MW00630225

Semiconductor Diode Lasers

VOLUME I

Progress in Lasers and Electro-Optics

Peter W. E. Smith, *Series Editor*

Integrated Optics: Devices and Applications, edited by Joseph T. Boyd
Coherent Lightwave Communications, edited by Paul S. Henry and Stewart D. Personick
Photonic Switching, edited by H. Scott Hinton and John E. Midwinter
Semiconductor Diode Lasers, Vol. 1, edited by William Streifer and Michael Ettenberg
Microlenses: Coupling Light to Optical Fibers, edited by Huey-Daw Wu and Frank S. Barnes

PROGRESS IN LASERS AND ELECTRO-OPTICS

Semiconductor Diode Lasers

VOLUME I

EDITED BY

William Streifer

Research Manager
Spectra Diode Labs

Michael Ettenberg

Director, Optoelectronics Research Laboratory
David Sarnoff Research Center

A Series published for the
IEEE LASERS AND ELECTRO-OPTICS SOCIETY
Peter W. E. Smith, *Series Editor*

The Institute of Electrical and Electronics Engineers, Inc., New York

IEEE PRESS
445 Hoes Lane, P.O. Box 1331
Piscataway, NJ 08855-1331

ISBN 0-87942-261-0

IEEE Order Number: PC0254-3

Printed in the United States of America

10 9 8 7 6 5 4 3 2 1

Library of Congress Cataloging-in-Publication Data

Semiconductor diode lasers / edited by William Streifer, Michael Ettenberg.
p. cm. -- (Progress in lasers and electro-optics)
Includes bibliographical references and indexes.
ISBN 0-87942-261-0 (v. 1 : case)
1. Semiconductor lasers. I. Streifer, William. II. Ettenberg, Michael. III. Series.
TA1700.S44 1991
621.36′6--dc20 90-5150
CIP

Contents

Foreword

THIS book is one of the first to appear in the new series "Progress in Lasers and Electro-Optics" (PLEOs). The IEEE Lasers and Electro-Optics Society is sponsoring this series to provide background and up-to-date information in rapidly evolving areas of laser technology, laser applications, optical and opto-electronic devices, and optical signal-processing.

Because the field has evolved so rapidly, there are very few contemporary books on lasers and electro-optics. In many cases, the topics of interest are still subjects of current research. This series has been designed to provide researchers, optical engineers, and professors teaching courses in these new areas of technology with access to the latest advances and understanding.

Other reprint volumes in the PLEOs series include:

Integrated Optics: Devices and Applications, edited by Joseph T. Boyd

Coherent Lightwave Communications, edited by Paul S. Henry and Stewart D. Personick

Photonic Switching, edited by H. Scott Hinton and John E. Midwinter

Microlenses: Coupling Light to Optical Fibers, edited by Huey-Daw Wu and Frank S. Barnes

The editors of each reprint volume are experts in their field and have written explanatory material to guide the reader through a carefully selected collection of reprints. I hope you will find this volume useful both for increasing your current knowledge and as a reference for years to come.

Peter W. E. Smith
Series Editor

Introduction

LITTLE more than twenty-five years have elapsed since semiconductor diode lasers were first demonstrated. These devices have progressed from laboratory curiosities operating at liquid helium temperatures to being the most widely manufactured lasers worldwide. Much has been learned of these complex, fascinating, and useful components. The richness of the phenomena displayed by diode lasers, however, continues to occupy increasing numbers of researchers, as has been witnessed by the ongoing expansion of the literature and the discovery of new effects, structures, and processes.

During the last two decades, diode lasers have been demonstrated from the red portion of the spectrum to the mid-infrared (>10 μm). Lasers are now available commercially over much of this band, and continuous-wave output powers from monolithic devices of over 50 watts have been reported; combinations of such lasers have been operated at significantly higher output powers. Applications range over space communications, solid-state laser pumps, compact disk players, computer printers, and supermarket scanners, for example, and the variety of uses, which is already vast, appears to be expanding at an increasing rate.

Scientific advances are being reported in many areas, including new materials, bandgap-engineered (quantum-effect) devices, and integrated opto-electronic circuits. It is likely that within the next few years short-wavelength, visible room-temperature lasers will be demonstrated, as will very low threshold lasers and useful surface emitters.

This first volume of collected papers represents our attempt to summarize the state of the field as of early 1989 in some areas. Several excellent textbooks [1–4] are available. They present background material, and the interested reader will find many additional articles in the trade and professional literature. In particular, the *IEEE Journal of Quantum Electronics* publishes a biannual special issue devoted to semiconductor diode lasers, and many letters and papers appear in the *IEEE Journal of Lightwave Technology, Applied Physics Letters, Electronics Letters*, and *Photonic Technology Letters*, as well as other publications. An interesting historical introduction to the field was included in the twenty-fifth anniversary issue of the *IEEE Journal of Quantum Electronics* [5].

Because of the limited space available in this (and its companion volume) and the overwhelming problem of doing justice to the vast literature, while not neglecting important new results, we have been unable to identify or include all deserving papers. Our bias has been to assign lower priority to, but not to ignore, historical contributions, especially those covered in the texts and earlier paper collections [6]. We ask the indulgence of our colleagues, who with justification may feel that their work has been overlooked, or unfairly omitted, to recognize and understand our difficulties.

References

[1] G. H. B. Thompson, *Physics of Semiconductor Laser Devices*. New York: Wiley, 1980.

[2] H. C. Casey, Jr., and M. Panish, *Heterostructure Lasers* (two volumes). New York: Academic, 1978.

[3] H. Kressel and J. K. Butler, *Semiconductor Lasers and Heterostructure LEDs*. New York: Academic, 1977.

[4] G. P. Agrawal and N. K. Dutta, *Long-Wavelength Semiconductor Lasers*. New York: Van Nostrand, 1986.

[5] *IEEE Journal of Quantum Electronics*, vol. 23, June 1987, Special Issue on Semiconductor Lasers, historical section guest editor, R. D. Dupuis; contributed section guest editor, P. D. Dapkus.

[6] J. K. Butler, ed., *Semiconductor Injection Lasers*. New York: IEEE Press and John Wiley, 1980.

Part 1
Semiconductor Laser Spectra

SEMICONDUCTOR lasers in which the lateral mode is confined by the gain profile almost invariably operate simultaneously in more than a single longitudinal mode. This behavior is in contrast to those devices with positive real-refractive-index waveguiding; the latter type most often emit in a single mode.

The spectral width of a single longitudinal mode laser is influenced by a variety of parameters. These include the antiguiding factor, length, facet reflectivities, and power. Furthermore, the lasing longitudinal mode can be selected or tuned, and the spectral width can be controlled by the use of external cavities (either with or without electronic control), and internal and external wavelength-selective elements such as gratings, etalons, or absorption lines. Papers describing external cavity effects, with the exception of stabilization to absorption lines, are included in a separate section; papers discussing spectra of distributed feedback and distributed Bragg reflector lasers are collected in that section; and papers relating to frequency chirp are reprinted in the section entitled ''Modulation'' in volume 2.

Still other areas of interest associated with the topics of diode laser spectra are those of mode stability, side-mode suppression, and the various effects of external reflections. These subjects are of particular significance in the fields of optical communications and memories.

REFERENCES

Gain-Guided Lasers

[1] Rivlin, L. A., ''Asymptotic nature of threshold conditions and multimode laser emission,'' *Sov. J. Quantum Electron.*, vol. 2, p. 464, 1973.

[2] Renner, D., and J. E. Carroll, ''Analysis of the effect of spontaneous emission coupling on the number of excited longitudinal modes in semiconductor lasers,'' *Electron. Lett.*, vol. 14, p. 779, 1978.

[3] Marcuse, D., ''Quantum mechanical explanation of spontaneous emission K-factor,'' *Electron. Lett.*, vol. 18, p. 920, 1982.

[4] Pietzsch, J., and T. Kamiya, ''Axial mode spectra of planar stripe geometry laser diodes,'' *Japan. J. Appl. Phys.*, vol. 21, p. L633, 1982.

Nonlinear Effects

[5] Yamada, M., and Y. Suematsu, ''A condition of single longitudinal mode operation in injection lasers with index guiding structure,'' *IEEE J. Quantum Electron.*, vol. 15, p. 743, 1979.

[6] Bogatov, A. P., P. G. Eliseev, O. G. Okhotnikov, M. P. Rakhaval'skii, and K. A. Khairetdinov, ''Interaction of modes and self-stabilization of single-frequency emission from injection lasers,'' *Sov. J. Quantum Electron.*, vol. 13, p. 1221, 1983.

[7] Henry, C. H., ''Phase noise in semiconductor lasers,'' *J. Light. Technol.*, vol. 4, p. 298, 1986.

Linewidth

[8] Welford, D., and A. Mooradian, ''Output power and temperature dependence of the linewidth of single-frequency CW (GaAl)As diode lasers,'' *Appl. Phys. Lett.*, vol. 40, p. 865, 1982.

[9] Vahala, K., L. C. Chiu, S. Margalit, and A. Yariv, ''On the linewidth enhancement factor in semiconductor injection lasers,'' *Appl. Phys. Lett.*, vol. 42, p. 631, 1983.

Frequency Locking to Absorption Lines

[10] Tsuchida, H., M. Ohtsu, T. Tako, N. Kuramochji, and N. Oura, ''Frequency stabilization of AlGaAs semiconductor laser based on the $^{85}Rb-D_2$ line,'' *Japan J. Appl. Phys.*, vol. 21, p. L561, 1982.

[11] Hori, H., Y. Kitayama, M. Kitano, T. Yabuzaki, and T. Ogawa, ''Frequency stabiliziation of GaAlAs laser using a Doppler-free spectrum of the Cs-D_2 line,'' *IEEE J. Quantum Electron*, vol. 19, p. 169, 1983.

(Invited) Theory of Single Mode Injection Lasers Taking Account of Electronic Intra-band Relaxation

Minoru YAMADA and Yasuharu SUEMATSU*

Department of Electrical Engineering,
Faculty of Technology, Kanazawa University,
Kodatsuno, Kanazawa 920, Japan
**Department of Physical Electronics,*
Tokyo Institute of Technology,
O-okayama, Meguro-ku, Tokyo 152, Japan

A new theory of injection lasers is given by taking account of the electronic intraband relaxation with the density matrix method. "Band tail" of the gain profile in nondoped crystal is explained with this relaxation. Gain saturations of lasing modes at band-to-band and band-to-impurity level transitions are theoretically given. In the case of band-to-band transition with k-selection rule, a small excess gain suppression affects the lasing behaviour. At the band-to-impurity level transition with no k-selection rule, the excess gain suppression disappears. The former effect corresponds to the "in-homogeneous gain profile", and the latter to the "homogeneous gain profile". Theoretical calculations are in good agreement with experiments. As an extention of this theory, a condition of single longitudinal mode oscillation is shown.

§1. Introduction

The double-hetero AlGaAs injection lasers[1] have been recently improved concerning static and dynamic lasing characteristics.[2-4] As the transverse mode is well controlled by adoption of the very narrow stripe structures, the modulation property inherent in these lasers is significantly improved and the longitudinal mode is also purified in such lasers.[5-11] After these improvements, unknown intrinsic properties of the injection laser appeared. Some of these intrinsic properties are found to conflict with the already established theories of the injection lasers. For example, gain and its saturation effect at lasing condition were measured in detail in the Transverse-Junction-Stripe (TJS) lasers which can show the single mode oscillation along both transverse and longitudinal directions.[8] The TJS laser showed so called "homogeneous gain profile" predicted by the established theories,[12-18] but the CSP laser showed "inhomogeneous gain profile" and strong gain suppression at lasing condition.[9] The latter phenomena cannot be explained by the previous theory, but seem to be analogous to the phenomena which were explained in the gas lasers as the mode-competition.[19-20]

Most theories of the injection lasers have been restricted in analysis of the linear gain to find the threshold condition.[12-18] In these analyses, the gain profile at lasing condition is simply assumed to be same to that of the threshold, namely "homogeneous gain profile" for photon energy.

As an exception, Nishimura and his co-workers postulated by an analogous treatment of the gas lasers by Lamb and others[19,21] that the gain profile is inhomogeneous at the lasing condition.[21]* However, the results by Nishimura *et al.* overestimated the gain saturation.

In this paper, we give a new theory of single mode injection lasers. It is found that the electronic intra-band relaxation affects significantly the gain profile, which is expressed by a function of injection current.[22] The difference of gain profiles at oscillation condition for the band to band and for the band to impurity transitions is given. The former and the latter correspond to the inhomogeneous and homogeneous gain saturations, respectively.[23] These results are in good agreement with experiment. A condition of single mode operation is also given analytically.

*The first analysis for the band to band transition is reported in Technical Report from IECE of Japan, QE71-22 (1971) by Y. Nishimura, K. Kobayashi, T. Ikegami and Y. Suematsu.

Reprinted with permission from *Japan. J. Appl. Phys.*, vol. 18, no. 18-1, pp. 347-354, 1978.

§2. Field Amplification and Density Matrix

The electric field is expressed with resonant modes of the cavity which has width of $2a_c$, thickness of $2b_c$ and length of l_c along x, y and z axes, respectively.

$$E=\sum_m [A_m(z)F_m(x, y) \exp(-j\beta_m z+j\omega_m t) + A_m(l_c-z)F_m(x, y) \exp(j\beta_m z+j\omega_m t) + c.c.],$$

$$F_m(x, y)=(a_c b_c)^{-1/2} \cos[(m_x+1)\pi x/(2a_c) - m_x\pi/2] \cos[(m_y+1)\pi y/(2b_c)-m_y\pi/2]. \quad (1)$$

Here, m is a mode number including transverse and longitudinal components. m_x and m_y are components of the mode number along x and y directions, respectively. The field is amplified by the laser polarization P which is introduced in the Maxwell's equation with relation to the dielectric flux density D as,

$$D=\varepsilon_0\varepsilon_r E+P. \quad (2)$$

Amplitude variation is obtained as,

$$d/dz\,|A_m(z)|^2=(\alpha_m-\alpha_m^{ab})|A_m(z)|^2 + C\sqrt{\mu/\varepsilon}\hbar\omega R(\ln(1/R))^2 I_{sp}/[4el_c(1-R)^2], \quad (3)$$

and

$$\alpha_m=\sqrt{\frac{\mu}{\varepsilon}}(\omega_m/A_m)Im\left[\frac{1}{\Delta T l_c}\int_t^{t+\Delta T}\int_0^{l_c} \times\int_{-b_c}^{b_c}\int_{-a_c}^{a_c} PF_m^*(x, y) \times \exp(j\beta_m z-j\omega_m t)\,dx\,dy\,dz\,dt\right],$$

$$\alpha_m^{ab}=\sqrt{\mu/\varepsilon}\sigma. \quad (4)$$

Here, α_m is the gain coefficient, α_m^{ab} is the loss coefficient and C is the spontaneous emission factor.[24] I_{sp} is component of the current for the spontaneous emission which will be shown later. The field is reflected at end-mirrors of the cavity which have power reflection coefficient R as

$$A_m(l_c)=\sqrt{R}A_m(l_c)=\sqrt{R}A_m(0)=A_m(0). \quad (5)$$

The polarization P is obtained as an expectation value of the dipole moment M, using the density matrix ρ for quantum statistics.

$$P-n\langle M\rangle=nTr(\rho M)=n\sum_{ll'}\rho_{ll'}M_{l'l}. \quad (6)$$

Here, n is the atomic density and l or l' is the energy level of the active region.

A dynamic equation of the density matrix in injection lasers is given by.

$$d\rho/dt=-[\rho, H]/(j\hbar)-\{(\rho-\bar{\rho})\Gamma_{in} + \Gamma_{in}(\rho-\bar{\rho})\}/2-\{(\rho-\tilde{\rho})\Gamma_s + \Gamma_s(\rho-\tilde{\rho})\}/2+\Lambda,$$

and $\quad (7)$

$$H=H_0-ME.$$

Here, H_0 is the Hamiltonian of the active region with characteristic energy W_l for level of l. In this paper, the energy level and the wave function of the electron are defined locally in smaller region than the wave-length of the field. Γ_s is an operator for spontaneous emission with expectation value of $1/\tau_s$ at diagonal elements, and $\tilde{\rho}$ is the distribution function (Fermi-Dirac function) at thermal equilibrium. Λ is an operator for pumping with expectation value of Λ_l at the diagonal element. Γ_{in} is an operator to show the intra-band relaxation or spatial diffusion caused by electron-electron, electron-phonon or electron-impurity scatterings with expectation value of $1/\tau_l$. Non-radiative transition from conduction band to donor level or acceptor level to valence band are included in this expression. $\bar{\tilde{\rho}}$ is an equilibrium function (not operator) at pumped condition, and is established only by the intra-band relaxation as illustrated in Fig. 1. Summations over all levels in one band and neighbouring impurity level, and spatial integration in the active region for $\bar{\tilde{\rho}}$ must be equal to existing electrons in that region.

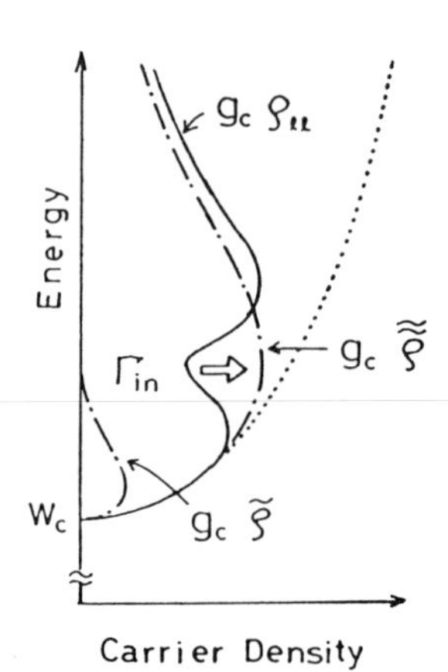

Fig. 1. Carrier distributions and relaxation effect in conduction band. g_c is the state density, $\bar{\tilde{\rho}}$ is an equilibrium function established by the intra-band relaxation Γ_{in}.

$$\int \sum_{l\in\text{band}} \tilde{\tilde{\rho}}_l/\tau_l \, dr = \int \sum_{l\in\text{band}} \rho_{ll}/\tau_l \, dr \tag{8}$$

Equation (7) is a non-linear equation with electric field E. Then the matrix element $\rho_{ll'} = \langle l|\rho|l'\rangle$ is obtained in form of a power series with E by purturbed approach.[22]

$$\rho_{ll'} = \rho_{ll'}^{(0)} + \rho_{ll'}^{(1)}(E) + \rho_{ll'}^{(2)}(E^2) + \rho_{ll'}^{(3)}(E^3) + \cdots \tag{9}$$

Diagonal elements ($l=l'$) and off-diagonal elements ($l \neq l'$) have only even and odd order components, respectively, in conventional semiconductor. Corresponding to this power expansion, the polarization of eq. (6) and gain coefficient of eq. (4) are expanded with the order of E. If we consider two modes which are numbered by p and m, the gain coefficient α_m is expressed approximately by the first and third order terms as,

$$\alpha_m = \alpha_m^{(1)} - \alpha_{m(m)}^{(3)}|A_m(l_c)|^2 - \alpha_{m(p)}^{(3)}|A_p(l_c)|^2. \tag{10}$$

Here, $\alpha_m^{(1)}$ is the first order (linear) gain coefficient, and $\alpha_{m(p)}^{(3)}$ is the third order gain coefficient which shows gain suppression due to mode P, where the back-ward component $A_p(l_c - z)$ is also included as the definition.

Here, we will note that the density matrix element caused by fields interacting in the order of $\omega_1, \omega_2, \cdots, \omega_i$ is $\rho_{ll'}^{(i)}(\omega_1, \omega_2, \cdots, \omega_i)$. Then, the linear gain coefficient $\alpha_m^{(1)}$ is calculated from $\rho_{ll'}^{(1)}(\omega_m)$, and the third order coefficient is calculated from

$$\begin{aligned}&\{\rho_{ll'}^{(3)}(\omega_m, -\omega_p, \omega_p) + \rho_{ll'}^{(3)}(\omega_p, -\omega_p, \omega_m) \\ &+ \rho_{ll'}^{(3)}(-\omega_p, \omega_m, \omega_p) + \rho_{ll'}^{(3)}(-\omega_p, \omega_p, \omega_m) \\ &+ \rho_{ll'}^{(3)}(\omega_m, \omega_p, -\omega_p) + \rho_{ll'}^{(3)}(\omega_p, \omega_m, -\omega_p)\} \\ &/(1 + \delta_{m,p}).\end{aligned}$$

Oscillation condition is determined by the relation of eqs. (3) and (5), neglecting influence from the spontaneous emission. Single mode oscillation for mode P is obtained from following conditions.

$$\begin{aligned}\alpha_p &= \alpha_p^{(1)} - \alpha_{p(p)}^{(3)}|A_p(l_c)|^2 \\ &= \alpha_{\text{th}} = \alpha^{ab} + 1/l_c \ln(1/R),\end{aligned}$$

and $\hfill (11)$

$$\alpha_m = \alpha_m^{(1)} - \alpha_{m(p)}^{(3)}|A_p(l_c)|^2 < \alpha_{\text{th}} \quad (m \neq p).$$

Here, α_{th} is the threshold gain for oscillation.

§3. Injection Current and Output Power

The injection current through the p-n junction is expressed as,

$$I = e\int n \sum_b \Lambda_b \, d\mathbf{r}. \tag{12}$$

Here, Λ_b is a matrix element for pumping at energy level b in the conduction band or donor level. From, the zeroth order element of the density matrix,

$$\rho_{ll'}^{(0)} = (\tilde{\tilde{\rho}}/\tau_l + \tilde{\rho}/\tau_s + \Lambda_l)\gamma_l \cdot \delta_{ll'}, \tag{13}$$

and with eq. (8), the injection current is calculated as[22]

$$\begin{aligned}I &= I_{sp} + I_{st}, \\ I_{sp} &= e/\tau_s \int n \sum_b (\rho_{bb}^{(0)} - \tilde{\rho}_b) \, dr, \\ I_{st} &= e\int n \sum_{b,a} (\rho_{aa}^{(2)} - \rho_{bb}^{(2)})/(\tau_a + \tau_b) \, d\mathbf{r}.\end{aligned} \tag{14}$$

Here, a is an energy level of the valence band or the acceptor level. I_{sp} is a current component contributing to the spontaneous emission. I_{st} is a component contributing to oscillating power. When the laser is not in oscillation, the current is counted only by I_{sp}. In the oscillation condition, I_{sp} is nearly fixed to the threshold value of I_{th}, and increased value is counted in I_{st}, because of τ_a, $\tau_b \ll \tau_s$. Especially, at the single mode oscillation of p, the I_{st} is obtained as,[23]

$$\begin{aligned}I_{st} &= 4\sqrt{\mu/\varepsilon} el_c(1-R)\alpha_{\text{th}}/[\ln(1/R)\hbar\omega_p]|A_p(l_c)|^2 \\ &\simeq I - I_{\text{th}}.\end{aligned} \tag{15}$$

From eq. (5) we can obtain the output power Q_p of the oscillating mode from both end-mirrors.

$$Q_p = \{\hbar\omega_p \ln(1/R)/[el_c\alpha_{\text{th}}]\}(I - I_{\text{th}}) \tag{16}$$

Gain suppression of other modes is rewritten with eqs. (11) and (15).

$$\begin{aligned}\alpha_m \simeq \alpha_m^{(1)} - \{&\sqrt{\mu/\varepsilon}\hbar\omega_p \ln(1/R)\alpha_{m(p)}^{(3)} \\ &/[4el_c(1-R)\alpha_{\text{th}}]\}(I - I_{\text{th}})\end{aligned} \tag{17}$$

This gain suppression is observed as output powers Q_m for amplified spontaneous emission.

$$Q_m = \{C\hbar\omega_m \ln(1/R)/[el_c\alpha_{\text{th}}]\}I_{sp}/(1 - \alpha_m/\alpha_{\text{th}}) \tag{18}$$

§4. Linear Gain Profile at Band to Band Transition

For lightly doped crystal, we can take the

radiative transition from conduction to valence bands, keeping the wave number conservation rule of $\boldsymbol{k}_{l'}\,\mathrm{d}\boldsymbol{k}=\boldsymbol{k}_{l'}\,\mathrm{d}\boldsymbol{k}$. If we rewrite the energy levels as b and a for conduction and valence bands, respectively, the linear gain is obtained from eqs. (6)–(10) with assumption of the parabolic state density and the Fermi-Dirac distribution function of electrons.[22,23]

$$\begin{aligned}\alpha_m^{(1)}=&B\omega_m\sqrt{\mu/\varepsilon}M^2\int(W_{ba}-W_G)^{1/2}\\&\times(1/\{1+\exp[\{m_v/(m_c+m_v)\}(W_{ba}-W_G)/(kT)-(F+\mu_v-W_v)/(kT)]\}\\&-1/\{1+\exp[-\{m_c/(m_c+m_v)\}(W_{ba}-W_G)/(kT)-(\mu_v-W_v)/(kT)]\})\\&\times(\hbar/\tau_{in})/\{(W_m-W_{ba})^2+\hbar^2/\tau_{in}^2\}\,\mathrm{d}W_{ba},\end{aligned}\tag{19}$$

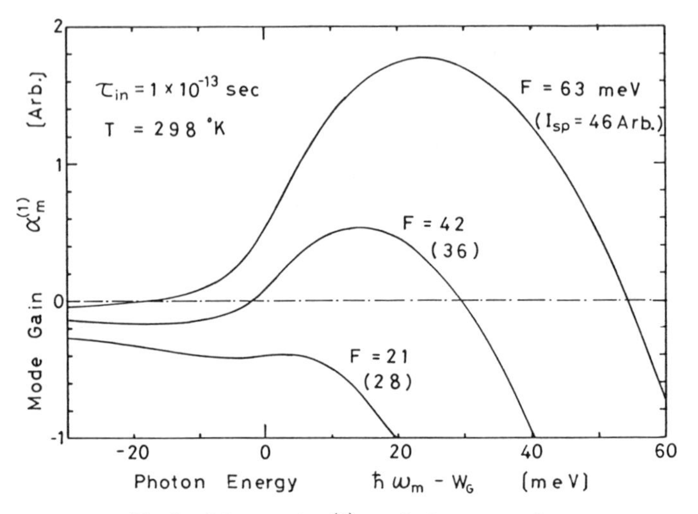

Fig. 2. Linear gain $\alpha_m^{(1)}$ vs. photon energy $\hbar\omega_m$.

where $W_{ba}=W_b-W_a=\hbar\omega_{ba}$. $W_G=W_c-W_v$ is the energy gap. W_c and W_v are the band edge levels, μ_c and μ_v are the quasi-fermi levels, and m_c and m_v are the effective masses, respectively. $F=\mu_c-\mu_v-W_G$ shows separation of the quasi-fermi levels. $\tau_{in}=2/(1/\tau_b+1/\tau_a)$ and $M^2=|M_{ab}|^2$ are assumed to be constant for all energy levels here. $B=\{2m_cm_v/(m_c+m_v)\}^{3/2}/(2\pi^2\hbar^3)$ is coefficient of the state density.

Numerical results of the linear gain for GaAs crystal are shown in Fig. 2 with assumption of $m_c=0.08$ m, $m_v=0.5$ m, $T=298$ K and $\tau_{in}=1\times10^{-13}$ sec. In Fig. 2, we can see the "band tail" at smaller photon energy than the band gap, $W_m-W_G<0$. This effect is remarkable for smaller τ_{in}. The peak value of the linear gain is named as $\alpha_p^{(1)}$. Relation between $\alpha_p^{(1)}$ vs. injection current $I=I_{sp}$ is shown in Fig. 3.

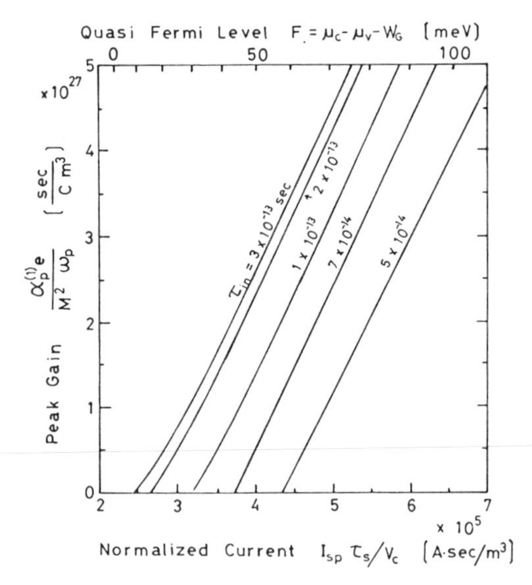

Fig. 3. Peak gain $\alpha_p^{(1)}$ vs. injection current $I=I_{sp}$.

§5. Gain Saturation at Band to Band Transition

At oscillating condition, the gain of the oscillating mode is fixed to $\alpha_p=\alpha_{th}$, and other modes suffer excess gain suppression due to the oscillating fields. The suppression is calculated from $\rho_{ab}^{(3)}$ and $\rho_{ba}^{(3)}$ in $\alpha_{m(p)}^{(3)}$. For band to band transition, we can assume that all intermediate states which are introduced in calculation of $\rho_{ab}^{(3)}$ and $\rho_{ba}^{(3)}$ are restricted to the level of b or a due to the wave number conservation as indicated in Fig. 4(a). Then, the third order coefficient is obtained as

$$\begin{aligned}\alpha_{m(p)}^{(3)} = & [2+\delta_{m,p}](2+\delta_{m_x,p_x})(2+\delta_{m_y,p_y})(1-R)/[(1+\delta_{m,p})(8a_cb_c)(\ln 1/R)] \\ & \times B\omega_m\sqrt{\mu/\varepsilon}M \times Re\int (W_{ba}-W_G)^{1/2} \\ & \times (1/\{1+\exp[\{m_v/(m_c+m_v)\}(W_{ba}-W_G)/(kT)-(F+\mu_v-W_v)/(kT)]\} \\ & -1/\{1+\exp[-\{m_c/(m_c+m_v)\}(W_{ba}-W_G)/(kT)-(\mu_v-W_v)/(kT)]\}) \\ & \times 1/[j(W_m-W_{ba})+\hbar/\tau_{in}](2[\tau_b+\tau_a]/\{\tau_{in}[(W_p-W_{ba})^2+\hbar^2/\tau_{in}^2]\} \\ & +\{1/[j(W_m-W_{ba})+\hbar/\tau_{in}]+1/[j(W_{ba}-W_p)+\hbar/\tau_{in}]\} \\ & \times\{1/[j(W_m-W_p)+\hbar/\tau_b]+1/[j(W_m-W_p)+\hbar/\tau_a]\})\,\mathrm{d}W_{ba}. \end{aligned} \tag{20}$$

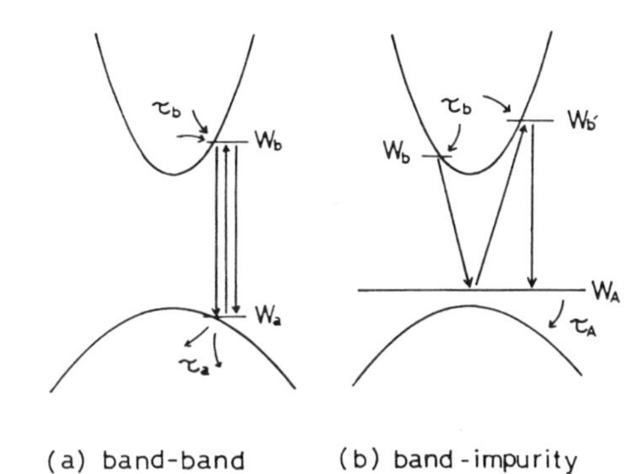

Fig. 4. Schematic explanation for radiative transitions at (a) band to band and (b) band to impurity level.

The coefficient $1/(1+\delta_{m,p})$ comes from field combination about $(\omega_m, -\omega_p, \omega_p)$ and $(\omega_p, -\omega_p, \omega_p)$ components in E^3. The difference between the coefficients for $m=p$ and $m\neq p$ is caused from phase rotation of the population inversion with frequancy of $\exp[j(\omega_m-\omega_p)t]$. This difference of the coefficients is ignored in conventional rate equation.[25] Coefficient $[2+\delta_{m,p}](1-R)(\ln 1/R)$ in eq. (20) is determined by the relation among $|A_m(z)|^2$, $|A_m(l_c-z)|^2$ and phase along z direction.[23] Spatial integrations along x and y directions give the following coefficient.

$$\int |F_m(x,y)|^2|F_p(x,y)|^2\,\mathrm{d}x\,\mathrm{d}y = (2+\delta_{m_x,p_x})(2+\delta_{m_y,p_y})/(16a_cb_c). \tag{21}$$

After all, gain suppression for non-oscillating modes $\alpha_{m(p)}^{(3)}$ is 4/3 times as large as that of the oscillating mode $\alpha_{p(p)}^{(3)}$, when all allowable modes are transverse fundamental ($m_x=m_y=p_x=p_y=0$). However, this suppression is released to 8/9 for transverse higher modes ($m_x\neq 0$ or $m_y\neq 0$) when the oscillating mode is the transverse fundamental ($p_x=0$). Numerical examples of the gain profile is shown in Fig. 5(a). Central part of the gain profile of the transverse higher modes ($m_x\neq 0$) is larger than to that of the threshold. There is possibility to oscillate with the transverse higher modes. Neverthless other longitudinal modes with transverse fundamental are not in oscillation. If we want to get single longitudinal mode oscillation, we must reduce the gains of the transverse higher modes by method of the "Transverse Mode Control".[10] Gain profiles with different τ_{in} are shown in Fig. 5(b), assuming that all modes are transverse fundamental. The gain reduction becomes small for smaller τ_{in}. The gain profile is sensitively deformed by temperature variation due to the band gap shift of crystal (GaAs) as,

$$W_G = 1433.6 - 0.4\,(T-298) \quad [\text{meV}]. \tag{22}$$

Examples of the calculation are shown in Fig. 5(c). The temperature variation is defined as $\Delta T = T - T_{th}$. T_{th} is temperature at the threshold.

The gain suppression is determined through the output powers as given in eq. (17). Comparison with the experiment of CSP laser is shown in Fig. 6 for the excess gain suppression. The amplitudes of the non-oscillating modes are reduced by the excess gain suppression, which is in good agreement with the present theory.

§6. Gain Saturation at Band to Impurity Level Transition

In case of heavily doped crystal, we must consider radiative transition from band to

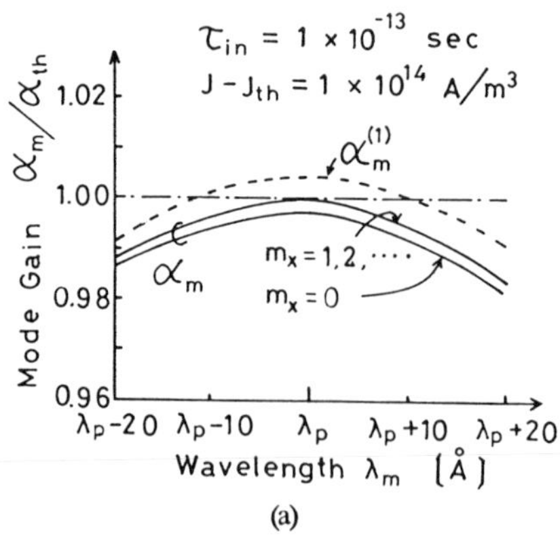

(a)

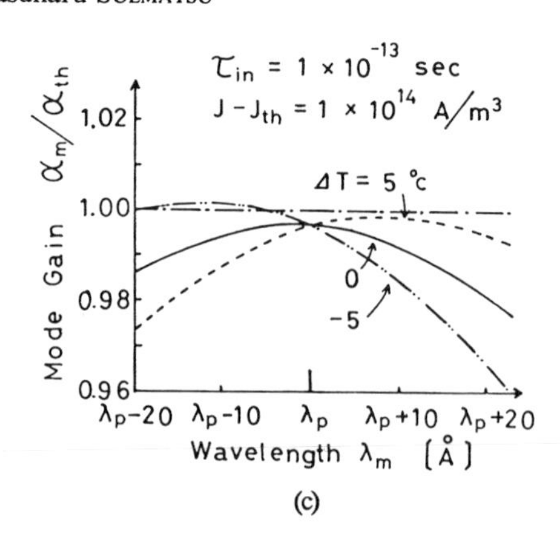

(c)

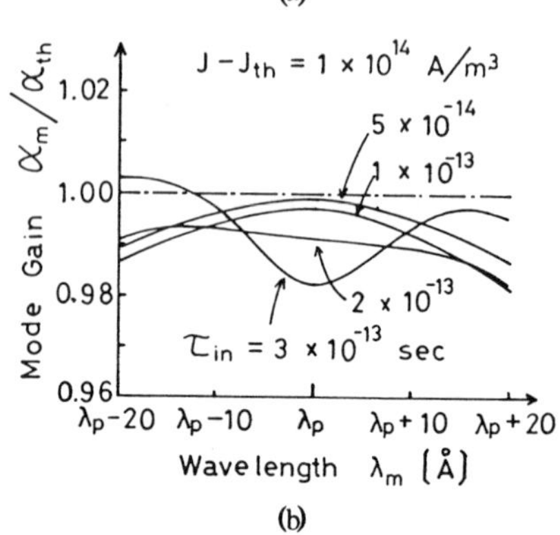

(b)

Fig. 5. Examples of the gain profile at oscillating condition. (R=0.3, $\tau_a=\tau_b=\tau_{in}$) (a) Relation for transverse modes. m_x is the transverse mode number. (b) Variation with the relaxation time. (c) Variation with temperature.

impurity level. Here, we approximately analyze the gain suppression for band to acceptor level transition.

The energy level of the impurity is labelled by A. The wave number of the impurity state is widened in $\boldsymbol{k}$ space as shown in Fig. 4(b). Then the intermediate states to calculate $\rho_{bA}^{(3)}$ or $\rho_{Ab}^{(3)}$ are A and b' which is not coincident with b in general. If we assume for convenience that τ_b is larger than 5×10^{-13} sec, the gains are obtained in explicit form as follows.[23)]

$$\alpha_m^{(1)}=\sqrt{\lambda/\varepsilon}\,\omega_m M_I^2 N_A V_c \pi g_c(W_m+W_A)[f_c(W_m+W_A)-f_v(W_A)], \tag{23}$$

$$\begin{aligned}\alpha_{m(p)}^{(3)}=&[2+\delta_{m,p}](1-R)(2+\delta_{m_x,p_x})(2+\delta_{m_y,p_y})/[(1+\delta_{m,p})(\ln 1/R)(16a_cb_c)]\omega_m\sqrt{\lambda/\varepsilon}\,M_I^4N_AV_c^2\pi^2\\&\times(\hbar/\{\tau_A[(W_m-W_p)^2+(\hbar/\tau_A)^2]\}g_c^2(W_m+W_A)][f_c(W_m+W_A)-f_v(W_A)]\\&+(2\tau_A/\hbar)g_c(W_m+W_A)g_c(W_p+W_A)[f_c(W_p+W_A)-f_v(W_A)]\\&+\hbar/\{\tau_A[(W_m-W_p)^2+(\hbar/\tau_A)^2]\}g_c^2(W_p+W_A)[f_c(W_p+W_A)-f_v(W_A)]),\end{aligned} \tag{24}$$

where $M_I=|M_{bA}|$ is dipole moment between conduction band and acceptor level. N_A is impurity density and $V_c=4a_cb_cl_c$ is the volume of the active region. τ_A is the relaxation time from impurity to valence band. $g_c(W)$ is the state density of the conduction band. Although we assumed that $\tau_b>5\times10^{-13}$ sec in calculation of eqs. (23) and (24), the results are not so different from those for $\tau_b<5\times10^{-13}$ sec.

An example of numerical result of the output powers affected by the gain suppression is shown in Fig. 7, comparing with experimental results of the heavily doped TJS laser.* From Fig. 7, it can be said that the excess gain suppression is negligible in this case. Therefore, this case corresponds to so called "homogeneous gain profile".

§7. Condition of Single Mode Oscillation

Single mode oscillation is well obtained when the excess gain suppression is large enough.

*The experimental data is reported in the Technical Report from IECE of Japan, Suzaki *et al.*, OQE77-23 (1977).

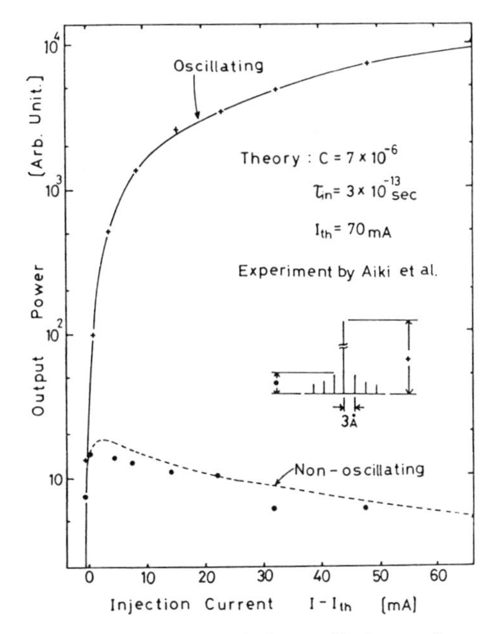

Fig. 6. Output powers of the oscillating and non-oscillating modes for band to band transition. The experimental result was obtained in CSP laser by Nakamura, Akiki *et al.* in reference 9.

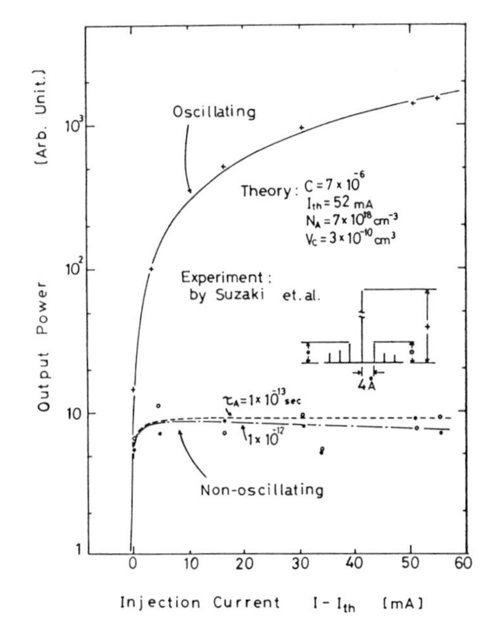

Fig. 7. Output powers of the oscillating and non-oscillating modes for band to impurity level transition The experiment was obtained in TJS laser by Suzaki *et al.* in the reference of foot notes.

Then, the transverse mode control is the most important factor for longitudinal single mode oscillation. Band to band transition with $\tau_{in}=1\sim2\times10^{-13}$ sec is also desired. However, the temperature variation at lasing condition is not good for stabilization of the operation.

Region of the single longitudinal mode oscillation is indicated in Fig. 8(a) about the injection level and the temperature variation. In case of CW operation, the temperature rises with the current as,

$$\Delta T=R_L V\Delta I \tag{25}$$

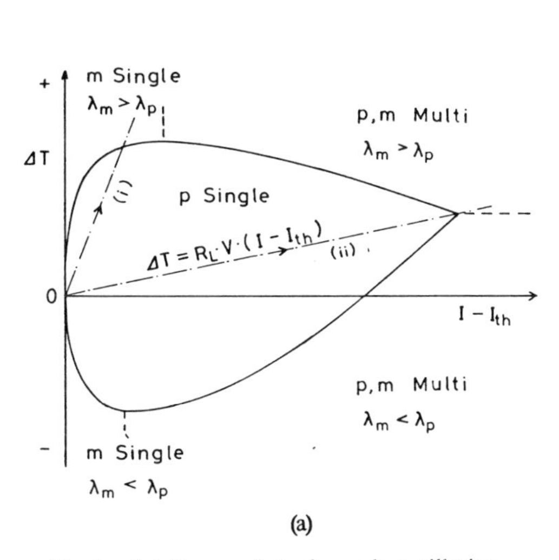

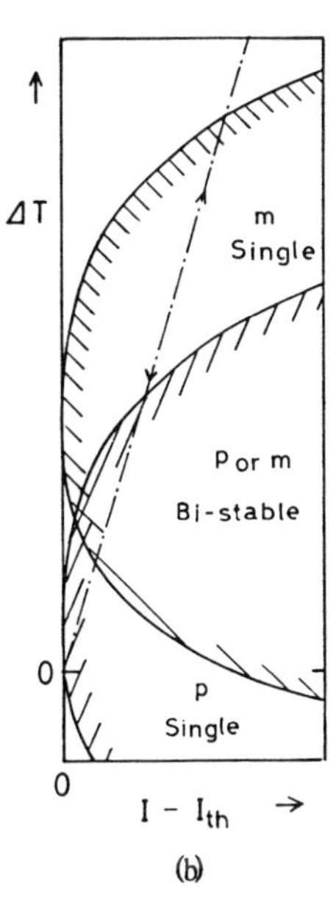

Fig. 8. (a) Range of single mode oscillation.
(b) Determination of mode change. The hysteresis phenomena is observed at overlapped (bi-stable) region.

Here, R_L is thermal resistance of the device and V is the supplied voltage. Then, the operating character is moving on the line such as (i) or (ii) in Fig. 8(a). The stabilization is achieved mostly on the line of (ii), at which the reduction of W_G is just compensated by increasing the quasi-fermi level F. This condition corresponds to $R_L \simeq 5°C/W$ in very narrow stripe AlGaAs laser. Succeeding changes of the oscillating modes are also determined by connection of Fig. 8(a) as shown in Fig. 8(b). When the regions of the succeeding single mode are overlapped as illustrated in Fig. 8(b), we can observe the hysteresis phenomena[9] for mode change at the overlapped (bi-stable) region. The hysteresis is hardly observed in lasers with condition of $\tau_{in} > 3 \times 10^{-13}$ sec, $\tau_{in} < 5 \times 10^{-14}$ sec or heavily doped active region, because of weak gain suppression.

§8. Conclusions

A new theory given in this paper shows the excess gain suppression for lightly doped lasers. The so called "inhomogeneous and homogeneous gain profiles" are theoretically discussed. The gain suppression generates wider range of the stable single longitudinal mode oscillation.

Acknowledgement

The authors acknowledge Y. Nishimura of Nikkei McGrow-Hill for his theoretical discussions, K. Aiki and M. Nakamura and their co-workers of Hitachi Corp. and W. Suzaki, K. Ikeda and their co-workers of Mitsubishi Electric for their experimental discussion. The authors also thank K. Hayano, H. Ishiguro and Prof. R. Ishibashi of Kanazawa Univ. for their co-operations. This research is partly supported by Sientific Research Grant-In-Aid from the Ministry of Education, Science and Culture.

References

1) I. Hayashi, M. B. Panish and S. Sumsky: Appl. Phys. Lett., **16** (1970) 326.
2) H. Yonezu, I. Sakuma, T. Kamejima, M. Ueno, K. Nishida, Y. Nannichi and I. Hayashi: Appl. Phys. Lett., **24** (1974) 18.
3) R. L. Hartman and R. W. Dixon: Appl. Phys. Lett., **26** (1975) 239.
4) H. Kan, H. Namizaki, M. Ishi and A. Ito: Appl. Phys. Lett., **27** (1975) 138.
5) J. C. Dyment: Appl. Phys. Lett., **10** (1967) 84.
6) H. Yonezu, I. Sakuma, K. Kobayashi, I. Kamejima, M. Ueno and Y. Nannichi: Japan. J. appl. Phys., **13** (1973) 1585.
7) T. Tsukada: J. appl. Pyys., **45** (1974) 4899.
8) H. Namizaki, H. Kan, M. Ishi and A. Ito: J. appl. Phys., **45** (1974) 2785.
9) M. Nakamura, K. Aiki, N. Chinone, R. Ito and J. Umeda: J. appl. Phys., to be published.
10) Y. Suematsu and M. Yamada: Trans. of IECE of Japan, **57-C**, (1974) 434, and IEEE J. of QE, **QE-9**, (1973) 305.
11) R. Lang: Japan J. appl. Pyys., **16** (1977) 205.
12) G. Lasher and F. Stern: Phys. Rev., **133** (1964) A553.
13) F. Stern: Phys. Rev., **148** (1966) 186.
14) C. J. Hwang: Phys. Rev., **B-2** (1970) 4117.
15) F. Stern: IEEE of of QE., **QE-9** (1973) 290.
16) H. Haug: Phys. Rev., **184** (1969) 338.
17) A. Scott: IEEE trans. Ed., **ED-11** (1964) 41.
18) H. Statz, C. L. Tang and J. M. Lavine: J. appl. Phys., **35** (1964) 2581.
19) W. E. Lamb Jr.: Phys. Rev. **134** (1964) A1429.
20) N. Bloembrgen: *Nonlinear Optics* (W. A. Benjamin Inc., New York, 1965).
21) Y. Nishimura and Y. Nishimura: IEEE J. of QE, **QE-9** (1973) 1011.
22) M. Yamada and Y. Suematsu: Technical Report from IECE of Japan, **OQE-77–21**, **OQE-77–22** (1977).
23) M. Yamaka, K. Hayano, H. Ishoguro and Y. Suematsu: Submitted to Japan J. appl. Phys., or Technical Report from IECE of Japan, **OQE-78–13** (1978).
24) Y. Suematsu, S. Akiba and T. Hong: IEEE J. of QE, **QE-13** (1977) 596.
25) For example; S. M. Kay and A. Maitland, *Quantum Optics* (Academic press, London and New York, 1970) p. 226.

Calculated Spontaneous Emission Factor for Double-Heterostructure Injection Lasers with Gain-Induced Waveguiding

KLAUS PETERMANN, MEMBER, IEEE

Abstract—The fraction of spontaneous emission going into an oscillating laser mode has been calculated. It is shown that this fraction strongly depends on the strength of astigmatism in the laser output beam. Therefore the spontaneous emission factor in planar stripe lasers with narrow stripe is in the order of 10^{-4} and by one order of magnitude larger than in injection lasers with a comparable active layer volume and with a built-in index waveguide. It is shown that the spontaneous emission factor is approximately proportional to the solid angle of laser radiation and nearly independent of the transverse active layer dimensions. Owing to the large spontaneous emission factor, the spectral width of narrow planar stripe lasers is significantly broader compared to narrow stripe lasers with a built-in index waveguide. In addition the large spontaneous emission coefficient also yields a much stronger damping of relaxation oscillations.

I. Introduction

The spectral characteristics of a semiconductor injection laser and its dynamic behavior are strongly affected by the ratio of spontaneous emission going into an oscillating laser mode versus the total rate of spontaneous emission [1]-[3]. The knowledge of this spontaneous emission factor is therefore important to characterize a semiconductor laser.

The spontaneous emission factor has been given for bulk material, for example in [4], and has been determined in [5] by taking the waveguide inside the laser into account. These calculations have been carried out for waveguides with real refractive indexes and, therefore, only hold as long as the lasing mode is predominately guided by the refractive index. In planar stripe lasers as in Fig. 1, however, the waveguiding parallel to the active layer (x-direction) is accomplished only by the carrier distribution $N(x)$, resulting in a gain-induced waveguiding mechanism [6] which is often combined with an index-antiguiding effect [7], [8].

The expression for the spontaneous emission ratio from [4], [5] cannot be used for lasers with gain induced waveguides since then the spatial orthogonality with respect to power between different modes does not hold any more.

We will show in the following that the value of the spontaneous emission factor is changed considerably in the case of injection lasers with gain-induced waveguiding.

Manuscript received November 14, 1978; revised February 15, 1979. This work was supported by the technological program of the Bundesministerium für Forschung und Technologie of the Federal Republic of Germany.

The author is with AEG-Telefunken Forschunginstitut, Abteilung Physik, Ulm, Germany.

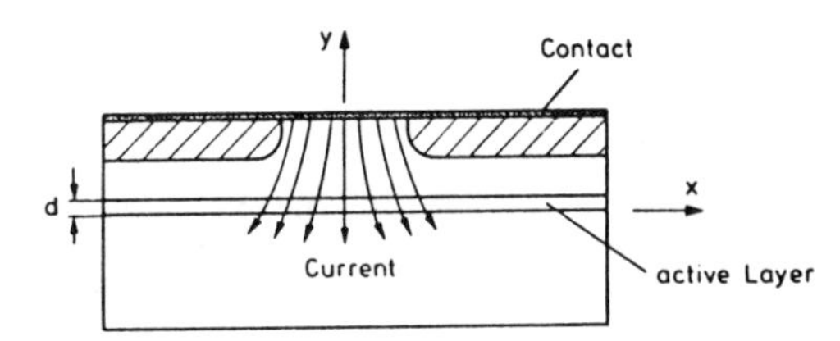

Fig. 1. Planar stripe laser.

II. Excitation Efficiency of a Spontaneously Emitting Dipole

The derivation of the spontaneous emission ratio is classically carried out similarly to [5] by representing the spontaneous emission as the radiation of arbitrarily oriented uncorrelated electric dipoles within the active layer. Compared with [5], a somewhat simplified formalism is used, yielding, however, equivalent results.

In order to determine the spontaneous emission ratio

$$\alpha = \frac{\text{rate of spontaneous emission into one oscillating mode}}{\text{total rate of spontaneous emission}}$$

the excitation efficiency of the dipoles into the oscillating laser mode has to be calculated. For a time dependent field $\overline{E}(t)$, oscillating with an angular frequency ω, we will use in the following the complex field amplitude $E(\omega)$ according to

$$\overline{E}(t) = \text{Re}\,(\sqrt{2}\,E(\omega)\exp(j\omega t)).$$

Let us consider an electric dipole, situated at (x_p, y_p, z_p) within the active layer (see Fig. 2). The oscillating laser modes, which are to be excited, are modes with predominating TE-character, where the electric field component E_x dominates and where $E_y, E_z << E_x$. For exciting these modes the electric dipole is assumed to be oriented in x-direction and to oscillate with an angular frequency ω. The current distribution is then given as

$$J_x = (I \cdot l)\,\delta(x - x_p)\,\delta(y - y_p)\,\delta(z - z_p) \tag{1}$$

with $\delta(x)$ denoting the Dirac function.

The complex electric field E_x is obtained from the wave equation

$$\Delta E_x + \omega^2 \mu_0 \epsilon_0 \epsilon_r E_x = j\omega\mu_0 J_x \tag{2}$$

with Δ denoting the Laplacian operator and ϵ_r denoting the generally complex permittivity. The scalar wave equation (2) holds as long as relative changes of ϵ_r in x-direction are small.

Reprinted from *IEEE J. Quantum Electron.*, vol. QE-15, no. 7, pp. 566–570, July 1979.

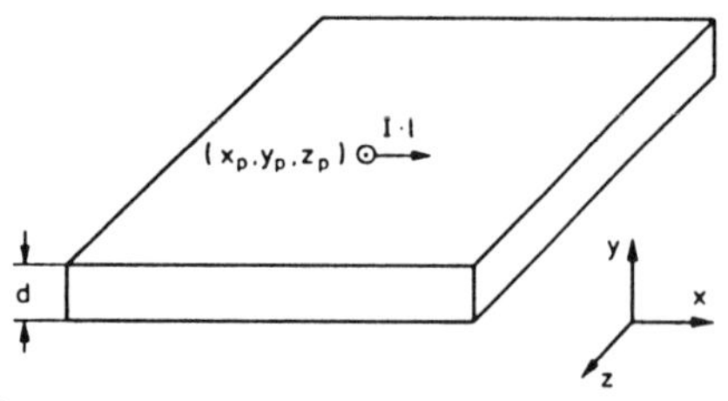

Fig. 2. Active layer and exciting dipole at (x_p, y_p, z_p).

The solutions of (2) for $J_x = 0$ are written as

$$E_x = E_m(x, y) \exp(\pm j\beta_m z). \tag{3}$$

The index m denotes the mth mode with the propagation constant β_m. $E_m(x, y)$ is generally complex. The dipole at (x_p, y_p, z_p) excites modes, traveling in $+z$ as well as in $-z$ direction. The modes traveling in $+z$-direction and $-z$-direction, respectively, are written as

$$E_{x+} = \sum_m D_{m+} \cdot E_m(x, y) \exp(-j\beta_m(z - z_p)) \quad z > z_p \tag{4}$$

$$E_{x-} = \sum_m D_{m-} \cdot E_m(x, y) \exp(+j\beta_m(z - z_p)) \quad z < z_p. \tag{5}$$

The electric field is continuous for $z = z_p$

$$E_{x-}\big|_{z=z_p} = E_{x+}\big|_{z=z_p}$$

so that

$$D_{m+} = D_{m-} = D_m.$$

An integration of (2) from $z = z_p - 0$ to $z = z_p + 0$ yields

$$\sum_m -2j\beta_m D_m E_m(x, y) = j\omega\mu_0(I \cdot l)\,\delta(x - x_p)\,\delta(y - y_p). \tag{6}$$

For calculating the excitation efficiency into the fundamental transverse mode $E_0(x, y)$, (6) is multiplied with $E_0(x, y)$ and integrated over the whole cross section. The orthogonality between modes is given as

$$\int_{-\infty}^{+\infty}\int_{-\infty}^{+\infty} E_0(x, y) E_m(x, y)\, dx\, dy = 0 \qquad \text{for } m \neq 0 \tag{7}$$

as can be shown with (2). Equation (6) then yields

$$D_0 = -\frac{\omega\mu_0(Il)\, E_0(x_p, y_p)}{2\beta_0 \iint E_0^2(x, y)\, dx\, dy}. \tag{8}$$

The required excitation efficiency η is given as

$$\eta = \frac{2P_0}{P_{\text{tot}}} \tag{9}$$

with P_{tot} denoting the total power radiated from the dipole and P_0 denoting the power in the fundamental transverse mode. The factor 2 in (9) takes into account that the mode traveling in $+z$-direction as well as the mode traveling in $-z$-direction contributes to the lasing mode. The power in the fundamental mode P_0 is obtained as

$$P_0 = \text{Re}\left\{\iint E_x H_y^*\, dx\, dy\right\} \tag{10}$$

where H denotes the magnetic field and * denotes "conjugate complex."

Since

$$H_y = E_x \frac{\beta_0}{\omega\mu_0} \tag{11}$$

the power in the fundamental mode is given as

$$P_0 = \text{Re}\left\{\frac{D_0 D_0^* \beta_0^*}{\omega\mu_0} \iint E_0 E_0^*\, dx\, dy\right\} \tag{12}$$

yielding with (8)

$$P_0 = \frac{1}{4}\sqrt{\frac{\mu_0}{\epsilon_0}}\,\frac{1}{n_e}\,(Il)^2\, |E_0(x_p, y_p)|^2\, \frac{\iint E_0 E_0^*\, dx\, dy}{\left|\iint E_0^2\, dx\, dy\right|^2} \tag{13}$$

where the index n_e is obtained as

$$\frac{1}{n_e} = \text{Re}\left\{\frac{\omega\sqrt{\mu_0\epsilon_0}}{\beta_0}\right\} \tag{14}$$

n_e approximately corresponds to the refractive index of the active layer.

The total power emitted from a dipole in a homogeneous material with refractive index n is given as [9]

$$P_{\text{tot}} = \frac{n}{6\pi}\,\omega^2\,\mu_0\sqrt{\mu_0\epsilon_0}\,(Il)^2. \tag{15}$$

Since the relative refractive index differences within the laser are small, (15) represents also a useful approximation for the radiated power of a dipole situated within the active layer.

η according to (9) is then given as

$$\eta = \frac{3\pi c^2}{n n_e \omega^2}\left|E_0(x_p, y_p)\right|^2 \frac{\iint E_0 E_0^*\, dx\, dy}{\left|\iint E_0^2\, dx\, dy\right|^2} \tag{16}$$

where the speed of light $c = 1/\sqrt{\mu_0\epsilon_0}$ has been introduced.

III. Calculation of the Spontaneous Emission Factor

By use of the excitation efficiency η, the spontaneous emission ratio α can be calculated. One obtains

$$\alpha = \frac{1}{3}\,\frac{\iint \eta \cdot i_{sp}(x_p, y_p)\, dx_p\, dy_p}{\iint i_{sp}(x_p, y_p)\, dx_p\, dy_p} \cdot f(\omega_0)\,\delta\omega. \tag{17}$$

The factor 1/3 takes into account, that the spontaneously emitting dipoles are arbitrarily oriented within the three coordinate directions and only those dipoles being oriented in x-direction contribute to the lasing TE-mode. The following integral expression averages the excitation efficiency η over all x_p, y_p, where $i_{sp}(x_p, y_p)$ denotes the intensity of spontaneous emission which is assumed to be independent of z. The excitation efficiency η according to (9) gives the excitation efficiency into the fundamental transverse mode without taking into account that the frequency of the radiating dipole must correspond to the lasing frequency $\omega = \omega_0$. Actually, the spectrum of the radiation of one dipole is considerably broader than the mode spacing between two longitudinal modes [5]. Under this condition the last term $f(\omega_0) \cdot \delta\omega$ accounts for the spectral part of the spontaneous emission which goes into the lasing mode. $\delta\omega$ denotes the difference in emission frequencies between two longitudinal modes and $f(\omega)$ denotes the normalized spontaneous emission line with $\int f(\omega)\, d\omega = 1$. The frequency difference between two longitudinal modes is given as

$$\delta\omega = \frac{\pi \cdot c}{L \cdot n_e'} \tag{18}$$

with $n_e' = \mathrm{Re}(d\beta_0/dk)$ where $k = 2\pi/\lambda \cdot L$ denotes the cavity length.

Inserting (16) and (18) into (17) yields

$$\alpha = \frac{\pi^2 c^3 f(\omega_0)}{n n_e n_e' \omega^2 L} \frac{\iint \left| E_0(x_p, y_p) \right|^2 i_{sp}(x_p, y_p)\, dx_p\, dy_p}{\iint i_{sp}(x_p, y_p)\, dx_p\, dy_p} \cdot \frac{\iint E_0 E_0^*\, dx\, dy}{\left| \iint E_0^2\, dx\, dy \right|^2}. \tag{19}$$

In the case of a constant active layer thickness $E_0(x, y)$ and $i_{sp}(x, y)$ may be written as

$$E_0(x, y) = F(x) \cdot G(y)$$

and

$$i_{sp}(x, y) = I_{sp}(x) \cdot R(y) \tag{20}$$

with

$$R(y) = \begin{cases} 1 \text{ within the active layer} \\ 0 \text{ outside the active layer.} \end{cases} \tag{21}$$

Equation (21) holds as long as the active layer thickness is small compared to the diffusion length. $I_{sp}(x)$ denotes the spatial distribution of spontaneous emission parallel to the active layer.[1]

[1] The shape of the distribution $I_{sp}(x)$ does not necessarily coincide with the spontaneous intensity distribution as observed at the mirror facets. The spatial spontaneous emission profile is visible only via the modes which are excited by $I_{sp}(x)$. These excited modes will reproduce $I_{sp}(x)$ at the facet, only, if the differences in propagation constants of the excited modes multiplied with the cavity length are sufficiently small, say $|\Delta\beta \cdot L| = |(\beta_m - \beta_n) \cdot L| << 1$. A better estimate for the spatial spontaneous emission profile $I_{sp}(x)$ may be obtained by observing the spontaneous emission perpendicular to the junction, as in [10].

Waveguiding perpendicular to the active layer (y-direction) is introduced via the heterojunctions of lower refractive index. Therefore index-guiding predominates in the y-direction and $G(y)$ is real:

$$G(y) = G^*(y).$$

$F(x)$, however, is complex owing to the gain-guiding mechanism. We introduce the confinement factor with respect to the active layer

$$\Gamma = \frac{\int_0^d G^2(y)\, dy}{\int_{-\infty}^{+\infty} G^2(y)\, dy} \tag{22}$$

with d denoting the active layer thickness.

The integration in (19) over y and y_p, respectively, can now be performed:

$$\alpha = \frac{\pi^2 c^3 f(\omega_0)}{n n_e n_e' \omega^2 L\, (d/\Gamma)} \frac{\int I_{st}(x) I_{sp}(x)\, dx}{\int I_{st}(x)\, dx \int I_{sp}(x)\, dx} \cdot K. \tag{23}$$

$I_{st}(x)$ denotes the intensity distribution of the stimulated emission parallel to the active layer in the fundamental transverse mode $I_{st}(x) = |F(x)|^2$. The factor K is given as

$$K = \frac{\left(\int \left| F(x) \right|^2 dx \right)^2}{\left| \int F^2(x)\, dx \right|^2} \tag{24}$$

and denotes the strength of astigmatism in the transverse fundamental mode. In the case of an index-guided mode with $F^2(x) = |F(x)|^2, K = 1$ is obtained. Otherwise K exceeds unity.

An effective laser width parallel to the active layer is introduced

$$w_{\mathrm{eff}} = \frac{\int I_{st}(x)\, dx \int I_{sp}(x)\, dx}{\int I_{st}(x) I_{sp}(x)\, dx}, \tag{25}$$

with which an effective volume of the active area is defined

$$V_{\mathrm{eff}} = L \cdot (d/\Gamma) \cdot w_{\mathrm{eff}} \tag{26}$$

yielding

$$\alpha = \frac{\pi^2 c^3 f(\omega_0) K}{n n_e n_e' \omega^2 V_{\mathrm{eff}}}. \tag{27}$$

Without astigmatism ($K = 1$) and for a dispersion-free fundamental transverse mode ($n_e' \approx n_e \approx n$) α according to (27) perfectly agrees with [5]. Taking the astigmatism into account, however, yields large deviations as discussed in the following.

It is often more convenient to write α with respect to the wavelength λ rather than with respect to the frequency ω. By introducing the emission line $g(\lambda) = f(\omega)\ (2\pi c/\lambda^2)$ with

$\int_0^\infty g(\lambda)\, d\lambda = 1$ one gets

$$\alpha = \frac{\lambda^4 g(\lambda_0) K}{8\pi n n_e n_e' V_{\text{eff}}}. \tag{28}$$

In the case of a Lorentzian line shape $g(\lambda)$ with the half-width (full width at half maximum) $\Delta\lambda$ with the maximum at λ_0 one arrives at

$$\alpha = \frac{\lambda^4 K}{4\pi^2 n n_e n_e' V_{\text{eff}} \Delta\lambda}. \tag{29}$$

Equation (29) differs by a factor of 2 from [5] although (27) perfectly agrees with [5].

IV. Discussion

The following discussion will be mainly devoted to the magnitude of the astigmatism parameter K and its influence on α. First of all, however, the effective width parallel to the junction w_{eff} will be given.

A. Effective Width Parallel to the Junction

The effective width w_{eff} is given according to (25) where we will assume a Gaussian distribution of $I_{st}(x)$ and $I_{sp}(x)$:

$$I_{st}(x) = I_0 \exp(-(x/w_{st})^2) \tag{30}$$

$$I_{sp}(x) = I_1 \exp(-(x/w_{sp})^2) \tag{31}$$

yielding

$$w_{\text{eff}} = \sqrt{\pi}\,\sqrt{w_{st}^2 + w_{sp}^2}. \tag{32}$$

From the experimental point of view it is more convenient to introduce the respective half widths (full width at half maximum) W_{st} and W_{sp}. We then obtain

$$w_{\text{eff}} = \sqrt{\frac{\pi}{4 \cdot \ln 2}}\,\sqrt{W_{st}^2 + W_{sp}^2} = 1.06\sqrt{W_{st}^2 + W_{sp}^2}. \tag{33}$$

B. Magnitude at the Astigmatism Parameter K

For estimating the magnitude of the astigmatism parameter we assume again a Gaussian field distribution

$$F(x) = F_0 \exp\left(-\tfrac{1}{2}(x/w_{st})^2 (1 + j\chi)\right) \tag{34}$$

where χ denotes the strength of astigmatism.

Evaluating (24) yields

$$K = \sqrt{1 + \chi^2}. \tag{35}$$

Equation (35) is not yet satisfactory, since the measurement of χ is difficult. A simple description is possible, however, via the far-field distribution. The far-field intensity distribution is obtained by the squared absolute value of the Fourier transform of (34) as

$$I(\varphi) = A \cdot \exp(-(\varphi/\gamma)^2) \tag{36}$$

with

$$\gamma = \frac{\sqrt{1 + \chi^2}}{w_{st} \cdot k} \tag{37}$$

where φ denotes the far-field angle parallel to the junction and k is the free space wavenumber $k = 2\pi/\lambda$. In (36), (37) we assume $\gamma << 1$ so that $\sin\gamma = \gamma$.

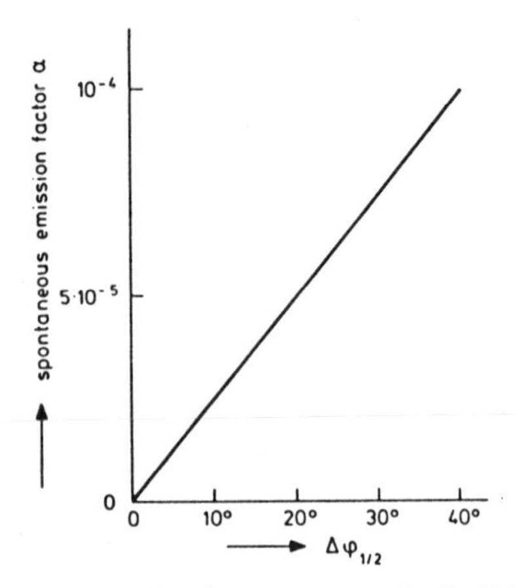

Fig. 3. Spontaneous emission factor α versus the far-field width $\Delta\varphi_{1/2}$ (full width at half maximum) parallel to the junction. Assumptions: $W_{sp} = W_{st}$, $n \approx n_e = 3.5$ $n_e' = 4.5$, $\lambda = 0.85$ µm, $L = 300$ µm, $\Delta\lambda = 300$ Å, $d = 0.2$ µm, $\Gamma = 0.6$ (corresponds to a difference in the Al-content of 30 percent between the heterojunctions and the active layer [13]).

Equations (35) and (37) yield

$$K = k \cdot \gamma \cdot w_{st}. \tag{38}$$

K thus represents the product of near- and far-field widths.

The Gaussian field distribution according to (35) occurs in an infinitely extending square-law gain- and index-profile [8]. In this case, the astigmatism parameter may be related to the ratio b between index guiding and gain guiding. By using (35) and the relations in [8] one gets

$$b = \frac{2 - K^2}{2\sqrt{K^2 - 1}}. \tag{39}$$

For $b = 0$ (pure gain guiding) one gets $K = \sqrt{2}$. In [8] index antiguiding up to $b = -3$ is reported, yielding much higher values for K; for $b = -3$, for example, one gets $K = 6.24$. It should be noted, that (39) only holds for the infinitely extending square-law profile. In the more interesting case of small stripe widths one obtains for a given b a still stronger astigmatism [11].

Equation (38) is now rewritten by introducing the half widths (full width at half maximum) in the far-field $\Delta\varphi_{1/2}$ and in the near-field W_{st}, respectively, instead of γ and w_{st}, yielding

$$K = \frac{1}{4 \ln 2} k \cdot \Delta\varphi_{1/2} \cdot W_{st}. \tag{40}$$

For planar stripe lasers with narrow stripe, which have been realized as a V-groove laser, one experimentally obtained the typical values $W_{st} = 8$ µm and $\Delta\varphi_{1/2} = 30°$ [12] yielding an astigmatism factor $K = 11$ at $\lambda = 0.85$ µm. The spontaneous emission factor thus becomes one order of magnitude larger than in lasers with a comparable volume of the active layer and with index guiding.

Inserting (40) into (29) finally yields

$$\alpha = \frac{\lambda^3 \Delta\varphi_{1/2}}{4\pi\sqrt{2\pi}\ln 2\, n n_e n_e' L (d/\Gamma) \Delta\lambda}. \tag{41}$$

In (41) the widths of spontaneous and stimulated emission, W_{sp} and W_{st}, respectively, are assumed to be equal. By additionally taking into account that d/Γ approximately corresponds to the extension of the optical field perpendicular to the junction, the expression $\lambda/(d/\Gamma)$ becomes approximately proportional to the far-field width perpendicular to the active layer. Therefore α becomes proportional to the solid angle of the laser radiation and is almost independent of the transverse dimensions of the active layer and the underlying guiding mechanism.

Fig. 3 shows the relation between the spontaneous emission ratio and the far-field half width $\Delta\varphi_{1/2}$ parallel to the junction (41) and Fig. 3 strictly holds only for a Gaussian field distribution. Otherwise (41) and Fig. 3 represent approximations only with which, however, the order of magnitude of α may be estimated.

V. Conclusions

We have shown that the spontaneous emission factor not only increases with decreasing volume of the active layer but also increases with increasing astigmatism.

The narrower the stripe width of planar stripe lasers the stronger is the astigmatism [8], [11]. Therefore, by narrowing the stripe width, the increase of the spontaneous emission factor is stronger than expected from the decrease of the active layer volume. Owing to the large spontaneous emission fraction narrow planar stripe lasers exhibit a much broader spectrum than lasers with a built-in index waveguide and a comparable volume of the active layer. The large spontaneous emission factor also yields an intensive superradiance around threshold as observed in [14] for very narrow planar strip lasers. The disappearance of relaxation oscillations may, at least partly, also be explained by the large fraction of spontaneous emission.

Acknowledgment

The author wishes to thank G. Arnold and P. Russer for helpful and stimulating discussions.

References

[1] R. Salathé, C. Voumard, and H. Weber, "Rate equation approach for diode lasers," *Opto-Electronics,* vol. 6, pp. 451-463, 1974.

[2] P. M. Boers, M. T. Vlaardingerbroek, and M. Danielsen, "Dynamic behavior of semiconductor lasers," *Electron Lett.*, vol. 11, pp. 206-208, May 15, 1975.

[3] K. Petermann, "Theoretical analysis of spectral modulation behavior of semiconductor injection lasers," *Opt. Quantum Electron.*, vol. 10, pp. 233-242, May 1978.

[4] J. Vilms, L. Wandinger, and K. L. Klohn, "Optimization of gallium arsenide injection lasers for maximum CW-power output," *IEEE J. Quantum Electron.*, vol. QE-2, pp. 80-83, Apr. 1966.

[5] Y. Suematsu and K. Furuya, "Theoretical spontaneous emission factor of injection lasers," *Trans. IECE Japan*, vol. E60, pp. 467-472, Sept. 1977.

[6] F. R. Nash, "Mode guidance parallel to the junction plane of double-heterostructure GaAs lasers," *J. Appl. Phys.*, vol. 44, pp. 4696-4707, Oct. 1973.

[7] D. D. Cook and F. R. Nash, "Gain-induced guiding and astigmatic output beam of GaAs lasers," *J. Appl. Phys.*, vol. 46, pp. 1660-1672, Apr. 1975.

[8] P. A. Kirkby, A. R. Goodwin, and G. H. B. Thompson, "Observations of self-focusing in stripe geometry semiconductor lasers and the development of a comprehensive model of their operation," *IEEE J. Quantum Electron.*, vol. QE-13, pp. 705-719, Aug. 1977.

[9] H. G. Unger, *Elektromagnetische Wellen I.* Braunschweig: Fr. Vieweg und Sohn, 1967.

[10] M. Nakamura, K. Aiki, and J. Umeda, "Direct observation of the saturation behavior of spontaneous emission in semiconductor lasers," *Appl. Phys. Lett.*, vol. 32, pp. 322-323, Mar. 1, 1978.

[11] K. Petermann, "Modes in active waveguides with inhomogeneous gain profiles as applied to injection lasers," *Arch. Elektron. und Übertragungstech.*, vol. 32, pp. 313-320, Aug. 1978.

[12] P. Marschall, E. Schlosser, and C. Wölk, "A new type of diffused stripe geometry injection laser," presented at the 4th European Conf. Optical Communication, Genova, Italy, post deadline paper XII.6, Sept. 1978.

[13] J. K. Butler and H. Kressel, "Design curves for double-heterostructure laser diodes," *RCA Rev.*, vol. 38, pp. 542-558, Dec. 1977.

[14] T. Kobayashi, H. Kawaguchi, and Y. Furukawa, "Lasing characteristics of very narrow planar stripe lasers," *Japan. J. Appl. Phys.*, vol. 16, pp. 601-607, Apr. 1977.

Single-Mode Stabilization by Traps in Semiconductor Lasers

JOHN A. COPELAND, SENIOR MEMBER, IEEE

Abstract—Recently it has been observed that certain single-transverse-mode semiconductor lasers continue to emit light predominantly in a particular longitudinal mode even after the optical gain peak has shifted by one or more mode spacings due to changes in bias current or temperature [1], [2]. The purpose of this paper is to show that this type of mode stabilization can be caused by the saturable optical absorption resulting from deep-level states or traps, which have been observed in AlGaAs laser structures [3]-[7]. The mode-selection mechanism is due to the spatial variation in the optical loss created by the standing-wave pattern of the single predominant mode. This loss pattern results in a lower average loss for the creating mode and a higher loss for all other modes. It is possible that laser devices with greatly improved single-mode stability can be made by introducing traps of the proper type and density during fabrication.

Saturable Loss Due to Traps

THE rate equation for deep levels in a laser previously used to explain sustained pulsations [8]-[10] can be used to derive the local optical absorption α as a function of the local photon density L (light intensity). First

$$\frac{dT}{dt} = \sigma_0 C_0 L (T_0 - T) - \sigma_e VNT \tag{1}$$

where T is the number of empty traps (whose electron or hole has been freed by optical stimulation into the conduction or valence band), σ_0 is the optical cross section, C_0 is the speed of light in the material, T_0 is the total number of traps, σ_e is the carrier capture cross section of an empty trap, N is the carrier density, and V is the carrier thermal velocity. The optical absorption is σ_0 times the density of filled traps:

$$\alpha = \sigma_0 (T_0 - T). \tag{2}$$

For a laser which is stable, the left side of (1) is zero and therefore

$$\alpha = \frac{\sigma_0 T_0}{1 + [\sigma_0 C_0/\sigma_e VN] \, L}. \tag{3}$$

This equation can be simplified by writing it in terms of the initial (low light) absorption due to traps α_0 and the photon density L_S where the absorption decreases by half. Then

$$\alpha(L) = \frac{\alpha_0}{1 + (L/L_S)} \tag{4}$$

where by definition

$$\alpha_0 = \sigma_0 T_0 \tag{5}$$

$$L_S = N\sigma_e V/\sigma_0 C_0. \tag{6}$$

Recently this type of saturable optical absorption was observed in $Al_{0.4}Ga_{0.6}As$ doped with Te by J. L. Merz, J. F. van der Ziel, and R. A. Logan [3]. This type of material is commonly used as a cladding layer in AlGaAs lasers. There appeared to be one deep level for each shallow donor, possibly due to lattice-defect complexing (similar behavior is expected for other common shallow donors, such as tin [3], [11]). The measured value of α_0 in $Al_{0.4}Ga_{0.6}As$ at 300 K was 6 cm^{-1}: however, in a laser structure with a 0.1 μm thick active layer, about 40 percent of the light is in the cladding layer so a smaller effective value will be used in the calculations to follow. The measured values of σ_0 and σ_n were 6×10^{-17} cm^2 and 5×10^{-17} cm^2, respectively, which indicated L_S was 8×10^{14} photons/cm^3. This corresponds to the average photon density in a laser emitting about 8 mW from a 0.1 by 5 μm facet.

Mode Loss

To compute the average loss for various modes when one mode predominates, it is assumed that the loss due to absorption by the traps can be calculated by first finding $\alpha(x)$ due to the photon density $L_d(x)$ of the dominant mode (mode number d)

$$L_d(x) = S_d \,|\exp(\beta_d x) - (-1)^d \exp(-\beta_d x)|^2 \tag{7}$$

$$\beta_d = \gamma_d + i2\pi/\lambda_d' \tag{8}$$

where x is zero at the center of the stripe and the mirrors are located at $x = -l/2$ and $l/2$. The mode amplitude is S_d and the wavelength in the cavity is λ_d'. The average optical gain parameter of the dominant mode γ_d is approximately equal to the cavity loss α_c which in the simplest case is related to the mirror reflectivity R by

$$\alpha_c = \ln(1/R)/l. \tag{9}$$

Now $\alpha(x)$ can be calculated using (4) and (7) for a given set of values of S_d/L_s, α_0, l, and R. Fig. 1 shows the calculated photon density at the center and near the end of a 300 μm laser (wavelength ≈ 0.25 μm) with a mirror reflectivity of 0.35 and mode amplitude S_d equal to $4L_s$. Below the photon density curves are plotted the calculated optical loss curves.

To calculate the loss due to traps for the various modes, it was assumed that the photon density for the nth mode would be given by (7) if the subscript d was replaced by n. The wavelength of mode n in the device is given by

Manuscript received November 11, 1979.
The author is with the Crawford Hill Laboratory, Bell Laboratories, Holmdel, NJ 07733.

Reprinted from *IEEE J. Quantum Electron.*, vol. QE-16, no. 7, pp. 721–727, July 1980.

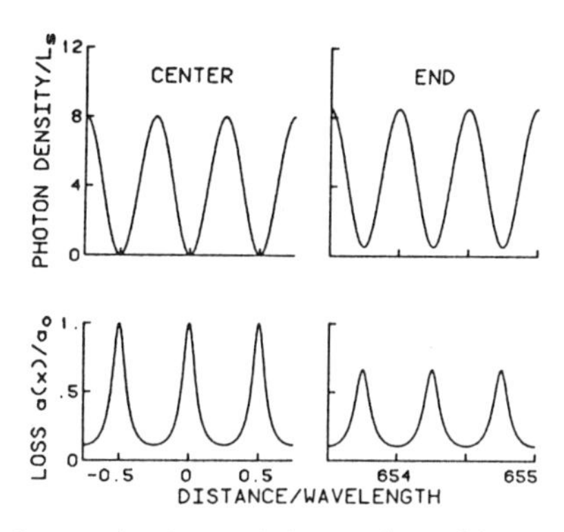

Fig. 1. The photon density variation and resulting variation of the saturable component of the optical absorption as a function of distance along the stripe for a region at the center and near the mirror (reflectivity = 0.35). The normalizing parameters L_S and α_0 are defined by (7) and (8).

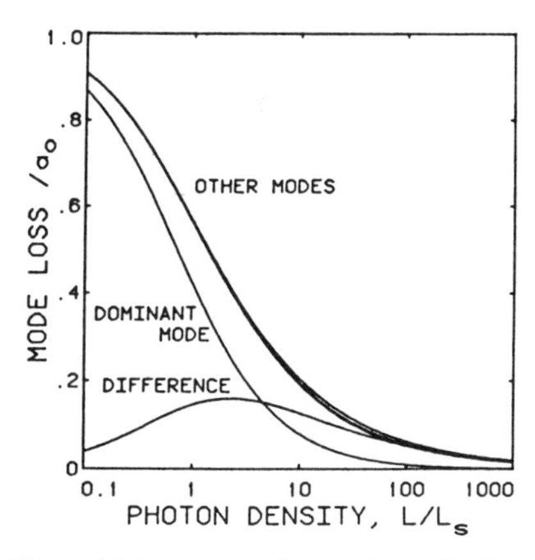

Fig. 2. The differential loss averaged over the cavity [see (11)] for the dominant mode and for other modes as a function of average photon density divided by L_S. The modes adjacent to the lasing mode have the highest loss. The difference is shown by the lower curve. A value of $L/L_S = 1$ corresponds to a power of 8 mW from a 0.1 by a 5 μm laser if the saturable absorption is due to the DX centers.

$$\lambda_n' = l/2n. \tag{10}$$

The wavelength in air λ_n is 3.65 times longer.

The average loss α_n is found by averaging $\alpha(x)$ with the normalized photon density as a weighting function

$$\alpha_n = \frac{\int_0^l \alpha(x) L_n(x)\, dx}{\int_0^l L_n(x)\, dx}. \tag{11}$$

By inspecting Fig. 1 it can be seen that the dominant mode will have the lowest mode loss because $\alpha(x)$ is always small when $L_d(x)$ is high and vice versa. All other modes have a higher loss because their standing-wave maxima are frequently situated in regions of higher loss.

Fig. 2 shows a plot of the average loss for the dominant (lasing) mode and a number of nearby modes as a function of the average photon density at the center S_n divided by the saturation parameter of the trap L_s. Also plotted is the difference in average loss between the adjacent modes and the dominant mode which is the important parameter for mode stabilization discussed in the next section.

Output Spectra

This section will develop the equations needed to calculate the mode spectra of a typical device with and without a small amount of saturable absorption due to traps. Parameter values will be chosen so that in the next section calculated results can be compared with the experimental results reported in [1].

By inspecting the functions $L_n(x)$ as shown in Fig. 1, it can be seen that the mode amplitude S_n differs from the average photon density by only a few percent if the mirror reflectivity R is greater than 0.3. For simplicity the mode amplitude S_n will be used interchangeably with the mode average photon density which appears in the rate equations below. These are similar to those presented by Y. Suematsu, S. Akiba, and T. Hong [12], except the effects of the traps and nonradiative carrier lifetime t_c have been added:

$$\frac{dN}{dt} = \frac{J}{ed} - \frac{N}{t_s} - \frac{N}{t_c} - C_\epsilon \sum_n \gamma_n S_n + \frac{dT}{dt} \tag{12}$$

$$\frac{dS_n}{dt} = \frac{cN}{t_s} + C_0 [\gamma_n - \alpha_c - \alpha_n] S_n. \tag{13}$$

Here J is the bias current density, t_s is the lifetime for spontaneous emission, γ_n is the medium gain (stimulated emission gain less band to band absorption) at the mode wavelength, and c is the spontaneous emission factor which can be found from [12, eq. (9)].

Optical confinement factors do not appear explicitly in the preceding equations so they should be considered as implicit in the various parameters. If Γ is the confinement factor for the active layer, the value for γ_n should be proportional to Γ when the active layer is thin and Γ is appreciably less than unity, as should the value of α_n if the traps are only in the active layer. If the traps are only in a cladding layer, the value of α_n should be scaled by $(1 - \Gamma)/2$. For the calculations here $\Gamma = 0.2$ will be used which is appropriate for an active layer thickness d of about 0.1 μm [13]. For stable operation, the spectra can be found from (13) to be given by

$$S_n = \frac{cN/C_0 t_s}{\alpha_c + \alpha_n - \gamma_n}. \tag{14}$$

To express the spectra in terms of radiated power per mode P_n

$$P_n = 0.4\,(1 - R)\, dwC_0 ES_n/\Gamma \tag{15}$$

$$= \frac{u}{\alpha_c + \alpha_n - \gamma_n} \tag{16}$$

where the factor 0.4 is used since the lasing filament usually occupies about 40 percent of the stripe width w when $w \lesssim 20$ μm.

Using the expression for the spontaneous emission factor given in [12], the mode-independent quantity u is given by

$$u = \frac{0.4\,(1 - R)\,\lambda^4 EN}{2\pi (n_s)^3 l \Delta\lambda t_s} \tag{17}$$

where w is the stripe width, E is the photon energy, and $\Delta\lambda$ is the spectral half width of the spontaneous emission. For a laser of the type used in [1], u has the value 0.03 mW/cm.

For the medium gain γ_n, the theoretical calculations of F. Stern [13] multiplied by Γ will be used. Since only the peak of the gain curve is important here, a parabolic fit can be used to obtain values of γ_n which are then given by

$$\gamma_n = \Gamma \times \{\gamma_p - [(\lambda_p - \lambda_n)/\lambda_0]^2\}. \tag{18}$$

Over the range of γ_n from 40 to 240 cm^{-1}, an approximate relation for the peak value (cm^{-1}) as a function of carrier density N is

$$\gamma_p = A\,(N - N_0) \tag{19}$$

where $A = 3.3 \times 10^{-16}\ \text{cm}^2$ and $N_0 = 1.1 \times 10^{18}\ \text{cm}^{-3}$. Stern's calculated gain curves for GaAs are fitted by a value of $0.9\ \text{nm} \cdot \text{cm}^{0.5}$ for λ_0.

Stern's calculations show that the wavelength, where γ_n is a maximum λ_p, becomes smaller by about 0.5 percent when N varies from 1.2 to $1.8 \times 10^{18}\ \text{cm}^{-3}$; however, the variation in N after a laser reaches threshold is much smaller than this. The predominant effect that shifts the gain peak in CW operation is an upward shift in λ_p due to heating [1] which reduces the bandgap energy. There is also a fixed shift in wavelength due to the aluminum content of the active layer. For the calculations here, a function which fits the experimental data in [1] will be used to obtain λ_p in nanometers.

$$\lambda_p = 841 + r_1 T_c \tag{20}$$

where the Celsius temperature T_c is related to current I by

$$T_c = T_A + r_2 I \tag{21}$$

where T_A is the ambient temperature. The experimental value for r_1 for AlGaAs lasers is 0.4 nm/°, and the value of r_2 depends on the device structure (0.06°/mA in [1]). For the calculations to follow, it will be assumed that the current I is related to the total power (sum of the mode powers) by

$$I = I_T + \eta^{-1} \sum_n P_n \tag{22}$$

with an efficiency factor η of about 0.25 mW/mA and a threshold current I_t of 70 mA.

The optical length of the cavity changes with temperature so that the cavity length l used in (11) to find the mode wavelength must be found by

$$l(T_c) = l_0\,[1 + aT_c]. \tag{23}$$

A value for a of $39 \times 10^{-6}\ \text{deg}^{-1}$ and a value for l_0 of 300 μm will be used.

Effect of α_0 on Spectra

Using the equations presented in the preceding sections, the laser spectra for five output powers P_T from 0.5 to 20 mW were calculated for $\alpha_0 = 0$ and for $\alpha_0 = 2.4\ \text{cm}^{-1}$ (corresponding to 6 cm^{-1} in the cladding layer). The results are shown in Fig. 3. The first column shows that with no saturable absorption the lines adjacent to the strongest line grow from 0.1 mW to about 1 mW as P_T increases from 1 to 20 mW.

The next two columns show that with $\alpha_0 = 2.4\ \text{cm}^{-1}$, the adjacent lines decrease slightly as the output increases above 3 mW, which is very similar to the behavior observed in [1] (see Figs. 1 and 2). Column 2 also shows the mode structure

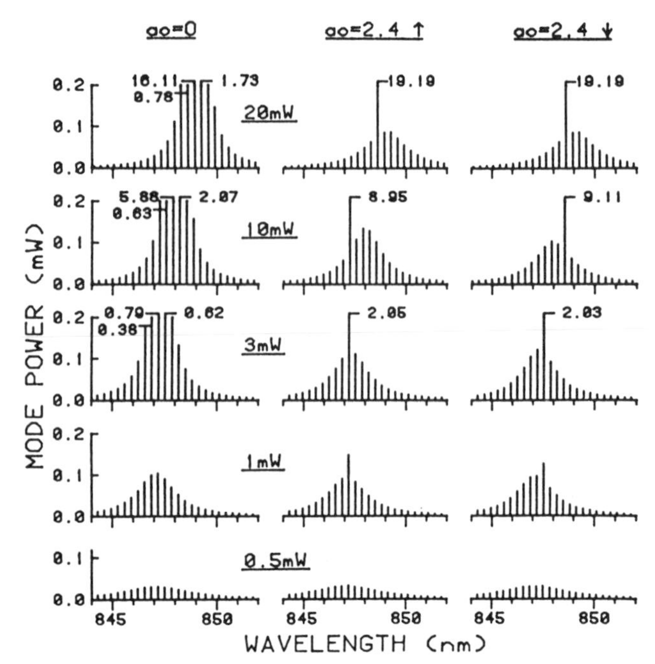

Fig. 3. The calculated mode spectra for five different power levels (rows) for $\alpha_0 = 0$ (first column) and $\alpha_0 = 2.4\ \text{cm}^{-1}$ with the output power increasing (second column) and decreasing (third column). The mode power is labeled in milliwatts when it exceeds 0.2 mW.

as output power increases. Notice that a single mode is dominant at a power level of 1 mW and this same mode remains dominant as the power is increased to 10 mW even though the gain peak, as shown by the peak in the subsidiary mode structure, has shifted by several mode spacings. Between 10 and 20 mW the mode, which is four mode numbers lower, suddenly becomes dominant, a phenomena known as "mode jumping." As the power is decreased again (column 3) the new dominant mode does not change until the power is reduced below 10 mW. This calculated hysteresis effect in the wavelength due to a value of $\alpha_0 = 2.4\ \text{cm}^{-1}$ is very similar to the hysteresis effect reported in [1, Fig. 6].

By varying the ambient temperature and keeping the total power constant, the wavelength for peak gain can be shifted without changing the value of the loss reduction $\Delta\alpha$ experienced by the dominant mode relative to the adjacent modes. Fig. 4 shows the power in the various modes as a function of temperature from 20 to 30°C with output power held equal to 3 mW. With no saturable absorption due to traps, the power in each of the modes from 2616 to 2630 grows and declines smoothly as the gain peak wavelength λ_p passes through the mode wavelength without hysteresis (bottom curves). The modes peak sequentially about every 0.7°.

When $\alpha_0 = 2.4\ \text{cm}^{-1}$ ($\Delta\alpha = 0.24\ \text{cm}^{-1}$), the initial dominant mode at 20°, 2630, remains dominant as the temperature increases (center curves) until at 22.0° the modes near mode 2627 begin to grow and then mode 2627 suddenly becomes dominant. As the temperature increases further the dominant mode changes suddenly every 2.1° to a mode three numbers lower.

At 30° the direction of temperature change was reversed (top curves). Initially mode 2618, which became dominant at 28.2°C when the temperature was rising, remains dominant as the temperature is decreased until a temperature 2.1° lower

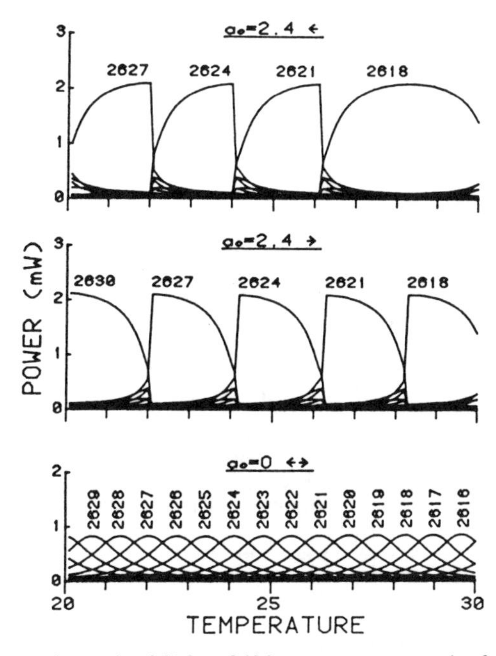

Fig. 4. Power in modes 2616 to 2630 as temperature varies from 20 to 30°C. The lower curves are for $\alpha_0 = 0$. The middle curves are for $\alpha_0 = 2.4 \text{ cm}^{-1}$ with temperature increasing, while the upper curves are for a subsequent decrease from 30°C. The total power is constant at 3 mW for a 0.1 × 5 × 200 μm device.

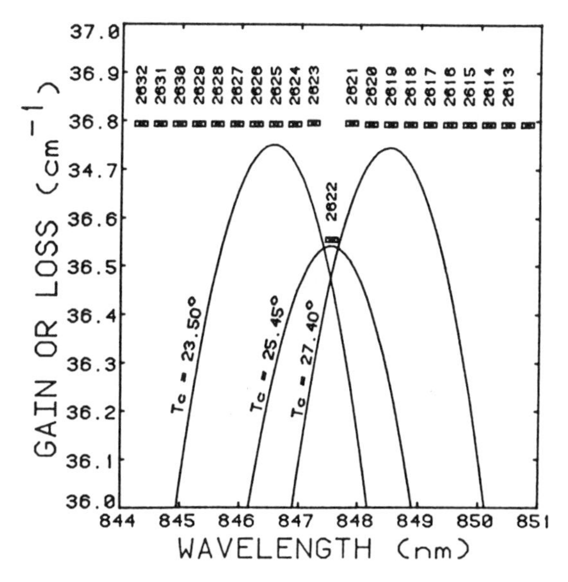

Fig. 5. The gain curve γ and the total mode losses $\alpha_c + \alpha_n$ for modes 2612 to 2632 when mode 2622 is the dominant mode at three temperatures. Three adjacent squares show the loss of the same mode at the three temperatures since the mode wavelength shifts upward with increasing temperature. The total power is 3 mW, so the difference between the loss and the gain of the dominant mode is approximately 0.01 cm^{-1}.

than 28.2°C is reached. After this the mode number of the dominant mode increases by three every 2.1°.

Once a mode n becomes dominant, it remains dominant as long as the temperature remains in the range of $T_n - \Delta T$ to $T_n + \Delta T$. The center of the stable range T_n is the temperature where the gain-peak wavelength λ_p equals the mode wavelength λ_n. If the temperature reaches the edge of this temperature range, the new dominant mode is the one whose wavelength is closest to λ_p at that temperature.

To explain this behavior, Fig. 5 shows the gain versus wavelength curve γ assuming mode 2622 is dominant at temperatures of 23.5, 25.45, and 27.40°. It also shows the total mode losses, $\alpha_n + \alpha_c$, for 3 mW total output. Keeping in mind that the mode powers are inversely proportional to $\alpha_c + \alpha_n - \gamma$, it can be seen why the mode three mode numbers away from the dominant mode becomes the next dominant mode ($\Delta n = 3$).

The mode jumps when

$$\Delta\alpha = \gamma_n - \gamma_{n+\Delta n} \tag{24}$$

or using (20)

$$\Delta\alpha = \Gamma (\Delta\lambda/\lambda_0)^2 \tag{25}$$

where $\Delta\lambda$ is the difference in wavelength between the dominant mode and the peak of the envelope of the other modes just before the jump. Thus

$$\Delta n = \text{int } [(\lambda_0/\lambda_s) \sqrt{\Delta\alpha/\Gamma}] \tag{26}$$

where λ_s is the mode spacing, int (x) means the nearest positive integer to x. Notice that Δn is proportional to the length of the laser ($\lambda_s \propto l^{-1}$) and to the square root of $(1 - \Gamma)/\Gamma$ if $\Delta\alpha$ is due to traps in the cladding layer ($\Delta\alpha \propto 1 - \Gamma$). For the present case where $d = 0.1$ μm and $\Gamma = 0.2$, the Γ dependent factor is equal to 2: however, for a laser with $d = 0.3$ μm and $\Gamma = 0.8$, this factor would be 0.5, and Δn would be 1. The effect of mode jumping by more than one mode will apparently be seen only in lasers with active layer thickness less than about 0.2 μm if the trap density is in the cladding layer and has the characteristics reported in [12] (10^{17} cm^{-3} *DX* centers).

Fig. 6 shows the wavelength of the dominant mode for five values of thickness from 0.10 to 0.40 μm. Notice that whether the range, where a particular mode is dominant when temperature is increasing overlaps or is separated from the mode's range when the temperature is decreasing, depends on whether the round off to the nearest integer implied by (26) is upward or downward. The experimental results reported in [1] show both a 35 percent overlap (see Fig. 6) and a 10 percent gap (see Fig. 5).

As the temperature changes the dominant mode will jump at temperature intervals ΔT_j given by

$$\Delta T_j = \Delta n \lambda_s / r_1 \tag{27}$$

where r_1 is the derivative of λ_p with temperature. A value of $\Delta T_j = 2°$ is reported in [1, Fig. 5], with $\Delta n = 2$ from 22 to 23.5° and $\Delta n = 1$ from 23.5 to 28° at a fixed current of 80 mA. The output power, about 2 mW, must have varied during this measurement because of variation of the threshold current with temperature. The lower temperature range would correspond to a higher output power and a larger $\Delta\alpha$ and Δn would be expected.

If the temperature change is due to a change in bias current, then $\Delta\alpha$ and consequently $\Delta\lambda$ and Δn will change also. In [1], the observed Δn was 3 at 85 mA (about 3 mW) and 4 at

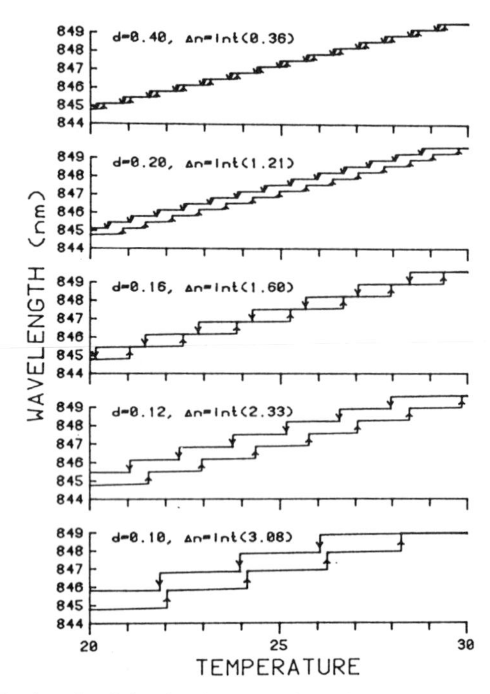

Fig. 6. Wavelength of the dominant mode as the temperature increases and subsequently decreases for five values of active layer thickness d from 0.10 to 0.40 μm. Also shown for each value of d is the value of the mode-jump interval Δn given by (26) before round off to the nearest positive integer.

110-140 mA (about 20 mW). For comparison, in the calculations described here, Δn is 1 at less than 0.5 mW, then 2 up to 1.6 mW, then 3 up to 6 mW, and 4 above 6 mW.

Other Considerations

One must carefully avoid reflections of laser output back onto one of the laser mirrors in an experimental setup. The difference between the middle spectra (3 mW) in columns 1 and 2 of Fig. 2 is due to a $\Delta\alpha$ of only 0.24 cm^{-1}. A reflection of one percent of the laser output back onto a mirror would create a comparable $\Delta\alpha_n$. A reflection which is even one-tenth of a percent or smaller would add a random fine structure to the mode envelope and cause premature dominant-mode jumps. Since the path length of such a reflection is usually several centimeters, the phase of the reflection would vary randomly between modes and would shift as the mode wavelength shifted, or as the setup vibrated.

If the effective value of α_0 becomes larger than about 6 cm^{-1}, the laser will exhibit sustained self-pulsations [8]-[10] unless the traps are hole traps or are electron traps situated so that the electrons excited from them do not contribute to the optical gain (e.g., in the cladding layer) [10].

The time required for a dominant mode to form a loss grating can be found from (1) and (5) to be about $(\alpha_0 C_0)^{-1}$ which is about 50 ps for $\alpha_0 = 2.4$ cm^{-1}. The saturable absorption due to traps can affect the instantaneous mode spectra of lasers which are pulsing. This may not be apparent in the time-averaged spectra, however, unless $\Delta n > 1$, since otherwise the dominant mode will jump during the pulse to follow the gain peak shift.

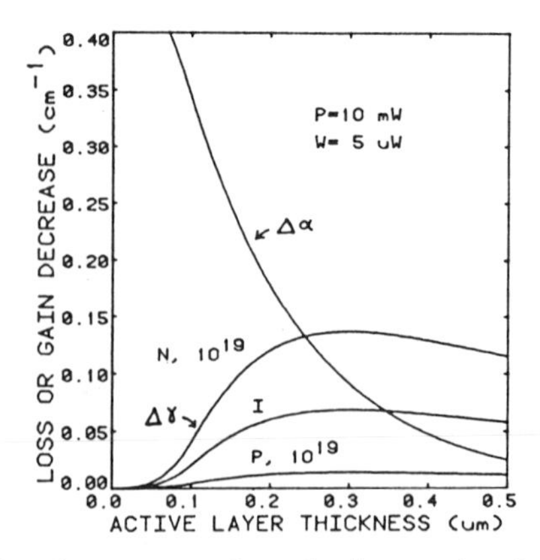

Fig. 7. The three lower curves show the decrease in gain for the dominant mode $\Delta\gamma$ due to spatial hole burning in the electron density as a function of active layer thickness for a heavily doped n-type active layer (N, 10^{19} cm^{-3}), a lightly doped active layer (I), and a heavily doped p-type active layer (P, 10^{19} cm^{-3}) for a power density equivalent to 10 mW from a 5-μm wide stripe ($\Delta\gamma$ for 10^{17} cm^{-3} DX centers in the n-type cladding layer.

The formation of a loss grating will be inhibited in devices where higher order transverse modes are present. Since there are more modes in the envelope and the average mode spacing is reduced, each mode will contain a smaller fraction of the total power and there will be more modes near the peak of the gain curve. For a parabolic gain curve (18), the output power required in order for the largest mode to contain a certain fraction of the total power increases as the inverse of the mode spacing squared.

Gain Grating

W. Streifer, R. D. Burnham, and D. R. Scifres discussed the fact that the standing-wave pattern of the dominant mode depletes the carrier density at the positions of the maxima and thus creates a decrease $\Delta\gamma$ in the gain γ_d of the dominant mode [14]. As they point out, this effect is greatly reduced at room temperature by the diffusion of carriers. To obtain a quantitative comparison of this effect with the effect of the decrease in loss $\Delta\alpha$, the following equation for $\Delta\gamma$ is derived in the Appendix:

$$\Delta\gamma = \frac{-\Gamma^2 A\gamma (\lambda_d')^2 P_d}{12.8\pi^2 (1-R)\, dwED} \tag{28}$$

where D is the ambipolar diffusion coefficient [14], [15] given by

$$D = \frac{(N+N_h) D_e D_h}{ND_e + N_h D_h} \tag{29}$$

where N_h is the hole density. Values for D_e and D_h, the electron and hole diffusion coefficients, used in [15], are 50 and 1 cm^2/s, respectively. If the active layer is doped less than 10^{18} cm^{-3}, D will be about $2D_h$ or 2 cm^2/s. Streifer, Burnham, and Scifres pointed out that a heavily doped (10^{19}) p-type active layer would have a value of D of about 10 cm^2/s which would decrease the magnitude of $\Delta\gamma$ by a factor of one fifth relative to a lightly doped layer.

Fig. 7 shows the values of $\Delta\gamma$ for n-type, intrinsic, and p-type active layers as a function of active layer thickness d for a power P_d of 10 mW and a stripe width of 5 μm. The value of $\Delta\alpha$ due to 10^{17} cm^{-1} DX centers in the n-type cladding layer is also shown. It can be seen that $-\Delta\alpha$ is an order of magnitude larger than $-\Delta\gamma$ when d is 0.1 μm or less, but that $-\Delta\gamma$ becomes larger than $-\Delta\alpha$ at a higher value of d (0.24 μm for n-type, 0.34 μm for intrinsic, and 0.60 μm for p-type).

It should be noted that $\Delta\gamma$ is proportional to the power density P_d/wd, whereas $\Delta\alpha$ varys more slowly with this quantity. The values of $\Delta\alpha$ due to DX centers will be proportional to the doping of the n-type cladding layer which varies in different devices. If the value of $\Delta\alpha$ had a component due to traps in the active layer, this component would increase with thickness since it would be proportional to Γ rather than $1 - \Gamma$.

The mode spectra presented earlier for $d = 0.1$ μm and $P_d \leqslant 20$ mW are not modified appreciably by adding the effect of $\Delta\gamma$. However, for devices with thicker active layers the effect of hole burning in the carrier density must be considered.

D. R. Scifres, R. D. Burnham, and W. Streifer report on devices with heavily doped p-type active layers 0.3 μm thick, which operated in a single mode at currents up to 2 amps [16]. While the p-type active layer would reduce $\Delta\gamma$ to 0.015 cm^{-1} at 10 mW, or 0.6 cm^{-1} at 400 mW (assuming the filament widths were 2 μm), these devices also had an unusually heavily doped n-cladding layer (10^{18} cm^{-3}) which would have produced a value of $\Delta\alpha$ of 0.9 cm^{-1}. From the work reported in this paper it would appear that both the 5×10^{18} cm^{-3} p-doped active layer and the 10^{18} n-doped cladding layer were necessary to keep $|\Delta\alpha| > |\Delta\gamma|$ at high power levels with an active layer that thick.

Conclusion

Calculations have been presented of the mode spectra of the AlGaAs laser with physical dimensions similar to the device used by Nakamura, Aiki, Chinone, Ito, and Umeda [1]. The calculated mode spectra which included the effect of deep levels in the n-cladding layer showed all the unusual effects observed by Nakamura *et al.*, such as predominance of a single mode, mode jumping by several mode numbers, and hysteresis effects as the power level or temperature varied. The physical characteristics used for the deep levels were those measured by Merz, Van der Ziel, and Logan [3]. There is quantitative agreement between the calculated mode spectra and the observed spectra suggesting that the effects observed may have been due to deep levels in the cladding layer.

Extending the calculations to other values of active layer thickness showed that the effect of the deep levels in the cladding layer is rapidly reduced as the thickness increases and will at some point, depending on device structure and power level, be suppressed by an opposite effect due to hole burning in the carrier density.

Having a laser which emits light primarily in a single mode which does not shift when output power and temperature change is very desirable for use in high-speed lightwave communications systems. If traps play the role that has been suggested, this characteristic can be enhanced by using thinner active layers and increasing the doping of the n-type cladding layer to increase the density of the deep levels. It should also be possible to enhance this effect by adding to the device structure appropriate dopants which form deep-level states, or by proton-bombarding the active region.

Appendix

To derive (28), which gives the value for the reduction in optical gain $\Delta\gamma$ due to the hole burning in the electron density N, one can start by adding a diffusion term to the right side of the rate equation (originally not needed since N was assumed spatially uniform), setting the time derivatives equal to 0, and assuming only one mode is present. Also, the photon density $L_d(x)$ is used in place of the average value S_d.

$$0 = \frac{J}{ed} - \frac{N}{t_s} - \frac{N}{t_c} - C_\epsilon \gamma L_d + D\frac{d^2N}{dx^2} \tag{A1}$$

where D is the ambipolar diffusion coefficient for the hole-electron plasma given by (29) [15].

It can be seen in Fig. 1 that the photon density (7) is given approximately by

$$L_d(x) = S_d\,(1 - \cos 4\pi x/\lambda_d') \tag{A2}$$

assuming d is even (the results are not affected if d is odd and a sine function is used). The electron density and optical gain are then expanded in Fourier series with the same periodicity as $L_d(x)$

$$N(x) = N_1 + N_2 \cos(4\pi x/\lambda_d) + \cdots \tag{A3}$$

$$\gamma(x) = \gamma_1 + \gamma_2 \cos(4\pi x/\lambda_d) + \cdots. \tag{A4}$$

When (A2)-(A4) are substituted into (A1), equating the terms with periodicity $\lambda_d/4\pi$ leads to

$$0 = -\frac{N_2}{t_s} - \frac{N_2}{t_c} - C_\epsilon S_d(\gamma_1 - \gamma_2) - N_2 D\left(\frac{4\pi}{\lambda_d}\right)^2. \tag{A5}$$

At this point the first two terms on the right of (A5) can be dropped since they are more than two orders of magnitude smaller than the last term. Thus, the amplitude of the electron density variation is given by

$$N_2 = \frac{C_\epsilon(\gamma_1 - \gamma_2) S_d (\lambda_d)^2}{16\pi^2 D}. \tag{A6}$$

Evaluating (A6) shows that N_2 is three to four orders of magnitude smaller than the average value of N. This suggests that γ_2 can be dropped from (A6) since it will be much smaller than γ_1 (0.1 cm^{-1} versus 35 cm^{-1}).

The spatially varying component of the optical gain (A4) can be found from (A3), (18), and (19) to be

$$\gamma_2 = \Gamma A N_2. \tag{A7}$$

Replacing α by γ in (13) to find the change in the average mode gain $\Delta\gamma$ due to the spatially varying component of γ leads to

$$\Delta\gamma = -0.5\,\gamma_2. \tag{A8}$$

Combining (A8), (A7), and (A6) and using the approximation $\gamma_1 - \gamma_2 = \gamma_d$ produces (28) which is the objective of this Appendix.

References

[1] M. Nakamura, K. Aiki, N. Chinone, R. Ito, and J. Umeda, "Longitudinal-mode behaviors of mode-stabilized $Al_xGa_{1-x}As$ injection tion lasers," *J. Appl. Phys.*, vol. 49, pp. 4644–4648, Sept. 1978.

[2] M. Yamada, K. Uayano, H. Ishiguro, F. Iida, S. Kido, and Y. Suematsu, "Stabilization of longitudinal mode in junction laser," presented at the 1978 IEEE Int. Semiconductor Laser Conf., Oct. 30, 1978; also in *OQE IECE*, vol. 78, pp. 65–70, Jan. 23, 1979.

[3] J. L. Merz, J. P. Van der Ziel, and R. A. Logan, "Optical absorption and saturation of the deep Te-complex center in $Al_xGa_{1-x}As$," *Phys. Rev.*, July 15, 1979.

[4] D. V. Lang, R. L. Hartman, and N. E. Schmaker, "Capacitance spectroscopy studies of degraded $Al_xGa_{1-x}As$ DH stripe geometry lasers," *J. Appl. Phys.*, vol. 47, pp. 4986–4992, 1976.

[5] H. Imai, K. Isozumi, and M. Takusagawa, "Deep level associated with the slow degradation of GaAlAs DH laser diodes," *Appl. Phys. Lett.*, vol. 33, pp. 330–332, 1978.

[6] T. Uji, "Deep levels in the n-$Al_{0.3}Ga_{0.7}As$ layer of (AlGa)As double-heterostructure lasers," *Japan. J. Appl. Phys.*, vol. 17, pp. 727–728, 1978.

[7] T. Kobayashi, "Recombination-enhanced annealing effect of AlGaAs-GaAs remote junction heterostructure lasers," presented at the 1978 IEEE Semiconductor Laser Conf., Oct. 30, 1978.

[8] M. J. Adams, "A theory of oscillations in the output of GaAs junction lasers," *Phys. Stat. Sol. (a)*, vol. 1, pp. 143–152, 1970.

[9] D. Kato, "Microscale degradation in (GaAl)As double-heterostructure diode lasers," *Appl. Phys. Lett.*, vol. 31, pp. 588–590, 1977.

[10] J. A. Copeland, "Semiconductor self-pulsing due to deep-level traps," *Electron. Lett.*, vol. 14, pp. 809–810, Dec. 7, 1978.

[11] B. Balland, G. Vincent, and D. Bois, "Donor-levels analysis in GaAlAs double heterostructure," *Appl. Phys. Lett.*, vol. 34, pp. 107–109, Jan. 1, 1979.

[12] Y. Suematsu, S. Akiba, and T. Hong, "Measurement of spontaneous-emission factor of AlGaAs double-heterostructure semiconductor lasers," *IEEE J. Quantum Electron.*, vol. QE-13, pp. 596–600, Aug. 1977.

[13] H. C. Casey, Jr. and M. B. Panish, *Heterostructure Lasers: Part A.* New York: Academic, 1978, p. 56 and 164.

[14] W. Streifer, R. D. Burnham, and D. R. Scifres, "Dependence of longitudinal mode structure on injected carrier diffusion in diode lasers," *IEEE J. Quantum Electron.*, vol. QE-13, 1977.

[15] J. P. McKelvey, *Solid State and Semiconductor Physics.* New York: Harper and Row, 1966, pp. 325–331.

[16] D. R. Scifres, R. D. Burnham, and W. Streifer, "Single longitudinal mode operation of diode lasers," *Appl. Phys. Lett.*, vol. 31, pp. 112–114, 1977.

Fundamental line broadening of single-mode (GaAl)As diode lasers

Mark W. Fleming [a] and Aram Mooradian
Lincoln Laboratory, Massachusetts Institute of Technology, Lexington, Massachusetts 02173

(Received 10 November 1980; accepted for publication 19 January 1981)

The spectral width of (GaAl)As cw single-mode diode lasers varied linearly with reciprocal output power at 300 K with a slope 50 times greater than that predicted by the Schawlow-Townes expression without partial inversion. While the spectral narrowing observed at 77 K for constant mode power is consistent with the predicted temperature dependence of the partial inversion contribution, the magnitude of the broadening can not completely be attributed to partial inversion.

PACS numbers: 42.55.Px

Although emission linewidths previously have been reported for various semiconductor lasers operating under diverse conditions,[1-4] heretofore no systematic determination of the dependence of linewidth on mode power has been published for a single-mode cw room-temperature injection laser. There are some indications, however, that the frequency broadening in single-mode lasers with tight optical confinement in active regions of small cross-sectional area, such as the channel-substrate-planar (CSP)-structure devices,[5] is considerably greater than the theoretical expections.[4,6] The importance of a thorough understanding of linewidth broadening in single-mode diode lasers is increasing as those devices are considered for practical applications in frequency-modulated data links, interferometric transducers, laser gyros, and high-resolution spectroscopy. In the experiment described here, the linewidth of two single-mode Hitachi HLP-1700 laser diodes was measured as a function of injection level, with the result that the width decreases linearly with reciprocal mode power but at a rate approximately 50 times greater than that predicted by the Schawlow-Townes formula without the partial inversion factor.[7]

The lasers studied had a threshold of about 68 mA and an emission spectrum which became essentially single-mode for injection currents above 80 mA. For currents above 88 mA the total intensity of the neighboring longitudinal modes was less than 1% of the lasing mode intensity. The devices oscillated at wavelengths of 817.5 and 832 nm at 295 K. The diodes were 280 μm long, with a 7-μm stripe width and a 0.1-μm active-region thickness. The material absorption coefficient α was determined to be 45 cm^{-1} from a measurement of the external differential efficiencies. Current was supplied to each device by a lead-acid storage battery connected through a temperature-compensated variable series resistance ranging from 50 to 100 Ω. A capacitive-input π filter was inserted between the diode and the variable current source in order to reduce the current noise bandwidth in the laser to 500 kHz. Within this bandwidth the current fluctuations due to Johnson noise in the series resistors and shot noise in the diodes themselves did not significantly contribute to the observed laser linewidths. The laser temperature was stabilized by mounting the diode packages on a copper heat sink in a vacuum. The temperature was sufficiently stable so that the laser drift was much less than 1 MHz/sec when thermal equilibrium was reached.

The diode laser linewidth was analyzed by a scanning Fabry-Perot confocal interferometer with 3.5-MHz resolution. Great care was exercised to eliminate optical feedback to the laser diode from reflecting surfaces in the beam path. The effects of this feedback could be identified as a rather dramatic linewidth narrowing which was extremely sensitive to acoustic or mechanical perturbations. When the feedback was eliminated, either by tilting the offending surface or by inserting optical attenuators in the beam path, the laser line spectrum resumed a steady shape. Throughout the experiment, the diode junction temperature was held constant enough to ensure that the characteristic laser mode hops occurred at well-defined injection levels which could be avoided when the linewidth measurements were taken. Besides the measurements taken with the Fabry-Perot interferometer, the linewidth of the single-mode diode laser was observed by heterodyning the output with a highly stabilized, narrow-linewidth external-cavity (GaAl)As diode laser operating in the same wavelength range.[8] The external-cavity diode laser had a short-term (one second) rms frequency jitter of 500 kHz. Analysis of the heterodyne spectra indicated that the spectral lineshape of the Hitachi lasers was Lorentzian.

Results of the determination of linewidth versus reciprocal power are illustrated in Fig. 1. The data corrected for instrumental resolution were fitted to a straight line described by $2\Gamma\,(\text{MHz}) = (114 \pm 5)P_0^{-1}\,(\text{mW}^{-1})$. The predicted linewidth due to quantum phase fluctuations is given by the modified Schawlow-Townes relation[7]

$$2\Gamma = (h\nu/8\pi P_0)\,(c/nl)^2(\ln R - \alpha l)\,(\ln R)\,n_{sp} \qquad (1)$$

[a] Present address: Central Research Laboratories, 3M Center, St. Paul, Minnesota 55144.

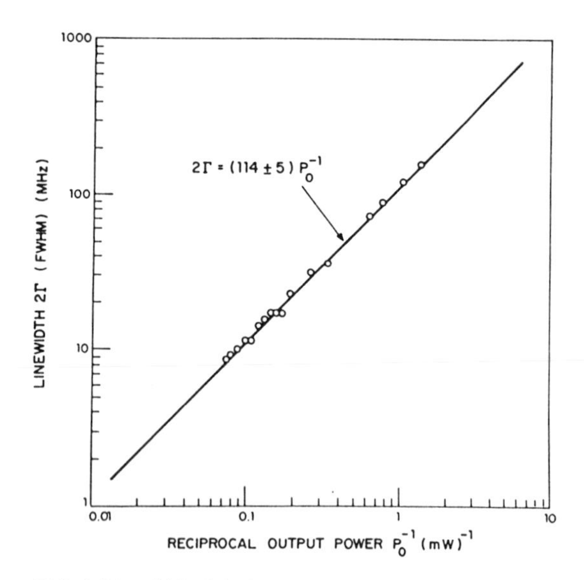

FIG. 1. Linewidth of single-mode output of Hitachi HLP-1700 diode lasers at room temperature as a function of reciprocal output power. The variance is $\pm$ 1.5 MHz for output powers greater than 5 mW and $\pm$ 5 MHz for the points at lower power. Solid line is a least squares fit to data.

where 2Γ is the full-width at half-maximum of the emission line at frequency ν, P_0 is the single-ended output power, n is the refractive index, l is the cavity length, α is the material absorption coefficient, R is the facet reflectivity, and n_{sp}, the spontaneous emission factor, is the ratio of the spontaneous emission rate per mode to the stimulated emission rate per laser photon. In a semiconductor laser, the spontaneous photon emission factor n_{sp} may be written as[9]

$$n_{sp} = \{1 - \exp[(h\nu + E_{Fv} - E_{Fc})/kT]\}^{-1}, \qquad (2)$$

where E_{Fc} and E_{Fv} are the conduction- and valence-band quasi-Fermi levels, k is the Boltzmann constant, and T is the temperature. In most lasers, n_{sp} is nearly unity, but for semiconductor lasers with nondegenerate carrier distribution functions, n_{sp} can become significantly grater than unity. The striking feature of Fig. 1 is the expected linear dependence of the linewidth on reciprocal power but with a slope 50 times greater than calculated from Eq. (1) for $n_{sp} = 1$. Parameter values for the (GaAl)As laser used here are known accurately enough to provide a cavity linewidth determination of better than $\pm$ 20%. The biggest uncertainty in the factor n_{sp} is the difference $(E_{Fc} - E_{Fv}) - h\nu$. Since n_{sp} is such a rapidly diverging function of $(E_{Fc} - E_{Fv}) - h\nu$, a value of nearly 0.5 meV would be necessary to account for the observed factor of 50. A value of 0.5 meV would seem too low at room temperature. Independent experimental determinations of this parameter[10] in (GaAl)As diode lasers with a somewhat different type of tight confining structure give a value of 12 meV.

Measurements were carried out at liquid-nitrogen temperature in order to determine if the linewidth narrowed as predicted by Eq. (2). For single-mode output powers from 0.5–4 mW the observed slope was 2.2 $\pm$ 0.3 times smaller than that observed at room temperature, where the measurements were made in the range 0.7–15 mW. This observation is entirely consistent with Eq. (2). It is interesting to note that the ratio $(n_{sp})_{300\,K}/(n_{sp})_{77\,K}$ is only weakly dependent upon the parameter $(E_{Fc} - E_{Fv}) - h\nu$, ranging from 3.9 to 2.0 as $(E_{Fc} - E_{Fv}) - h\nu$ goes from 0 to 15 meV. Values of the parameter $(E_{Fc} - E_{Fv}) - h\nu$ greater than 15 meV would be unlikely for the range of conditions in the present experiment and less than 0 would not satisfy the laser threshold condition. For power levels above 4 mW at liquid-nitrogen temperatures and all power levels at liquid-helium temperature, the diode outputs became multimode, causing appreciable broadening to the width of each frequency owing to mode competition. Changes in the cavity parameters with temperature were estimated to be small enough not to significantly alter the linewidth.

Equation (1) describing the phase-fluctuation contribution to the laser frequency emerges from the assumption that the laser gain is not strongly saturated. This case was treated for semiconductor lasers by Haug and Haken.[9] Elesin and Rusakov[11] later showed theoretically that in the strongly saturated regime the Schawlow-Townes formula must be multiplied by a power-independent factor of the order of 100–1000. In the low-intensity regime the standard Schawlow-Townes relation was recovered. The situation in the intermediate case unfortunately was not analyzed by Elesin and Rusakov, but it is reasonable to assume that a continuous transition should connect the two extreme cases, with line broadening by a factor ranging from 1 to 100. If the Elesin and Rusakov mechanism is operative for the present range of measurements, then the observed P^{-1} dependence would be quite fortuitous, since a non-P^{-1} dependence is expected in the intermediate saturation regime. This theory may contribute to the linewidth, but experiments should be carried out at liquid-helium temperature on a single-mode device in order to reduce n_{sp} to unity and thus determine any residual contributions to the broadening.

In conclusion, we have observed that the spectral width of single-mode room-temperature cw (GaAl)As diode lasers increases linearly with reciprocal output power. The observed decrease in single-mode linewidth from 300 to 77 K is consistent with predictions for a partially inverted system.

We would like to acknowledge the technical assistance of B. Feldman and R. Hancock as well as helpful discussions with P. L. Kelley and B. Lax. This work was sponsored by the Department of the Air Force.

[1]J. A. Armstrong and Archibald W. Smith, Appl. Phys. Lett. **4**, 196 (1964).
[2]W. E. Ahearn and J. W. Crowe, IEEE J. Quantum Electron. **QE-2**, 597 (1966).
[3]E. D. Hinkley and Charles Freed, Phys. Rev. Lett. **23**, 277 (1969).
[4]V. I. Annenkov, Yu M. Mironov, V. I. Molochev, and A. S. Semenov, Sov. J. Quantum Electron. **8**, 795 (1978).
[5]K. Aiki, M. Nakamura, T. Kuroda, and J. Umeda, Appl. Phys. Lett. **30**, 649 (1977).
[6]Kenichi Iga (private communication).
[7]Melvin Lax, in *Physics of Quantum Electronics*, edited by P. L. Kelley, B. Lax and P. E. Tannenwald, (McGraw-Hill, New York, 1966), p. 735.
[8]M. W. Fleming and A. Mooradian, IEEE J. Quantum Electron. **QE-17**, 44 (1981).
[9]H. Haug and H. Haken, Z. Phys. **204**, 262 (1967).
[10]C. H. Henry, R. A. Logan, and F. R. Merritt, J. Appl. Phys. **51**, 3042 (1980).
[11]V. F. Elesin and V. V. Rusakov, Sov. J. Quantum Electron. **5**, 1239 (1976).

Frequency-Locking of a GaAlAs Laser to a Doppler-Free Spectrum of the Cs–D_2 Line

Tsutomu YABUZAKI, Akira IBARAGI*, Hirokazu HORI, Masao KITANO and Toru OGAWA

Radio Atmospheric Science Center, Kyoto University, Uji, Kyoto 611

(Received April 30, 1981; accepted for publication May 12, 1981)

Preliminary results are reported on the first frequency-locking of a cw GaAlAs laser, operating at room temperature on a single mode, to a Doppler-free spectrum in the saturated absorption of the Cs–D_2 line at 852.1 nm.

§1. Introduction

Recently diode lasers have extensively been developed, and cw operation on a single longitudinal mode is now possible at room temperature, the oscillation frequencies covering the spectral range from infrared to visible. Because of the small size, low electric power to operate, and easy operation on a single mode, they are now being used in various fields and considered to have a high potentiality in wide variety of future applications. The diode lasers have, however, rather poor frequency-stability in the free-running condition, which is a reflection of their high frequency-tunability.

The frequency-stabilization of a diode laser has been done so far mainly by using a Fabry-Perot interferometer as an external reference.[1–3] Recently Tsuchida *et al.* used the Fabry-perot interferometer controlled by a stabilized He-Ne laser in the frequency-stabilization of a GaAlAs laser and obtained the Allan variance between 2×10^{-9} and 2×10^{-11} at the averaging time between 10 ms and 500 s.[4] Another way of stabilization is to lock the laser frequency directly to an atomic or molecular line. To this direction, Ohi reported the frequency-locking of a PbSnTe laser, operating at the liquid nitrogen temperature, to methane absorption lines in the ν_4 band at the wavelengths around 7.7 μm, and the minimum Allan variance was estimated to be 4.3×10^{-11} at the averaging time of 15 s.[5]

In this letter we report the preliminary experimental results on the first frequency-locking of a GaAlAs laser to a Doppler-free spectrum in the saturated absorption of the Cs-D_2 line at 852.1 nm. Since the laser operates at about room temperature, the temperature control can easily be done by using a small thermoelectric cooler, by which either cooling or heating is possible. In addition, a small Cs cell can be used at room temperature (the corresponding vapor pressure of Cs being $\sim10^{-6}$ Torr), so that the frequency-locking can be made without sacrificing the advantages of a diode laser such as its small size, which may be important particularly in practical applications.

§2. Experiments

The GaAlAs laser used was a commercially available double-heterostructure type, operating on a single mode with the maximum output power ~5 mW. The diode laser with the oscillation frequency close to the Cs–D_2 line at room temperature was selected, and it was mounted on an aluminum block attached tightly to a thermoelectric cooler (Peltier element) to control the temperature. As is well known, with the increase of the laser temperature, the oscillation frequency shifts toward the lower frequency side, repeating a continuous change and a mode-hopping. In the case of the laser used in the present experiment, the rate of change in wavelength was measured to be 0.04 nm/°C in the continuously changing region. Similar shift of the oscillation frequency occurs when the driving current of the laser is changed. It should be noted that, in most lasers used, the resonance frequency can be put in a continuously changing region by choosing

*Present address: Research Center, Sanyo Electric Co. Ltd., Hirakata-shi, Osaka 573.

Reprinted with permission from *Japan. J. Appl. Phys.*, vol. 20, no. 6, pp. L452–L454, June 1981.

an adequate combination of the temperature and the driving current. In order to get the first derivative of resonances, the driving current was modulated at 100 Hz with the amplitude of few μA, which gives the frequency deviation of few MHz in the frequency-modulation of the emitted light.

The laser beam was splitted into two beams, which were used as a saturating beam and a probe beam. These beams were applied to a cylindrical Cs cell with the length of 5 cm from the opposite directions to each other. The power of the saturating beam was reduced to about 0.4 mW by a neutral density filter in order to decrease the power broadening of Doppler-free spectra observed as an intensity change of the weak probe beam ($\sim 5\ \mu$W). Both of these two beams were detected by photodiodes after transmitted through the cell. When we swept the laser frequency through the D_2 line by sweeping the laser current or temperature, we could observe small but sharp signals on the Doppler-broadened background directly in the output of the photodiode detecting the probe beam, while the output of the photodiode detecting the saturating beam showed only the Doppler-broadened resonance. So, we used the latter signal to reduce the Doppler-broadened background by applying the outputs of both photodiodes to a divider circuit, whose output was then applied to a lock-in amplifier tuned at 100 Hz. The time constant in the lock-in detection was kept constant at 1 s throughout the present experiment.

Figure 1 shows the derivative of resonances obtained by sweeping the laser frequency ν through the absorption lines from the hyperfine state with $F=4$ in the ground state $6^2S_{1/2}$. Since the $F=4$ state is optically connected with three hyperfine states with $F=3$, 4 and 5 in the $6^2P_{3/2}$ state, six resonances are expected to appear; three being the ordinary Lamb dips,[6] and other three being the crossover resonances.[7] In Fig. 1 we show also the positions of these resonances expected from the theoretical calculation of hyperfine separations in $6^2P_{3/2}$.[8] Similar signals could be obtained when the laser frequency was swept through the absorption lines from the $F=3$ state in the ground state.

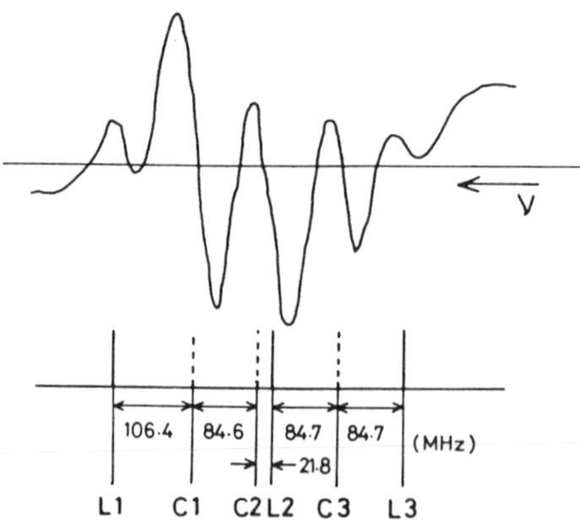

Fig. 1. First derivative of Doppler-free resonances and their positions expected from the theoretical calculation. The laser frequency was swept through the absorption lines from the hyperfine state with $F=4$ in the ground state of Cs. The symbols L1, L2 and L3 represent the Lamb dips due to the transitions to the states with $F=5$, 4 and 3 in the $6^2P_{3/2}$ state, and C1, C2 and C3 represent the crossover resonances due to the pairs of transitions to the states with $F=5$ and 4, $F=5$ and 3, and $F=4$ and 3 in $6^2P_{3/2}$, respectively.

Before locking the laser frequency at one of the resonances shown in Fig. 1, the laser temperature was stabilized. The change of the temperature was detected by measuring the change of the resistance of a thermistor mounted close to the laser on the aluminum block. The thermistor was inserted into a bridge circuit, whose output, proportional to the difference from the preset resistance, was amplified and fed back to the driving current of the thermoelectric cooler. By stabilizing the temperature in this way, the fluctuation of the laser frequency was measured to be within 15 MHz for 1 hour at least, which corresponds to the temperature fluctuation within 7.5×10^{-4}°C (see Fig. 2(b)).

After stabilizing the temperature, we locked the laser frequency to a Doppler-free signal by feeding back the error signal from the lock-in amplifier to the laser current. Figure 2(a) shows the trace of the output of the lock-in amplifier in the case that the laser frequency was locked at the center of the crossover resonance Cl in Fig. 2. (The crossover resonance Cl occurs at the arithmetic mean frequency of the transitions from the $F=4$ state in the ground state to the $F=4$ and 5 states in the $6^2P_{3/2}$ state). From Fig. 2(a) we see that the short term fluctuation is within 400 kHz. For comparison, we show in Fig. 2(b) and (c) the

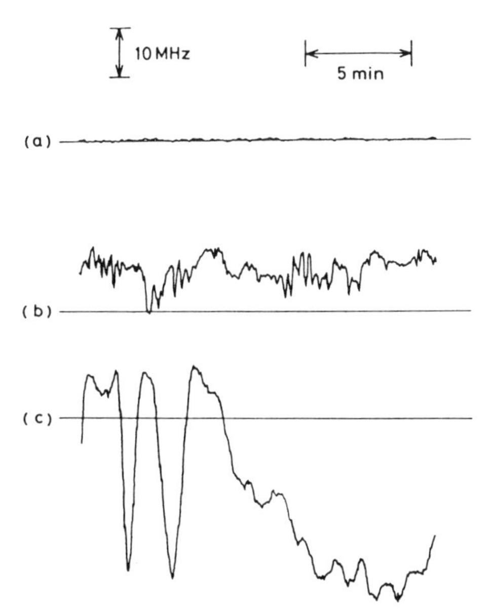

Fig. 2. Recorder traces showing the output of the lock-in amplifier in the three cases that (a) both of the laser current and temperature were stabilized, (b) only the temperature was stabilized, and (c) both were not stabilized. The laser frequency was initially tuned at about the center of the crossover resonance C1 shown in Fig. 1. The fluctuation in the cases (a) and (b) can be regarded as that of the laser frequency, since the laser frequency is in the central region of the resonance. The frequency scale shown is the one estimated from the slope in the derivative of the resonance.

traces of the output of the lock-in amplifier in the cases that only the laser temperature was stabilized and that both of feed-back loops were open, respectively. These traces were obtained by setting the laser frequency initially at about the center of the crossover resonance C1. The Allan variance[9] in the low frequency region was estimated from such a trace as shown in Fig. 2(a), and the result is shown in Fig. 3, where we see that the minimum value is about 1.6×10^{-10} at the averaging time τ between 15 s and 240 s.

§3. Conclusions

We have shown the preliminary results of the first experiment on the frequency-locking of a GaAlAs laser to a Doppler-free spectrum in the saturated absorption of the Cs–D_2 line. The frequency-locking was carried out after stabilizing the laser temperature, and the minimum Allan variance was estimated to be about 1.6×10^{-10}. We found that this value

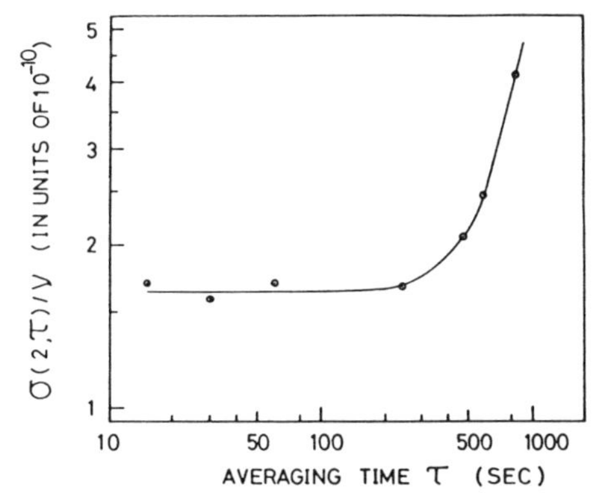

Fig. 3. Long term Allan variance $\sigma(2, \tau)/\nu$ estimated from the recorder trace of the output of the lock-in amplifier.

was mainly determined by the noise and relatively large temperature dependence of the electronic circuits used in the present experiment. The improvement of the electronic circuits is now under way, together with the optimization of gains and time constants of the feed-back loops, and other parameters such as the power and diameters of laser beams. The details of the experiments and the results will be reported later.

It may be possible to make a compact optical system, since all of the components are so small that they can be mounted on a small platform. (For example, few cm is enough for the length of the Cs cell.) Such a compact frequency-stabilized system should promote further applications of a diode laser. Finally, it must be noted that the frequency-locking of a diode laser may be possible, without difficulties, to the D lines of Rubidium (780.0 nm/794.8 nm) and Potassium (766.5 nm /769.9 nm) by using the techniques used in the present experiment.

Acknowledgments

The authors thank Mr. Y. Kitayama for his experimental assistance. This work was supported in part by the Ministry of Education, Science and Culture, Japan, under a Grant-in-Aid for Scientific Research.

References

1) Yu. A. Bykovskii, V. L. Velichnskii, I. G. Goncharov and V. A. Maslov: Sov. Phys.-JETP **30** (1970) 605; Sov. Phys.-Semicond. **4** (1970) 580.
2) J. L. Picqué and S. Roizen: Appl. Phys. Lett. **27** (1975) 340.

3) T. Okoshi and K. Kikuchi: Electron. Lett. **16** (1980) 179.
4) H. Tsuchida, S. Sanpei, M. Ohtsu and T. Tako: Jpn. J. Appl. Phys. **19** (1980) L721.
5) M. Ohi: Jpn. J. Appl. Phys. **19** (1980) L541.
6) W. E. Lamb, Jr.: Phys. Rev. **134** (1964) 1929.
7) H. R. Schrossberg and A. Javan: Phys. Rev. **150** (1966) 267.
8) D. A. Jackson: Proc. R. Soc. (London) **A174** (1934) 500.
9) D. W. Allan: Proc. IEEE **54** (1966) 221.

Longitudinal mode spectra of diode lasers

W. Streifer, D. R. Scifres, and R. D. Burnham
Xerox PARCs, 3333 Coyote Hill Road, Palo Alto, California 94304

(Received 10 November 1981; accepted for publication 30 November 1981)

A theory is presented which explains the longitudinal mode spectra of diode lasers. The theory is based on spontaneous emission coupling into the longitudinal modes and the excellent agreement with experimental data for both gain guided and real refractive index waveguide diode lasers is obtained because of the more accurate and detailed modeling of the spontaneous emission coupling and the laser itself.

PACS numbers: 42.55.Px, 42.80.Sa, 42.55.Bi, 42.60.Da

Although the longitudinal mode spectra of diode lasers have long been a subject of interest, there is still little agreement as to the relative importance of the factors governing that behavior. Among the many effects considered[1] are inhomogeneous broadening,[2] lateral charge inhomogeneity,[3,4] intensity induced longitudinal charge periodicity,[5-7] and spontaneous emission driving the longitudinal modes.[8-10,21] Herein we describe a theory based on spontaneous emission as the principal determinant of longitudinal mode spectra and show that the results agree remarkably well with observations for both gain guided and real refractive index guided lasers.

The basic idea was proposed and examined by Casperson in an important seminal paper,[9] but in several respects his analysis is insufficiently detailed for application to modern semiconductor lasers. Specifically, the large band-to-band absorption at lasing wavelengths in semiconductors is ignored; low gain is assumed whereas rather high gain is present especially if antireflection facet coatings are employed, the spontaneous emission coupling in actuality differs greatly, gain dependence on charge or equivalently pumping current is not included, the saturation constant is not calculated in terms of device parameters, transverse modal intensity and charge variations are disregarded. Whereas none of these limitations is of great consequence singly, together they restrict the theory in its present form to being qualitative in nature. Thus it cannot be used for quantitative comparisons. Our analysis removes the above qualifications and is therefore amenable to direct experimental verification.

The fundamental idea is that in the homogeneously broadened laser the spontaneous emission couples to all the longitudinal modes in differing degree depending upon the emission lineshape. These modes all experience gain in propagating back and forth within the laser cavity whilst receiving power from the spontaneous emission. Because the spontaneous emission continuously excites the lasing modes, they need never quite experience gain sufficient to compensate for the internal losses and the facet transmission. Therefore many lase simultaneously with differing intensities. Below threshold the output spectral envelope is indeed broad, rivaling that of a light-emitting diode but as the device passes through threshold, the stimulated emission causes the injected carriers to recombine, the charge density (hence the gain) begins to saturate, and the spectral envelope narrows significantly.

Mathematically it is necessary to express the gain of each longitudinal mode in terms of the lateral charge density variation, $n(y)$, within the active region. Even below threshold $n(y)$ depends not only on the pumping current but also on the lateral optical mode dependence $G(y)$, because of stimulated emission. These effects are incorporated within the diffusion equation[11] and in our analysis that equation is integrated to obtain an expression for the modal gain α_j, of longitudinal mode j. Next, differential equations for the traveling waves of each mode within the cavity are formulated. These include the modal gain, internal losses α_l, and the spontaneous emission coupling into the mode. Under the constraint that the intensity reproduces itself in a round trip through the cavity, the equations are solved for each mode. Since stimulated recombination depends upon the total optical power, the modal powers are appropriately summed to yield nonlinear algebraic equations, whose solution is the output light versus pumping current characteristic as well as the spectral envelope width.

Our derivation applies to lasers operating in a single TE transverse mode (usually TE_{00}) and the effects of longitudinal charge inhomogeneity as well as spectral inhomogeneity are ignored. Furthermore the lasers are well behaved in that they do not exhibit kinks at low power, do not pulsate, their facets are uniformly reflective, no regions of saturable absorption occur, and they are uniformly pumped along their lengths. The results of the complicated analysis described above are, however, relatively simple for the dependence of the longitudinal spectral envelope full width half-maximum (FWHM), λ_s, on the output power, viz.

$$\lambda_s = \lambda_h \left[(P_t^2/4P_s^2 + 1)^{1/2} - P_t/2P_s \right]. \tag{1}$$

Here λ_h is the homogeneous spontaneous linewidth, P_t is the total TE_{00} output power transmitted through facet 1, and P_s is on the order of the power output in the TE_{00} modes just below threshold. It is given by

$$P_s = \left(\frac{1 - R_1}{R_1} \frac{\sqrt{R_1} + \sqrt{R_2}}{2\sqrt{R_2}} \frac{(1 - \sqrt{R_1 R_2})}{\ln(1/R_1 R_2)} \right) \frac{hc\lambda_0 K}{4\pi \eta_a \eta_e \mathscr{A}}, \tag{2}$$

where R_1 and R_2 are the facet power reflectivities, hc is Planck's constant multiplying the speed of light ($hc = 1.99 \times 10^{-23}$ J cm), λ_0 is the free space wavelength, η_a, η_e are the active region and modal refractive indices, and K is the spontaneous emission factor, also called the astigmatism factor.[12]

Reprinted with permission from *Appl. Phys. Lett.*, vol. 40, no. 4, pp. 305-307, Feb. 15, 1982.

$$K=\left\{\int_{-\infty}^{\infty}|G(y)|^2dy\right\}^2\left|\int_{-\infty}^{\infty}G^2(y)dy\right|^{-2}. \quad (3)$$

Evidently $K = 1$ for lasers utilizing real refractive index waveguidance in which case the lateral modal variation $G(y)$ is a real function. However, K increases with astigmatism, varies inversely with stripe width in a gain guided laser, and may even approach 90 in extreme cases.[13] Finally, $\mathscr{A}$ is a material parameter which may be obtained from measurements on a broad-area laser. Specifically

$$\mathscr{A}=\frac{et}{\Gamma_x}\frac{d\alpha_g}{dJ}, \quad (4)$$

where e is the electronic charge, the filling factor Γ_x is the fractional modal power in the active region of thickness t, and the derivative $d\alpha_g/dJ$ is the slope of the modal gain α_g vs current density J, curve below threshold.[14] That slope is approximately constant for particular laser samples.[14,15]

Interestingly, P_s as given by Eq. (2) is apparently independent of laser dimensions (with the proviso that the device operate single transverse mode), but P_s does depend on K and $\mathscr{A}$. Since the modal phase of gain guided lasers varies greatly with stripe width s, and to a somewhat lesser extent with active region thickness t, and laser length L,[16] K is indeed a function of these dimensions. Furthermore, $\mathscr{A}$ also changes with laser s, t, and L, as a consequence of its sensitivity to the active region charge density, but relatively weakly. Doping level, species, and polarity influence $\mathscr{A}$ as well. Other than the above dependences, P_s varies linearly with λ_0 and increases greatly as R_1 is diminished (by antireflection coating or angling the stripe for example). For $R_1 = R_2 = 0.3$, $\lambda_0 = 0.83\ \mu$m, $\eta_a = 3.6$, $\eta_e = 3.45$, and $\mathscr{A} = 0.6\times10^{-24}$ cm^2 s, which applies to a laser with $\Gamma_x = 0.3$, $t = 0.1\ \mu$m, and $\Delta\alpha_g/\Delta J = 110$ cm^{-1}/1 kA/cm^2, we obtain $P_s = 12\,K\mu$W, so that with $K = 40$, $P_s = 480\,\mu$W. Better material quality or device design, interpreted as larger $\mathscr{A}$ values lead to smaller P_s and conversely.

For small output powers, [from (1)], $P_t < P_s$

$$\lambda_s \approx \lambda_h[1-\tfrac{1}{2}(P_t/P_s)], \quad (5)$$

whereas above threshold, $P_t > 2P_s$,

$$\lambda_s \approx \lambda_h\ P_s/P_t. \quad (6)$$

This simple relationship predicts that in the lasing regime, the spectral envelope FWHM varies inversely with output power with the proportionality constant $\lambda_h P_s$, the homogeneous spontaneous emission linewidth multiplying P_s. Because Eq. (6) is independent of most individual laser parameters, the spectral dependence above threshold is uncomplicated and in fact Eq. (6), as well as its more complete form (1), indicate that the spectra of all real refractive index guided lasers e.g. CSP, BH, PCW etc. with the same materials properties, narrow identically as a function of P_t regardless of the detailed means of providing the waveguidance. Furthermore, decreasing R_1 to enlarge P_s by angling the stripe relative to the facet increases the spectral width in agreement with reported observations.[17]

In Fig. 1, we plot λ_s vs P_t according to (1) at several K values for the laser parameters listed above. Also shown are spectral measurements of cw 4- and 8-μm gain guided lasers

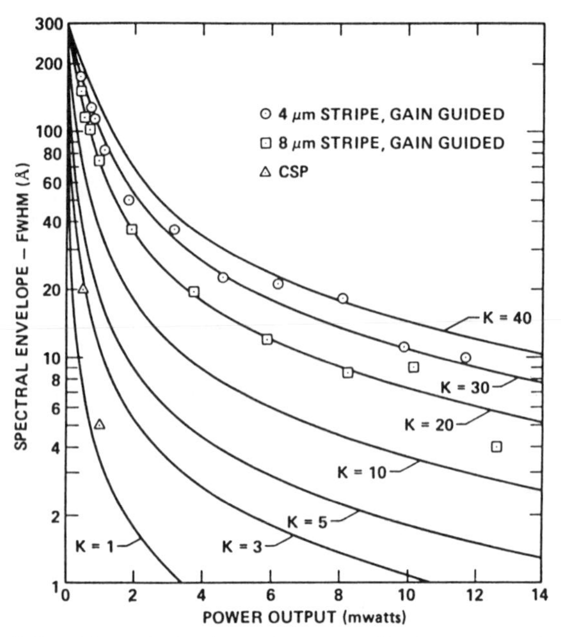

FIG. 1. Theoretical and experimental results of spectral envelope width (FWHM) vs output power. The circles and squares are for 4- and 8-μm stripe gain guided lasers, respectively. The triangles are for a CSP laser.

versus output power excluding TM polarization. These devices grown by metal-organic chemical vapor deposition[16] in our laboratory, of $L = 185\ \mu$m have longitudinal modes separated by 4.6 Å and operate kink-free in excess of 15 mW. The measured FWHM for the 4- and 8-μm stripe lasers agree quite well with the calculations for $K = 30$ and 20 respectively. These values in turn are appropriate for those stripe widths and $L = 185\ \mu$m as computed by the method outlined in Ref. 13 (see also Fig. 1 of Ref. 13 for $L = 400\,\mu$m). In obtaining the data at low power levels no difficulty was experienced in estimating the spectral envelope width, but at elevated powers only two or three modes lase with substantial power within the spectral envelope. In these cases Lorentzian profiles were employed to estimate λ_s, and this procedure produces some of the irregularities in the plotted points. Moreover at these elevated power levels, the spectra are no longer truly symmetrical, with more longitudinal modes lasing on the short wavelength side of the dominant mode. Such behavior, observed in Fig. 2 for the 4-μm stripe laser spectrum at 11.8 mW, is most likely caused by nonlinear effects not encompassed by our theory, which were alluded to briefly in the introductory remarks. Additionally, in Fig. 1 are displayed two data points for the Hitachi CSP laser taken from their data sheet.[18] These are not corrected to exclude TM polarized light, which may total 100 μW. This correction accounts to some extent for the small deviation from the $K = 1$ curve, but that discrepancy is quite small in any case. Other measurements of CSP lasers,[19] show continuing reduction in subsidiary longitudinal modes with increasing power, but the data points fall below the scale of our plot. We also note that spectral plots of Hitachi CSP and BH lasers[18] appear to be of roughly equal width at 1-mw output power. Since $K = 1$ for both devices and $\mathscr{A}$ is probably comparable this result is in agreement with our theory. Of course, if some phase front distortion exists within a real

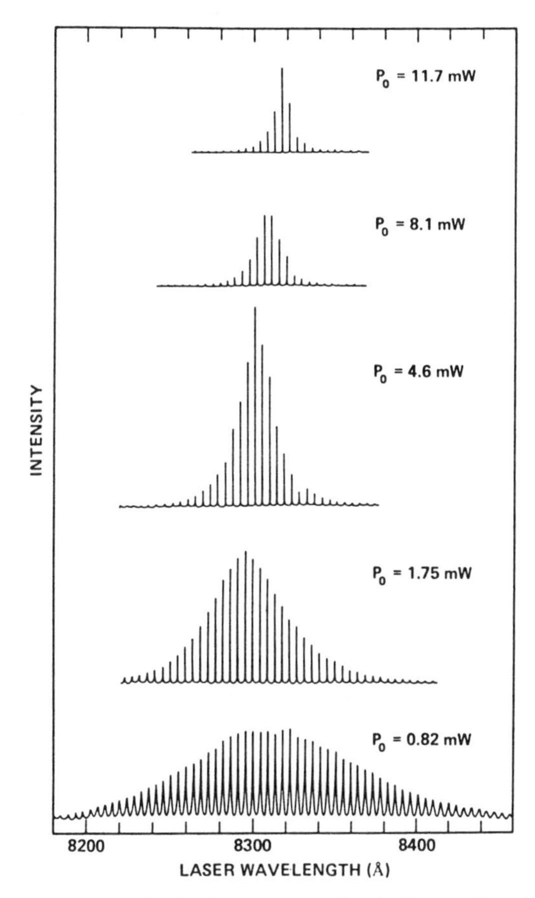

FIG. 2. Longitudinal mode spectra for the 4-μm stripe gain guided laser.

refractive index waveguide laser, such as may result from side wall scattering in a BH device, for example, K may exceed unity and the spectrum may broaden.

Finally, let us compare the spectra of (InGa)(AsP) and (GaAl)As diode laser. According to Eqs. (2) and (6) the spectral envelope of the quaternary should exceed that of the ternary as a result of the larger values of λ_0 and λ_h; however, it is very likely that the K values are substantially smaller for the gain guided quaternary lasers both because of wider stripe contacts and greater thermal waveguiding. Furthermore, since the longitudinal mode separation, $\Delta\lambda = \lambda_0^2/(2L\eta_e')$, where η_e' is the modal dispersion index, is much larger in the case of the longer wavelength quaternary, that gain guided device may well lase single longitudinal mode. However, very narrow stripe quaternaries with astigmatic modes and therefore larger values of K have been observed to emit multiple longitudinal mode spectra.[20]

In summary, we have presented the results of a theory based on spontaneous emission exciting the longitudinal modes in diode lasers that explains observed spectral differences between gain guided and real refractive index waveguide lasers. Analytic results, including dependences on device parameters, for the longitudinal spectral envelope as a function of output power have been shown to agree very well with experimental observations.

The authors acknowledge useful discussions with Dr. R. V. Schmidt. Dr. T. L. Paoli informed us of Ref. 8, and Dr. D. Botez of Ref. 20. We also thank M. Bernstein for assistance with the measurements.

[1]P. G. Eliseev and N. N. Shuikin, Sov. J. Quantum Electron. **3**, 181 (1973).
[2]M. Yamada, K. Hayano, H. Ishiguro, and Y. Suematsu, Jpn J. Appl. Phys. **18** 1531 (1979).
[3]C. Y. Chen and S. Wang, J. Appl. Phys. **52**, 614 (1981).
[4]K. Seki, T. Kamiya, and H. Yanai, IEEE J. Quantum Electron. **QE-17** 706 (1981).
[5]H. Statz and C. L. Tang, J. Appl. Phys. **35**, 1377 (1964).
[6]H. G. Danielmeyer, J. Appl. Phys. **42**, 3125 (1971)
[7]W. Streifer, R. D. Burnham, and D. R. Scifres, IEEE J. Quantum Electron. **13**, 403 (1977).
[8]L. A. Rivlin, Sov. J. Quantum Electron. **2** 464 (1973).
[9]L. W. Casperson, J. Appl. Phys. **46** 5194 (1975).
[10]D. Renner and J. E. Carroll, Electron. Lett. **14** 779 (1978).
[11]W. Streifer, R. D. Burnham, and D. R. Scifres, IEEE J. Quantum Electron. **QE-17**, 736 (1981).
[12]K. Petermann, IEEE J. Quantum Electron. **15** 566 (1979).
[13]W. Streifer, D. R. Scifres, and R. D. Burnham, Electron. Lett. **17**, 1933 (1981).
[14]B. W. Hakki and T. L. Paoli, J. Appl. Phys. **46** 1299 (1975).
[15]C. H. Henry, R. A. Logan, and F. R. Merritt, J. Appl. Phys. **51** 3042 (1980).
[16]D. R. Scifres, W. Streifer, and R. D. Burnham, IEEE J. Quantum Electron. **QE-17**, December (1981).
[17]D. R. Scifres, W. Streifer, and R. D. Burnham, IEEE J. Quantum Electron. **QE-14** 223 (1978).
[18]Hitachi Laser Diode, HLP 1000, HLP 2000, and HLP 3000 Series Applications Manual.
[19]Jerome E. May, Xerox Corp., Webster Research Center (private communcation).
[20]D. Renner and G. Henshall, IEEE J. Quantum Electron. **QE-17**, 199 (1981).
[21]G. H. B. Thompson, *Physics of Semiconductor Laser Devices* (Wiley, New York, 1980), p. 121 and following.

SIMPLE FORMULA GIVING SPECTRUM-NARROWING RATIO OF SEMICONDUCTOR-LASER OUTPUT OBTAINED BY OPTICAL FEEDBACK

K. KIKUCHI
T. OKOSHI

Department of Electronic Engineering
University of Tokyo
Hongo, Bunkyo-ku, Tokyo 113, Japan

24th November 1981

Indexing terms: Lasers, Optics

The letter presents a theory of the spectrum-narrowing effect of semiconductor lasers by optical feedback. A simple formula for the 3 dB spectral width is derived as a function of the intensity and phase of the returning beam and the round-trip time of the feedback circuit. The spectrum-narrowing ratio of a GaAlAs laser with a small amount of optical feedback was measured as a function of the optical feedback power ratio. The derived formula and experiment show very good agreement.

Introduction: It has been reported that a certain amount of optical feedback (typically -40 dB) can narrow the spectral width of semiconductor-laser output appreciably.[1] However, no theory has been presented to give the spectrum-narrowing ratio quantitatively. In this letter, this spectrum-narrowing effect is analysed on the basis of Van der Pol's equation. A simple formula is derived which gives the 3 dB spectral width as a function of the intensity and phase of the returning beam and the round-trip time of the feedback circuit.

The spectrum-narrowing ratio in a GaAlAs laser has been measured by using the delayed self-heterodyne method.[2] The measured narrowing ratio shows very good agreement with the derived formula.

Theory: If we consider only the returning light from the first round trip, we can write Van der Pol's equation as[3]

$$\frac{dE(t)}{dt} + \{\gamma - \alpha + \beta E^*(t)E(t)\}E(t) = \gamma\sqrt{(\eta)}E(t-\tau)e^{-j2\pi f_0\tau} + \Gamma \tag{1}$$

where τ is the round-trip time of the external resonator, $E(t)$ the phasor representation of the electric field (including noise), γ the damping constant of the main resonator, α the gain of the lasing material, η the feedback power ratio, f_0 the centre oscillation frequency in the free-running state, Γ the random disturbance given to the oscillating system, and the term βE^*E represents the gain saturation.

The phasor $E(t)$ can be expressed in terms of the amplitude $|E(t)|$ and the phase fluctuation $\phi_n(t)$ as

$$E(t) = |E(t)|e^{j\phi_n}(t) + j2\pi\,\Delta ft \tag{2}$$

where Δf represents the frequency shift induced by optical feedback. From eqns. 1 and 2, we obtain
where Γ_i denotes the imaginary part of $\Gamma e^{-j2\pi\Delta ft}/|E(t)|$. By averaging eqn. 3, we have

$$2\pi\,\Delta f = -\gamma\sqrt{(\eta)}\sin\{2\pi(f_0 + \Delta f)\tau\} \tag{4}$$

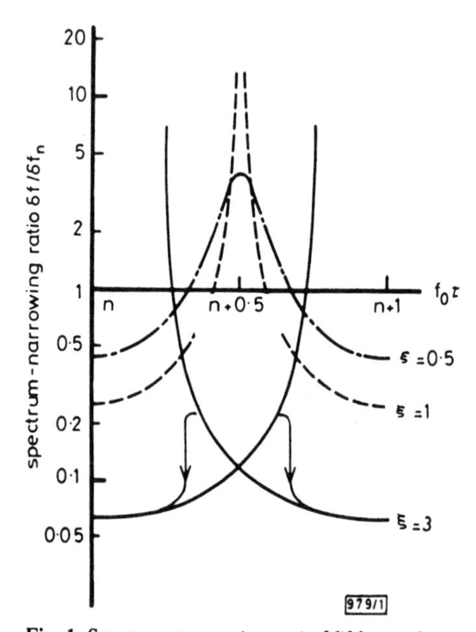

Fig. 1 *Spectrum-narrowing ratio $\delta f/\delta f_n$ as a function of $f_0\tau$ (n = integer)*

which determines the oscillation frequency $f_0 + \Delta f$ when the returning beam is present. When the feedback level is relatively high, the solution of eqn. 4 shows the 'multistability' in the oscillating mode, as described in Reference 4.

When τ is much shorter than the coherence time of the laser output, eqns. 3 and 4 lead to a simple equation:

$$\frac{d\phi_n}{dt} = \frac{\Gamma_i}{1+\delta} \tag{5}$$

where

$$\delta = \gamma\sqrt{(\eta)}\tau\cos\{2\pi(f_0 + \Delta f)\tau\} \tag{6}$$

the phase factor $\cos\{2\pi(f_0 + \Delta f)\tau\}$ being determined by eqn. 4.

Suppose that when the laser is oscillating without feedback, the output spectrum has a Lorentzian shape whose 3 dB spectral width is δf_n. Then we find from eqn. 5 that the spectral shape of the laser output with optical feedback is also Lorentzian, but the width is now given by

$$\delta f = \frac{\delta f_n}{[1 + \gamma\sqrt{(\eta)}\tau\cos\{2\pi(f + \Delta f)\tau\}]^2} \tag{7}$$

because δf_n is originally proportional to the time average of

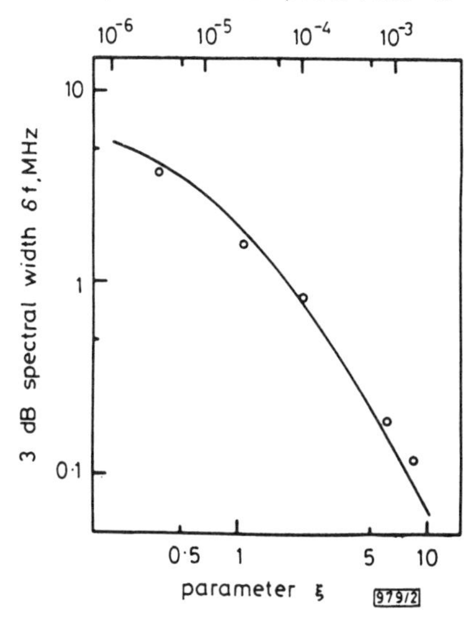

Fig. 2 *3 dB spectral width δf as a function of optimal feedback power ratio R and spectrum-narrowing parameter ξ*

○ measured —— theoretical

Γ_i^2.[5] Note that δf is strongly dependent on the phase of the returning light.

Fig. 1 shows the spectrum-narrowing ratio $\delta f/\delta f_n$ as a function of the normalised oscillation frequency without feedback, i.e. $f_0 \tau$. The parameter ξ is given as

$$\xi = \gamma\sqrt{(\eta)}\tau$$

which we tentatively call the spectrum-narrowing parameter. When $\xi \leq 1$ the ratio is single-valued. The spectral width δf becomes wider than the original value δf_n when $f_0 \tau \simeq 0{\cdot}5$ (where n = integer), i.e. when the emitted light field and the returning light field are out of phase each other on the laser end surface. This effect appears most strongly when $\xi \simeq 1$.

When $\xi > 1$, the ratio becomes multivalued. It has been found experimentally that the spectral width changes abruptly, being accompanied by a mode jumping, as indicated by arrows in Fig. 1. It has also been found by experiment that the mode jumping always occurs in the direction in which the spectral width becomes narrower.

Experiment and result: The laser under test is a single longitudinal-mode GaAlAs laser (λ = 840 nm). The driving current is 1·5 times the threshold current. Both the temperature and driving current are highly stabilised.[6] The length of the feedback circuit (external resonator) L = 1 m. The 3 dB spectral width was measured as a function of the power ratio R of the returning light power to the emitted one. The delayed self-heterodyne method[2] was used in the measurement.

The small circles and solid curve in Fig. 2 show the measured and theoretical values of 3 dB spectral width δf, respectively.

It was found that only a slight variation of the driving current changes the spectral width drastically. In particular, when the feedback level is relatively high, the spectral width changes abruptly being accompanied by a jump in the oscillation frequency. These phenomena can be explained well by the above theory as the effect of the phase variation of the returning beam.

The measured data shown in Fig. 2 are the minimum values of the spectral width (for each value of R) obtained by a fine adjustment of the driving current. We presume that, in such a state, the emitted light field and the returning light field are in a same phase on the laser end surface.

Discussion: In the present measurement, we can assume that the in-phase condition ($f_0 n$ = integer) is achieved. Therefore, δf is given as

$$\delta f = \frac{\delta f_n}{[1 + \gamma\tau\sqrt{(\eta_c R)}]^2} \tag{9}$$

where η_c is the coupling efficiency of the returning beam into the lasing mode of the laser main resonator; hence $\eta = \eta_c R$.

The solid curve in Fig. 2 shows $\delta f/R$ relation given by eqn. 9 where $\gamma\tau\sqrt{(\eta_c)} = 220$. The lower abcissa gives the parameter $\xi = \gamma\tau\sqrt{(n_c R)}$. The measured values of δf are in good agreement with the theoretical curve. If we assume that $\gamma = 3 \times 10^{11}$ s^{-1}, η_c is calculated to be 1×10^{-2}, which seems to be a reasonable value.

References

1 SAITO, S., and YAMAMOTO, Y.: 'Direct observation of Lorentzian lineshape of semiconductor laser and linewidth reduction with external grating feedback', *Electron. Lett.*, 1981, **17**, pp. 325–327

2 OKOSHI, T., KIKUCHI, K., and NAKAYAMA, A.: 'Novel method for high resolution measurement of laser output spectrum', *ibid.*, 1980, **16**, pp. 630–631

3 KANADA, T., and NAWATA, K.: 'Injection laser characteristics due to reflected optical power', *IEEE J. Quantum Electron.*, 1979, **QE-15**, pp. 559–565

4 LANG, R., and KOBAYASHI, K.: 'External optical feedback effects on semiconductor injection laser properties', *ibid.*, 1980, **QE-16**, pp. 347–355

5 YARIV, A.: 'Quantum electronics' (John Wiley & Sons, Inc., New York, 1975), p. 307

6 KIKUCHI, K., OKOSHI, T., and KAWANISHI, S.: 'Achievement of 1 MHz frequency stability of semiconductor lasers by double-loop AFC scheme', *Electron. Lett.*, 1981, **17**, pp. 515–516

Theory of the Linewidth of Semiconductor Lasers

CHARLES H. HENRY

Abstract—A theory of the spectral width of a single-mode semiconductor laser is presented and used to explain the recent measurements of Fleming and Mooradian on AlGaAs lasers. They found the linewidth to be inversely proportional to power and to have a value of 114 MHz at 1 mW per facet. This value is 30 times greater than can be explained by existing theories. The enhanced linewidth is attributed to the variation of the real refractive index n' with carrier density. Spontaneous emission induces phase and intensity changes in the laser field. The restoration of the laser to its steady-state intensity results in changes in the imaginary part of the refractive index $\Delta n''$. These changes are accompanied by changes in the real part of the refractive index $\Delta n'$, which cause additional phase fluctuations and line broadening. The linewidth enhancement is shown to be $1 + \alpha^2$, where $\alpha = \Delta n'/\Delta n''$. A value of $\alpha \approx 5.4$, needed to explain the observed linewidth, is close to the experimental values of α of 4.6 and 6.2.

I. Introduction

The spectral linewidth of a semiconductor injection laser is an interesting property that deserves careful study. It may also be an important device parameter in future applications of injection lasers that utilize the coherence of the laser light, such as heterodyne detection of optical signals.

The first careful measurements of the linewidth of an AlGaAs injection laser versus optical power were recently reported by Fleming and Mooradian [1]. They found the spectrum to be Lorentzian in shape, with a full width at half intensity Δf that varied inversely with output power P_0. These features have also been established for gas lasers [2] and are expected for lasers in general [3], [4]. Surprisingly, however, they reported [1] that at 300 K the magnitude of Δf was about 50 times greater than they had expected according to conventional theories of semiconductor laser linewidth.

Fleming and Mooradian [1] were unable to explain this unexpected broadening. They did mention that Elesin and Rusakov [5] predicted a sizable broadening of semiconductor laser lines at high power due to spectral gain saturation. However, this explanation seemed unlikely, because it would also predict deviations from the relation $\Delta f \sim P_0^{-1}$, which were not observed. Furthermore, no independent evidence for spectral hole burning has been found in semiconductor injection lasers [6].

The purpose of this paper is twofold: first, to explain the measured linewidth, and second, to present an intuitive and self-contained theory of line broadening in semiconductor lasers.

In general, the width of the laser line can be thought of as due to fluctuations in the phase of the optical field [3], [4]. These fluctuations arise from spontaneous emission events, which discontinuously alter the phase and intensity of the lasing field, as illustrated in Fig. 1.

Manuscript received June 19, 1981; revised September 21, 1981.
The author is with Bell Laboratories, Murray Hill, NJ 07974.

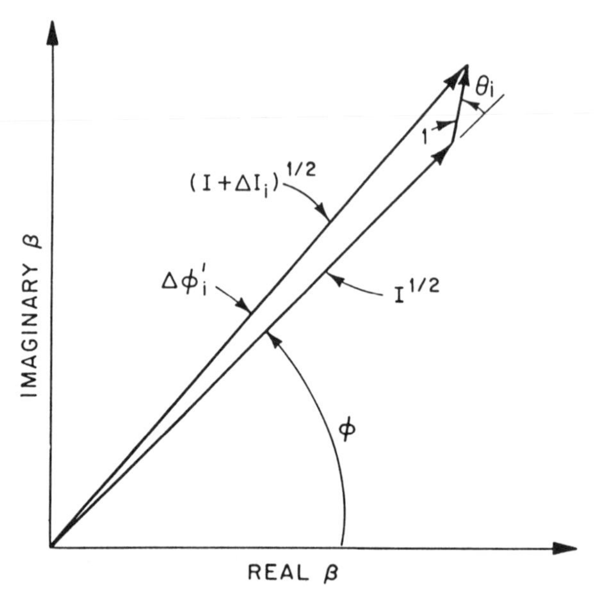

Fig. 1. The instantaneous changes of the phase ϕ and intensity I of the optical field caused by the ith spontaneous emission event. The field amplitude $\beta = I^{1/2} \exp(i\phi)$ increases by $\Delta\beta_i$ having an amplitude of unity and phase $\phi + \theta_i$, where θ_i is a random angle.

Besides the instantaneous phase change caused by spontaneous emission, there will be a delayed phase change resulting from the instantaneous change in field intensity. To restore the steady-state field intensity, the laser will undergo relaxation oscillations, which last about 1 ns. During this time, there will be a net gain change $\Delta g(t) = (-2\omega/c)\, \Delta n''(t)$, where $\Delta n''(t)$ is the deviation of the imaginary part of the refractive index from its steady-state value. The change in n'' is caused by a change in carrier density, which will also alter the real part of the refractive index n'. The ratio of these changes is

$$\alpha = \frac{\Delta n'}{\Delta n''}. \tag{1}$$

A change in $\Delta n'$ during a limited period of time results in an additional phase shift of the laser field and in additional line broadening.

The gross broadening of the spectral lines of pulsating lasers has been attributed to the change in refractive index with carrier density [7], [8]. In this paper we show that this same effect causes a substantial broadening of the lines of stable lasers. In Section II, a formula for the linewidth of a single-mode injection laser is derived and it is shown that the coupling of phase to intensity fluctuations increases the laser linewidth by $1 + \alpha^2$. In Section III, the linewidth formula

Reprinted from *IEEE J. Quantum Electron.*, vol. QE-18, no. 2, pp. 259–264, Feb. 1982.

is compared with the experimental results of Fleming and Mooradian [1]. It is shown that their data can be explained with $\alpha \approx 5.4$ and this is close to the values of $\alpha \approx 6.2$ of Henry *et al.* [9] and $\alpha \approx 4.6$ determined from the measurements of Turley *et al.* [10].

The problem of line broadening due to the coupling of phase and intensity in a semiconductor laser is mathematically identical to a similar problem that occurs in detuned gas lasers, where the cavity resonance and optical transition frequencies do not coincide. This problem was solved by Lax [3], [4] and results in a $1 + \alpha^2$ enhancement, where α is the detuning parameter. While the linewidth formula for a semiconductor laser can be obtained by adapting Lax's equations to the semiconductor case, instead a less rigorous but more intuitive derivation is given in Section II.

A quantum mechanical treatment of noise in semiconductor lasers was given by Haug and Haken [11]. They gave a formula for the linewidth, without detailed derivation, that included the $1 + \alpha^2$ enhancement. Haug and Haken stated without giving their reasons that α will be small compared to unity and the linewidth enhancement will be very small. They seemed to have reached this conclusion by considering only light-induced changes in the complex refractive index due to spectral hole burning.

In general, a narrow spectral change in gain (or absorption) is accompanied by a change in n'' of the same shape and a change in n' of comparable magnitude, but with a dispersive shape having two peaks of opposite sign occurring on either side of the peak in n''. For spectral hole burning, the peak in $\Delta n''$ is centered at the laser line and, therefore, $\alpha = \Delta n'/\Delta n''$ will be small compared to unity. On the other hand, the peak change in gain due to a change in carrier density occurs well above the energy of the laser line, so that in this case α is large compared to unity. This is clearly shown in the data of Henry *et al.* [9]. In this paper, we attribute α to changes in $\Delta n'$ and $\Delta n''$ due to changes in carrier density and neglect light-induced changes in $\Delta n'$ and $\Delta n''$ occurring at fixed carrier density.

II. Derivation of the Linewidth Formula

Following the notation of Lax [4], we will represent the field by a complex amplitude β normalized so that the average intensity $I = \beta^*\beta$ also equals the average number of photons in the cavity

$$\beta = I^{1/2} \exp(i\phi) \tag{2}$$

where $I(t)$ and $\phi(t)$ represent the intensity and the phase of the laser field.

Our basic assumption is that the ith spontaneous emission event alters β by $\Delta\beta_i$, where $\Delta\beta_i$ has unit magnitude and a random phase

$$\Delta\beta_i = \exp(i\phi + i\theta_i) \tag{3}$$

where θ_i is random. This is illustrated in Fig. 1. The justification of this assumption is that it leads to the correct average rate of increase in I due to spontaneous emission and the correct noise fluctuations (Langevin forces) for I and ϕ. This is discussed in the appendixes. The classical rate equations for I and ϕ are derived from the wave equation in Appendix I. Using the above assumption about $\Delta\beta_i$, the complete rate equations including noise generation are derived in Appendix II. Except for notation, these equations are identical to those of by Lax [4], who begins with an atomic model and a quantized optical field.

We will now solve for the phase change $\Delta\phi_i$ due to a single spontaneous emission event that alters I from the steady-state value. When I is altered, the laser undergoes damped relaxation oscillations, which return I to the steady state. The equations describing small oscillations of the laser about its steady state are linear; consequently, the principle of superposition holds, and the total phase change for many spontaneous emission events overlapping in time is just the sum of the individual phase changes $\Delta\phi_i$.

There are two contributions to the phase change, and these are denoted by $\Delta\phi_i'$ and $\Delta\phi_i''$. The change $\Delta\phi_i'$ is due to the out-of-phase component of $\Delta\beta_i$. It is clear from Fig. 1 that this change is

$$\Delta\phi_i' = I^{-1/2} \sin(\theta_i). \tag{4}$$

The second contribution $\Delta\phi_i''$ is due to the intensity change and the fact that the intensity and phase changes are coupled. From Fig. 1, using the law of cosines, we see that the amplitude changes from $I^{1/2}$ to $(I + \Delta I_i)^{1/2}$, where

$$\Delta I_i = 1 + 2I^{1/2} \cos(\theta_i). \tag{5}$$

The second term in (5) averages to zero, so that on the average spontaneous emission causes a field intensity change equivalent to adding one photon to the mode. However, $I \approx 40\,000$, even at power of only 1 mW per facet [see (22)], so that the second term in (5), which causes fluctuations in light intensity due to interference, is equivalent to a change of several hundred photons.

In Appendix I we show that the rate equations for I and ϕ are

$$\dot{\phi} = \frac{\alpha}{2}(G - \gamma) \tag{6}$$

$$\dot{I} = (G - \gamma)I \tag{7}$$

where G is the net rate of stimulated emission and γ is the rate of cavity loss caused by facet and waveguide losses. Combining (6) and (7), we have

$$\dot{\phi} = \frac{\alpha}{2I}\dot{I}. \tag{8}$$

We will approximate I in (8) as constant and equal to the steady-state value. Initially $I(0) = I + \Delta I_i$ and, finally, after the relaxation oscillations have died out, $I(\infty) = I$; therefore, upon integrating (8), we find

$$\Delta\phi_i'' = -\frac{\alpha}{2I}\Delta I_i = -\frac{\alpha}{2I}(1 + 2I^{1/2}\cos(\theta_i)). \tag{9}$$

The total phase change is given by (4) and (9):

$$\Delta\phi_i = \Delta\phi_i' + \Delta\phi_i'' = -\frac{\alpha}{2I} + \frac{1}{I^{1/2}}[\sin(\theta_i) - \alpha\cos(\theta_i)]. \tag{10}$$

The first term is a small but constant phase change. If the average spontaneous emission rate is R, then the first term will result in an average phase change

$$\langle \Delta\phi \rangle = -\frac{\alpha R t}{2I} \tag{11}$$

or an angular frequency shift

$$\Delta\omega = \langle \Delta\dot{\phi} \rangle = -\frac{\alpha R}{2I}. \tag{12}$$

This frequency shift can be thought of as caused by spontaneous emission, which alters the steady-state stimulated emission rate from $G = \gamma$ to $G = \gamma - R/I$.

The total phase fluctuation for $N = Rt$ spontaneous emission events will be

$$\Delta\phi = \sum_{i=1}^{N} I^{-1/2} (\sin(\theta_i) - \alpha \cos(\theta_i)). \tag{13}$$

The value of $\langle \Delta\phi^2 \rangle$ is easily computed from (13) because, for random angles, the average of all cross terms vanishes and

$$\langle \Delta\phi^2 \rangle = \frac{R(1+\alpha^2)t}{2I}. \tag{14}$$

Due to the random spontaneous emission events, the phase ϕ executes Brownian motion and has a Gaussian probability distribution [3]. It is then readily shown [3] that

$$\langle \beta(t)^* \beta(0) \rangle = |\beta(0)|^2 \exp(-|t|/t_{\text{coh}}) \tag{15}$$

where the coherence time t_{coh} is given by

$$t_{\text{coh}}^{-1} = \frac{\langle \Delta\phi^2 \rangle}{2t}. \tag{16}$$

The power spectrum of the laser can be shown [3] to be the Fourier transform of $\langle \beta(t)^* \beta(0) \rangle$. It is Lorentzian with a full width at half maximum of

$$\Delta f = (\pi t_{\text{coh}})^{-1} = \frac{R}{4\pi I}(1+\alpha^2). \tag{17}$$

To relate Δf to experiment, I must be expressed in terms of the output power per facet P_0. Let u be the number of photons per unit length propagating toward $+z$ in the cavity. The population u will increase across the laser as

$$u(z) = u(0) \exp[(g - \alpha_L)z] \tag{18}$$

where g is the gain, α_L is the waveguide loss of the laser and

$$I = 2\int_0^L u\,dz = 2u(0)\,[(\exp(g - \alpha_L)L) - 1]/(g - \alpha_L). \tag{19}$$

In a dispersive medium, the ratio of photon flux to photon density is v_g, the group velocity [12]. Therefore,

$$P_0 = (1 - r_m)\, v_g u(L)\, h\nu \tag{20}$$

where $h\nu$ is the energy of the laser line and r_m is the facet reflectivity. Using the relations $u(0) = r_m u(L)$, $r_m \exp[(g - \alpha_L)L] = 1$, (18), and defining the facet loss α_m as

$$\alpha_m \equiv g - \alpha_L = -L^{-1} \ln(r_m) \tag{21}$$

where L is the cavity length, we find

$$I = \frac{2P_0}{h\nu\, v_g\, \alpha_m}. \tag{22}$$

The rate of spontaneous emission R and the gain g are related by [13]

$$R = v_g r = v_g a \exp\left[\frac{\text{eV} - h\nu}{kT}\right] \tag{23}$$

$$G = v_g g = v_g a \left[\exp\left[\frac{\text{eV} - h\nu}{kT}\right] - 1\right] \tag{24}$$

where a is the optical absorption coefficient at the laser line and eV is the separation of quasi-Fermi levels. Combining (23) and (24), we have

$$\frac{R}{v_g} = r = \frac{g}{1 - \exp[-(\text{eV} - h\nu)/kT]} = a + g = g n_{\text{sp}} \tag{25}$$

where n_{sp} is referred to as the spontaneous emission factor. Combining (17), (22), and (25), we have

$$\Delta f = \frac{v_g^2\, h\nu\, g\, n_{\text{sp}}\, \alpha_m (1+\alpha^2)}{8\pi P_0}. \tag{26}$$

III. Comparison with Experiment

Fleming and Mooradian [1] compared their data to a theoretical formula that is identical to (26), but with $\alpha = 0$ and v_g replaced by the phase velocity $v_p = c/n'$. Using $\alpha_L = 45$ cm^{-1} as reported [1], $\alpha_m = 39$ cm^{-1}, $g = \alpha_L + \alpha_m = 84$ cm^{-1}, $h\nu = 1.5$ eV, $n_{\text{sp}} = 1$, and $P_0 = 1$ mW, we find $\Delta f = 2.3$ MHz and $\Delta f(\text{exp})/\Delta f = 114/2.3 = 49.6$, in agreement with Fleming and Mooradian's [1] assertion that the theoretical formula with $n_{\text{sp}} = 1$ is a factor of 50 too small.

Let us now set our corrections to the formula of Fleming and Mooradian equal to this factor of 50 and solve for α:

$$50 = \frac{v_g^2 (1+\alpha^2) n_{\text{sp}}}{v_p^2}. \tag{27}$$

The assumption $r/g = n_{\text{sp}} = 1$ is correct for laser transitions in which the ground state is unoccupied. This is not the case for semiconductor lasers, where $r = g + a$ and $a \neq 0$. In (17) and (18) of [13], n_{sp} was obtained directly from the spontaneous emission spectrum and found to be $n_{\text{sp}} \approx 2.7$. More recently, this measurement was repeated [13] and n_{sp} was found to be ≈ 2.6. If we use $n_{\text{sp}} = 2.6$ and $v_g = c/4.33$, as determined from mode spacing [14], and $v_p = c/3.5$, then $(v_p/v_g)^2 = 1.53$ and (27) becomes

$$1 + \alpha^2 \approx 29.4$$

or

$$\alpha \approx 5.4.$$

The approximate value of α can be deduced from measurements of refractive index and gain change. Henry *et al.* [9] measured the spectrum of the gain change within the active layer from analysis of spontaneous emission in buried heterostructure lasers. Using their estimate of $\Gamma = 0.6$ for the confinement factor, they found a differential change in mode gain

$$\Delta g = \frac{dg}{dN} N_{TH} = 258 \text{ cm}^{-1}$$

where dg/dN is evaluated at threshold and where N_{TH} is the carrier density at threshold, resulting in a change in a differential change in n'' of

$$\Delta n'' = -\frac{c}{2\omega} \Delta g = -1.82 \times 10^{-3}.$$

A Kramers-Kronig inversion of the $\Delta n''$ spectrum resulted in a similarly defined differential change in $\Delta n' = -10.2 \times 10^{-3}$ at the laser line. To this value was added the calculated change in index due to free carriers of -1.11×10^{-3}, for a total change of

$$\Delta n' = -11.3 \times 10^{-3}.$$

The ratio of $\Delta n'$ and $\Delta n''$ is

$$\alpha = \frac{11.3}{1.82} = 6.2.$$

The error in this value is at least ±10 percent.

Turley *et al.* [10] measured the mode shifts of a twin-transverse-junction laser and found them to be linear in carrier density. They reported a dielectric constant change of $2n'\Delta n' = -5.92 \times 10^{-2}$. Using $n' = 3.5$, the change in n' is

$$\Delta n' = 8.5 \times 10^{-3}.$$

If the mode change in gain is the same as that measured by Henry *et al.* [12] for this laser, then

$$\alpha = \frac{8.5}{1.82} = 4.6.$$

IV. Summary and Discussion

Fleming and Mooradian [1] have reported a careful measurement of laser linewidth versus optical power that was 50 times greater than expected by conventional theories of laser linewidth. When their analysis is corrected for optical dispersion and the fact that n_{sp} is greater than unity, the measured linewidth is still about 30 times wider than expected.

The factor of 30 is attributed to enhanced broadening due to the change of refractive index with carrier density, which couples phase and intensity fluctuations and broadens the line by $1 + \alpha^2$, where $\alpha = \Delta n'/\Delta n''$. To explain the factor of 30, $\alpha = 5.4$ is needed.

The results of index- and gain-change measurements on a buried heterostructure laser by Henry *et al.* [9] gave $\alpha = 6.2$. From the index-change measurements on twin-transverse-junction lasers made by Turley *et al.* [10], a value of $\alpha = 4.6$ was deduced. It is not yet clear whether the discrepancy in these two values is due to experimental uncertainties or these are real differences in α for different types of lasers. In any case, these values are within ±15 percent of the value of $\alpha = 5.4$ needed to account for the measured linewidth and thereby confirm our explanation.

An intuitive derivation of the linewidth formula was presented that agrees with the more formal calculations of Lax [3], [4]. The derivation is based on the physical idea, illustrated in Fig. 1, that spontaneous emission events instantaneously add increments to the laser field, each increment having a magnitude of unity and a random phase angle.

If several longitudinal laser modes are above threshold, we expect that the phase shifts due to carrier density fluctuations will be the same in each mode. Therefore, the enhancement in line broadening due to changes in n' with carrier density will not show up in observations of the spectrum of the difference frequency of two modes. For example, the beat frequency of two counter-rotating modes of a semiconductor-fiber ring laser should not have enhanced broadening.

Appendix I
Derivation of the Rate Equations for I and ϕ

The wave equation for the electric field E is

$$\frac{\partial^2 E}{\partial z^2} = \frac{1}{c^2} \cdot \frac{\partial^2}{\partial t^2} (\epsilon E). \tag{A1}$$

The electric field can be written as

$$E \sim \beta \exp [i(\omega t - kz)] + \beta^* \exp [-i(\omega t - kz)]. \tag{A2}$$

To take into account that the change in the dielectric constant ϵ due to dispersion, caused by the time dependence of β, we write

$$\epsilon E \sim \left(\epsilon(\omega)\beta + i \frac{\partial \epsilon}{\partial \omega} \dot{\beta}\right) \exp [i(\omega t - kz)] + \text{c.c.} \tag{A3}$$

where $\dot{\beta} = \partial\beta/\partial t$. Substitution of (A2) and (A3) into (A1) results in two equations, one for β and one for β^*, which are complex conjugates of each other. If derivatives of β, higher than first order are neglected, the equation for β is

$$\frac{2i\omega}{c^2}\left(\epsilon + \frac{\omega \partial\epsilon}{2\partial\omega}\right)\dot{\beta} = \left[\frac{\omega^2}{c^2}\epsilon - k^2\right]\beta. \tag{A4}$$

The dielectric constant ϵ is complex and can be written as the square of a complex refractive index $n' - in''$, where n'' determines the net gain according to

$$g - \alpha_\gamma = -\frac{2\omega}{c} n'' \tag{A5}$$

g is the gain per unit length, and α_γ is the loss, including facet losses, which we approximate as uniformly distributed over the cavity. At threshold $g = \alpha_\gamma$, ϵ is real and ω is chosen so that

$$\frac{\omega}{c} n' = k. \tag{A6}$$

Changes in carrier density will cause n' and n'' to deviate from the threshold values. To include this, we write ϵ as

$$\begin{aligned} \epsilon &= n'^2 + 2n'(\Delta n' - i\Delta n'') \\ &= n'^2 - 2in'\Delta n''(1 + i\alpha) \end{aligned} \tag{A7}$$

where

$$\alpha \equiv \frac{\Delta n'}{\Delta n''}. \tag{A8}$$

The bracketed term on the left side of (A4) is related to the group velocity v_g:

$$\epsilon + \frac{\omega \partial \epsilon}{2 \partial \omega} = n'\left(n' + \omega \frac{\partial n'}{\partial \omega}\right) = \frac{c}{v_g} n'. \quad \text{(A9)}$$

Substituting (A6), (A7), and (A9) into (A4), we find

$$\dot{\beta} = -\frac{\omega}{c} v_g \Delta n''(1 + i\alpha)\beta$$

$$= \frac{(g - \alpha_\gamma)v_g}{2}(1 + i\alpha)\beta. \quad \text{(A10)}$$

In a dispersive medium, the ratio of energy flux to energy density is the group velocity v_g [12]. Consequently, the rate of stimulated emission G minus the rate of loss γ is given by

$$(G - \gamma) = v_g(g - \alpha_\gamma). \quad \text{(A11)}$$

Therefore, the final equation for β is

$$\dot{\beta} = \left[\frac{G - \gamma}{2}\right](1 + i\alpha)\beta. \quad \text{(A12)}$$

Similarly,

$$\dot{\beta}^* = \left[\frac{G - \gamma}{2}\right](1 - i\alpha)\beta^*. \quad \text{(A13)}$$

We can transform to the I, ϕ representation using

$$I = \beta\beta^* \quad \text{(A14)}$$

$$\phi = \frac{1}{2i} \ln(\beta/\beta^*) \quad \text{(A15)}$$

and find

$$\dot{I} = (G - \gamma)I \quad \text{(A16)}$$

$$\dot{\phi} = \frac{\alpha}{2}(G - \gamma). \quad \text{(A17)}$$

Appendix II
Derivation of the Langevin Forces Due to Spontaneous Emission

In Section II, a model of spontaneous emission was proposed that is illustrated in Fig. 1. According to this model, each spontaneous emission event causes a phase and an intensity change

$$\Delta\phi_i = I^{-1/2} \sin(\theta_i) \quad \text{(A18)}$$

$$\Delta I_i = 2I^{1/2} \cos(\theta_i) + 1. \quad \text{(A19)}$$

These changes occur at random times t_i where the average rate of spontaneous emission events is R.

The effect of spontaneous emission can be incorporated into the classical rate equations for ϕ and I derived in Appendix I [(A16) and (A17)] by adding Langevin force terms $F_\phi(t)$ and $F_I(t)$. The equations are then

$$\dot{\phi} = \frac{\alpha}{2}(G - \gamma) + F_\phi(t) \quad \text{(A20)}$$

$$\dot{I} = (G - \gamma)I + R + F_I(t) \quad \text{(A21)}$$

where the term R in (A21) is the average rate caused by the second term in (A19) and F_ϕ and F_I are given by

$$F_\phi(t) = \sum_i I^{-1/2} \sin(\theta_i)\,\delta(t - t_i) \quad \text{(A22)}$$

$$F_I(t) = \sum_i 2I^{1/2} \cos(\theta_i)\,\delta(t - t_i). \quad \text{(A23)}$$

The delta functions are necessary in order to produce discontinuous changes in intensity and phase during spontaneous emission events.

Langevin forces must satisfy the general relations [15]

$$\langle F_a(t) \rangle = 0 \quad \text{(A24)}$$

and

$$\langle F_a(t) F_b(u) \rangle = 2D_{ab}\,\delta(t - u). \quad \text{(A25)}$$

It is obvious that $\langle F_\phi \rangle = \langle F_I \rangle = 0$, since the angles θ_i are random. To determine the coefficients $D_{\phi\phi}$, we compute $\langle F_\phi^2(t) \rangle$. The quantity $F_\phi(t) F_\phi(u)$ is the product of two sums of delta functions. All cross terms of this product are zero, since $\delta(t - t_i)\,\delta(u - t_j)$ is zero unless $t_i = t_j$; hence

$$F_\phi(t) F_\phi(u) = \sum_i I^{-1} \sin^2(\theta_i)\,\delta(t - t_i)\,\delta(u - t_i). \quad \text{(A26)}$$

The delta function product can be rewritten as

$$\delta(t - t_i)\,\delta(u - t_i) = \delta(t - u)\,\delta(u - t_i) \quad \text{(A27)}$$

since it is zero unless $u = t = t_i$. Equation (A26) can be averaged by replacing $\sin^2 \theta_i$ by its average value $\frac{1}{2}$ and replacing Σ_i by $R \int dt_i$; hence

$$\sum_i \delta(u - t_i) = R \int dt_i\,\delta(u - t_i) = R. \quad \text{(A28)}$$

With these changes, the average of (A24) is

$$\langle F_\phi(t) F_\phi(u) \rangle = 2D_{\phi\phi}\,\delta(t - u) \quad \text{(A29)}$$

where

$$2D_{\phi\phi} = R\langle I^{-1} \sin^2(\theta_i) \rangle = \frac{R}{2I}. \quad \text{(A30)}$$

Similarly, we can show that

$$2D_{II} = R\langle 4I \cos^2(\theta_i) \rangle = 2RI \quad \text{(A31)}$$

$$2D_{I\phi} = 2R\langle \cos(\theta_i) \sin(\theta_i) \rangle = 0. \quad \text{(A32)}$$

The coefficients D_{II}, $D_{\phi\phi}$, and $D_{I\phi}$ are identical, except for changes in notation, to those derived by Lax [4] from a model of atoms interacting with a quantized optical field.

It is interesting that (A21), with the same value of D_{II}, can also be derived from considerations of photon shot noise occurring in absorption and stimulated emission. The above derivation emphasizes the wave aspects of the optical field, whereas the shot-noise arguments emphasize the particle properties. Phase is a wave property and therefore it is doubtful that (A20) and (A30) could be derived from the particle properties of light.

ACKNOWLEDGMENT

The author benefited from discussions with M. Lax, G. L. Miller, F. K. Reinhart, and R. G. Smith.

REFERENCES

[1] M. W. Fleming and A. Mooradian, "Fundamental line broadening of single-mode (GaAl)As diode lasers," *Appl. Phys. Lett.*, vol. 38, p. 511, 1981.
[2] H. Gerhardt, H. Welling, and A. Guttner, "Measurements of the laser linewidth due to quantum phase and quantum amplitude noise above and below threshold. I," *Z. Physik*, vol. 253, p. 113, 1972.
[3] M. Lax, "Classical noise V. Noise in self-sustained oscillators," *Phys. Rev.*, vol. 160, p. 290, 1967.
[4] —, "Quantum noise X. Density-matrix treatment of field and population-difference fluctuations," *Phys. Rev.*, vol. 157, p. 213, 1967.
[5] V. F. Elesin and V. V. Rusakov, "Theory of the natural width of a semiconductor laser emission line," *Sov. J. Quantum Electron.*, vol. 5, p. 1239, 1976.
[6] M. W. Fleming and A. Mooradian, "Spectral characteristics of external-cavity controlled semiconductor lasers," *IEEE J. Quantum Electron.*, vol. QE-17, pp. 44–59, Jan. 1981.
[7] J. P. van der Ziel, "Spectral broadening of pulsating $Al_xGa_{1-x}As$ double heterostructure lasers," *IEEE J. Quantum Electron.*, vol. QE-15, pp. 1277–1281, Dec. 1979.
[8] B. Hakki, "Optical and microwave instabilities in injection lasers," *J. Appl. Phys.*, vol. 51, p. 68, 1980.
[9] C. H. Henry, R. A. Logan, and K. A. Bertness, "Spectral dependence of the change in refractive index due to carrier injection in GaAs lasers," *J. Appl. Phys.*, vol. 52, pp. 4451–4461, 1981.
[10] S.E.H. Turley, G.H.B. Thompson, and D. F. Lovelace, "Effect of injection current on the dielectric constant of an inbuilt waveguide in twin-transverse-junction stripe lasers," *Electron. Lett.*, vol. 15, p. 256, 1979.
[11] H. Haug and H. Haken, *Z. Physik*, vol. 204, pp. 262–275, 1967.
[12] L. D. Landau and E. M. Lifshitz, *Electrodynamics of Continuous Media*. Reading, MA: Addison-Wesley, 1960, sect. 63.
[13] C. H. Henry, R. A. Logan, and F. R. Merritt, "Measurement of gain and absorption spectra in AlGaAs buried heterostructure lasers," *J. Appl. Phys.*, vol. 51, p. 3042, 1980.
[14] C. H. Henry, R. A. Logan, and K. A. Bertness, "Measurement of spectrum, bias dependence and intensity of spontaneous emission in GaAs lasers," *J. Appl. Phys.*, vol. 52, pp. 4453–4456, 1981.
[15] M. Lax, "Fluctuations from the nonequilibrium steady state," *Rev. Mod. Phys.*, vol. 32, p. 25, 1960.

Short-Cavity InGaAsP Injection Lasers: Dependence of Mode Spectra and Single-Longitudinal-Mode Power on Cavity Length

TIEN-PEI LEE, SENIOR MEMBER, IEEE, CHARLES A. BURRUS, FELLOW, IEEE,
JOHN A. COPELAND, SENIOR MEMBER, IEEE, ANDREW G. DENTAI, MEMBER, IEEE,
AND DIETRICH MARCUSE, FELLOW, IEEE

Abstract—Simple expressions are given to describe the lower and upper limits of the single-mode (single-frequency) power as a function of the cavity length for InGaAsP injection lasers. It has been found that the lower limit of the single-mode power is proportional to the cavity length, while the upper limit is inversely proportional to the cavity length. Thus, a short-cavity laser provides a favorable geometry for obtaining single mode output over a wide range of power levels and currents above threshold. The mode stability versus temperature is also improved by a short-cavity design. The theoretical results agree with our recent experiments on very-short-cavity (50-75 μm) stripe-geometry InGaAsP lasers, which have shown consistent single-mode output over wide current ranges.

I. Introduction

SINGLE-LONGITUDINAL-MODE operation has been observed in virtually every variety of injection laser—channeled-substrate planar configurations [1], transverse-junction-stripe (TJS) devices [2], and numerous buried-heterostructure (BH) types [3]—having narrow index-guiding cavities with lengths which have come to be considered "normal," i.e., 200-300 μm or so. However, it appears that, for the most part, these observations have been relatively rare, usually occurring over limited ranges of temperature and output power and in only a few samples. In spite of many proposed mode-confinement and mode-stabilization schemes [4]-[6], the routine production of single-mode injection lasers has proved to be elusive.

Recently, we have reported relatively consistent single-mode operation over wide current ranges in very short-cavity (50-75 μm), stripe-geometry InGaAsP injection lasers with metal-coated mirrors on the cleaved facets [7]. Observations on these experimental devices have led to a theoretical investigation, summarized here, of the dependence of the longitudinal mode spectra on the laser output power and cavity length.

In previous theoretical treatments, the assumption of single-mode output of injection lasers has always been based [8] on the theory of homogeneously broadened linewidth. More recently, attention has been paid to the fact that the large spontaneous emission rates in semiconductor lasers may be responsible for the multimode behavior observed in these lasers near threshold [5], [9]-[12]. It is well known [13] that the rate of spontaneous emission into each cavity mode in semiconductor lasers is four to five orders of magnitude larger than that in both gas lasers and solid state lasers. It is this spontaneous emission rate which also affects the noise in the intensity fluctuation of the laser output [13], as well as the relaxation oscillation characteristics of the injection laser when modulated by PCM signals [14], [15] or by high-frequency sinusoidal currents [16].

The large spontaneous emission in a semiconductor laser can be considered as a noise source in the gain medium, and the cavity modes can be considered to be selectively amplified spontaneous emission at frequencies for which the cavity resonant conditions are satisfied [17]. The primary mode at the peak of the gain spectrum then produces the largest amplitude. Because of the large gain in the medium and the large spontaneous emission into cavity modes, however, the amplitude of the secondary modes can be appreciable at currents near or slightly above threshold, although these modes eventually saturate at high injection currents in a homogeneously broadened laser. Thus, single-mode output is achieved only at currents appreciably above threshold when the primary mode power is substantially larger than the power of the secondary modes. Because the difference in gain between the primary mode and the secondary mode depends on the mode spacing, it is expected that the minimum primary mode power required to produce single-mode output will also depend on the mode spacing, and therefore on the length of the cavity.

On the other hand, a large single-mode (single-frequency) amplitude can induce spatial hole-burning in the carrier densities at the peaks of the standing wave pattern within the cavity [18], [19]. Thus, when the depletion of electrons by stimulated emission occurs faster than the diffusion rates of injected carriers, suppression of the primary mode gain will result. An upper limit on single-mode power then exists due to the gain broadening by spatial hole-burning. Since the width of the broadened gain curve is proportional to the single-mode power, and the difference of mode gain is proportional to the mode spacing, this upper limit of single-mode power is expected to be a function of mode spacing, and also a function of the length of the cavity.

It is the purpose of this paper to derive simple formulas relating both the lower limit and the upper limit of single-mode power as a function of the cavity length for InGaAsP lasers.

Manuscript received December 31, 1981; revised February 25, 1982.
The authors are with Crawford Hill Laboratory, Bell Laboratories, Holmdel, NJ 07733.

Reprinted from *IEEE J. Quantum Electron.*, vol. QE-18, no. 7, pp. 1101–1113, July 1982.

The validity of the estimated limits is supported by the mode characteristics observed in lasers reported in the literature and by recent results on our very short cavity lasers [7].

II. Model Used for Mode Computation

As a fundamental base from which to establish a lower bound on the power output required to reach single-mode operation, we assume the simplest model for a semiconductor laser; i.e., a medium with a homogeneously broadened gain spectrum. (This assumption is justified for power levels less than a few mW.) The amplitude of each cavity mode is built up, essentially, by amplification of spontaneous emission.

For a given cavity length L, the longitudinal cavity modes must satisfy the resonance condition

$$\lambda_m = 2nL/m \tag{1}$$

where λ_m is the free space wavelength of the mth mode and n is the refractive index of the laser medium. The spacing between adjacent modes is

$$\delta\lambda = \lambda_m - \lambda_{m-1} = \frac{\lambda_m^2}{2n_g L} \tag{2}$$

where n_g is the group index of the medium. Each of these modes grows, upon injection of current, according to the rate equations

$$\frac{dN}{dt} = \frac{J}{qd} - \frac{N}{\tau_s} - \left(\frac{c}{n}\right) \sum_m g_m S_m \tag{3}$$

$$\frac{dS_m}{dt} = \frac{\Gamma\gamma N}{\tau_s} + \left(\frac{c}{n}\right) [\Gamma g_m - \alpha_c] S_m \tag{4}$$

where N is the injected electron density and S_m is the photon flux density of the mth cavity mode in the active region. γ is the spontaneous emission factor defined as the ratio of the rate of spontaneous emission into each cavity mode to the total spontaneous emission rate. Derivation of γ is given in [10] and [12] and also in Appendix C. The value of γ is about 10^{-4} for semiconductor lasers as compared to a value of 10^{-9} for gas lasers and solid-state lasers [13]. All other symbols have their conventional definitions, which are given, along with values assigned in the computation, in Table I.

A parabolic approximation of the medium gain g_m as a function of wavelength is used. It can be written as [6]

$$g_m = g_p - [(\lambda_p - \lambda_m)/G_0]^2 \tag{5}$$

where the peak of the gain varies with the electron density according to

$$g_p = A_0(N - N_0). \tag{6}$$

Equation (5) is fitted to the theoretical gain curves [20] for InGaAsP near $\lambda_p = 1.3\ \mu m$ to obtain $G_0 = 2.1\ nm \cdot cm^{1/2}$. The parabolic approximation is satisfactory for gain in the range of 40-280 cm^{-1}. The values of $A_0 = 2.5 \times 10^{-16}\ cm^2$, $N_0 = 4.5 \times 10^{17}\ cm^{-3}$, and $\tau_s = 3 \times 10^{-9}$ s are used in (6) to yield a normalized threshold current density of 3.6 kA/$cm^2 \cdot \mu m$, a best value [21] experimentally obtained for InGaAsP lasers.

TABLE I
List of Symbols and Assigned Values

Symbol	Definition	Value	Unit
A	cross-sectional area of laser cavity	$w \cdot d$	cm^2
A_0	gain parameter	2.5×10^{-16}	cm^2
c	velocity of light in vacuum	3×10^{10}	cm/s
d	active layer thickness	0.2×10^{-4}	cm
E	photon energy	0.95	eV
G_0	parabolic gain fitting factor	2.1	$nm \cdot cm^{1/2}$
g_m	gain of the mth cavity mode		cm^{-1}
g_p	gain at the peak of the gain curve		cm^{-1}
h	Planck's constant	6.625×10^{-34}	J · s
I	current		mA
J	current density		kA/cm^2
J_{th}	threshold current density		kA/cm^2
L	cavity length		cm
m	mode number		
N	electron density		
N_o	electron density to reach population inversion		
n	index of refraction		
n_g	group index of refraction	4	
P_m	power output of mth mode		W
P_0	power output of lasing mode		W
P_1	power output of the adjacent secondary mode		W
P_{sat}	saturated power output of the adjacent secondary mode		W
q	electronic charge	1.6×10^{-19}	C
R	mirror reflectivity	0.3	
S_m	photon density of mth mode		cm^{-3}
t	time		s
τ_s	spontaneous radiative recombination lifetime	3×10^{-9}	s
V	volume of the active cavity		cm^3
w	width of the active cavity		cm
α_c	cavity loss		cm^{-1}
α_o	loss due to absorption	20	cm^{-1}
Γ	confinement factor	0.5	
γ	spontaneous emission factor	10^{-4}	

The steady-state photon-flux density of each mode can be expressed by

$$S_m = \frac{\gamma N/\tau_s}{\left(\frac{c}{n}\right) [(\alpha_c/\Gamma) - g_m]} \tag{7}$$

so that, if N and g_m are known, the power of the mth mode emitted from one facet can be obtained by (see Appendix A)

$$P_m = 0.5\, R^{-1/2}(1 - R) wd \left(\frac{c}{n}\right) E S_m/\Gamma \tag{8}$$

where w is the stripe width, and E is the photon energy in J.

It will be shown later that γ plays an important role in determining the mode spectra.

III. Numerical Results

With the model described above, restricted to the case of a fundamental transverse mode by choice of a reasonably narrow stripe width, $w = 5\ \mu m$, and a thin active layer, $d = 0.2\ \mu m$, we calculate the following (see Appendix B): 1) the growth of each longitudinal mode amplitude, or photon density S_m, as a function of injection current (or current density); 2) the power output as a function of injection current, i.e., the *L-I* curve, where, to determine I_{th}, the linear region of the *L-I* curve is extrapolated, and I_{th} is taken to be at the intersection on the current axis; 3) the mode spectra as a function of power output and as a function of I/I_{th}; 4) the effect of the spontaneous emission factor γ on the output spectra; and finally 5) the dependence of the output spectra on the cavity length.

A. Mode Spectra versus Current

We assume a standard cavity length of 250 μm, and a nominal value of $\gamma = 10^{-4}$. The wavelength of the central mode ($m = 0$) is assigned to be 1.3 μm, which is the wavelength of the gain peak. At a low injection current, below threshold, the envelope of the mode spectrum is as broad as the spontaneous emission. As the current increases, the width of the mode-spectrum envelope narrows. According to our laser model, the central mode (lasing mode, $m = 0$) grows faster than the adjacent modes at currents near threshold, I_{th}, and eventually the amplitudes of the adjacent modes effectively saturate. Thus, at a particular output level, additional increases in power are due to growth of a single primary mode. This general behavior is not surprising. However, the interesting point is that the amplitudes of a number of modes are still growing at currents substantially above threshold. Fig. 1 shows the photon densities (scale on the left side) of the primary mode ($m = 0$) and eight adjacent modes as a function of injection current (100 percent lateral current confinement and unity internal quantum efficiency were assumed). The power output (per facet) in mW is also shown (scale on the right side). The threshold current I_{th}, indicated by the arrow at the bottom of the figure, was obtained from the *L-I* plot as shown in Fig. 2. The total power of the amplified secondary modes at saturation can be significant, with the value depending upon the spontaneous emission factor and on the cavity length, as we shall discuss later. The larger the total power from the secondary modes, the higher is the power output of the primary mode required to achieve a "single-mode" spectrum. Here, the term "single-mode" is a matter of definition: we define "single-mode" operation to occur when the primary mode is 20 times larger than the adjacent secondary modes. Thus, in the example of Fig. 1, we note that the nearest secondary mode ($m = \pm 1$) is 13 dB down from the primary mode ($m = 0$) at $I \sim 2.8\ I_{th}$.

B. L-I Characteristic and Output Spectra

Fig. 2 is a plot of the power output (per facet) versus the injection current. I_{th} is determined by extrapolating the linear *L-I* curve to intersect with the current axis, and for this calculation $I_{th} = 13$ mA. The normalized output spectra at various currents are shown in the inserts. Mode spacings are 0.85 nm ($L = 250\ \mu m$). The differential quantum efficiency (output from both facets) is 66 percent. At $I = 1.5\ I_{th}$, the output spectrum appears to be multimode. The output spectra become single-mode at currents above 2.8 I_{th}.

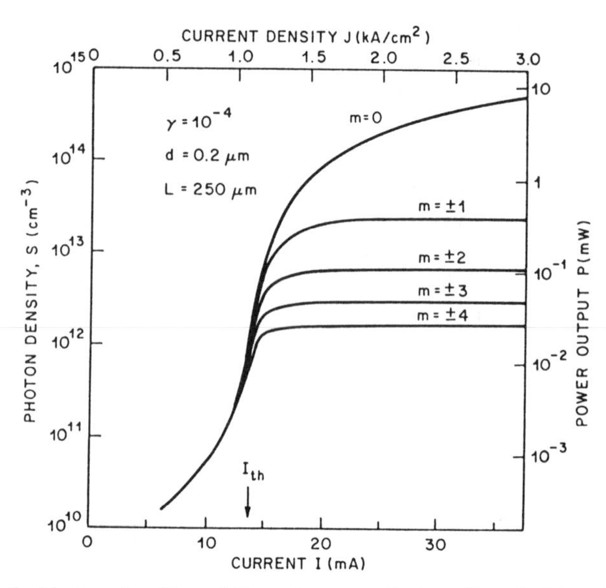

Fig. 1. Photon densities of the primary mode ($m = 0$) and eight adjacent secondary modes as a function of the injection current for a laser with 250 μm cavity length. The output power is shown on the right-hand scale.

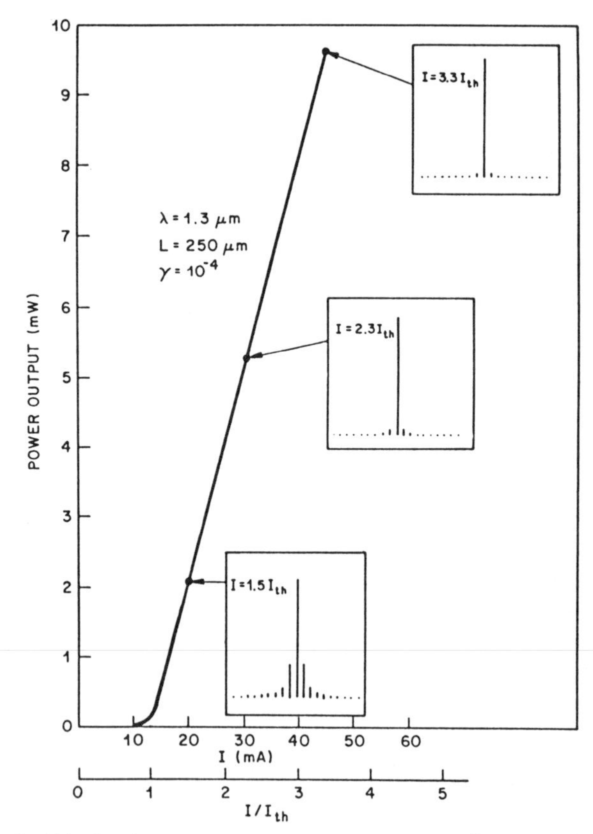

Fig. 2. Calculated power output versus current (and I/I_{th}) for the same laser shown in Fig. 1. The inserts are the mode spectra at three different current levels, mode spacing $\delta\lambda = 0.85$ nm.

C. The Effect of the Spontaneous Emission Factor on the Mode Spectra

The spontaneous emission factor γ plays an important role in determining the output spectra, as illustrated in Fig. 3. Above threshold, the power output versus current characteristics are essentially the same for all values of γ. However, the output spectra are very different. At a given output of 2 mW for $\gamma = 10^{-5}$ the power is nearly all in one mode, while for $\gamma = 10^{-4}$, 80 percent of the power is in one mode, and for $\gamma = 10^{-3}$, the power is shared by many modes. It will be shown later in (14) that the power in the secondary modes at saturation is proportional to γ. As is shown in (16), γ varies inversely with the volume of the laser cavity and in proportion to the square of the wavelength.

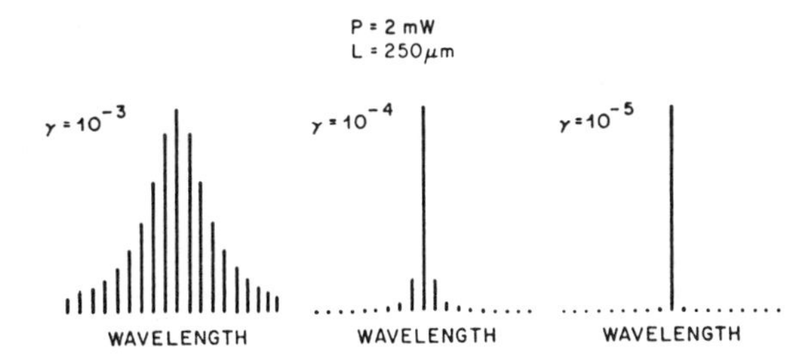

Fig. 3. Mode spectra of a 250 μm long laser at 2 mW output power when (a) $\gamma = 10^{-3}$, (b) $\gamma = 10^{-4}$, and (c) $\gamma = 10^{-5}$.

D. The Effect of Cavity Length on Mode Spectra

It is clear from (2) that the longitudinal mode spacing increases with decreasing cavity length, and that by virtue of (5) a large gain difference exists between the mode at the gain peak and all other modes; thus, single-mode operation is favored in lasers with very short cavities. Fig. 4 illustrates that, for $\gamma = 10^{-4}$ and for a power output of 2 mW, the output spectrum of a laser with a 50 μm cavity length shows essentially one mode, whereas the spectrum of a laser with a standard 250 μm cavity length has 20 percent of the power in the secondary modes.

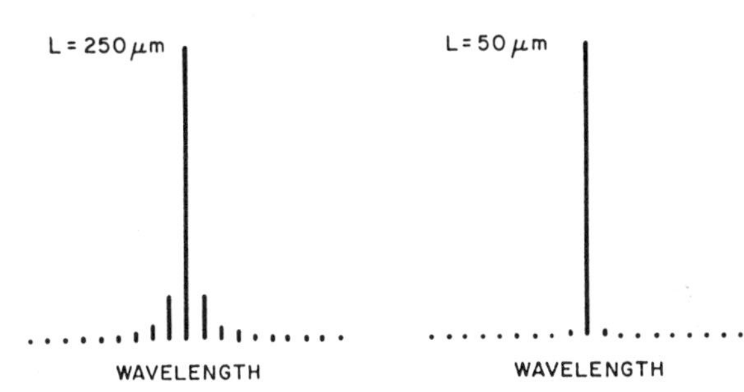

Fig. 4. Comparison of the output spectra of a 250μm long laser ($\delta\lambda$ = 0.85 nm) and that of a 50μm long laser ($\delta\lambda$ = 4.25 nm), for both outputs at 2 mW and $\gamma = 10^{-4}$.

Fig. 5 shows an L-I curve for the 50 μm long laser. As in Fig. 2, the output spectra at two different currents are shown in the inserts. A clear single-mode spectrum is obtained at 1.5 I_{th}, as opposed to the multimode spectrum shown in Fig. 2, also at $I = 1.5\ I_{th}$, for a 250 μm long cavity.

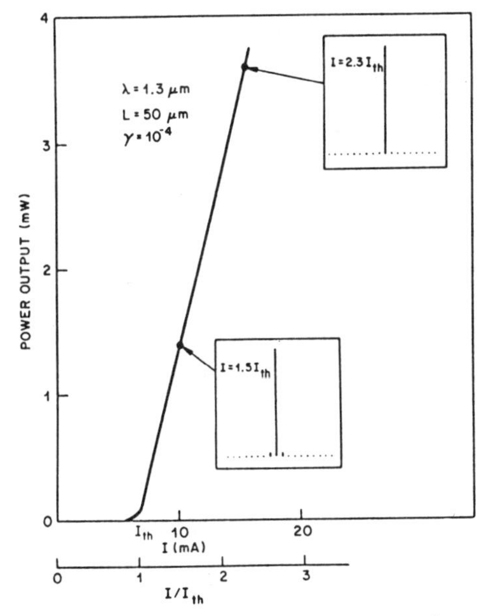

Fig. 5. Calculated power output versus current (and I/I_{th}) for a 50 μm long laser. The inserts are output spectra at two current levels, mode spacing $\delta\lambda$ = 4.25 nm.

IV. Condition for Single-Mode Operation

From examination of the above numerical examples, we come to the following conclusion: even in a homogeneously broadened injection laser, because of the large rate of spontaneous emission there still is significant power in the secondary modes near threshold, and this secondary-mode power saturates only at current levels substantially above threshold. The larger the power in the secondary modes, the higher is the current (above threshold) required for single-mode operation. Thus, we examine the effects of material variables and device geometry on the magnitude of the secondary-mode saturation power.

The power in the secondary modes can be obtained by (5)-(8). Using (7), we obtain the photon density

$$S_0 = \frac{\gamma N/\tau_s}{\left(\frac{c}{n}\right)(\alpha_c' - g_p)} \tag{9}$$

for the central mode ($m = 0$, and $\lambda_0 = \lambda_p$), where $\alpha_c' = \alpha_c/\Gamma$, and

$$S_m = \frac{\gamma N/\tau_s}{\left(\frac{c}{n}\right)\left[\alpha_c' - g_p + \left(\frac{m\delta\lambda}{G_0}\right)^2\right]} \tag{10}$$

for the mth mode, where $\delta\lambda$, given by (2), is the mode spacing. Substituting (9) into (10), we have

$$S_m = \frac{1}{\frac{1}{S_0} + \left(\frac{c}{n}\right)\left(\frac{\tau_s}{\gamma N}\right)\left(\frac{m\delta\lambda}{G_0}\right)^2}. \tag{11}$$

We define

$$S_{m\,\text{sat}} = \lim_{S_0 \to \infty} S_m = \left(\frac{n}{c}\right)\left(\frac{\gamma N}{\tau_s}\right)\left(\frac{G_0}{m\delta\lambda}\right)^2; \tag{12}$$

then

$$\frac{S_m}{S_0} = \frac{1}{1 + S_0/S_{m\,\mathrm{sat}}}. \tag{13}$$

The saturated power output of the mth mode, from one facet, is

$$P_{m\,\mathrm{sat}} = AR^{-1/2}(1-R)\left(\frac{c}{n}\right)E \cdot S_{m\,\mathrm{sat}}/2\Gamma$$

$$= \frac{A}{2}\left(\frac{1}{R^{1/2}}\right)\left(\frac{1-R}{\Gamma}\right)\left(\frac{\gamma N}{\tau_s}\right)\left(\frac{hc}{\lambda}\right)\left(\frac{G_0}{m\delta\lambda}\right)^2 \tag{14}$$

where $A = w \cdot d$ is the cross-sectional area of the active region. Because the value of N varies very slowly above threshold, we can use (6) for N by letting $g_p = \alpha_c/\Gamma = A(N - N_0)$. For $L = 250\ \mu$m, $N = 10^{18}$ cm^{-3}, and $\gamma = 0.34 \times 10^{-4}$, (14) gives, at $\lambda = 1.3\ \mu$m and $m = 1$

$$P_{1\,\mathrm{sat}} = 0.1\ \mathrm{mW}/(\mu\mathrm{m})^2. \tag{15}$$

Thus, for $A = 5 \times 0.2\ (\mu\mathrm{m})^2$, the saturation power of the nearest secondary mode is 0.1 mW when $L = 250\ \mu$m.

The factor γ can be expressed as

$$\gamma = \frac{\lambda^4 K}{8\pi^2 n^2 n_g \Delta\lambda \cdot V} \tag{16}$$

where $V = A \cdot L$ is the volume of the active region and $\Delta\lambda$ is the spectral width of the spontaneous emission. The factor $K = 1$ for index-guided lasers and $K > 1$ for gain-guided lasers [12]. Equation (16) differs from (29) in [12] by a factor of two to account for both TE and TM polarizations (see Appendix C). Substituting (2) and (16) into (14) we have

$$P_{m\,\mathrm{sat}} = \left(\frac{K}{R^{1/2}}\right)\left(\frac{1-R}{\Gamma}\right)\left(\frac{n_g L}{4\pi^2 n^2 \Delta\lambda}\right)\left(\frac{N}{\tau_s}\right)\left(\frac{hc}{\lambda}\right)\left[\frac{G_0^2}{m^2}\right]. \tag{17}$$

It is interesting to note that $P_{m\,\mathrm{sat}}$ increases linearly with cavity length. Since both $\Delta\lambda$ and G_0 are proportional to λ^2, $P_{m\,\mathrm{sat}}$ is directly proportional to the wavelength. Finally, the power ratio of the mth mode to the primary lasing mode is

$$\frac{P_m}{P_0} = \frac{1}{1 + (P_0/P_{m\,\mathrm{sat}})}. \tag{18}$$

It can been seen readily that the dependence of the output spectra on the parameters γ, L, R, and P_0, discussed in the numerical examples, is contained explicitly in (14), (17), and (18). For instance, in a nearly single-mode (single-frequency) output, (P_m/P_0) must be small, which demands a small value of $P_{m\,\mathrm{sat}}$. From (17), we can immediately observe that a high reflectivity R, a short cavity length L, and a small value of K (such as in an index guided laser) tend to be favorable for single-mode output. Thus, if we define "single-mode" operation by the criterion $(P_1/P_0) \leqslant 0.05$, then single-mode operation is reached when the lasing output exceeds $P_{l\,\mathrm{sat}}$ by

$$\frac{P_0}{P_{1\,\mathrm{sat}}} = 10 \log_{10}\left[\left(\frac{P_0}{P_1}\right) - 1\right]\ \mathrm{dB} \tag{19}$$

or 12.8 dB. Therefore, once $P_{1\,\mathrm{sat}}$ is obtained by (17), the minimum power level for single-mode operation can be determined.

Fig. 6 gives the calculated $P_{1\,\mathrm{sat}}$ versus the cavity length L in μm by use of (17) for various values of mirror reflectivity R at $\lambda = 1.3\ \mu$m. Values of the other parameters have been given previously. The power ratio P_1/P_0 is then calculated from Fig. 6 and (18) for $m = 1$ and is plotted in Fig. 7 as a function of P_0, the power of the central mode. The curves are plotted for $L = 250\ \mu$m, $R = 0.3$; $L = 100\ \mu$m, $R = 0.7$; and $L = 50\ \mu$m, $R = 0.9$. It is seen that either shortening the laser cavity or increasing the mirror reflectivity or both improves the laser spectrum toward a purer single-frequency output.

V. Effect of Temperature on the Mode Spectra

In the computations above, the wavelength of one of the longitudinal cavity modes is assumed to coincide with the wavelength of the gain peak. Since the gain peak changes with temperature, this condition can be met by varying the operating temperature. On the other hand, if the temperature drifts away from the optimum so that no cavity mode is at the gain peak, the difference in gain between the primary mode and the nearest secondary mode decreases. As a result, the secondary mode power saturates at a higher level, and the power of the primary mode required to reach the "single-mode" condition is proportionally larger. Any increase in power of the primary mode increases the junction temperature further. Thus, a positive feedback situation, which can inhibit single-mode operation, exists. In the following we derive a simple expression which predicts the range of temperature deviation from the optimum (or equivalently the range of wavelength deviation from the gain peak wavelength) allowable for stable single mode output.

If λ_0 is the wavelength of the primary mode, and λ_1 is the wavelength of the nearest secondary modes, the photon densities of these modes are

$$S_0 = \frac{\gamma N/\tau_s}{\left(\frac{c}{n}\right)\left[\alpha_c' - g_p + \left(\frac{\lambda_p - \lambda_0}{G_0}\right)^2\right]} \tag{20}$$

$$S_1 = \frac{\gamma N/\tau_s}{\left(\frac{c}{n}\right)\left[\alpha_c' - g_p + \left(\frac{\lambda_p - \lambda_1}{G_0}\right)^2\right]}. \tag{21}$$

Defining $a = |\lambda_p - \lambda_0|/(\delta\lambda/2)$, it can be shown that

$$S_1 = \frac{1}{\frac{1}{S_0} + \frac{1}{S_{1\,\mathrm{sat}}'}} \tag{22}$$

if $a < 1$. $S_{1\,\mathrm{sat}}'$ in (22) is the saturated photon density of the nearest secondary mode, and is given by

$$S_{1\,\mathrm{sat}}' = \left(\frac{1}{1-a}\right)\left(\frac{n_g}{c}\right)\left(\frac{\gamma N}{\tau_s}\right)\left(\frac{G_0}{\delta\lambda}\right)^2$$

$$= S_{1\,\mathrm{sat}}/(1-a) \tag{23}$$

where $S_{1\,\mathrm{sat}}$ is given by (12), with $m = 1$. Thus

$$P_{1\,\mathrm{sat}}' = P_{1\,\mathrm{sat}}/(1-a) \tag{24}$$

is the saturated power output of the secondary mode. When $a = 1$, the gain peak is at the midpoint between the two cavity

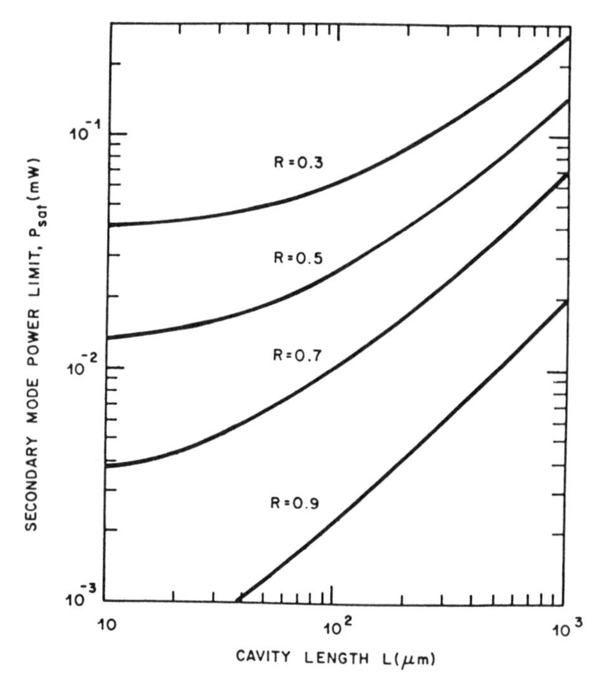

Fig. 6. The saturated secondary mode output power as a function of cavity length.

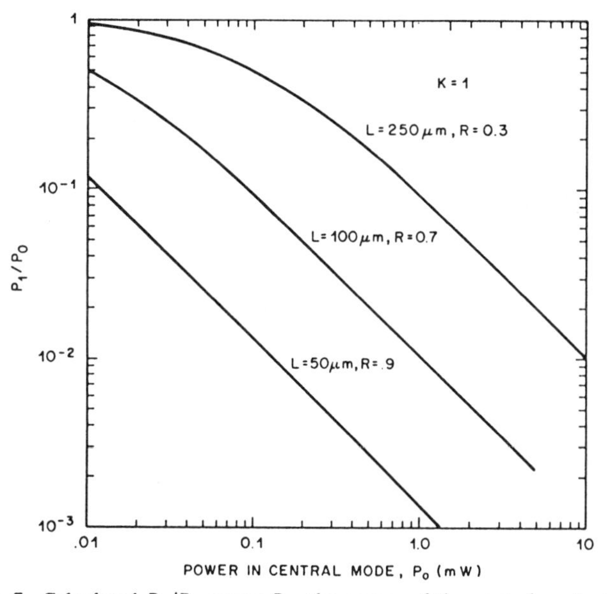

Fig. 7. Calculated P_1/P_o versus P_o, the power of the central mode, for various cavity lengths and mirror reflectivities.

modes, both of which are excited equally. The primary "mode" then is composed of two modes of equal amplitude. This is an undesirable type of operation because the increased spectral width of such a light source increases the partition noise and reduces the useful bandwidth of a single-mode optical fiber [22].

The shift in wavelength at the gain peak versus temperature has been obtained experimentally (near room temperature), as described in Section VII-A, using an InGaAsP diode laser with a cavity length of 70 μm. It was found that the peak of the gain curve shifted one longitudinal-mode spacing (2.93 nm) for a 14 °C temperature change, or about 0.21 nm/°C. Using this value, we obtain $a = 2 \times 10^{-3}\,(L \cdot \Delta T)$, and

$$P'_{sat} = \frac{0.75 + .005\,L}{1 - 2 \times 10^{-3}\,(L \cdot \Delta T)}\ \text{mW} \tag{25}$$

where L is in μm and ΔT is in °C, and $P_{1sat} = 0.75 + 0.005\,L$(mW) is obtained from Fig. 6.

Fig. 8 is a plot of (25) for $L = 50\ \mu$m, and $L = 250\ \mu$m. Five periods are shown for $L = 250\ \mu$m, where each minimum corresponds to the alignment of the gain peak with one primary mode. Single-mode operation requires a minimum output of 2 mW when the gain peak coincides with one cavity mode, in agreement with the previous calculation. The required power doubles if the gain peak drifts ±0.2 nm, or if the temperature changes by ±1 °C. However, for the 50 μm short-cavity laser, a drift of the gain peak by ±1 nm and a change of temperature by ±5 °C would be tolerable.

VI. Single-Mode Power Limitation by Spatial Hole-Burning

The result in Section IV predicts a lower limit on the output power required to reach single-mode operation in a homogeneously broadened laser. As the single-mode power increases, a standing wave arises in the laser cavity. Carriers are depleted faster at the peaks of the standing wave than in the surrounding areas, which results in a decrease in the average mode gain. This effect is known as "spatial hole burning" [18], [19]. The depleted carriers have to be replenished by carriers diffusing into these regions. Thus, the amount of gain suppression of the lasing mode depends upon the diffusion rates of electrons and holes. By use of a similar derivation given in [6], we obtain an expression for the decrease in the mode gain given by

$$\Delta g = \frac{R^{1/2}\Gamma A_0 g_p \lambda_p^2 P}{16\pi^2 n^2 (1 - R) w d E D} \tag{26}$$

where D is the ambipolar diffusion coefficient [6], [19]. We define the onset of spatial hole burning to occur when Δg is equal to the difference in gain between the lasing mode and the nearest neighboring mode; i.e., when

$$\Delta g = g_0 - g_1 = \Gamma\left(\frac{\delta\lambda}{G_0}\right)^2. \tag{27}$$

Using (2) for $\delta\lambda$, and $g_p = (1/\Gamma)[\alpha_0 + (1/L)\ln(1/R)]$, the single-mode power limitation P_{max} due to spatial hole burning can be estimated by (26) and (27), and is given by

$$P_{max} = \frac{4\pi^2 n^2 \Gamma}{n_g^2}\left(\frac{hc\lambda}{A_0 G_0^2}\right)\frac{(1 - R)}{R^{1/2}[\alpha_0 L + \ln(1/R)]}\left(\frac{D}{L}\right)A \tag{28}$$

where $A = w \cdot d$ is the cross-sectional area of the active region, and L is the cavity length. Fig. 9(a) is a plot of (28). The straight line is the lower limit of the single-mode power output as a function of the cavity length as derived previously. The curve, indicating the limitation due to spatial hole burning, is shown as a function of the cavity length for an ambipolar diffusion constant $D = 2$ cm^2/s which corresponds to an n-type carrier concentration less than 10^{18} cm^{-3} in the active layer. Fig. 9(b) shows a similar curve for $D = 10$ cm^2/s corresponding to a heavily p-type doped active layer [6]. Since it is clear

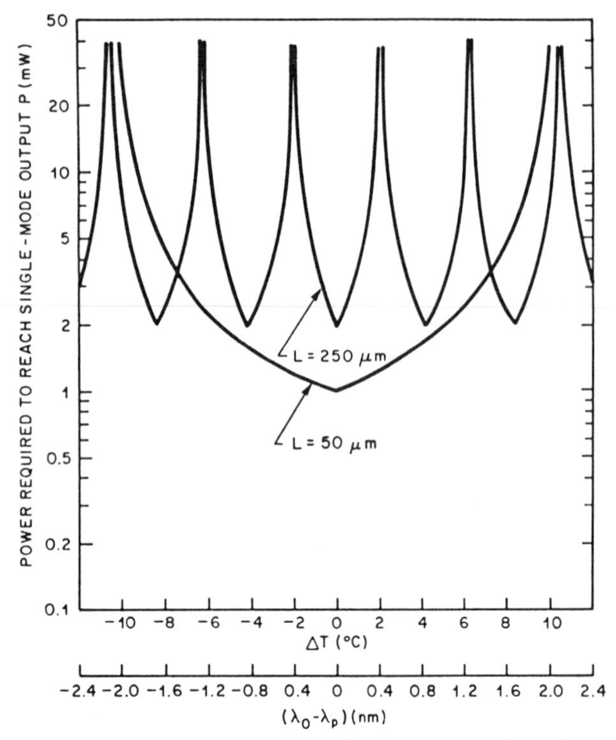

Fig. 8. Calculated output power required to reach single-mode operation as a function of drift in termperature (or wavelength of the gain-peak) from optimum.

from (28) and Fig. 9 that spatial hole burning occurs at low output powers in lasers with a long cavity length, the power range of single-mode output is reduced. Conversely, single-mode output is maintained over a wide output power range in lasers with a short-cavity structure.

VII. Experiments

Our initial experiments have been carried out on conventional oxide-masked stripe-geometry lasers (6 μm stripe width) made from InGaAsP/InP wafers grown by liquid-phase epitaxy for operation near 1.3 μm wavelength. Lasers with cavity lengths varying between 40 μm and 250 μm were made. The threshold current ($I = 200$ mA for $L = 250\ \mu$m[1]) of devices with cleaved-mirror facets decreased linearly with cavity length to $L \cong 125\ \mu$m, reached a minimum of 90 mA at $L \cong 75\ \mu$m, and increased again to 100 mA at $L \cong 50\ \mu$m, as described in more detail previously [7].

For some of the short-cavity lasers, high-reflectivity mirrors were applied to the cleaved facets. It was shown previously [7] that a) reduction of threshold current by a factor of 2 to 3 and b) nearly single-mode (single frequency) output were obtained by application of the mirror coatings. The mirrors consisted of deposited gold films, opaque on the back face and semitransparent on the front, applied over very thin dielectric films. The reflectivity of the back-face mirror was estimated to be greater than 95 percent, and that of the front-face 80-85 percent, from measurements at 1.3 μm on glass-deposited samples; the transmission of the front (output) mirror, also measured on glass-deposited samples, was ~10 percent. The best CW threshold for a 64 μm long mirror-coated laser was 40 mA at 22 °C.

[1]The threshold current is comparable to those reported for oxide-mask narrow stripe geometry lasers. The lack of index-guiding and poor current-confinement gave rise to the high I_{th} compared with the ideal values obtained in the calculated I_{th}.

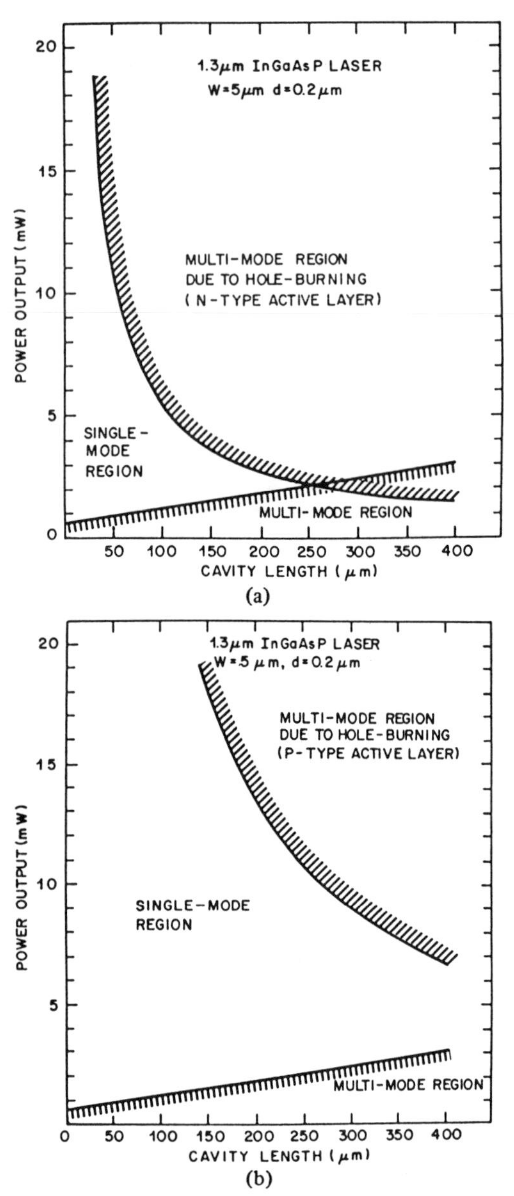

Fig. 9. Estimated upper bound of single-mode power as a function of cavity length. D is the ambipolar diffusion coefficient of electrons and holes. The straight line is the lower bound of the single-mode power derived from (17) and (19). (a) $D = 2$ cm^2/s and (b) $D = 10$ cm^2/s.

Three basic groups of lasers were used in the mode-spectra study, namely a) lasers with cleaved mirrors and standard cavity lengths, 200-250 μm, b) lasers with cleaved mirrors and short lengths, 50-75 μm, and c) lasers with coated mirrors and short lengths, 50-75 μm. About six units from each group were selected for detailed mode spectra measurements.

A. Measurement of Gain Peak Wavelength Shift versus Temperature

Because the peak of the gain curve shifts toward longer wavelength with increasing temperature, calibration of the wavelength shift was made by observing the shift of the laser output spectrum. Lasers were driven by a pulse current, 100 ns dura-

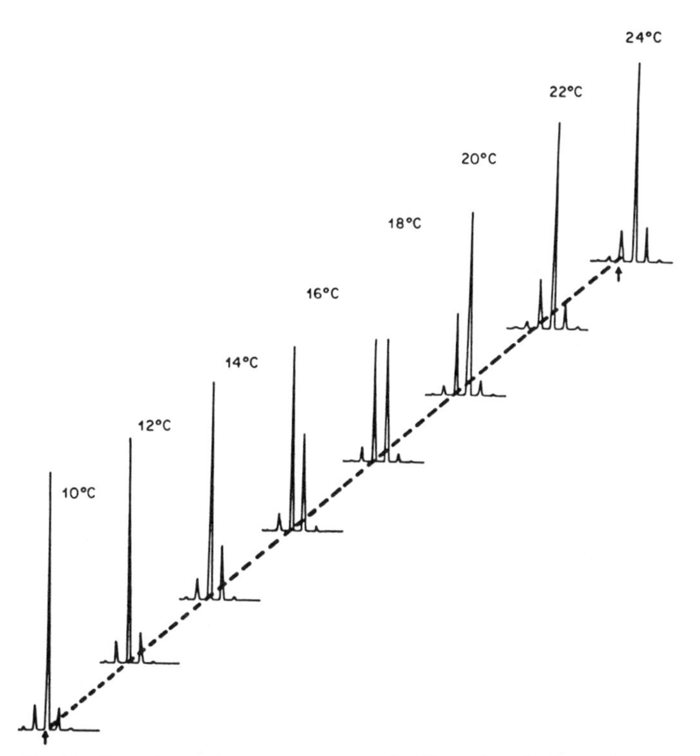

Fig. 10. Experimental output spectra of a 70 μm long InGaAsP laser at different temperatures with the injection current kept constant (I = 190 mA, I_{th}(22 °C) = 150 mA). The primary mode shifted from 1.287 μm (shown by an arrow) at 10 °C to 1.290 μm at 24 °C, corresponding to a gain peak shift of 0.21 nm/°C.

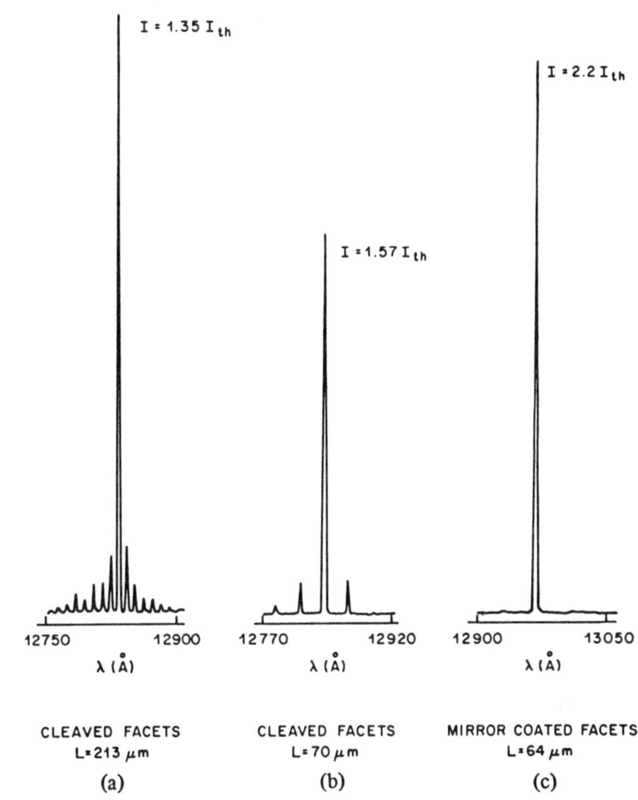

Fig. 11. Measured mode spectra of experimental laser diodes. (a) Long cavity (213 μm) cleaved facet. (b) Short cavity (70 μm), cleaved facet laser. (c) Short cavity (64 μm), mirror-coated laser.

tion typically, and at a low duty cycle ($\sim 10^{-5}$). Furthermore, a box-car integrator was used in observing the time-resolved spectra. A 5 ns gate width was set for the box-car integrator to ensure that all the modes observed were indeed oscillating simultaneously at the same temperature. The temperature was then controlled by a thermoelectric device attached to the laser heat sink.

Fig. 10 shows the output spectra of a laser diode, cavity 70 μm long with cleaved facets, as the heatsink temperature was varied from 10 to 24 °C. For a 14 °C temperature change, the wavelength of the peak mode shifted exactly one longitudinal mode spacing (2.93 nm), corresponding to a wavelength shift of 0.21 nm/°C. At the two endpoint temperatures the spectrum appeared quite symmetrical, implying that the central cavity mode was aligned with the gain peak. Furthermore, at 16 °C two strong cavity modes were excited equally, implying that the gain peak was at the midpoint between the two cavity modes. Thus, the amplitude of all cavity modes observed was qualitatively in agreement with the theory as described by (7) and (8).

B. Mode Spectra versus Cavity Length and Mirror Reflectivity

Spectral measurements were made in an experimental arrangement similar to that described above. The peak of the gain curve was aligned to coincide with one of the cavity modes by adjusting the heat-sink temperature by a few degrees, so that even at currents much above threshold a nearly symmetrical spectrum with respect to the same central frequency was maintained. To achieve symmetry in the spectra at high currents, the heat-sink temperature was readjusted (usually cooled) by a few degrees to keep the actual junction temperature constant throughout the maximum possible current range.

Fig. 11 compares the spectra of the best diode in each group. For the long-cavity laser the spectrum was quite "clean" up to $I = 1.4\, I_{th}$ and $P = 3$ mW, as shown in Fig. 11(a), at which point higher order transverse modes began to grow and a symmetrical spectrum could no longer be maintained by adjusting the temperature. For the short-cavity laser, in Fig. 11(b), a nearly single-mode spectrum was seen even near lasing threshold. The mode remained stable up to $I = 1.8\, I_{th}$, at which point a second-order transverse mode began to oscillate. For the mirror-coated short-cavity lasers [Fig. 11(c)], stable single-mode output was maintained up to $3\, I_{th}$.

Fig. 12 plots the experimental value of the ratio P_1/P_0 as a function of P_0 for lasers shown in Fig. 11(a) and (c). These results are compared with the calculated curves using (18) along with Fig. 6 for the value of P_{1sat} with K as an adjustable parameter. We found that the experimental spectral shapes agreed reasonably well with the calculated ones if we assumed $K \cong 2$. This is a reasonable value for K because the laser used here had a gain-guided structure which produced a nonplanar wavefront, resulting in a K-value larger than unity.[2] In other oxide-masked, narrow stripe geometry, gain-guided GaAlAs/GaAs lasers K-values larger than 10 have been measured [12]. Fig. 13 is an plot of the experimental ratio of the power in the central mode to the total emitted power as a function of I/I_{th}, for the best diode of each group. Again, it is obvious that for

[2] *Note added in proof:* The K-value was measured by the curvature of the wavefront at the mirror face and a value of 1.8 was obtained, which is in close agreement with the value obtained here by curve fitting.

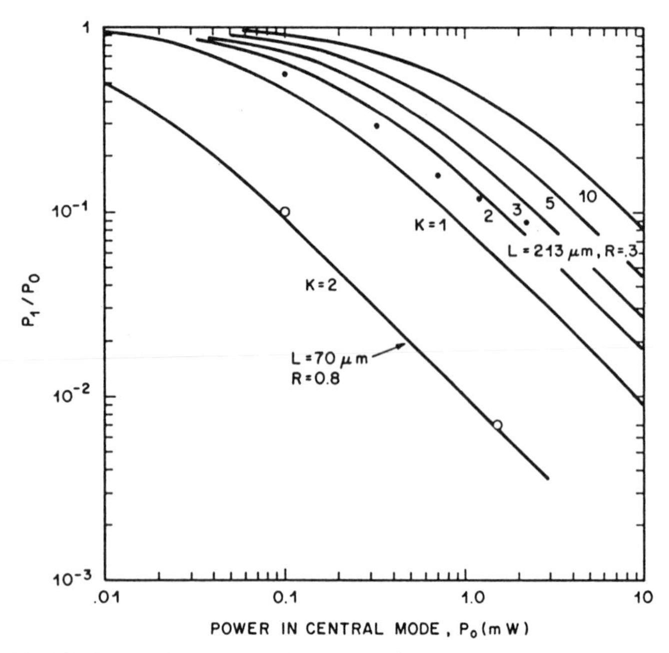

Fig. 12. Comparison of the measured P_1/P_0 versus P_0 with calculated results shown in solid curves. K is used as an adjustable parameter. $K = 2$ best fits the measured results.

the 213 μm long cleaved-facet laser, curve (a), substantial power remained in the side modes near threshold. The power ratio of the central mode to the total emission reached a maximum of 65 percent at $I = 1.4\, I_{th}$, beyond which the ratio decreased because of the onset of the second-order transverse mode. For the 70 μm short-cavity lasers, curve (b), 70 percent of the power was in the central mode near threshold, and reached a maximum of 86 percent at $I = 1.7\, I_{th}$. The best stable single-mode output was obtained with the mirror-coated short-cavity laser, curve (c), where 80 percent of the output power was in the central mode near threshold, but increased to 99.3 percent at 2.2 I_{th}. The central-mode wavelength of this coated device was absolutely stable with increasing current up to 3 I_{th}, remaining at the same wavelength without any temperature adjustment. Furthermore, a time-domain spectral measurement indicated that it was single wavelength throughout the entire duration of the 200 ns drive pulse.

These experimental observations have confirmed that stable single-mode (single frequency) oscillation in short-cavity lasers, especially mirror-coated lasers, starts at low current levels above threshold and remains single-mode over wide current ranges as predicted by the theory. Because of the lack of index guiding in the laser structures used in the experiments, the output power did not reach a level producing hole-burning before the second-order transverse mode set in; therefore, an experimental test of the upper power limit was not possible. Further experimental work, including modulation experiments, is in progress.

VIII. Discussion

Our computations have assumed that the output is in a single transverse mode. It is well known that many stripe-geometry lasers without an index-guiding structure develop higher order transverse modes (represented by so-called "kinks" in the L-I curves) at a certain power level, as shown in the experiments, and that if this power level is less than the value given by (19), single-longitudinal-mode operation cannot be obtained, also as observed in the long-cavity laser in our experiments described above. Thus, single-mode (single frequency) operation is possible only in lasers which have single-transverse-mode stability to sufficiently high power levels (as in some of the index-guiding structures previously reported). If higher order transverse modes appear at a certain power level for a certain type of guiding stripe, then it may be possible to obtain stable single-frequency operation at a lower power level if the laser cavity is short, as observed in our experiments.

We note also that the semiconductor medium is highly nonlinear and that many parameters used in the equations here are interdependent. For instance, the peak of the gain shifts toward shorter wavelengths when the injected carrier density is increased. On the other hand, it shifts toward longer wavelengths when the junction temperature is raised (a situation which usually accompanies the increase of injection current in CW operation). In addition, both the gain coefficient A_0 in (6) and the parameter of the gain width G_0 in the approximation of (5) may also depend on temperature. Although the interdependence of these variables is important, it is not included in the calculations presented here because it does not change significantly the effect of the cavity length on the steady-state output spectra.

Other mechanisms may help in stabilizing single-mode output. For example, the introduction of a controlled number of electron traps in the active region, to act as a saturable absorber, has been proposed [6] as a way to stabilize single-mode operation. Also, there have been many recent papers on the effect of distortion of the gain curve by various effects and the resulting changes in output spectra. In cases where these effects are significant, they would perturb the basic behavior described here.

IX. Conclusions

A simple multimode rate-equation model of injection lasers has been developed to investigate the mode spectra as a function of output power and cavity length. It is found that because of the large value of the spontaneous emission factor the power in the secondary modes is significant even above threshold, and thus a multimode output spectrum usually is present in semiconductor lasers. The magnitude of the power in the secondary modes has been derived and found to reduce with decreasing cavity length and to reduce with increasing mirror reflectivity. Thus, single-mode operation is expected at low power levels and at currents near threshold for lasers with short cavity lengths and/or with mirror-coated facets, provided that single-transverse-mode stability is maintained. These expectations have been verified qualitatively by experiments.

The temperature range in which stable single-mode single-frequency operation can be obtained is also wider for short-cavity lasers, so that the usual stringent requirement on regulation of the laser operating temperature can be relaxed somewhat with short-cavity devices.

Spatial hole burning in the carrier densities at the peaks of the primary mode standing wave selectively reduces the gain of the primary mode and, thus, sets an upper bound on the single-mode power output.

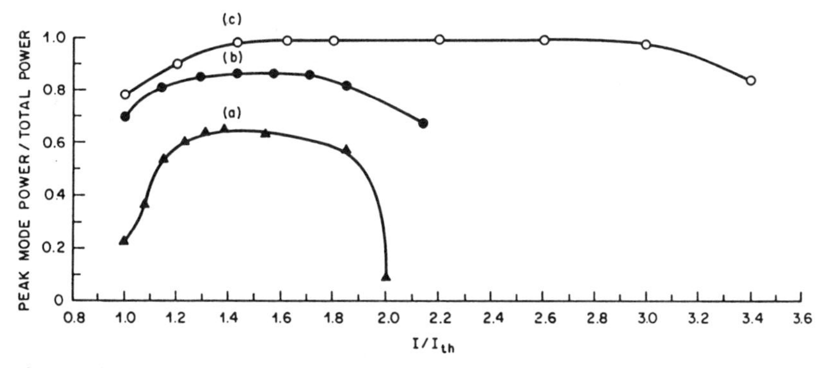

Fig. 13. Ratio of power in the central mode to the total emitted power for three different types of laser cavities shown in Fig. 11.

The unique contribution of the present studies is that a quantitative limit on both the lower bound of the single-mode power, which is proportional to the cavity length, and the upper bound of the single-mode power, which is inversely proportional to the cavity length, has been established. These relationships allow the utilization of cavity length and mirror reflectivity as design parameters in the realization of single-mode lasers.

Appendix A

Relation Between Output Photon Density and the Photon Density Inside the Cavity

Referring to Fig. 14, the photon density at x in the cavity can be written as

$$S(x) = S_+(0)e^{gx} + S_-(0)e^{-gx} \tag{A1}$$

where $S_+(0)$ and $S_-(0)$ are the amplitudes of the photon flux at the center of the cavity ($x = 0$), which are propagating in the $+x$ and $-x$ directions, respectively, and g is the gain coefficient. The resonance condition of the cavity requires

$$R^2 e^{2gL} = 1 \tag{A2}$$

where equal mirror reflectivity R has been assumed.

The output photon density is

$$S = (1 - R)S_+(L/2) = (1 - R)S_+(0)e^{gL/2}. \tag{A3}$$

Combining (A2) and (A3), we obtain

$$S = \left(\frac{1}{R}\right)^{1/2} (1 - R)S_+(0). \tag{A4}$$

Using $S_0 = S_+(0) + S_-(0)$ as the total photon density at the center of the cavity, and $S_+(0) = S_-(0) = \frac{1}{2} S_0$, (A4) can be written as

$$S = \frac{1}{2}\left(\frac{1}{R}\right)^{1/2} (1 - R)S_0 \tag{A5}$$

which is the relation used in conjunction with (7) in the text to obtain (8).

It can be shown that the photon density is not constant over the length of the cavity. The photon density at the mirror facet is higher than that at the center, and is given by

$$\frac{S(L/2)}{S_0} = \frac{1}{2}\left(\sqrt{R} + \frac{1}{\sqrt{R}}\right). \tag{A6}$$

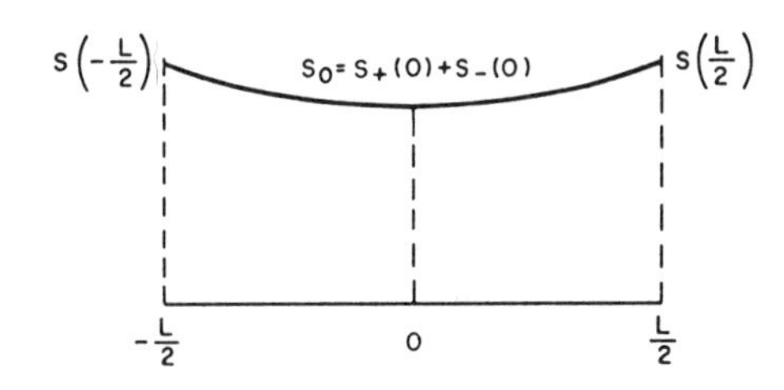

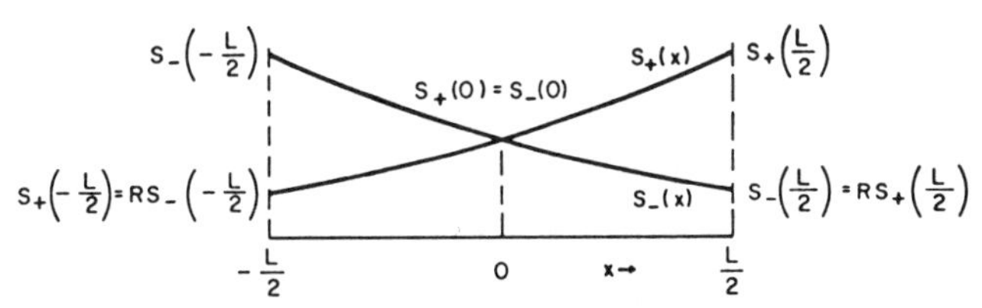

Fig. 14. Photon densities along the stripe are composed of a component moving left S_- and a component moving right S_+.

For $R = 0.3$, $S(L/2)/S_0 = 1.185$ and for $R = 0.9$, $S(L/2)/S_0 = 1.001$.

Appendix B

Comments on Computer Solution

When the laser has reached steady state operation the time derivatives in (3) and (4) vanish and we obtain from (3)

$$N = \tau_s \left[\frac{J}{qd} - \left(\frac{c}{n}\right) \sum_m g_m S_m\right] \tag{A7}$$

and from (4)

$$S_m = \frac{\gamma N/\tau_s}{\left(\frac{c}{n}\right) D_m} \tag{A8}$$

with D_m defined by

$$D_m = D_o + [(\lambda_p - \lambda_m)/G_o]^2 \tag{A9}$$

where

$$D_o = \frac{\alpha_c}{\Gamma} - A_o(N - N_o) \tag{A10}$$

is the denominator of the central mode, $m = 0$. The system of equations (5), (6) and (A7)–(A10) is highly nonlinear. Attempts to obtain solutions by straightforward iteration fail because the denominator D_o appearing in S_o may become negative, contrary to the requirement that the photon density S_o is a positive quantity. The problem is complicated by the fact that for operation above threshold D_o becomes very small. In order to overcome this difficulty we replace D_o in the denominator of S_o by a parameter D_o' that is always positive. As a starting value we let $D_o' = 0.5$. Thereafter we reduce the value of D_o' by division with $(1 + \epsilon)$ whenever $D_o - D_o' < 0$ and we increase the value of D_o' by multiplication with $(1 + \epsilon)$ whenever $D_o - D_o' > 0$. To ensure convergence, the value of ϵ is reduced (from an initial value of 0.1) by division with the factor 1.5 each time $D_o - D_o'$ changes sign. This technique ensures that the denominator D_o' of S_o is always a positive quantity that converges toward the true value of D_o. Simultaneously with this operation on the denominator we compute iterative values for N and S_m from (A6) and (A7) starting with $S_m = 0$. For current values high above threshold, approximately 150-200 iteration steps are required until successive iterations of S_o as well as the values of D_o and D_o' differ by less than 0.001. This iterative calculation of solutions of the rate equations takes only a few minutes on a small desk-top computer.

Appendix C

Derivation of Spontaneous Emission Factor

The spontaneous emission factor γ was introduced in (4) to account for the fact that only a fraction of all spontaneously emitted photons actually contribute to a given cavity mode m. To facilitate the derivation of a simple (approximate) expression for γ we begin by rewriting the spontaneous emission term on the right-hand side of (4) as follows.

$$\frac{\gamma N}{\tau_s} = \frac{\bar{\gamma} n_m}{\tau_s}. \tag{A11}$$

(For simplicity we set $\Gamma = 1$.) In this expression, n_m is the fraction of the total electron density that contribute to photon emission into the mth laser mode. This fractional electron density is related to the total electron density N via

$$n_m = D_m N. \tag{A12}$$

D_m is a distribution function that is normalized to unity

$$1 = \sum_m D_m \approx \frac{1}{\Delta\lambda_c} \int_{-\infty}^{\infty} D(\lambda) d\lambda \tag{A13}$$

so that

$$\sum_m n_m = N. \tag{A14}$$

In (A13) $\Delta\lambda_c$ is the spacing between adjacent laser modes. The relation between γ and $\bar{\gamma}$ in (A11) is given by

$$\gamma = \bar{\gamma} D_m. \tag{A15}$$

Since the distribution function (A15) cannot be normalized, we assume that D_m has Lorentzian shape

$$D_m = \frac{C_D}{1 + [(\lambda_m - \lambda_p)/\Delta\lambda]^2} \tag{A16}$$

of spontaneous spectral width $\Delta\lambda$ which peaks at $\lambda = \lambda_p$. From the normalization condition (A13) we obtain

$$C_D = \frac{\Delta\lambda_c}{\pi \Delta\lambda}. \tag{A17}$$

We are now ready to derive a formula for the coefficient $\bar{\gamma}$ which represents the fraction of spontaneously emitted photons into a given laser mode relative to all photons spontaneously emitted into all directions and into the wavelength interval $\Delta\lambda_c$.

The waveguide in the laser amplifier has width w and thickness d and forms a resonator of length L. The propagation vector of the modes of this resonator is

$$\vec{\beta} = \left(\frac{2\pi}{w} n_x, \frac{2\pi}{d} n_y, \frac{2\pi}{L} n_z \right). \tag{A18}$$

The integers n_x, n_y, and n_z represent coordinates in mode number space. One guided mode in the laser occupies the volume

$$V_{n1} = dn_x dn_y dn_z = 1 \tag{A19}$$

in mode number space. This volume corresponds to

$$V_{\beta 1} = \frac{(2\pi)^3}{wLd} \tag{A20}$$

in β-space. A general volume in β-space can be expressed as

$$V_{\beta 2} = 2 \int_\Omega \beta^2 d\beta d\Omega. \tag{A21}$$

The factor two takes care of the fact that each mode can exist in two mutually orthogonal polarizations. By integrating over the whole 4π range of solid angles we have

$$V_{\beta 2} = 8\pi\beta^2 \Delta\beta. \tag{A22}$$

The propagation constant can be expressed as

$$\beta = \frac{2\pi}{\lambda_p} n \tag{A23}$$

and its differential is

$$|\Delta\beta| = \frac{2\pi}{\lambda_p^2} n_g \Delta\lambda_c \tag{A24}$$

with n being the refractive index, n_g is the group index of the laser medium, and $\Delta\lambda_c$ is the wavelength spacing between adjacent laser modes. We thus have the following expression for the volume in β-space that is occupied by photons that are spontaneously emitted into the wavelength range $\Delta\lambda_c$ and in all possible directions in space:

$$V_{\beta 2} = 8\pi(2\pi)^3 \frac{n^2 n_g}{\lambda_p^4} \Delta\lambda_c. \tag{A25}$$

By definition, the factor $\bar{\gamma}$ is the ratio of the volume in β-space occupied by one guided mode relative to the whole volume receiving photons by spontaneous emission in the wavelength interval $\Delta\lambda_c$

$$\bar{\gamma} = \frac{V_{\beta 1}}{V_{\beta 2}} = \frac{\lambda_p^4}{8\pi n_g n^2 \Delta\lambda_c wLd}. \tag{A26}$$

Equation (A26) is only approximately valid. The derivation of an exact expression would require an exact treatment of the guided and radiation modes of the waveguide embedded in the laser.

According to (A15) and (A16) the spontaneous emission factor appearing in (4) is actually a function of the wavelength. However, for our purposes we are interested only in its value near the peak of the gain curve so that we have

$$\gamma = \bar{\gamma} C_D \tag{A27}$$

or after substitution of (A17) and (A26)

$$\gamma = \frac{\lambda_p^4}{8\pi^2 n_g n^2 \Delta\lambda wLd}. \tag{A28}$$

Except for the factor K, this formula is equal to the expression (16) if we identify $V = wLd$ as the effective mode volume.

The derivation of (A28) holds for index guided laser modes with plane phase fronts. Petermann [12] and Streifer *et al.* [23] have shown that the spontaneous emission factor is larger by a factor K if the mode inside the laser cavity has curved phase fronts. This happens when the mode is not guided by total internal reflection but by the difference in gain and loss inside and outside of the active laser region. The factor K can be quite large. Its value is hard to predict since it depends on the details of the waveguiding mechanism in the laser under consideration.

Acknowledgment

J. F. Ferguson assisted in the epitaxial growth, F. Favire in device processing, and W. B. Secsa in device evaluation.

References

[1] M. Nakamura, K. Aiki, N. Chinone, R. Ito, and J. Umeda, "Longitudinal-mode behavior of mode-stablized $Al_xGa_{1-x}As$ injection lasers," *J. Appl. Phys.*, vol. 49, pp. 4644-4648, Sept. 1978.

[2] H. Namizaki, "Transverse-junction-strip lasers with a GaAs p-n homojunction," *IEEE J. Quantum Electron.*, vol. QE-11, pp. 427-431, July 1975.

[3] M. Hirao, A. Doi, S. Tsuji, M. Nakamura, and K. Aiki, "Fabrication and characterization of narrow strip InGaAsP/InP buried hetero-structure lasers," *J. Appl. Phys.*, vol. 51, pp. 4539-4540, Aug. 1980.

[4] D. R. Scifres, R. D. Burnkham, and W. Streifer, "Single longitudinal mode operation of diode lasers," *Appl. Phys. Lett.*, vol. 31, pp. 112-114, July 1977.

[5] M. Yamada and Y. Suematsu, "A condition of single longitudinal mode operation in injection lasers with index-guiding structure," *IEEE J. Quantum Electron.*, vol. QE-15, pp. 743-749, Aug. 1979.

[6] J. A. Copeland, "Single-mode stabilization by traps in semiconductor lasers," *IEEE J. Quantum Electron.*, vol. QE-16, pp. 721-727, July 1980.

[7] C. A. Burrus, T. P. Lee, and A. G., Dentai, "Short-cavity single-mode 1.3 μm InGaAsP lasers with evaporated high-reflectivity mirrors," *Electron. Lett.*, vol. 17, pp. 954-956, Dec. 1981.

[8] For example, H. Kressel and J. K. Butler, *Semiconductor Lasers and Heterojunction LEDs.* New York: Academic, 1977, ch. 17; also *Semiconductor Devices for Optical Communication* (Topics in Applied Physics, vol. 39), H. Kressel, Ed. Berlin: Springer-Verlag, 1980, ch. 7.

[9] L. W. Casperson, "Threshold characteristics of multimode laser oscillators," *J. Appl. Phys.*, vol. 46, pp. 5194-5201, Dec. 1975.

[10] Y. Suematsu and K. Furuya, "Theoretical spontaneous emission factor of injection lasers," *Trans. IECE, Japan*, vol. E60, pp. 467-472, Sept. 1977.

[11] K. Petermann, "Theoretical analysis of spectral modulation behavior of semiconductor injection lasers," *Opt. Quantum Electron.*, vol. 10, pp. 233-242, May 1978.

[12] —, "Calculated spontaneous emission factor for double-heterostructure injection lasers with gain induced waveguiding," *IEEE J. Quantum Electron.*, vol. QE-15, pp. 566-570, July 1979.

[13] D. E. McCumber, "Intensity fluctuations in the output of cw laser oscillators I," *Phys. Rev.*, vol. 141, pp. 306-322, Jan. 1966.

[14] Y. Suematsu, S. Akiba, and T. Hong, "Measurement of spontaneous-emission factor of AlGaAs double-heterostructure semiconductor lasers," *IEEE J. Quantum Electron.*, vol. QE-13, pp. 596-600, Aug. 1977.

[15] R. Lang and K. Kobayashi, "Suppression of relaxation oscillation in modulated output of semiconductor lasers," *IEEE J. Quantum Electron.*, vol. QE-12, pp. 194-199, Mar., 1976.

[16] S. Tarucha and K. Otsuka, "Response of semiconductor laser to deep sinusoidal injection current modulation," *IEEE J. Quantum Electron.*, vol. QE-17, pp. 810-816, May 1981.

[17] E. I. Gordon, "Optical maser oscillators and noise," *Bell Syst. Tech. J.*, vol. 43, pp. 507-539, Jan. 1964.

[18] H. G. Danielmeyer, "Effects of drift and diffusion of excited states on spatial hole burning and laser oscillation," *J. Appl. Phys.*, vol. 42, pp. 3125-3132, July 1971.

[19] W. Streifer, R. D. Burnham, and D. R. Scifres, "Dependence of longitudinal mode structure on injected carrier diffusion in diode laser," *IEEE J. Quantum Electron.*, vol. QE-13, pp. 403-404, June 1977.

[20] N. K. Dutta, "Calculated absorption, emission, and gain in $In_{0.72}Ga_{0.28}As_{0.6}P_{0.4}$," *J. Appl. Phys.*, vol. 51, pp. 6095-6099, Dec. 1980.

[21] D. Botez, "InGaAsP/InP double-heterostructure lasers: Simple expressions for wave confinement, beamwidth, and threshold current over wide ranges in wavelength (1.1-1.65 μm)," *IEEE J. Quantum Electron.*, vol. QE-17, pp. 178-186, Feb. 1981.

[22] K. Ogawa, "Analysis of mode partition noise in laser transmission systems," *IEEE J. Quantum Electron.*, vol. QE-18, pp. 849-855, May 1982.

[23] W. Streifer, D. R. Scifres, and R. D. Burnham, "Spontaneous emission factor of narrow-strip gain-guided diode lasers," *Electron. Lett.*, vol. 17, p. 933, 1981.

Longitudinal mode self-stabilization in semiconductor lasers

R. F. Kazarinov, C. H. Henry, and R. A. Logan
Bell Laboratories, Murray Hill, New Jersey 07974

(Received 16 November 1981; accepted for publication 9 March 1982)

A general mechanism of self-stabilization of longitudinal modes in semiconductor lasers is presented. The stabilization is due to the modulation of the inverted population by the beating of the fields of lasing and nonlasing modes, thereby modulating the rate of stimulated emission. This leads to two optical nonlinearities: one causing gain suppression of nonlasing modes and the other causing coupling of pairs of nonlasing modes that are equally separated from the laser line. The two nonlinearities nearly cancel, but their net effect is a weak suppression of the nonlasing modes and stabilization of the lasing mode. Buried optical guide lasers were stabilized in a single longitudinal mode for currents greater than 6mA above threshold. The mode intensity spectra of the lasers were measured over 5 decades and converted to gain spectra, which could be compared with the theory. The gain spectrum is parabolic at threshold. At 20 mA above threshold it remains continuous at the laser line but narrows and becomes structured. The structure is characterized by a dip in the gain and in the mode intensities occurring about 3 modes from the laser line. The laser line also causes a pronounced dip in the gain spectra of the nonlasing first order transverse modes. All of these features can be approximately accounted for by the theory.

PACS numbers: 42.55.Px, 42.65.Gv, 42.80.Sa, 85.30.De

I. INTRODUCTION

A number of types of semiconductor lasers display single longitudinal mode behavior.[1–3] The only feature that these lasers have in common is the ability to operate up to high power densities in a stabilized tranverse mode. Therefore, the longitudinal mode selection in semiconductor lasers does not appear to be a peculiarity of device design, but is more likely related to the optical properties of the semiconductor under conditions of intense stimulated emission.

In semiconductor lasers, the width of the gain spectrum considerably exceeds the separation of two adjacent modes of the Fabry-Perot cavity. Even in this unfavorable situation, single mode operation is still possible if the gain spectrum is "homogeneously broadened," so that it rigidly retains its shape as laser optical power increases. Under these circumstances almost all of the optical power will be emitted from the one or two modes nearest the peak of the gain spectrum. However, continuously operated semiconductor lasers exhibit stability that goes beyond what can be attributed to homogeneous broadening. A study by Nakamura *et al.*,[2] of channeled-substrate planer (CSP) lasers, showed that nonlasing modes near the laser line decreased in intensity with increasing laser power. These lasers also showed a reluctance to change to a new lasing mode as the temperature was varied and the gain envelope shifted. The changes occurred suddenly in jumps of one or more modes and showed "hysteresis" with the jump occurring at different temperatures, depending on whether temperature was increasing or decreasing.

In this paper, we consider only spectral gain changes. The effects of spatial hole burning on the longitudinal modes, such as discussed by Streiffer *et al.*,[4] are neglected. We show theoretically that longitudinal mode stability can arise from gain suppression of nonlasing modes caused by nonlinear optical interactions with the lasing mode. The nonlinearities originate from stimulated emission altering the inverted population of the semiconductor. The phenomena of spectral hole burning in the gain spectrum about the laser line, caused by stimulated emission decreasing the inverted population, is well known and leads to single mode instability.[5,6] However, we will show that there are several other effects of the same order of magnitude as spectral hole burning and which lead to single mode stability. These new phenomena result from modulation of the inverted population by the beating of lasing and nonlasing fields producing a modulation of the rate of stimulated emission. The theory of these phenomena is presented in Sec. III and in Appendices B and C.

Probably any mechanism of longitudinal mode stability containing adjustable parameters can account for the observed high ratio of lasing to nonlasing mode intensities and the hysteresis effect observed by Nakamura *et al.*[2] On the other hand, the changes in the mode intensity spectra that accompany single mode stabilization are similar in both our lasers and those reported by Nakamura *et al.*,[2] and these changes can probably distinguish between different stabilization mechanisms. Prior to presenting the theory, we report in Sec. II an experimental study of mode intensity spectra in loss stabilized buried optical guide (LSBOG) lasers[7] exhibiting single longitudinal mode stability. ("Loss stabilized" refers to stabilization of the transverse mode.) The mode intensities of a simple laser with uncoupled modes are inversely proportional to the difference of loss and gain for each mode. We use this relation, derived in Appendix A, to convert the mode intensity data to "effective gain" spectra which are readily compared with theory. The effective gain spectrum of the fundamental transverse TE_{00n} modes shows three features: It is continuous at the laser line; it narrows about the laser line, stabilizing the lasing mode; it is structured with a dip in gain developing on the high energy side about 3 modes from the laser line. In contrast to the fundamental TE_{00n} modes, the gain profile of the nonlasing TE_{01n} modes does

Reprinted with permission from *J. Appl. Phys.*, vol. 53, no. 7, pp. 4631–4644, July 1982.

not vary smoothly at the laser line, but exhibits there a sharp asymmetric dip in gain. The theory of Sec. III can explain all of the basic features of the effective gain spectra. This gives us confidence that while the theory is approximate, it is essentially correct. Furthermore, the theory contains three parameters, two relaxation times and an optical matrix element, and fits to the data allow us to approximately determine these parameters.

There have been several papers published on the mechanism of longitudinal mode stability in semiconductor lasers. Copeland[8] has suggested that deep traps acting as saturable absorbers can cause stability and he has also proposed that the *D-X* center in $Al_xGa_{1-x}As$ lasers, acting as a saturable absorber in the *n*-cladding layer, is present in high enough concentrations to account for the stability observed by Nakamura *et al.*[2] Lang *et al.*[9] has shown that the energy level of the *D-X* center is above the conduction band unless the Al concentration is greater than 30–35%. If it is above the conduction band, the level will be ionized and unable to absorb light. We are certain that this center is not important in the stability of our lasers, because the optical field has a negligible penetration in regions with $x \geqslant 30\%$.

Yamada *et al.*[10,11] have attempted to account for longitudinal mode stability using a mechanism similar to ours: optical nonlinearities. Both our paper and their paper use a density matrix formalism to calculate the optical nonlinearities, but we arrive at different conclusions, principally because Yamada *et al.* do not include the nonlinear coupling between modes equally separated from the laser line. Without including this term, the spectral features discussed in this paper cannot be accounted for. We will elaborate on this point in Sec. IV, where our results are summarized and discussed.

II. MEASUREMENTS OF MODE INTENSITY SPECTRA

A. Experimental

1. Lasers

The lasers used in this experiment were AlGaAs loss stabilized buried optical guide (LSBOG) lasers. The properties of these lasers and their construction have been described in an earlier paper.[7] The lasers had thresholds of 20–25 mA and active layer dimensions of 2.5 μm wide, 0.2 μm thick, and 380 μm long, with a mode occupation factor $\Gamma \cong 0.3$. The lasers operate in the lowest transverse mode up to currents of 20–40 mA above threshold and have differential quantum efficiencies of approximately 50%. The data in this paper was taken on $Al_xGa_{1-x}As$ lasers with $x = 0$ active layers, surrounded vertically by 1/2-μm-thick $x = 0.15$ guiding layers and $x = 0.30$ cladding layers and horizontally by $x = 0.36$ cladding layers. Similar performance and spectra were observed with lasers having $x = 0.08$ active layers.

The lasers were heat sunk in a simple manner by bonding them to copper foils with epoxy. Both active-side-down and substrate-side-down mounted lasers exhibited similar performance and mode stability. The lasers were held in a temperature controlled dewar in which temperature was varied by evaporated N_2 gas passing through a heater coil.

2. Oscilloscope display of mode spectra

The experiments were greatly aided by construction of an instantaneous display of the mode spectra. Light from the continuously operating laser was collected with a $\times 8$ objective. Half of the light was sent to a spectrometer for careful spectral measurements. The other half was sent to a grating of 1200 lines per mm. The first order reflection from the grating was focused by a 100-cm focal length lens onto a slit in front of an RCA 8852 photomultiplier. The dispersed light was reflected off a General Scanning Inc. electrically driven mirror prior to reaching the slit. This enabled the dispersed light to be scanned across the slit and the mode spectrum to be displayed on an oscilloscope. This display was used in selecting lasers having single mode stability and also used in returning the laser to the same operating mode when current or temperature was changed.

Lasers with defects or which degraded and acquired defects during operation lost their single mode stability. An LSBOG laser free of defects would operate in a dominant mode at currents less than 1 mA above threshold. Within a few mA of threshold, changes in temperature were accompanied by smooth changes in the mode spectrum in which the dominant mode decreases in intensity and the next mode increases in intensity.

For currents more than 6 mA above threshold the smooth transitions between lasing modes ceased. Only one dominant mode could be seen. The mode shifted with temperature but remained constant in intensity until the laser suddenly switched to a new lasing mode. For currents more than 12 mA above threshold, the range of temperature over which a given mode was dominant increased and hysteresis was observed[2,3]; the temperature at which the mode jump occurred depended on whether the temperature was increasing or decreasing. In our lasers the newly lasing mode was always the mode adjacent to the formerly lasing mode.

3. Mode spectra

Mode spectra were recorded using a Spex double spectrometer and an RCA 8852 photomultiplier. Spectra were only recorded for lasers showing hysteresis, which is indicative of single mode stability, and showing similar behavior in different spectral regions. The output of the photomultiplier was amplified with a Hewlett-Packard 7563A log amplifier. This permitted us to record spectra over 5 decades of intensity. The double spectrometer was valuable in removing scattered light and grating ghosts which distorted the nonlasing mode spectrum near the laser line. A polarizer was used to remove the nonlasing TM modes.

B. Effective gain spectra of the TE_{00n} modes

The light in each mode arises from amplified spontaneous emission. It is shown in Appendix A that the power in the *i*th mode is inversely proportional to the difference between the loss γ and the gain g_i.

$$P_i \sim (\gamma - g_i)^{-1}. \quad (1)$$

The constant of proportionality is also calculated in Appendix A and for the lasing mode with $I - I_{th} = 20$mA and

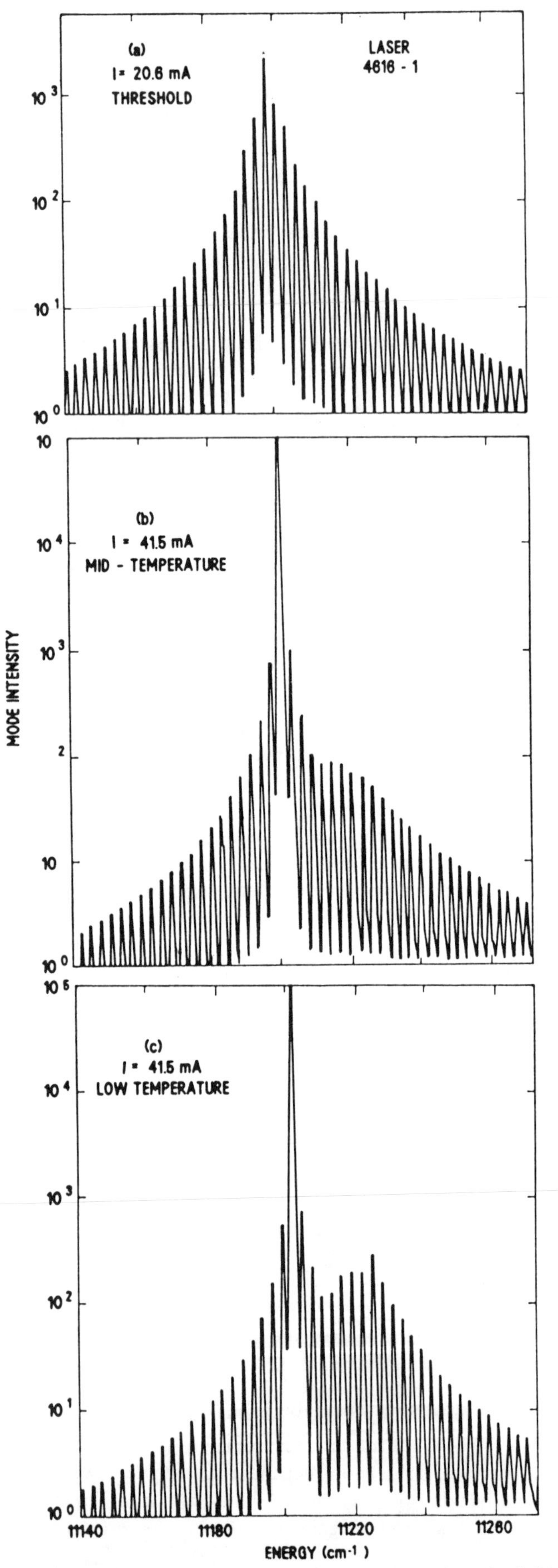

FIG. 1. Mode intensity spectra at threshold and at 20 mA above threshold. Mid-temperature and low temperature refer to the middle and low end of the range of mode stability. The total range is about 2 K.

50% quantum efficiency, it is shown that $\gamma - g_0 = 6.2\times 10^{-4}\,\text{cm}^{-1}$. The values of $\gamma - g_i$ for the non-lasing mode can then be found from the ratio of intensities P_i/P_0. and Eq. (1).

Figures 1(a) and 1(b) show the spectra of an LSBOG laser at threshold and at 20 mA above threshold. As current was increased, the temperature of the heat sink was changed to keep the laser operating on the same mode. This corresponds to little or no change in the temperature of the active layer. At 20 mA above threshold, the laser will operate in the same mode over a range of temperature of about 2 K. Figure 1(b) shows the spectrum for the center of this range and Fig. 1(c) shows the spectrum for the low temperature end of the range. The midtemperature and low temperature mode intensity spectra have a structured appearance, which is most apparent in the low temperature spectra, Fig. 1(c), where there is a dip in intensities occurring near the third mode from the laser line. This dip is a consistently occurring feature of the mode spectra and occurs in the data of Nakamura *et al.*,[2] as well as in ours.

The mode intensities of the threshold data and mid-temperature data for 20 mA above threshold are converted to effective gain spectra in Fig. 2 using Eq. (1). We call them "effective gain spectra" because the theory presented in Sec. III shows that the TE_{00n} modes of the laser are coupled in pairs about the laser line. In this case, the relation between $\gamma - g_i$ and P_i is more complex than described in Appendix A and Eq. (1). Nevertheless, the conversion is helpful because the effective gain spectra are more useful as a basis of comparison of theory and experiment and of different lasing conditions than the original mode intensity spectra.

The effective gain curve at threshold is nearly parabolic in shape. It can be fitted with

$$g(\text{cm}^{-1}) = \gamma - \left(\frac{N-\overline{N}}{4.9}\right)^2, \tag{2}$$

where $N-\overline{N}$ are the number of modes from the peak of the gain curve and the mode energy separation is 3.0 cm^{-1} (2.35

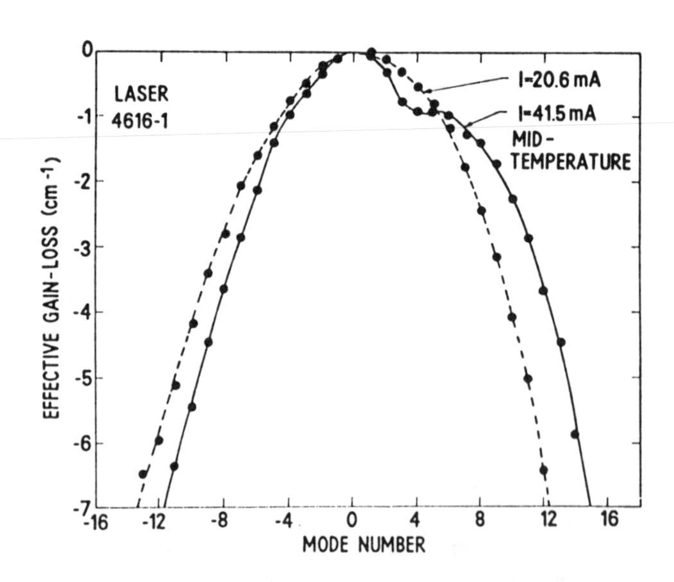

FIG. 2. Effective gain spectra for the mode intensity spectra of Fig. 1(a) and 1(b).

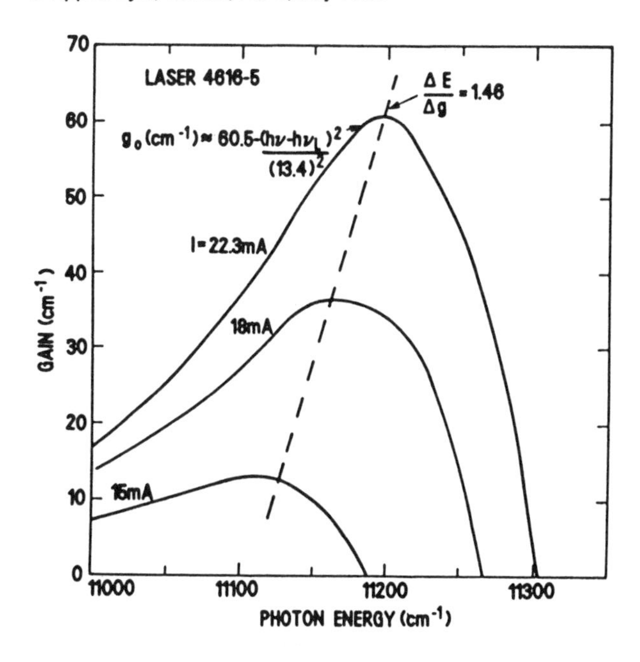

FIG. 3. Gain spectra for threshold and below threshold data deduced from analysis of spontaneous emission spectra. For a mode separation of 3.0 cm^{-1}, the width parameter of 13.4 cm^{-1} equals 4.5 modes.

Å). The overall gain curves at and below threshold have been determined for a laser from the same wafer by analysis of the spontaneous emission spectrum, using methods published earlier.[12] The spectra are shown in Fig. 3. The peak of the gain curve at threshold can be fitted with

$$g(\text{cm}^{-1}) = \gamma - \left(\frac{N-\bar{N}}{4.5}\right)^2, \qquad (3)$$

where $\gamma = 60$ cm^{-1}. Comparison of Eqs. (2) and (3) shows that the two methods agree within 10%. This justifies our use of mode intensities to measure gain.

The data of Figs. 2 and 4 show the effective gain curves of the laser operating 20 mA above threshold at the mid, low, and high temperature ends of the temperature range of a single lasing mode. These curves show several features when compared with the parabolic curve of effective gain at threshold. First, the curves appear continuous with no sign of discontinuity in gain at the laser line. Second, there is a narrowing of the gain profile about the maximum which provides the stability of the lasing mode, and this narrowing persists even when the temperature is changed and the linear gain profile shifts to higher or lower energy. Third, the effective gain curve becomes structured with a prominent dip occurring in the low temperature effective gain spectra. (Under higher current and more stable operation than we achieved, Nakamura *et al.*[2] also observed a dip in the low energy mode intensities in spectra for the high temperature end of the range.)

C. Gain spectra of the nonlasing TE_{01n} modes

The cavity of the LSBOG lasers support many transverse modes. Most of these modes are kept well below threshold by side wall scattering losses, but in some lasers the TE_{01n} modes become prominent. Figure 5 shows the

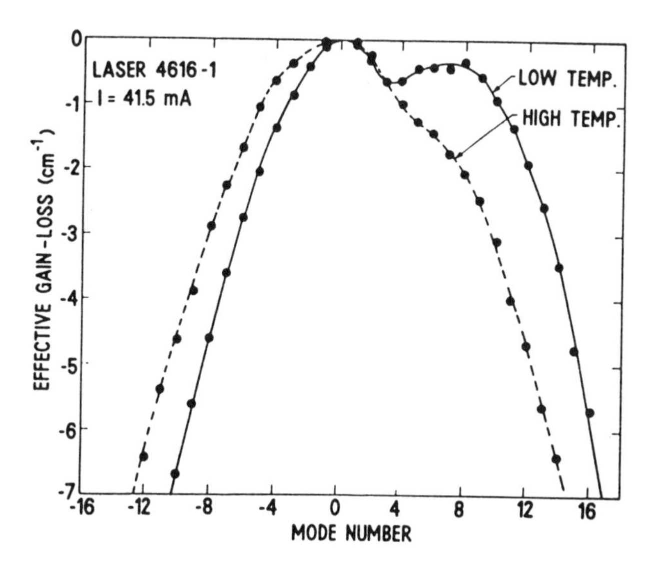

FIG. 4. Effective gain spectra for the low and high temperature ends of the stability range at 20 mA above threshold. The high and low temperatures are separated by about 2 K.

mode intensity spectra of such a laser. The corresponding effective gain profiles are shown in Fig. 6. Near threshold (not shown) both modes had parabolic gain profiles peaking

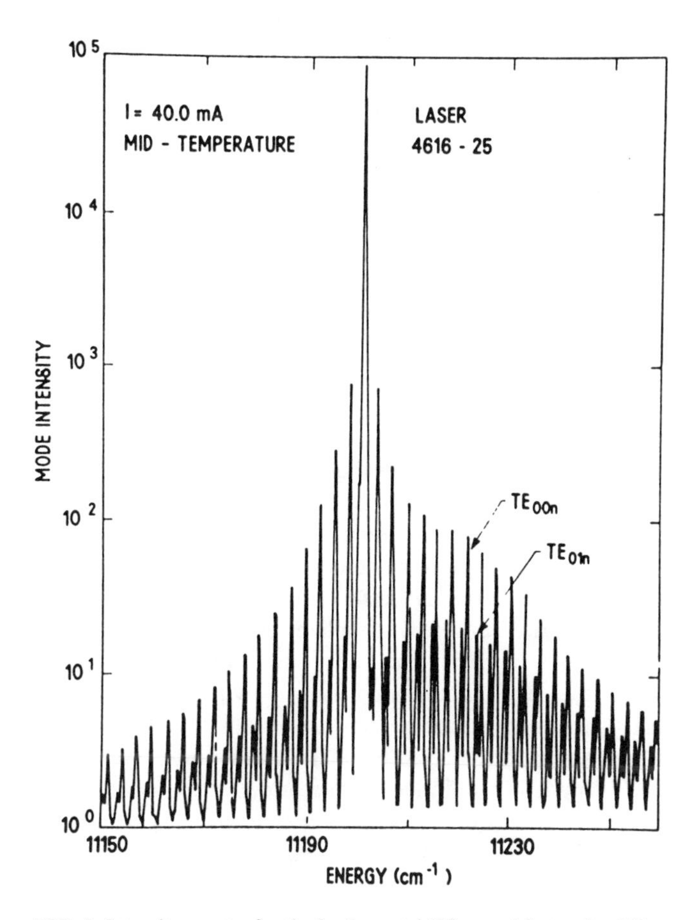

FIG. 5. Intensity spectra for the fundamental TE_{00n} and first-order TE_{01n} modes. The intensities of the TE_{01n} modes are actually about ×2 greater than they appear due to the lower efficiency of collection of light for this mode.

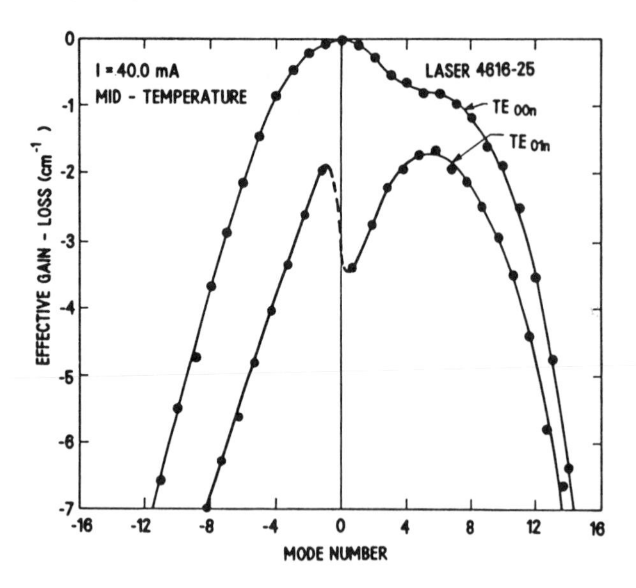

FIG. 6. Effective gain spectra of the TE_{00n} and TE_{01n} modes of Fig. 5.

at the same energy with the TE_{01n} modes suppressed by 9 cm^{-1}. As the current increased above threshold, the TE_{01n} modes shifted to higher energy and increased in gain.

The data in Figs. 5 and 6 show the remarkable effect of the laser line on the nonlasing first order transverse modes near the laser line. The laser line has a tremendous effect despite the fact that the fundamental (lasing) and the first order transverse modes have different spatial distributions.

III. THEORY OF LONGITUDINAL MODE STABILIZATION

In this section we will first derive expressions for the nonlinear dielectric functions caused by spectral hole burning and modulation of the inverted population. We will then solve Maxwell's equations for the mode intensities, with these nonlinear terms included. Finally, we will compare our derived effective gain curves with the measure curves of Sec. II.

The chief result of Sec. III A is Eq. (29) for the nonlinear polarization ΔP. The nonlinear polarization has 3 contributions expressed as 3 nonlinear dielectric functions ϵ_1,ϵ_2, and χ. The term with ϵ_1 expresses the change in polarization at the lasing or nonlasing modes due to the decrease in inverted population caused by stimulated emission [Eq. (19), later]. The terms ϵ_2 and χ express additional polarizations (at the nonlasing modes only) that arise from modulation of the inverted population caused by stimulated emission induced by the beating of lasing and nonlasing modes. The beating of the lasing field ω_0 and a nonlasing field at ω_1 will modulate the inverted population at $\Omega = \omega_1 - \omega_0$ [Eq. (22), later]. As a consequence of the inverted population being modulated at Ω, the lasing field will induce polarizations at $\omega_1 = \omega_0 + \Omega$ and $\omega_2 = \omega_0 - \Omega$. Conversely, a field at ω_2 beating with the lasing field and causing stimulated emission will result in an additional polarization at ω_1 [Eq. (22), later]. The term ϵ_2 expresses the additional polarization at ω_1 caused by a field at ω_1 beating with the lasing field and the term χ expresses the additional polarization at ω_1 due to a field at ω_2 beating with the laser field.

In Sec. III B, the mode intensities are calculated by solving Maxwell's equations, including ΔP. The nonlinear dielectric function χ causes a coupling of nonlasing modes which are equally spaced about the laser line [Eq. (61), later]. As a consequence of this coupling, there are two nonlasing modes at each cavity resonance. In the simplest symmetrical case [Eq. (71), later], the nonlinear gains of these modes are $g_1 + g_2 \pm g_\chi$, where g_1,g_2, and g_χ are proportional to the imaginary part of ϵ_1,ϵ_2, and χ, respectively [Eqs. (43)–(45)].

A. Dielectric functions

The dielectric functions for the active medium containing electric fields of the lasing and nonlasing modes

$$E_i(t) = E(\omega_i) \exp(-i\omega_i t) + E(\omega_i)^* \exp(i\omega_i t), \qquad (4)$$

will now be derived using a phenomenological theory employing the density matrix method.[13]

1. Density matrix equations

The polarization $P(t)$ caused by the fields $E_i(t)$ can be expressed through the dipole matrix elements $d_{12} = d_{21}^*$ and the off diagonal density matrix elements $\rho_{12}(t) = \rho_{21}(t)^*$, corresponding to transitions between the conduction band state 1 and valence band state 2, separated by energy $\hbar\omega_{12}$.

$$P(t) = \sum_{\omega_{12}} [d_{21}\rho_{12}(t) + d_{12}\rho_{21}(t)]. \qquad (5)$$

The equation for the density matrix operator ρ is

$$\dot{\rho} = -\frac{i}{\hbar}[H,\rho], \qquad (6)$$

where

$$H = H_0 + H_{\rm rad} + H_s, \qquad (7)$$

is the Hamiltonian of the system. The first term H_0 describes the unperturbed electronic states of the crystal and is diagonal in $|1\rangle$ and $|2\rangle$, with energies E_1 and E_2. The second term $H_{\rm rad}$ is the interaction between the electron and the electric fields of the light waves

$$H_{\rm rad} = -d\sum_i E_i(t), \qquad (8)$$

where it is assumed that the electric dipole operator d has only off-diagonal matrix elements.

The third term H_s describes the electron scattering processes that establish thermal equilibrium among the electrons in each band and also cause the polarization $P(t)$ to die away in the absence of driving electric fields. In the absence of electric fields, the diagonal part of Eq. (6) would reduce to Boltzmann's equation.

A correct treatment of the contribution of H_s to Eq. (6) would involve all the interactions that couple a single electron to the lattice phonons and the other electrons of the crystal. Such a treatment has not been properly made for electrons near the band edges and is beyond the scope of this paper. Instead, we will represent H_s phenomologically by two relaxation times: The decay time T_1 of a nonequilibrium electron population and the decay time T_2 of the electric polarization. The diagonal contribution of H_s to $\dot{\rho}$ is given by

$$(\dot{\rho}_{11})_s = -\frac{i}{\hbar}[H_s,\rho]_{11} = -\frac{(\rho_{11}-\bar{\rho}_{11})}{T_1}, \quad (9)$$

where $\bar{\rho}_{11}$ is the equilibrium electron state occupation determined by the quasi-Fermi level of the conduction band. The offdiagonal contribution of H_s to $\dot{\rho}$ is given by

$$(\dot{\rho}_{12})_s = -\frac{i}{\hbar}[H_s,\rho]_{12} = -\frac{\rho_{12}}{T_2}. \quad (10)$$

Since it is known that, due to the higher density of states of the valence band, relaxation time T_1 is much shorter for valence band electrons than for conduction band electrons, we make the simplifying assumption that the valence band electrons are in thermal equilibrium determined by the quasi-Fermi level of the valence band.

$$\rho_{22} = \bar{\rho}_{22}. \quad (11)$$

We will describe the changes in the electron population caused by stimulated emission by writing

$$\rho_{11}(t) = \bar{\rho}_{11} + \Delta\rho_{11}(t). \quad (12)$$

Substituting Eqs. (8), (9), (10), and (12) into Eq. (6), we find equations for $\Delta\rho_{11}(t)$ and $\rho_{12}(t)$.

$$\Delta\dot{\rho}_{11} + \frac{\Delta\rho_{11}}{T_1} = -\frac{i}{\hbar}(d_{21}\rho_{12} - d_{12}\rho_{21}) \times \sum_i [E(\omega_i)\exp(-i\omega_i t) + \text{c.c.}], \quad (13)$$

$$\dot{\rho}_{12} + \left(i\omega_{12} + \frac{1}{T_2}\right)\rho_{12} = -\frac{i}{\hbar}d_{12}(\bar{\rho}_{11} - \bar{\rho}_{22} + \Delta\rho_{11}) \times \sum_i [E(\omega_i)\exp(-i\omega_i t) + \text{c.c.}], \quad (14)$$

where $\omega_{12} = (E_1 - E_2)/\hbar$. Equation (13) simply describes the change in occupation of level 1 due to stimulated emission. Equation (14) determines the contribution of the interband transition between levels 1 and 2 to the electric polarization.

2. *Linear and nonlinear dielectric functions*

Equations (13) and (14) are readily solved by expanding $\Delta\rho_{11}(t)$ and $\rho_{12}(t)$ as a sum of terms proportional to $\exp(\pm i\omega_i t)$ and equating terms on both sides having the same time dependence. The equation for ρ_{12} is only resonant for terms with $\exp(-i\omega_i t)$. Neglecting the nonresonant terms, we write

$$\rho_{12}(t) = \sum_i \rho_{12}(\omega_i)\exp(-i\omega_i t). \quad (15)$$

From the symmetry $\rho_{21}(t) = \rho_{12}(t)^*$ and Eq. (15), we find

$$\rho_{21}(\omega_i) = \rho_{12}(\omega_i)^*. \quad (16)$$

We will write $\rho_{12}(\omega_i)$ as a sum of a linear and a nonlinear term

$$\rho_{12}(\omega_i) = \bar{\rho}_{12}(\omega_i) + \Delta\rho_{12}(\omega_i). \quad (17)$$

The linear term $\bar{\rho}_{12}(\omega_i)$ can be determined immediately from Eq. (14) by neglecting $\Delta\rho_{11}(t)$.

$$\bar{\rho}_{12}(\omega_i) = \frac{d_{12}(\bar{\rho}_{11} - \bar{\rho}_{22})}{\hbar\left(\omega_i - \omega_{12} + \frac{i}{T_2}\right)} E(\omega_i). \quad (18)$$

Before we can solve for $\Delta\rho_{12}(\omega_i)$, we must first solve for $\Delta\rho_{11}(t)$. Equation (13) shows that $\Delta\rho_{11}(t)$ will only be large for static or slowly varying components, where $\Delta\rho_{11}(t)$ is driven by the difference of two frequencies ω_i, at least one of which is the laser frequency ω_0. The term $\Delta\rho_{11}(t)$ is real and can be written as

$$\Delta\rho_{11}(t) = \Delta\rho_{11}(0) + \sum_\Omega [\Delta\rho_{11}(\Omega)\exp(i\Omega t) + \Delta\rho_{11}(\Omega)^* \exp(-i\Omega t)], \quad (19)$$

where $\omega_i = \omega_0 + \Omega$. The static change in the electron level occupation $\Delta\rho_{11}(0)$ can be calculated using Eq. (13), and keeping only the largest terms, which are second order in the laser field

$$\Delta\rho_{11}(0) = -\frac{i}{\hbar}T_1[d_{21}\bar{\rho}_{12}(\omega_0)E(\omega_0)^* - \text{c.c.}]$$
$$= -\frac{iT_1|d_{12}|^2(\bar{\rho}_{11} - \bar{\rho}_{22})}{\hbar^2} \times \left(\frac{1}{\omega_0 - \omega_{12} + \frac{i}{T_2}} - \frac{1}{\omega_0 - \omega_{12} - \frac{i}{T_2}}\right)|E(\omega_0)|^2. \quad (20)$$

In a similar manner, $\Delta\rho_{11}(\Omega)$ which determines the modulation of the inverted population is found keeping the largest terms on the right side of Eq. (13) that are at the difference frequency Ω. These terms are first order in the laser field. Let $\omega_1 = \omega_0 + \Omega$ and $\omega_2 = \omega_0 - \Omega$, then

$$\Delta\rho_{11}(\Omega) = \frac{-iT_1}{\hbar(1 - i\Omega T_1)}[d_{21}\bar{\rho}_{12}(\omega_1)E(\omega_0)^* - d_{12}E(\omega_1)\bar{\rho}_{12}(\omega_0)^* + d_{21}\bar{\rho}_{12}(\omega_0)E(\omega_2)^* - d_{12}E(\omega_0)\bar{\rho}_{12}(\omega_2)]. \quad (21)$$

Using Eq. (18), we find

$$\Delta\rho_{11}(\Omega) = \frac{-iT_1|d_{12}|^2(\bar{\rho}_{11} - \bar{\rho}_{22})}{\hbar^2}\left\{\left[\frac{1}{\omega_1 - \omega_{12} + \frac{i}{T_2}} - \frac{1}{\omega_0 - \omega_{12} - \frac{i}{T_2}}\right]E(\omega_1)E(\omega_0)^* + \left[\frac{1}{\omega_0 - \omega_{12} + \frac{i}{T_2}} - \frac{1}{\omega_2 - \omega_{12} - \frac{i}{T_2}}\right]E(\omega_0)E(\omega_2)^*\right\}. \quad (22)$$

Finally, we can find the largest contribution to $\Delta\rho_{12}(\omega_1)$, which are second order in the laser field, by substituting the expressions for $\Delta\rho_{11}(0)$ and $\Delta\rho_{11}(\Omega)$ into Eq. (14).

$$\Delta\rho_{12}(\omega_1) = \frac{d_{12}[\Delta\rho_{11}(0)E(\omega_1) + \Delta\rho_{11}(\Omega)E(\omega_0)]}{\hbar\left(\omega_1 - \omega_0 + \frac{i}{T_2}\right)}. \quad (23)$$

The polarization can also be written as the sum of a linear and a nonlinear term

$$P(t) = \sum_i [\overline{P}(\omega_i) + \Delta P(\omega_i)] \exp(-i\omega_i t) + \text{c.c.}, \tag{24}$$

where

$$\overline{P}(\omega_i) + \Delta P(\omega_i) = \frac{1}{V} \sum_{\omega_{12}} d_{21} [\overline{\rho}_{12}(\omega_i) + \Delta\rho_{12}(\omega_i)]$$
$$= \int d_{21} D(\omega_{12}) [\overline{\rho}_{12}(\omega_i) + \Delta\rho_{12}(\omega_i)] \times d\omega_{12}, \tag{25}$$

and $D(\omega_{12})$ is the density of states per unit volume. The polarization can be linearly related to a field at the same frequency by the dielectric function. For the linear polarization

$$\overline{P}(\omega_1) = \frac{[\epsilon_0(\omega_1) - 1]}{4\pi} E(\omega_1). \tag{26}$$

From Eqs. (18) and (25), the linear dielectric function $\epsilon_0(\omega_0 + \Omega)$ is given by

$$\epsilon_0(\omega_1) - 1 = \frac{1}{\hbar} \int d\omega_{12} \frac{f(\omega_{12})}{\omega_1 - \omega_{12} + \dfrac{i}{T_2}}, \tag{27}$$

where $f(\omega_{12})$ is

$$f(\omega_{12}) = 4\pi^2 |d_{12}|^2 (\overline{\rho}_{11} - \overline{\rho}_{22}) D. \tag{28}$$

Similarly, the nonlinear polarization is related to the field in terms of 3 nonlinear dielectric functions

$$\Delta P(\omega_1) = \frac{1}{4\pi} [\epsilon_1 + \epsilon_2] E(\omega_1) + \frac{\chi}{4\pi} \exp(i\phi) E(\omega_2), \tag{29}$$

where ϵ_1, ϵ_2, and χ are nonlinear dielectric functions that are found from substitution of $\Delta\rho_{12}(\omega_1)$ [Eq. (23)] into Eq. (25). The function ϵ_1 comes from $\Delta\rho(0)$ in Eq. (23) and is due to static hole burning in the electron population. The functions ϵ_2 and χ come from $\Delta\rho_{11}(\Omega)$ and are due to the modulation of the electron population by the beating of the laser field and fields at ω_1 and ω_2, respectively. The phase ϕ is defined by

$$E(\omega_0)^2 = |E(\omega_0)|^2 \exp(i\phi). \tag{30}$$

The nonlinear dielectric functions are

$$\epsilon_1 = -i \frac{1}{\pi} \int \frac{f(\omega_{12}) C}{\left(\omega_1 - \omega_{12} + \dfrac{i}{T_2}\right)} \times \left[\frac{1}{\omega_0 - \omega_{12} + \dfrac{i}{T_2}} - \frac{1}{\omega_0 - \omega_{12} - \dfrac{i}{T_2}} \right] d\omega_{12}, \tag{31}$$

$$\epsilon_2 = \frac{-i}{(1 - i\Omega T_1)} \frac{1}{\pi} \int \frac{f(\omega_{12}) C}{\left(\omega_1 - \omega_{12} + \dfrac{i}{T_2}\right)} \times \left[\frac{1}{\omega_1 - \omega_{12} + \dfrac{i}{T_2}} - \frac{1}{\omega_1 - \dfrac{i}{T_2}} \right] \times d\omega_{12}, \tag{32}$$

$$\chi = \frac{-i}{(1 - i\Omega T_1)} \frac{1}{\pi} \int \frac{f(\omega_{12}) C}{\left(\omega_1 - \omega_{12} + \dfrac{i}{T_2}\right)} \times \left[\frac{1}{\omega_0 - \omega_{12} + \dfrac{i}{T_2}} - \frac{1}{\omega_2 - \omega_{12} - \dfrac{i}{T_2}} \right] \times d\omega_{12}. \tag{33}$$

The terms are nonlinear because C is quadratic in the laser field.

$$C = \frac{T_1 |d_{12}|^2 |E(\omega_0)|^2}{\hbar^2}. \tag{34}$$

A calculation of ϵ_1, ϵ_2, and χ from first principles requires a knowledge of $f(\omega_{12}) \sim |d_{12}|^2 D (\overline{\rho}_{11} - \overline{\rho}_{22})$. This is not readily known, since a realistic model must include exciton effects and the screening of the electron-hole attraction by the high carrier density present during laser operation. Furthermore, at room temperature the absorption edge of GaAs and other semiconductors develop an exponential "Urbach" tail and lasing occurs within this tail region at about 10 meV (80 cm^{-1}) below the band gap.[12] In view of these difficulties, we have taken an empirical approach to the evaluation of $f(\omega_{12})$.

The function $f(\omega_1)$ is approximately proportional to the linear gain curve $g_0(\omega_1)$. The gain is related to the imaginary part of the dielectric function by

$$g(\omega) = -\frac{\omega^2}{c^2 k} \epsilon''(\omega), \tag{35}$$

and the imaginary part of the linear dielectric function is given by Eq. (27) as

$$\epsilon_0''(\omega_1) = -\frac{1}{\pi T_2} \int \frac{d\omega_{12} f(\omega_{12})}{(\omega_{12} - \omega_1)^2 + \dfrac{1}{T_2^2}}. \tag{36}$$

If $1/T_2$ is small compared to the width of $f(\omega_{12})$, we can remove $f(\omega_{12})$ from the integral. The remaining integral is equal to πT_2, hence $\epsilon_0''(\omega_1) \cong -f(\omega_1)$ and

$$f(\omega_1) \cong \frac{c^2 k g_0(\omega_1)}{\omega^2}. \tag{37}$$

In Eqs. (31)–(33) for ϵ_1, ϵ_2, and χ, the essential region of integration over ω_{12} is the interval $\omega_0 - T_2^{-1} \lesssim \omega_{12} \lesssim \omega_0 + T_2^{-1}$. The integrals for ϵ_1, ϵ_2, and χ can be approximately evaluated by assuming $f(\omega_{12})$ to be slowly varying in the essential region of integration and approximately given by

$$f(\omega_{12}) \cong f(\omega_0) + f'(\omega_0)(\omega_{12} - \omega_0). \tag{38}$$

Then, Eqs. (31)–(33) can be immediately evaluated by contour integration in the complex plane of ω_{12} and the results are

$$\frac{\omega^2}{c^2 k} \epsilon_1 = \frac{i d g_0}{\left(1 - i \dfrac{\Omega}{2} T_2\right)} \left[1 - \frac{i f'(\omega_0)}{f(\omega_0) T_2}\right], \tag{39}$$

$$\frac{\omega^2}{c^2 k} \epsilon_2 = \frac{i d g_0}{(1 - i\Omega T_1)\left(1 - i \dfrac{\Omega}{2} T_2\right)} \left[1 - \frac{i f'(\omega_0)}{f(\omega_0) T_2}\right], \tag{40}$$

$$\frac{\omega^2}{c^2 k} \chi = \frac{i d g_0}{(1 - i\Omega T_1)(1 - i\Omega T_2)} \times \left[1 - \frac{i f'(\omega_0)(T_2^{-1} - i\Omega)}{f(\omega_0)}\right], \tag{41}$$

where $dg_0 = (\omega^2/c^2k)CT_2$ or using Eqs. (34) and (37)

$$dg_0 = \omega^2 T_1 T_2 |d_{12}|^2 f(\omega_0)|E(\omega_0)|^2 \cong \frac{T_1 T_2 |d_{12}|^2 g_0(\omega_0)|E(\omega_0)|^2}{\hbar^2}. \quad (42)$$

It is convenient for later work to define the gain changes due to ϵ_1,ϵ_2, and χ as the negative of the imaginary parts of Eqs. (39), (40), and (41). This definition is consistent with Eq. (35). In the absence of mode coupling ($\epsilon_\chi = 0$), g_1 and g_2 are the actual gain changes.

$$g_1 \equiv -\frac{\omega^2}{c^2}\epsilon_1'' = \frac{-dg_0\left[1 + \frac{f'(\omega_0)}{f(\omega_0)} - \frac{\Omega}{2}\right]}{1+\Omega^2 T_2^2/4}, \quad (43)$$

$$g_2 \equiv -\frac{\omega^2}{c^2}\epsilon_2'' = \frac{-dg_0\left[1 - \frac{\Omega^2 T_1 T_2}{2} + \frac{f'(\omega_0)}{f(\omega_0)}\left(\frac{T_1}{T_2} + \frac{1}{2}\right)\Omega\right]}{(1+\Omega^2 T_1^2)(1+\Omega^2 T_2^2/4)}, \quad (44)$$

$$g_\chi = -\frac{\omega^2}{c^2}\chi = \frac{-dg_0}{(1+\Omega^2 T_1^2)}\left[\frac{1-\Omega^2 T_1 T_2}{1+\Omega^2 T_2^2} - \frac{f'(\omega_0)T_1}{f(\omega_0)T_2}\Omega\right]. \quad (45)$$

Notice that at $\Omega = 0$

$$g_1(\omega_0) = g_2(\omega_0) = g_x(\omega_0) = -dg_0. \quad (46)$$

B. Calculation of mode intensities and comparison of theory and experiment

For simplicity, we will assume that the losses are uniform along the length of the cavity (replacing the facet losses at the ends by a distributed loss), then the cavity field has the form

$$E(x,y,z,t) = \sum_i \Psi_m(x,y)f_n(z) \times [E(\omega_i)\exp(-\omega_i) + \text{c.c.}], \quad (47)$$

where $\omega_i = \omega_0 + \Omega$, and $\Psi_m(x,y)$ is the normalized eigenfunction of the transverse mode satisfying

$$\nabla_\perp^2 \Psi_m + \frac{\omega^2}{c^2}\epsilon_0'(x,y)\Psi_m = \frac{\omega^2}{c^2}\epsilon_m'\Psi_m, \quad (48)$$

and $f_n(z)$ is the eigenfunction of the longitudinal mode given by

$$f_n(z) = \left(\frac{2}{L}\right)^{1/2}\sin(k_n z),$$

where $k_n = n\pi/L$. Maxwell's equations for nearly transverse cavity fields reduce to

$$\nabla^2 E = \frac{1}{c^2}(\ddot{E} + 4\pi\ddot{P}). \quad (49)$$

Substitution of Eq. (47) into Eq. (49), using Eqs. (26) and (29) to express P in terms of the dielectric functions and using Eq. (48) to eliminate $\nabla_\perp^2$ results in

$$\left\{\left[-k_1^2 - \frac{\omega_1^2}{c^2}(\epsilon_m' + i\epsilon_0'' + \epsilon_1 + \epsilon_2)\right]E(\omega_1) + \frac{\omega_1^2}{c^2}\chi\exp(i\phi)E(\omega_2)^*\right\} \times \Psi_m(x,y)f_n(z) = \frac{4\pi\omega_1^2}{c^2}P_n(\omega_1), \quad (50)$$

where $\omega_1 = \omega_0 + \Omega, \epsilon_0'', \epsilon_1, \epsilon_2$, and χ depend on x, y, and Ω. The term $P_n(\omega_1)$ on the right side of Eq. (50) is a phenomelogical polarization term needed to generate spontaneous emission at ω_1.

Proceeding the same way as in first order perturbation theory in quantum mechanics, we multiply Eq. (50) by $\Psi_m f_n$ and integrate over x, y, and z. Equation (50) reduces to

$$[-k_1^2 + \frac{\omega^2}{c^2}(\epsilon_m' + i\epsilon_0''(\omega_1) + \epsilon_1 + \epsilon_2)]E(\omega_1) + \frac{\omega^2}{c^2}\chi\exp(i\phi)E(\omega_2)^* = \frac{\omega^2}{c^2}N(\omega_1), \quad (51)$$

where

$$\epsilon_1 = \int \Psi_n^2 \epsilon_1(x,y)dxdy, \quad (52)$$

etc., and

$$N(\omega_1) = \int \Psi_m(x,y)f_n(z)4\pi P_n(x,y,z,\omega_1)dxdydz. \quad (53)$$

If we define $k(\omega_1)^2 = (\omega^2/c^2)\epsilon_m'(\omega_1)$ and the group velocity $v_g = d\omega/dk(\omega_1)$, then the cavity resonances occur at $\omega_0 + \Omega_1$, where $k(\omega_0 + \Omega_1) = k_1 = n_1\pi/L$. The first two terms in Eq. (51) can be written as

$$k(\omega_0+\Omega)^2 - k_1^2 \cong 2k_1(k(\omega_0+\Omega) - k_1) = \frac{2k_1}{v_g}\Delta\Omega \equiv \frac{\omega^2}{c^2}y, \quad (54)$$

where $\Delta\Omega = \Omega - \Omega_n$ and y is a new variable proportional to $\Delta\Omega$. With these changes Eq. (54) becomes

$$[y + i\epsilon_0'' + \epsilon_1 + \epsilon_2]E(\omega_1) + \chi\exp(i\phi)E(\omega_2)^* = N(\omega_1). \quad (55)$$

1. Intensity of the laser line

The nonlinear dielectric functions ϵ_2 and χ do not apply for the case of the lasing mode. Neglecting these terms and approximating $N(\omega_1) = N(\omega_0)$ and setting $\Omega = 0$, Eq. (55) becomes

$$E(\omega) = \frac{N(\omega_0)}{y + i\epsilon_0''(\omega_0) + \epsilon_1}. \quad (56)$$

The intensity of each mode will be proportional to $\int|E(\omega_1)|^2 d\Omega$. It is convenient to define the relative intensity I of the nth mode as

$$\frac{\omega^2}{c^2k}I = \frac{1}{\pi}\int\frac{|E(\omega_n)|^2}{|N(\omega_n)|^2}dy. \quad (57)$$

Using Eq. (56), the intensity of the laser line I_0 becomes

$$\frac{\omega^2}{c^2k}I_0 = \frac{1}{\pi}\int\frac{dy}{[y+\epsilon_1'(\omega_0)]^2 + [\epsilon_0''(\omega_0)+\epsilon_1''(\omega_0)]^2}$$

$$= \frac{1}{\epsilon_0''(\omega_0) + \epsilon_1''}, \quad (58)$$

and using Eqs. (39), (43) and (46) we find

$$I_0 = \frac{1}{\gamma - g_0(\omega_0) - g_1(\omega_0)} = \frac{1}{\gamma - g_0(\omega_0) + dg_0}. \quad (59)$$

The gain at the laser line is $g_0(\omega_0) - dg_0$. The decrease in gain by dg_0 is due to spectral hole burning and must be compensated by increased $g_0(\omega_0)$ and increased carrier density.

2. Coupled nonlasing TE_{00n} modes

a. Solution of coupled mode equations. Equation (55) shows that the nonlinear term χ couples the field amplitudes $E(\omega_1)$ and $E(\omega_2)$ at $\omega_1 = \omega_0 + \Omega$ and $\omega_2 = \omega_0 - \Omega$. Let us regard Eq. (55) as the equation for the field at ω_1. The corresponding equation for the field at ω_2 can be found by substituting $\Omega \to -\Omega$ and interchanging ω_1 and ω_2 in Eq. (55) and redefining y. The quantity y will now be y_2 given by $(\omega_2^2/c^2)y_2 = (2k_2/v_g)(-\Omega - \Omega_2)$. *We will assume the modes are evenly spaced so that* $\Omega_2 = -\Omega_1$. Therefore, if we approximate $\omega_2 \approx \omega_1$ and $k_2 \approx k_1$

$$y_2 = \frac{-2c^2}{\omega^2}\frac{k}{v_g}(\Omega - \Omega_1) = -y. \quad (60)$$

Taking the complex conjugate of the equation for the field at ω_2, the two coupled equations become

$$[y + i\epsilon_0''(\omega_1) + \epsilon_1(\Omega) + \epsilon_2(\Omega)]E(\omega_1) + \chi(\Omega)\exp(i\phi)E(\omega_2)^* = N(\omega_1), \quad (61a)$$

$$[-y - i\epsilon_0''(\omega_2) + \epsilon_1(-\Omega)^* + \epsilon_2(-\Omega)^*]E(\omega_2)^* + \chi(-\Omega)^*\exp(-i\phi)E(\omega_1) = N(\omega_2)^*. \quad (61b)$$

The expressions for $\epsilon_1(\Omega)$, $\epsilon_2(\Omega)$, and $\chi(\Omega)$ are given by Eqs. (39)–(41). The modes of interest are near the maximum of the gain curve and hence near the maximum of $f(\omega_{12})$, so we will neglect the second terms in Eqs. (39)–(41) that depend on $f'(\omega_0)/f(\omega_0)$. With this simplification, Eqs. (39)–(41) show that $\epsilon_1(-\Omega)^* = -\epsilon_1(\Omega)$, $\epsilon_2(-\Omega)^* = -\epsilon_2(\Omega)$, and $\chi(-\Omega)^* = -\chi(\Omega)$. Let us write $\epsilon_0''(\Omega)$ as the sum of two terms that are symmetric and antisymmetric in Ω

$$\epsilon_0''(\omega_1) = \epsilon_s''(\omega_1) + \epsilon_a''(\omega_1), \quad (62)$$

and define

$$\alpha \equiv i\epsilon_s''(\omega_1) + \epsilon_1 + \epsilon_2, \quad (63)$$

and

$$\beta \equiv i\epsilon_a''. \quad (64)$$

Then Eqs. (61) can be rewritten as

$$(y + \alpha + \beta)E(\omega_1) + \chi\exp(i\phi)E(\omega_2)^* = N(\omega_1), \quad (65a)$$

$$(y + \alpha - \beta)E(\omega_2)^* + \chi\exp(-i\phi)E(\omega_1) = -N(\omega_2)^*, \quad (65b)$$

where $\chi = \chi(\omega_1)$. Eliminating $E(\omega_2)^*$ we find

$$E(\omega_1) = \frac{(y + \alpha - \beta)N(\omega_1) + \chi\exp(i\phi)N(\omega_2)^*}{(y + \alpha)^2 - (\beta + \chi)^2}. \quad (66)$$

The intensity of mode at ω_1 is given by Eq. (57). We assume that the squared amplitudes of $N(\omega_1)$ and $N(\omega_2)$ are equal and there is no correlation between them, so on average, the product $N(\omega_1)N(\omega_2)$ is zero. The mode intensity at ω_1 is then

$$\frac{\omega^2}{c^2k}I = \frac{\omega^2}{c^2k}(I_1 + I_2) = \int \frac{(|y + \alpha - \beta|^2 + |\chi|^2)dy}{|y + \alpha - \delta|^2|y + \alpha + \delta|^2}, \quad (67)$$

where $\delta = (x^2 + \beta^2)^{1/2}$. The mode intensity at ω_1 is the sum of two terms I_1 and I_2 which arise from spontaneous emission at ω_1 and ω_2, respectively. The relative intensity I_2/I is therefore a measure of the coupling of the modes at ω_1 and ω_2. The integral in Eq. (67) is calculated in Appendix B using contour integration. It is given by

$$\frac{\omega^2}{c^2}I = \frac{\alpha''(\alpha'' - \beta'') + \chi'^2}{2(\alpha''^2 + \delta'^2)}\left(\frac{1}{\alpha'' - \delta''} + \frac{1}{\alpha'' + \delta''}\right), \quad (68)$$

where

$$\frac{I_2}{I} = \frac{\chi'^2 + \chi''^2}{2[\alpha''(\alpha'' - \beta'') + \chi'^2]}. \quad (69)$$

b. Symmetric case. The equations (68) and (69) for I and I_2/I are more transparent in the symmetric case when the laser line is at the center of the parabolic gain profile. Then $i\epsilon_a''(\Omega) = \beta = 0$, $\delta = \chi(\Omega)$, and Eq. (68) becomes

$$\frac{\omega^2}{c^2k}I = \frac{1}{2}\left(\frac{1}{\alpha'' - \chi''} + \frac{1}{\alpha'' + \chi''}\right). \quad (70)$$

The equation for I can be written more explicitly using Eqs. (63) and (43)–(45):

$$I = \frac{1}{2}\left(\frac{1}{\gamma - g_0 - g_1 - g_2 + g_\chi} + \frac{1}{\gamma - g_0 - g_1 - g_2 - g_\chi}\right), \quad (71)$$

where all functions are evaluated at Ω_1. As a consequence of the coupling of the fields at $\omega_0 \pm \Omega$, there are two modes at each cavity resonance with gains of $g_0 + g_1 + g_2 \pm g_\chi$.

The value of effective gain defined by $\gamma - g_{eff} = I^{-1}$ is plotted as a function of mode number in Fig. 7 for the case of $T_1 = 1.0$ psec and $T_2 = 0.1$ psec, using the expressions for g_0, g_1, g_2, and g_χ given by Eqs. (38)–(40) and (44). The dashed curve corresponds to the threshold case, where $dg_0 = 0$ and $g_{eff} = g_0(\omega_1)$ with $\overline{N} = 0$. The solid curve illustrates the narrowing of the g_{eff} for $dg_0 = 4\ \text{cm}^{-1}$. The small dashed curve is a plot of I_2/I. This function approaches 0.5 at $\Omega = 0$ showing the strong coupling of the modes near the laser line.

The contributions to the change in gain that occur above threshold are illustrated in Fig. 8. The changes in gain are an overall increase of dg_0 to maintain $g \approx \gamma$ for the laser line and the contributions of g_1, g_2, and $-g_\chi$ to the nonlasing mode with maximum gain. The curve g_1 causes a greater reduction in gain at the laser line than at the nonlasing modes, but this is a small effect because g_1 is slowly varying with Ω. The contributions of g_2 and g_χ cancel at $\Omega = 0$, but away from the laser line, the cancellation is incomplete and $g_2 - g_\chi$ causes a slight gain suppression of order $0.15\ \text{cm}^{-1}$ of the nonlasing modes relative to the lasing mode, that stabilizes the laser in the lasing mode.

The mode coupling results in two contributions to each integrated mode intensity with gains differing by $2g_\chi$. Near

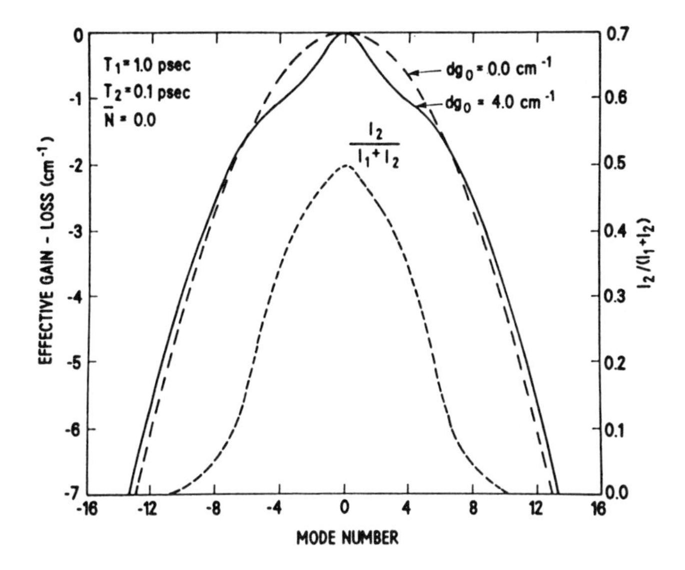

FIG. 7. Calculated effective gain curves for the symmetric case. I_1 and I_2 are the contributions to the intensity at ω_1 due to spontaneous emission at $\omega_1 = \omega_0 + \Omega$ and $\omega_1 = \omega_0 - \Omega$, respectively.

the laser line the low gain mode is strongly suppressed and $\gamma - g_{eff}$ is about twice $\gamma - g_0 - g_1 - g_2 + g_\chi$. This effect enhances the observed structure in g_{eff} and makes the lasing mode appear somewhat more stable than it actually is.

c. Asymmetric case. Figure 9 illustrates the predictions of Eq. (68) for the asymmetric case where the peak of $g_0(\Omega)$ is shifted away from the laser line. The shift is $\bar{N}$ modes, where $\bar{N} = 0$, 1.5, and 3.0. The same parameters are used as were used in Figs. 7 and 8, namely, $dg_0 = 4\ \text{cm}^{-1}$, $T_1 = 1.0$ psec, and $T_2 = 0.1$ psec. The calculated curves resemble the measured curves in Figs. 2 and 4 with a dip and a peak developing in the gain profile as the profile is shifted to higher energies.

The parameters are not uniquely determined by fitting the data. For example, an equally good fit was obtained with $T_1 = 0.6$ psec, $T_2 = 0.2$ psec, and $dg_0 = 3\ \text{cm}^{-12}$. Of course,

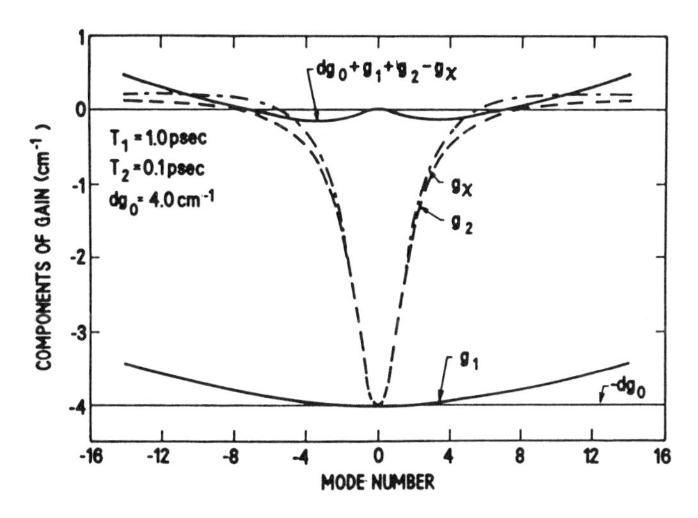

FIG. 8. Nonlinear contributions to the gain in the symmetric case. The three components are g_1, g_2, and g_χ and the net change is $dg_0 + g_1 + g_2 - g_\chi$.

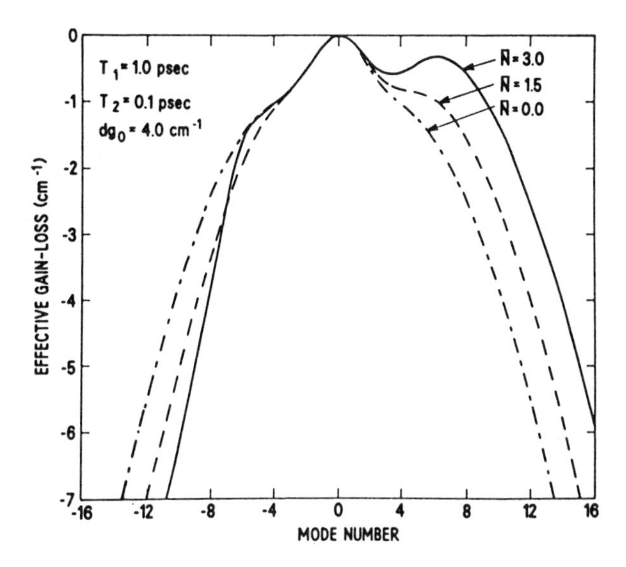

FIG. 9. Calculated effective gain in the asymmetric case, when the maximum of the linear gain curve g_0 is shifted by $\bar{N}$ modes from the laser line.

much worse fits were obtained with other values and the chosen parameters are probably accurate to about a factor of 2.

d. Theoretical estimate of dg_0. The parameter dg_0 is given by

$$\frac{dg_0}{T_1 T_2} \cong \frac{|d_{12}|^2}{\hbar^2} \int |E(\omega_0)|^2 g_0(\omega_0) \Psi_m^2(x,y)\,dx\,dy. \tag{72}$$

The product $|E(\omega_0)|^2 g_0(\omega_0)$ is proportional to the rate of stimulated emission and therefore proportional to the current above threshold $I - I_{th}$. The optical absorption coefficient α is proportional to $|d_{12}|^2 D$, where D is the density of states per unit volume entering into the optical transition. Therefore, $|d_{12}|^2$ can be determined from α / D, where α is the measured optical absorption coefficient and D is calculated. However, D can only be calculated above the band gap where a simple parabolic band model of the band edges is approximately valid. In Appendix C we evaluate $|d_{12}|^2$ for an energy of 0.19 eV above the band gap. Using this value of $|d_{12}|^2$ obtained, we find

$$\frac{dg_0}{T_1 T_2} = 29.2\ \text{cm}^{-1}\ (\text{psec})^{-2},$$

for $T_1 = 1.0$ psec and $T_2 = 0.1$ psec, $dg_0 = 2.9\ \text{cm}^{-1}$, a value close to $dg_0 = 4\ \text{cm}^{-1}$ used in fitting the data. It is encouraging that the calculated value of dg_0 has the same order of magnitude as the measured value.

e. Intensities of nonlasing first order modes. The first-order TE_{01n} modes are not coincident with the fundamental TE_{00n} modes. Consequently, fields of the TE_{01n} modes, equally spaced about the laser line at $\omega_0 + \Omega$ and $\omega_0 - \Omega$, cannot both be resonant in the Fabry-Perot cavity. Therefore, the coupling, due to $\chi(\omega_1)$ in Eq. (61), is nonresonant and can be neglected. Neglecting this term,

$$E(\omega_1) = \frac{N(\omega_1)}{\gamma + i\epsilon_0''(\omega_1) + \epsilon_1 + \epsilon_2}, \tag{73}$$

and

$$I = \frac{1}{\gamma - g_0(\omega_1) - g_1(\omega_1) - g_2(\omega_1)}. \tag{74}$$

We have already remarked that the laser line has a surprisingly large effect on the mode intensities and gain of the first-order mode shown in Figs. 5 and 6. The experimental gain curve in Fig. 6 shows a sharp asymmetric dip at the laser line. We believe the large magnitude of this nonlinear effect is due to the absence of the coupling term χ for the first-order mode. Consequently the effect of g_2 is not nearly canceled out by g_χ as it is in the case of the fundamental mode.

Offsetting this enhancement is the fact that the fundamental lasing mode and the first-order nonlasing modes have different spatial distributions. In Appendix C we calculate that this effect decreases dg_0 (and therefore g_1 and g_2) by $\times 3$ compared to the values for the fundamental modes. This is probably an overestimate because carrier motion (even in times of 1 psec) are substantial and will tend to smear out the spatial changes in the inverted population and decrease the differences in dg_0 for the first-order and fundamental modes. Therefore, in trying to obtain a theoretical fit, we will take $dg_0 = 2\ \text{cm}^{-1}$ or half the amount for the nonlinearities of the fundamental mode.

In order to try to explain the asymmetry in the measured gain curve of Fig. 6, we will keep terms proportional to $f'(\omega_0)$ in Eqs. (39) and (40) that were neglected up till now. They are more important in this case because the peak in the gain curve occurs farther from the laser line ω_0. The gain change $g_1(\Omega)$ is slowly varying and any narrow structure near the laser line will have to be explained by $g_2(\Omega)$. The first term in Eq. (40) for $g_2(\Omega)$ produces a narrow dip in gain about the laser line and the second term produces an asymmetry with the correct sign, but with too small a magnitude to quantitatively explain the experimental data. The theoretical curve for the gain of the TE_{01n} modes is shown in Fig. 10.

The theoretical curve in Fig. 10 could be brought closer to the experimental curve in Fig. 6 by changing parameters from those used in fitting the TE_{00n} data. The asymmetry will be enhanced by increasing the ratio of T_1 and T_2 or increasing $f'(\omega_0)/f(\omega_0)$. According to Eq. (36) and (37), the shape function $f(\omega)$ is narrower than the measured gain curve $g_0(\omega)$ and therefore there will be some enhancement of $f'(\omega_0)/f(\omega_0)$ over $g'(\omega_0)/g(\omega_0)$. To take account of this, we write

$$\frac{f'(\omega_0)}{f(\omega_0)} = \eta \frac{g'(\omega_0)}{g(\omega_0)}. \tag{75}$$

In the dashed curve in Fig. 10 the asymmetry has been increased by choosing $\eta = 3$, $T_1 = 1.5$ psec, and $T_2 = 0.05$ psec. While these changes produce a curve in better agreement with experiment, we are not at all certain that these changes can be justified and they decrease the fit to the effective gain curves for the TE_{00n} modes.

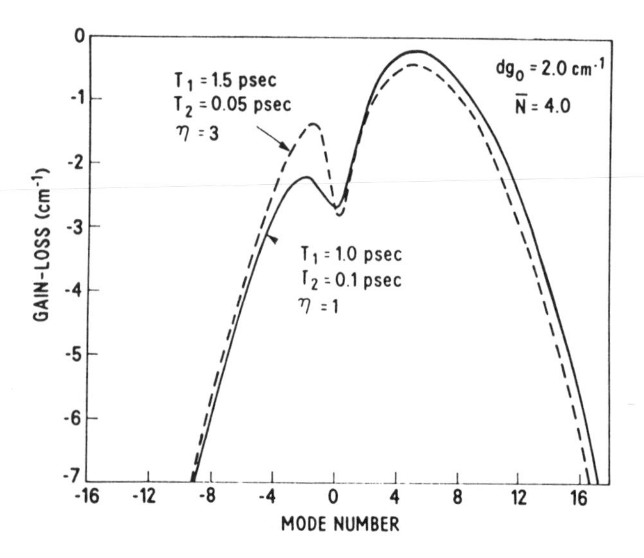

FIG. 10. Calculated gain for the TE_{01n} mode. The solid curve uses the same relaxation times as was used to fit the TE_{00n} mode data and dg_0 decreased by $\times 2$. The dashed curve alters the relaxation times and uses increased derivative enhancement η in order to increase asymmetry.

IV. SUMMARY AND DISCUSSION

In Sec. II we presented an experimental study of mode intensity spectra of LSBOG lasers, self-stabilized in a single longitudinal mode. A theory of self-stabilization was presented in Sec. III which explains the observed spectral features and provides a general mechanism for longitudinal mode self-stabilization of injection lasers.

Using a grating and an electrically driven mirror, an oscilloscope display of the laser modes was achieved. The lasers had thresholds of about 21 mA. Near threshold, the mode intensities smoothly changed as the linear gain curve was shifted by varying temperature. About 6 mA above threshold, the laser spectrum stabilized, and the mode pattern would snap from one lasing mode to the next as the temperature was changed. At 12 mA above threshold and higher currents, hysteresis, previously reported by Nakamura *et al.*[2] and by Saito and Ito,[3] was observed. Our observations were made up to currents of 20 mA above threshold. It was difficult to obtain data above this current for a variety of reasons including the onset of pulsations, the appearance of a second lasing mode, and a high degradation rate. *Mode stability and hysteresis were observed for cw operation but not for pulsed operation.* It may be that temperature changes during the 1μsec pulses that we tried prevent the delicate mode stabilization from taking place.

The mode spectra were recorded over five decades of intensity using a double spectrometer. At 20 mA above threshold, the ratio of the lasing to the most intense nonlasing modes was about 100:1. This indicates that the amount of stability achieved in our lasers was less that of Nakamura *et al.*, who reported ratios as high as 250:1 at currents of 20 mA above threshold and about 1000:1 at 70 mA above threshold in CSP lasers. When the lasing mode in our lasers changed due to varying the current or temperature, the laser line always jumped to the nearest neighboring mode, whereas both single and multiple mode jumps were reported by Nakamura *et al.*[2] Our lasers appeared to behave similarly to the buried heterostructure lasers of Saito and Ito.[3] Despite the differences in the degree of stability of our lasers and the CSP lasers of Nakamura *et al.*,[2] the similarity of the mode spectra in these two types of lasers lead us to believe that the self-stabilizing mechanism in both lasers is of the same nature.

We have attempted to deduce the experimental gain

spectrum of our lasers from the intensities of the lasing and nonlasing modes. It is shown in Appendix A that for a single laser having independently oscillating modes, the net loss minus gain of each mode is inversely proportional to the mode intensity and the constant of proportionality is calculated. Therefore, the spectrum of net mode gain can be determined from the relative intensities of the modes. For a laser with coupled modes the gain is not as simply related to mode intensity and therefore we have referred to the "gain" deduced from mode intensity spectra as "effective gain."

The effective gain profile in Fig. 2 is parabolic at threshold and the width of the parabola agrees reasonably well with the gain profile determined from analysis of the spontaneous emission spectrum and shown in Fig. 3.

Above threshold the effective gain profile narrows near the laser line and becomes structured. The structure is most prominent when the gain envelope is shifted to higher energy relative to the laser line by lowering the temperature several degrees. Then the effective gain profile exhibits a dip at about three modes from the laser line followed by a peak about seven modes from the laser line, both on the high energy side. The dip and peak were as found by Nakamura *et al.*,[2] who could also observe the same phenomena on the low energy side of the laser line when the laser operated high above threshold and the gain envelope was shifted to low energies by raising the temperature.

Another important feature of the effective gain profiles of the fundamental TE_{00n} modes is their continuity. The gain curves vary smoothly through the region of the laser line. Figure 6 shows that in contrast to the smooth behavior near the laser line of the fundamental TE_{00n} modes, the first-order transverse TE_{01n} modes show an abrupt change near the lasing line that has the appearance of an asymmetric dip.

All of the observed features of effective gain profiles, the narrowing, continuity, structure, and differences between the fundamental and first order transverse modes can be accounted for by the theory of mode stabilization presented in Sec. III. In contrast, the earlier theories of Copland[8] and Yamada *et al.*[9,10] cannot explain these features. The theories of Yamada *et al.* predict greatest gain suppression at the nearest-neighbor modes and both theories predict a discontinuity in gain profile at the laser line.

The theory developed in this paper explains self-stabilization as due to nonlinear optical effects, which arise when the inverted population is modified by intense stimulated emission. These nonlinearities result in 3 changes in gain, g_1, g_2, and g_χ, illustrated in Fig. 8. The change g_1 is due to the decrease in inverted population caused by stimulated emission (spectral hole burning). It is slowly varying and causes a slight reduction in single mode stability. The slowly varying nature of $g_1(\omega_1)$ probably explains why spectral hole burning has not been observed in spontaneous emission up till now.[14]

The changes g_2 and g_χ arise from modulation of the inverted population due to beating of lasing and nonlasing fields, which modulate the rate of stimulated emission. As a result, the dielectric function is modulated and when $\Delta\epsilon(\Omega)$ acts on the laser field $E(\omega_0)$, polarizations at $\omega_0 \pm \Omega$ are set up. These polarizations cause gain reduction g_2 at the nonlasing modes. The polarizations also couple modes equally separated on either side of the laser line resulting in an enhancement in gain by g_χ. The two changes g_χ and g_2 exactly cancel at the laser line, but away from the laser line the cancellation is incomplete and the net effect is to cause a slight stabilization of the lasing mode, with maximum gain suppression occurring several modes away from the laser line. The near cancellation of g_2 and g_χ accounts for the continuity of the effective gain curve and the dip in gain occurrring away from the laser line. The gains g_1 and g_2 were calculated by Yamada *et al.*[9,10], but they did not take into account mode coupling and calculate g_χ. Yamada *et al.*[9,10] did not try to explain the spectral features we have mentioned, which would be very hard to interpret without the g_χ term.

The first-order TE_{01n} modes are not equally spaced about the laser line and therefore, the coupling phenomena is not resonant and is negligible for these modes. In this case, g_2 is not nearly canceled out and has a much more dramatic effect on the gain near the laser line. In this way, we can qualitatively explain the differences between the TE_{00n} and TE_{01n} gain profiles in Figs. 5 and 6. However, our theoretical curves in Fig. 10 do not quantitatively account for the experimental curves, so the theory is still imperfect.

The theory presented in this paper is only an approximate description of the nonlinear optical behavior of the semiconductor. It has two weaknesses. First, it is a theory describing the response of free electrons to stimulated emission. In reality, the semiconductors have an exponential Urbach tail[12] extending below the energy gap and lasing occurs within this tail. A consensus has not been reached on the nature of this tail, which may involve momentarily trapped electrons[15] or phonon side bands. Consequently, we do not know theoretically the density of states D or the optical matrix element d_{12} appropriate for the lasing region. Second, the actual many body interactions in which the electrons are scattered have been replaced by two phenomenological time constants T_1 and T_2, which attempt to describe electron level occupancy relaxation and polarization relaxation. (Here we differ from Yamada *et al.*,[9] who claims these two relaxation times are related and that $T_1 = 2T_2$).

The time T_1 is the characteristic time for electron levels to refill after depletion. The time T_2 is the decay time for the polarization associated with the optical field. The two time constants were evaluated from fitting the observed gain curves to be $T_1 \approx 1$ psec and $T_2 \approx 0.1$ psec. The time T_2 determines the width of spectral hole burning described by $g_1(\Delta\omega = 4/T_2)$. Because T_2 is so small, spectral hole burning is broad and has little destabilizing effect on single mode operation. Despite the large width of spectral hole burning, narrow structure in the gain curves occurs because the spectral widths of g_2 and g_χ are determined largely by $T_1(\Delta\omega \approx 2/T_1)$ and are more than an order of magnitude narrower than g_1. The gains g_2 and g_χ result from modulation of the inverted population at $\omega_1 - \omega_0$. This modulation falls off for $\omega_1 - \omega_0 > T_1^{-1}$ because the electron levels do not have time to refill

The three parameters used in the theoretical description seem to be reasonable. The $T_1 = 1.0$ psec is not very different than the energy relaxation time of 2.5 psec measured by Glover.[16] The time $T_2 = 0.1$ psec may be related to the time associated with the total scattering rate (whether scattering causes a change in level occupation or not) which has been estimated to be about 0.1 psec under lasing conditions by Nishimura.[17] In Appendix C, we showed that our choice of $|d_{12}|^2$ needed to fit the data was about equal to the value of $|d_{12}|^2$ evaluated from optical absorption measurements at 0.19 eV above the energy gap.

While the theory is a simplified description of the actual semiconductor, the good overall agreement of the theory with experiment in explaining the measured effective gain spectra indicates that the self-stabilization mechanism set forth in this paper is probably the dominant one for semiconductor injection lasers.

ACKNOWLEDGMENTS

We thank H. G. White, A. Savage, L. Kozi, and F. R. Merritt for their assistance in crystal growth, laser preparation, and measurements.

APPENDIX A: RELATION OF LOSS-GAIN AND POWER FOR UNCOUPLED MODES

Consider a simple laser with uncoupled modes with the jth mode having distributed loss α_L and facet reflectivity r_m. Let $u_j(z)$ be the number of photons per unit length at position z in the cavity and traveling in the z direction. The power emitted from each facet by the jth mode is

$$P_j = h\nu v_g u_j(L)(1-r_m). \tag{A1}$$

The rate of growth of $u_j(z)$ is

$$\frac{du_j}{dz} = (g_j - \alpha_I)u_j + \frac{r}{2L}, \tag{A2}$$

where $v_g r$ is the rate of spontaneous emission into the mode.[12] The solution of Eq. (A2) using the boundary condition $u(0) = r_m u(L)$ gives

$$u_j(L) = \frac{r}{2L}\,\frac{\exp[(g_j-\alpha_L)L]-1}{1-r_m\exp[(g_j-\alpha_L)L]}\,\frac{1}{(g_j-\alpha_L)}. \tag{A3}$$

We define the average loss of the cavity as

$$\gamma = \alpha_L + \frac{1}{L}\ln\left(\frac{1}{r_m}\right). \tag{A4}$$

For lasing and nearly lasing modes $g_j \approx \gamma$, therefore Eq. (A3) becomes

$$u_j(L) \cong \frac{1-r_m}{2r_m \ln\left(\frac{1}{r_m}\right)}\,\frac{r}{(\gamma-g_j)L}. \tag{A5}$$

The coefficient r can be shown to be related to gain at threshold by [12]

$$r = g n_{sp}, \tag{A6}$$

where

$$n_{sp} = \left[1-\exp\left(\frac{h\nu - \text{eV}}{kT}\right)\right]^{-1}, \tag{A7}$$

where eV in the separation of quasi-Fermi levels. Combining Eqs. (A1), (A5), and (A6) we find

$$\gamma - g_j = \frac{(1-r_m)^2}{r_m \ln\left(\frac{1}{r_m}\right)}\,\frac{g n_{sp} v_g h\nu}{2P_j L}. \tag{A8}$$

The power in the lasing mode is related to the current above threshold by

$$2P_L = \eta\frac{(I-I_{th})h\nu}{e}, \tag{A9}$$

where η is the differential quantum efficiency. Combining Eqs. (A8), and (A9), we find

$$\gamma - g_j = \frac{(1-r_m)^2}{r_m \ln\left(\frac{1}{r_m}\right)}\,\frac{g n_{sp} v_g e}{\eta(I-I_{th})L}\,\frac{P_L}{P_j}. \tag{A10}$$

In our experiments $I - I_{th} = 20$ mA, $g = 60$ cm^{-1}, $v_G = c/4.33, n_{sp} \cong 2.6,$[12] $e = 1.6\times10^{-19}$ C, $L = 380\times10^{-4}$ cm, $r_m = 0.3$, and $\eta \cong 0.5$, then

$$\gamma - g_j = 6.17\times10^{-4}\frac{P_L}{P_j}\ \text{cm}^{-1}. \tag{A11}$$

APPENDIX B: EVALUATION OF INTEGRALS FOR THE MODE INTENSITIES

The integrals for I_1 and I_2, given by Eq. (67), can be evaluated by contour integration. We assume the poles $\alpha+\delta$ and $\alpha-\delta$ are above the real axis, then completing the contour in the upper half plane, we find

$$\frac{\omega^2}{c^2k}I_1 = -\frac{1}{2\delta}\left[\frac{(\beta-\delta)(\alpha-\alpha^*+\beta^*-\delta)}{(\alpha''-\delta'')(\alpha-\alpha^*-\delta-\delta^*)} - \frac{(\beta+\delta)(\alpha-\alpha^*+\beta^*+\delta)}{(\alpha''+\delta'')(\alpha-\alpha^*+\delta+\delta^*)}\right]. \tag{B1}$$

Using $\beta = i\beta'' = -\beta^*$, $\alpha-\alpha^* = 2i\alpha''$, $\delta+\delta^* = 2\delta'$ and $\chi^2 = \delta^2 - \beta^2$, we find

$$\frac{\omega^2}{c^2k}I_1 = \frac{1}{4\delta}\left[\frac{2i\alpha''(i\beta''-\delta)+\chi^2}{(\alpha''-\delta'')(\delta'-i\alpha'')} + \frac{2i\alpha''(i\beta''+\delta)+\chi^2}{(\alpha''+\delta'')(\delta'+i\alpha'')}\right]. \tag{B2}$$

This expression must simplify further because it is real and therefore, all imaginary terms must cancel out. By forming a common denominator, it is readily shown that those terms not canceling in the numerator have a common factor δ, which cancels with δ in the denominator. The resulting expression is

$$\frac{\omega^2}{c^2k}I_1 = \frac{\alpha''[2\alpha''(\alpha''-\beta'')+\chi'^2-\chi''^2+2i(\chi'\chi''-\delta'\delta'')]}{2(\alpha''^2+\delta'^2)(\alpha''^2-\delta''^2)}. \tag{B3}$$

Taking the imaginary part of $\chi^2 = \delta^2 - \beta^2$ shows that $\delta'\delta'' = \chi'\chi''$ so that the imaginary part of the numerator cancels out. We have finally

$$\frac{c^2}{\omega^2k}I_1 = \frac{2\alpha''(\alpha''-\beta'')+\chi'^2-\chi''^2}{4(\alpha''^2+\delta'^2)}\left(\frac{1}{\alpha''-\delta''}+\frac{1}{\alpha''+\delta''}\right). \tag{B4}$$

Evaluation of the integral for I_2 by a similar, but simpler calculation yields

$$\frac{c^2}{\omega^2 k} I_2 = \frac{(\chi'^2 + \chi''^2)}{4(\alpha''^2 + \delta''^2)} \left(\frac{1}{\alpha'' - \delta''} + \frac{1}{\alpha'' + \delta''} \right). \quad \text{(B5)}$$

The total intensity $I = I_1 + I_2$ is given by

$$\frac{c^2}{\omega^2 k} I = \frac{\alpha''(\alpha'' - \beta'') + \chi'^2}{2(\alpha''^2 + \delta'^2)} \left(\frac{1}{\alpha'' - \delta''} + \frac{1}{\alpha'' + \delta''} \right), \quad \text{(B6)}$$

and the fraction I_2/I is

$$\frac{I_2}{I} = \frac{\chi'^2 + \chi''^2}{2[\alpha''(\alpha'' - \beta'') + \chi'^2]}. \quad \text{(B7)}$$

APPENDIX C: ESIMATE OF dg_0

The parameter dg_0 is approximately given by

$$\frac{dg_0}{T_1 T_2} = \frac{|d_{12}|^2}{\hbar^2} \int \overline{|E(\omega_0)|^2} g_0(\omega_0) \Psi_m^2(x,y) dx dy, \quad \text{(C1)}$$

where the bar over $|E(0)|^2$ represents an average along the cavity length. We average over spatial variations along the cavity length because carrier motion will largely smooth out variations in the inverted population that are 1/2 wave length apart. (With a velocity of 2×10^7 cm sec^{-1}, an electron will travel about 1 wave length in a psec.)

The squared field amplitude is related to the electromagnetic energy density U by

$$U = \frac{1}{8\pi} \left(\frac{\partial(\omega\epsilon_0')}{\partial\omega} \bar{E}^2 + \bar{H}^2 \right) = \frac{n_0' c}{2\pi v_g} \overline{|E(\omega_0)|^2}. \quad \text{(C2)}$$

The matrix element $|d_{12}|^2$ can be expressed in terms of the ratio of optical absorption to the density of states D.

$$\alpha = \frac{\omega^2}{c^2 k} \frac{4\pi^2}{\hbar} |d_{12}|^2 D = \frac{4\pi^2 \omega}{\hbar c n_0'} |d_{12}|^2 D, \quad \text{(C3)}$$

where α and D are to be evaluated at the laser line in the absence of excitation ($\rho_{11} = 0, \rho_{22} = 1$). Eliminating $\overline{|E(0)|^2}$ and $|d_{12}|^2$, Eq. (C1) becomes

$$\frac{dg_0}{T_1 T_2} = \frac{\alpha}{2\pi \hbar \omega D} v_g \int U g_0 \Psi_m^2 dx dy. \quad \text{(C4)}$$

The LSBOG lasers used in our experiments have weak optical confinement perpendicular to the active layer with $\gamma \approx 0.3$ and strong optical confinement in the lateral direction. The eigenfunctions of the fundamental and first transverse modes are approximately

$$F_0(X) = \left(\frac{1}{W} \right)^{1/2} \cos\left(\frac{\pi X}{W} \right), \quad \text{(C5a)}$$

$$F_1(X) = \left(\frac{1}{W} \right)^{1/2} \sin\left(\frac{\pi X}{W} \right), \quad \text{(C5b)}$$

and $U(X)$ is approximately

$$U = U_{\max} \cos^2\left(\frac{\pi X}{W} \right). \quad \text{(C6)}$$

We can approximate the integral in Eq. (C4) as

$$\int U g_0 \Psi_m^2 dx dy = \Gamma U_{\max} g_0 \int_{-W/2}^{W/2} dx F_m^2(X) \cos^2\left(\frac{\pi X}{W} \right) = \begin{cases} \frac{3}{4} \Gamma g_0 U_{\max} & m = 0 \\ \frac{1}{4} \Gamma g_0 U_{\max} & m = 1 \end{cases}. \quad \text{(C7)}$$

The optical power generated by stimulated emission is

$$\frac{\hbar\omega(I - I_{th})}{e} = \int v_g U g_0 \, d^3x = \frac{v_g U_{\max} g_0 V}{2}, \quad \text{(C8)}$$

where V is the volume of the active layer. Eliminating the integral from Eq. (C4) with Eqs. (C7) and (C8), we have for the fundamental transverse mode $m = 0$

$$\frac{dg_0}{T_1 T_2} = \frac{3\Gamma\alpha(I - I_{th})}{4\pi D e V}. \quad \text{(C9)}$$

Above the band gap, D can be calculated using a parabolic band model

$$D = \frac{1}{2\pi^2 \hbar^2} (2\mu)^{3/2} (\hbar\omega - E_g)^{1/2}, \quad \text{(C10)}$$

where $\mu = 0.059\, m_e$ is the reduced mass of the electron and hole. At $\hbar\omega = 13\,000$ cm^{-1} $= E_g + 0.191$ eV, $\alpha \cong 1.74 \times 10^4$ cm^{-1}. The dimension of the active layer are 380 μm long, 2.5 μm wide, and 0.2 μm thick. Evaluating Eq. (9) for $I - I_{th} = 20$ mA we find

$$\frac{dg_0}{T_1 T_2} = 29.2 \text{ cm}^{-1} (\text{psec})^{-2}. \quad \text{(C11)}$$

[1] H. Namizaki, IEEE J. Quantum Electron. **QE-11**, 427 (1975).
[2] M. Nakamura, K. Aiki, N. Chinone, R. Ito, and J. Umeda, J. Appl. Phys. **49**, 4644 (1978).
[3] K. Saito and R. Ito, IEEE J. Quantum Electron. **QE-16**, 205 (1980).
[4] W. Streiffer, R. D. Burnham, and D. R. Scifres, IEEE J. Quantum Electron. **QE-13**, 403 (1977).
[5] Y. Nishimura and Y. Nishimura, IEEE J. Quantum Electron. **QE-9**, 1011 (1973).
[6] B. Zee, IEEE J. Quantum Electron. **QE-14**, 727 (1978).
[7] C. H. Henry, R. A. Logan, and F. R. Merritt, IEEE J. Quantum Electron. **QE-17**, 2196 (1981).
[8] J. A. Copeland, IEEE J. Quantum Electron. **QE-16**, 721 (1980).
[9] D. V. Lang, R. A. Logan, and M. Jaros, Phys. Rev. B **19**, 1015 (1979).
[10] M. Yamada, K. Hoyono, H. Isighuro, and Y. Suematzu, Jpn. J. Appl. Phys. **18**, 1531 (1979).
[11] M. Yamada and Y. Suematzu, IEEE J. Quantum Electron. **QE-15**, 743 (1979).
[12] C. H. Henry, R. A. Logan, and F. R. Merritt, J. Appl. Phys. **51**, 3042 (1980).
[13] C. P. Slichter, "Principles of Magnetic Resonance, Section 5.4," in *Density Matrix-General Equations* (Springer-Verlag, New York, 1978).
[14] M. W. Fleming and A. Mooradian, IEEE J. Quantum Electron. **QE-17**, 44 (1981).
[15] H. Sumi and Y. Toyazawa, J. Phys. Soc. Jpn. **31**, 342 (1971).
[16] G. H. Glover, Appl. Phys. Lett. **21**, 409 (1972).
[17] Y. Nishimura, Jpn. J. Appl. Phys. **13**, 109 (1974).

Measurement of the linewidth enhancement factor α of semiconductor lasers

Christoph Harder, Kerry Vahala, and Amnon Yariv
California Institute of Technology, Watson 128-95, Pasadena, California 91125

(Received 15 October 1982; accepted for publication 23 November 1982)

A theory of the amplitude and phase modulation characteristic of a single mode semiconductor laser is presented. In this model the amplitude modulation couples through the complex susceptibility of the gain medium to the phase. We show that this coupling constant can be obtained by a high-frequency modulation experiment. This measured coupling constant is used to infer the linewidth enhancement factor α as discussed by Henry, and Vahala and Yariv. Experiments confirmed the model and we measured a linewidth enhancement factor $|\alpha| = 4.6 \pm 1.0$ for a GaAlAs buried optical guide laser.

PACS numbers: 42.55.Px, 42.60.Fc, 42.60.He, 42.80.Sa

The spectral purity of semiconductor lasers is of utmost importance in applications that utilize the coherence properties of the laser, such as heterodyne detection of optical signals. The extremely high gain in injection lasers as well as strong amplitude-phase coupling causes their spectral properties to differ markedly from other laser systems. Recently, Henry[1] presented a model of the linewidth of single mode semiconductor lasers, which takes line broadening due to the coupling of phase and intensity into account. Independently, Vahala and Yariv[2] developed a semiconductor laser noise theory which treats the carrier density as a dynamic variable and which includes the carrier density dependence of the index of refraction. Both treatments predict a spectral linewidth Δf of the modified Schawlow–Townes form:

$$\Delta f = \frac{v_{gr}^2 h\nu g n_{sp} \alpha_{mir}}{8\pi P_0}(1+\alpha^2), \tag{1}$$

where v_{gr} is the group velocity of the light, $h\nu$ the lasing energy, g the gain, n_{sp} is the spontaneous emission factor,[3] α_{mir} the mirror loss, P_0 the output power per facet, and α the linewidth enhancement factor.[1,2] Until now no direct measurement of this important device parameter was available and its approximate value had to be estimated from frequency shift measurements,[4,5] gain measurements,[4] or gain calculations[6,7] and a subsequent Kramers–Kronig analysis.

The purpose of this letter is twofold: first, we derive the relationship between the small-signal modulation characteristic of a semiconductor laser and the linewidth enhancement factor α, and second, we apply this result to measure α through a high-frequency modulation experiment.

This small-signal analysis is based on the electromagnetic field equation of a laser as derived by Lamb[8] and is applied to the case of index guided single mode lasers with a spatially inhomogeneous carrier density. The polarization $\mathbf{P}(\mathbf{r},t)$ due to the carriers injected into the semiconductor material is given as a function of the electric field $\mathbf{E}(\mathbf{r},t)$ by

$$\mathbf{P}(\mathbf{r},t) = \epsilon_0 \chi(n(\mathbf{r},t),\mathbf{r})\mathbf{E}(\mathbf{r},t), \tag{2}$$

where $\chi = \chi_r + i\chi_i$ is the complex susceptibility which is an explicit function of the carrier density and of the position (in the case where the material is inhomogeneous).

The equation for the time evolution of the cavity mode $E_m(t)$ is obtained by substituting the polarization $\mathbf{P}$, as given by Eq. (2), into the electromagnetic field equation[8]

$$\frac{d^2}{dt^2}\left[\left(1+\frac{\chi_m(t)}{N^2}\right)E_m(t)\right] + \frac{1}{\tau_p}\frac{d}{dt}E_m(t) + \omega_m^2 E_m(t) = -\frac{1}{\epsilon_0 N^2}\frac{d^2 P_{sp,m}}{dt^2}, \tag{3a}$$

$$\mathbf{E}(\mathbf{r},t) \equiv E_m(t)\mathbf{e}_m(\mathbf{r}), \tag{3b}$$

$$\chi_m = \int_V \chi[n(\mathbf{r},t),\mathbf{r}]\,\mathbf{e}_m(\mathbf{r})\cdot\mathbf{e}_m(\mathbf{r})dV, \tag{3c}$$

$$\tau_p \equiv \frac{1}{v_{gr}[\alpha_{sc} + (1/L)\ln(1/R)]}, \tag{3d}$$

$$N^2 \equiv \epsilon/\epsilon_0, \tag{3e}$$

$$\omega_m \equiv 2\pi(c/2LN)m. \tag{3f}$$

The optical mode profile is given by $e_m^2(\mathbf{r})$ and χ_m is the effective susceptibility for the mode m. τ_p, N, and ω_m are the photon lifetime, index of refraction, and resonance frequency, respectively, of the cold cavity, that is, of the cavity when the effects of the lasing transition are removed. The spontaneous emission can be taken into account by adding a driving term $P_{sp,m}$.[2] The explicit form can be obtained from a Langevin noise source treatment which is rather tedious. Fortunately, there is a simpler way to obtain the effects of $P_{sp,m}$ since we are only interested in its average contribution. It is a basic result of quantum mechanics that the ratio of stimulated emission to average spontaneous emission into the lasing mode is equal to the number of photons in the mode, P_m. The average effect of $P_{sp,m}$ can therefore be accounted for in a small-signal analysis by changing the second term (the loss term) in the field equation (3a) from $(1/\tau_p)(dE/dt)$ to

$$\frac{1}{\tau_p}\left(1-\frac{n_{sp}}{P_m}\right)\frac{dE}{dt},$$

where n_{sp} is equal to the ratio of the total to the net stimulated emission rate.

For the small-signal analysis the mode $E_m(t)$ and the mode susceptibility $\chi_m(t)$ are assumed to be of the following form:

$$E_m(t) = E_0[1+\delta(t)]\cos[\omega_1 t + \varphi(t)], \tag{4a}$$

$$\chi_m(t) = \chi_{m,0} + \chi_{m,1}(t) = \chi_{m,0,r} + \chi_{m,1,r}(t) + i[\chi_{m,0,i} + \chi_{m,1,i}(t)]. \tag{4b}$$

The solution for the operating point shows that the mode

Reprinted with permission from *Appl. Phys. Lett.*, vol. 42, no. 4, pp. 328–330, Feb. 15, 1983.

gain $\chi_{m,0,i}$ is clamped and the lasing frequency ω_1 is shifted slightly from the cold cavity resonance ω_m.

$$\chi_{m,0,i} = \frac{N^2}{\omega_1 \tau_p}\left(1 - \frac{n_{sp}}{P_m}\right), \tag{5a}$$

$$\omega_1^2 = \frac{\omega_m^2}{(1 + \chi_{m,0,r}/N^2)}. \tag{5b}$$

The small-signal behavior is given by the solution of

$$\dot{\varphi}(t) + \frac{1}{2}\frac{\chi_{m,1,r}(t)}{N^2}\omega_1 = 0, \tag{6a}$$

$$\dot{\delta}(t) + \frac{1}{2\tau_p}\frac{n_{sp}}{P_m}\delta(t) - \frac{1}{2}\frac{\chi_{m,1,i}(t)}{N^2}\omega_1 = 0. \tag{6b}$$

In the experiments described below the semiconductor laser is biased above threshold and a small sinusoidally varying current at the frequency Ω is superimposed. Therefore, the steady state sinusoidally modulated solution of the field $E_m(t)$ is of interest. To obtain it we substitute

$$E_m(t) = E_0[1 + (m/2)\cos(\Omega t)]\cos[\omega_1 t + \beta\cos(\Omega t + \Phi)] \tag{7}$$

into Eqs. (6a) and (6b), where m and β are the intensity and phase modulation indices, respectively. For large modulation frequencies Ω $[\Omega \gg (n_{sp}/P_m)(1/\tau_p)]$ the solution is

$$\beta = -\tfrac{1}{2}\alpha_m m, \tag{8a}$$

$$\Phi = 0, \tag{8b}$$

$$\alpha_m(\Omega) \equiv \frac{\chi_{m,1,r}}{\chi_{m,1,i}} = \int_V \frac{\partial \chi_r(n)}{\partial n}\bigg|_{n=n_0(\mathbf{r})} N_1(\mathbf{r},\Omega)e_m^2(\mathbf{r})dV \bigg/ \int_V \frac{\partial \chi_i(n)}{\partial n}\bigg|_{n=n_0(\mathbf{r})} N_1(\mathbf{r},\Omega)e_m^2(\mathbf{r})dV. \tag{8c}$$

As can be seen from Eq. (8a), the phase and intensity modulation indices are proportional to each other, independent of bias point and optical confinement factor. This result suggests a simple way to obtain the exact value of α_m through a measurement of the ratio of intensity and phase modulation depths, two relatively straightforward measurements, as will be shown below. The factor $\alpha_m(\Omega)$ is defined in Eq. (8c), where $n_0(\mathbf{r})$is the quiescent carrier density at location $\mathbf{r}$, $N_2(\mathbf{r},\Omega)$ the small-signal frequency dependent carrier density fluctuation at position $\mathbf{r}$, and $e_m^2(\mathbf{r})$ the normalized photon density. If the susceptibility $\chi(n,\mathbf{r})$ is linear in n and does not depend on $\mathbf{r}$, then it can be seen from Eq. (8c) that α_m is independent of Ω. Using the relation between the index of refraction N_{ind} and the susceptibility χ, $\epsilon_0 N_{ind}^2 \equiv 1 + \chi$, one obtains that in this case α_m is equal to the linewidth enhancement factor α as defined by Henry.[1]

$$\alpha_m = \frac{\partial \chi_r/\partial n}{\partial \chi_i/\partial n} = \frac{\Delta N_{ind,r}}{\Delta N_{ind,i}} = \alpha. \tag{8d}$$

Please note that in this linear case α_m is totally independent of the spatial distribution of the carrier density modulation (e.g., the incomplete carrier clamping in the wings of the optical mode, or diffusion effects do not enhance the phase modulation as suggested in Ref. 9). However, if the susceptibility $\chi(n,\mathbf{r})$ is not linear in the carrier density or depends on the location (e.g., the optical field penetrates into a material with a different band gap[4]), then the factor α_m is dependent on the modulation frequency and its value measured at high frequencies cannot be used to infer the linewidth broadening factor α.

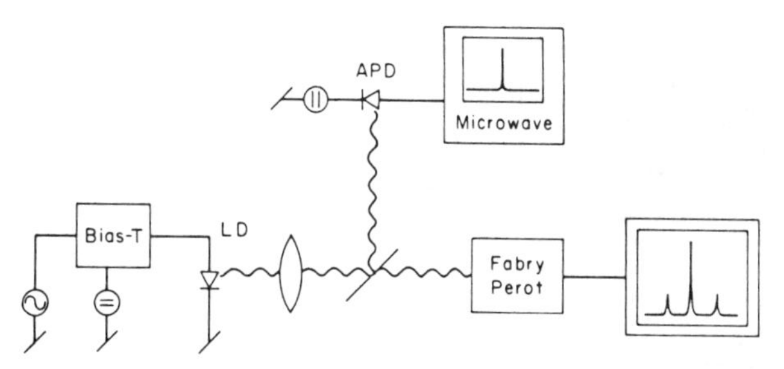

FIG. 1. Setup for measuring the intensity and phase modulation index. The laser diode (LD) is biased well above threshold and a small-signal current at frequency Ω is superimposed. The intensity modulation depth is measured with an avalanche photodiode (APD) and the spectral density with a scanning Fabry–Perot.

The experimental arrangement for measuring the intensity and phase modulation index is shown in Fig. 1. The semiconductor laser is biased above threshold and a small sinusoidally varying current at frequency Ω is superimposed. The intensity and spectral density of the radiation field are given by

$$\text{Intensity} \sim E_0^2[1 + m\cos(\Omega t)], \tag{9a}$$

$$\text{Spectrum: center line at } \omega_1: E_0^2[J_0^2(\beta) + m^2 J_1^2(\beta)] \tag{9b}$$

$$\text{First sidebands at } \omega_1 \pm \Omega: E_0^2\{J_1^2(\beta) + 1[(m/2)(J_2(\beta) - J_0(\beta))]^2\}, \tag{9c}$$

where $J_n(\beta)$ are nth order Bessel functions. Note that the calculated spectrum is symmetric.

The intensity modulation index m was measured with an avalanche photodiode (S171P Telefunken) calibrated in the measurement setup from dc to 3.5 GHz to an accuracy of ± 1 dB. The optical spectrum was measured with a confocal scanning Fabry–Perot (Tropel 240). Care was taken to avoid any back reflection into the laser. In a typical measurement, as shown in Fig. 2, the modulation current at frequency Ω was adjusted to produce a desired intensity modulation depth m, which was measured with the photodiode. The phase modulation index β can be found by measuring the relative sideband strength and using Eqs. (9b) and (9c). The factor α_m is then obtained as $\alpha_m = -2(\beta/m)$. Since only the absolute value of β can be measured, the sign of α_m must be obtained by other means. A measurement of the α_m of a buried optical guide laser (BOG Hitachi 3400, $\lambda = 816$ nm) at $\Omega = 2$ GHz, a bias level of 1.3 times threshold, and an intensity modulation depth of 10%, gave $|\alpha_m| = 4.5$. Repetition of this measurement for about 50 different conditions (Ω varied between 1 and 3.5 GHz, bias level varied between 1.3 and 1.9 times threshold, and modulation depth varied between 10% and 30%) gave $|\alpha_m| = 4.6 \pm 0.5$. This value has an additional uncertainty of $\pm 10\%$ due to the inaccuracy of the photodiode calibration. A simple structure such as the BOG laser is expected to have the required simple form of the susceptibility so as to render α_m as given by Eq. (8c)

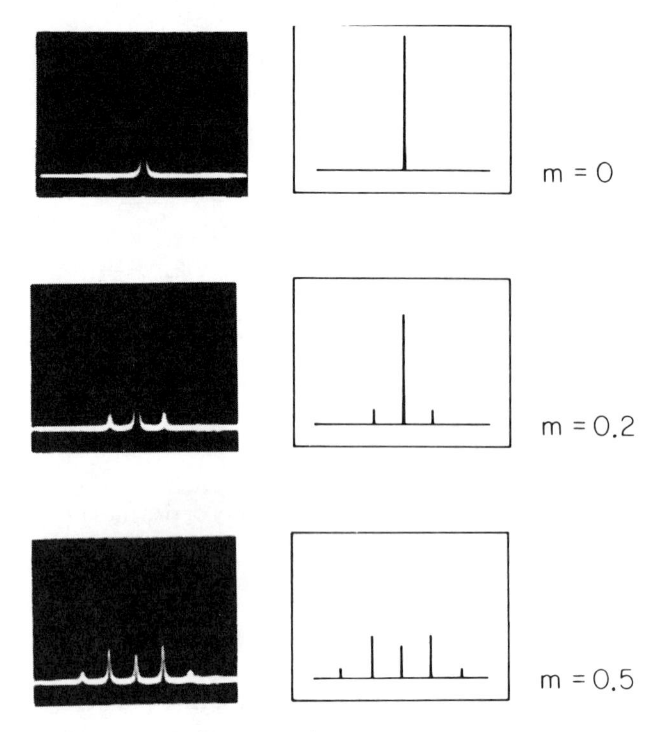

FIG. 2. Measured and calculated optical spectra of a laser diode with an intensity modulation $m = 0$, 20% and 50%. The modulation frequency is $\Omega = 1$ GHz$\times 2\pi$.

frequency independent. Indeed, our measurements of α_m could not detect any dependence on Ω in the range 1–3.5 GHz. Therefore, we conclude that for this BOG laser $|\alpha| = 4.6 \pm 1.0$.

Attempts to measure α for a channeled substrate planar laser (CSP) failed because the measured α_m was strongly dependent on the modulation frequency Ω. This is expected since the optical field penetrates into the GaAs substrate (which has a smaller band gap than the active region) in order to stabilize the transverse mode. As discussed above the susceptibility in such a case is no longer of the required simple form to render Eq. (8c) frequency independent.

In conclusion, we have developed a model for calculating the amplitude and phase modulation of the radiation field of the family of index guided, single mode semiconductor lasers with an inhomogeneous carrier density. In the model amplitude and phase are coupled through the complex susceptibility of the gain medium. We have shown that this coupling constant can be obtained by measuring the ratio of amplitude to phase modulation at high frequencies. Since the same coupling mechanism causes the spectral linewidth broadening, this method enables us to measure directly the linewidth enhancement factor α. Our measurements confirmed the model and we measured a linewidth enhancement factor $|\alpha| = 4.6 \pm 1.0$ for a buried optical guide laser.

The authors thank Dr. M. Nakamura of Hitachi Central Research Laboratories for providing the BOG and CSP lasers used in this experiment. This research was supported by the Office of Naval Research, the National Science Foundation under the Optical Communication Program and by the Army Research Office.

[1]C. H. Henry, IEEE J. Quantum Electron. **QE-18**, 259 (1982).
[2]K. Vahala and A. Yariv, IEEE J. Quantum Electron (to be published).
[3]H. Haug and H. Haken, Z. Phys. **204**, 262 (1967).
[4]C. H. Henry, R. A. Logan, and K. Bertness, J. Appl. Phys. **52**, 4457 (1981).
[5]D. Welford and A. Mooradian, Appl. Phys. Lett. **40**, 865 (1982).
[6]J. G. Mendoza-Alvarez, F. D. Nunes, and N. B. Patel, J. Appl. Phys. **51**, 4365 (1980).
[7]F. Stern, Phys. Rev. A **133**, 1653 (1964).
[8]W. E. Lamb, Jr., Phys. Rev. A **134**, 1429 (1964).
[9]S. Kobayashi, Y. Yamamoto, M. Ito, and T. Kimura, IEEE J. Quantum Electron. **QE-18**, 582 (1982).

Heterodyne determination of the width of the emission lines of injection lasers in the beat frequency stabilization regime

A. M. Akul'shin, N. G. Basov, V. L. Velichanskiĭ, A. S. Zibrov, M. V. Zverkov, V. V. Nikitin, O. G. Okhotnikov, N. V. Senkov, V. A. Sautenkov, D. A. Tyurikov, and E. K. Yurkin

P. N. Lebedev Physics Institute, Academy of Sciences of the USSR, Moscow

(Submitted March 24, 1983)
Kvantovaya Elektron. (Moscow) **10**, 1527–1529 (August 1983)

A servo system was used to lock the beat frequency of injection lasers operating under conditions of self-stabilization of single-frequency emission in an anomalously wide continuous tuning range. The width of the beat spectrum was found to be ~500 Hz.

PACS numbers: 42.55.Px, 42.60.He

A method for narrowing the emission line of injection lasers by use of an external resonator was proposed and implemented by Velichanskiĭ *et al.*[1] Measurements were made by the method of heterodyne mixing of radiation from two injection lasers of the same type. The same method was used to determine the width of the emission line of a laser with an external resonator, which was of the order of 15–50 kHz (Ref. 2). However, investigations reported in Refs. 1 and 2 were concerned with lasers operating under free-running conditions and the precision of the measurements was limited by fluctuations of the difference frequency. In the present study the width of an emission line of an injection laser with an external resonator was determined under conditions of stabilization of the beat frequency.

APPARATUS

All the components of two laser systems with external resonators were identical, they were placed on pyroceramic supports, and included injection lasers operating at 300 K, matching objectives with a numerical aperture 0.65 and a focal length 6.2 mm, rotatable mirrors made of a piezoceramic, and holographic selectors. A similar system was described in Ref. 3. One of the injection laser mirrors was given an antireflection coating to increase the range of tuning by a selector. Since the antireflection effect was incomplete, lasing was possible only when the selector band coincided with the injection laser mode. A complete coverage of the spectrum was achieved when the mode positions were varied by altering the temperature of a heat sink. The laser frequencies were brought together by a diffraction grating and two scanning interferometers with free spectral ranges 40 and 1.5 GHz. The method used to match the wavefronts and the details of the apparatus were described in Ref. 1.

Radiations from the two laser systems were mixed in an avalanche photodiode and the signal of this photodiode was applied to an S4-27 or S4-12 spectrum analyzer and to an automatic frequency control (AFC) unit. In the locking regime the beat frequency was determined by that of a reference AFC oscillator and could be varied within the range 6–20 MHz. The frequency of the "slave" laser system was controlled using two methods: variation of the voltage on a piezoelectric ceramic plate, i.e., variation of the length of the external part of the resonator (with a pass band of 1.5 kHz) and variation of the injection current (with a pass band 20 kHz).

LASER OPERATION REGIME

It is very easy to control the frequency by the self-stabilization single-frequency emission regime, because of its high stability against excitation of neighboring modes[4] and, as reported below, because it can increase considerably the range of continuous tuning of the emission frequency both in the case when the length of the external part of the resonator is varied and when the optical length of the injection laser is modulated. We used injection lasers with a conventional stripe contact as well as lasers with a waveguide buried in a mesastructure. A single-frequency regime was manifested by a strong asymmetry of the characteristic[5] observed when the mode of the injection laser resonator was tuned over the selector profile (Fig. 1a) and a characteristic feature of the self-stabilization regime was the absence of a step structure[4] and an anomalously wide tuning range.

The continuous tuning range was estimated using interferometers (Figs. 1b and 1c). The lower oscillogram in Fig. 1b confirmed the continuity of the frequency tuning in a wide range resulting from variation of the length of the external part of the resonator (mode hopping would have resulted in discontinuities in the curve), whereas the upper oscillogram enabled us to

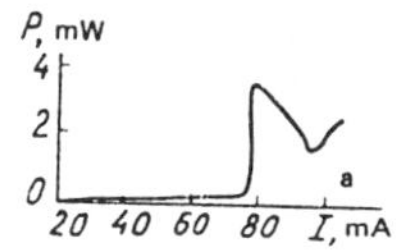

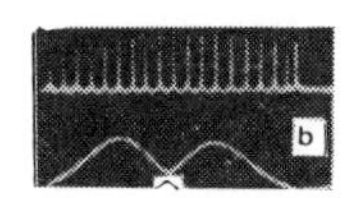

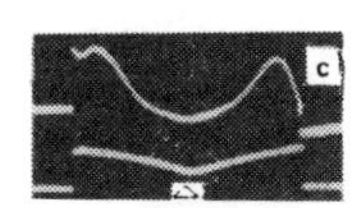

FIG. 1. Watt-ampere characteristic of a laser with an external resonator (a), resonances of the transmission of interferometers with instrumental widths 16 MHz (upper trace) and 1.2 GHz (lower trace) recorded with the aid of the laser when the length of the external part was varied (b), and dependences on transmission of an interferometer with an instrumental width 30 MHz (upper trace) and of the output power (lower trace) on the current (c). The resonator length and the current were modulated in accordance with a sawtooth law and the arrow identifies the top of the peak.

measure the tuning range. The maximum deviation of the frequency due to a change in the length of the external part amounted to 2 GHz when the length of the external resonator was $L = 60$ cm, which was eight times greater than the tuning range under normal conditions (250 MHz). The corresponding value in the case of tuning by variation of the injection current was 60 MHz, which was two orders of magnitude wider than the usual tuning range.

A transmission resonance of an interferometer (represented by the upper oscillogram in Fig. 1c) was observed when the injection current was varied and it demonstrated the continuity of the frequency tuning. In this case the total tuning range was estimated from the width of an interferometer resonance. A change in the sign of tuning occurring after an abrupt onset of lasing (represented by the watt-ampere characteristics shown in the lower part of Fig. 1c) was due to unsteady cooling because of a corresponding abrupt reduction in the power dissipated in the active region, which gradually changed to an increase in the temperature because of an increase in the current.

BEAT SPECTRUM

It was practically impossible to detect the beat spectrum with a high resolution without frequency locking. When the frequency was stabilized by means of the first method, a stable beat signal was obtained on the screen of an analyzer for 10–100 min (depending on the drift of the laboratory temperature). The width of the beat spectrum was then 20–200 kHz for ten pairs of lasers. Broadening of the bands by the second method reduced the width of the beat spectrum. The minimum width at the 0.5 level was 500 Hz (Fig. 2). The spectrum was recorded using an S4-12 analyzer with a resolution of 30 Hz.

DISCUSSION

According to Ref. 6, the width of the laser emission line is $\Gamma = \Gamma_0'\chi^2 + \Gamma_0''\chi$, where Γ_0' is the contribution of the spontaneous noise, Γ_0'' is the contribution of fluctuations of the number of electrons in the active region to the width of the injection laser line in the absence of an external resonator; $\chi = Q_0/Qk$; Q and Q_0 are the Q factors of the external and internal (intrinsic) resonators, respectively; k is the power coupling coefficient of the resonators. This expression is valid in the case of a single-frequency regime when both broadening mechanisms are statistically independent and give rise to a Lorentzian line profile (Γ, Γ_0', and Γ_0'' are the total widths) and if the contribution of technical fluctuations is negligible. In the absence of an external resonator the injection lasers operated in the multimode regime, so that it was impossible to determine Γ_0' and Γ_0'' directly. The order of magnitude of χ was estimated using the experimental values $\Gamma_0' = 20$ MHz and $\Gamma_0'' = 2$ MHz (Ref. 7), obtained for the single-frequency regime (it was reasonable to assume that in the case of generation of a specific oscillation mode of a laser with a resonator the broadening mechanisms associated with multimoding were suppressed). In estimating Γ_0' and Γ_0'' an allowance was made for small corrections associated with the difference between the injection laser parameters. The values of Q and Q_0 were determined by the resonator lengths and were approximately equal to losses on the mirrors so that $Q/Q_0 = L/n'l = 6 \cdot 10^2$ (n' is the effective refractive index of the injection laser material and l is the length of the resonator of the injection laser). Then, assuming that $k = 0.1-0.3$, we found that $\Gamma_0'\chi^2 = 5 - 0.5$ kHz and $\Gamma_0''\chi = 30 - 10$ kHz. Clearly, the sum of these two quantities exceeded the experimental line width. The contribution of the second type of perturbation probably decreased because of AFC. Further narrowing of the line could be achieved by increasing the resonator length or the effective number of transits in the resonator.[7]

One should point out that whereas external resonators reduce the spectra of each of the lasers, electronic self-tuning in the above experiments suppresses only fluctuations of the difference frequency. In practice, the spectra emitted by laser with external resonators are broadened because of technical low-frequency fluctuations of the carriers. However, it is important that in the case of the available systems of resonators with external mirrors and of control components these perturbations can be removed by frequency stabilization using an atomic line with a high-Q resonator. It is now possible to stabilize the emission frequency of two lasers with external resonators using neighboring modes of a confocal interferometer with a mode spacing 240 MHz.

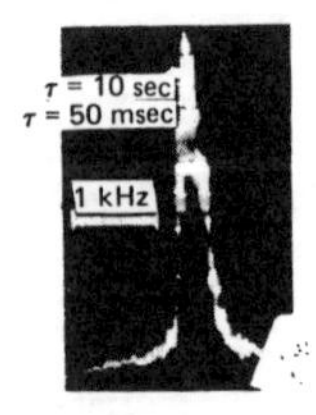

FIG. 2. Spectrum of the beat signal in the case of mutual locking of the frequencies of two lasers with external resonators (outward power ~3 mW). This was obtained using a feedback channel including a piezoelectric ceramic plate with maximal control of the current. The beat signal frequency was 6 MHz, the duration of a scan was 10 sec, the integration time constant was 50 msec.

CONCLUSIONS

The proposed method makes it possible to suppress technical fluctuations in the beat spectrum of an injection laser and to achieve a very narrow spectrum of beats with a width amounting to ~500 Hz. The tuning characteristics of lasers with external resonators were obtained for the first time in the self-stabilization regime. Stabilization of the beat frequency of a laser with an external resonator in combination with stabilization with the aid of atomic lines and high-Q interferometers opens up new opportunities for the use of lasers with external resonators in precision ultra high-resolution spectroscopy.

[1]V. L. Velichanskiĭ, A. S. Zibrov, V. S. Kargopol'tsev, V. I. Molochev, V. V. Nikitin, V. A. Sautenkov, G. G.

Kharisov, and D. A. Tyrukov, Pis'ma Zh. Tekh. Fiz. 4, 1087 (1978) [Sov. Tech. Phys. Lett. 4, 438 (1978)].

[2]V. Yu. Bazhenov, A. P. Bogatov, Yu. V. Gurov, P. G. Eliseev, O. G. Okhotnikov, G. T. Pak, M. P. Rakhval'skiĭ, M. S. Soskin, V. B. Taranenko, and K. A. Khaĭretdinov, Kvantovaya Elektron. (Moscow) 7, 2642 (1980) [Sov. J. Quantum. Electron. 10, 1546 (1980)]; S. Saito and Y. Yamamoto, Electron. Lett. 17, 325 (1981); A. Mooradian, D. Welford, and M. W. Fleming, Proc. Fifth Intern. Conf. on Laser Spectroscopy, Jasper Lodge, Alberta, Canada, 1981, publ. by Springer Verlag, Berlin (1981), p. 67.

[3]A. S. Zibrov, A. M. Akul'shin, V. L Velichanskiĭ, V. I. Malakhova, V. V. Nikitin, V. A. Sautenkov, D. A. Tyurikov, and E. K. Yurkin, Kvantovaya Elektron. (Moscow) 9, 804 (1982) [Sov. J. Quantum Electron. 12, 502 (1982)].

[4]V. Yu. Bazhenov, A. P. Bogatov, P. G. Eliseev, O. G. Okhotnikov, G. T. Pak, M. P. Rakhvalskii (Rakhvalsky), M. S. Soskin, V. G. Taranenko, and K. A. Khaĭretdinov, IEE Proc. I 129, 77 (1982).

[5]V. L. Velichanskiĭ, A. S. Zibrov, V. I. Molochev, V. V. Nikitin, V. A. Sautenkov, D. A. Tyurikov, and G. G. Kharisov, Kvantovaya Elektron. (Moscow) 8, 1925 (1981) [Sov. J. Quantum Electron. 11, 1165 (1981)].

[6]É. M. Belenov, V. L. Velichanskiĭ, A. S. Zibrov, V. V. Nikitin, V. A. Sautenkov, and A. V. Uskov, Kvantovaya Elektron. (Moscow) 10, 1232 (1983) [Sov. J. Quantum Electron. 13, 792 (1983)].

[7]D. Welford and A. Mooradian, Appl. Phys. Lett. 40, 560 (1982).

Translated by A. Tybulewicz

DEPENDENCE OF SEMICONDUCTOR LASER LINEWIDTH ON MEASUREMENT TIME: EVIDENCE OF PREDOMINANCE OF 1/f NOISE

K. KIKUCHI
T. OKOSHI

Department of Electronic Engineering
University of Tokyo
Bunkyo-ku, Tokyo 113, Japan

3rd September 1985

Indexing terms: Lasers and laser applications, Semiconductor lasers

Linewidths of 1·3 μm InGaAsP lasers were measured by using delayed self-heterodyne set-ups with two different delay-line lengths, i.e. with two equivalent measurement times. It has been found that in high-power operation the linewidth increases as the measurement time becomes longer, and that this dependence is explained well by a calculation assuming that the 1/f noise in the FM noise spectrum is the predominant cause of the spectral broadening. The significance of this fact in coherent optical communications is discussed.

Introduction: The Schawlow–Townes formula predicts that the linewidth Δf of lasers is proportional to the inverse of the output power P.[1] However, Welford and Mooradian showed experimentally that an additional spectral broadening existed in AlGaAs lasers;[2] it appeared as the power-independent component of the linewidth in the Δf against P^{-1} diagram, bringing forth a residual linewidth in the limit $P^{-1} \rightarrow 0$. This observation suggests that an unknown source exists for the spectral broadening in addition to spontaneous emission events. Specialists' interest in this power-independent spectral broadening has grown rapidly, because it determines the lower limit of the linewidth of semiconductor lasers.

The authors have previously observed in the spectrum of the instantaneous frequency fluctuation (abbreviated as FM noise spectrum) of AlGaAs lasers a power-independent noise component, whose spectral density was approximately inversely proportional to the frequency, and pointed out that this power-independent 1/f noise could induce the residual linewidth.[3] Shortly afterwards O'Mahony and Henning showed theoretically that the strong dependence of the linewidth on the measurement time (in their case, the time required for a single scan of a Fabry–Perot interferometer) could be caused by the 1/f noise.[4]

In this letter we show first experimental data on the dependence of the lineshape of 1·3 μm InGaAsP DFB lasers on the measurement time. The lineshape is measured by using delayed self-heterodyne set-ups[5] with fibre delay lines having different lengths (1·5 km and 27 km). The result shows that the linewidth with the longer delay line is larger than that measured with the shorter delay line. Furthermore, an analysis of the data suggests that the 1/f noise in the FM noise spectrum is the principal cause of the power-independent line broadening. The possibility of linewidth reduction using a narrowband automatic frequency control scheme is also discussed.

Lineshape determined by delayed self-heterodyne method: We assume first that the FM noise spectrum $S(f)$ consists of the power-dependent white noise and power-independent 1/f noise:

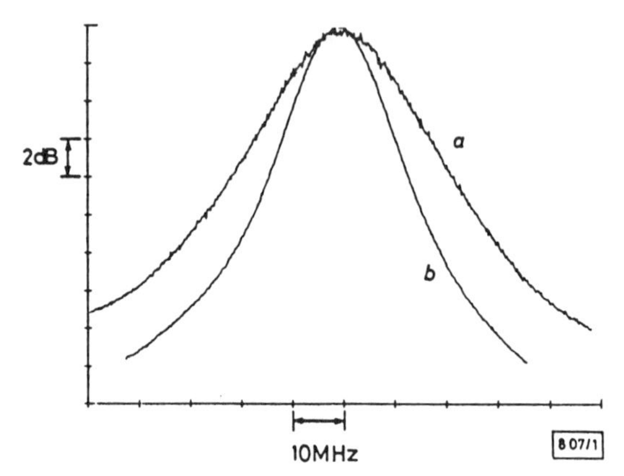

Fig. 1 *IF spectra measured by delayed self-heterodyne method*
a Length of delay line = 27 km
b Length of delay line = 1·5 km

$$S(f) = C + K/f \tag{1}$$

where K and C are frequency-independent, whereas C is inversely proportional to the output power.

The lineshape determined by a scanning Fabry–Perot interferometer with a finite measurement time τ_m is not affected by the FM noise component having frequencies below $1/\tau_m$, because the finite measurement time is equivalent to a high-pass filter which eliminates frequency fluctuations below $1/\tau_m$. Consequently, as shown theoretically by O'Mahony and Henning,[4] the measured lineshape depends strongly on the measurement time only when 1/f noise exists in the FM noise.

Next, we consider the delayed self-heterodyne method, whose principle is described in Reference 5. The delay time τ_d in the delayed self-heterodyne method corresponds to the measurement time τ_m of a scanning Fabry–Perot interferometer. The reason is given in the following. We consider a frequency fluctuation component whose frequency is much lower than $1/\tau_d$. For such a component the phase difference between the signal beam and the reference beam after travelling through the delay line is small; hence the frequency component of the FM noise below $1/\tau_d$ is eliminated automatically in the delayed self-heterodyne method. Therefore, similarly to the case of a scanning Fabry–Perot interferometer, the measured IF linewidth will depend strongly on the delay-line length only when the 1/f noise exists. When it does not exist, the linewidth increase is practically negligible in most cases.

The lineshape $I(f)$ of the IF signal obtained by the delayed self-heterodyne method is related to the FM noise spectrum

Reprinted with permission from *Electron. Lett.*, vol. 21, no. 22, pp. 1011–1012, Oct. 24, 1985.

$S(f)$ as

$$I(f) = \mathscr{F}\left[\exp\left\{-8\int_0^\infty S(f')\frac{\sin^2 \pi f' t}{f'^2} \times (1 - \cos 2\pi f'\tau_d)\, df'\right\}\right] \quad (2)$$

where $\mathscr{F}$ denotes a Fourier transform. Derivation of this equation will be given elsewhere. In eqn. 2 the fact that lower-frequency components are cut off is expressed by the term $(1 - \cos 2\pi f'\tau_d)$.

Experimental results: The laser under test was a 1·3 μm InGaAsP DFB laser. Lineshapes were measured by using the delayed self-heterodyne set-ups with 1·5 km and 27 km single-mode fibre delay lines. Fig. 1 shows lineshapes of the IF signal measured when the bias current level was six times the threshold. The FM noise spectrum of the laser was also measured, giving $K = 1{\cdot}44 \times 10^{12}$ Hz^2.

Discussion: In Fig. 1 the linewidth (FWHM) measured with the 27 km fibre is 21 MHz, and that with the 1·5 km fibre is 14 MHz; a remarkable change is observed in the linewidth.

We calculate here the linewidth of the IF signal using eqns. 1 and 2. We assume temporarily that the white noise component in the FM noise spectrum is negligible ($C = 0$ in eqn. 1) because the bias current level is fairly high. Under such an assumption, the linewidth calculated for the 27 km fibre is 21 MHz, and that for the 1·5 km fibre is 17 MHz. These results support the assumption that the $1/f$ noise is the predominant cause of the spectral broadening in such high-power operation of a DFB laser. (Note that the dependence of the linewidth on the delay-line length is even stronger in the experiment than in the theory.)

The above conclusion is particularly important in the application of such lasers to coherent communications, because it means that the lineshape could be improved effectively by an automatic frequency control (AFC) having a relatively narrow bandwidth. It has generally been believed for the AFC-oriented lineshape improvement techniques at microwave frequencies that an AFC circuit with a bandwidth f_m reduces the spectral density of noise sideband within $\pm f_m$ of the carrier. This statement is valid when the origin of the spectral spread is white noise, but not valid when it is $1/f$ noise. When the $1/f$ noise is predominant, an AFC in narrow bandwidth may reduce the linewidth drastically. In heterodyne optical communications, such a reduction can also be achieved in the receiver by an AFC scheme in the local oscillator. Experiments are now being performed and will be reported later.

Acknowledgments: We thank Dr. K. Kobayashi of Opto-Electronics Research Laboratories, NEC, for supplying DFB lasers. This work is supported by a Scientific Research grant-in-aid from the Japanese Ministry of Education, Science & Culture.

References

1 YARIV, A.: 'Quantum electronics' (J. Wiley & Sons, New York, 1975), eqn. 13.2-18
2 WELFORD, D., and MOORADIAN, A.: 'Output power and temperature dependence of the linewidth of single-frequency CW (GaAl)As diode lasers', *Appl. Phys. Lett.*, 1982, **40**, pp. 865–867
3 KIKUCHI, K., and OKOSHI, T.: 'Measurement of spectra of and correlation between FM and AM noises in GaAlAs lasers', *Electron. Lett.*, 1983, **19**, pp. 812–813
4 O'MAHONY, M. J., and HENNING, I. D.: 'Semiconductor laser linewidth broadening due to $1/f$ carrier noise', *ibid.*, 1983, **19**, pp. 1000–1001
5 OKOSHI, T., KIKUCHI, K., and NAKAYAMA, A.: 'Novel method for high resolution measurement of laser output spectrum', *ibid.*, 1980, **16**, pp. 630–631

Linewidth enhancement factor in InGaAsP/InP multiple quantum well lasers

C. A. Green, N. K. Dutta, and W. Watson
AT&T Bell Laboratories, Murray Hill, New Jersey 07974

(Received 4 February 1987; accepted for publication 23 March 1987)

The linewidth enhancement factor α in an InGaAsP/InP multiple quantum well (MQW) laser has been determined from the spontaneous emission spectra below threshold. It is demonstrated that the measured value of α in the MQW laser is appreciably smaller than that in a conventional double heterostructure laser as expected from theoretical calculations.

The linewidth enhancement factor α is a key parameter in semiconductor lasers both under cw operation[1-3] and under high-frequency modulation.[4,5] It characterizes the linewidth broadening due to fluctuations in the carrier density altering the refractive index.[2,3,6,7] The factor α is the ratio of the change of the refractive index with carrier density N to the change in optical gain g with carrier density. This is expressed as[3]

$$\alpha = -\frac{4\pi}{\lambda}\frac{dn/dN}{dg/dN}, \qquad (1)$$

where λ is the wavelength of the laser light.

Arakawa *et al.*[8] and Burt[9] have calculated the value of α in quantum well lasers. It was predicted that α at lasing frequency is considerably reduced as compared to that in conventional double heterostructure (DH) lasers since the differential gain dg/dN is enhanced in multiple quantum well (MQW) lasers owing to its large density of states at the band edge.

In this paper, we report on the observation of the dispersion of α in a MQW laser and on a DH laser. The results obtained demonstrate that a reduction in α is realized in MQW lasers as predicted by the calculations.[8,9]

Experiments were performed on an InGaAsP/InP MQW laser and on an InGaAsP/InP DH laser. The MQW laser fabricated by the liquid phase epitaxy (LPE) growth technique consisted of an active region containing four 150-Å-thick InGaAsP wells and three 150-Å-thick InP barriers. The threshold current was at 55 mA and the lasing wavelength was at 1.33 μm. The DH laser, also fabricated by LPE growth technique, had a threshold current of 63 mA and the lasing wavelength was at 1.31 μm. Both types of lasers had a nominal cavity length of 250 μm and were strongly index-guided buried heterostructure type devices. The lasers were mounted on heat sinks whose temperature was controlled to within ± 0.05 °C. The spectral characteristics of the light output from the laser were analyzed using a 1-m grating monochromator. A polarizer was inserted between the laser and the monochromator to ensure that only TE polarizer radiation was measured.

The change in the mode refractive index dn_m was determined from the wavelength shift $d\lambda$ of a Fabry–Perot mode with two different injection currents below threshold according to the relation[10]

$$dn_m = \lambda/(2L\Delta\lambda)d\lambda, \qquad (2)$$

where $\Delta\lambda$ is the Fabry–Perot mode spacing, L is the capacity length, λ the nominal wavelength, and $d\lambda$ the wavelength shift between the two different currents.

The mode gain G_m was obtained from the depth of the modulation in the spontaneous emission intensity using its relation[11]

$$G_m = L^{-1}\{\ln[(r^{1/2}-1)/(r^{1/2}+1)] - \ln R\}, \qquad (3)$$

where $r = P_{max}/P_{min}$, P_{max} and P_{min} being the intensities at the adjacent peak and valley in the emission spectra, respectively, and R is the power reflectivity at the laser facets. The change in the optical gain between current No. 1 and current No. 2 is $dg = G_{m1} - G_{m2}$.

Substituting Eqs. (2) and (3) into (1) and canceling the carrier density term we have

$$\alpha = \frac{4\pi}{2\Delta\lambda}\frac{d\lambda}{dg}. \qquad (4)$$

Figure 1 represents a plot of α as a function of photon

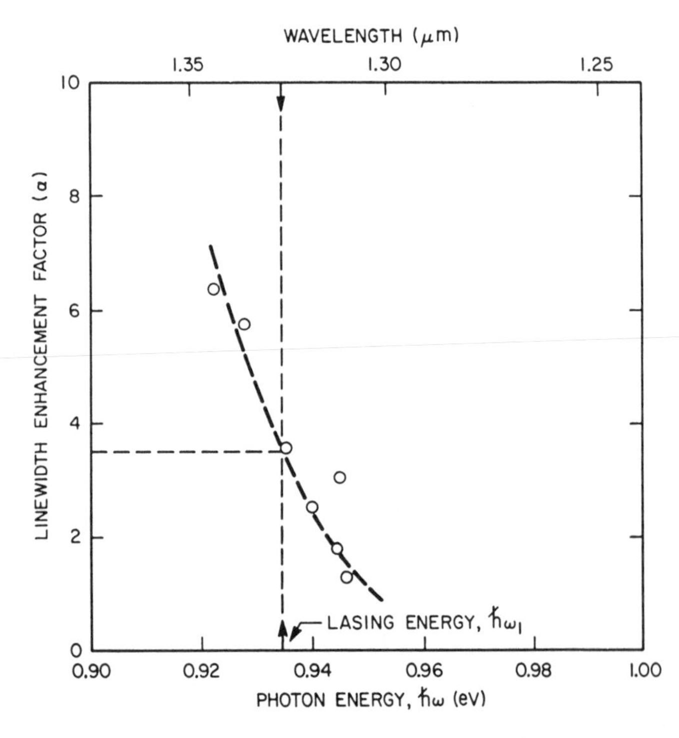

FIG. 1. Plot of α as a function of photon energy $\hbar\omega$ for the MQW laser. The lasing photon energy $\hbar\omega_l$, denoted by the arrow, is 0.9345 eV.

Reprinted with permission from *Appl. Phys. Lett.*, vol. 50, no. 20, pp. 1409–1410, May 18, 1987.

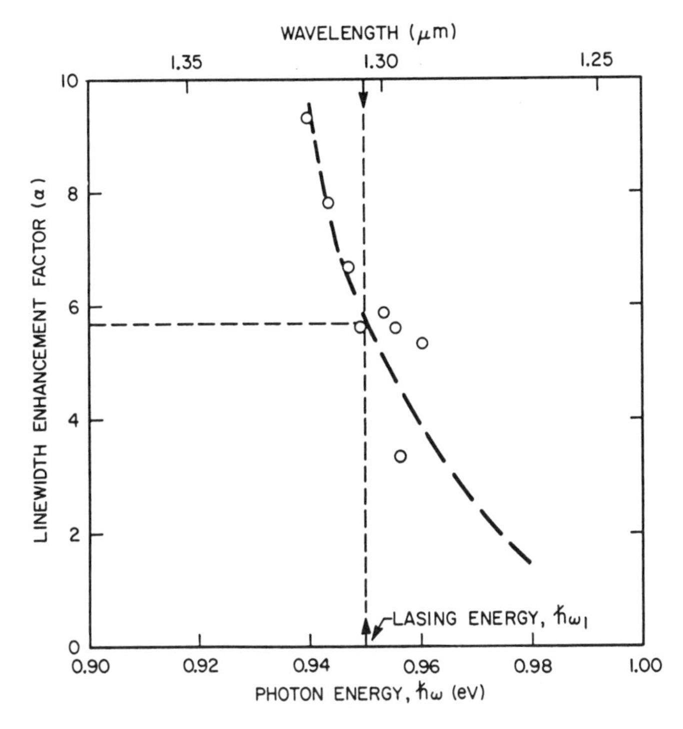

FIG. 2. Plot of α as a function of photon energy $\hbar\omega$ for the DH laser. The lasing photon energy $\hbar\omega_l$, denoted by the arrow, is 0.9500 eV.

energy $\hbar\omega$ for the MQW laser and Fig. 2 is the same plot but for the DH laser. The lasing photon energy $\hbar\omega_l$, denoted by the arrow, is 0.9345 eV for Fig. 1 and 0.9500 eV in Fig. 2. One can see that α is reduced for the MQW laser compared with the DH laser. At the lasing wavelength $\hbar\omega_l$, α for the MQW laser is ~ 3.5 and is about 60% of the value ~ 5.7 for the DH laser.

In conclusion, α in a MQW laser has been experimentally determined. A decrease in α as compared to conventional DH lasers has been found. The results show that MQW lasers may have smaller linewidth under modulation compared to regular DH lasers as observed previously.[12] This is a feature advantageous in the application of MQW lasers as light sources in optical communication systems.

[1] D. Welford and A. Mooradian, Appl. Phys. Lett. **40**, 865 (1982).
[2] C. H. Henry, IEEE J. Quantum Electron. **QE-18**, 259 (1982).
[3] K. Vahala and A. Yariv, IEEE J. Quantum Electron. **QE-19**, 1069 (1983).
[4] C. H. Harder, K. Vahala, and A. Yariv, Appl. Phys. Lett. **42**, 328 (1983).
[5] T. L. Koch and J. E. Bowers, Electron. Lett. **20**, 1038 (1984).
[6] R. Schimpe and W. Harth, Electron. Lett. **19**, 136 (1983).
[7] M. J. Adams, Electron. Lett. **19**, 136 (1983).
[8] Y. Arakawa, K. Vahala, and A. Yariv, Appl. Phys. Lett. **45**, 950 (1984).
[9] M. G. Burt, Electron. Lett. **20**, 27 (1985).
[10] N. Ogasawara, R. Ito, K. Tone, and H. Nakae, Jpn. J. Appl. Phys. **23**, L518 (1984).
[11] B. W. Hakki and T. L. Paoli, J. Appl. Phys. **46**, 1299 (1975).
[12] N. K. Dutta, S. G. Napholtz, R. Yen, T. Wood, T. M. Shen, and N. A. Olsson, Appl. Phys. Lett. **46**, 1036 (1985).

LINEWIDTH ENHANCEMENT IN QUANTUM-WELL LASERS

L. D. WESTBROOK
M. J. ADAMS
British Telecom Research Laboratories
Martlesham Heath
Ipswich IP5 7RE, United Kingdom

11th September 1987

Indexing terms: Lasers and laser applications, Semiconductor lasers, Quantum optics

We have developed explicit approximations for the linewidth enhancement factor in quantum-well lasers. These simple expressions represent a quick and easy means of calculating the linewidth enhancement factor under a variety of operating conditions, and help us to understand the physics influencing this important parameter.

Introduction: The α-parameter, usually known as the linewidth enhancement factor, profoundly influences the emission linewidth of semiconductor injection lasers.[1] The reduction of $|\alpha|$ is one of the avenues currently being explored in the development of narrow line sources for coherent optical communications and fibre sensor applications. To this end, Burt[2] and Arakawa *et al.*[3] have shown that the linewidth enhancement factor is smaller in quantum-well lasers than in bulk devices, while other workers have demonstrated a reduction in $|\alpha|$ in bulk lasers by detuning the emission wavelength.[4–6] These results suggest that the combination of quantum wells and detuning may be the best route to achieve minimum linewidth in a discrete device.

Clearly, optimisation of α will involve repeated calculation of this parameter under different operating conditions (well width, injection level etc.), but calculations to date have relied on numerical methods. Recently, we reported explicit approximations for the linewidth enhancement factor in bulk lasers,[7] and in this letter we present the first explicit algebraic forms for α in quantum-well lasers. These formulas not only represent an uncomplicated means of estimating α; they also provide us with insight into the physics influencing α, which was hitherto obscured by computation.

Analysis: In the analysis which follows, we concentrate on the contribution to the linewidth enhancement factor due to band-to-band transitions only, ignoring the contribution due to free carriers on the grounds that it is small in quantum-well lasers as a result of the larger gain constant compared with bulk lasers. The real and imaginary parts of the complex susceptibility $\chi = \chi_r + j\chi_i$ are both functions of the injected carrier density N, and the linewidth enhancement factor may be defined as $\alpha \equiv (d\chi_r/dN)/(d\chi_i/dN)$. For the case of strict conservation of crystal momentum, $d\chi_i/dN$ is given by

$$\frac{d\chi_i}{dN} = \frac{n_0 \hbar c B_{12}}{E v_g} \frac{m_r}{\pi \hbar^2 L_z} \frac{d[f_c(E) - f_v(E)]}{dN} \qquad E > E_{g1} \quad (1)$$

where E_{g1} is the effective bandgap, n_0 is the (real) refractive index in the absence of carrier injection, E is the photon energy, B_{12} is the Einstein coefficient, v_g is the group velocity, m_r is the reduced mass and L_z is the well width. In eqn. 1 it has been assumed that all optical transitions take place between the first sub-bands in both the conduction and valence bands. This assumption is valid for narrow wells and/or low injected carrier densities, where the number of electrons and holes in higher sub-bands is small.

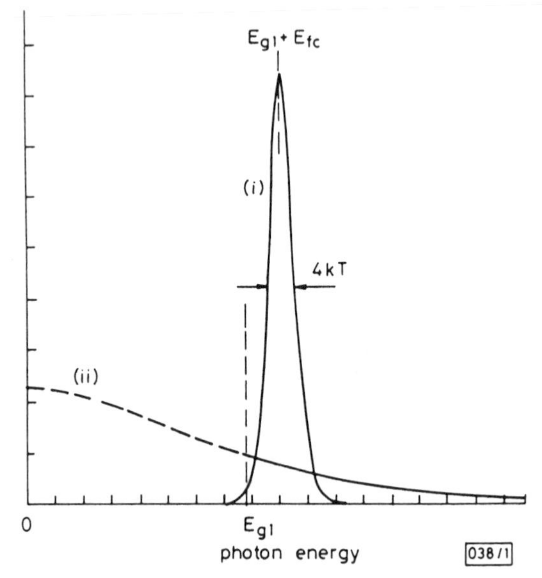

Fig. 1 *Dependence of Fermi derivatives on photon energy, showing (i) df_c/dN and (ii) df_v/dN*

Note that derivatives do not contribute to $d\chi_i/dN$ below E_{g1}

In Fig. 1 we plot the Fermi–Dirac occupation functions df_c/dN and df_v/dN for a typical quantum-well laser. In Reference 7 we showed that these derivatives are, to a good approximation, Lorentzian. We also noted[7] that, in the material systems of current interest, the overall contribution to $d\chi_i/dN$ due to df_c/dN is much greater than that due to df_v/dN as a result of the greatly different effective masses for electrons and holes ($m_c \ll m_v$). Under these assumptions, $d\chi_i/dN$ may be described as a single Lorentzian of peak energy $\simeq E_{g1} + E_{fc}$ (E_{fc} is the electron quasi-Fermi level measured from the effective band edge) and FWHM $\simeq 4kT$, the Lorentzian being truncated for $E < E_{g1}$ due to the step-like density of states.

Calculation of α necessitates the evaluation of the real part of the derivative of the susceptibility $d\chi_r/dN$ through the Kramers–Kronig transform:

$$\frac{d\chi_r}{dN} = \frac{2}{\pi} \Pr \int_0^\infty \frac{E}{E^2 - E'^2} \frac{d\chi_i}{dN} \, dE \qquad (2)$$

where Pr denotes the Cauchy principle part. We have been able to evaluate this integral analytically by ignoring the slowly varying energy dependence of the prefactor to the Lor-

Reprinted with permission from *Electron. Lett.*, vol. 23, no. 23, pp. 1223–1225, Nov. 5, 1987.

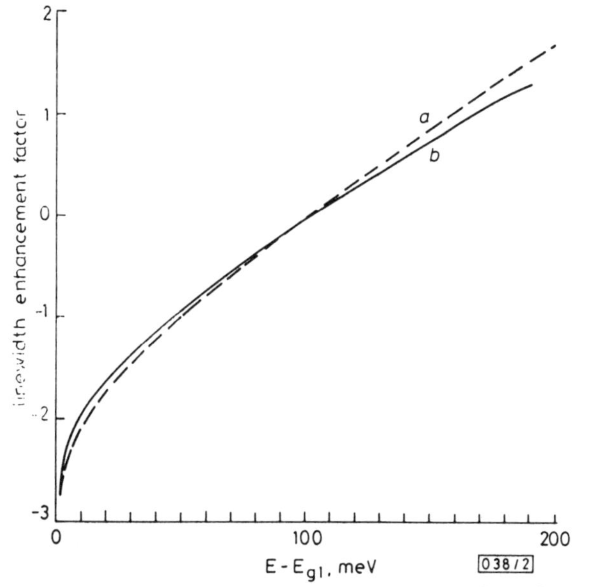

Fig. 2 *Spectral dependence of linewidth enhancement factor for a 100 Å GaInAs quantum well, showing (a) eqn. 3 and (b) a numerical Kramers–Kronig transformation of eqn. 1*

entzian and by using the approximation $E/(E^2 - E'^2) \simeq 1/2(E - E')$ in eqn. 2, obtaining

$$\alpha \simeq \left(\frac{E - E_{g1} - E_{fc}}{2kT}\right)\left[\frac{1}{2} + \frac{1}{\pi}\tan^{-1}\left(\frac{E_{fc}}{2kT}\right)\right] + \frac{1}{2\pi}\log\left[\frac{(E - E_{g1})^2}{E_{fc}^2 + (2kT)^2}\right] \quad (3)$$

It can be shown that a similar expression for α may be obtained for quantum wells for the case of partial conservation of crystal momentum rules.*

In this case α is given by

$$\alpha \simeq \frac{\left(\frac{E - E_{g1} - E_{fc}}{2kT}\right)\left[\frac{1}{2} + \frac{1}{\pi}\tan^{-1}\left(\frac{E_{fc}}{2kT}\right)\right] + \frac{1}{2\pi}\log\left[\frac{(E - E_{g1})^2 + (\hbar/\tau)^2}{E_{fc}^2 + (2kT)^2}\right]}{\frac{1}{2} + \frac{1}{\pi}\tan^{-1}\left(\frac{E - E_{g1}}{\hbar/\tau}\right)} \quad (4)$$

where τ is the intraband relaxation time.

At this point we note that a useful insight into the α-parameter can be obtained from the well known Lorentz oscillator model. We postulate an analogous Lorentz oscillator in which the derivative $d\chi_i/dN$ has the same Lorentzian parameters as given above, with the exception that it is not truncated at E_{g1}. The usefulness of the Lorentz model is that we know both real and imaginary parts of χ. The α-parameter for the Lorentz oscillator is given as the ratio of the real and imaginary parts of the Lorentzian, giving $\alpha \simeq (E - E_{g1} - E_{fc})/2kT$. Note that when the photon energy is close to $E_{g1} + E_{fc}$, eqns. 2 and 3 both reduce to

$$\alpha(E \simeq E_0) \simeq \left(\frac{E - E_{g1} - E_{fc}}{2kT}\right) + \frac{1}{2\pi}\log\left[\frac{E_{fc}^2}{E_{fc}^2 + (2kT)^2}\right] \quad (5)$$

The first term on the right-hand side of eqn. 5 is just that obtained from the Lorentz oscillator model. The second (smaller) term therefore accounts for the truncation of $d\chi_i/dN$ at E_{g1}. This deceptively simple expression shows us that the primary influences on α are the photon energy, the electron quasi-Fermi level E_{fc} and the absolute temperature, only. In addition, it is now clear from inspection of eqn. 5 just why quantum wells are so useful in reducing α. As the active layer well width decreases, E_{fc} (and hence the peak energy of the Lorentzian) also decreases, since $E_{fc} \simeq (\pi hNL_z/m_c)$. Thus, for a given energy difference $E - E_{g1}$ (with $E < E_{g1} + E_{fc}$) the linewidth enhancement factor decreases with decreasing well width.

The accuracy of eqn. 3 may be judged from Fig. 2, in which we plot the dispersion of α for an undoped GaInAs quantum-well laser. Here, the well width is 100 Å ($\lambda_{bandgap} \simeq 1{\cdot}5\,\mu m$) and $E_{fc} = 92$ meV. Eqn. 3 is plotted together with the result of an exact numerical Kramers–Kronig transformation of $d\chi_i/dN$, given by eqns. 1 and 2. This Figure shows that our approximation for α is sufficiently accurate to be useful for even the most critical applications.

In conclusion, we have presented simple explicit approximations for the linewidth enhancement factor in quantum-well lasers. These expressions provide the device engineer with a quick and easy means of calculating the linewidth enhancement factor under a variety of operating conditions, while at the same time contributing to our understanding of the physical influences on α.

Acknowledgment: We thank M. G. Burt for discussions, and acknowledge the Director of Research, British Telecom for permission to publish this letter.

* WESTBROOK, L. D., and ADAMS, M. J.: to be published

References

1 HENRY, C. H.: 'Theory of the linewidth of semiconductor lasers', *IEEE J. Quantum Electron.*, 1982, **QE-18**, pp. 259–264
2 BURT, M. G.: 'Linewidth enhancement factor for quantum-well lasers', *Electron. Lett.*, 1984, **20**, pp. 27–29
3 ARAKAWA, Y., VAHALA, K., and YARIV, A.: 'Quantum noise and dynamics in quantum well and quantum wire lasers', *Appl. Phys. Lett.*, 1984, **45**, pp. 950–952
4 WESTBROOK, L. D.: 'Dispersion of linewidth-broadening factor in 1·5 μm laser diodes', *Electron. Lett.*, 1985, **21**, pp. 1018–1019
5 KOJIMA, K., NODA, S., TAI, S., KYUMA, K., and NAKAYAMA, T.: 'Measurement of spectral linewidth of AlGaAs/GaAs distributed feedback lasers', *ibid.*, 1986, **22**, pp. 425–427
6 OGITA, S., YANO, M., ISHIKAWA, H., and IMAI, H.: 'Linewidth reduction in DFB laser by detuning effect', *ibid.*, 1987, **23**, pp. 393–394
7 WESTBROOK, L. D., and ADAMS, M. J.: 'Simple expressions for the linewidth enhancement factor in direct-gap semiconductors', *IEE Proc. J, Optoelectron.*, 1987, **134**, pp. 209–214

Carrier-induced refractive-index change in quantum-well lasers

Weng W. Chow

Hughes Aircraft Company, 1600 Randolph Court, S.E., Albuquerque, New Mexico 87106

Dave Depatie

U.S. Air Force, Kirtland Air Force Base, New Mexico 87117-6008

Received July 28, 1987; accepted January 22, 1988

We investigated the loaded gain and the carrier-induced refractive-index change in quantum-well lasers. A quantum-well laser is found typically to have a higher gain and a smaller refractive-index change than a conventional diode laser. We also found that the gain and the refractive-index change for these two types of semiconductor lasers saturate similarly, with the refractive index being a much weaker function of laser intensity.

Quantum-well semiconductor lasers have received considerable attention because of their superior operating characteristics and potential scalability to high-power efficient devices. Whether the latter is achievable without the loss of beam quality depends on the carrier-induced refractive-index change, δn, which leads to gain antiguiding.[1] Recently there have been several papers describing the application of semiclassical laser theory to quantum-well lasers.[2] Since these treatments do not explicitly include the effects of cross-relaxation (spectral-hole filling) collisions, their results can be correctly interpreted as giving the gain and δn only in terms of the optical flux saturated carrier density. However, comparison of theory with experiment requires that the gain and δn be known as functions of the local unsaturated carrier density (or injection current) and laser field. The calculation described in this Letter accomplishes this by modifying semiclassical laser theory to take into account that in diode lasers $\gamma_R \gg S$, where γ_R and S are the cross-relaxation and stimulated-emission rates, respectively. The usual semiclassical laser theory for inhomogeneously broadened lasers assumes that $\gamma_R \ll S$, which is true for a gas laser.[3] We derive the nonlinear equations describing the evolution of the intracavity laser field. These equations are solved for the saturated gain and δn, as functions of the laser field and the unsaturated carrier density, for typical diode-laser configurations.

In a quantum-well medium, the conduction band is divided into a series of subbands. Similarly, the valence band consists of a series of heavy-hole and light-hole subbands. Radiative transitions occur between distributions of electronic states in the conduction and valence heavy- or light-hole subbands. These transitions are broadened by intraband electron–electron and electron–phonon collisions. Within the conduction and valence bands, the electron–electron and electron–phonon collisions also tend to maintain a Fermi–Dirac distribution in the carrier population.

The summation over states in quantum-well structures may be approximated by[2]

$$\frac{1}{V}\sum_{\text{states}} \rightarrow \sum_n \sum_j \int_{\omega_{0nj}}^{\infty} \mathrm{d}\omega_{nj} \frac{m_{rj}}{w\pi\hbar}, \tag{1}$$

where n labels the subband, j indicates whether the radiative transition terminates in a heavy- or a light-hole band, m_{rj} is the reduced effective mass, w is the well width, ω_{nj} is the frequency difference between the two states involved with the transition, $\hbar\omega_{0nj} = E_g + E_{cn} + E_{vnj}$, E_g is the band-gap energy, E_{cn} is the nth conduction subband-edge energy measured from the edge of the conduction band, and E_{vnj} is the nth heavy- or light-hole subband-edge energy measured from the edge of the valance band. By using relation (1), the results of Ref. 4 may be readily modified to give the following local saturated intensity gain and derivative of the carrier-induced phase shift in a quantum-well active layer:

$$G = \sum_j \sum_n \int_{\omega_{0nj}}^{\infty} \mathrm{d}\omega_{nj} F_{nj} L\left(\frac{\omega_{nj}-\nu}{\gamma}\right) \times [f(\omega_{nj}) + g(\omega_{nj}) - 1] \tag{2}$$

and

$$\frac{\mathrm{d}\phi}{\mathrm{d}z} = -\frac{1}{2}\sum_j \sum_n \int_{\omega_{0nj}}^{\infty} \mathrm{d}\omega_{nj} F_{nj} L\left(\frac{\omega_{nj}-\nu}{\gamma}\right) \times [f(\omega_{nj}) + g(\omega_{nj})]\left(\frac{\omega_{nj}-\nu}{\gamma}\right), \tag{3}$$

where $F_{nj} = \nu m_{rj} d_{nj}^2/(\epsilon_0 \bar{n} c \hbar^2 \gamma w \pi)$, d_{nj} is the dipole transition matrix element,[5] $\bar{n}$ is the average refractive index of the gain medium, γ is the transition linewidth, $L(x) = 1/(1 + x^2)$, ν is the laser frequency, and f and g are the Fermi–Dirac distributions for the saturated conduction-electron and valence-hole populations, respectively. The first summation is over the light- and heavy-hole states, and the second summation is over the subbands. The Fermi–Dirac distributions for the saturated carriers may be determined

Reprinted with permission from *Opt. Lett.*, vol. 13, no. 4, pp. 303–305, Apr. 1988.

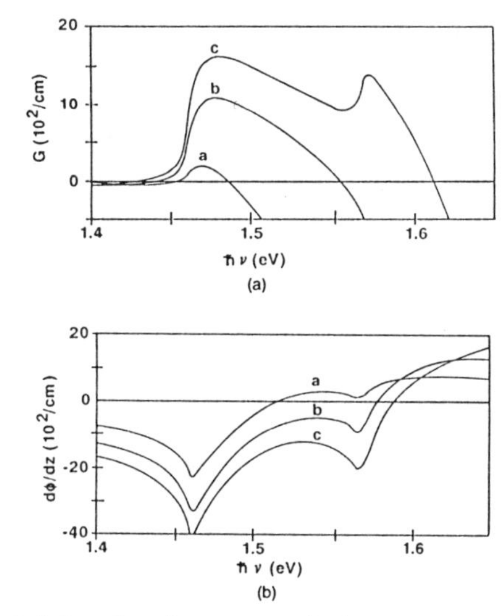

Fig. 1. (a) Local gain versus photon energy. (b) Local derivative of the carrier-induced phase shift versus photon energy. The injected carrier densities for curves a, b, and c are $2 \times 10^{18}/cm^3$, $4 \times 10^{18}/cm^3$, and $6 \times 10^{18}/cm^3$, respectively. We assumed $\gamma_R = \gamma = 5 \times 10^{13}$/sec and a dipole matrix element of 14.42 D for the bulk GaAs gain medium.[7]

from the saturated minority carrier density, N, which obeys the equation

$$\gamma_{nr}(N_0 - N) + W_{sp}(N_0) - W_{sp}(N) = GI/\hbar\nu, \quad (4)$$

where I is the local laser intensity, γ_{nr} is the nonradiative decay rate, W_{sp} accounts for the recombination of carriers by spontaneous emission,[6] and N_0 is the unsaturated minority carrier density, which may be determined from the injection current. Equation (4) is derived from the density operator equation.[4] For given N_0 and I, the local saturated gain may be computed by solving Eqs. (2) and (4) simultaneously. The saturated carrier distributions, which are also obtained in the solution of Eqs. (2) and (4), are used in Eq. (3) to compute $d\phi/dz$. The carrier-induced refractive index is then found by $k_0\delta n = d\phi/dz$, where k_0 is the laser wave vector in vacuum.

Figure 1(a) depicts the local gain in a quantum-well layer, Eq. (2), versus laser frequency for different carrier densities. The curves are computed for a laser consisting of undoped GaAs in the 10-nm-wide active regions and $Ga_{0.8}Al_{0.2}As$ in the barriers. For a carrier density of $2 \times 10^{18}/cm^3$, the population inversion is appreciable only between the $n = 1$ conduction and heavy-hole subbands. At the laser frequency where the gain is maximum, the dominant transition involves the recombination of an electron from an $n = 1$ conduction subband and a heavy hole from an $n = 1$ valence subband ($1 - 1h$). For a carrier density of $4 \times 10^{18}/cm^3$, the hole population in the $n = 1$ light-hole subband is also appreciable, causing the peak gain to shift to a higher frequency, where the transitions contributing to the gain are 1–$1h$ and 1–$1l$ ($1l$ represents a laser lower level that is in the $n = 1$ light-hole subband). Here, the onset of the 1–$1l$ transitions does not lead to two distinct peaks in the gain curve because $E_{1l} - E_{1h} \approx \hbar\gamma$. Finally, for a density of $6 \times 10^{18}/cm^3$, an inversion is established between the $n = 2$ conduction and heavy-hole subbands. The secondary peak in the gain curve is due to the transitions 1–$1h$, 1–$1l$, and 2–$2h$. At higher densities, the gain maximum shifts to the higher-frequency peak. For the well width used in this example, there are only two conduction subbands, so that further increases in the carrier density do not lead to the appearance of more gain peaks. Figure 1(b) depicts the corresponding $d\phi/dz$ curves predicted by Eq. (3). The values of $d\phi/dz$ for most frequencies

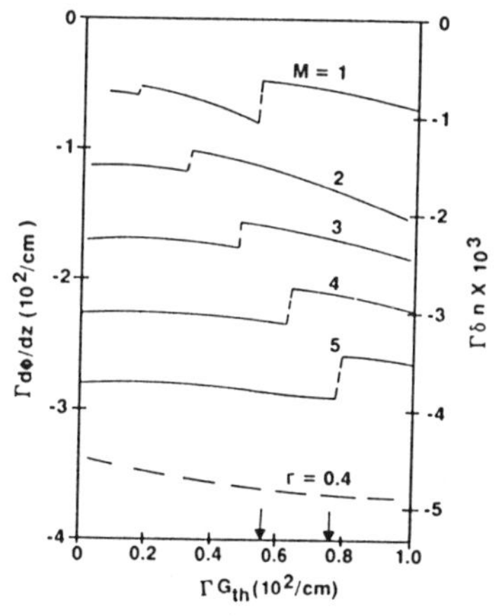

Fig. 2. $\Gamma d\phi/dz$ versus ΓG_{th} in multiple-quantum-well lasers. $\Gamma\delta n$ is plotted on the right-hand margin. M is the number of quantum wells in the laser, and the thickness of each quantum well is 10 nm. The arrows at $\Gamma G_{th} = 55.6$/cm and at $\Gamma G_{th} = 76.4$/cm indicate the threshold gain for lasers with facet reflectivities of $R_1 = R_2 = 0.32$, and $R_1 = 0.20$, $R_2 = 0.95$, respectively. The dashed curve is for a conventional diode laser with an undoped-GaAs active region and a fill factor of 0.4. All other parameters are similar to those in Fig. 1.

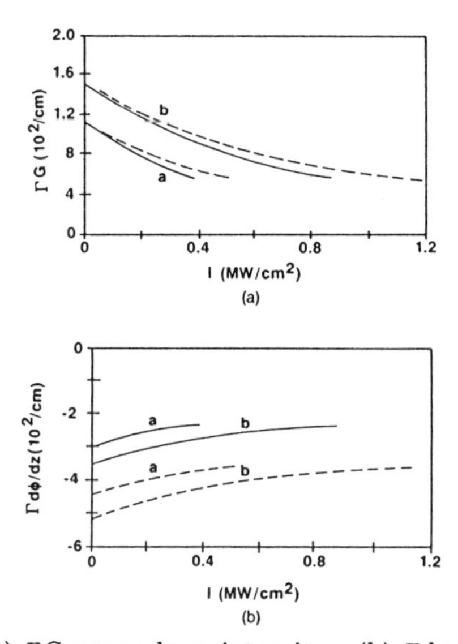

Fig. 3. (a) ΓG versus laser intensity. (b) $\Gamma d\phi/dz$ versus laser intensity. Curves a and b are for unsaturated carrier densities of $1.5 \times N_{th}$ and $2.0 \times N_{th}$, respectively, where $N_{th} = 2.4 \times 10^{18}/cm^3$. The dashed curves are for the conventional diode laser used in Fig. 2. All other parameters are similar to those in Fig. 1.

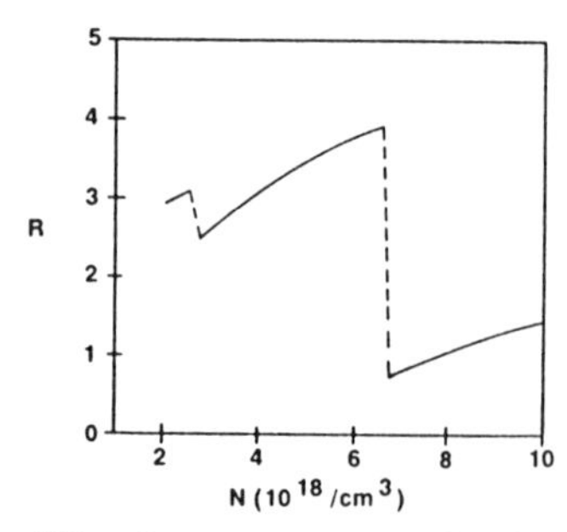

Fig. 4. Antiguiding factor versus carrier density for a multiple-quantum-well laser. The laser has four quantum-well layers, each 10 nm thick. All other parameters are the same as those in Fig. 1.

are appreciable because of the asymmetrical carrier distributions.

An indication of the importance of the carrier-induced phase shift for a quantum-well laser may be obtained by examining $\Gamma d\phi/dz$ as a function of the laser threshold gain, ΓG_{th}, where Γ is the fill factor (Fig. 2). In this figure, we assume that the combined width of the gain, barrier, and waveguide layers is 200 nm and that the cladding layers are p and n $Ga_{0.6}Al_{0.4}As$, so that $\Gamma = 0.3\ Mw/100$ nm, where M is the number of wells.[2] The discontinuities in the curves are due to the jumps in the peak gain frequency with carrier density. Note that $\Gamma|d\phi/dz|$ increases with the number of wells and decreases with the onset of transitions from higher-order subbands. Therefore, in terms of minimizing the effects of gain antiguiding, it may sometimes be advantageous to operate at a higher threshold. For comparison, we have plotted $\Gamma d\phi/dz$ for a conventional diode laser with $\Gamma = 0.4$ and an undoped-GaAs active region. Since the carrier-induced phase shift in quantum-well lasers can be smaller than that in conventional diode lasers, we expect better mode control in broader-area devices with quantum-well structures. The results for different well widths are essentially the same as above.

The dependence of gain on laser intensity may be obtained by solving Eqs. (2) and (4) simultaneously. In Fig. 3, curves a and b are computed for unsaturated injected carrier densities of 1.5× and 2× the threshold density. In this example, the gain region contains four quantum-well layers, the facet reflectivities equal 0.32, the internal optical loss is 10/cm, and the laser length is 250 μm. The computed threshold modal gain and carrier density are 55.6/cm and $2.46 \times 10^{18}/cm^3$, respectively. Based on a homogeneously broadened gain model, the saturation intensity is defined as the laser intensity when the laser is operated with a small-signal gain that is twice the threshold gain. Using curve b of Fig. 3, we get a saturation intensity for the quantum-well structure of 0.4 MW/cm^2, which is essentially the same as for conventional diode lasers. The dashed curves are computed for the conventional diode laser used previously. The carrier densities are adjusted so that these curves have the same small-signal gains as curves a and b. Note that the gains of quantum-well and conventional diode lasers saturate similarly.

Figure 3(b) depicts the corresponding curves of $\Gamma d\phi/dz$. The dashed curves are for the conventional diode laser. Note that although $\Gamma d\phi/dz$ for the quantum-well and the conventional diode lasers are different in magnitude, they saturate similarly. The similarity in the saturation characteristics of G and $d\phi/dz$ for these two types of laser is due to the rapid cross-relaxation rate, which causes both types of laser to saturate homogeneously, with the inversion depletion occurring throughout the entire carrier spectral distributions.[4] An important result of this Letter is that the decrease in $|d\phi/dz|$ with intensity is much smaller than that of G for both laser types.

Many semiconductor-laser models[8] use a constant antiguiding factor to approximate the carrier-induced phase shift. By using the general definition for the antiguiding factor,

$$R = -2\frac{d\phi/dz}{(dG/dN)N},$$

we show in Fig. 4 that R actually varies with carrier density. The values of R computed for the quantum-well laser are in most cases smaller than those for conventional diode lasers.[1,8]

In summary, we have investigated the loaded gain and the carrier-induced refractive-index change in quantum-well lasers. We found that, owing to the differences in the density of states and in the fill factors, a quantum-well laser typically has a smaller $\Gamma|d\phi/dz|$ than a conventional diode laser with the same threshold gain. We also found that, because of the rapid intraband cross-relaxation collisions, G and $d\phi/dz$ for these two types of laser saturate similarly, with $d\phi/dz$ being a much weaker function of laser intensity than G. These results have important implications for determining the transverse mode structure of quantum-well lasers, particularly in the formation of filaments. While this Letter contains predictions only for a $w = 10$ nm GaAs/GaAlAs quantum-well structure, we have found that simulations of quantum-well structures of different widths and materials give essentially the same results.

The authors are grateful to A. Elci, G. Dente, and R. Craig for discussions about aspects of this work.

References

1. J. Manning, R. Olshansky, and C. Su, IEEE J. Quantum Electron. **QE-19,** 1525 (1983).
2. M. Asada, A. Kameyama, and Y. Suematsu, IEEE J. Quantum Electron. **QE-20,** 745 (1984); Y. Arakawa and A. Yariv, IEEE J. Quantum Electron. **QE-22,** 1887 (1986).
3. M. Sargent III, M. Scully, and W. E. Lamb, Jr., *Laser Physics* (Addison-Wesley, Reading, Mass., 1977).
4. W. Chow, G. Dente, and D. Depatie, IEEE J. Quantum Electron. **QE-23,** 1314 (1987).
5. M. Yamanishi and I. Suemune, Jpn. J. Appl. Phys. **23,** L35 (1984).
6. G. Thompson, *Physics of Semiconductor Laser Devices* (Wiley, New York, 1985).
7. M. Asada and Y. Suematsu, IEEE J. Quantum Electron. **QE-21,** 434 (1985).
8. G. Agrawal, J. Appl. Phys. **56,** 3100 (1984).

Part 2
External Cavity Effects

SEMICONDUCTOR laser spectra are greatly affected by external reflections and/or placement in an external cavity. The external cavity can be employed to stabilize the wavelength, to narrow the linewidth, or both simultaneously; however, external reflections may also be detrimental and cause mode-hopping noise. In this section we have collected papers on these subjects. Included are reports of cavities with etalons or gratings, cavities formed by external reflectors or fibers, the interaction of two active resonators (the C^3 laser), and the effects of reflection noise.

Other papers relating to spectra are reprinted in several sections, namely, "Semiconductor Laser Spectra," "Distributed Feedback and Distributed Bragg Reflectors Lasers," and "Modulation," in volume 2.

REFERENCES

External Gratings

[1] Rossi, J. A., S. R. Chinn, and H. Heckscher, "High-power narrow-linewidth operation of GaAs diode lasers," *Appl. Phys. Lett.*, vol. 23, p. 25, 1973.

[2] Paoli, T. L., and J. E. Ripper, "Single longitudinal mode operation of CW junction lasers by frequency selective optical feedback," *Appl. Phys. Lett.*, vol. 25, p. 744, 1974.

[3] Nilsson, O., S. Saito, and Y. Yamamoto, "Oscillation frequency, linewidth reduction, and frequency modulation characteristics for a diode laser with external grating feedback," *Electron. Lett.*, vol. 17, p. 589, 1981.

[4] Andrews, J. R., "Single mode operation of a current pulsed GaAlAs laser with dispersive external feedback," *Appl. Phys. Lett.*, vol. 44, p. 5, 1984.

[5] Kuo, C.-Y., and J. P. van der Ziel, "Linewidth reduction of 1.5 μm grating loaded external cavity semiconductor laser by geometric reconfiguration," *Appl. Phys. Lett.*, vol. 48, p. 885, 1986.

[6] Favre, F., D. Le Guen, J. C. Simon, and B. Landousies, "External-cavity semiconductor laser with 15 nm continuous tuning range," *Electron. Lett.*, vol. 22, p. 795, 1986.

External Cavity Control

[7] Voumard, C., "External-cavity-controlled 32-Mhz narrow-band CW GaAlAs-diode lasers," *Opt. Lett.*, vol. 1, p. 61, 1977.

[8] Chinone, N., K. Aiki, and R. Ito, "Stabilization of semiconductor laser outputs by a mirror close to a laser facet," *Appl. Phys. Lett.*, vol. 33, p. 990, 1978.

[9] Tsuchida, H., S. Sanpei, M. Ohtsu, and T. Tako, "Frequency stability measurement of feedback stabilized AlGaAs DH laser," *Japan. J. Appl. Phys.*, vol. 19, p. L721, 1980.

[10] Goldberg, L., H. F. Taylor, A. Dandridge, J. Weller, and R. O. Miles, "Spectral characteristics of semiconductor lasers with optical feedback," *IEEE J. Quantum Electron.*, vol. 18, p. 555, 1982.

[11] Nielsen, C. J., and J. H. Osmundsen, "Linewidth stabilization of semiconductor lasers in an external cavity," *J. Opt. Commun.*, vol. 5, p. 42, 1984.

[12] Dahmani, B., L. Hollberg, and R. Drullinger, "Frequency stabilization of semiconductor lasers by resonant optical feedback," *Opt. Lett.*, vol. 12, p. 876, 1987.

[13] Sollberger, A., A. Heinamaki, and H. Melchior, "Frequency stabilization of semiconductor lasers for application in coherent communication systems," *J. Light. Technol.*, vol. 5, p. 485, 1987.

External Fiber Cavities

[14] Liou, K.-Y., Y. K. Jhee, C. A. Burrus, and K. L. Hall, "Narrow-linewidth fiber-external-cavity injection lasers," *Electron Lett.*, vol. 21, p. 933, 1985.

[15] Eisenstein, G., U. Koren, R. S. Tucker, G. Raybon, A. G. Dentai, L. W. Stulz, and B. I. Miller, "High power extended-cavity laser at 1.3 μm with a single-mode fiber output port," *Appl. Phys. Lett.*, vol. 50, p. 1567, 1987.

Reflection Noise

[16] Fujiwara, M., K. Kubota, and R. Lang, "Low-frequency intensity fluctuation in laser diodes with external optical feedback," *Appl. Phys. Lett.*, vol. 38, p. 217, 1981.

[17] Matsui, S., H. Takiguchi, H. Hayashi, S. Yamamoto, S. Yano, and T. Hijikata, "Suppression of feedback induced noise in short cavity V-channeled substrate inner stripe lasers with self oscillation," *Appl. Phys. Lett.*, vol. 43, p. 219, 1983.

[18] Chinone, N., T. Kuroda, T. Ohtoshi, T. Takahashi, and T. Kajimura, "Mode-hopping noise in index-guided semiconductor lasers and its reduction by saturable absorbers," *IEEE J. Quantum Electron.*, vol. 21, p. 1264, 1985.

[19] Temkin, H., N. A. Olsson, J. H. Abeles, R. A. Logan, and M. B. Panish, "Reflection noise in index-guided InGaAsP lasers," *IEEE J. Quantum Electron*, vol. 22, p. 286, 1986.

C^3 Lasers

[20] Allen, L. B., H. G. Koenig, and R. R. Rice, "Single frequency injection laser diodes for integrated optics and fiber optics applications," *SPIE*, vol. 157, p. 110, 1978.

[21] Chang, M. B., and E. Garmire, "Amplification in cleaved-substrate lasers," *IEEE J. Quantum Electron.*, vol. 16, p. 997, 1980.

[22] Tsang, W. T., and N. A. Olsson, "Enhanced frequency modulation in cleaved-coupled-cavity semiconductor lasers with reduced spurious intensity modulation," *Appl. Phys. Lett.*, vol. 43, p. 527, 1983.

[23] Coldren, L. A., T. L. Koch, C. A. Burrus, and R. G. Swartz, "Intercavity coupling gap width dependence in coupled-cavity lasers," *Electron. Lett.*, vol. 20, p. 350, 1984.

[24] Streifer, W., D. Yevick, T. L. Paoli, and R. D. Burnham, "Coupling strength and influence in cleaved-coupled-cavity lasers," *Electron. Lett.*, vol. 20, p. 553, 1984.

USE OF A FABRY-PEROT RESONATOR FOR THE STABILIZATION OF THE FREQUENCY OF AN INJECTION LASER

Yu. A. Bykovskii, V. L. Velichanskii, I. G. Goncharov, and V. A. Maslov

Moscow Engineering Physics Institute
Translated from Fizika i Tekhnika Poluprovodnikov, Vol. 4, No. 4, pp. 685-689, April, 1970
Original article submitted July 29, 1969

The frequency characteristics of gallium arsenide injection lasers were determined under continuous working conditions. It was found that the laser emission frequency depended strongly on the injection current. A Fabry-Perot interferometer could be used quite simply to determine the laser threshold, the mode structure of the radiation, and the region of the linear dependence of the emission frequency on the current. The strong dependence of the emission frequency on the current was used to stabilize the frequency to within 1 part in 10^7.

The problem of the stabilization of the laser emission frequency is attracting increasing interest because of new suggestions of simple stabilization methods [1], such as the use of a nonlinearly absorbing cell in the laser resonator. The interest in the frequency stabilization is due to the great importance of high coherence of laser radiation in communications and navigation, as well as in the establishment of a universal standard of length and time, in high-resolution spectroscopy, etc. The first attempts to stabilize the laser emission frequency by means of a nonlinearly absorbing cell were carried out on gas lasers and have ensured stability within 1 part in 10^9-10^{10}.

It is reported in [2] that an absorbing methane cell in a helium–neon laser ($\lambda = 3.39\ \mu$) gives a reproducibility of 1 in 10^{11} with respect to the center of the methane line. Even better stabilization of the frequency of gas lasers by means of a low-pressure cell has been reported in later papers.

However, gas lasers have the disadvantage of emitting a relatively small number of lines and permitting only very restricted frequency tuning of each line. This makes it difficult to select suitable substances for nonlinearly absorbing cells with the necessary properties of a large absorption coefficient and a long excited-state lifetime.

Since solid solutions of ternary compounds can be used to fabricate lasers of any required wavelength within a wide spectral range [3] and since the relatively large width of the amplified line (~ 100 Å) makes it possible to tune continuously the laser emission frequency within the limits of this line, it follows that stabilization of the emission frequency of semiconductor lasers would be very desirable.

Preliminary results on the stabilization of the frequency of semiconductor lasers with external resonators are reported in [4]. The present paper describes similar results of an investigation of the spectral characteristics and stabilization of the emission frequency of injection lasers by means of Fabry-Perot interferometers.

In order to stabilize the frequency of an injection laser, we must determine the influence of various factors on the emission frequency in order to compensate the undesirable effects by a suitably selected parameter.

It is known that the laser emission frequency can be altered by varying the pressure [5] and temperature [6]. When the temperature is increased, the forbidden-band width decreases, the positions of the quasi-Fermi levels of the electrons and holes change, and the refractive index of the active re-

Reprinted with permission from *Sov. Phys.—Semicon.*, vol. 4, no. 4, pp. 580-583, Oct. 1970.

gion is affected. The wavelength of each resonator mode increases mainly due to the increase in the refractive index [6]. Investigations of the spectral characteristics of injection lasers working under pulse conditions have demonstrated [7] that the emission wavelength increases during an injection current pulse because of the heating of the active region.

We investigated the spectral characteristics of injection lasers under continuous-wave (CW) conditions as a function of the injection current, which determined the temperature of the active region under steady-state conditions. A preliminary investigation was carried out on the laser emission spectrum using a DFS-12 spectrograph with ~ 1 Å resolution in order to select those samples which emitted just one mode.

The laser diodes were prepared from GaAs by the liquid epitaxy method. These diodes were 50-200 μ long; their width was approximately the same as the length. The CW operation was ensured by placing the diodes in a cryostat in nitrogen vapor, keeping the p- and n-type regions of the diode in contact with a heat conductor. The threshold currents were 150-500 mA, depending on the quality of the diode and its dimensions. The emission wavelength at the threshold level ranged from 8625 to 8715 Å for different diodes. When the injection current was increased, the single-mode operation was retained by the better samples when the frequency changed within the range up to 100 GHz. Further increase in the injection current produced additional modes. When the injection current was raised, the wavelengths of all the modes shifted simultaneously and by the same amount in the direction of longer wavelengths. The separation between the modes remained constant.

A Fabry-Perot interferometer whose mirrors were separated by 3 cm and had a reflection coefficient of 80% was used to investigate lasers with a high spectral resolution (10^{-6}) operating under single-mode conditions. The laser radiation was concentrated into a parallel beam by means of an objective lens. The radiation passed through the interferometer, as well as a filter, before being focused on the photocathode of an FÉU-22 photomultiplier. The photomultiplier signal was applied to an S1-15 oscillograph. The dependence of the laser emission frequency on the injection current was investigated more thoroughly by applying a constant voltage as well as an additional sawtooth signal. The amplitude of the sawtooth current through the diode could be varied continuously from 0 to 100 mA. The frequency of the sawtooth voltage was 50 or 100 Hz. (The oscillograph scan was triggered by the sawtooth voltage source.)

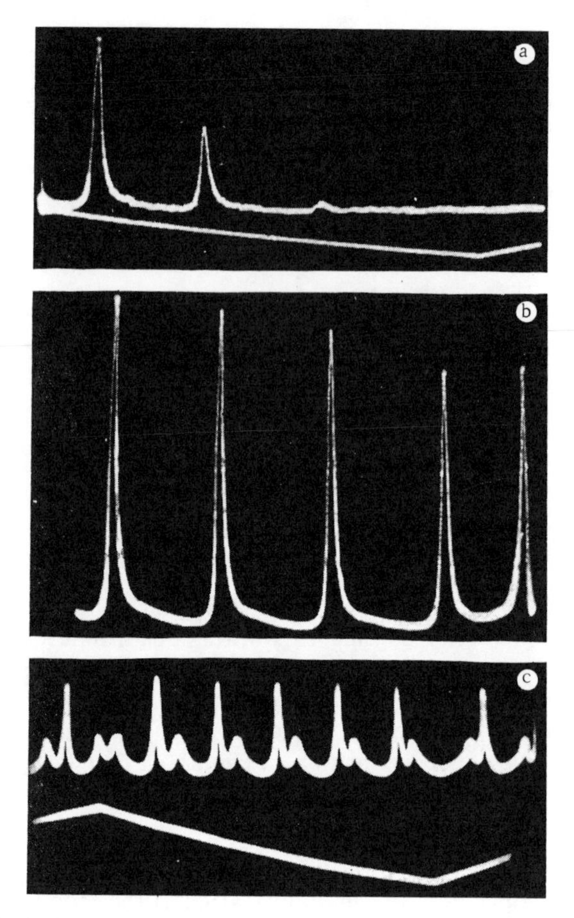

Fig. 1. Explanations in text. Frequency interval between neighboring peaks is 5 GHz in all three oscillograms.

The application of the sawtooth voltage produced equidistant peaks on the oscillograph screen. These peaks corresponded to transmission resonances of the Fabry-Perot resonator. The range of currents in which the emission was of the single-mode type and the radiation intensity suffered only weak fluctuations was found by varying the constant component of the injection current and the amplitude of the sawtooth voltage.

Figure 1 shows oscillograms of the transmission of an external Fabry-Perot resonator, obtained for a diode working under different conditions. Figure 1a shows the development of laser emission at the threshold value of the current. In this range of currents, the radiation intensity depended strongly on the current.

When the injection current was increased above the threshold value, we found a region in which the radiation intensity depended weakly on the injection level (Fig. 1b).

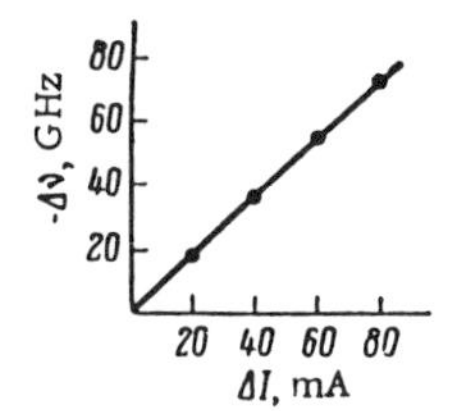

Fig. 2. Explanations in text: $\Delta\nu$ is the frequency increment; ΔI is the current increment.

The frequency scale of the horizontal scan was deduced from the known separation between the resonance frequencies in the external resonator. The passband of the resonator was $\sim$500 MHz. This method was found to be very convenient in the observation of the appearance and development of additional modes.

Figure 1c shows the appearance of a second laser mode.

The dependence of the frequency shift on the injection current is shown in Fig. 2. This dependence was deduced from the oscillogram in Fig. 1b using the known amplitude of the sawtooth-like variation of the current. It is evident from Fig. 2 that the laser frequency shift was a linear function of the injection current. The slope of the dependence of the shift on the current, deduced from Fig. 2, was -0.9 GHz / mA. The sign of the derivative $d\nu / dI$ was governed by the influence of a change in the linear dimensions of the external interferometer on the direction of shift of the transmission peaks when the injection current was increased. The better laser samples exhibited a linear dependence of the single-mode emission frequency on the injection current in the range up to 10^{11} Hz.

This method allowed us to determine rapidly, and with a high spectral resolution, some of the important spectral characteristics of semiconductor injection lasers, including the laser threshold, mode structure, and the linear region of the dependence of the emission frequency on the injection current.

Our investigations showed that the dependence of the emission frequency on the current could be used for the purpose of frequency stabilization.

Figure 3 shows a block diagram of the apparatus employed to stabilize the frequency of an injection laser. A laser 1 was supplied with power from a stabilized current source 2, which provided a current continuously variable from 0 to 10 A. A sawtooth voltage was applied simultaneously to the laser diode from an oscillator of the NGPK-3 type 3 and a sinusoidal voltage was obtained from a G3-33 oscillator 4. The output radiation of the laser was passed through an external Fabry-Perot resonator 5 and a filter. This radiation

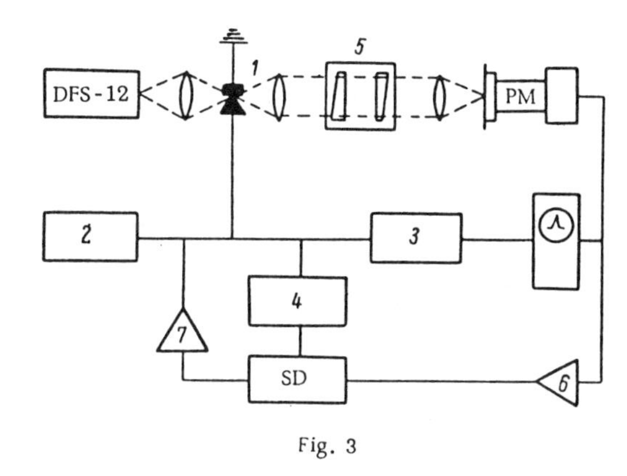

Fig. 3

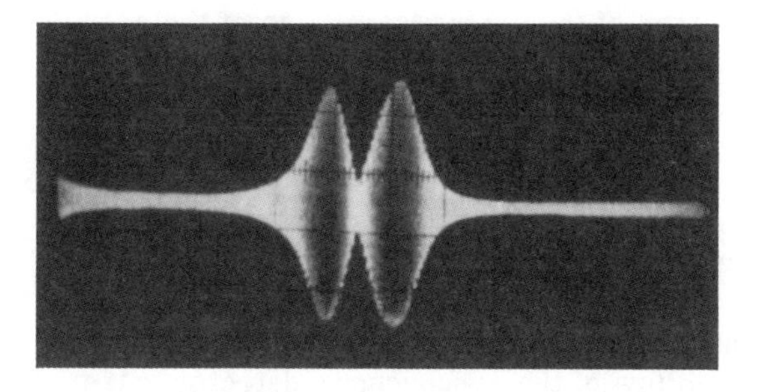

Fig. 4

was focused on the photocathode of an FÉU-22 photomultiplier (PM). The photomultiplier signal was applied to the input of a U2-6 amplifier 6.

Figure 4 shows an oscillogram of the signal after it had passed through the narrow-band amplifier. This signal was obtained when the sawtooth and sinusoidal voltages were applied simultaneously to the laser diode. The sinusoidal modulation frequency was 25 kHz, and it was limited by the amplifier. The oscillogram in Fig. 4 could be used to plot the discrimination curve of the Fabry-Perot resonator (Fig. 5), if the frequency scale of the scan were known. The width of the discrimination curve was about 500 MHz for this interferometer. The discrimination curve rep-

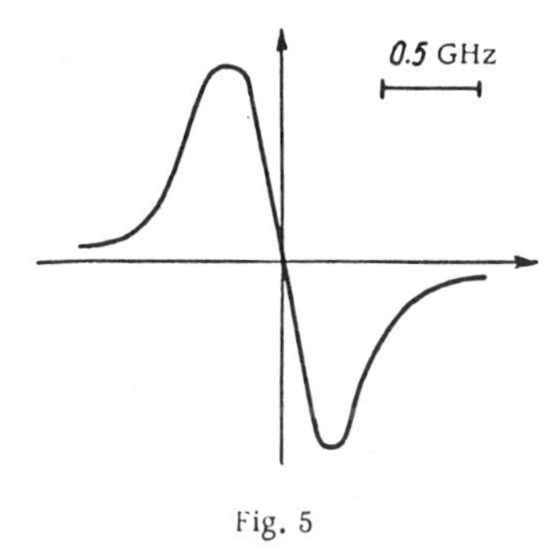

Fig. 5

resented the possibility of converting a deviation of the laser frequency into an error signal whose amplitude and phase would depend on the difference between the laser emission frequency and the center of the transmission line of the external resonator. The error signal was obtained by applying the output of the narrow-band amplifier to a synchronous detector (SD in Fig. 3), in conjunction with a reference signal provided by a suitable oscillator 4. After it had passed through the synchronous detector, the error signal was amplified by a dc amplifier 7 and fed into the feedback circuit of the laser power supply.

The instability of the laser frequency relative to the center of the transmission line of the external resonator, observed after a long time interval (~ 10 min), was deduced from the shift of the interferometer transmission peaks relative to a reference line inscribed on the oscillograph screen. Usually, the instability amounted to a few gigahertz in a period of several minutes. The drift of the laser frequency, observed in a short time interval without feedback, was determined from readings of the synchronous-detector voltmeter whose scale had first been calibrated in megahertz. Before the measurements were made the laser frequency was selected by adjusting the constant component of the injection current so that the voltmeter reading was zero. After a few seconds, the laser frequency drifted outside the limits of the discrimination curve. The relative instability in short intervals of time was $5 \cdot 10^{-6}$.

The stability of the emission frequency of a laser with negative feedback was governed by the position of the average laser frequency relative to the center of the transmission resonance of the interferometer in an interval of the order of the time constant of the synchronous detector. Repeated measurements showed that the relative instability of the average laser frequency was less than 10^{-7} in a period of several minutes.

The working range of the negative feedback system was governed by the discriminator band. The dynamic range of frequency stabilization was 10 GHz and the band of the feedback system was a few hertz (it was governed mainly by the time constant of the synchronous detector).

The use of a high-Q interferometer and the extension of the feedback circuit band should make it possible to improve the relative stability of the laser emission frequency.

The emission frequency of semiconductor lasers can be stabilized also using the absorption lines of gases. Of special interest is the stabilization by means of the absorption line of cesium (λ = 8521 Å) since the absorption involves the ground state of cesium atoms.

The authors are grateful to V. V. Nikitin for his very valuable and numerous comments, and to Yu. P. Zakharov for supplying the injection laser samples.

LITERATURE CITED

1. N. G. Basov and V. S. Letokhov, Usp. Fiz. Nauk, 96, 585 (1968) [Sov. Phys.—Usp., 11, 855 (1969)].
2. R. L. Barger and J. L. Hall, Phys. Rev. Lett., 22, 4 (1969).
3. M. I. Nathan, TI IÉR, 54, 55 (1966).
4. Yu. A. Bykovskii, V. L. Velichanskii, I. G. Goncharov, and V. A. Maslov, Zh. Eksp. Teor. Fiz., 57, 1109 (1969).
5. J. E. Ripper and C. G. Whitney, IEEE J. Quantum Electron., QE-3, 202 (1967).
6. T. F. Nikitina, Yu. M. Popov, G. M. Strakhovskii, and N. N. Shuikin, Fiz. Tekh. Poluprov., 3, 164 (1969) [Sov. Phys.—Semicond., 3, 139 (1969)].
7. W. Engeler and M. Garfinkel, Solid-State Electron., 8, 585 (1965).

External Optical Feedback Effects on Semiconductor Injection Laser Properties

ROY LANG AND KOHROH KOBAYASHI

Abstract—**Influences on the semiconductor laser properties of external optical feedback, i.e., return of a portion of the laser output from a reflector external to the laser cavity, have been examined. Experimental observations with a single mode laser is presented with analysis based on a compound cavity laser model, which has been found to explain essential features of the experimental results. In particular, it has been demonstrated that a laser with external feedback can be multistable and show hysteresis phenomena, analogous to those of nonlinear Fabry-Perot resonator. It has also been shown that the dynamic properties of injection lasers are significantly affected by external feedback, depending on interference conditions between returned light and the field inside the laser diode.**

I. Introduction

MUCH attention has recently been drawn to the fact that semiconductor laser behaviors can be significantly affected by external optical feedback, that is, feedback of a portion of the laser output back into the laser cavity from a reflecting surface external to it. On one hand, it is potentially of practical use. For example, the external feedback enhances the longitudinal mode selection, which can be used to narrow the emission spectrum width [1], [2]. It has been used to reduce wave form distortion in the modulated output [3]. A novel scheme has also been proposed [4], in which a semiconductor diode laser is used not only as a light source, but also as a detector, making use of the output power or junction voltage variation caused by the external feedback. On the other hand, serious problems arise in practice because of unintentional external feedback. For example, reflection at a fiber facet in a diode-to-fiber optical coupling circuit degrades the modulation response characteristics and increases intensity noise [5]-[8].

As has been pointed out previously [9], [10], the effects of external feedback on laser behaviors are expected to differ characteristically depending on the distance between a laser diode to an external reflector. When the distance is smaller than the output coherence length, the combined laser and external reflector system will behave as a laser with a compound cavity.

The compound cavity effects in conventional lasers have been well known. However, previous experimental observations of external feedback effects in semiconductor lasers did not appear to permit simple interpretation. One possible reason for this is that many of the previous experiments used diode lasers with unstable transverse modes, oscillating in multilongitudinal modes, which exhibited rather erratic behaviors even without external feedback. In addition, as is shown in the following, some of the properties of the semiconductor lasers tend to make the appearance of the external feedback effects somewhat complex. They are: 1) broad gain spectrum half width, typically around 50 Å, which permit different longitudinal modes of the diode cavity to be excited with a slight change in the external feedback conditions, 2) very sensitive dependence of the crystal refractive index on temperature, and 3) strong dependence of the active medium refractive index on the excited carrier density.

This paper presents results of experimental and theoretical analysis of the influences of the externally reflected light on the static and dynamic behaviors of semiconductor injection lasers. Particular attention is paid to the case where the laser diode to external reflector distance is around a few centimeters, and the compound cavity effects are most easily and clearly demonstrated. In particular, it is demonstrated that the external feedback can make the injection laser multistable and cause hysteresis phenomena, similar to those demonstrated recently with a dye laser [11]. The mechanism causing the multistability is analogous to that of the nonlinear Fabry-Perot resonator [12].

The external feedback effects on the dynamic properties of semiconductor injection lasers have also been examined. It has been found that the coherent interference effects are responsible for enhancing or prolonging the relaxation oscillation in the transient output, as well as for suppressing it.

II. Experiment

Experiments have been performed with CW AlGaAs double-heterostructure stripe-geometry diode lasers with builtin (effective) refractive index profile for lateral mode stabilization [13]. The stripe width ranged between 6 and 10 μm. Cavity length l_D was about 290 μm. As shown in Fig. 1, the laser diode (LD), a coupling circuit and a flat mirror with a gold reflecting layer are mounted on a plate to make a stable feedback optics. The coupling circuit is the same one as used to couple the light from LD to an optical fiber, and it consists of a SELFOC® rod lens with 1.8 mm diameter and 4.5 mm long. The flat mirror is driven by a piezo-electric positioner with an accuracy around a tenth of 1 μm. Backward emission from LD is coupled to a monochromator and a photocell to observe the emission spectra and light output versus current characteristics (L-I curves).

The LD was driven by dc current. The only oscillating lateral transverse mode (parallel to the junction plane) was

Manuscript received August 1, 1979; revised September 27, 1979.

The authors are with the Laser Equipment Development Division, Nippon Electric Company, Ltd., Kawasaki 213, Japan.

Reprinted from *IEEE J. Quantum Electron.*, vol. QE-16, no. 3, pp. 347-355, Mar. 1980.

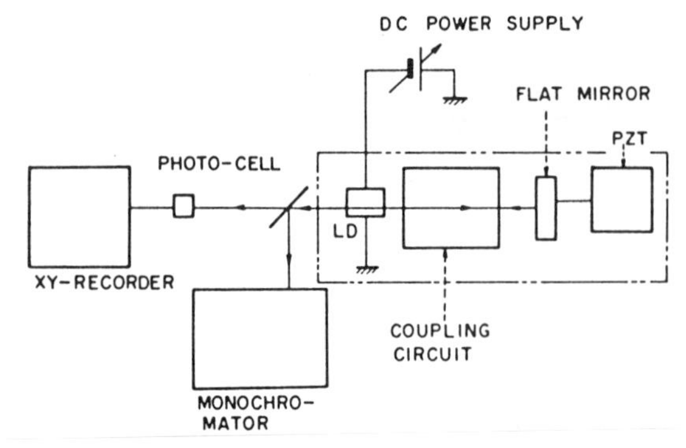

Fig. 1. Block diagram of the experiment.

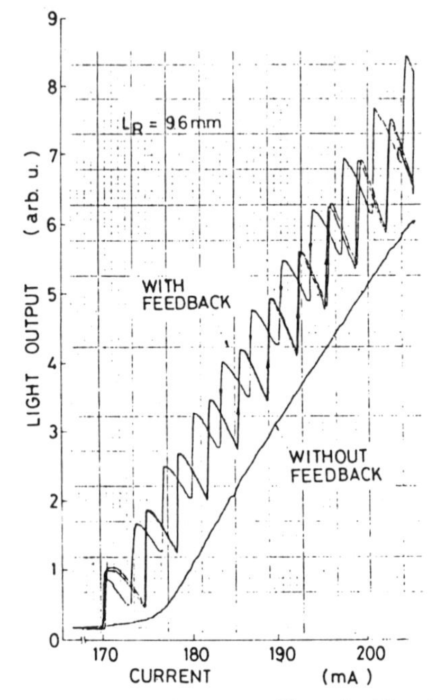

Fig. 2. Output versus current curves with and without external feedback. Hysteresis is seen in that with feedback.

the fundamental mode, which was stable within a current range used in the experiments.

The laser plus an external mirror system, shown in Fig. 1, can be viewed as a compound cavity laser, consisting of a diode cavity and an external cavity formed by the external reflector (with reflectivity R_3) and the diode facet facing it (with reflectivity R_2), which are mutually coupled through the partially transparent diode facet. The presence of the coherent interference effects, between reflected light and the field inside the laser diode, has been confirmed in the present experiments with a single mode injection laser and careful control of the LD to external mirror distance L_R, which is defined as the optical path length between the external reflector and the diode facet facing it. For example, at a fixed dc excitation level, the output power varied periodically as L_R was varied. The period in L_R was equal to a half of the oscillation wavelength of 8300 Å, as expected from a simple compound cavity model. The output undulation as depicted in Fig. 2 was also found to take place at a fixed mirror distance L_R, with a change in the dc excitation current level. When the amount of external feedback was large, the undulation was found to have hysteresis, depending on the current direction, as seen in this

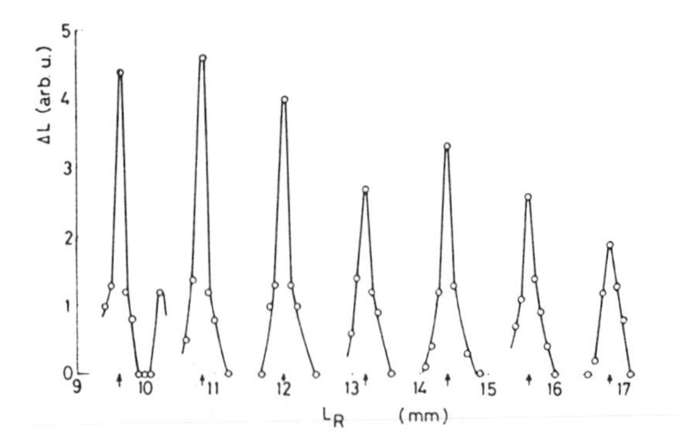

Fig. 3. Amplitude of output undulation ΔL versus effective external mirror distance L_R. Arrows indicate where L_R equals integral multiples of effective diode cavity length L_D.

figure. Analysis presented later in this paper will indicate that the undulation with hysteresis results from the variation in the diode cavity optical path length L_D, which is caused by crystal refractive index variation due to the active region temperature change with current. In this respect, variation in L_R is equivalent to variation in the crystal refractive index with current.

It has been found, however, that there is a little complication caused by the presence of a large number of diode cavity longitudinal modes within the broad gain spectrum width; that is, amplitude ΔL of the output undulation depends on the external mirror distance L_R, as depicted in Fig. 3. Arrows in this figure indicate the external cavity lengths equaling integral multiples of the effective diode cavity length L_D, defined as $L_D = \eta_{eff} l_D$, where

$$\eta_{eff} = \eta + \Omega \frac{\partial \eta}{\partial \Omega} \tag{1}$$

is the effective refractive index, η is the active region refractive index, and Ω is the laser oscillation frequency. It can be determined with the observed oscillating wavelength λ and the longitudinal mode separation $\Delta\lambda_D$ of the diode cavity as

$$L_D = \lambda^2 / 2\Delta\lambda_D. \tag{2}$$

Observed λ and $\Delta\lambda_D$, in this case, were 2.9 and 8300 Å, respectively. As is clearly seen in this figure, undulation amplitude ΔL takes its maximum where L_R equals an integral multiple of L_D, that is, when the longitudinal mode separation of the diode cavity equals an integral multiple of that of the external cavity.

Results of the precise spectral measurement, as depicted in Figs. 4 and 5, have also indicated that there are marked difference in the spectral behaviors of the output, depending on whether L_R closely equals an integral multiple of L_D or not. In the example depicted in Fig. 4, $L_R = 8L_D + 50\ \mu m$, corresponding to the latter case. As the current was increased from point c to l on the accompanying L-I curve, which showed a *small* amplitude undulation, the oscillating wavelength was found to jump successively by an amount equaling the longitudinal mode separation of the *diode cavity*. At point m, which was at a bottom of the undulation, oscillation wavelength jumped back to a value very close to that at point c, another bottom of the undulation, but shifted to the longer wavelength by an amount equaling the longitudinal mode separation of the *external cavity*. When L_R was smaller than

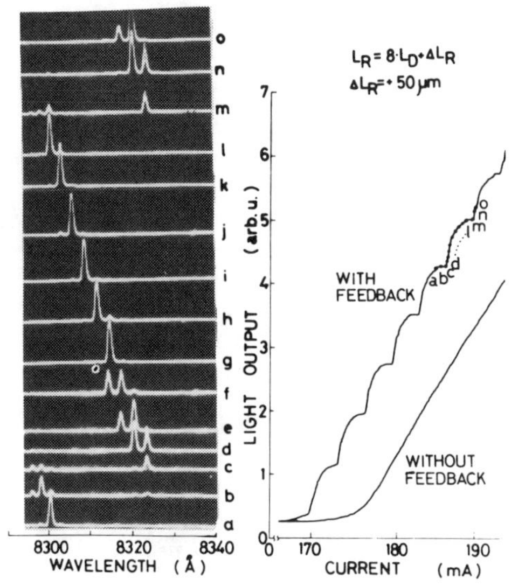

Fig. 4. Spectral changes and output undulation with current increase, when L_R is greater by 50 μm than the nearest integral multiple of L_D.

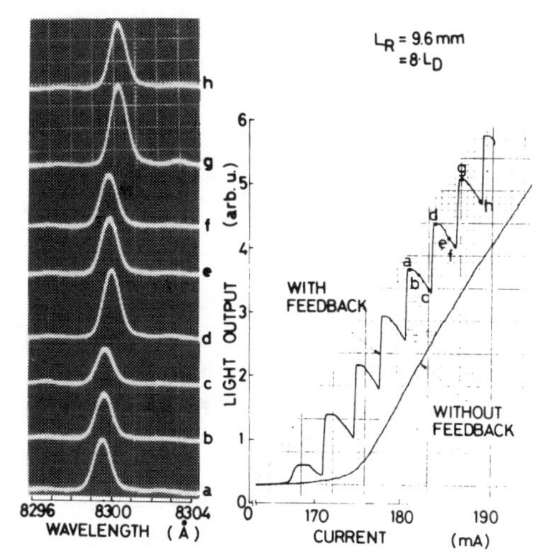

Fig. 5. Spectral changes and output undulation with current increase when L_R equals an integral multiple of L_D.

the nearest integral multiple of L_D, the wavelength jumped in the same way, except that the direction of the mode jump among the diode's longitudinal modes were in the opposite direction, towards the longer wavelength side.

Wavelength varied with current in a very different way, when L_R was almost equal to an integral multiple of the effective diode length, as depicted in Fig. 5. In this case, the output showed a large amplitude undulation. As the current increased, the wavelength changed continuously, without jumps, between points a and c on the accompanying L-I curve, and made a discontinuous jump by about 0.36 Å, an amount equaling the external cavity mode separation, from points c to d.

The dependence of the L-I curve undulation amplitude as well as the wavelength variation pattern on L_R (mode L_D) can be explained as follows. The distribution of resonant modes of the diode and the external cavities is illustrated in Fig. 6. When L_R equals an integral (m) multiple of L_D, the diode cavity mode separation is an integral multiple of the external cavity mode separation, as illustrated in Fig. 6(a). If one of

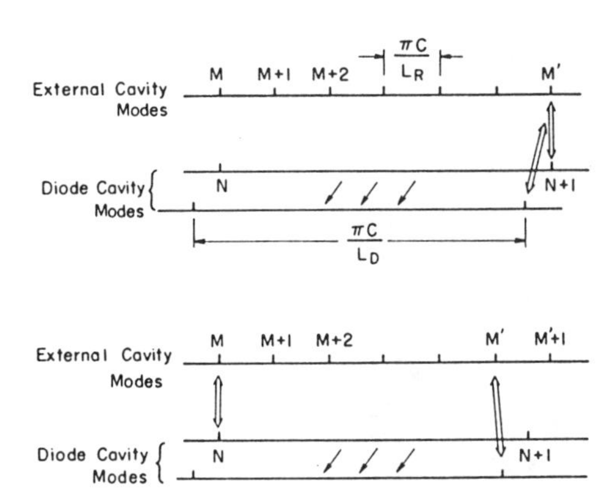

Fig. 6. Relationship between the diode cavity modes and external cavity modes. (a) When $L_R = mL_D$, and (b) when $L_R \neq mL_D$.

the diode cavity modes (mode $N + 1$) coincides in frequency with an external cavity mode (mode M'), there will also be coincidence in neighboring diode modes. The laser will oscillate at the combination of modes closest to the gain peak, say, at the pair $N + 1$ and M'. When the dc excitation current is increased, the active region temperature rises, and the crystal refractive index increases. This shifts the diode cavity resonant modes towards the low frequency side, relative to the external cavity modes. Frequency mismatching develops at the oscillating mode pair, which results in a less constructive interference condition between the externally reflected light and the field inside the laser cavity. It also results in a reduction in the output, compared with the perfect matching state. However, in this case, mismatching of the same extent also develops at other mode pairs. Therefore, the laser oscillation is maintained at the original mode pair ($N + 1$ and M'), until the mismatching develops to such a large extent that the new combination $M' - 1$ and $N + 1$ becomes better matched.

In case L_R is not close to an integral multiple of L_D, the situation is different. For example, if L_R is a little larger than the nearest integral multiple of L_D, the resonant modes are distributed as illustrated in Fig. 6(b). Assume that there is a perfect matching of frequencies between modes M and N, near the gain spectral peak. The laser will be oscillating at this pair. As the diode cavity resonance frequencies are lowered with the current increase, mismatching develops at this pair. However, the matching improves at the neighboring diode cavity mode $N + 1$ and the external cavity mode M' closest to it, which are on the higher frequency side. Therefore, the laser will switch its oscillation frequency to the latter mode pair, with a frequency jump by an amount almost equaling the diode cavity mode separation. The frequency jumps will be repeated with the current increase, until the oscillation frequency becomes so far away from the gain spectrum peak that the oscillation frequency jumps back to another matching mode pair located on the lower frequency side of the gain spectrum. Because of this additional freedom of mode switching among the diode cavity modes, the frequency mismatching does not develop as severely in this case as the former case. Hence, the undulation in the L-I curve has smaller amplitude. Obviously, the compound cavity effects will take their simplest form when $L_R = mL_D$. In the following, only situations of this kind will be considered.

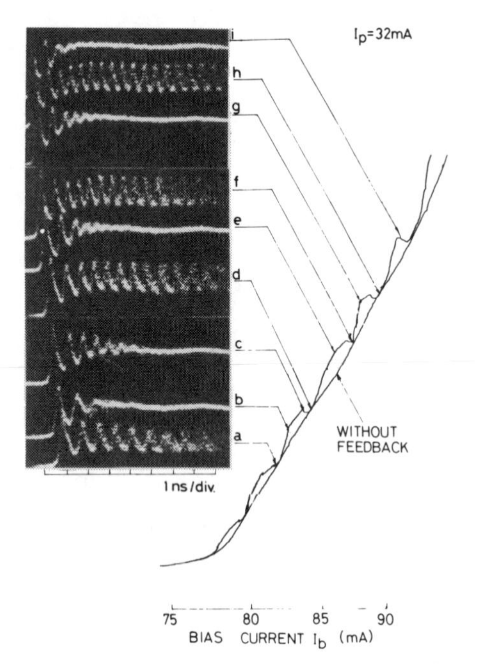

Fig. 7. The transient output response to a current pulse at various points on the undulated L-I curve. Pulse height was 32 mA, which was superimposed on the dc bias current.

It has been found that the L-I curve shows hysteresis when the external feedback is sufficiently large, as seen in Fig. 2. In this figure, the arrows indicate the current change direction. The L-I curve in the direction of the current increase has been traced twice in this figure, to confirm that the hysteresis did not result from any experimental imperfections. The hysteresis will be shown to result from the multistability of the compound cavity laser.

Several reports [5]-[10] have been published recently on the influence of the external feedback on the transient behaviors and noise properties of semiconductor injection lasers. In particular, Chinone *et al.* [8] has examined the external feedback effect on transient behaviors for the case where the external mirror distance L_R ranged between a few millimeters and several centimeters. It has been found that, for L_R exceeding about 5 cm, external feedback tends to enhance the relaxation oscillation or induce self-sustained pulsation of the output, with the oscillation period locked to the transit time $\tau = 2L_R/c$ in the external cavity. On the other hand, the relaxation oscillation in the transient output has been found to be reduced when L_R is less than about 2 cm.

The present investigation has found that there is also finer dependence on L_R, reflecting the interference effects, as well as on the amount of the external feedback. When L_R is between 1 to 2 cm, the relaxation oscillation of the modulated output tends to be suppressed at dc bias current levels corresponding to the peaks of the undulation of the L-I curve. However, it tends to be enhanced or prolonged at bias levels corresponding to the undulation valleys. In particular, as the external feedback is reduced to the level where the hysteresis almost disappeared, the output exhibited sustained pulsations at bias levels corresponding to the valleys in the undulation, as shown in the example depicted in Fig. 7. It is interesting to note that the pulsations at undulation valleys are less pronounced when external feedback is large enough to cause hysteresis.

At dc excitation condition, intensity noise properties have been found to have similar dependence on L_R. At current levels near the undulation peaks, the noise frequency spectrum had a peak which is much lower and broader than the well-known resonance peak of an isolated diode laser. At current levels near the undulation valleys, however, sharp resonance peak appeared.

III. Theory

A. Basic Equations

Under lasing conditions, the diode cavity is filled with gain medium, which, to a large extent, compensate for the diode cavity loss. It, therefore, has substantially greater effective quality factor, and consequently, greater influence on the laser behaviors, than the passive external cavity. For this reason, the following form of field equation has been adopted for a compound cavity laser configuration, obtained by adding an external feedback term to a standard laser equation in complex form; that is,

$$\frac{d}{dt}E(t)\,e^{i\Omega t} = \left\{i\omega_N(n) + \frac{1}{2}(G(n) - \Gamma_0)\right\}E(t)e^{i\Omega t} + \kappa E(t-\tau)e^{i\Omega(t-\tau)} \tag{3}$$

Here, $\omega_N(n)$ is the diode cavity longitudinal mode resonant frequency, which is defined with an integer N as

$$\omega_N = N\pi c/\eta l_D. \tag{4}$$

Γ_0 is the cavity loss of the diode cavity, and c is the light velocity. The last term on the right-hand side represents the external feedback. As derived in the Appendix, coefficient κ is related to cavity parameters as

$$\kappa = ca/2\eta l_D \tag{5}$$

where parameter a, defined with the facet and external mirror reflectivities R_2 and R_3 as

$$a = (1 - R_2)(R_3/R_2)^{1/2} \tag{6}$$

is a measure of the coupling strength between the two cavities. In the above expression for external feedback, multiple reflections in the external cavity have been neglected.

A usual form of rate equation has been adopted for carrier density n, which can be expressed, assuming appropriate normalization for field amplitude E, as

$$\frac{d}{dt}n = -\gamma n - G(n)|E|^2 + P \tag{7}$$

where P denotes the number injection rate per unit volume of the excited carriers, which is related to current density J, electronic charge e and the diode active layer thickness d as $P = J/ed$. γ is the inverse spontaneous lifetime of the excited carriers.

B. Steady-State Conditions

Stationary lasing conditions can be obtained from (3), by setting E to be constant. The real and the imaginary parts of the equation, when they are separated, can be written as

$$G(n) - \Gamma_0 + 2\kappa \cos(\Omega\tau) = 0 \tag{8}$$

$$\omega_N(n) - \Omega - \kappa \sin(\Omega\tau) = 0. \tag{9}$$

Since both gain G and resonance frequency ω_N, as defined by (4), are dependent on excited carrier density n, these equations are mutually coupled.

These equations describe the changes in laser oscillation frequency Ω and carrier density n with a change in the external mirror distance L_R or an external parameter x, which is assumed to represent temperature in the following. In order to study the behaviors in a more explicit way, the following linear approximation for the refractive index is adopted, for small variations Δn, $\Delta\Omega$, and Δx of n, Ω, and x around their respective reference values n_r, Ω_r, and x_r.

$$\eta(n, \Omega, x) = \eta_r + \eta_n \cdot \Delta n + \eta_\Omega \cdot \Delta\Omega + \eta_x \cdot \Delta x. \tag{10}$$

Here, $\eta_r = \eta(\eta_r, \Omega_r, x_r)$, and the coefficients have been defined as

$$\eta_n = \left.\frac{\partial \eta}{\partial n}\right|_{n=n_r,\ \Omega=\Omega_r,\ x=x_r} \tag{11}$$

and likewise for others. With this approximation, the diode cavity resonance frequency is expressed as

$$\omega_N = \omega_r - \frac{\omega_r}{\eta_r}(\eta_n \cdot \Delta n + \eta_\Omega \cdot \Delta\Omega + \eta_x \cdot \Delta x). \tag{12}$$

Gain G can be approximated similarly. However, since the gain spectrum half width (~50 Å) is much broader than the typical diode axial mode separation (a few angstrom), dependence on frequency and the external parameters are not explicitly considered for the moment, and it is approximated as

$$G(n) = G_r + G_n \cdot \Delta n. \tag{13}$$

In the following, it is assumed that $\Omega = \Omega_r$, $n = n_r$, and $x = x_r$ satisfy (8) and (9), and that $\omega_r = \Omega_r$. In this case, it is found, from (8), that

$$G_r = \Gamma_0 - 2\kappa. \tag{14}$$

Substituting (10)-(13) into (8) and (9), and combining the two equations to eliminate Δn, one obtains

$$\eta_x \cdot \Delta x = (\eta_{\text{eff}}/\omega_r\tau)\{\beta[R \cos(\Delta\Omega \cdot \tau) - \sin(\Delta\Omega \cdot \tau) - R] - \Delta\Omega \cdot \tau\} \tag{15}$$

where

$$\beta = aL_R/L_D. \tag{16}$$

The factor R, defined as

$$R = 2\omega_r\eta_n/\eta_r G_n \tag{17}$$

is the ratio, multiplied by twice the wave vector k, of the derivatives with respect to carrier density n of refractive index η to gain per unit length $\eta_r G/c$. This ratio has been found to critically affect the lateral transverse mode stability in stripe geometry lasers against spatial hole burning [13], [14]. Experimentally, it has been found to vary between -0.5 and -3 in case of GaAs active region [15].

An example of calculated frequency versus refractive index curve is depicted in Fig. 8. In this example, adopted parameter values for a, β, and R are 0.15, 1.5 and -1, respectively, and ω_r has been assumed to be 2.2×10^{15} s^{-1} which is appropriate for GaAs/AlGaAs lasers emitting at around 8300 Å.

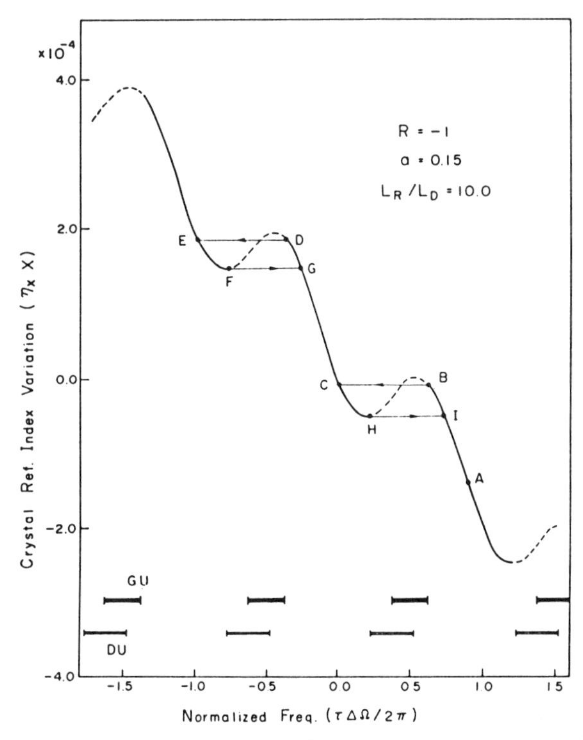

Fig. 8. Calculated crystal refractive index variation versus normalized oscillation frequency. Regions indicated as DU and GU are dynamically unstable and gain-wise unstable, respectively. The broken lines also indicate where the time independent solution is unstable in either sense.

It is seen in Fig. 8 that the frequency is a multivalued function of the external parameter x, and that a compound cavity laser is multistable in this case. The multistability arises, because of the presence of sine and cosine functions in (8) and (9), reflecting the interference effects, when parameter κ is large enough to cause singularities in $d\Omega/dx$. Differentiating (15), one obtains

$$d\Omega/dx = -(\eta_x\omega_r/\eta_{\text{eff}})/\{1 + \beta[\cos(\Delta\Omega \cdot \tau) + R \sin(\Delta\Omega \cdot \tau)]\} \tag{18}$$

from which it is found that the singularities, and hence, the multistability, arises when

$$(1 + R^2)^{1/2}\, aL_R/L_D > 1. \tag{19}$$

The above criterion indicates that the multistability is more likely to show up when coupling parameter a and mirror distance L_R are sufficiently large, and effective diode cavity length L_D is sufficiently small. It also indicates that multistability readily results when R is large, as in semiconductor lasers.

C. Dynamic Stability

Not all solutions for (8) and (9) may represent dynamically stable states. The stability of a stationary solution has been examined by studying the time development of infinitesimal fluctuations in the field and the carrier density around it, as described in the following.

Complex field amplitude strength E can be expressed as

$$E = (E_0 + e) \exp (i\varphi) \tag{20}$$

where E_0 is a stationary solution for the field, for a given external parameter value, and it has been assumed to be real without loss of generality. Real parameters e and φ represent the infinitesimal deviations from the stationary value of the amplitude and phase. Deviation of the carrier density n is denoted as δn. Substituting these expressions into (3), neglecting terms of the second and higher order in the infinitesimal deviations, and separating the real and imaginary parts, one obtains

$$\dot{e}(t) = -\kappa E_0 \sin (\Omega\tau)\, \Delta_\tau \varphi - \kappa \cos (\Omega\tau)\, \Delta_\tau\, e + \tfrac{1}{2} G_n E_0 \delta n \tag{21}$$

and

$$\dot{\varphi}(t) = -\kappa \cos (\Omega\tau)\, \Delta_\tau \varphi + \kappa \sin (\Omega\tau)\, \Delta_\tau\, e/E_0 - (\omega_r/\eta_r) \cdot (\eta_n \cdot \delta n + \eta_\Omega \cdot \nu) \tag{22}$$

where

$$\Delta_\tau \varphi = \varphi(t) - \varphi(t - \tau); \qquad \Delta_\tau\, e = e(t) - e(t - \tau). \tag{23}$$

Note that fluctuation in the oscillating frequency ν have been introduced as $\nu = \dot{\varphi}$, while keeping Ω as a constant.

Similarly, from (7), it is possible to obtain

$$\delta \dot{n} = -\gamma \delta n - G_n E_0^2 \delta n - 2G_r E_0\, e. \tag{24}$$

Equations (21), (22), and (24) govern the time development of infinitesimal fluctuations around a stationary solution. Since they are linear and homogeneous with respect to the fluctuations, one may seek for solutions for e, φ, and δn, which are proportional to $\exp (zt)$. Substitution of this form into these equations yields a set of algebraic equations, whose secular determinant is found to be

$$D(z) = (z + \gamma_e)[z^2 + \kappa_c(1 + \eta_r/\eta_{\rm eff})(1 - e^{-z\tau})\, z + \kappa^2 (\eta_r/\eta_{\rm eff})(1 - e^{-z\tau})^2] + \omega_R^2 [z + (R\kappa_s + \kappa_c)(\eta_r/\eta_{\rm eff})(1 - e^{-z\tau})] = 0 \tag{25}$$

where

$$\kappa_c = \kappa \cos (\Delta\Omega \cdot \tau), \qquad \kappa_s = \kappa \sin (\Delta\Omega \cdot \tau) \tag{26}$$

and

$$\omega_R^2 = G_n G_r E_0^2, \qquad \gamma_e = \gamma + G_n E_0^2. \tag{27}$$

When all the roots of (25) have a negative real part, fluctuations decay in time, and the corresponding stationary solution represents a dynamically stable state, or otherwise an unstable state.

Equation (25) has been derived under a rather general context, and it is expected to be applicable for a wide range of the compound cavity configurations with various L_R and the coupling coefficient values. In case κ is sufficiently small and $\kappa\tau << 1$, the solutions of (25) will satisfy $|\tau z| << 1$. In such cases, $1 - \exp (-z\tau)$ can be approximated as $z\tau$, and (25) can be reduced to a product of z and a quadratic equation. The roots of the quadratic equation are found as

$$z = -[\gamma_e \pm (\gamma_e^2 - 4F)^{1/2}]/2 \tag{28}$$

where

$$F = \omega_R^2 [1 + (\eta_r/\eta_{\rm eff})(R\kappa_s + \kappa_c)\tau] / [1 + (1 + \eta_r/\eta_{\rm eff})\kappa_c\tau + (\eta_r/\eta_{\rm eff})(\kappa\tau)^2]. \tag{29}$$

From (28) it is found that the stationary solutions of (15), for which $F < 0$ represent dynamically unstable states. In Fig. 8, the frequency domains where the stationary solutions yield dynamically unstable states are indicated with bars denoted as DU.

D. Gain Spectrum Peak Shift

In the preceding analysis, the frequency dependence of gain $G(n)$ has been negelected on the account that the gain spectrum width is very large compared with the resonant mode separation of the diode cavity. Typical longitudinal mode separation in a semiconductor diode laser is a few angstroms, while the gain spectrum half width is around 50 Å at room temperature. The relative difference in gain at a mode in the gain spectrum peak and its nearest neighbor mode is on the order of 10^{-4}-10^{-3}. Therefore, incorporation of the frequency dependence of gains give rise to only negligible corrections to the carrier density and the field amplitude determined by (7)-(9).

The gain spectrum shape cannot be entirely neglected, however, since the mode (or, rather, the combination of the modes in the compound cavity), which actually oscillates, is selected by the gain spectrum shape. Assume that $n = n_1$ and $\Omega = \Omega_1$ is an allowed stationary state when $x = x_1$. For fixed values of x_1 and n_1, there are, in general, other possible solutions (9) which will be called subsidiary modes. They are the compound cavity modes established when the laser is oscillating at $\Omega = \Omega_1$ with $n = n_1$ and $x = x_1$. The laser will oscillate stably at $\Omega = \Omega_1$, if the net gain, defined as the left-hand side quantity of (8), is greater for this mode than the subsidiary modes. However, if the gain spectrum peak is sufficiently shifted from this frequency Ω_1, some of the subsidiary modes may have greater gain. In that case, the mode at Ω_1 does not oscillate in reality. The solution corresponds to an unstable physical state. In semiconductor lasers, the gain spectrum peak shifts appreciably, not only with temperature and pressure, but also with the carrier density. This complicates the selection of oscillation frequency for the compound cavity injection lasers. To examine the consequences of this effect, the gain spectrum shape has been approximated as

$$G(n, \Omega, x) = G_r - (\Delta\Omega - \epsilon\Delta n - \mu\Delta x)^2/w^2 \tag{30}$$

where w is the gain spectrum half width in angular frequency units. Parameters ϵ and μ are coefficients for the gain peak shift with carrier density and the external parameter. In adopting this form, it has been assumed that, when $x = x_r$ and $n = n_r$, the gain peak is located exactly at $\Omega = \Omega_r$. When x represents temperature, μ is determined essentially as the temperature coefficient of the energy band gap, which is -6.87×10^{11} s^{-1}/K at room temperature [16]. For value of ϵ, 2.61×10^{-5} $s^{-1} \cdot cm^{-3}$ has been adopted, which was deduced from the unpublished theoretical gain curves by Stern quoted as

Fig. 3.7-7 in [16]. In Fig. 8, the frequency regimes where the compound cavity laser is dynamically unstable (DU) and gain spectrum-wise unstable (GU) are indicated at the bottom of the figure. Also, the broken line portions of the curve are the regimes unstable in either sense.

E. Hysteresis in Frequency versus x

Fig. 8 indicates the presence of hysteresis in the oscillation frequency change, as the crystal refractive index of the diode is varied with an external parameter, e.g., temperature. Suppose that the laser is initially at a state corresponding to point A in this figure. As the refractive index is increased the frequency will change along $A \rightarrow B \rightarrow C \rightarrow D \rightarrow E$, avoiding the unstable regime, and making discontinuous jumps between B and C and between D and E. Once the direction of the refractive index change is reversed at E, the frequency change will follow a different path, $E \rightarrow F \rightarrow G \rightarrow H \rightarrow I$. The hysteresis originates from the interference effects in the diode cavity with the gain and refractive index varying with the laser intensity. In this respect, it is analogous to that exhibited by a nonlinear Fabry-Perot resonator [12].

F. Hysteresis in L-I Curve

Since the interference conditions in a compound cavity laser change with the oscillation frequency, the hysteresis in the frequency versus x accompanies hysteresis in the output variation. As has been demonstrated with the experimental result in Fig. 2, the hysteresis shows up in undulated L-I curve for a dc operated injection laser, even without intentional means to vary L_R or crystal refractive index. This is because the refractive index of the GaAs depends sensitively on temperature, while the latter varies appreciably with the dc excitation current. Thermal resistance of a $GaAs/Al_xGa_{1-x}As$ DH laser with narrow (~4 μm) stripe width is typically 40 K/W [16]. When contact voltage is 1.6 V, an injection current increase by 5 mA raises the temperature at 0.3 K. The temperature coefficient of the refractive index $\partial\eta/\partial T$ of GaAs at room temperature is about 5.5×10^{-4}/K, so this current increase can reduce the oscillating wavelength at about 8300 Å approximately by 0.3 Å, an amount comparative to the axial mode separation in the external cavity when L_R is on the order of 1 cm. Therefore, when there is an external reflecting surface at a distance of around 1 cm or greater, injection current change by a few milliamperes can appreciably vary the compound cavity resonance condition by inducing the oscillating mode jump, which is reflected in the output versus current curve as undulation with hysteresis. In case of the observed example depicted in Fig. 2, external cavity mode separation was 0.36 Å, while wavelength shift due to the crystal refractive index change with current was measured, in the absence of the external mirror, to be 0.092 Å/mA. Calculated period 3.9 mA agrees, within the accuracy of the measurement, with the observed period of 3.6 mA, indicating that the undulation was indeed caused by temperature variation with current. Conversely, the compound cavity effects shows up most easily when L_R is around a few centimeters, where the external cavity mode separation is small enough to be comparable to the temperature shift of the oscillation frequency, but larger than the resolution of a high resolution monochromator.

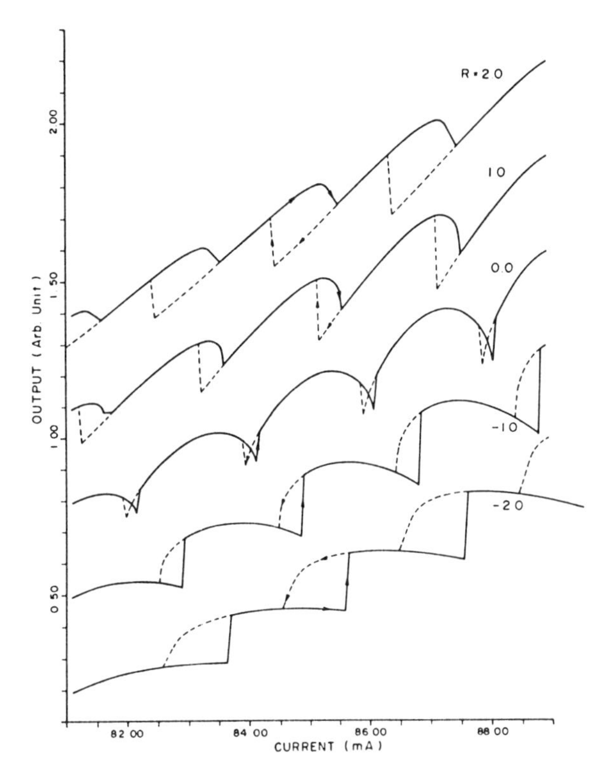

Fig. 9. Calculated L-I curves with hysteresis. Parameters are $R = 2k(\partial\eta/\partial n)/(\partial x/\partial n)$, where α is the gain per unit length.

Calculated L-I curves are shown in Fig. 9. The curves were obtained as a steady state solution of (7), with carrier density n and oscillation frequency Ω calculated through (8) and (9). Assumed parameter values for L_D, L_R and a are 0.1 cm, 1 cm and 0.15, respectively. The rate of refractive index change with current $\partial\eta/\partial I$ are assumed to be 10^{-4} mA^{-1}. Increment ratio R for the refractive index and gain were varied from -2 to 2. It is seen in this figure that, while the undulation period is determined solely by $\partial\eta/\partial I$, the shape of the undulated curve and the extent of the hysteresis depend sensitively on the R value.

The calculated curves with $R < 0$ appear to explain the essential features of the observed L-I curve depicted in Fig. 2. For one, the output is, on the average, greater for decreasing current direction, than the opposite. For another, as the current is increased, the output decreases between the discontinuous increases at mode jumps. Note that the output would have varied in the other way, if R had positive values.

G. Transient Responses

Effects of external feedback on the dynamic response of the laser output to a small amplitude current modulation can also be studied with (21)-(24), adding a modulation term, $P_m \exp(i\omega t)$, to the right-hand side of (24). The amplitude response $e(\omega)$ to a sinusoidal modulation, normalized with that at $\omega = 0$, is found to be

$$e(\omega)/e(0) = \omega_R^2 \left[i\omega + (R\kappa_s + \kappa_c)(\eta_r/\eta_{\text{eff}})(1 - e^{-i\omega\tau})\right]/D(i\omega) \quad (31)$$

where $D(z)$ has been defined by (25). The above equation indicates that the external feedback effects depend on τ, or mirror distance L_R, through factors $\cos(\Delta\Omega\tau)$ and $\sin(\Delta\Omega\tau)$

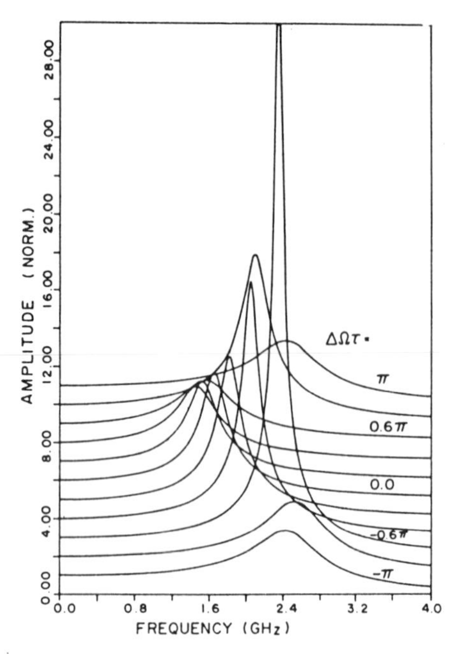

Fig. 10. Calculated field amplitude response spectra to a small amplitude sinusoidal modulation. Parameter is $\Delta\Omega\tau$, which was varied from $-\pi$ to π in step of 0.2π. $\omega_R\tau$ and γ_e were, respectively, assumed to be $\pi/4$ and 0.75×10^{10} s^{-1}. For clarity the curves are successively shifted vertically by one unit in the vertical scale.

and through $1 - \exp(-i\omega\tau)$. The former represents the interference effect, while the latter represents the phase retardation effects of the intensity variation between the returned beam and the optical intensity in the diode cavity. An example of output response spectrum, for the case $\omega_R = 2\pi \times 2$ GHz, $\gamma_e = 0.5 \times 10^9$ s^{-1}, $\omega_R\tau = \pi/4$ ($L_R = 0.94$ cm), and $\kappa = 0.75 \times 10^{-10}$ s^{-1} are shown in Fig. 10. The parameter is $\Delta\Omega\tau$, which is varied between $-\pi$ and π in step of $\pi/5$. Curves are successively shifted vertically by one unit. It is found that the sharp resonance peak at $\omega = \omega_R$, which is well known in the response spectrum of an isolated injection laser, almost entirely disappears with the external feedback with small mirror distance ($L_R \simeq 1$ cm), except when $\Delta\Omega\tau \simeq -0.6\pi$, where the peak is taller and narrower than that in the response spectrum of an isolated diode. The latter corresponds to the valleys of the L-I curve undulation. These curves, therefore, indicate that the relaxation oscillation in the laser output will be suppressed when the returned light favorably interferes ($\Delta\Omega\tau \cong 0$) with the field in the diode, while it is enhanced and prolonged when $\Delta\Omega\tau$ has negative values of an appreciable magnitude. Calculations have also indicated that this tendency of relaxation oscillation enhancement *increases* as the external feedback *decreases*, even to such a small feedback level corresponding to the κ value of 2×10^8 s^{-1}. This seems to explain the observed fact that the external feedback tends to instabilize the dynamic behaviors of lasers diodes, particularly when the feedback is weak.

The physical origin of the relaxation oscillation enhancement can be explained as follows. In an isolated laser diode, the gain saturation tends to smooth out the intensity fluctuation. For example, the increase of the laser intensity beyond its stationary value is damped because of the corresponding decrease of the carrier density and gain, although the phase retardation in carrier density change at high frequency intensity fluctuation results in the resonance-like peak in the response spectrum. In a coupled cavity laser, the change in the interference condition with the carrier density modifies the situation. Suppose that the diode cavity resonance frequency ω_N is too large for the interference condition to be optimum, causing $\Delta\Omega = \Omega - \omega_N$ to be negative. The intensity increase reduces the carrier density, with decrease of the gain and increase of the refractive index in the diode cavity. The refractive index increase results in the decrease of ω_N and, hence, the improvement in the interference condition and the reduction of the compound cavity laser threshold, which compensates for the gain reduction to some extent. For this reason, the field increase above its stationary value is encouraged, giving rise to an enhanced relaxation oscillation, when $\Delta\Omega\tau$ is sufficiently negative, while it is strongly damped out when $\Delta\Omega\tau \gtrsim 0$.

The intensity noise spectrum can be calculated as the output response to fluctuations in carrier injection as well as photon emission and absorption, which can be regarded to have a white spectrum. It, therefore, resembles very closely the modulation response spectrum in Fig. 10. Therefore, the calculated results described above appear to explain well the observed transient and noise behaviors presented in the preceding section.

IV. Summary

To summarize, the influence of the optical feedback on semiconductor laser properties, with an external reflector placed 1-2 cm apart from the laser diode, has been investigated in detail. Experiments with transverse mode stabilized GaAs/AlGaAs lasers and carefully controlled mirror distance have found the periodic change in the output and its spectrum with the change in mirror distance and dc excitation current. The observation has been explained to result from the changes in the interference conditions in the compound laser cavity, formed by the laser diode and the external mirror. Some complications have been found to arise when the mirror distance is not closely equal to an integral multiple of the effective diode cavity length, because, in such a case, different longitudinal modes of the diode cavity compete for lasing with slight change in the interference conditions.

It has also been found that the external optical feedback can, when it is sufficiently strong, cause the laser to be multistable and to show hysteresis phenomena. In a semiconductor laser, the multistability can more easily show up than in other lasers because of the strong dependence of the refractive index of the laser active region on the carrier density.

The hysteresis phenomena, discussed in the present paper, have an entirely different origin from those reported recently by Nakamura *et al.* [17] and by Paoli [18]. The phenomena reported in [17] are caused by strong coupling among longitudinal modes via occupation number pulsation at k states interacting directly with the laser field, at the beat frequency equaling the difference in neighboring mode frequencies [19]. The other phenomena [18] are caused by saturable absorption within the diode cavity. The laser diodes used in this investigation showed neither of these kinds of hysteresis phenomena. The theoretical analysis presented in this paper has also neglected these other possibilities. The hysteresis phenomena, due to the compound cavity effects, can be easily controlled externally, e.g., by varying the mirror distance or dc current level, and appear to be potentially applicable for optical logic or memory devices, as expected for the nonlinear Fabry-Perot resonators [12].

The interference effects in the compound cavity have been found to affect also the dynamic properties of semiconductor lasers. When the interference condition is nearly optimum, corresponding to the output undulation peaks, the external feedback tends to suppress the relaxation oscillation in the transient output. The peak in the intensity noise frequency spectrum is reduced in height and broadened. When the interference condition is less favorable, corresponding to the valleys of the output undulation, and if the feedback is not sufficiently strong, the relaxation oscillation tends to be enhanced, or sustained and a sharp peak appears in the noise spectrum, correspondingly. These changes in the dynamic behaviors appear also be explainable as compound laser cavity effects.

Appendix

Derivation of (5)

The feedback coefficient appearing in (3) can be readily related to the cavity parameters as follows. Assume that stationary field $E_i \exp(i\Omega t)$ is incoming to the right diode facet in Fig. 1 from the left. The total reflected field $E_r \exp(i\Omega t)$ at this facet is

$$E_r e^{i\Omega t} = [\sqrt{R_2} + (1 - R_2)\sqrt{R_3}\, e^{-i\Omega\tau} + (1 - R_2) R_3 \sqrt{R_2}\, e^{-2i\Omega\tau} + \cdots] E_i e^{i\Omega t}.$$

The effective amplitude reflectivity r_{eff} can be defined [3] as the ratio E_r/E_i, which is found, when the multiple reflections in the external cavity is neglected, to be

$$r_{eff} = \sqrt{R_2}\,(1 + a\, e^{-i\Omega\tau})$$

where a has been defined by (6). The total cavity loss Γ of the compound cavity can be computed, using the standard expression for the mirror loss, as

$$\Gamma = \Gamma_w - \frac{c}{\eta \cdot l_D} \ln(\sqrt{R_1} \cdot r_{eff}) = \Gamma_0 - \frac{c}{\eta \cdot l_D} \ln(1 + a\, e^{-i\Omega t})$$

where Γ_w is the waveguide loss in the diode cavity, and Γ_0 is the cavity loss of the diode laser without the external mirror. Since the damping rate of the field in the diode equals $\frac{1}{2}\Gamma E \exp(i\Omega t)$, comparison of this expression with (3) yields, when $a \ll 1$, expression (5).

Acknowledgment

The authors are grateful to T. Uchida, I. Hayashi, S. Sugimoto, F. Saito, and A. Ueki for helpful comments and encouragement. Assistance in the experiment by Y. Odagiri is gratefully acknowledged. One of the authors (R. L.) is also grateful to R. Bonifacio for stimulating conversation.

References

[1] A. P. Bogatov, P. G. Eliseev, L. P. Ivanov, A. S. Logginov, M. A. Manko, and K. Ya. Senatorov, "Study of the single-mode injection laser," *IEEE J. Quantum Electron.*, vol. QE-9, pp. 392-398, Feb. 1973.

[2] C. Voumard, R. Salathe, and H. Weber, "Resonance amplifier model describing diode lasers coupled to short external resonators," *Appl. Phys.*, vol. 12, pp. 369-378, 1977.

[3] K. Kobayashi, "Improvements in direct pulse code modulation of semiconductor lasers by optical feedback," *Trans. IECE Japan*, vol. E59, pp. 8-14, Dec. 1976.

[4] Y. Mitsuhashi, T. Morikawa, K. Sakurai, A. Seko, and J. Shimada, "Self-coupled optical pickup," *Opt. Commun.*, vol. 17, pp. 95-97, Apr. 1976.

[5] R. F. Broom, E. Mohn, C. Risch, and R. Salathe, "Microwave self-modulation of a diode laser coupled to an external cavity," *IEEE J. Quantum Electron.*, vol. QE-6, pp. 328-334, June 1970.

[6] T. Morikawa, Y. Mitsuhashi, and J. Shimada, "Return-beam induced oscillations in self-coupled semiconductor lasers," *Electron. Lett.*, vol. 12, pp. 435-436, Aug. 1976.

[7] I. Ikushima and M. Maeda, "Self-coupled phenomena of semiconductor lasers caused by an optical fiber," *IEEE J. Quantum Electron.*, vol. QE-14, pp. 331-332, May 1978.

[8] N. Chinone, K. Aiki, and R. Ito, "Stabilization of semiconductor laser outputs by a mirror close to a laser facet," *Appl. Phys. Lett.*, vol. 33, pp. 990-992, Dec. 1978.

[9] O. Hirota and Y. Suematsu, "Noise properties of injection lasers due to reflected waves," *IEEE J. Quantum Electron.*, vol. QE-15, pp. 142-149, Mar. 1979.

[10] T. Kanada and K. Nawata, "Injection laser characteristics due to reflected optical power," *IEEE J. Quantum Electron.*, vol. QE-15, pp. 559-565, July 1979.

[11] K. H. Levin and C. L. Tang, "Optical switching and bistability in tunable lasers," *Appl. Phys. Lett.*, vol. 34, pp. 376-378, Mar. 1979.

[12] A. Szoke, V. Daneu, J. Goldhar, and N. A. Kurnit, "Bistable optical element and its applications," *Appl. Phys. Lett.*, vol. 15, pp. 376-379, Dec. 1969.

[13] R. Lang, "Lateral transverse mode instability and its stabilization in stripe geometry injection lasers," *IEEE J. Quantum Electron.*, vol. QE-15, pp. 718-726, Aug. 1979.

[14] G. H. B. Thompson, D. F. Lovelace, and S. E. H. Turley, "Kinks in the light/current characteristics and near-field shifts in (GaAl)As heterostructure stripe lasers and their explanation by the effect of self-focusing on a built-in optical waveguide," *IEE J. Solid-State and Electron Devices*, vol. 2, pp. 12-30, Jan. 1978.

[15] P. A. Kirkby, A. R. Goodwin, G. H. B. Thompson, and P. R. Selway, "Observation of self-focusing in stripe geometry semiconductor lasers and the development of a comprehensive model of their operation," *IEEE J. Quantum Electron.*, vol. QE-13, pp. 705-719, Aug. 1977.

[16] H. C. Casey, Jr. and M. B. Panish, *Heterostructure Lasers, Part A*. New York: Academic, 1978.

[17] M. Nakamura, K. Aiki, N. Chinone, R. Ito and J. Umeda, "Longitudinal mode behaviors of mode-stabilized $Al_xGa_{1-x}As$ injection lasers," *J. Appl. Phys.*, vol. 49, pp. 4644-4648, Sept. 1978.

[18] T. L. Paoli, "Saturable Absorption effects in the self-pulsing (AlGa)As junction laser," *Appl. Phys. Lett.*, vol. 34, pp. 652-655, May 1979.

[19] R. Lang, in preparation.

Feedback-induced line broadening in cw channel-substrate planar laser diodes

R. O. Miles, A. Dandridge, A. B. Tveten, H. F. Taylor, and T. G. Giallorenzi
Naval Research Laboratory, Washington, D. C. 20375

(Received 4 August 1980; accepted for publication 29 September 1980)

The effect of optical feedback on the spectral characteristics of channel-substrate planar single-mode laser diodes operating at room temperature is reported. The impact on the performance of interferometric sensor systems using such sources is discussed. The linewidth for the free-running laser at 10-mW output power was determined to be less than 5 MHz at room temperature. Broadening on the order of 40 times the intrinsic linewidth was observed for 0.1% feedback and increased with increasing feedback. The presence of self-oscillation modes was observed at 0.04% feedback. Satellite modes symmetrically located with respect to the primary mode appeared in the spectrum for feedback greater than 0.04%. These satellite modes are attributed to self-oscillation in the laser induced by feedback. As the feedback was increased, the satellite mode spectrum began to overlap that of the primary mode, reducing the effective coherence length from 60 m (for the single-mode linewidth) to less than a few centimeters.

PACS numbers: 42.55.Px, 42.60.By

Recently the deleterious effects of optical feedback on laser diode noise properties have been reported.[1-3] In this letter we report the effect of feedback on the coherence properties of single-mode channel-substrate planar (CSP) diode lasers[4] and its impact on possible sources used in interferometric sensor systems. The results presented here were obtained using the Hitachi HLP 1400 single-mode CSP diode laser.

Most interferometric sensors consist of a signal and reference arm in a Mach Zehnder configuration, with the sensitivity of the device proportional to the length of the signal arm.[5] Some sensor configurations which are being investigated require unequal optical path lengths for signal and reference arms. The laser source for such configurations must have a coherence length considerably longer than this path length difference, and spectral characteristics which remain stable as other system parameters change. For a laser source with linewidth Δf the corresponding coherence length L_C is

$$L_c = c/\Delta f, \tag{1}$$

where c is the velocity of light. A simple expression approximating the linewidth, (full width at half maximum) of a single-mode diode laser source is[6]

$$\Delta f = 4\pi N h \nu_0 (\Delta \nu_{cav})^2 / P, \tag{2}$$

where P is the total power emitted in the fundamental lasing mode of frequency ν_0, and N is proportional to the population inversion. In general, the value of N depends on junction temperature and field intensity across the radiating surface; N is an integer and can range from 1 to 10 for low temperature and/or low field intensity, and can go as high as 10^3 for strong fields. The condition for strong fields in a diode laser is given by Mironav *et al.*[7] as

$$P/S \gg 10^5 \text{ W/cm}^2, \tag{3}$$

where S is the radiating surface area, the cold-cavity linewidth $\Delta \nu_{cav}$ is the mode half-width at half power of the passive laser cavity. This expression is written

$$\Delta \nu_{cav} = (c/2\pi \bar{n} l)(1 - \text{Re}^{-\alpha L})/(\text{Re}^{-\alpha L})^{1/2}, \tag{4}$$

where $\bar{n}$ is the effective refractive index for the laser waveguide which allows for dispersion in the medium and is expressed as

$$\bar{n} = \left(1 - \frac{\lambda_0}{n} \frac{\lambda n}{\partial \lambda}\right), \tag{5}$$

where n is the refractive index of the medium at λ_0, α is the absorption loss, and l and R are the cavity length and reflectivity of the cavity facets. For the HLP 1400 laser,[4] $R = 0.32$, $l = 300\,\mu$m, $\bar{n} = 4.2$, and $\alpha = 7$ cm^{-1}. For a total output power of approximately 10 mW the power density in the laser cavity is on the order of 5×10^5 W/cm^2, which is still within the low field intensity regime specified by Eq. (3). Population-inversion ratios for the low-intensity case and for room-temperature operation are estimated to lie within the range $1 < N < 10$. The spectral linewidth can be calculated from Eq. (2) to lie within the range $0.3 < \Delta f < 3$ MHz.

The linewidth of cw diode laser has been measured by several authors.[8-10] Nakamura *et al.*[8] reported measuring a linewidth less than 30 MHz at room temperature, using the Hitachi 1000 series CSP laser with a 10-cm Fabry Perot etalon. This measurement was instrument limited by the finesse of the etalons. Voumard,[9] using a stripe-geometry diode laser with the front facet antireflection coated and an external reflector to define the laser cavity, observed a linewidth of 17 MHz. This was achieved using a low-finesse Fabry Perot etalon placed in the cavity. This measurement too was limited, however, by the finesse of the measuring instrument. Ahearn and Crowe[10] measured Δf to be 150 kHz using a GaAlAs laser cooled to 77 K and operating at 250 mW. Their measurement procedure consisted of a homodyne detection scheme of correlated noise in an unbalanced Michelson interferometer.

To observe the effects of optical feedback on the laser

linewidth, an experiment was set up as described in detail elsewhere[2] and as illustrated in Fig. 1. Initially, all sources of optical feedbck into the laser were reduced below detectable levels ($< 10^{-4}\%$). The linewidth of the free-running single-mode laser was measured at room temperature. Operating with a driving current 1.3 times threshold with 10 mW total output power, the linewidth of the Hitachi HLP 1400 CSP diode laser was found to be less than 5 MHz. The measurement was made using a scanning Fabry Perot interferometer with a free spectral range (FSR) of 900 MHz and was limited by the resolution of the interferometer. The calculated coherence length from Eq. (1) for this linewidth is about 60 m.

Emitted light was fed back into the laser with amplitude and phase controlled independently. Using a Fabry Perot with a variable FSR, the linewidth and model characteristics were measured as a function of feedback. For small amounts of feedback $\sim 0.1\%$, the linewidth was broadened by a factor of about 40. At 0.04% feedback a fine structure was observed on the fundamental mode. The fine structure was observed to be in the form of two satellite modes located on either side of the primary mode. Frequency displacement of the satellite modes from the primary mode was not observed to be dependent upon the phase of the feedback, but a 20–30% change in relative amplitude of the peaks was observed as the phase was varied through 2π rad. However, the frequency difference between the satellite modes and the principle mode was an increasing function of dc bias current ranging from 2.5 GHz at $1.2I_{th}$ to 4 GHz at $2I_{th}$. Peak amplitude of the modes increased with increased feedback until equal in amplitude with the primary mode. Figures 2(a), 2(b), and 2(c) compare the spectra for the free-running single-mode laser and the spectra taken with a FSR of 66 GHz at 0.04% and 0.06% feedback.

The satellite modes are apparently sidebands generated by intensity fluctuations in the laser output. The observed increase in mode spacing with current is consistent with previous observations[11] on the dependence of the frequency of self-oscillation in injection lasers on bias current level. However, neither the spacing between the primary and satellite peaks nor the relative amplitude of these peaks was found to be strongly dependent on external cavity spacing. Apparently, in our experiment the influence of cavity transit time on the self-pulsation frequency is not as important as in the work of Figueroa *et al.*[12] This difference could be due to the stronger coupling to the external cavity in their experiment, in which the feedback was between 1 and 20%.

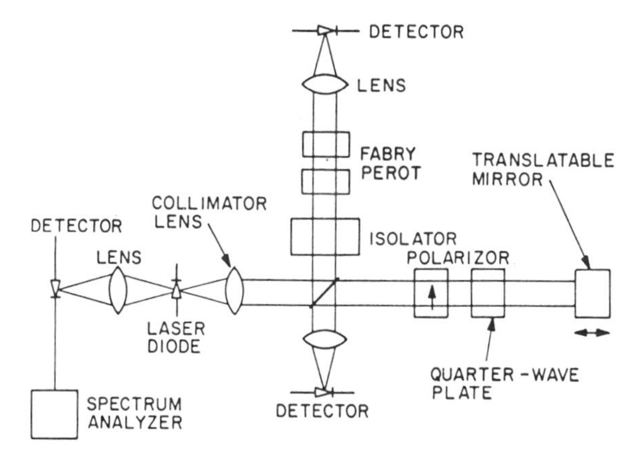

FIG. 1. Diagram of experimental method to determine the effect of feedback on laser characteristics.

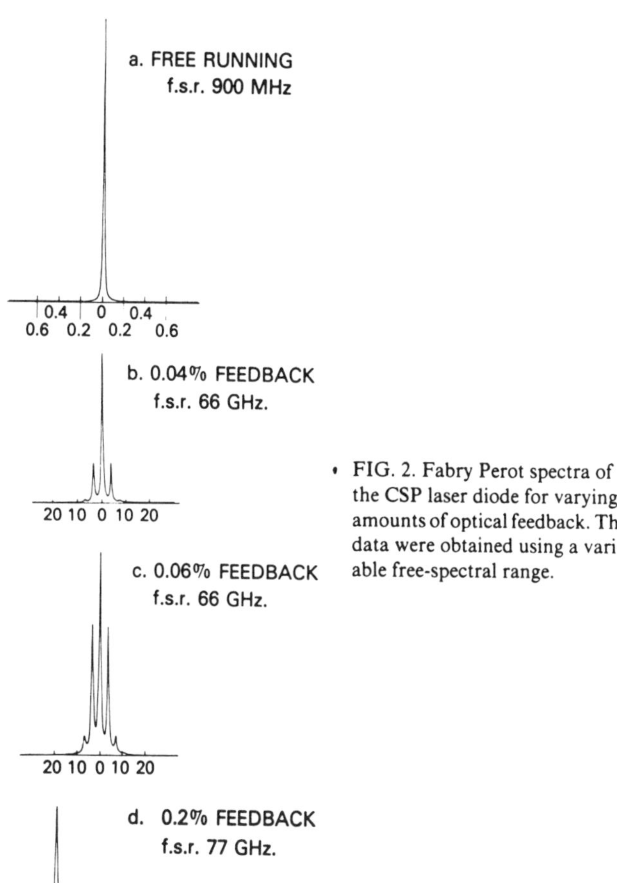

FIG. 2. Fabry Perot spectra of the CSP laser diode for varying amounts of optical feedback. The data were obtained using a variable free-spectral range.

With increasing feedback, multiple longitudinal modes appear and the spectrum of each continues to broaden. This is illustrated in the emission spectra of Fig. 2(d), which were recorded using a Fabry Perot with a FSR of 77 GHz. Note that the satellite modes are associated with each of the longitudinal modes. The apparent near proximity of the longitudinal modes in this figure is a consequence of the overlapping orders of the Fabry Perot interferometer. The modes in reality are well separated in frequency space (1.2×10^{11} Hz). The effects of broadening on the coherence of the laser becomes apparent with the significant overlap in frequency space of the satellite and primary modes with increased feedback. This effect is clearly seen in Fig. 2(e) as feedback is increased to 0.3%. In this case the linewidth of the individual modes has broadened about 2 GHz. The overlap in frequency space has become so significant that the effective coherence width of this mode is essentially that of a convoluted linewidth of 6 GHz, which corresponds to a coherence length of about 5 cm.

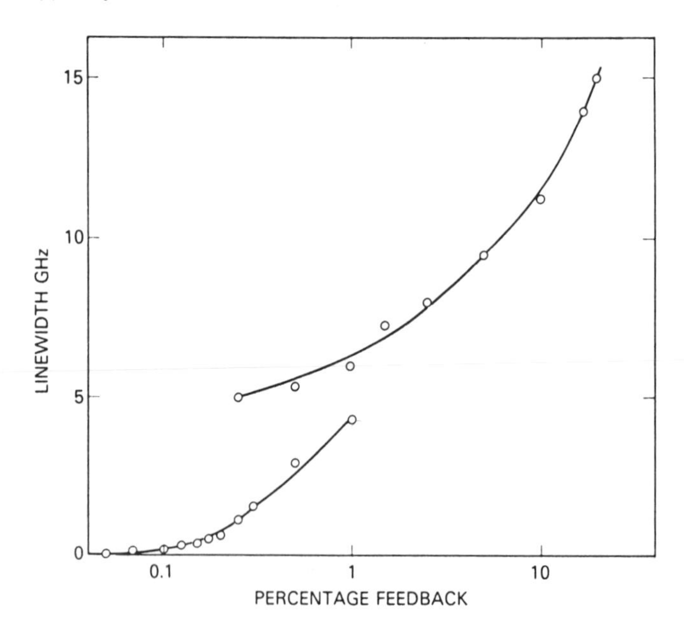

FIG.3 Linewidth as a function of feedback. Lower curve: increase in Δf for fundamental mode. Upper curve: effective convoluted linewidth due to overlapping in frequency space.

Figure 3 shows the increased linewidth as a function of feedback. The lower curve is the increase of Δf as a function of feedback for the individual mode, while the upper curve is the effective convoluted linewidth due to overlapping in frequency space also as a function of feedback.

From the above results it is observed that optical feedback in the CSP laser diode source induces three types of modal behavior which can reduce the fringe visibility in an interferometric sensor system.[13,14] Feedback-induced line broadening reduces the coherence length from 60 m to 30 cm at 0.2% feedback. An interferometric sensor system using this laser would require a path difference of less than a few millimeters to obtain good fringe visibility.The induced satellite modes present in the 0.04%–0.1% feedback region cause a periodic modulation in the fringe visibility every 8 cm as the path difference is increased, and therefore require the path difference to be controlled to within 1 cm to obtain high-contrast fringes. At the onset of multi-longitudinal-mode operation, the fringe visibility is again modulated for increased path length with a periodicity of 2 mm. This requires the path difference in the interferometer sensor to be controlled to within 0.1 mm to insure good fringe visibility,.

In conclusion, we have observed a 5-MHz linewidth in a free-running CSP laser diode operating at room temperature with 10-mW output. With increasing feedback of emitted light into the laser cavity, the linewidth was observed to broaden by a factor of 40 at 0.1% feedback. At 0.04% fine structure in the form of symmetrical satellite modes appeared. The frequency separation of the satellite mode from the primary mode was observed to be a function of dc bias current and ranged from 2 to 4 GHz. The frequency separation was found to be independent of cavity length for the range of feedback investigated. The amplitudes of the satellite modes, however, were phase dependent and observed to change by 20–30% as the phase was varied by 2π rad. These results are consistent with self-oscillation phenomena in diode lasers and represents the first time that self-oscillations have been observed above 2 GHz and the first observations of phase dependence of the amplitude of the induced oscillations. Furthermore, feedback-induced oscillations have not been reported for feedback less than 1%. The effect of the presence of the satellite modes is to overlap the primary mode in frequency space with increasing feedback. The overlapping in effect increases the emission linewidth of the laser to the convoluted width of the primary and the two symmetrical satellite modes. This results in an increase in the linewidth by several GHz, effectively reducing the coherence length of the laser to less than a few centimeters.

[1]T. Kanada, K. Nawata, IEEE J. Quantum Electron. **QE-15**, 559 (1979).
[2]R. Miles, A. Dandridge, A. B. Tveten, T. Giallorenzi, and H. F. Taylor (unpublished).
[3]O. Hirota and V. Suematsu, IEEE J. Quantum Electron. **QE-15**, 142 (1979).
[4]K. Aiki, M. Nakamura, T. Kuroda, J. Umeda, R. Ito, N. Chinone, and M. Maeda, IEEE J. Quantum Electron. **QE-14**, 89 (1978).
[5]A. Dandridge, A. B. Tveten, G. H. Sigel, E. J. West, and T. G. Giallorenzi, Electron. Lett. **16**, 408 (1980).
[6]V. Elesin and V. Rusakov, Sov. J. Quantum Electron. **5**, 1239 (1976).
[7]Y. Mironav, V. Molochev, V. Nikitin, and A. Semenov, Sov. J. Quantum Electron. **6**, 123 (1976).
[8]M. Nakamura, K. Aiki, N. Chinone, R. Ito, and J. Umeda, J. Appl. Phys. **49**, 4644 (1978).
[9]C. Voumard, Opt. Lett. **1**, 61 (1977).
[10]W. Ahearn and J. Crowe, IEEE J. Quantum Elecctron. **2**, 597 (1966).
[11]R. Broom, E. Mohn, C. Risch, and R. Salathe, IEEE J. Qunatum Electron. **6**, 328 (1970).
[12]L. Figueroa, K. Lau, and A. Yariv, Appl. Phys. Lett. **36**, 248 (1980).
[13]A. Reisinger, C. David, K. Lawley, and A. Yariv, IEEE J. Quantum Electron. **15** 1382 (1979).
[14]A. Dandridege, A. B. Tveten, and R. O. Miles (unpublished).

DIRECT OBSERVATION OF LORENTZIAN LINESHAPE OF SEMICONDUCTOR LASER AND LINEWIDTH REDUCTION WITH EXTERNAL GRATING FEEDBACK

S. SAITO
Y. YAMAMOTO

Musashino Electrical Communication Laboratory
Nippon Telegraph & Telephone Public Corporation
Musashino-shi, Tokyo 180, Japan

1st April 1981

Indexing terms: Lasers, Optical communications

The Lorentzian lineshape of a single longitudinal mode AlGaAs semiconductor laser is directly observed by optical heterodyne detection. A remarkable reduction in the spectral linewidth to less than 50 kHz is achieved with external grating feedback. The experimental linewidth is in reasonable agreement with the theoretical value, which is obtained by finesse calculation of the active Fabry-Perot cavity.

Introduction: The possibility of coherent optical fibre transmission systems using a semiconductor laser transmitter and a local oscillator has been investigated.[1,2] The spectral linewidth determined by the quantum phase noise of lasers affects the signal/noise ratio in optical heterodyne detection of phase or frequency modulated light.[2] Precise measurement of the spectral lineshape and reduction in the spectral linewidth, as well as frequency stabilisation, are indispensable for system performance evaluation. The linewidth of AlGaAs double heterostructure lasers has been so far by means of interference measurement using a 4.15 fibre,[3] a delayed self-heterodyne method,[4] Fourier spectroscopy,[5] Fabry-Perot interferometry[6] and a phase-amplitude noise conversion measurement.[7]

This letter reports direct observation of the beat note spectrum between two distinct AlGaAs laser outputs. Effects of the pumping level and the external grating feedback on the spectral linewidth are studied experimentally and theoretically.

Free-running AlGaAs laser spectrum: Experimental set-up is similar to the configuration previously shown as Fig. 1 in Reference 1. The AlGaAs channelled substrate planar (CSP) lasers,[8] which oscillate in a single longitudinal mode at identical 825 nm wavelengths, are installed in temperature stabilised chambers. Two additional optical isolators are inserted to eliminate undesired reflection feedback from optical elements into the two lasers.

Beat note spectra between free running lasers are shown in Figs. 1*a* and *b* for pumping rates $I/I_{th} = 1{\cdot}20$ and $1{\cdot}49$, respectively. Hereafter, the pumping rate refers to the arithmetic mean of pumping rates for the two lasers, since they are chosen to be approximately similar values. The pumping rates corresponding to Fig. 1*b*, for example, are $I/I_{th} = 1{\cdot}46$ and $1{\cdot}52$ for the two lasers. The noise floor with a white spectral distribution decreases with respect to the beat note peak as the pumping rate increases. Oscillation lineshapes for different pumping rates are plotted in Fig. 2 as a function of the frequency deviation from the centre frequency. The experimental results, except for the noise floor, mostly agree with the solid lines which reveal Lorentzian distribution. The spectral linewidths (full width at half the maximum) are shown in Fig. 3 by open circles as a function of the pumping rate.

Linewidth reduction with grating feedback: Frequency selective feedback with a diffraction grating[9] is tested to improve the lineshape. The externally mounted diffraction gratings have 750 nm blaze wavelength, 0·83 μm groove pitch and 26·7° blaze angle, and are arranged in the Littrow configuration.[10] Light

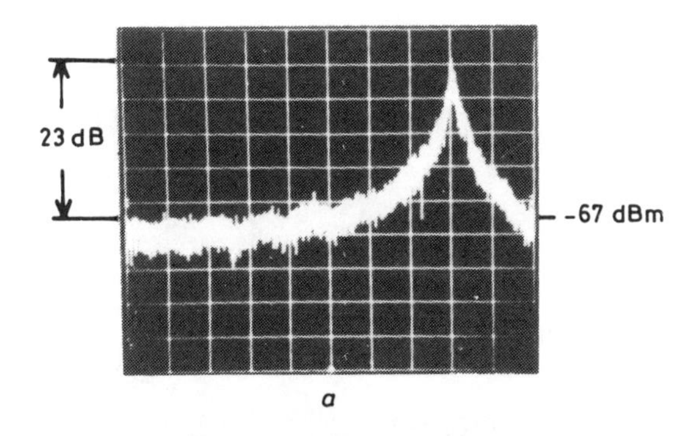

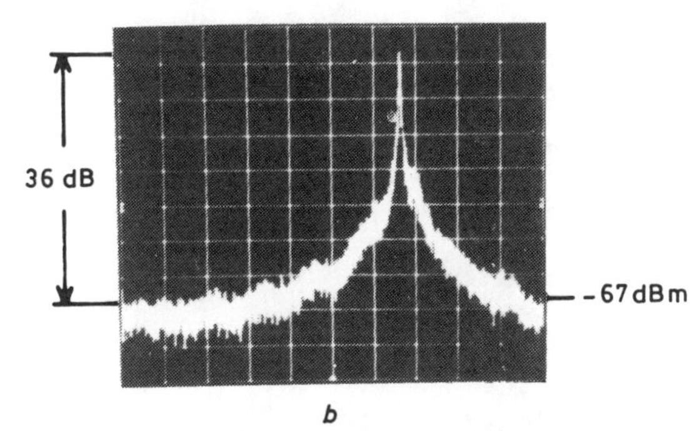

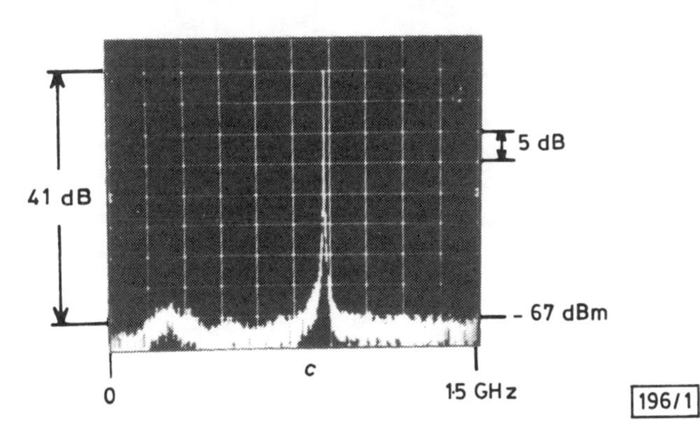

Fig. 1 *Beat note spectrum between two distinct semiconductor lasers*

a Lasers in free-running state at $I/I_{th} = 1{\cdot}20$
b Lasers in free-running state at $I/I_{th} = 1{\cdot}49$
c Lasers with external grating feedback at $I/I_{th} = 1{\cdot}44$

emitted from the rear facet of the laser travels out of the temperature stabilised chamber. The beam is aligned to focus at about 10 m distance from the laser with a 15 mm focal length lens. The beam divergent angle is estimated to be about 1×10^{-4} rad. The grating, with rulings parallel to the junction plane, is fixed at a 22 cm distance from the laser. The first order diffraction is used for feedback.

The beat note spectrum between two lasers, both with grating feedback, is shown in Fig. 1*c*. Remarkable improvements in

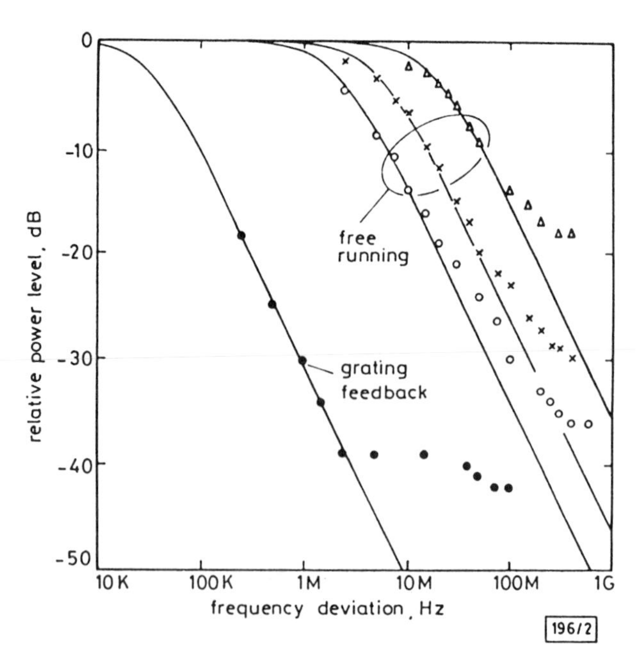

Fig. 2 *Oscillation lineshape of a single semiconductor laser*

Solid lines denote the Lorentzian lineshape

I/I_{th}:

△ 1·165 × 1·36

○ 1·49 ● 1·44

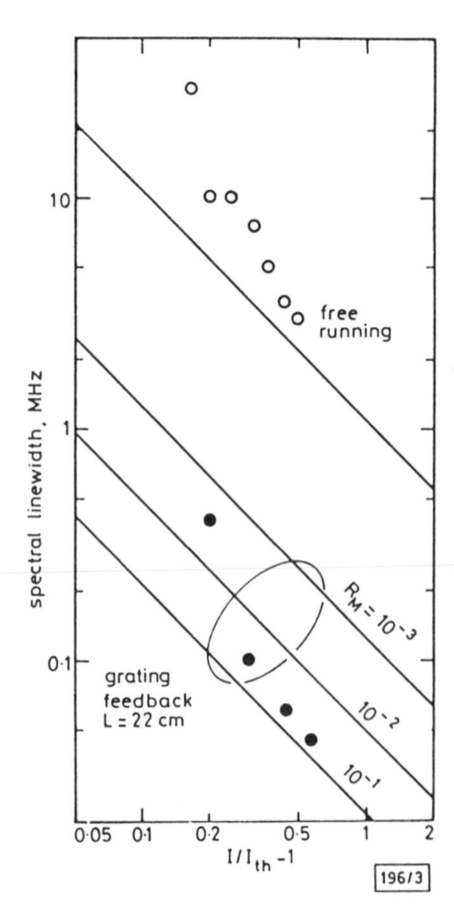

Fig. 3 *Spectral linewidth of a single semiconductor laser*

Open and solid circles are measured linewidths of a laser in free running state and with external grating feedback, respectively. Solid lines are theoretical spectral linewidth. L is distance from laser to external grating, and R_M is equivalent reflectivity of grating

the noise floor level and in the spectral linewidth are achieved with the external feedback. The spectral lineshape and the spectral linewidth are shown in Figs. 2 and 3 by solid circles, respectively.

Discussion and conclusion: The Lorentzian lineshape of the semiconductor laser was directly observed by optical heterodyne detection and displayed in an RF spectrum analyser. Discrepancy from the theoretical Lorentzian lineshape at the tail shown in Fig. 2 is caused by the beat component between amplified spontaneous emission light oscillating in the spurious longitudinal modes.

The solid lines in Fig. 3 reveal theoretical linewidths for the CSP laser, with and without the external grating feedback. The theoretical curves are obtained by calculating finesse for an active Fabry–Perot cavity, in which a single pass gain is estimated by rate equation analysis.[11] The spectral linewidth decreases with the pumping rate in proportion to $(I/I_{th} - 1)^{-1}$. The experimental values are in reasonable agreement with the theoretical results.

Remarkable reduction in linewidth as well as noise floor was achieved with the external feedback. Similar improvement was confirmed with an external mirror feedback without wavelength selectivity. Grating feedback, however, was superior to mirror feedback with respect to stable single longitudinal mode operation and wideband frequency tunability.

The linewidth is expected to be reduced further by enlarging the distance from the laser to the grating. When the grating is separated further, however, a spurious external cavity mode begins to build up and two mode oscillations are observed during the small laser temperature fluctuation.

In order to realise a 400 Mbit/s optical FSK heterodyne detection system with 10^{-9} error rate, for example, the optical carrier wave spectral linewidth should be less than 100 kHz.[2] The semiconductor laser with external grating feedback is promising for such coherent optical fibre transmission application, owing to the less than 100 kHz spectral linewidth and the over 1 THz oscillation frequency tunability.

Acknowledgment: The authors wish to thank T. Kimura and A. Kawana for their useful suggestions and discussions.

References

1 SAITO, S., YAMAMOTO, Y., and KIMURA, T.: 'Optical heterodyne detection of directly frequency modulated semiconductor laser signals', *Electron. Lett.*, 1980, **16**, pp. 826–827

2 YAMAMOTO, Y., and KIMURA, T.: 'Coherent optical fiber transmission systems', *IEEE J. Quantum Electron.*, June 1981, to be published

3 MACHIDA, S., KAWANA, A., ISHIHARA, K., and TSUCHIYA, H.: 'Interference of an AlGaAs laser diode using 4·15 km single mode fiber cable', *ibid.*, 1979, **QE-15**, pp. 155–157

4 OKOSHI, T., KIKUCHI, K., and NAKAYAMA, A.: 'Novel method for high resolution measurement of laser output spectrum', *Electron. Lett.*, 1980, **16**, pp. 630–631

5 NEMOTO, K., HAYASHI, K., and HIRANO, H.: 'Measurement of spectral width of single longitudinal mode semiconductor laser'. Record of Annual Meeting of IECE Japan, 1980, 222 (in Japanese)

6 TAKAKURA, T., IGA, K., and TAKO, T.: 'Measurement of spectral width of a single longitudinal mode semiconductor laser', *Japan. J. Appl. Phys.*, 1980, **19**, pp. L725–L727

7 YAMAMOTO, Y., MUKAI, T., and SAITO, S.: 'Quantum phase noise and linewidth of a semiconductor laser', see pp. 327–329

8 AIKI, K., NAKAMURA, M., KURODA, T., UMEDA, J., ITO, R., CHINONE, N., and MAEDA, M.: 'Transverse mode stabilized $Al_xGa_{1-x}As$ injection lasers with channeled-substrate-planar structure', *IEEE J. Quantum Electron.*, 1978, **QE-14**, pp. 89–94

9 FLEMING, M. W., and MOORADIAN, A.: 'Spectral characteristics of external-cavity controlled semiconductor lasers', *ibid.*, 1981, **QE-17**, pp. 44–59

10 ITO, M., and KIMURA, T.: 'Oscillation properties of AlGaAs DH lasers with an external grating', *ibid.*, 1980, **QE-16**, pp. 69–77

11 YAMAMOTO, Y.: to be published

Monolithic two-section GaInAsP/InP active-optical-resonator devices formed by reactive ion etching

L. A. Coldren, B. I. Miller, K. Iga, and J. A. Rentschler
Bell Telephone Laboratories, Holmdel, New Jersey 07733

(Received 27 October 1980; accepted for publication 10 December 1980)

Narrow, high-aspect-ratio grooves formed by reactive ion etching (RIE) are shown to be useful as partially transmissive mirrors for coupled active laser-detector, laser-modulator, and laser-etalon two-section monolithic devices. Results emphasize control of the longitudinal mode spectrum by active etalon action.

PACS numbers: 42.55.Px, 42.82. + n, 41.80.Gg, 85.60.Me

The GaInAsP material system has been well established as important for sources and detectors in the 1.1–1.7 μm wavelength region where efficient optical fiber communication systems show promise.[1] A common desire of many workers in the field is to integrate sources, detectors, and various signal manipulating devices together in a simple and reliable manner.[2–6]

A key optical component in this integration is an efficient, partially transmissive mirror that can be used for laser feedback and output coupling to other devices aligned on the same substrate. Such devices might be as simple as a monitoring detector, or as complex as several more active laser-resonator sections for obtaining improved mode and frequency stability. In most cases, the partially transmissive mirror should transmit nearly all the radiation it does not reflect, and the energy should be retained within a waveguide.

In this letter we report the first creation and use of a deep, narrow-etched groove to perform the desired partially transmissive mirror function in a double-heterostructure (DH) GaInAsP/InP laser substrate. The groove, which is formed by reactive ion etching (RIE),[6] divides the laser into two coupled sections. The first is used as the primary laser cavity, and the second can be used alternatively as (i) a monitoring detector, (ii) an active gain modulator, or (iii) an active etalon for spectrum control. In this letter, we will concentrate on the novel, active etalon results.

Previous work in this area includes a number of early suggestions[7–10] that multiple electrodes or cavities may be advantageous for controlling laser outputs, and some of these[8–10] discuss the potential advantages of etalon action as demonstrated here. Experimental work on GaAlAs has demonstrated the integration of a laser-amplifier/detector using a separate waveguide and wet chemically etched (WCE) mirrors.[11] Quaternary experiments have made use of relatively wide grooves formed by WCE to couple a monitoring detector with a laser,[3] and the use of Bragg reflective gratings in a separate low-loss waveguide channel.[4] Both of these latter techniques, however, are relatively inefficient at transmitting to a second device waveguided energy that is

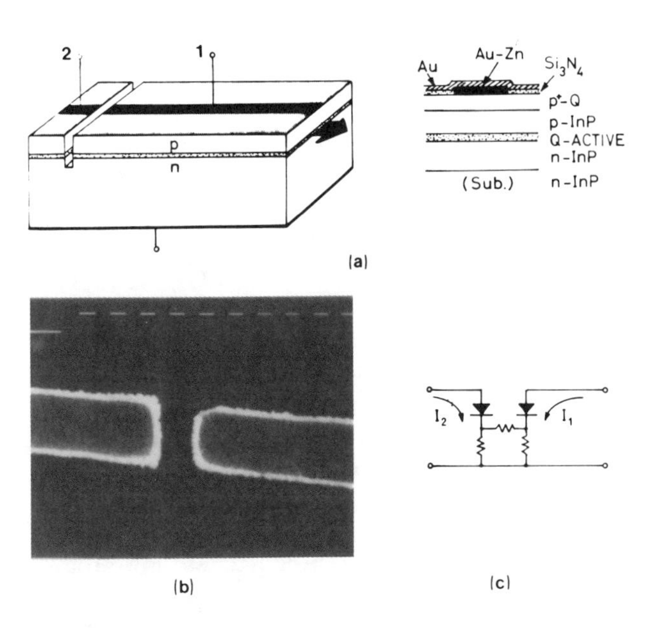

FIG. 1. Device configuration. (a) schematic cross section; (b) SEM photo of 5-μm-wide strip contacts at etched groove (marker segements = 1 μm); (c) simplified equivalent circuit.

not reflected. Other work has integrated modulators without an interveneing mirror.[5]

Figure 1(a) shows schematically the experimental DH chips illustrating the stripe geometry used. Two different groove-depth cases, which provide different regimes of operation, will be considered. In the first case (deep groove), the groove cuts through and well beyond the active layer providing a maximum of reflection and minimum of coupling to the second section. In the second case (shallow groove), the groove does not reach the active layer, thus providing a weaker reflection and a stronger coupling to the second sections. In testing, separate connections are made to the two sections so that separate bias signals can be applied. Figure 1(b) is a scanning electron microscopy (SEM) illustration of a deep-groove device where the stripe contacts meet the reflective groove, and Fig. 1(c) is a simple dc equivalent circuit of the three terminal device.

Reprinted with permission from *Appl. Phys. Lett.*, vol. 38, no. 5, pp. 315–317, Mar. 1, 1981.

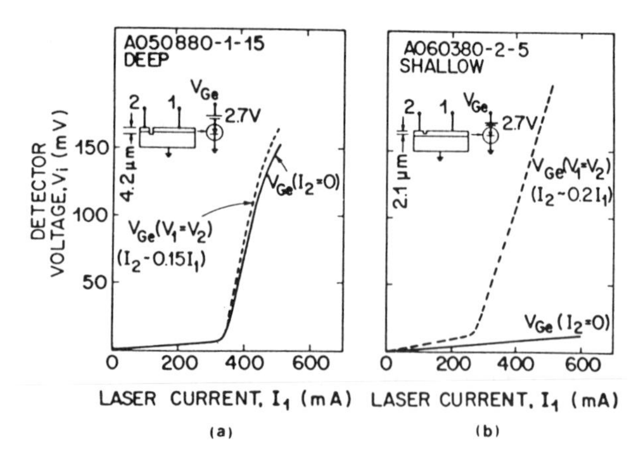

FIG. 2. Photodetector voltage vs laser current, I_1 with various biases on terminal 2, for example deep and shallow groove devices. Cavity lengths in Fig. 3.

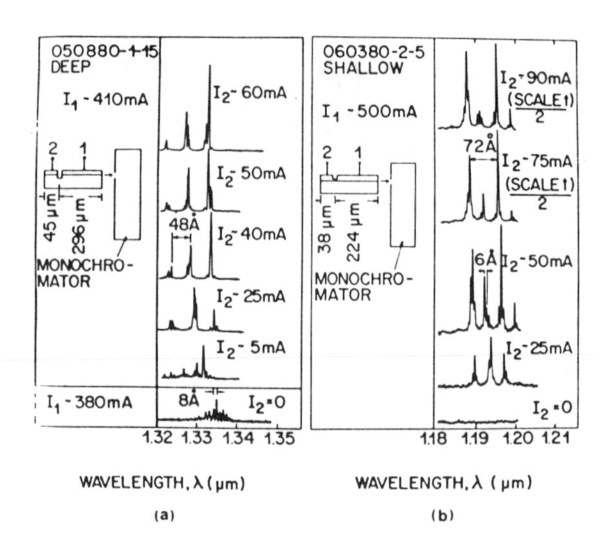

FIG. 3. Laser output spectra from section 1 and I_2 is changed for deep and shallow groove devices.

The DH substrate wafers are grown by conventional liquid phase epitaxial (LPE) techniqes. A 1-μm gap in a deposited Ti layer forms the mask during RIE in a 80% Cl_2 + 20% O_2 gas mixture for the narrow groove. After Ti mask removal the substrates are coated with 1000 Å of Si_3N_4, stripe contact windows are opened by plasma etching, and plated contacts are formed. The wafers are then cleaved and sawed to form the test chips.

In Fig. 2 the detector voltage output versus pulsed laser current I_1 is plotted for the deep and shallow reflector groove cases with I_2 bias as a parameter. The condition ($V_2 = V_1$) determined the maximum I_2 applied. As one would expect, the second-section bias current I_2 has little effect on the output level in the deep-groove case where the sections are weakly coupled, but has a large effect in the shallow-groove case where the coupling is strong. This behavior can be understood more quantitatively by studying the effective reflectance of the "active mirror" at the groove for section 1,

$$r = r_g + r_c t_g^2 e^{-2j\beta_2 l_2}(1 - r_c r_g e^{-2j\beta_2 l_2})^{-1}, \quad (1)$$

where r_g and t_g are the complex groove reflection and transmission coefficients for the guided mode, r_c is the cleaved end reflectance, l_2 is the length of section 2, and $\beta_2 = \beta_{20} + j\alpha_2$ is the complex propagation constant for the guided mode in section 2. For the cases depicted we estimate[12] $|r_g(\text{deep})| \sim 0.3$; $|t_g\ (\text{deept})| \sim 0.4$; $|r_g(\text{shallow})| \sim 0.1$; $|t_g\ (\text{shallow})| \sim 0.7$ and $r_c \sim 0.55$.

A significant loss occurs in the present cases because the groove walls are somewhat rough and slope about 10° from the vertical. It has been shown, however, that vertical smooth walls are possible with reactive ion etching (RIE).[6] Also, there is inherent mode conversion loss in the shallow-groove case.

Figure 3 shows output spectra as the bias I_2 is changed. In the deep-groove case laser section 1 will operate with $I_2 = 0$ as shown in Fig. 2(a), and it does so with a typical multilongitudinal mode spectrum shown just above threshold for $I_1 \sim 380$ mA. Further above threshold ($I_1 \sim 410$ mA) the 8-Å mode spacing still persists until a significant current I_2 is applied. As can be shown from Eq. (1), the effective laser mirror reflectivity r developes ripples as a function of wavelength λ as I_2 is increased. The groove-transmission phase (controlled by its width) and the second-section length l_2 primarily determine where the two terms in Eq. (1) will interfere constructively or destructively. The loss (or gain) $\alpha_2(I_2)$ controls the relative magnitude of the two terms, and the combination of α_2 with the reflectances r_c and r_g determine the Q of the ripple. The 48-Å ripple period resulting from the short 45-μm cavity in Fig. 3(a) determines the allowed output modes for the laser section as I_2 is increased. Every sixth mode is selected in this case. Also note how the base line becomes cleaner as the relatively high-Q short-cavity section modulates $r(\lambda)$. Spurious transverse modes prohibit a still cleaner response.

Another interesting result observed in Fig. 3(a) is the tuning capability afforded by the active etalon. As the bias I_2 is increased from 40 to 60 mA, for example, the modes shift ~ 16 Å with little change in output level. Control of both I_1 and I_2 allows the level to be held constant. Shifts in both the index and the gain spectrum in the etalon are believed to be the cause of this tuning capability.

For shorter second sections the ripple period will become large enough to provide single-mode operation analogous to the work of Smith.[13] We calculate that $l_2/l_1 < 0.1$ is required to assure single-mode behavior at any output level. Alternatively, the second-section length could be made just slightly different from section 1. Then the longitudinal mode combs of the two cavities coincide only at widely spaced wavelengths, again providing probable single-mode operation.[9]

In the shallow-groove case of Fig. 3(b), the situation is somewhat different. Here I_2 has a large effect on output level [see Fig. 2(b)], and the etalon action is evident as soon as the lasing threshold is reached. Because of the low effective groove reflectance, the short-cavity Q is always low and mode selectivity is not as sharp.

The above two-section devices have also been used in other experiments. An integrated monitoring detector is obtainable by reverse biasing the second section in deep groove devices.[14] In this case, we have found that a wider groove is desirable to better isolate the detected signal from the laser bias current, although a differential detection scheme should solve the inherent "cross-talk" problem evident from the dc equivalent circuit in Fig. 1(c). For our 1×4.2-μm-deep grooves the depicted resistors are all comparable in value at $\sim 0.5\ \Omega$.

In addition, the second section of a shallow groove device can serve as a low-capacitance, low-current modulation port as suggested by the strong output dependence on I_2 shown in Fig. 2(b). On/off ratios > 20 dB are easily obtainable. High speed is promised by the relatively low current to be switched.

In summary, we have shown that a narrow high-aspect ratio RIE slot can be used as a partially transmissive mirror for integrated optical circuits, and that a two-section device made with such a mirror can provide a monolithic laser-etalon combination. Laser-detector and laser-modulator functions are possible with the same devices. Threshold levels comparable to simple, cleaved stripe geometry devices suggest that coupling losses are tolerable. Use of multiple grooves to create multiple sections will provide more degrees of freedom for leveling, stabilizing, and manipulating laser outputs. Only with RIE are the necessary high-aspect-ratio grooves possible.

The authors would like to achnowledge A. A. Ballman and W. A. Bonner for supplying the InP substrates, and R. J. Martin for technical advice.

[1]T. Miya, Y. Terumina, T. Hasaka, and T. Miyashita, Electron. Lett. **15**, 106 (1979).
[2]R. F. Leheny, R. E. Nahory, M. A. Pollack, A. A. Ballman, E. D. Beebe, J. C. DeWinter, and R. J. Martin, Electron. Lett. **16**, 353 (1980).
[3]K. Iga and B. I. Miller, Electron. Lett. **16**, 342 (1980).
[4]K. Utaka, Y. Suematsu, K. Kobayashi, and H. Kawanishi, Jpn. J. Appl. Phys. **19**, L137 (1980).
[5]D. Z. Tsang, J. N. Walpole, S. H. Groves, J. J. Hsieh, and J. P. Donnelly, *38th Annual Device Research Conference Program* (IEEE, New York, 1980), IVB-6.
[6]L. A. Coldren, K. Iga, B. I. Miller, and J. A. Rentschler, Appl. Phys. Lett. **37**, 681 (1980).
[7]G. J. Lasher, Solid-State Electron. **7**, 707 (1964).
[8]A. B. Fowler, U. S. Patent No. 3, 303, 431 (7 February 1967).
[9]R. Lange and K. Kobayashi, U. S. Patent No. 3,999,146 (21 December 1976).
[10]P. Russer, U. S. Patent No. 4,101,845 (18 July 1978).
[11]K. Kishino, Y. Suematsu, K. Utaka, H. Kawanishi, Jpn. J. Appl. Phys. **17**, (1978).
[12]K. Iga and B. Miller. (unpublished).
[13]P. W. Smith, Proc. IEEE **60**, 422 (1972).
[14]L. A. Coldren, K. Iga, B. I. Miller, and J. A. Rentschler, *38th Annual Device Research Conference Program* (IEEE, New York, 1980), IVB-5.

Longitudinal mode control in GaAs lasers using a three-mirror active-passive cavity

E. Garmire,[a] G. Evans, and J. Niesen
Electronics Research Laboratory, The Aerospace Corporation, P. O. Box 92957, Los Angeles, California 90009

(Received 7 November 1980; accepted for publication 26 August 1981)

Integrated optics techniques have been used to form a three-mirror laser diode configured to form a long active cavity and a short passive cavity. The third mirror results from an abrupt etched step down to the waveguide layer of a large optical cavity heterostructure laser. We have observed predominantly single-frequency operation at current levels up to 1.5 times threshold. For certain ratios of passive-to-active cavity length, these devices operated multimode within a narrow frequency range, whereas diodes with different length ratios emit two modes widely separated in frequency.

PACS numbers: 42.55.Px, 42.60.By

Techniques for obtaining single longitudinal mode operation of GaAs lasers have typically involved distributed feedback (DFB) or distributed Bragg reflectors (DBR),[1,2] designs to provide single spatial mode,[3–7] or coupling between active and passive waveguides.[8–10] Other techniques include the use of a very short activity cavity,[11] a bent-guide structure,[12] or an external cavity.[13] In this letter single longitudinal mode operation is reported at current levels up to 1.5 times threshold by using the monolithic three-mirror active-passive (AP) arrangement shown in Fig. 1. In this structure an integrated optics equivalent of an external cavity is used in which an etched step between the active and passive regions effectively introduces a third mirror between the two cleaves. The use of a short passive cavity introduces the mode control which makes possible single frequency, two frequency, or multimode narrow band operation. This approach does not require grating fabrication, epitaxy over etched substrates, controlled diffusion or special electrode stripe geometries. Planar epitaxial material was used for the AP devices.

The epitaxial structure used in these devices is similar to that which has been used for DBR lasers.[2] It is a large optical cavity (LOC) structure that contains a waveguide layer below a thin active layer. The AP devices were fabricated by removing some of the epitaxial layers in the passive region, down through the active layer. To remove the layers, ion beam etching was used on the cap layer and AB etchant (1:1:8) on the p isolation and active layers. The active laser cavity was protected by photoresist. The waveguide discontinuity at the etched step results in a partially reflecting mirror which divides the laser into a long active cavity and a short passive cavity. This partial reflection is the origin of the mode control with the AP structure.

An example of the single-mode output is shown in Fig. 2, in which weak satellite modes can be observed at spacings equal to the spacing of both the passive cavity (20 Å) and the active cavity (2.2 Å). Linewidths were broadened to 1 Å because of thermal chirping. The lasers were operated pulsed, without heat sinks, and p side up.

Mode selectivity results from the overlap of the resonance for transmission of the active cavity with the peak in the reflectivity of the passive cavity, and the mutual overlap of both these resonances with the peak of the gain lines. The requirement that all three effects overlap constrains the cavity dimensions. However, since the peak of the gain spectrum and the optical path lengths within the diode are temperature and current sensitive, the device temperature and operating current can be varied to obtain the appropriate overlap.

A wide range of geometries was tested in the AP structure. In Fig. 3, a compilation of data on the 13 diodes tested is shown. When the passive cavity length was one-tenth the active cavity length, single-mode operation was achieved at current levels typically 50% above threshold. For passive cavity lengths up to 40% of the active cavity length, single-mode operation was still achieved near threshold. The mode selectivity of the AP structure is determined by the fractional decrease in gain from the peak of the gain curve at the adjacent mode of the passive cavity $\delta G/G_0$, and the fractional decrease in reflectivity of the passive cavity at the adjacent mode of the active cavity $\delta R/R$. These quantities, plotted in

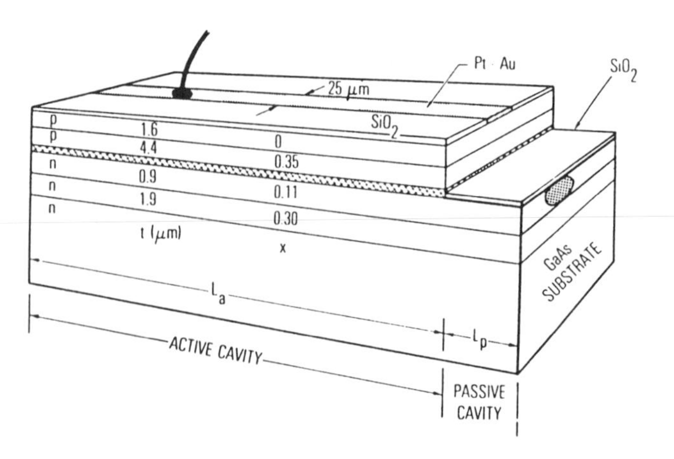

FIG. 1. Geometry for two-cavity single longitudinal mode lasers that were fabricated and tested. The epilayer structure is described by p,n representing majority carriers, t representing layer thickness, and x representing the fraction of AlAs in each layer. The active layer is cross hatched, 0.12 μm thick, and contains 7% AlAs. The abrupt etched step in the waveguide layer causes a reflection. The length of the active cavity L_A and of the passive cavity L_p, were varied over a wide range.

[a] Also at Center for Laser Studies, University of Southern California, University Park, Los Angeles, Ca 90007.

Reprinted with permission from *Appl. Phys. Lett.*, vol. 39, no. 10, pp. 789-791, Nov. 15, 1981.

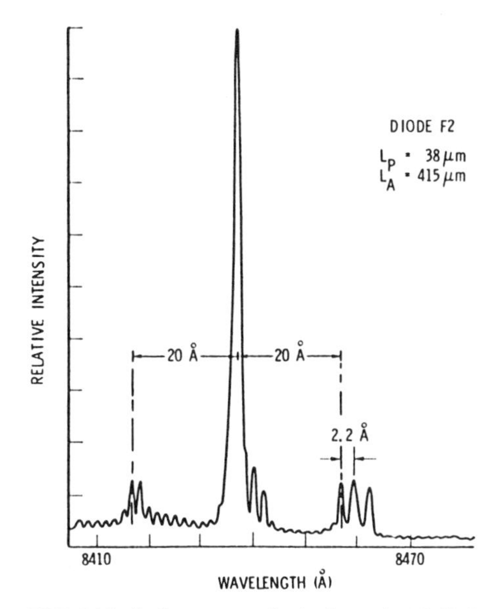

FIG. 2. Typical spectrum of a single-mode AP diode, operating at a current level 44% above threshold. The closely spaced modes of the active cavity and the more distantly spaced modes of the passive cavity are also apparent.

Fig. 3, were determined by following procedure.

Estimates for the decrease in gain were obtained by fitting measured fluorescence spectra near the peak of the emission with a Gaussian model[14]:

$$G = G_0 \exp[-((\lambda - \lambda_0)/\Delta\lambda)^2]. \quad (1)$$

Within 200 Å of the emission peak, the fluorescence could be fitted by $\Delta\lambda \sim 20$ Å, the exact value depending on the particular diode and operating conditions. Assuming that single-mode operation is achieved near the peak of the gain spectrum, a short passive region further reduces the overall gain at the next resonance of the passive cavity to provide additional discrimination against oscillation at that wavelength.

To estimate the effect of the passive cavity on the spectral output of the AP laser, consider that it acts like a Fabry–Perot cavity in reflection. Assume the etched step has a field transmission coefficient t_+ and a field reflection coefficient $-r_+$ for light incident from the active cavity. The transmission and reflection coefficients t_-, r_-, for light incident on the etched step from the passive cavity will, in general, be different. Assume the reflection coefficient at the cleave is $-r_c$. When $r_- \ll 1$, the effective reflectivity of the passive cavity[15] can be written

$$R_{\text{eff}} = (r_+ + r_c\eta)^2 - 4r_+ r_c \eta \sin^2\phi_0, \quad (2)$$

where $\eta = t_+t_- + r_+r_-$, which is less than one if the etched step introduces loss. The number of modes of the active cavity that oscillate depends on how much the reflectivity of the passive cavity decreases at the next mode of the active cavity. The frequency dependence of the reflectivity is contained in the phase ϕ_0. The phase $\phi_0 = 2\pi n_0 L_p (\nu_0 - \nu_1)/c$, where ν_0 is the frequency of light at the peak reflectivity, ν_1 is the frequency of the next active cavity mode, n_0 is the refractive index in the passive cavity at ν_0, and c is the velocity of light. The phase ϕ_0 depends only on the ratio between the passive and active cavity lengths since $(\nu_0 - \nu_1)/c = (2n_d L_A)^{-1}$, where n_d is the index of refraction of the active cavity with

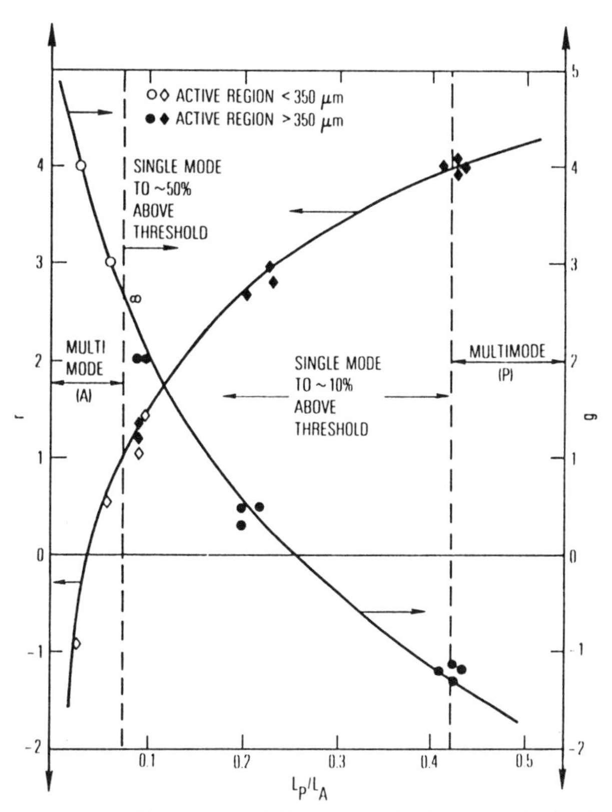

FIG. 3. Compilation of all AP diodes tested. Ordinate to the left is related to the fractional change of reflectivity at adjacent modes of the active cavity: $r \equiv \ln(100\delta R/R)$. The right ordinate is related to the decrease in gain at adjacent modes of the passive cavity: $g \equiv \ln(100\delta G/G_0)$. When $r < 1$, the AP diode operates multimode in the active cavity A; when $g < 1$, the AP diode operated multimode in the passive cavity P. Abscissa is the ratio of passive-to-active cavity length. Single-mode lasers operate most successfully when $L_p/L_A = 0.14$.

dispersion of the Fabry–Perot taken into account. Thus $\phi_0 = \pi (n/n_d)(L_p/L_A)$.

The fractional decrease in reflectivity of the passive cavity from its peak value to that of the next mode of the active cavity (choosing the temperature to match the resonance of the active cavity with the peak reflectivity of the passive cavity) is given by

$$\delta R/R = (4r_c r_+ t_+ \sin^2\phi_0)/(r_+ + r_c t_+)^2. \quad (3)$$

Numerical estimates for the quantities in Eq. (3) are taken from Ref. 16. With power reflectivity of the etched step taken as 2%, transmission as 50% and reflectivity of the cleave as 30%, the curve shown in Fig. 3 is obtained. The computer calculations of Ref. 16 indicate that this reflectivity occurs with a fractional change in step height of 10%. These estimates were confirmed by comparing the optical power output from the active and passive ends of the AP laser. This ratio was typically a factor of 2, independent of the length of the passive cavity, which indicates that the loss in the passive waveguide was negligible compared to the loss at the etch step. The graph of Fig. 3 indicates a strong dependence of r on L_p/L_A although r is not strongly dependent on the assumed values for r_+.

Figure 3 also indicates the decrease in gain from the peak to the next mode of the passive cavity, determined from Eq. (1). Plotted on this figure are points for all the lasers tested. The diodes can be grouped into three categories:

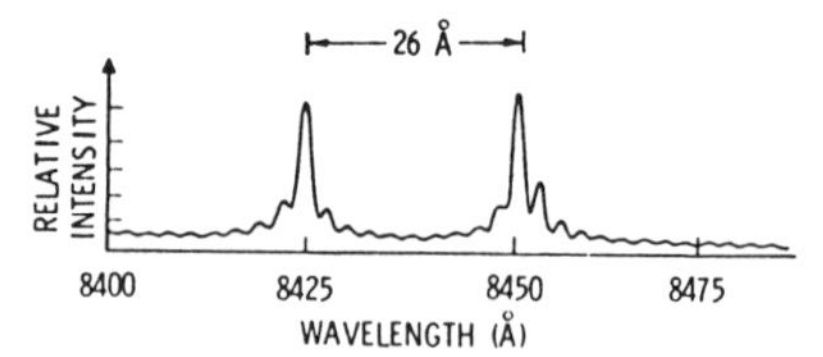

FIG. 4. Two-frequency operation of AP lasers. $L_p = 27\,\mu m$, $L_A = 275\,\mu m$, and the diode temperature and/or current is chosen to position the peak of the gain curve between modes of the passive cavity.

emitting multiple active cavity modes (when r is small), diodes with multimodes at the passive cavity resonant frequencies (when g is small), and diodes for which a regime single mode behavior was observed. Either single-mode behavior was observed only near threshold, or the devices operated single mode at current drives up to 50% above threshold. The best geometry for single-mode operation is with $L_p/L_A \sim 0.1$. For the same L_p/L_A, no strong dependence on L_A was observed for $310\,\mu m \leqslant L_A \leqslant 485\,\mu m$.

The single-mode operation of the lasers for values of r just greater than 1 confirms that reduction of approximately 3% in reflectivity at the adjacent modes was sufficient to result in single-mode operation, even at current levels 50% above threshold. For these same lasers, a 10% decrease in gain at adjacent modes of the passive waveguide would also result in single-mode operation. This indicates that the lasers are homogeneously broadened and that the addition of the passive cavity results in a single mode, eliminating multimode operation that occurs because of longitudinal mode hopping or spatial hole burning. Note that the lasers had relatively wide ($25\,\mu m$) electrodes and operated in more than one transverse mode, but there were ranges of single-frequency operation for each diode with a proper value of L_p/L_A. A more careful analysis of the relative roles of the active and passive cavity mode selectivities may provide further information on the operation of stripe geometry lasers that have several transverse modes.

To achieve single-mode operation, certain operating requirements on both temperature and current must be met. The gain curve must be tuned so that its peak is centered on a passive cavity resonance. Since these resonances are at most 40 Å apart (our fabrication technique limits the passive cavity length to $10\,\mu m$), and the peak in the gain spectrum shifts typically 3 Å/deg, this means that a temperature tuning of 10 °C is sufficient to match gain peak and passive resonance. In addition, the wavelength of the gain peak also shifts with drive current as the band fills, so that the optimum temperature may vary somewhat with current drive.

The temperature stability must be sufficiently good to maintain a single mode of the activity cavity. This is the same requirement that applies to all single-mode Fabry–Perot lasers, if hopping to the next longitudinal mode is to be avoided. Since the cavity modes are separated by at lease 2 Å, a temperature control of a quarter of a degree should suffice to maintain the active and passive cavities in resonance. We encountered no problem maintaining single-mode operation even though no temperature control was used.

If the peak of the gain curve is halfway between the two modes of the passive cavity, it is possible to obtain a two-frequency laser with a wide spacing between the modes, as shown in Fig. 4. Such a laser may be useful for multiplexing, heterodyning, and mixing applications. Temperature tuning this same device may transform it into a single-mode laser.

The longitudinal mode control available with the AP structure can be used to decrease the bandwidth of the emitted spectra of a multimode laser. Diodes with $r < 0.1$ operate multimode in the active cavity but their bandwidths are narrowed by the presence of the passive cavity. We have fabricated lasers with $L_p/L_A = 0.06$ which operated in six closely spaced modes, with a FWHM of 5 Å. This is considerably narrower than the spectra of typical multimode lasers. ' ch narrow bandwidth, multimode lasers may be useful for optical fiber communications, in which single frequency lases introduce modal noise.

The laser described herein are the first attempts at three-mirror structures. The thresholds were approximately $17\ kA/cm^2$, roughly the same as for two-mirror diodes fabricated from the same LOC wafer. These thresholds were very high because the aluminum concentration difference between the active layer and the waveguide layer was too small to confine the carriers properly. Theoretical calculations[17] and experimental results[18] on DBR lasers indicate that it should be possible to obtain cw operation from the AP structure, when the proper layer dimensions and aluminum concentrations are obtained. Experiments are under way to fabricate the AP structure on LOC material, which has a lower Fabry–Perot geometry threshold.

The authors wish to acknowledge the able technical assistance of M. P. Ziegler and J. A. Osmer and to thank F. L. Vernon, Jr. for critical comments on the manuscript. The wafer was grown at Laser Diode Laboratories by J. Menella. This work was performed under Air Force contract F04701-80-C-0081 and was supported in part by PM TRADE, NTEC.

[1] M. Nakamura, K. Aiki, J. Omeda, A. Katzir, A. Yariv, and H. W. Yen, IEEE J. Quantum Electron. **QE-11**, 436 (1975).
[2] K. K. Shams and S. Wang, Appl. Phys. Lett. **33**, 170 (1978).
[3] W. Susaki, T. Tanaka, H. Kan, and M. Ishii, IEEE J. Quantum Electron. **QE-13**, 587 (1977).
[4] M. Nakamura, K. Aiki, N. Chinone, R. Ito, and J. Umeda, J. Appl. Phys. **49**, 4644 (1978).
[5] W. T. Tsang, R. A. Logan, and M. Ilegems Appl. Phys. Lett. **32**, 311 (1978).
[6] D. Botez, Appl. Phys. Lett. **33**, 872 (1978).
[7] R. D. Dupuis and P. D. Dapkus, Appl. Phys. Lett. **33**, 725 (1978).
[8] Y. Suematsu, K. Kishino, and T. Kambayashi, IEEE J. Quantum Electron. **QE-13**, 619 (1977).
[9] D. R. Schifres, R. D. Burnham, and W. Steifer, Appl. Phys. Lett. **32**, 658 (1978).
[10] J. L. Merz and R. A. Logan, Appl. Phys. Lett. **32**, 661 (1978).
[11] N. Matsumoto, IEEE J. Quantum Electron. **QE-13**, 560 (1977).
[12] N. Matsumoto and S. Ando, Jpn. J. Appl. Phys. **16**, 1697 (1977).
[13] R. Salathe', Appl. Phys. **20**, 1 (1979).
[14] This approximation is used because of lack of detailed knowledge of gain spectra for these devices: B. W. Hakki and T. L. Paoli, J. Appl. Phys. **46**, 1299 (1975).
[15] M. Rousseau and H. Blaker, *Problems in Optics* (Pergamon, New York, 1973), p. 54.
[16] J. L. Merz, R. A. Logan, and A. M. Sergent, IEEE J. Quantum Electron. **QE-15**, 72 (1979).
[17] M. B. Chang and E. Garmire, Appl. Opt. **19**, 2370 (1980).
[18] Zh. I. Alferov, S. A. Gurevich, M. N. Mizerov, and E. L. Portnoy, Topical Meeting on Integrated and Guided Wave Optics, Technical Digest, January, 1978, p. MD4.

Optical Feedback Effects Upon Laser Diode Oscillation Field Spectrum

FRANCOIS FAVRE, DANIEL LE GUEN, AND JEAN CLAUDE SIMON

Abstract—**Optical feedback effects on spectral properties of a semiconductor laser diode coupled to a single-mode fiber cavity are investigated. Linewidth reduction from 6 MHz to less than 30 kHz and frequency stability improvement with increasing feedback are reported. Experiments are in good agreement with theory for short fiber cavities.**

I. Introduction

The possibility of coherent type single-mode fiber transmission systems has recently been reported [1]-[3]. The performances of these systems depend on the spectral purity and frequency stability of optical sources. For a single-mode laser operating far above the oscillation threshold, the theoretical minimum linewidth is determined by the random phase fluctuations. Due to the low Q value of a semiconductor laser cavity, the linewidth is not compatible with the requirements of coherent communication systems.

Spectral narrowing by optical feedback from a mirror or a grating has been reported [4]-[8]. Feedback effects were investigated for relatively short external cavities.

This paper reports experimental results on linewidth reduction and center frequency stabilization for a semiconductor laser coupled to a single-mode fiber whose output end has been carefully cleaved. A single-mode fiber cavity is insensitive to mechanical disturbances and easy to stabilize thermally. The overall dimensions of the external cavity can be reduced independently of the optical length. The power mode coupling efficiency between the laser diode and the fiber can be easily controlled experimentally. Measurements of the power feedback ratio, linewidth reduction, and satellite lines frequency separation for various external cavity lengths agree with the semiconductor laser feedback theory [9]. Our experimental results are in good agreement with theoretical predictions. Linewidth reduction from 6 MHz to less than 30 kHz has been obtained and center oscillation frequency stability greatly improved with feedback.

II. Experimental Setup

A. Laser Diode

The two lasers used in the experiments are AlGaAs CSP (Hitachi 1400) laser diodes coming from the same wafer. Their light versus current characteristics are almost identical. They oscillate on a single-mode near 820 nm and emit 8 mW per facet at 61 percent above threshold, which occurs at 74.5 mA and is practically unchanged in weak optical feedback conditions investigated in the following. The laser temperature is stabilized by a thermoelectric element.

Manuscript received March 11, 1982.

The authors are with the Centre National d'Etudes de Télécommunications, Lannion, France.

B. Single-Mode Fiber Cavity

The single-mode fiber cavity is end-butt coupled to the laser chip, the end of which oversteps the heat sink and is mounted on a three-axis piezoelectric translator. The output end of the single-mode fiber is carefully cleaved in order to obtain a reflecting interface orthogonal to the fiber axis.

The experimental setup used to control the fiber facet orthogonality is described in Fig. 1. A He-Ne laser beam is focused on the fiber facet and partially launched in the fiber mode. The distance separating a dot placed at the front focal point of the lens to its image formed on the same focal plane after reflection on the fiber facet is related to the local facet orthogonality. The orthogonality at the fiber core was found to be good to 1° and it is assumed in the following that the light power reflected back by the rear facet is entirely launched into the fiber backward mode.

The fiber is wound around a 30 mm diameter PZT ceramic in order to adjust the optical length of the cavity. Fiber and ceramic are immersed in oil and thermally stabilized by a thermoelectric element. The state of polarization (SOP) of the fiber output is analyzed through a polarizer. The fiber output SOP is maintained as linear as possible (with a cross polarized power ratio less than 5×10^{-3}) by monitoring the external cavity temperature. The light launched back into the laser mode is thus linearly polarized with the same SOP as that of the lasing mode whenever SOP changes along the fiber.

C. Spectral Measurements Method

A delayed self-heterodyne method is used to measure the laser linewidth [10]. The experimental arrangement is displayed in Fig. 2. The laser beam is launched in a two-wave interferometer consisting of a 3.9 km long single-mode fiber in one arm and an acoustooptic frequency shifter (71 MHz) in the other (a Faraday optical isolator avoids reflections from the interferometer). The two beams are then mixed in a short single-mode fiber and the photocurrent fluctuation spectrum is measured around the beat frequency with an RF spectrum analyzer. The photocurrent spectrum is directly related to the output intensity fluctuation spectrum $S(\Delta F)$ whose analytical expression is given in [11] as

$$S(\Delta F) = \frac{2}{\pi \Delta \nu} \exp(-2\pi \Delta \nu \tau_d) \cdot \left[\frac{\Delta F/\Delta \nu \sin(2\pi \Delta F \tau_d) + \sinh(2\pi \Delta \nu \tau_d)}{1 + (\Delta F/\Delta \nu)^2} - \frac{\sin(2\pi \Delta F \tau_d)}{\Delta F/\Delta \nu} \right] \quad (1)$$

Reprinted from *IEEE J. Quantum Electron.*, vol. QE-18, no. 10, pp. 1712–1717, Oct. 1982.

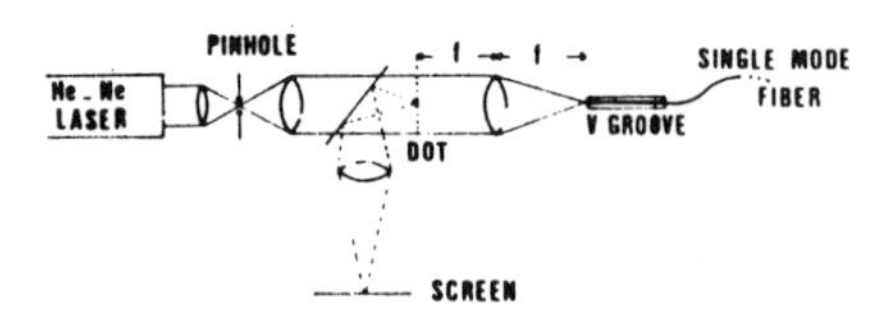

Fig. 1. Schematic of experimental arrangement used for measurements of fiber end orthogonality.

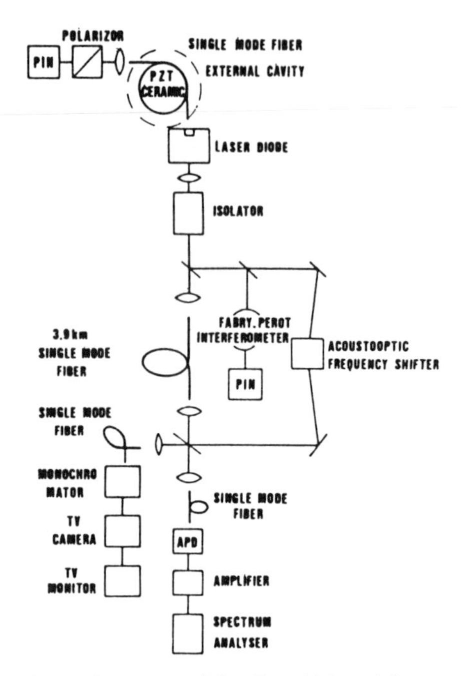

Fig. 2. Experimental setup used for linewidth and frequency fluctuations measurements on semiconductor laser coupled to external single-mode fiber cavity.

where τ_d is the delay time between the arms of the interferometer, $\Delta\nu$ is the oscillation field linewidth, and ΔF is the frequency deviation. The photocurrent spectrum is proportional to the autocorrelation function of the field spectrum as long as the linewidth $\Delta\nu$ is large compared to the interferometer resolution τ_d^{-1}. When $\Delta\nu \lesssim \tau_d^{-1}$, $\Delta\nu$ can be derived from the spectrum half width $\Delta F_{1/2}$ through a correction factor $\Delta F_{1/2}/\Delta\nu$ which is plotted in Fig. 3 against $2\pi\Delta\nu\tau_d$.

III. Oscillation Field Spectrum

A. Theoretical Expressions

An analytical expression of the oscillation field spectrum for a semiconductor laser with external mirror feedback has recently been proposed [9]

$$P(\Delta\nu) = \left\{1 + \left(\frac{2\Delta\nu}{\Delta\nu_{SL}}\right)^2 \left[\left(1 + X\frac{\sin 2\pi\Delta\nu\tau}{2\pi\Delta\nu\tau}\right)^2 + X^2\left(\frac{1-\cos 2\pi\Delta\nu\tau}{2\pi\Delta\nu\tau}\right)^2\right]^2\right\}^{-1} \quad (2)$$

where $\Delta\nu_{SL}$ is the full linewidth for the solitary laser, τ is the roundtrip time of the external cavity, and X is a feedback influence parameter given by

$$X = \gamma\sqrt{\eta}\,\tau. \quad (3)$$

η is the power feedback ratio, and γ is a coefficient derived from steady-state oscillation condition for a diode laser with external mirror [9], [12]

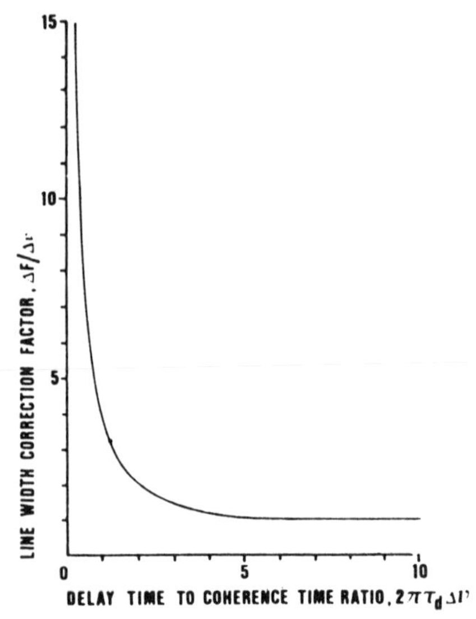

Fig. 3. Calculated photocurrent spectrum half width to laser linewidth ratio $\Delta F_{1/2}/\Delta\nu$ versus $2\pi\Delta\nu\tau_d$ where τ_d is the delay time between interferometer arms.

$$\gamma = \frac{c}{2n_D l_D} \quad (4)$$

where l_D is the laser diode length, n_D is the refractive index, and c is the light velocity.

Another expression for γ can be derived from a modified van der Pol equation and written as [7], [13], [14].

$$\gamma = \frac{c}{2n_D l_D}\left[\alpha_D l_D - \ln R_D\right] \quad (5)$$

where α_D is the free carrier absorption loss coefficient and R_D is the diode facet reflectivity. γ as given in (5) is equal to $(2\tau_p)^{-1}$, τ_p being the photon lifetime. A typical value for $\alpha_D - (1/l_D)\ln R_D$ is 45 cm^{-1} for a 300 μm long CSP laser diode [15] providing $\gamma = 135$ GHz from (5) against $\gamma = 100$ GHz from (4).

An expression of $\Delta\nu_{SL}$ can be derived from the modified Schawlow-Townes expression giving the linewidth of a solitary laser [16]

$$\Delta\nu_{SL} = \frac{h\nu}{8\pi P_o}\left(\frac{c}{n_D l_D}\right)^2 (\ln R_D - \alpha_D l_D)(\ln R_D)\, n_{sp} \quad (6)$$

where P_o is the single ended output power and n_{sp} is the spontaneous emission factor which lies in the 2.3-2.7 range at room temperature [16].

The oscillation field spectrum is narrowed with increasing the feedback influence parameter X as derived from (2) when in-phase condition is achieved (the emitted field and the returning field are then in phase on the laser end facet). In feedback condition, the linewidth is given by [7], [9]

$$\Delta\nu = \Delta\nu_{SL}(1 + X)^{-2}. \quad (7)$$

The oscillation field spectrum shows satellites which are enhanced and pushed to the external cavity mode frequency with increasing X. The normalized frequency deviation $\tau\delta\nu$ is calculated from (2) and plotted versus X in Fig. 4. The parameter X can be derived from measurements of $\tau\delta\nu$ using Fig. 4. The corresponding value for the linewidth reduction ratio can then be compared with the theoretical value given by (7).

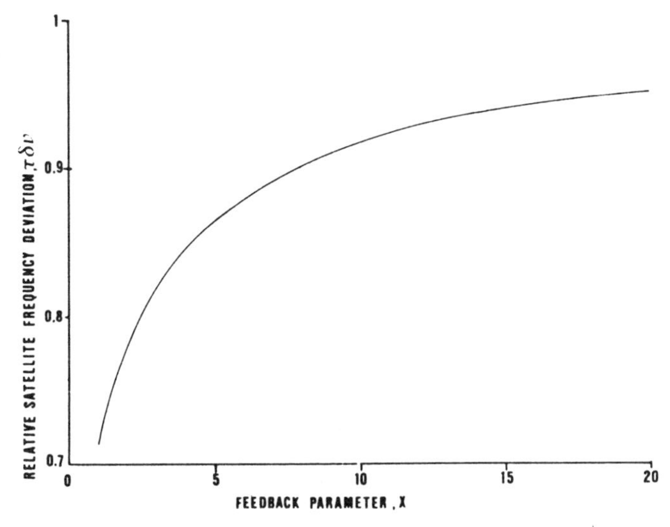

Fig. 4. Calculated normalized satellite line frequency deviation $\tau\delta\nu$ versus feedback parameter X. τ is the external cavity roundtrip time. The function $\tau\delta\nu(X)$ can be approximated by $X/(X+1)$ for $X > 20$.

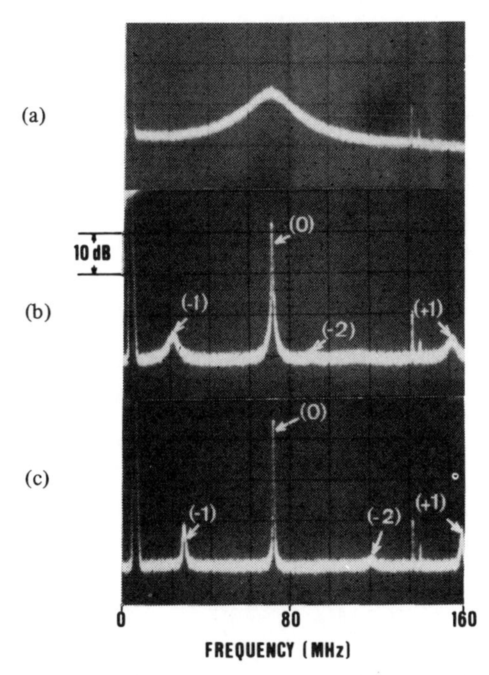

Fig. 5. Photocurrent fluctuations spectrum with increasing feedback from a 1.027 m long single-mode fiber. Photovoltage output V is proportional to fiber output light power. (a) $V = 0$ (solitary laser diode), (b) $V = 4$ mV, (c) $V = 10$ mV, $I/I_{th} = 1.61$. (b) and (c) show satellite lines due to feedback and labeled (+1), (−1), (−2). (−1) and (−2) lines are displayed in negative frequency domain. Spectrum analyzer bandwidth: 300 kHz.

B. Experimental Results

1) Power Feedback Ratio: The power feedback ratio η is defined as the relative power returning into the laser diode mode and given by [9], [12]

$$\eta = \rho^2 (1 - R_D)^2 R_D^{-1} (1 - R_F)^2 R_F \exp(-2\alpha_F L_F) \tag{8}$$

where R_F is the mode power reflectivity of the fiber output end, α_L is the propagation loss coefficient due to absorption and curvatures, L_F is the fiber length, and ρ is the power mode coupling efficiency between the laser diode and the fiber. η can be related to the feedback fiber output by

$$\eta = (1 - R_D)^2 R_D^{-1} (1 - R_F)^{-2} R_F V_D^{-2} V^2 \tag{9}$$

where V and V_D are photovoltages respectively proportional to the fiber output power and to the laser diode output power. It should be pointed out that propagation losses are taken into account in (9). Measurements give $V_D = 220$ mV at $I = 1.61 I_{th}$ and calculated values for R_D and R_F are, respectively, 0.32 and 0.035. In the following, linewidth measurements are performed for decreasing roundtrip time values by shortening the fiber while the output end is kept unchanged.

2) Satellite Lines Frequency Separation: An example of photocurrent fluctuations spectrum alteration with feedback is shown in Fig. 5. The frequency separation $\delta\nu$ between lines is measured as a function of the fiber output V for various external cavity lengths. The feedback parameter X is then derived from its theoretical dependence of $\tau\delta\nu$ given in Fig. 4; results are depicted in Fig. 6 as a function of the fiber output photovoltage V for different values of the external cavity roundtrip time τ. Each straight line is a least square fit to the data. The mean value of X/V obtained from Fig. 6 as a function of τ is shown in Fig. 7. The solid line represents the linear law derived from (3) and (9) and given by

$$\frac{X}{V} = (1 - R_D) R_D^{-1} (1 - R_F)^{-1} R_F V_D^{-1} \gamma\tau \tag{10}$$

with $\gamma = 135$ GHz as given by (5). Experimental points deviate from the linear law with increasing τ.

3) Linewidth Reduction Ratio: The linewidth reduction ratio $\Delta\nu/\Delta\nu_{SL}$ is measured as a function of the output fiber photovoltage V and displayed in Fig. 8 versus the corresponding X values derived from Fig. 6. The minimum value for $\Delta\nu$ is obtained by monitoring the fiber optical length to achieve in-phase condition. Experimental points are in good agreement with the theory except for $\tau = 10$ ns.

4) Frequency Stability: Fig. 9 shows the output of a low finesse scanned Fabry-Perot interferometer (free spectral range: 940 MHz; resolution: 135 MHz). Short term frequency stability is improved with increasing X. External cavity mode jumping can be observed during the time exposure of 5 s for low X values. Oscillograms are also made using a 4 MHz resolution Fabry-Perot interferometer (FSR: 300 MHz) and shown in Fig. 10. Center frequency fluctuations are estimated to lie in the ±2 MHz range during 5 s in feedback condition. Using a 15 GHz FSR Fabry-Perot interferometer with a finesse of 18, it has not been possible to observe self-pulsing phenomena as previously reported in similar conditions [17].

5) Linewidth Versus Laser Output Power Dependence: The linewidth has been measured as a function of the normalized bias current for solitary lasers and with feedback influence. Experimental results are shown in Fig. 11. A theoretical linewidth of 200 kHz at $I = 1.61 I_{th}$ (corresponding to $P_o = 8$ mW) is derived from the modified Schawlow-Townes expression (6) while the measured value is 30 times greater. A factor of 20 between experimental and theoretical values has previously been reported [16]. The enhanced linewidth is attributed to the variation of the real refractive index with carrier density [18].

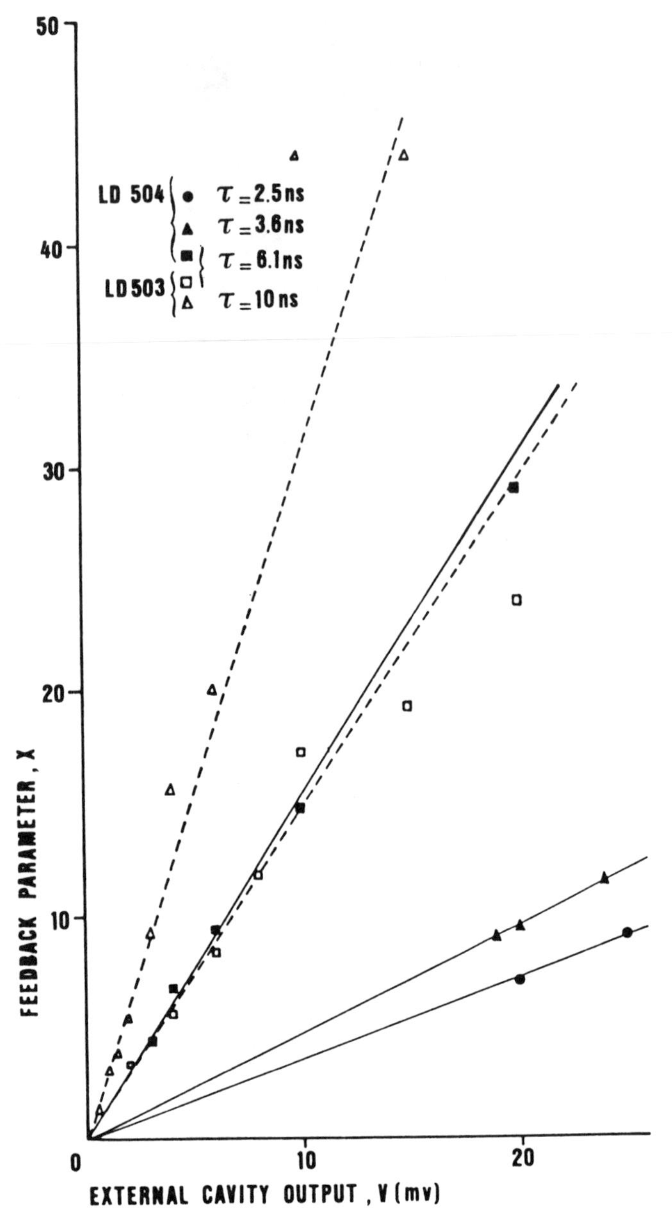

Fig. 6. Feedback parameter X as a function of fiber output V for various fiber cavity lengths. X is derived from line frequency separation through the theoretical law displayed in Fig. 4. Each straight line is a least square fit to the data. Two laser diodes are used: LD 504 (solid lines); and LD 503 (dashed lines). I/I_{th} = 1.61.

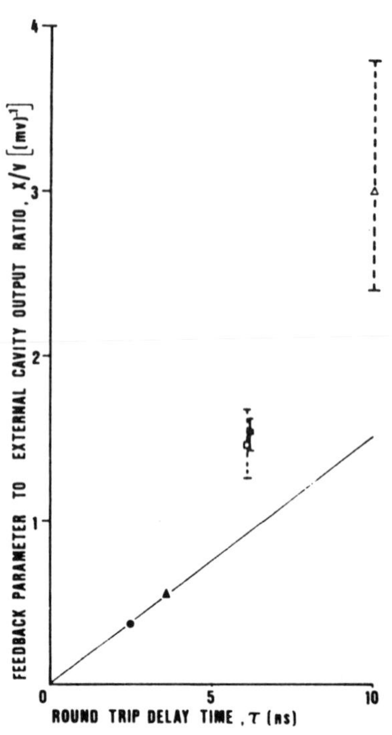

Fig. 7. Mean values of X/V obtained from Fig. 6 as a function of roundtrip time τ. Solid line is the calculated result (relation (10) with γ = 135 GHz).

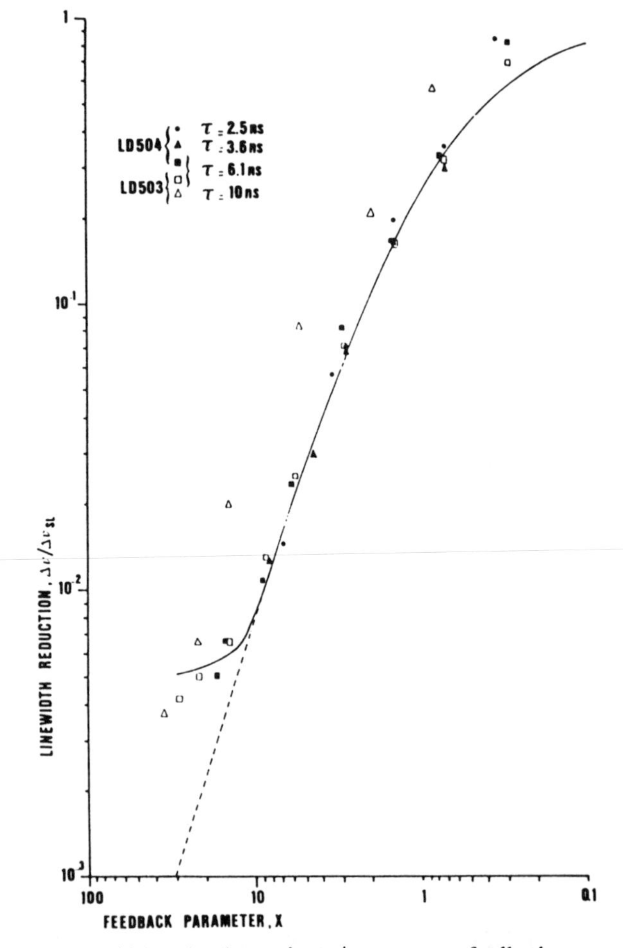

Fig. 8. Linewidth reduction ratio $\Delta\nu/\Delta\nu_{SL}$ versus feedback parameter X. Dashed line is the plot of $(1 + X)^{-2}$. Solid line is the theoretical linewidth reduction ratio when measurements are achieved using the two beams interferometer with a delay time τ_d = 19 μs.

6) Feedback Effects Due to the Front Facet of the Fiber: Cyclic laser diode mode jumping is observed when the external fiber cavity is continuously moved away from the laser diode. It can be explained considering the frequency selectivity arising from the three-mirror laser cavity consisting of the laser diode of optical length L and the fiber input facet at a distance d. Let us consider the cavities of lengths L and $L + d$ as shown in Fig. 12(a). Assume the laser matching occurs for the mth mode of the laser cavity [Fig. 12(b)] and for the nth mode of the longest cavity [Fig. 12(c)], these modes being on the high frequency side with regard to the gain spectrum peak. Frequency mismatching between mth and nth modes develops with increasing d while it decreases between $(m - 1)$th and $(n - 1)$th modes until the laser frequency jumps to the $(m - 1)$th modes. Mode jumps will be repeated until frequency

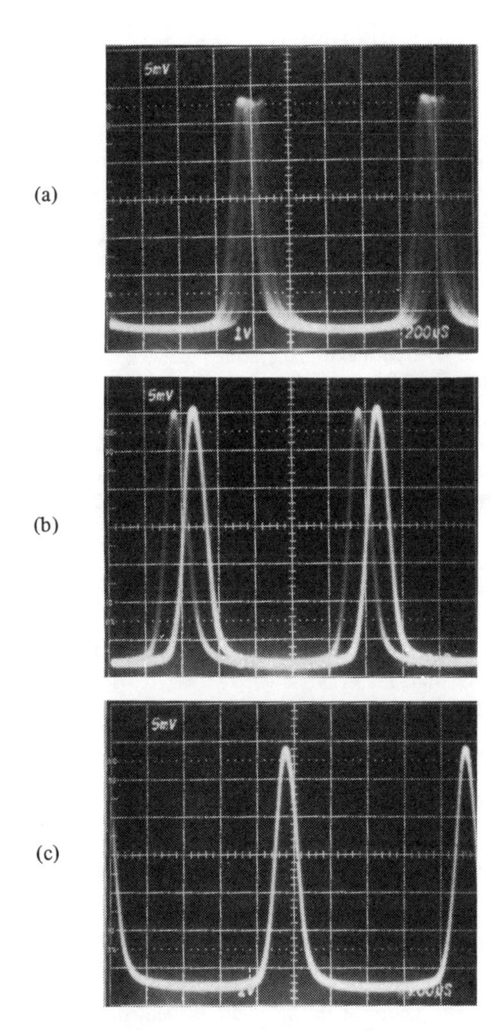

Fig. 9. Linearly scanned Fabry-Perot interferometer output with increasing feedback (a) $X = 0$ (solitary laser), (b) $X = 10$, (c) $X = 25$. $\tau = 10$ ns, FSR = 940 MHz, resolution = 135 MHz. Oscillograms are the superposition of 2500 scans corresponding to a time exposure of 5 s. $I/I_{th} = 1.61$.

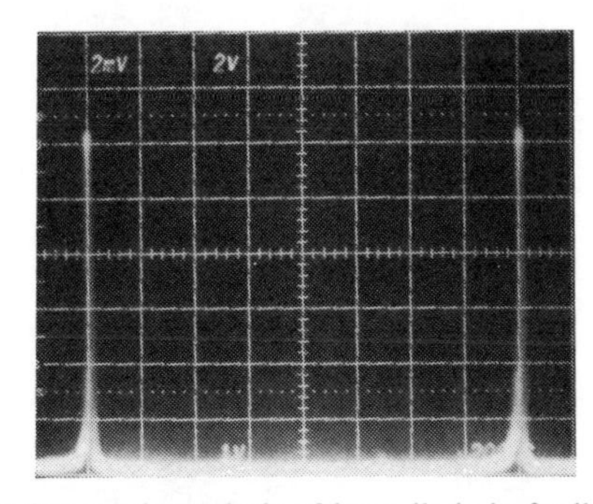

Fig. 10. Interferometric analysis of laser diode in feedback conditions given in Fig. 9(c). FSR = 300 MHz, resolution = 4 MHz, exposure time is 5 s.

matching occurs between mth and $(n + 1)$th modes. The number of jumps per cycle is approximately given by

$$N \approx \frac{L}{d}. \quad (11)$$

Experimental determination of N is reported in Fig. 13 and compared to the theoretical expression (11). Effects upon the linewidth remain negligible due to low values of the cavity

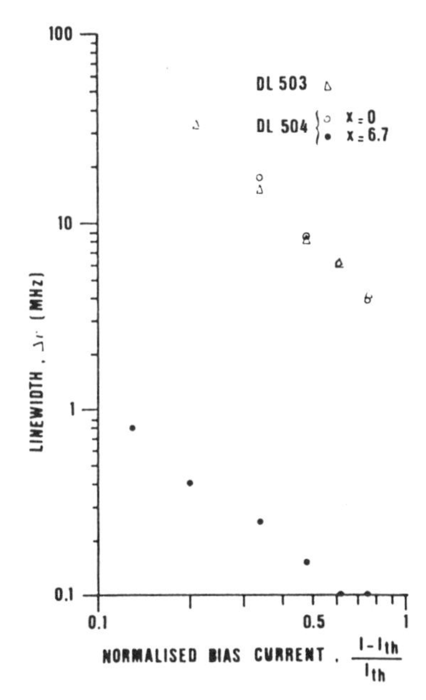

Fig. 11. Linewidth measurements as a function of normalized bias current in solitary and feedback conditions ($\tau = 2.5$ ns, $X = 6.7$).

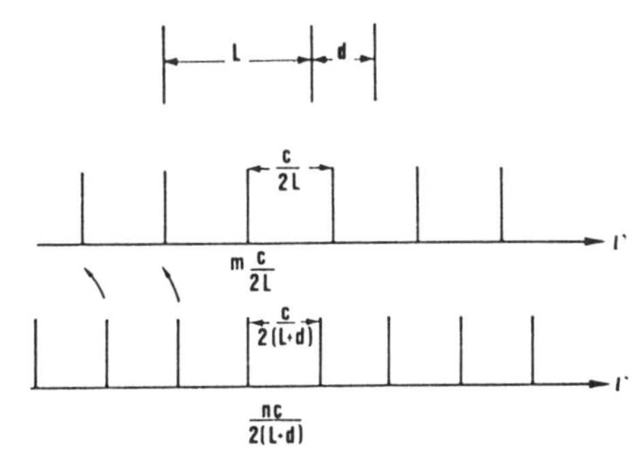

Fig. 12. Schematic of modes of the three-mirror cavity.

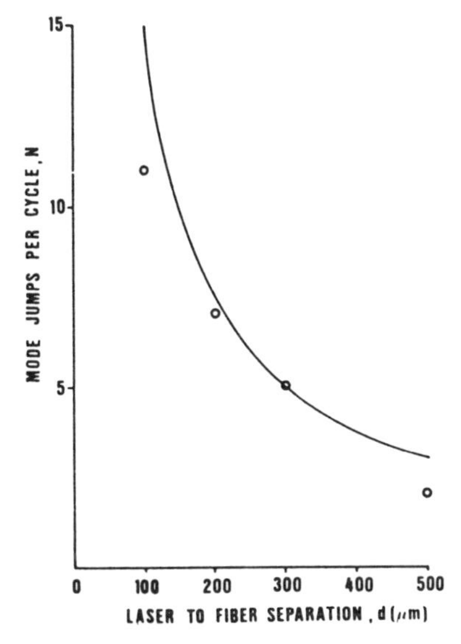

Fig. 13. Number N of mode jumps per cycle as a function of d. Solid line corresponds to theoretical predictions.

length and of the feedback ratio (provided $d \geq 100$ μm). These results have been confirmed by using a silica plate in the position of the fiber input face.

IV. Conclusion

Optical feedback effects upon spectral properties of semiconductor lasers have been investigated. Linewidth reduction from 6 MHz to less than 30 kHz has been obtained for a single-mode semiconductor laser diode coupled to a single-mode fiber whose output end is cleaved. Experimental results are in good agreement with theory for fiber length below 50 cm. The use of a single-mode fiber makes the external cavity insensitive to mechanical disturbances and overall dimensions can be easily reduced. These features associated with the high spectral purity make this optical source compatible with the requirements of coherent communication systems.

Acknowledgment

The authors are grateful to Dr. Monerie for his encouragement and many fruitful discussions during the course of this work. They are also indebted to Dr. L. Rivoallan, Dr. P. Sansonetti, and F. Alard for their help in cleaving and characterizing the fiber.

References

[1] Y. Yamamoto and T. Kimura, "Coherent optical fiber transmission systems," *IEEE J. Quantum Electron.*, vol. QE-17, pp. 919-935, June 1981.
[2] F. Favre, L. Jeunhomme, I. Joindot, M. Monerie, and J. C. Simon, "Progress towards heterodyne-type single-mode fiber communication systems," *IEEE J. Quantum Electron.*, vol. QE-17, pp. 897-906, June 1981.
[3] T. Okoshi and K. Kikuchi, "Heterodyne-type optical fiber communications," *J. Opt. Commun.*, vol. 2, pp. 82-88, 1981.
[4] F. Favre and D. Le Guen, "Laser-diode emitter for heterodyne communication systems," presented at IOOC, San Francisco, CA, Apr. 1981.
[5] S. Saito and Y. Yamamoto, "Direct observation of Lorentzian lineshape of semiconductor laser and linewidth reduction with external grating feedback," *Electron. Lett.*, vol. 17, pp. 325-327, Apr. 1981.
[6] L. Golberg, A. Dandridge, R. O. Miles, T. G. Giallorenzi, and J. F. Weller, "Noise characteristics in line-narrowed semiconductor lasers with optical feedback," *Electron. Lett.*, vol. 17, pp. 677-678, 1981.
[7] K. Kikuchi and T. Okoshi, "Simple formula giving spectrum-narrowing ratio of semiconductor laser output obtained by optical feedback," *Electron. Lett.*, vol. 18, pp. 10-11, Jan. 1982.
[8] S. J. Petuchowski, R. O. Miles, A. Dandridge, and T. G. Giallorenzi, "Phase sensitivity and linewidth narrowing in a Fox-Smith configured semiconductor laser," *Appl. Phys. Lett.*, vol. 40, pp. 302-304, Feb. 1982.
[9] O. Nilsson, S. Saito, and Y. Yamamoto, "Oscillation frequency, linewidth reduction and frequency modulation characteristics for a diode laser with external grating feedback," *Electron. Lett.*, vol. 17, pp. 589-591, Aug. 1981.
[10] T. Okoshi, K. Kikushi, and A. Nakayama, "Novel method for high resolution measurement of laser output spectrum," *Electron. Lett.*, vol. 16, pp. 630-631, July 1980.
[11] J. A. Armstrong, "Theory of interferometric analysis of laser phase noise," *J. Opt. Soc. Amer.*, vol. 56, pp. 1024-1031, Aug. 1966.
[12] R. Lang and T. Kobayashi, "External optical feedback effects on semiconductor injection laser properties," *IEEE J. Quantum Electron.*, vol. QE-16, pp. 347-355, Mar. 1980.
[13] O. Hirota and Y. Suematsu, "Noise properties of injection lasers due to reflective waves," *IEEE J. Quantum Electron.*, vol. QE-15, pp. 142-149, Mar. 1979.
[14] T. Kanada and K. Nawata, "Injection laser characteristics due to reflected optical power," *IEEE J. Quantum Electron.*, vol. QE-15, pp. 559-565, July 1979.
[15] K. Aiki, M. Nakamura, T. Kuroda, J. Umeda, R. Ito, N. Chinone, and M. Maeda, "Transverse mode stabilized $Al_xGa_{1-x}As$ injection lasers with channeled-substrate-planar structure," *IEEE J. Quantum Electron.*, vol. QE-14, pp. 89-94, Feb. 1978.
[16] M. W. Fleming and A. Mooradian, "Power-dependent linewidth measurements on single-mode (GaAl)As injection lasers," *IEEE J. Quantum Electron.*, vol. QE-17, pp. 166-169, Dec. 1981.
[17] A. Dandridge and R. O. Miles, "Spectral characteristics of semiconductor laser diodes coupled to optical fibres," *Electron. Lett.*, vol. 17, pp. 273-275, Apr. 1981.
[18] C. H. Henry, "Theory of the linewidth of semiconductor lasers," *IEEE J. Quantum Electron.*, vol. QE-18, pp. 259-264, Feb. 1982.

Single-mode operation of coupled-cavity GaInAsP/InP semiconductor lasers

K. J. Ebeling, L. A. Coldren, B. I. Miller, and J. A. Rentschler
Bell Telephone Laboratories, Holmdel, New Jersey 07733

(Received 6 August 1982; accepted for publication 5 October 1982)

Monolithic two-section GaInAsP/InP lasers are shown to operate in a single longitudinal mode under high-speed pulsed current modulation. The length of the emitted monomode light pulses is less than 500 ps. The suppression of secondary modes is described in a rate equation model that is generally useful for a variety of coupled-cavity configurations. It is found that 10% increase in cavity loss for the unwanted modes is sufficient to provide 17 dB suppression.

PACS numbers: 42.55.Px, 42.82. + n, 42.60.By

Single longitudinal mode operation has now been observed for a wide class of semiconductor lasers. In most cases single-mode operation is constricted to limited ranges of temperature and pumping current. For high-speed modulation the number of oscillating modes usually increases and the individual modes broaden due to a frequency chirp.[1]

A greater spectral purity of the laser emission under high-speed pulsed operation has been obtained in external cavity lasers with common spherical mirrors[2] or in lasers with distributed Bragg reflectors.[3,4] In this letter we show that monolithic two-section GaInAsP/InP lasers[5,6] can operate in a single longitudinal mode under high-speed current modulation. The observed suppression of higher modes is then described in a simple multimode rate equation model. As shown schematicaly in Fig. 1(a) the monolithic two-section laser studied in the experiments has a total length $l_1 + l_2 \sim 420\,\mu$m, corresponding to a mode spacing of 5.9 Å. The two sections are separated by a narrow groove of about 1 μm width,[5] and the relative lengths of the two sections $l_2/l_1 \sim 1/8$. A simple Si_3N_4 defined stripe that provides transverse gain guiding is used in these experiments.

As previously suggested,[5] this coupled-cavity geometry provides reinforcement of every eighth mode in the long cavity and suppression of the intervening modes. If a reinforced (low loss) mode is coincident with the gain maximum, we find that the normal gain roll-off is sufficient to also suppress the adjacent reinforced modes, even during a turn-on transient.

In the experiment the two-section laser was pumped with a current pulse of 2.8-ns length at 1.5 threshold level without any bias. The current pulse is just long enough that the laser emits the first peak of the relaxation oscillation. The output pulse of less than 500-ps length is shown in Fig. 1(b). This energy build-up delay and relaxation oscillation period is in good correspondence with the theory shown below. Figure 1(c) shows the output spectra for operation at two different ambient temperatures. The monomode spectrum at 37 °C corresponds to the situation where a low loss mode is tuned to the center of the line. At 27 °C two dominating modes lie symmetrically around the line center. The distance of 47 Å between the modes corresponds to the spacing of eight longitudinal modes. The mode shift with temperature is obtained to be $\delta\lambda/\delta T = 0.5$ Å/°C. As indicated in Fig. 1(d) the change of the spectrum with increasing temperature can be explained by a shift of the gain peak of $\delta\lambda_{\rm peak}/\delta T = 2.85$ Å/°C. This value is in good agreement with measurements for GaAs lasers.[7]

The spectra shown in Fig. 1 were recorded with current injected to the longer of the two sections only. In this case the short section is pumped only through an internal interconnection resistance[6] $\sim 40\ \Omega$. Similar spectra were observed when both sections were pumped at the same current density. Mode selection was found to be not sensitive to pumping current level. Monomode output was observed up to more than twice the threshold current. Although strong relaxation oscillations were observed (as predicted by theory below), no evidence of self-pulsation was observed for any of the possible bias configurations.

For a homogeneously broadened laser oscillating in several longitudinal modes of lowest transversal order, the rate equations for the excess carrier density N and the photon density S_m in mode number m are given by[8,9]

$$\frac{dN}{dt} = \frac{J}{qd} - \frac{N}{\tau_{\rm sp}} - \frac{c}{n}\left(\sum_m g_m S_m\right), \tag{1}$$

$$\frac{dS_m}{dt} = \frac{\Gamma\gamma N}{\tau_{\rm sp}} + \frac{c}{n}\,(\Gamma g_m - \alpha_{tm})\,S_m, \tag{2}$$

where $J = J(t)$ is the pumping current density, q is the electronic charge, c is the velocity of light, n is the refractive index, and we assume an active layer thickness $d \sim 0.2\,\mu$m, a spontaneous emission lifetime $\tau_{\rm sp} \sim 3\times10^{-9}$ s, a confine-

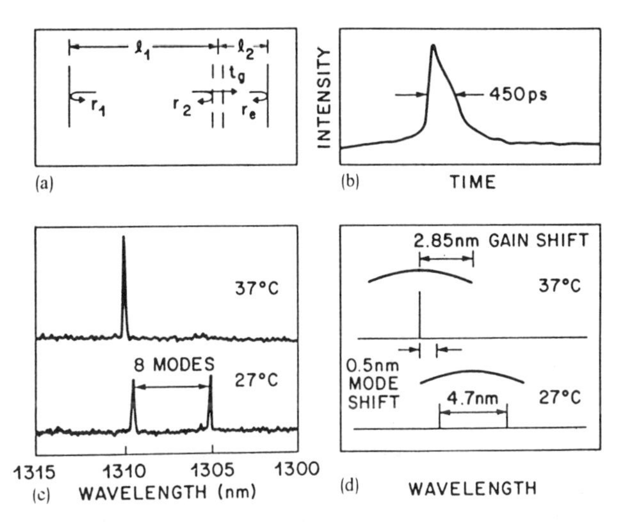

FIG. 1. Two-section laser results for high-speed pulse current modulation: (a) coupled-cavity schematic; (b) output light pulse of ca. 450 ps half-width; (c) spectra at 37 °C and 27 °C; (d) schematical sketch of the mode shift and the shift of the line center with temperature.

Reprinted with permission from *Appl. Phys. Lett.*, vol. 42, no. 1, pp. 6–8, Jan. 1, 1983.

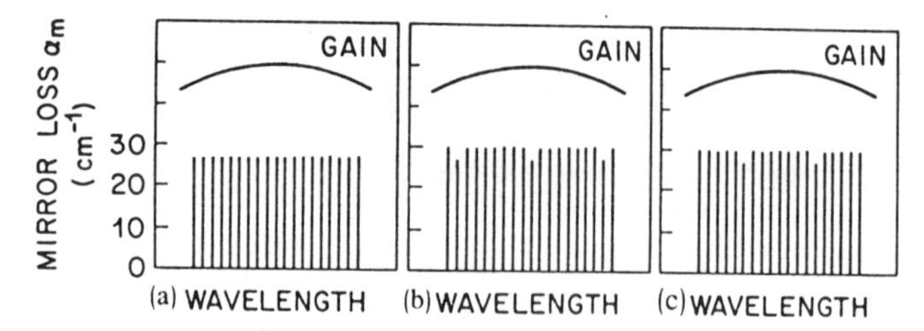

FIG. 2. Mirror loss α_m of modes and gain curve (schematically): (a) equal quality modes in standard Fabry–Perot cavity; (b) dominant mode ($m = 0$) of a two-section laser in line center; (c) dominating modes ($m = \pm 4$) of two-section laser outside of line center.

ment factor $\Gamma \sim 0.5$, a spontaneous emission factor $\gamma \sim 10^{-4}$, and a mode gain g_m that varies linearly with N and parabolically with wavelength deviation $\Delta\lambda$.

$$g_m = a(N - N_0) - b\Delta\lambda_m^2, \tag{3}$$

and we use $a \sim 2.5 \times 10^{-16}$ cm^2, $b = 0.23$ nm^{-2} cm^{-1}, and $N_0 = 4.5 \times 10^{17}$ cm^{-3}.

The total cavity loss term α_{tm} is the sum of internal absorption α_{abs} and output coupling α_m losses for mode m. In standard Fabry–Perot type resonators all modes have the same loss, as illustrated in Fig. 2(a), but in two-section lasers or others with external or grating reflectors, the "mirror" loss α_m varies from mode to mode depending on the geometry. Figures 2(b) and 2(c) illustrate an idealized case where every eighth mode has lower loss than the others, in correspondence with the experimental configuration in Fig. 1. For the two-section the desired mode loss can be typically 10% lower than for the undesired modes.[10]

For a two-cavity laser, either external cavity or monolithic two-section, the mode loss variation can be calculated from the wavelength dependent reflectance $r_2(\lambda_m)$ of an equivalent complex mirror at the coupling facet of the primary (longer) laser cavity. For a groove coupled two-section configuration,[5] as illustrated in Fig. 1(a),

$$r_2(\lambda_m) = r_g + r_e t_g^2 e^{-2j\beta_2 l_2}(1 - r_e r_g e^{-2j\beta_2 l_2})^{-1}, \tag{4}$$

where r_g and t_g are the complex groove reflection and transmission, r_e is the second cavity end (external mirror) reflectance, l_2 is the length of the second (external) section, and β_2 is the complex propagation constant in the short (external) section.

For studying dynamical effects of mode suppression the rate equation system has been solved numerically. Examples of intensity versus time curves for the modes are shown in Fig. 3. The computation has been performed for a total number of 19 modes. It is assumed that a pumping current step of $J = 1.5\, J_{threshold}$ is applied at time $t = 0$ without any bias. The curves in Fig. 3(a) correspond to a Fabry–Perot cavity, the mode loss pattern of which is sketched in Fig. 2(a). Only the intensity curves for the central mode and the adjacent mode are plotted. After a turn-on delay of about 2.4 ns the emission starts with damped relaxation oscillations. At the beginning of the oscillation both modes have almost the same intensity and the intensity difference slightly increases with increasing time.

The mode suppression is quite different in a laser with

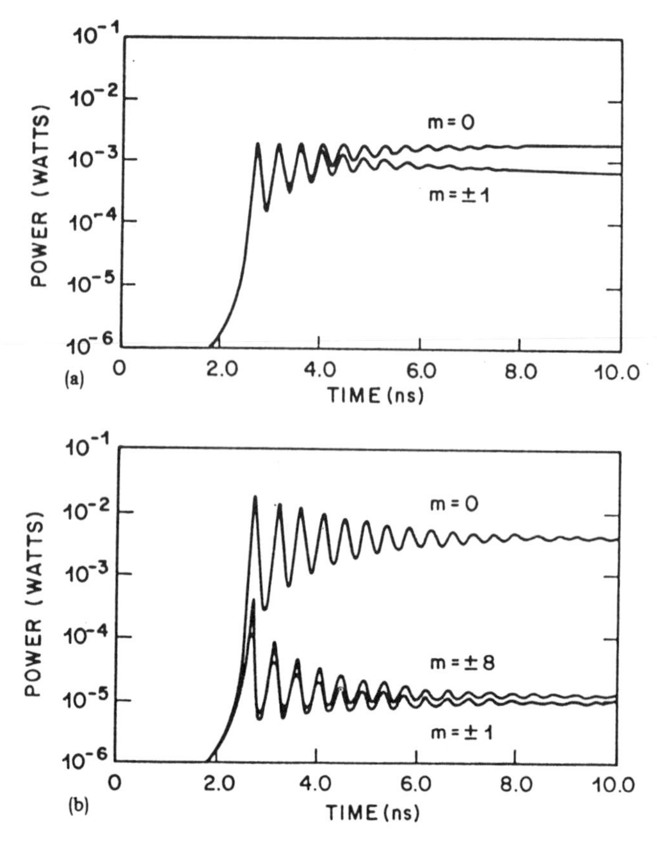

FIG. 3. Computed dynamical response of laser output to a pumping current step applied at time $t = 0$ (power output $\propto S_m$): (a) Fabry–Perot cavity, with all α_m equal; (b) two-section laser with $\alpha_0 = \alpha_{\pm 8} = 0.9\alpha_m$ ($m \neq 0,8$).

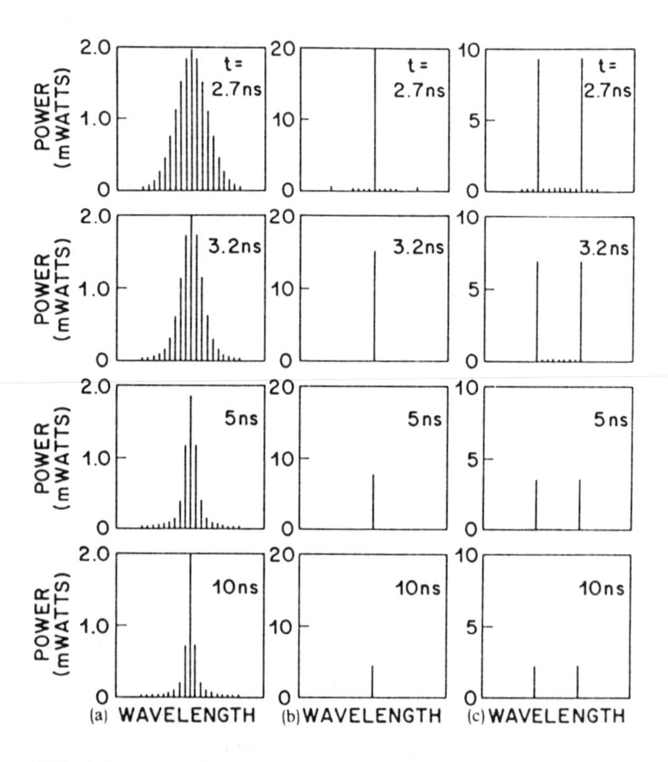

FIG. 4. Computed time-resolved mode spectra. t denotes the time after the current step is applied. (a) Fabry–Perot cavity. (b) dominating mode ($m = 0$) of two-section laser in center of laser line. (c) low loss modes ($m = \pm 4$) of two-section laser out of line center.

different α_m (e.g., two-section laser) as demonstrated in Fig. 3(b). The curves are computed for the loss pattern of Fig. 2(b). Only the intensity curves for the low loss modes and the high loss modes adjacent to the line center are plotted. The emission occurs almost completely in the central low loss mode. Other modes are strongly suppressed even in the first peak of the relaxation oscillation. Similar mode suppression behavior is found when the pumping current is pulsed from a bias level or when the current is modulated with a series of pulses. Comparison of Fig. 3(a) and 3(b) clearly demonstrates the effect of the α_m difference on mode selection.

Figure 4 gives an overview over the time development of the output spectra. The spectra in parts (a), (b), and (c) are computed for the mode loss patterns of Figs. 2(a), 2(b), and 2(c), respectively. The parameter t is the time after application of the pumping current step. The increasing suppression of secondary modes with increasing time in a Fabry–Perot cavity can be seen in the left column from the top to the bottom. The relative intensity of the strongest secondary mode eventually decreases to a value of 36%. The monomode output in the central column is obtained for a modulated α_m (two-section) laser, a low loss mode of which coincides with the gain peak. The relative power of secondary modes remains below 2% at every instant of time. Compared to the case of multimode oscillation the power of the central mode is much higher in particular in the first peak of the relaxation oscillation. In the right column, two dominating modes are present lying outside the line center at equal gain points. Other modes are again strongly suppressed. These later two cases closely correspond to the experimental results in Fig. 1(c).

In conclusion, it has been shown that monolithically integrated two-section lasers can operate in a single mode under high-speed pulsed conditions. The observed spectra can be well described with a rate equation model when different losses are introduced for different modes. When the quality of the dominant mode is about 10% larger than that of the rest of the modes within the line the laser operates single mode. The experiments show that such an amount of discrimination between the modes can be achieved in a monolithic two-section laser, the two sections of which are separated by a narrow groove of 1-μm width. The use of the transverse gain-guided geometry, which generally has a greater tendency to emit multimode spectra, is believed to be a "worst-case" test of this coupled-cavity technique for longitudinal mode selection. From the theory, single-longitudinal mode operation is expected quite generally for other resonator geometries that have low loss modes the α_m of which are about 10% higher than that of the rest of the modes. Possible mode selective structures are multielement or external cavity lasers, for example.

[1]K. Kishino, S. Aoki, and Y. Suematsu, IEEE J. Quantum Electron. **18**, 343 (1982).
[2]K. R. Preston, K. C. Wooland, and K. H. Cameron, Electron. Lett. **17**, 931 (1981).
[3]Y. Sakakibara, K. Furuya, K. Utaka, and Y. Suematsu, Electron. Lett. **16**, 456 (1980).
[4]K. Utaka, K. I. Kobayashi, and Y. Suematsu, IEEE J. Quantum Electron. **17**, 651 (1981).
[5]L. A. Coldren, B. I. Miller, K. Iga, and J. A. Rentschler, Appl. Phys. Lett. **38**, 315 (1981).
[6]L. A. Coldren, K. Furuya, B. I. Miller, and J. A. Rentschler, IEEE J. Quantum Electron. **QE-18**, 1679 (1982).
[7]K. Aiki, M. Nakamura, and J. Umeda, IEEE J. Quantum Electron. **12**, 597 (1976).
[8]T. P. Lee, C. A. Burrus, J. A. Copeland, A. G. Dentai, and D. Marcuse, IEEE J. Quantum Electron. **QE-18**, 1101 (1982).
[9]R. P. Salathé, Appl. Phys. **20**, 1 (1979).
[10]K. J. Ebeling and L. A. Coldren (unpublished).

10 kHz LINEWIDTH 1·5 μm InGaAsP EXTERNAL CAVITY LASER WITH 55 nm TUNING RANGE

R. WYATT
W. J. DEVLIN

British Telecom Research Laboratories
Martlesham Heath
Ipswich, Suffolk IP5 7RE, England

20th December 1982

Indexing terms: Lasers and applications, Semiconductor lasers

An InGaAsP 1·5 μm laser, with one facet antireflection coated, has been incorporated into a diffraction grating external cavity. The lasing wavelength could be tuned over a 55 nm range about the centre wavelength of 1·5 μm by rotating the grating. It was found that the emission spectrum was extremely narrow; beat-frequency measurements at 1523 nm against an HeNe laser showed it to be of the order of 10 kHz.

Introduction: High-performance coherent optical-fibre systems[1] require narrow-linewidth laser transmitters in the low-loss 1·5 μm spectral region in order to realise the full benefits of coherent detection. Presently available 1·5 μm semiconductor lasers do not possess sufficient phase coherence for use in such systems unless external line-narrowing techniques are used. In a recent paper[2] we described a reduction in linewidth from 1 GHz to below 1 MHz by injection-locking a semiconductor laser to the output from a single-mode 1·5 μm HeNe laser; this type of transmitter has been successfully used in a number of coherent transmission experiments.[3–5] However, the limited tuning range of the HeNe laser places stringent requirements on the semiconductor laser wavelength, and so we report here an alternative, more versatile line-narrowing configuration, based on strong feedback from an external grating. Using a laser diode, antireflection coated on one facet, single-mode oscillation is reliably obtained, with output linewidths in the order of 10 kHz.

Experimental: The InGaAsP/InP laser used for these experiments was of the channel substrate, buried crescent type[6] with a 53 mA pulse threshold at 20°C for a 190 μm-long cavity. This was the threshold value before antireflection coating. It was In-bonded, *p*-side-down, to a gold-plated copper heatsink, which allowed access to both facets. The dominant wavelength at 20°C under pulsed conditions was 1516 nm. Antireflection coating was applied to one facet to approximately quarter-wave thickness. The light/current characteristics are shown in Fig. 1 both before and after antireflection coating. The reflectivity of the coated facet R_c was calculated from the ratio of the coated to uncoated differential quantum efficiencies η_c/η_u of the laser in its modified reflectivity state, using the formula[7]

$$\frac{\eta_c}{\eta_u} = \sqrt{\left(\frac{R_u}{R_c}\right)\frac{(1 - R_c)}{(1 - R_u)}}$$

Using a value of the uncoated reflectivity, $R_u = 0{\cdot}31$,[7] the coated reflectivity is estimated to be 3–4%. Assuming the threshold current to be proportional to the sum of internal and mirror losses, the internal loss is calculated to 40 to 50 cm^{-1}.

The output from the antireflection coated laser facet was

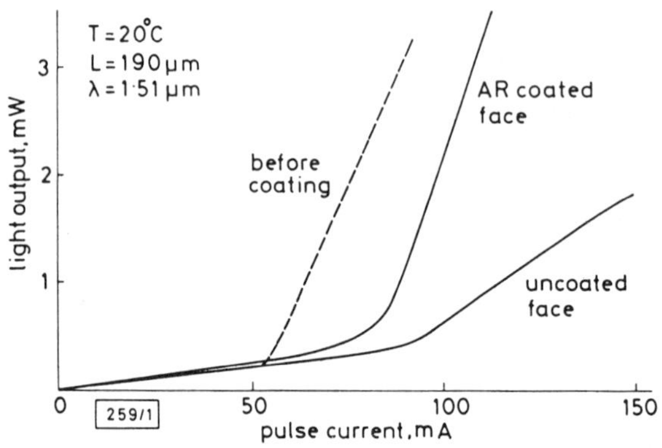

Fig. 1 *Light/current characteristics of channel substrate, buried crescent laser, both before (– – – –) and after (———) antireflection-coating one facet*

collimated by a × 18, 0·45 NA, long working distance microscope objective, and reflected back into the laser cavity from a gold-coated, 1200 line/mm diffraction grating. The efficiency of the diffraction grating was measured as 83% at 1·5 μm for light polarised perpendicular to the rulings, and the overall reflectivity back into the laser was about 4%, taking into account the objective coupling efficiency. (It is important to realise that this experimental arrangement represents strong external cavity coupling as the amount of feedback is of the same order as the antireflection coated facet reflectivity.) The uncoated front facet of the semiconductor laser forms the output mirror of the external cavity; overall cavity lengths from 15 to 50 cm have been used. A collimating lens × 10, 0·3 NA served to couple the output beam, through a polariser and quarter-wave plate for isolation, into a scanning monochromator, or scanning etalon for spectral measurements.

Results: The minimum CW threshold current of the laser with external cavity was 58 mA, compared to 75 mA with the grating reflection blocked, at a temperature of 16°C. The variation of threshold current over the central portion of the tuning range was very low, as shown in Fig. 2. The points correspond to wavelengths of the residual laser cavity modes and were selected by rotating the grating. At 80 mA drive current, tuning up to 30% of the semiconductor mode spacing could be obtained. Wavelengths not accessible by grating rotation required a change in laser temperature and/or drive current.

Emission in a single longitudinal mode of the external cavity could be obtained for cavity lengths up to the maximum used of 50 cm, with no additional frequency-selective elements. The linewidth of this single mode was measured with a scanning confocal etalon of 2 GHz free spectral range, and also by beat-frequency measurements against a 1523 nm

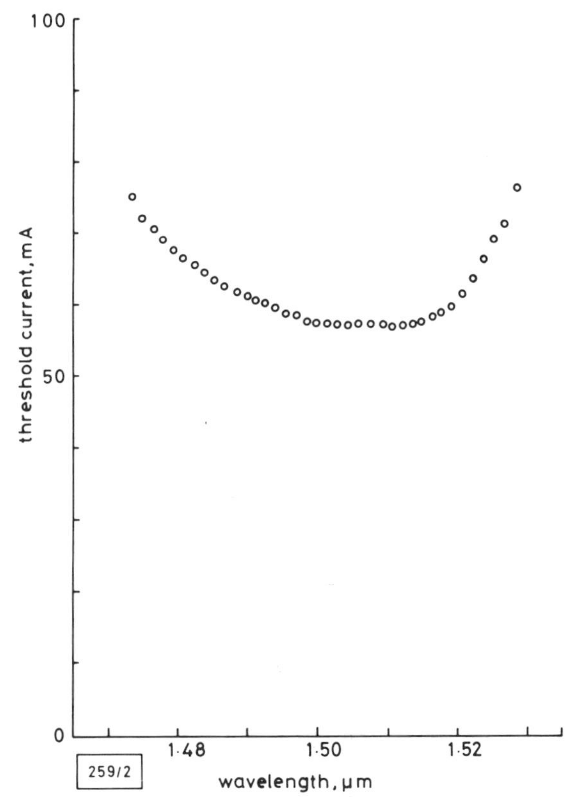

Fig. 2 *Threshold current of laser in external grating cavity as a function of lasing wavelength*

Points correspond to residual cavity modes and were selected by rotating the grating

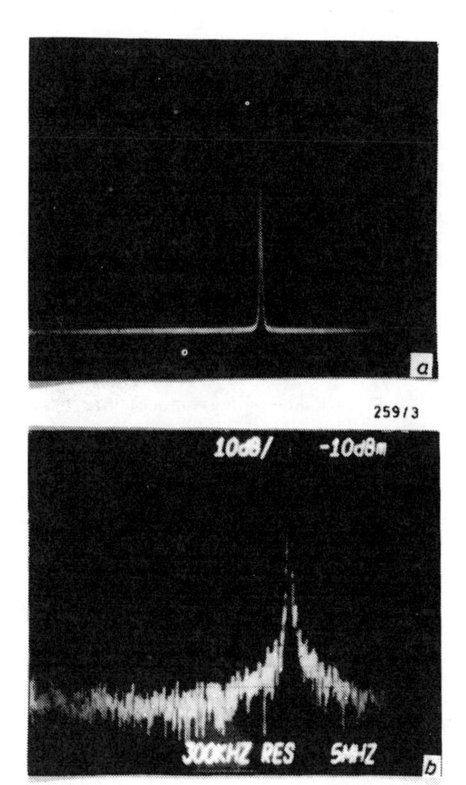

Fig. 3

a Single-mode output of laser in external cavity showing a linewidth below instrument resolution (12 MHz)
Free spectral range of this scanning etalon is 2 GHz. Horizontal scale is 250 MHz/div. with a linear vertical scale
b Heterodyne beat-frequency measurement of linewidth using a 1523 nm HeNe local oscillator, showing a 3 MHz beat width 50 dB down from the peak
Horizontal scale is 5 MHz/div.; vertical scale is 10 dB/div.

HeNe laser. Fig. 3*a* shows the output from the scanning etalon, displaying an instrument-limited linewidth of 12 MHz. Fig. 3*b* shows the result of the higher resolution heterodyne beat-frequency measurement. A Lorentzian lineshape is obtained, as expected for line broadening caused by quantum phase fluctuations. (The HeNe laser is assumed to have a much narrower linewidth than the semiconductor laser.) From the 3 MHz beat-frequency width at -50 dB relative to the peak intensity we can deduce a linewidth due to fundamental phase fluctuations of 10 kHz FWHM. This is in reasonable agreement with a width of 2 kHz calculated from the modified Schawlow–Townes formula[8] for the 20 cm cavity length and the 0·1 mW output power of these measurements, assuming a 31% reflectivity of the uncoated laser facet.

It should be noted that, at the laser current of 90 mA at which these measurements were taken, the semiconductor laser alone, without the external cavity, has a multilongitudinal-mode output, the single-mode output only being obtained with the external cavity present. Thus, calculations of the expected output based on a reduction factor characteristic of the external cavity and applied to the linewidth of the free-running laser (see Reference 9, for example) are not appropriate for our experimental results. Although these measurements were taken at 1523 nm, similar etalon traces were obtained over the entire 1473 nm to 1528 nm tuning range of the device, and it is expected that sub-megahertz output linewidths are available throughout this range.

The laser frequency was very insensitive to drive current changes, as expected for operation in a long external cavity. A change of < 2 MHz/mA was measured with a 20 cm external cavity within the range of single-mode operation, compared to about 1 GHz/mA for the free-running laser.

It was also possible to operate the laser at much higher currents, e.g. 150 mA, and obtain single-mode operation without external feedback. Results similar to those reported in Reference 10 were obtained; a free-running linewidth of 500 MHz was reduced to about 5 MHz by small amounts of feedback (10^{-4}). Any increase in feedback beyond this level caused a rebroadening of the single mode. The mode was also not rigidly held in frequency by the external cavity, but tuned from mode to mode of the external cavity at the normal rate of about 1 GHz/mA, in complete contrast to the strong feedback situation described above. Results in the weak feedback mode were therefore much less satisfactory.

Conclusion: An InGaAsP/InP semiconductor laser with one facet antireflection coated has been incorporated into a grating-tuned external cavity. A wide tuning range of 55 nm around 1·5 μm was obtained, with single-mode linewidths of 10 kHz. The lasing frequency was very insensitive to drive current variations. A stabilised version of this type of laser source is being used to evaluate the potential of coherent optical-fibre systems.

Acknowledgments: The authors are grateful to colleagues in the epitaxial growth areas for providing the InGaAsP wafer and to the Director of Research, British Telecom, for permission to publish this letter.

References

1 YAMAMOTO, Y., and KIMURA, T.: 'Coherent optical fibre transmission systems', *IEEE J. Quantum Electron.*, 1981, **QE-17**, pp. 919–934

2 WYATT, R., SMITH, D. W., and CAMERON, K. H.: 'Megahertz linewidth from a 1·5 μm semiconductor laser with HeNe laser injection', *Electron. Lett.*, 1982, **18**, pp. 292–293

3 HODGKINSON, T. G., WYATT, R., and SMITH, D. W.: 'Experimental assessment of a 140 Mbit/s coherent optical receiver at 1·52 μm', *ibid.*, 1982, **18**, pp. 523–525

4 HODGKINSON, T. G., WYATT, R., MALYON, D. J., NAYAR, B. K., HARMON, R., and SMITH, C. W.: 'Experimental 1·5 μm coherent optical fibre transmission system'. Eighth ECOC, Cannes, France, 21–24 Sept. 1982, pp. 414–418

5 HODGKINSON, T. G., SMITH, D. W., and WYATT, R.: '1·5 μm optical heterodyne system operating over 30 km of monomode fibre', *Electron. Lett.*, 1982, **18**, pp. 929–930

6 DEVLIN, W. J., WALLING, R. H., FIDDYMENT, P. J., HOBBS, R. E., MURRELL, D., SPILLETT, R. E., and STEVENTON, A. G.: 'Low-threshold channelled-substrate buried crescent InGaAsP lasers emitting at 1·54 μm', *ibid.*, 1981, **17**, pp. 651–653

7 HIGUCHI, H., NAMIZAKI, H., OOMURA, E., HIRANO, R., SAKIBARA, Y., SUSASKI, W., and FUJIKAWA, K.: 'Internal loss of InGaAsP/InP buried crescent (1·3 μm) laser', *Appl. Phys. Lett.*, 1982, **41**, pp. 320–321

8 FLEMING, M. W., and MOORADIAN, A.: 'Spectral characteristics of external cavity controlled semiconductor lasers', *IEEE J. Quantum Electron.*, 1981, **QE-17**, pp. 44–59

9 KIKUCHI, K., and OKOSHI, T.: 'Simple formula giving spectral narrowing ratio of semiconductor laser output obtained by optical feedback', *Electron. Lett.*, 1982, **18**, pp. 10–12

10 GOLDBERG, L., TAYLOR, H. F., DANDRIDGE, A., WELLER, J. F., and MILES, R. O.: 'Spectral characteristics of semiconductor lasers with optical feedback', *IEEE J. Quantum Electron.*, 1982, **QE-18**, pp. 555–563

High-speed direct single-frequency modulation with large tuning rate and frequency excursion in cleaved-coupled-cavity semiconductor lasers

W. T. Tsang, N. A. Olsson, and R. A. Logan
Bell Laboratories, Murray Hill, New Jersey 07974

(Received 7 February 1983; accepted for publication 18 February 1983)

We report a new mechanism of direct frequency modulation, the cavity-mode enhanced frequency modulation (CME-FM), using the newly developed cleaved-coupled-cavity (C^3) semiconductor laser. In this operation, one of the diode of the C^3 laser was operated as a laser, while the other diode was operated as a frequency modulator. It was shown that a very large frequency excursion of 150 Å and frequency tuning rate of 10 Å/mA have been obtained with a C^3 GaInAsP crescent laser operating at 1.3 μm. Time-resolved spectral and spectral-resolved pulse response measurements also showed that such C^3 lasers operated in highly stable single-longitudinal mode at all times even under high-speed direct frequency modulation. In addition to the important application as the optical source in FM optical communication systems, the present CME-FM C^3 laser can also be used as the optical source in wavelength-division multiplexing systems. Further, it opens the possibility of ultrahigh capacity multilevel optical FM information transmission systems.

PACS numbers: 42.55.Px, 42.60.By, 42.60.Da, 42.80.Sa

All optical fiber communication systems developed so far are based on amplitude modulation (AM) and direct detection of the optical energy. Recently, some interest has been placed on optical frequency modulation[1,2] (FM) and demodulation[3,4] of coherent laser waves. Such coherent optical fiber transmission systems[5] are expected to improve system performance towards longer repeater spacings and higher information capacity. However, the development of FM optical systems has been relatively difficult due to the lack of suitable frequency tunable lasers that can be conveniently used as the transmitter in such systems. One approach has been using electro-optic frequency modulators, either integrated[6,7] or discrete devices in external cavity semiconductors lasers.[8,9] Also, a small frequency shift can be obtained by direct modulation of the injection current of laser diodes.[1,4,10] An envelope spectrum shift of 0.4 Å (15 GHz) or 20 Å was obtained by the electro-optic effect[6] or by the threshold gain variation obtained through the modulation of the effective mirror reflectivity.[7] However, only broad-area diodes were demonstrated. But the most important drawback of this scheme is the complexity involved in fabricating such complicated integrated structure. For directly modulated lasers the frequency shift is extremely small, for example, the ratio of the frequency deviation to modulation current for an (AlGa)As channeled-substrate planar laser is $\sim$100 MHz/mA in the modulation frequency region of 10 MHz–1 GHz.[2,10] Thus, only a relatively small frequency shift can be achieved without serious unintended intensity modulation.

Earlier studies of cracked and multiple cavity laser diodes of broad area[11] or wide (50 μm) oxide stripes[12] have demonstrated optical amplification. In this letter we report a new mechanism of achieving very wide range (over 150 Å), very high rate (10 Å/mA), ultrahigh speed (1.5×10^{10} Å/s), direct frequency modulation in the newly developed cleaved-coupled-cavity (C^3) semiconductor laser. Figure 1 shows a schematic diagram of a C^3 laser. The detailed fabrication procedures of such C^3 laser are described in Ref. 13. The C^3 laser consists of two standard Fabry–Perot (F–P) cavity 1.3-μm wavelength GaInAsP crescent laser diodes[14] of 136-μm and 121-μm length, respectively, which were self-aligned and very closely coupled to form a two-cavity resonator. The active strip from each diode is precisely aligned with respect to the other on a straight line and they are separated from each other by a distance $<5\ \mu$m. All the reflecting facets are formed by cleaving along crystallographic planes and hence are perfectly mirror-flat and parallel to each other. Complete electrical isolation (>50 kΩ) between the two individual F–P diodes also results. The total length of the C^3 laser can be as short as 100 μm with typical length of 200–400 μm.

The basic working principle is illustrated schematically in Fig. 2. The propagating mode in each active stripe can have a different effective refractive index N_{eff} even though they have the same geometric shape, size, and material composition. This is because N_{eff} is a function of carrier density in the active stripe. This can be varied by varying the injection current below threshold when the junction voltage is not

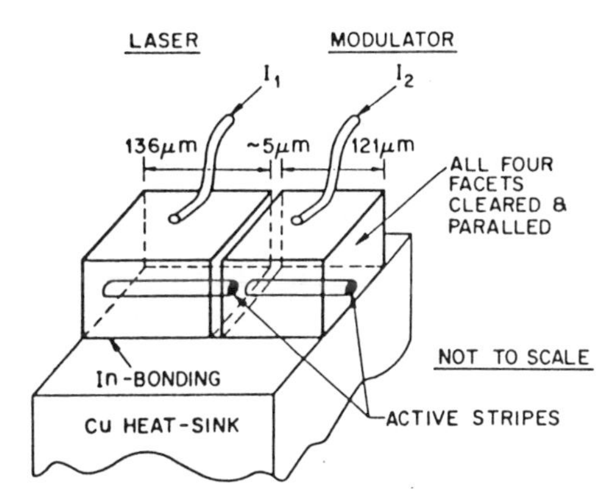

FIG. 1. Schematic diagram of a cleaved-coupled-cavity 1.3-μm wavelength GaInAsP crescent laser.

Reprinted with permission from *Appl. Phys. Lett.*, vol. 42, no. 8, pp. 650–652, Apr. 15, 1983.

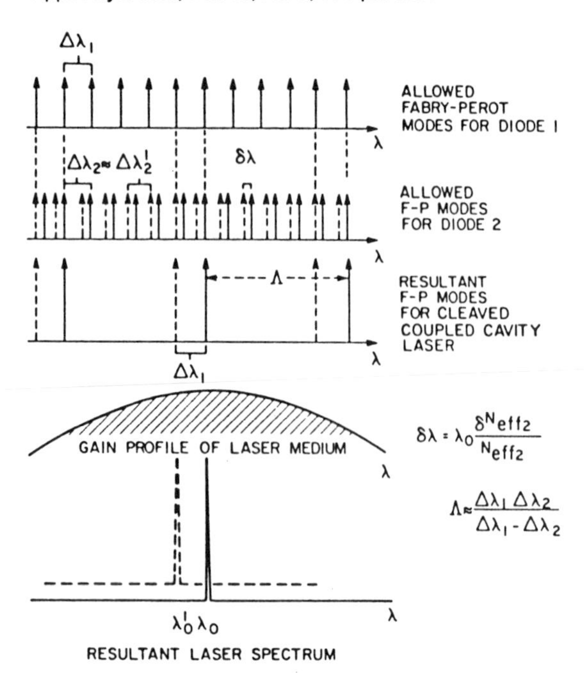

FIG. 2. Basic working principle of direct frequency modulation in C^3 laser. In this operation, the left F–P diode was operated as laser, while the right F–P diode was operated as the modulator. The solid and dashed lines correspond to a pulsed current of I_2 and I_2' applied to the modulator, respectively.

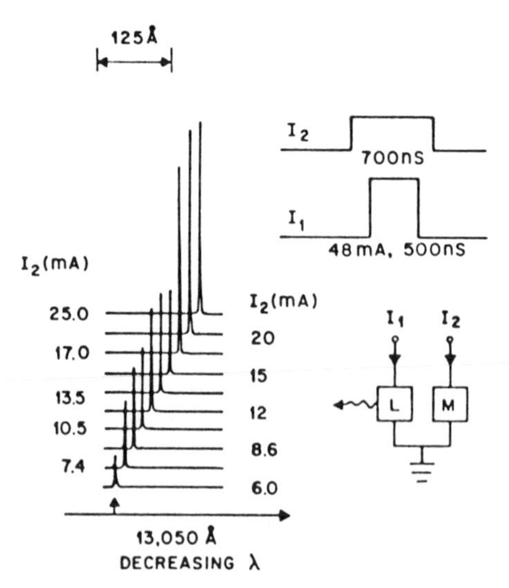

FIG. 3. Various specrtra obtained with different current levels applied to the modulator. The inset shows the detailed operation conditions. The C^3 laser operated in single-longitudinal mode under all conditions.

saturated.[15] Thus, the F–P mode spacings for active stripes 1 and 2 will be different and given by $\Delta\lambda_1 \sim \lambda_0^2/2N_{\text{eff1}} L_1$ and $\Delta\lambda_2 \sim \lambda_0^2/2N_{\text{eff2}} L_2$, respectively, and are represented schematically by the solid lines in Fig. 2. Since the two cavities are coupled, those F–P modes from each cavity that coincide spectrally will interfere constructively and become the enforced F–P modes of the coupled-cavity resonator while the others interfere destructively and become suppressed. The spectral spacing Λ of these enforced F–P modes will be significantly larger than either of the original individual F–P mode spacings depending on the difference of $N_{\text{eff1}} L_1$ and $N_{\text{eff2}} L_2$ and is given approximately by

$$\Lambda = \Delta\lambda_1 \Delta\lambda_2/|\Delta\lambda_1 - \Delta\lambda_2| = \lambda_0^2/2|N_{\text{eff1}} L_1 - N_{\text{eff2}} L_2|, \quad (1)$$

where we have assumed $\Delta\lambda_1 \approx \Delta\lambda_2$. Thus, for the enforced mode near the gain maximum, the normal gain roll-off, which is quite fast for GaInAsP at $\sim 1.3\ \mu$m, is sufficient to suppress the adjacent enforced modes[15] even under high-speed direct modulation.

With the above understanding, one can then easily show how wide-range direct frequency modulation with a large frequency tuning rate can be achieved in C^3 lasers. Let laser 1 be biased with an injection current level I_1 above lasing threshold, thus it acts as a laser. Let laser 2 be biased with some current I_2 below threshold, thus it acts as an etalon. Under these conditions, the situation is described by the solid lines in Fig. 2. Now, if one increases I_2 to I_2' and keeping I_1 the same, a change in carrier density in active stripe 2 will correspondingly induce a decrease from N_{eff2} to N_{eff2}'. This results in a shift of the modes of laser 2 towards shorter wavelength as shown by the dashed lines in Fig. 2. As a result of such changes, the F–P modes from laser 1 and etalon 2 that originally coincide become misaligned and the adjacent mode on the shorter wavelength side comes into coincidence and becomes enforced instead. This results in a shift by one F–P mode spacing of the laser towards the shorter wavelength. Since the change in N_{eff2} necessary to shift the next adjacent modes into alignment is small, only a small change in I_2 is sufficient.

The amount of frequency shift is greatly enhanced by the necessity to jump at least a discrete F–P mode spacing of laser 1 (~ 15 Å for a 136-μm cavity). Further increase in I_2 will continue to shift the lasing mode to the next one. This new mechanism which we called cavity-mode enhanced frequency modulation (CME-FM) thus resulted in a very large frequency tuning rate and a very wide frequency tuning range, at least half of the spectral width of the gain profile, i.e., $\gtrsim 150$ Å. The range can be further increased by temperature control. In addition, the C^3 laser is also always operating in highly stable single-longitudinal mode even under high-speed direct amplitude[16] or frequency modulation. The former[16] has been shown recently and the latter will be shown in the following.

Figure 3 shows the various spectra obtained with different current levels applied to the modulator (right) diode. The inset shows the detailed operation conditions. The laser (left) diode was biased with a 48-mA current pulse of 500-ns length. This corresponds to 1.3 times the threshold of this diode when no current was applied to the right diode. The current threshold of the right diode alone was 30 mA. The total threshold with both diodes pumped together was 46 mA. It is seen that a frequency shift of 150 Å has been achieved. Such frequency shift represents the widest range ever achieved so far. This is to be compared with 0.4-Å shift obtained in intracavity electro-optically modulated lasers[6] and >1 GHz shift in direct modulation of single laser diodes.[1,2,10] Further, a frequency tuning rate of 10 Å/mA was obtained. Even larger value can be obtained by having shorter cavities. Such value is again to be compared with ~ 100 MHz/mA in direct modulation of single laser diodes[1,2,10] or 0.02 Å/V in intracavity electro-optic modula-

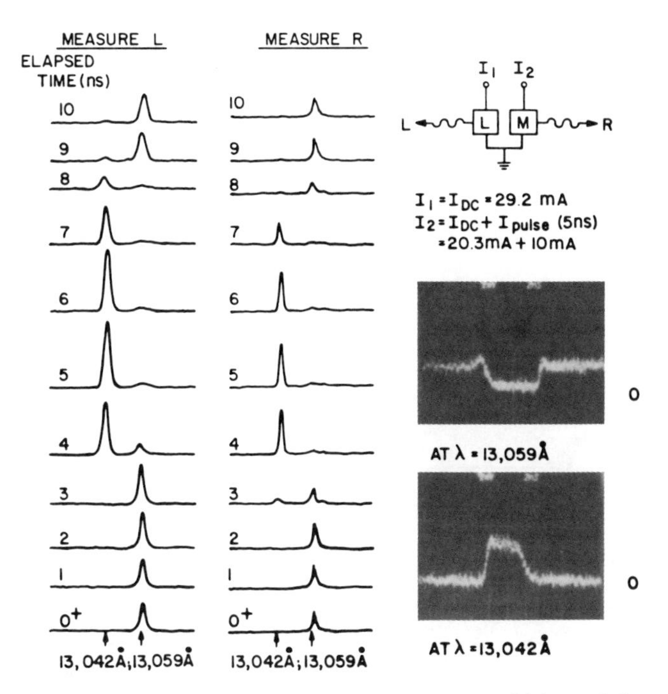

FIG. 4. (a) Time-resolved transient mode spectra under high-speed direct frequency modulation achieved under conditions described by the inset. The rise time of the current pulse applied to the modulator was ~1 ns. (b) Spectral-resolved optical pulse responses at the single-longitudinal modes before frequency switching (13.058 Å) and after frequency switching (13.042 Å).

tion.[6] Very important is also the fact that the C^3 laser operated in a clean single-longitudinal mode under the conditions shown in Fig. 3. With such large frequency shifts one can, in fact, use the C^3 lasers as optical sources for multilevel FSK transmission system employing a single optical fiber. Each individual wavelength can be utilized as one level. The spectral separation of each level can be controlled by using the proper cavity lengths for the C^3 laser. They can also be used as sources in wavelength-division multiplexing systems.

Figure 4(a) shows the time-resolved transient mode spectra under high-speed direct frequency modulation achieved under conditions described by the inset. The spectra on the left and right of the figure were measured from the left and right sides of the C^3 laser, respectively. A dc current of 29.2 mA was applied to the laser (left) diode and a dc current of 20.3 mA with a superimposed pulse current of 10 mA (~1 ns rise time) was applied to the modulator (right diode). The spectra shown were taken at various elapsed times at 1-ns interval starting 4 ns before the onset of the frequency switch due to the application of the current pulse to the modulator. Complete frequency switching (from 13.058 to 1.3042 Å) was accomplished in ~1 ns which was limited by the rise time of the current pulse used. Further, at *all times*, the laser operated *stably* in single-longitudinal mode. No mode hopping was observed. To investigate the pulse-to-pulse spectral variations, the real-time optical pulse responses at the single-longitudinal modes before frequency switching (13.058 Å) and after frequency switching (13.042 Å) as selected by the spectrometer were displayed with a sampling oscilloscope as shown by the top and bottom photographs in Fig. 4(b), respectively. The clean flat pulse responses indicate that there was no pulse-to-pulse spectral variations.

In summary, we have reported a mechanism of direct frequency modulation, the cavity-mode enhanced frequency modulation (CME-FM), using the newly developed cleaved-coupled-cavity semiconductor lasers. It was shown that a very large frequency excursion of 150 Å and a frequency tuning rate of 10 Å/mA have been obtained with a 1.3-μm wavelength GaInAsP crescent C^3 laser.

Furthermore, time-resolved spectral and spectral-resolved pulse response measurements also showed that such C^3 lasers were highly single-longitudinal moded with excellent spectral purity and stability at all times even under high-speed direct frequency modulation. Because of the large frequency excursion that can be achieved, the FM optical demodulator can simply be a filter or monochromator followed by a photodetector. Without the need for heterodyne detection, there is no need for the local laser oscillator in the receiver or for stringent requirements on the components and on the overall system as required in direct FM of single F–P laser diodes. In addition to the important application as the optical source in FM optical communication systems, the present CME-FM C^3 laser can also be used as an optical source in wavelength-division multiplexing systems. Further, it opens the possibility of ultrahigh capacity multilevel optical FM information transmission systems.

[1] S. Kobayashi, Y. Yamamoto, M. Ito, and T. Kimura, IEEE J. Quantum Electron. **QE-18**, 582 (1982).
[2] S. Saito, Y. Yamamoto, and T. Kimura, Electron. Lett. **18**, 468 (1982).
[3] S. Saito, Y. Yamamoto, and T. Kimura, IEEE J. Quantum Electron. **QE-17**, 935 (1981).
[4] S. Saito, Y. Yamamoto, and T. Kimura, Electron. Lett. **16**, 826 (1980).
[5] Y. Yamamoto and T. Kimura, IEEE J. Quantum Electron. **QE-17**, 919 (1981).
[6] F. K. Reinhart and R. A. Logan, Appl. Phys. Lett. **27**, 532 (1975).
[7] F. K. Reinhart and R. A. Logan, Appl. Phys. Lett. **36**, 954 (1980).
[8] C. L. Tang, V. Kreismanis, and J. Ballantyne, Appl. Phys. Lett. **30**, 113 (1977).
[9] A. Olsson, and C. L. Tang, IEEE J. Quantum Electron. **QE-15**, 1085 (1979).
[10] A. Dandridge and L. Goldberg, Electron. Lett. **18**, 303 (1982).
[11] W. F. Kosnocky and R. H. Covnely IEEE J. Quantum Electron. **QE-4**, 125 (1968).
[12] M. B. Chang and Elsa Garmire, IEEE J. Quantum Electron. **QE-16**, 997 (1980).
[13] W. T. Tsang and N. A. Olsson (unpublished).
[14] R. A. Logan, J.P. Van der Ziel, H. Temkin, and C. H. Henry, Electron. Lett. **18**, 95 (1982).
[15] L. A. Coldren, D. I. Miller, K. Iga, and J. A. Rentschler, Appl. Phys. Lett. **38**, 315 (1981).
[16] W. T. Tsang, N. A. Olsson, and R. A. Logan (unpublished).

1·5 μm WAVELENGTH GaInAsP C^3 LASERS: SINGLE-FREQUENCY OPERATION AND WIDEBAND FREQUENCY TUNING

W. T. TSANG
N. A. OLSSON

Bell Laboratories
Murray Hill, NJ 07974, USA

R. A. LINKE
R. A. LOGAN

Bell Laboratories
Crawford Hill, Holmdel, NJ 07974, USA

22nd April 1983

Indexing terms: Lasers and applications, Semiconductor laser

We have characterised the temporal-spectral behaviour of 1·5 μm wavelength cleaved-coupled-cavity (C^3) lasers. Single longitudinal mode discrimination ratios in excess of 500:1 have been obtained under high bit rate modulation. Bit error rates of less than $\lesssim 10^{-9}$ were obtained under single-frequency operation with direct modulation up to 1 Gbit/s. Averaged frequency tuning rates as large as 26 Å/mA and frequency tuning excursion of 300 Å were achieved when the C^3 laser was operated in a frequency modulation mode.

Recently, we have described a new batch processing technique for forming self-aligned coupled cavity laser diodes by a simple modification of the usual cleaving procedures.[1–3] It was shown that in addition to stable single longitudinal mode operation under high-speed direct modulation[3] a large frequency tuning rate of 10 Å/mA and frequency tuning excursion of 150 Å,[2] can be obtained when operated under different regimes. These results were obtained with 1·3 μm wavelength cleaved-coupled cavity (C^3) lasers.

Since stable single-frequency operation under high bit-rate direct modulation is particularly important for optical transmission in dispersive single-mode fibre at 1·5 μm range, we report in the present letter the spectral-temporal properties of the newly developed C^3 laser operating at 1·5 μm.

A 1·5 μm wavelength GaInAsP crescent laser wafer was used in this experiment.[4] However, C^3 lasers can be formed from any other laser structure. A detailed description about the fabrication of C^3 lasers has been reported previously.[1] Fig. 1*a* shows the CW light/current (*L/I*) curves at room-temperature of a 1·5 μm wavelength C^3 laser under the operation conditions shown in the inset. This result confirmed the strong optical coupling between the two cleaved cavities as also observed in gain-guided two-section lasers by Coldren *et al.*[5] For curves with $I_R < 20$ mA (the threshold of the right diode), the *L/I* curves were smooth both below and above lasing. However, for curves with $I_R > 20$ mA, a modulation or ripple structure was observed in the *L/I* curves below threshold. Sometimes the same structure is seen above threshold but in that case the ripples are more widely separated in current. Spectral measurements show that these structures are associated with the currents where longitudinal-mode switching occurred. A detailed study will be given elsewhere. Briefly, when one of the diodes of the C^3 laser is operated as a laser and the other diode is operated below threshold as a frequency modulator, a change in current applied to the modulator gives a change in carrier density. This in turn gives a corresponding change in the effective refractive index, which results in a shift in the Fabry–Perot (F–P) modes of the modulator with respect to the laser diode. Because of the coupling of the two cavities, such a slight shift results in a large shift

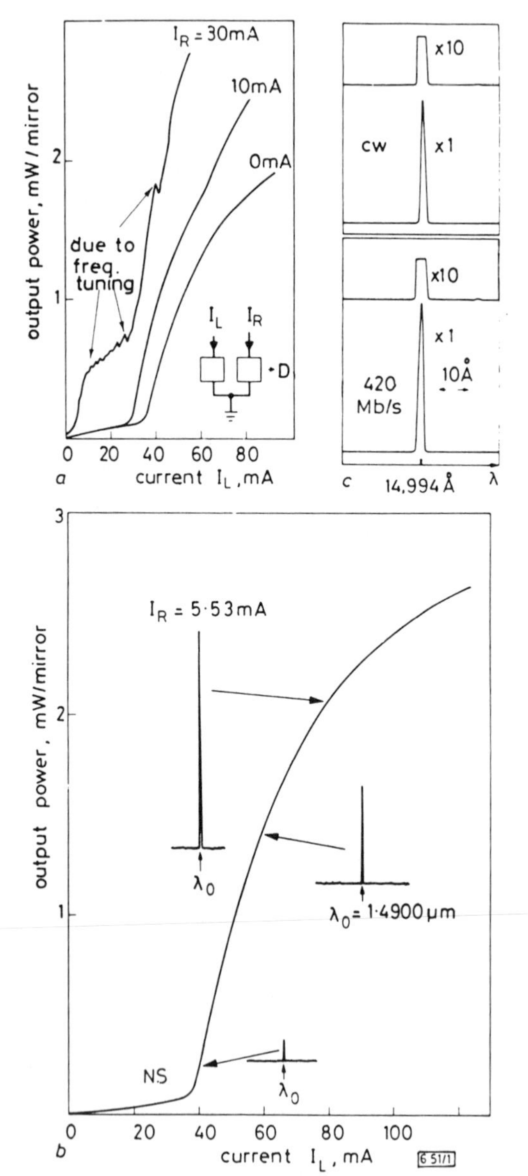

Fig. 1

a CW *L/I* curves at room temperature under operation conditions shown in the inset

b CW *L/I* and spectra of another C^3 laser showing the wide range of stable single-frequency operation

c CW and high-speed modulated (420 Mbit/s) spectra for the same C^3 laser as in *b*

Reprinted with permission from *Electron. Lett.*, vol. 19, no. 11, pp. 415–417, May 26, 1983.

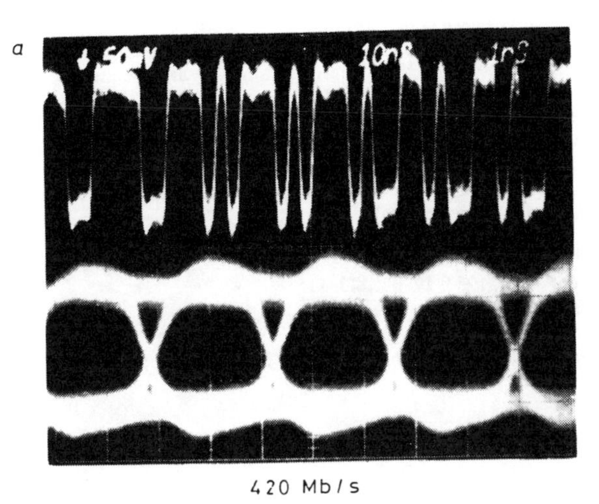

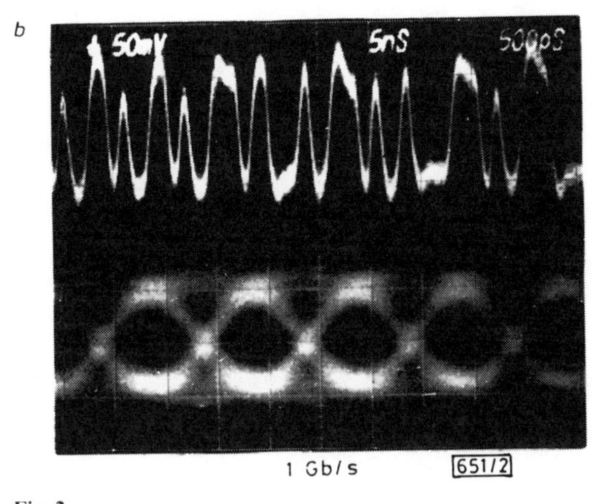

Fig. 2

a and *b* are the eye diagrams and optical pulse patterns at 420 Mbit/s and 1 Gbit/s, respectively, for the same C^3 laser shown in Figs. 1*b* and *c*

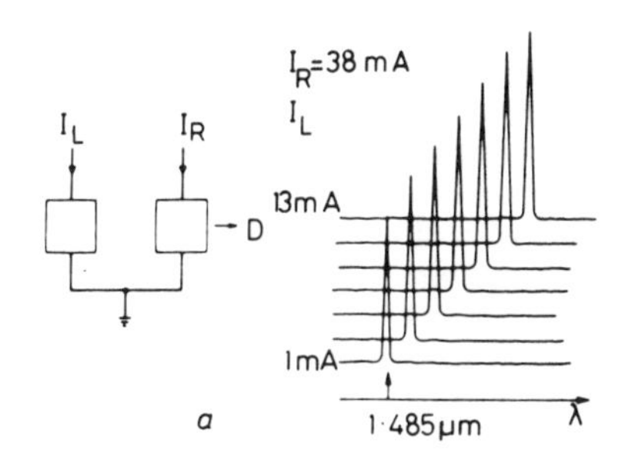

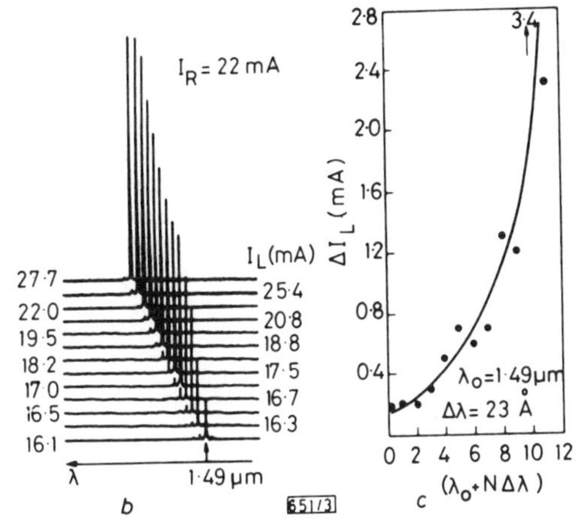

Fig. 3

a Typical example of frequency tuning by changing the current to the modulator diode of a 1·5 μm wavelength C^3 laser
b shows a 1·5 μm wavelength C^3 laser with the largest frequency tuning range of 300 Å and tuning rate of 26 Å/mA
c the increment in modulator current needed for the C^3 laser wavelength to shift by one longitudinal mode spacing plotted as function of lasing wavelength

($\sim$ 20 Å) of the enforced mode of the coupled-cavity to the adjacent F–P mode of the laser diode.[2] This longitudinal mode shift is manifested by the ripples in the *L/I* curves. The ripples are closer together below threshold than above. This is because, below threshold, carrier density builds up with increasing injection current up to threshold. Ideally, when threshold is reached, the carrier density should be pinned and no further increase in density should occur with increasing injection current. Subsequently, above threshold, no further mode switching should occur. However, most 1·5 μm wavelength crescent C^3 lasers tested in this experiment were not ideal and mode-switching still could occur above threshold. Fig. 1*b* shows the *L/I* and the spectra at various current levels of another C^3 laser. A wide range of stable single-frequency operation was obtained even with highly non-ideal original lasers. Mode discrimination in excess of 500:1 was measured both under CW and high-speed modulation as shown by the spectra given in Fig. 1*c*. The low-power saturation was not due to the C^3 structure but present in the original 1·5 μm wavelength crescent structure. It is believed to be due to serious current leakage across or/and around the reverse-biased current blocking junction. A typical threshold-temperature dependence coefficient T_0 of $\sim$ 30 K was measured for both diodes pumped together. Again this value is similar to that of the original crescent laser.

The present C^3 lasers were subjected to 420 Mbit/s and 1 Gbit/s NRZ high-speed modulation tests with one diode operated under CW condition and the other diode biased with a DC component and a pseudorandom word superimposed on it. Fig. 2*a* and *b* show the eye diagrams and the optical pulse patterns at 420 Mbit/s and 1 Gbit/s, respectively, for the same diodes as shown in Figs. 1*b* and 1*c*. A bit error rate of $\lesssim 10^{-9}$ were obtained through a spectrometer with the spectrometer slit to pass only the dominant longitudinal mode indicating that the C^3 laser operated truly as a single-frequency source even under high bit-rate direct modulation.

As explained above, with the laser diode operated above threshold and the modulator diode under threshold, an extremely large frequency tuning rate and excursion can be obtained. Fig. 3*a* shows a typical example of the various spectra obtained with different current levels applied to the modulator diode for a 1·5 μm wavelength C^3 crescent laser. A frequency excursion of $\sim$ 150 Å and a tuning rate averaged over many steps of $\sim$ 13 Å/mA was typically obtained. Highly single longitudinal mode operation was obtained at the same time. In Fig. 3*b* we show a 1·5 μm C^3 crescent laser that allowed a frequency shift as large as 300 Å in 13 discrete steps and an averaged frequency tuning rate as large as 26 Å/mA. These values are at least twice as large as those obtained previously with any C^3 lasers.[2] Fig. 3*c* shows the increment in current ΔI_L needed for the C^3 laser to shift by one longitudinal mode spacing as a function of lasing wavelength. It is seen that ΔI_L increased parabolically with increasing lasing wavelength (or I_L). This is consistent with the fact that as the modulator diode approached threshold the carrier density (or junction voltage) begins to saturate.

In summary, we have characterised the temporal-spectral behaviour of 1·5 μm wavelength C^3 lasers fabricated from crescent laser wafers. Single longitudinal mode discrimination ratio in excess of 500:1 has been obtained even under high bit rate modulation. Bit error rates of $\lesssim 10^{-9}$ were obtained under single-frequency operation with direct modulation up to 1 Gbit/s. Averaged frequency tuning rate as large as 26 Å/mA and frequency tuning excursion of 300 Å were achieved when the C^3 laser was operated in a frequency modulation mode.

References

1 TSANG, W. T., and OLSSON, N. A.: 'A technique for fabricating cleaved coupled-cavity semiconductors in batch form' (unpublished)

2 TSANG, W. T., OLSSON, N. A., and LOGAN, R. A.: 'High speed direct single-frequency modulation with large tuning rate and frequency excursion in cleaved-coupled-cavity semiconductor laser', *Appl. Phys. Lett.*, 1983, **43**, (Apr. 15th)

3 TSANG, W. T., OLSSON, N. A., and LOGAN, R. A.: 'Stable single-longitudinal mode operation under high speed direct modulation in cleaved-coupled-cavity GaInAsP semiconductor lasers', *Electron. Lett.* (under consideration)

4 VAN DER ZIEL, J. P., TEMKIN, H., and LOGAN, R. A.: 'Quaternary 1·5 μm (InGaAsP/InP) buried crescent lasers with separate optical confinement', *ibid.*, 1983, **19**, pp. 113–115

5 COLDREN, L. A., FURUYA, K., MILLER, B. I., and RENTSCHLER: 'Etched mirror and groove-coupled GaInAsP/InP laser devices for integrated optics', *IEEE J. Quantum Electron.*, 1982, **QE-18**, pp. 1679–1688

NEW APPROACH TOWARDS FREQUENCY STABILISATION OF LINEWIDTH-NARROWED SEMICONDUCTOR LASERS

C. J. NIELSEN
J. H. OSMUNDSEN

Electromagnetics Institute
Technical University of Denmark
DK-2800 Lyngby, Denmark

9th June 1983

Indexing terms: Semiconductor devices and materials, Lasers and laser applications, Frequency stabilisation

By means of controlling the injection current and the phase of optical feedback, simultaneous frequency stabilisation and line-width reduction of a semiconductor laser are demonstrated. Line-width reduction from 24 MHz to 300 kHz and mean frequency stability better than 800 Hz relative to a Fabry–Perot etalon were obtained.

For use in coherent optical-communication systems and interferometric sensors, it is essential that the spectral purity of the semiconductor laser is improved.

Reduction of the frequency drift of semiconductor lasers to less than 2 kHz has been achieved using an automatic-frequency-control (AFC) loop with feedback to the injection current.[1]

In order to reduce the phase noise, a fast electronic feedback loop has been applied yielding a reduction of 30 dB.[2] Also, optical feedback has been used by several authors to obtain a narrow spectral linewidth.[3]

Both frequency stability and narrow linewidth have been obtained using two identical lasers placed on the same heatsink and biased in parallel.[4] Locking the frequency of one of the lasers to a Fabry–Perot interferometer (FPI) by means of a current-feedback loop and placing the other laser in an external cavity, a frequency-stabilised laser unit with narrow spectral linewidth was obtained. However, the frequency drift of the second laser induced by variations in the external cavity length is not corrected by the AFC loop.

In this letter we describe a system by which a frequency stability better than 800 Hz relative to an FPI passband and a linewidth of 300 kHz has been obtained simultaneously using only one semiconductor laser.

The frequency stabilisation is achieved by controlling the phase of the optical feedback from an external cavity by means of a piezoelectric transducer (PZT). Owing to the low bandwidth of the mirror positioning mechanics, a conventional current-controlled AFC loop is applied in order to improve performance.

The experimental set-up is shown in Fig. 1. From the external mirror a part of the emitted light is reflected back into the active layer of the laser yielding a reduction in spectral linewidth and frequency tunability.[5]

A confocal FPI with a free spectral range (FSR) of 2 GHz and finesse of $F \sim 150$ was used as optical-frequency discriminator. The power transmitted through the FPI is detected by a photodiode and the electrical signal fed into a differential amplifier. A reference voltage to the differential amplifier is used to determine the operating point of the frequency discriminator.

The error signal from the differential amplifier was fed to the PZT via an integrator followed by a high-voltage amplifier. The cutoff frequency of this branch was approximately

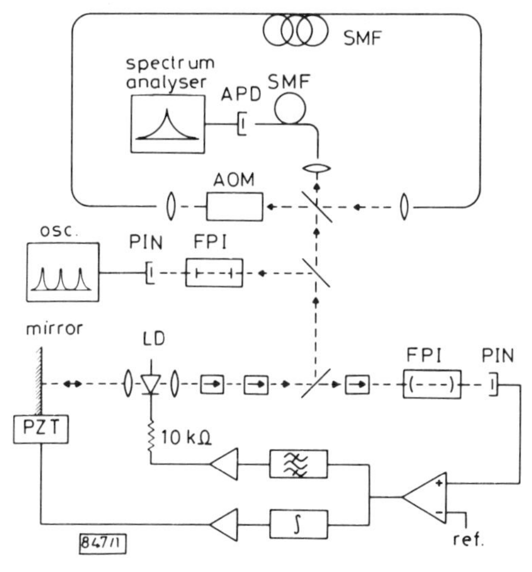

Fig. 1 *Experimental set-up*

20 Hz, determined by the PZT, and the total loop gain from output to input of the integrator was approximately 60.

Frequency components beyond 20 Hz of the error signal were fed back to the injection current via a bandpass filter with passband approximately 20–500 Hz. The open-loop gain within the passband was approximately 20.

The mean frequency stability is evaluated by recording the error signal by means of a recorder with a bandwidth of 4 Hz. The high-frequency components of the error signal are monitored by a spectrum analyser.

A scanning planar FPI with adjustable FSR from 2 GHz to 800 GHz was used to monitor the emission spectrum in order to ensure that single-longitudinal-mode operation without self-pulsations was maintained.

The laser was placed on a heatsink and temperature stabilised by means of a Peltier element ($23 \pm 0{\cdot}01$°C). In order to avoid mode jumps between external cavity modes, it was necessary to shield the laser from air turbulences causing rapid temperature variations.

Experimental results: The linewidth of the laser, which was measured by a self-heterodyne set-up, was in the free running state 24 MHz. The amount of optical feedback was adjusted for minimum obtainable linewidth which for the laser (HLP 1400) used in this experiment was 300 kHz (Fig. 2). Further increment of the optical-feedback level induced self-pulsations and multimode operation. Throughout the experiment it was observed that the power level of adjacent cavity modes was at least 30 dB below the dominant mode.

The mean frequency stability of the laser placed in the

Reprinted with permission from *Electron. Lett.*, vol. 19, no. 16, pp. 644-646, Aug. 4, 1983.

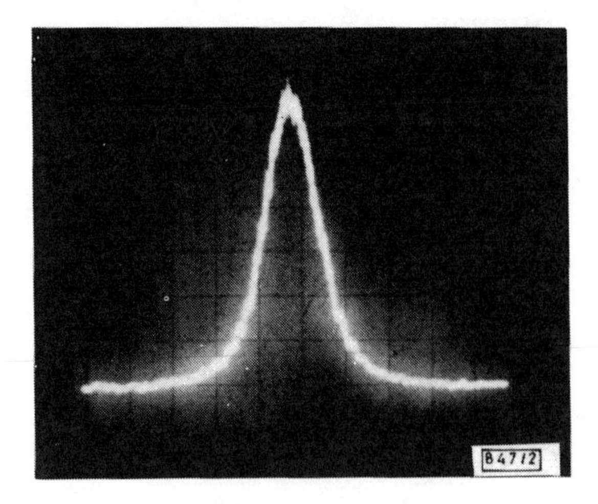

Fig. 2 *Beat note of the laser in the line narrowed case, obtained from the self-heterodyne set-up*

Horizontal: 150 kHz/division
Vertical: linear scale

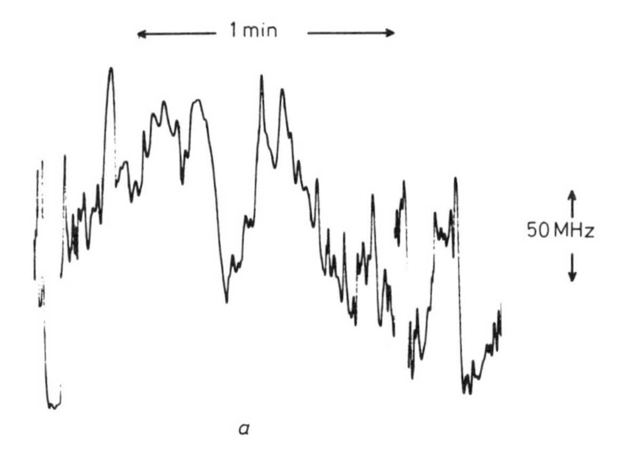

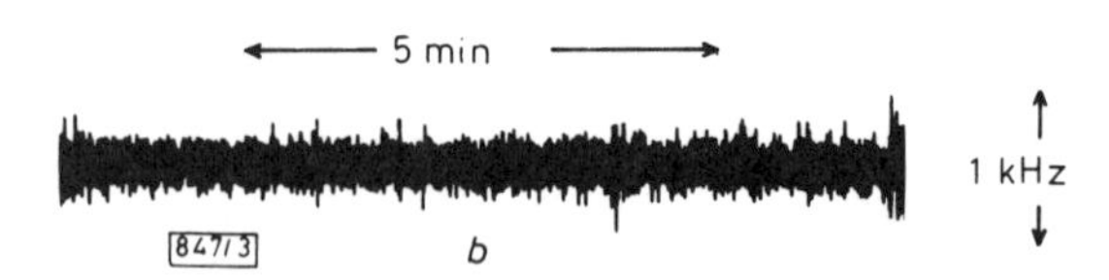

Fig. 3 *Frequency drift of the laser in the external cavity*

a Without AFC
b With AFC

external cavity, but without any electronic feedback, is shown in Fig. 3*a*. Over a period of 2 min the frequency drift is approximately 185 MHz, probably due to temperature variations of the external cavity and the laser.

Fig. 3*b* shows the frequency drift of the laser stabilised by the double-loop AFC scheme and as seen from this Figure a mean frequency stability better than 800 Hz is obtained.

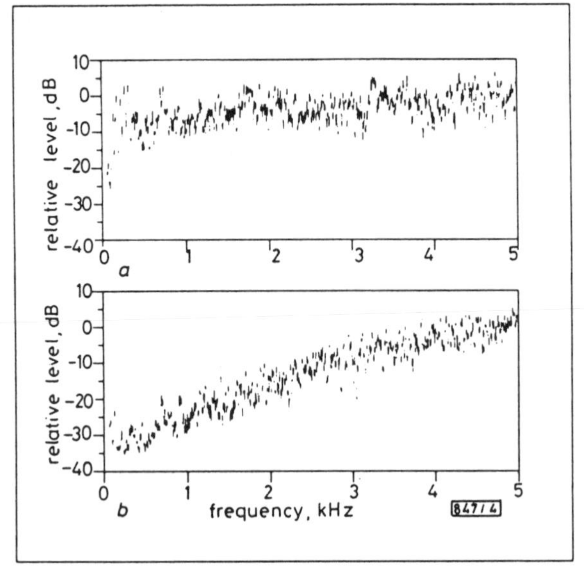

Fig. 4 *Spectrum of the error signal*

a Without current controlled AFC
b With current controlled AFC

The effect of the current-controlled AFC loop is demonstrated in Figs. 4*a* and *b*. Fig. 4*a* shows the spectrum of the error signal, when the current-controlled AFC is switched off.

Applying feedback to the injection current, the level of the error signal is reduced in the frequency region below 5 kHz. The reduction within the passband of the filter is approximately 25 dB.

Conclusion: We have demonstrated a double-loop AFC system yielding a frequency stability better than 800 Hz and a linewidth of 300 kHz simultaneously.

The results obtained are promising for future work in order to make the optical source compatible with the requirements of coherent communication systems.

Future work could include the application of a high-bandwidth feedback system in order to further reduce the phase noise of semiconductor lasers.

Acknowledgments: This work was supported by the US Army Research Office (contract DAJA 37-82-6-9735) and the Danish Council for Scientific & Industrial Research (STVF).

References

1 NIELSEN, C. J.: 'and JACOBSEN, G.: 'Frequency stabilisation of single-mode semiconductor lasers at 830 nm and 1·3 μm', *J. Opt. Commun.*, to be published

2 COBB, K. W., and CULSHAW, B.: 'Reduction of optical phase noise in semiconductor lasers', *Electron. Lett.*, 1982, **18**, pp. 336–337

3 FAVRE, F., LE GUEN, D., and SIMON, J. C.: 'Optical feedback effects upon laser diode oscillation field spectrum', *IEEE Trans.*, 1982, **MTT-30**, pp. 1700–1705

4 FAVRE, F., and LE GUEN, D.: 'Effect of semiconductor laser phase noise on BER performance in an optical DPSK heterodyne-type experiment', *Electron. Lett.*, 1982, **18**, pp. 964–965

5 GOLDBERG, L., TAYLOR, H. F., DANDRIDGE, A., WELLER, J. F., and MILES, R. O.: 'Spectral characteristics of semiconductor lasers with optical feedback', *IEEE Trans.*, 1982, **MTT-30**, pp. 401–409

SINGLE-LONGITUDINAL-MODE OPERATION OF INJECTION LASER COUPLED TO A GRINROD EXTERNAL CAVITY

K. -Y. LIOU

Bell Laboratories
555 Union Boulevard
Allentown, PA 18103, USA

3rd August 1983

Indexing term: Lasers and applications

We have demonstrated CW and pulsed single-longitudinal-mode operation of a conventional InGaAsP buried-heterostructure laser butt-coupled to a short GRINROD lens with reflective coating on the far end. The GRINROD lens was prepared using a ≲1/4 pitch graded-index fibre which was used as an external cavity with controlled optical coupling to the laser.

Single-longitudinal-mode laser sources are of great interest for high-bandwidth single-mode-fibre communication systems when the data bit rate is limited by chromatic dispersion. High-speed light output pulses can be generated by either direct modulation of the laser or CW operation of the laser with an external modulator. In this letter we describe CW and pulsed single-longitudinal-mode operation of conventional multimoded InGaAsP BH laser diodes achieved by coupling the laser to a short graded-index cavity with Cr-Au reflective coating on the far end.

Longitudinal-mode selection by a coupled cavity[1,2] has been investigated as an approach to achieve single-longitudinal-mode operation of semiconductor lasers. The second cavity optically coupled to the laser can be either an air-spaced passive cavity[3-5] or an active laser cavity with bias-current control.[6,7] The lasing wavelength of the active-active coupled laser can be tuned by controlling the injection currents.[7] The passive external cavity laser can also be tuned by adjusting the external cavity length.[4,8] The external cavity approach is attractive for its simplicity and can be applied to existing lasers of proven designs. Either an Au-coated planar mirror[5,8] or a concave spherical mirror[4] has been used as the external reflector. For the external cavity laser the ratio of the optical lengths of the laser ($n_l L_l$) and the external cavity ($n_e L_e$) are usually chosen in the range of 3:1 to 6:1 for effective single-mode operation. In our experiment, a simple GRINROD lens was used as the external cavity. This GRINROD cavity provides a controlled amount of optical coupling to the laser. It can also be used at the same time as an optical coupler to other electro-optical components in a practical transmitter module.

Short GRINROD lenses for this experiment were prepared from graded-index multimode fibre with 0·29 numerical aperture and 70 μm core diameter. The fibre was epoxied inside a glass capillary tube, and was polished from both ends to a predetermined length. One end was coated with Cr-Au for high reflectivity. The coated end was then epoxied on a glass rod for handling. The coupling geometry of this GRINROD cavity to the laser is shown schematically in Fig. 1. Conventional InGaAsP/InP BH lasers which operate with multi-longitudinal modes were used to demonstrate the GRINROD external cavity laser design. The laser was mounted on a Cu heat sink with a thermo-electric cooler for temperature

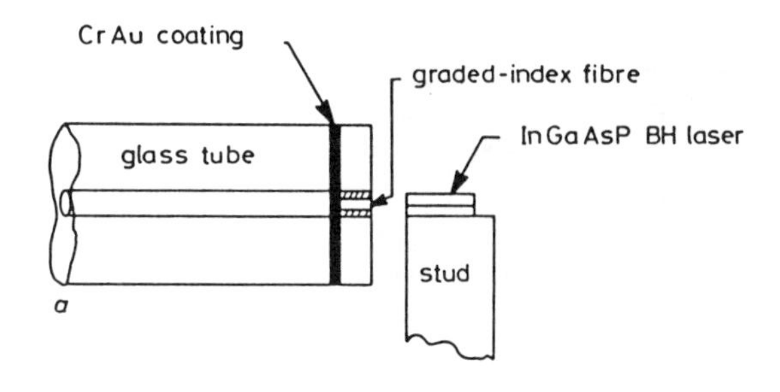

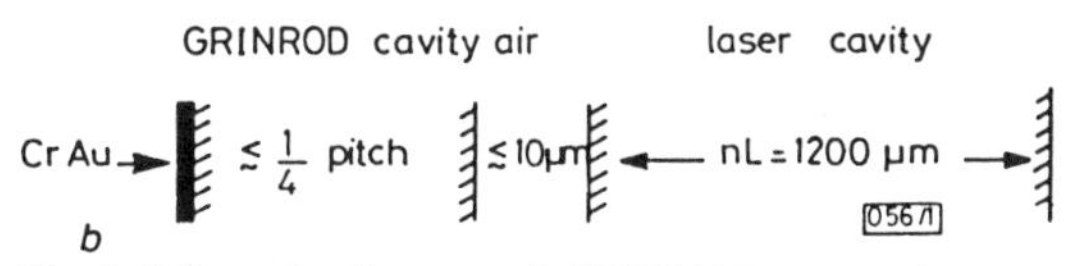

Fig. 1 *Schematic diagram of GRINROD external cavity laser (not drawn to scale)*

control. The airgap between the front face of the GRINROD and the laser facet was ≲10 μm. This airgap cavity did not have any significant mode selection effect due to its large cavity mode spacing (≳120 × laser mode spacing). An anti-reflection coating on the front face of the GRINROD lens can be applied if necessary. The GRINROD cavity which was 170 μm long was made slightly shorter than 1/4 pitch to have the focal point outside the glass near the laser facet. The ratio of the laser to the external cavity length ($n_l L_l / n_e L_e$) was approximately 4:1.

The 6 mW/facet CW spectrum for the InGaAsP BH laser with current at 51 mA (I_{th} = 23 mA) at 23°C is shown in Fig. 2*a*. A maximum of 40% increase in light output was observed when the GRINROD cavity was coupled to the laser. After reducing the laser current to again give 6 mW CW output, the single-longitudinal-mode spectrum at the same heat sink temperature is shown in Fig. 2*b*. The laser with the coupled external cavity was pulsed by a square-wave generator from threshold to a peak power of 6 mW. A beam splitter was used for simultaneous measurements of the spectrum and the light output pulses detected with a high-speed InGaAs/InP PIN photodiode. The on/off extinction ratio was better than 30:1. The spectra of the GRINROD external cavity laser under 300 MHz and 500 MHz square-wave modulation are also shown in Fig. 2*b*. The corresponding multimoded spectra for the laser alone are shown in Fig. 2*a*. The same longitudinal mode was stabilised with the external cavity as the modulation rate was varied. The most significant side mode intensity relative to the main mode intensity at 300 MHz and 500 MHz was suppressed by 23 dB and 20 dB, respectively. Under CW operation the side mode suppression ratio was better than 25 dB. When the laser was pulsed from above I_{th}, the amplitude

Reprinted with permission from *Electron. Lett.*, vol. 19, no. 19, pp. 750–751, Sept. 15, 1983.

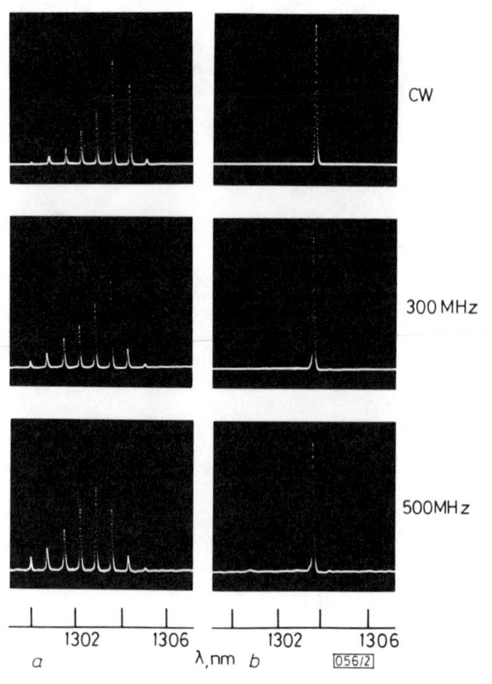

Fig. 2 *CW and square-wave pulsed spectra for the laser alone (a) and the GRINROD external cavity laser (b)*

CW spectra are scaled to have the same peak height as the pulsed spectra. The intensity scale of (*a*) is 2·5 times the scale of (*b*)

of the first relaxation oscillation peak decreased and the mode suppression ratio approached that under CW operation with the penalty of a decreased on/off light output extinction ratio.

The GRINROD cavity plays the dual role of the external cavity and an optical coupler. The laser to external cavity optical coupling efficiency and the L_l/L_e ratio can be separately optimised for single-mode operation. If the Cr-Au reflective coating used in the experiment is replaced by a partially transmitting coating, the GRINROD cavity can also couple a portion of the light to a photodiode which can serve as a laser monitor for control purposes. If a 1/2 pitch lens is used, the GRINROD cavity can focus and couple laser light to a transmission fibre if desirable. The design of a single-longitudinal-mode laser is dependent on the system requirements. The mode suppression ratio in the present experiment can be improved by using lasers with shorter cavity lengths as suggested by Lin and Burrus.[5] An optimised optical coupling possible with the GRINROD cavity, however, permits single-mode operation with a longer laser cavity than is possible for the nonfocusing external cavity schemes. Since a short cavity laser may have a short practical life due to an increased junction temperature and current density,[9] reliability and laser length are among the factors to be considered for optimised performance in communication systems.

In summary, we have proposed and demonstrated single-longitudinal-mode operation of a GRINROD external cavity laser. The passive cavity is a $\lesssim 1/4$ pitch GRINROD lens prepared from a short section (170 μm) of a graded-index optical fibre. Used as an external cavity and an optical coupler, the GRINROD cavity approach shows promise for use in practical lightwave transmitters.

Acknowledgment: I am indebted to S. W. Granlund and F. H. Levinson for processing of the GRINROD lenses from optical fibre for the experiment, and to L. A. Coldren, C. B. Swan and R. G. Smith for helpful discussions.

References

1 KLEINMAN, D. A., and KISLIUK, P. P.: 'Discrimination against unwanted orders in the Fabry-Perot resonator', *Bell Syst. Tech. J.*, 1962, **41**, pp. 453–462

2 SMITH, P. W.: 'Mode selection in lasers', *Proc. IEEE*, 1972, **60**, pp. 422–440

3 RENNER, D., and CARROLL, J. E.: 'Simple system for broadband single-mode tuning of DH GaAlAs lasers', *Electron. Lett.*, 1979, **15**, pp. 73–74

4 PRESTON, K. R., WOOLLARD, K. C., and CAMERON, K. H.: 'External cavity-controlled single-longitudinal-mode laser transmitter module', *ibid.*, 1981, **17**, pp. 931–933

5 LIN, C., and BURRUS, C. A.: 'CW and high-speed single-longitudinal-mode operation of a short InGaAsP injection laser with external coupled cavity'. Postdeadline paper PD5-1, Topical meeting on optical fiber communication, New Orleans, Feb. 28–March 2, 1983

6 EBELING, K. J., COLDREN, L. A., MILLER, B. I., and RENTSCHLER, J. A.: 'Single-mode operation of coupled-cavity GaInAsP/InP semiconductor lasers', *Appl. Phys. Lett.*, 1983, **42**, pp. 6–8

7 TSANG, W. T., OLSSON, N. A., LOGAN, R. A., and LINKE, R. A.: 'Demonstration of multilevel multichannel optical frequency shift keying (FSK) with cleaved-coupled-cavity (C^3) semiconductor lasers', *Electron. Lett.*, 1983, **19**, pp. 341–343

8 PRESTON, K. R.: 'Simple spectral control technique for external cavity laser transmitters', *ibid.*, 1982, **18**, pp. 1092–1094

9 ENDO, K., MATSUMOTO, S., KAWANO, H., FURUSE, T., and SAKUMA, I.: 'Cavity length dependence of practical life of long wavelength semiconductor laser (II)'. National Convention of the Institute of Electronics & Communication Engineers of Japan (IECEJ), 2–4 April 1983, Sendai, Japan, Paper 954

Instability of Semiconductor Lasers Due to Optical Feedback from Distant Reflectors

CHARLES H. HENRY AND RUDOLF F. KAZARINOV

Abstract—We explain an istability occurring in continuously operating lasers due to moderate feedback from distant reflectors. This instability occurs despite the fact that the laser is stable with respect to small deviations from steady-state operation. It is the result of finite phase and carrier number changes caused by fluctuations in spontaneous emission. We predict several properties that agree with recent experimental observations: 1) the instability only occurs when the laser reaches a steady state that maximizes coherent feedback and laser light intensity; 2) the instability vanishes at strong feedback levels; and 3) at moderate feedback levels, the laser will be nearly stable at threshold, but unstable when operated well above threshold. The latter behavior results in a nonlinear "kinked" shape in the light versus current relation.

I. Introduction

We will discuss the stability of semiconductor lasers operating continuously in the presence of moderate external feedback. We have in mind power reflectivities greater than -30 dB and external reflectors separated by a distance of many semiconductor cavity lengths from the laser, e.g., a few centimeters to kilometers. These effects should be considered important in applications of lasers such as video recording, stabilization of lasers for coherent communications, use of external modulators, etc.

It is well known that external reflectors can have a profound effect on continuously operating semiconductor lasers [1]-[7]. Weak reflections have been shown to cause appreciable line narrowing [4], [8], [9]. More surprisingly, the laser line has been observed to broaden under higher levels of feedback [2], [3], [10]. Recently, Lenstra *et al.* [10] demonstrated that for moderate levels of optical feedback, the laser line becomes enormously broadened to a line width on the order of 25 GHz. They called this phenomenon "coherence collapse" and attributed it to a puzzling lack of coherence between the field of a continuously operating laser and the steady-state reflected field.

Another rather baffling behavior of CW lasers is their tendency to exhibit periodic low-frequency intensity fluctuations in the presence of moderate external feedback [11]-[13]. While there is some understanding of the dependence of the period of the fluctuations on laser current and reflector separation [13], the cause of the fluctuations has not been explained.

An experiment that provides insight into both the line broadening and the self-pulsation phenomena was recently done by Temkin *et al.* [14]. They show that under conditions of moderate reflecting feedback (-35 to -15 dB power reflectivity), the laser exhibits low-frequency self-pulsations. The pulsation period is determined by the external cavity length and takes a time of about ten roundtrips in the external cavity. Near threshold, the pulsating behavior can be described as one in which light is amplified through many roundtrips in the external cavity, and just as it approaches a steady-state intensity, it abruptly drops to zero. The substantial line broadening (up to 40 GHz), also observed by Temkin *et al.*, is merely the frequency change (chirp) as the laser repetitively goes from the initially on state to steady-state operation.

This instability is unexpected because conventional analysis of the stability of steady-state behavior of a laser with external mirrors (or equivalently, injection-locked lasers [15]) shows that the laser should be stable. This stability is usually established in the following way. The differential equations governing laser operation are strongly nonlinear. However, they are readily solved for conditions of steady operation by putting all time derivatives to zero. The equations are then linearized with respect to small derivations from the steady-state solutions. We will show that at the point of steady-state operation with minimum threshold gain, these deviations decay to zero and, in fact, are strongly damped, thereby satisfying the linear condition for stability. However, we will show that, in this case, the linear analysis of stability is insufficient, and when second-order deviations are considered, we find an instability that can explain the behavior observed by Temkin *et al.* [14].

In a simple laser without external feedback, there are forces which keep the system at the point of steady-state operation. For example, if the carrier number increases, the gain will increase. This in turn causes the light intensity to increase, thereby increasing the rate of stimulated emission. The increased stimulated emission reduces the carrier number. This leads to conventional relaxation oscillations which are damped by additional effects.

The instability arising in second order can be briefly explained as follows. The laser seeks a steady-state operation which maximizes feedback.

When external feedback is present, the state corresponding to maximum feedback occurs when there is phase alignment between the semiconductor cavity field and the reflected field. A carrier number change n will

Manuscript received April 18, 1985.
The authors are with AT&T Bell Laboratories, Murray Hill, NJ 07974.
IEEE Log Number 8406669.

Reprinted from *IEEE J. Quantum Electron.*, vol. QE-22, no. 2, pp. 294-301, Feb. 1986.

change the resonance frequency of the semiconductor cavity. This in turn causes a phase change ϕ between the laser field and the reflected field. This acts to decrease the light intensity in proportion to $1 - \cos \phi \approx \phi^2/2$, which decreases the rate of stimulated emission and further increases n. This increase in n again raises the cavity resonance frequency, causing the phase misalignment ϕ to continue to grow. Instability occurs for finite fluctuations of ϕ and n when this effect becomes greater than the restoring forces giving rise to the relaxation oscillations described above. We will show that once the point of steady-state operation is reached (phase alignment of the cavity field and reflected field), the probability of such a sufficiently strong fluctuation is high enough to explain the experimental observations.

We believe our explanation for the cause of the instability is new. It differs greatly from recent papers claiming that the unstable behavior of semiconductor lasers with reflective feedback is a form of "optical chaos" [16]-[18]. These studies do not include spontaneous emission noise. In steady-state operation, the laser with reflective feedback can be thought of as phase locked to the reflected field. The phenomenon that we describe is driven by large fluctuations in spontaneous emission that dislodge the laser from this locked state that is stable for small fluctuations.

II. Analysis

In this section, we will present the equations governing a laser in the presence of weak or moderately strong reflections. We will discuss steady-state behavior and derive the condition for instability. The instability will be shown to be caused by fluctuations that take the system from the steady-state operating point to over the top of a restraining barrier. Finally, we will calculate the approximate time for the instability to occur and compare our results to the experiments of Temkin *et al.* [14].

A. Basic Equations

Our starting point is the equation commonly used to describe the complex laser field $\beta(t)$ in the presence of a reflections [1], [9]:

$$\dot{\beta} = \left[-i\omega_0 + \frac{\Delta G}{2}(1 - i\alpha) \right] \beta + \kappa\beta(t - \tau_0) + F_\beta(t) \quad (1)$$

where the light intensity measured in photons in the semiconductor cavity is $I = |\beta|^2$. The feedback parameter κ can be shown to be [1], [9]

$$\kappa = \frac{(1 - R)R_0^{1/2}}{R^{1/2}\,\tau_s} \quad (2)$$

where R is the facet power reflectivity, R_0 is the external power reflectivity including coupling losses, and τ_s is the roundtrip time in the semiconductor cavity. The other parameters in (1) are ω_0, the cavity resonance angular frequency at the threshold in the absence of reflections, α, the linewidth parameter [19], τ_0, the roundtrip time in the external cavity, ΔG, the deviation of the laser gain from that at threshold, and $F_\beta(t)$, a random Langevin force that causes spontaneous emission. Equation (1) is restricted in validity to moderate levels of reflectivity where $\kappa\tau_s \lesssim 1/2$.

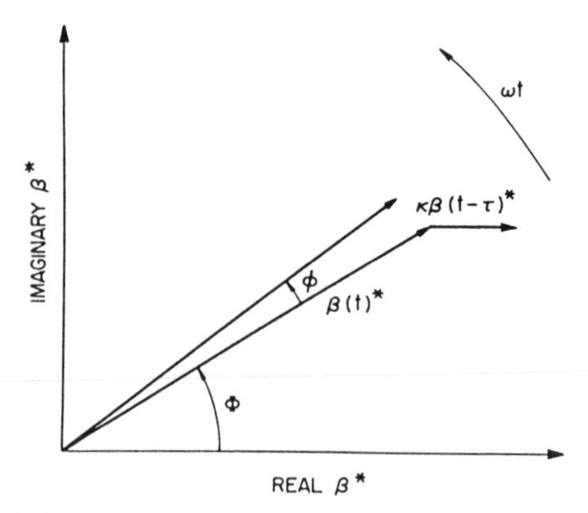

Fig. 1. Relative phase alignment of the steady-state laser field $\beta(t)$ and reflected field $\beta(t - \tau_0)$. The complex conjugate fields, which rotate positively in time, are shown. Parameter κ (2) determines the level of feedback.

B. Steady-State Operation

The steady-state condition is immediately found by substituting

$$\beta(t) = I^{1/2} \exp(-i\omega t) \quad (3)$$

into (1) and neglecting $F_\beta(t)$. (This neglects spontaneous emission.) The real and imaginary parts of (1) result in two relations determining ω and ΔG:

$$\Delta G = -2\kappa \cos \Phi \quad (4)$$

$$\omega - \omega_0 = -\kappa(\alpha \cos \Phi + \sin \Phi) \quad (5)$$

where $\Phi = \omega\tau_0$ is the roundtrip phase change in the external cavity. The cavity field $\beta(t)$ rotating at $-\omega$ will lead the reflected field by Φ (see Fig. 1).

Regarding Φ as a continuous parameter, (4) and (5) result in a relation between ΔG and ω which has the form of an ellipse (see Fig. 2). The operating point, corresponding to the steady state with lowest threshold, occurs at the bottom of the ellipse where $\Phi = 0$, $\Delta G = -2\kappa$, and $\omega - \omega_0 = -\alpha\kappa$. Typical numerical parameters are $\kappa\tau_s = 0.1$, corresponding to a power reflection of about -21 dB, a gain change $\Delta G/v_g = -4.0\ \text{cm}^{-1}$ where v_g is the semiconductor group velocity, and $\omega - \omega_0 = -2\pi(14\ \text{GHz})$.

We have regarded $\Phi = \omega\tau_0$ to be continuous. Actually, the solutions of (4) and (5) are points along the ellipse in Fig. 2 corresponding to the modes of the system. The phase Φ determines the phase relation between the laser field and the reflected field as shown in Fig. 1. We will assume that Φ is quasi-continuous. We mean by this that the laser may be operating in several or many very closely spaced modes; however, the phase relation between the cavity field and the laser field for each mode is given by

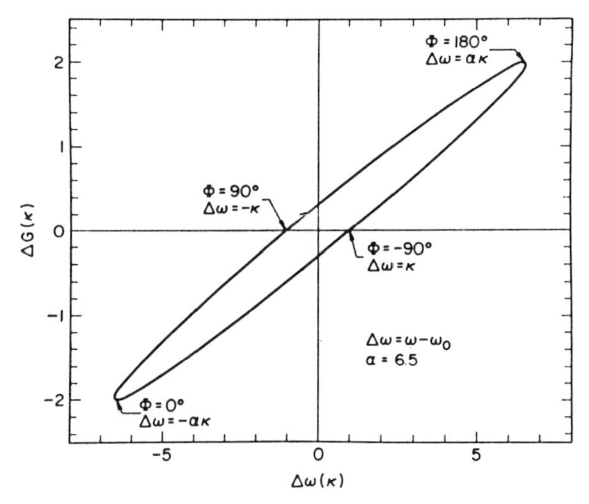

Fig. 2. Gain change versus angular frequency change for the possible steady states of operation. The laser modes are actually points along the ellipse which become closely spaced when the locking range contains many modes (6).

TABLE I
PARAMETERS

$\lambda = 1.55\ \mu m$	wavelength
$L = 250\ \mu m$	length
$d = 0.2\ \mu m$	active layer thickness
$w = 1.5\ \mu m$	strip width
$\eta = 0.4$	quantum efficiency of two facets
$R = 0.35$	facet reflectivity
$v_g = c/4 = 0.75 \times 10^{10}\ cm \cdot s^{-1}$	group velocity
$g = (1/\eta L) \ln (1/R) = 105\ cm^{-1}$	threshold gain per unit length
$G = v_g g$	threshold gain per unit time
$n_{sp} = 1.7$	spontaneous emission factor
$n_c = 2.7 \times 10^{18}\ cm^{-3}$	carrier density at threshold
$N = n_c Lwd = 2.0 \times 10^8$	carrier number
$G_N = \delta G/N = 2G/N$	$\partial G/\partial N$
$C = 32.5\ mA/q$	threshold current
$S = C/2$	spontaneous emission rate
$1/T = \beta S/N = 3S/N = (0.67\ ns)^{-1}$	$\partial S/\partial N$
$\tau_s = 2L/v_g = 6.7\ ps$	laser cavity roundtrip time
L_0	external reflector separation
$\tau_0 = 2L_0/c$	external cavity roundtrip time

approximately the same value of Φ. We also assume that the mode spacing is fine enough so that the steady-state operating point is $\Phi \approx 0$, corresponding to the lowest value of threshold gain. These assumptions should be valid if the number of modes along the ellipse in going from $\Delta\omega = 0$ to $\Delta\omega = -\alpha\kappa$ is large compared to unity.

$$\frac{\alpha\kappa\tau_0}{2\pi} >> 1. \qquad (6)$$

For example, for $\kappa\tau_s = 0.1$ (and other parameters listed in Table I), this requires $L_0 >> 1$ cm.

C. Stability

In order to study the stability of the steady state, we have to consider small deviations in intensity and phase. This can be done with

$$\beta(t) = (I + p(t))^{1/2} \exp(-i\omega t - i\phi(t)) \qquad (7)$$

where p and ϕ are small deviations. We must also consider changes in carrier number $n(t)$ which alters the gain:

$$\Delta G(t) = \Delta G + G_N n(t). \qquad (8)$$

Substitution of (7) and (8) into (1) results in two real equations:

$$\dot{\phi} = \frac{1}{2}\alpha G_N n - \kappa[\sin(\Phi + \phi) - \sin\Phi] - \frac{\kappa p}{2I} + F_\phi(t) \qquad (9)$$

$$\dot{p} = G_N I n - 2\kappa I[\cos\Phi - \cos(\Phi + \phi)] - \kappa\cos\Phi p + F_I(t). \qquad (10)$$

We will only consider fluctuations occurring for times less than the roundtrip time in the external cavity τ_0. During this time, the reflected field cannot respond to any changes. Therefore, we have set $\omega(t - \tau_0)$ equal to the steady-state value $I^{1/2} \exp[-i\omega(t - \tau_0)]$ in deriving (9) and (10).

We have found that $F_I(t)$ in (10) describing intensity fluctuations is the dominant random force. To keep the discussion as simple as possible, we will drop the source of phase fluctuations F_ϕ in (9) and not include a source of carrier number fluctuations. We will also drop the small term $\kappa p/(2I)$ in (9).

The equation for carrier number fluctuations is well known [19] and is given by

$$\dot{n} = -\frac{n}{T} - Gp \qquad (11)$$

where $1/T$ is the change in spontaneous emission (radiative and nonradiative) with carrier number and G is the steady state gain (see Table I).

Expanding $\cos(\Phi + \phi)$ and $\sin(\Phi + \phi)$ in (9) and (10) and keeping only the linear and quadratic terms in ϕ,

$$\dot{\phi} = \frac{\alpha}{2} G_N n - \kappa\cos\Phi\phi \qquad (12)$$

$$\dot{p} = G_N I n - \kappa\cos\Phi p - \kappa I(2\sin\Phi\phi + \cos\Phi\phi^2) + F_I(t). \qquad (13)$$

In the absence of reflections ($\kappa = 0$), the characteristic frequency of these equations is the relaxation oscillation frequency Ω given by

$$\Omega^2 = GG_N I. \qquad (14)$$

Experimentally, the instability occurs only for moderately strong reflections where $\kappa > \Omega$.

In the vicinity of the steady-state operating point, $\cos\Phi \approx 1$ and the characteristic decay time for ϕ is κ^{-1}. As we shall see later, this time is short compared to the characteristic time in which n changes. Therefore, we can neglect $\dot{\phi}$ in (12). That is, ϕ adiabatically follows changes in n and any deviations from this motion decay rapidly at rate κ. The adiabatic motion of ϕ is found by neglecting $\dot{\phi}$ in (12); then

$$\phi = \frac{\alpha G_N n}{2\kappa}. \tag{15}$$

We are left with two first-order equations for n and p [(11) and (13)]. We can eliminate one of these variables by forming a second-order equation. For simplicity, we will only derive this equation for the steady-state operating point of minimum threshold gain $\Phi = 0$. Eliminating p, the equation for n is

$$\ddot{n} = -\left(\frac{1}{T} + \kappa\right)\dot{n} - \left(\Omega^2 + \frac{\kappa}{T}\right)n + \frac{\alpha^2\Omega^2 G_N}{4\kappa}n^2 - GF_I(t). \tag{16}$$

This equation is analogous to a mechanical equation for a particle of mass unity and coordinate n moving in a potential well

$$U(n) \sim n^2 - \frac{2n^3}{3n_0}$$

where

$$n_0 = \frac{4\kappa}{\alpha^2 G_N}\left(1 + \frac{\kappa}{\Omega^2 T}\right). \tag{17}$$

The potential $U(n)$ is sketched in Fig. 3. The form of this potential is valid in the vicinity of $\Phi = 0$, but not generally. For small deviations in carrier number n, the conditions for stability are satisfied; there is a returning force and positive damping. The damping rate $1/T + \kappa \approx \kappa$ is significantly greater than in the absence of external feedback.

There is a characteristic decay rate γ for which the particle displaced from the origin $n = 0$ will return by sliding to the bottom of the potential well under friction. The rate γ is given by $\dot{n}/n$ in (16) when $\ddot{n}$, n^2, and random force terms are neglected.

$$\gamma = \left(\frac{1}{T} + \frac{\Omega^2}{\kappa}\right). \tag{18}$$

These parameters will be evaluated later. We will show that for power reflectivities greater than -30 dB, this characteristic rate γ is small compared to κ so that our assumption that ϕ adiabatically follows n is justified.

D. Fluctuations Over the Potential Barrier

If the carrier number change is greater than n_0, we see from Fig. 3 that the system will not return to $n = 0$; carrier number n and phase ϕ continue to increase and p continues to decrease. This is an instability destroying the locked constructive interference between the cavity field and the reflected field.

The motion of n is that of a particle undergoing overdamped sliding motion in potential well $U(n)$ while acted on by a random force. The second derivative $\ddot{n}$ in (15) can be neglected in describing the overdamped motion; the equation for n is then given by

$$\dot{n} = -\frac{\partial U}{\partial n} + F(t) \tag{19}$$

where

$$U(n) = \gamma\left(\frac{n^2}{2} - \frac{n^3}{3n_0}\right) \tag{20}$$

and

$$F(t) = -\frac{G}{\kappa}F_I(t). \tag{21}$$

We see that the barrier height

$$U(n_0) = \frac{\gamma n_0^2}{6} \tag{22}$$

increases with κ and the random force diminishes with κ. We will find that the barrier is readily crossed for values of κ corresponding to small and moderate feedback, but not for strong feedback. On the other hand, our analysis which assumes adiabatic following is not valid weak feedback.

Equation (19) is a nonlinear Langevin force equation [20]. The random force $F(t)$ is characterized by a diffusion coefficient D defined by

$$\langle F(t)F(u)\rangle = 2D\delta(t - u). \tag{23}$$

The diffusion coefficient is

$$D = \frac{G^2}{\kappa^2}D_{II} = \frac{G^2 RI}{\kappa^2} \tag{24}$$

where $D_{II} = RI$ is the well-known diffusion coefficient for $F_I(t)$ [19].

The instantaneous probability distribution $P(n)$ for $n(t)$ obeying (19) is a solution of the Fokker–Planck equation [20]

$$\frac{\partial P}{\partial t} = \frac{\partial}{\partial n}\left(P\frac{\partial U}{\partial n}\right) + D\frac{\partial^2 P}{\partial n^2}. \tag{25}$$

In the steady state, it is easily shown [21] that

$$P(n) = P(0)\exp\left\{-\frac{U(n)}{D}\right\} \tag{26}$$

which is analogous to a Boltzmann distribution, but with kT replaced by D describing quantum fluctuations. The probability distribution $P(n)$ is sketched in Fig. 3.

The motion in the potential well in Fig. 3 involves two characteristic times: the time for a small displacement from $n = 0$ to return to $n = 0$, and the time for a small displacement beyond the top of the barrier to leave the barrier top. It is easily shown that for the sliding motion described by (19), both times are γ^{-1}. This time results in a characteristic diffusion length $L = (D\gamma^{-1})^{1/2}$ characterizing the width of the distribution $P(n)$ about the origin and the decay of $P(n)$ beyond the barrier top.

We are seeking the average time t_I for an instability associated with crossing the barrier to occur. A careful

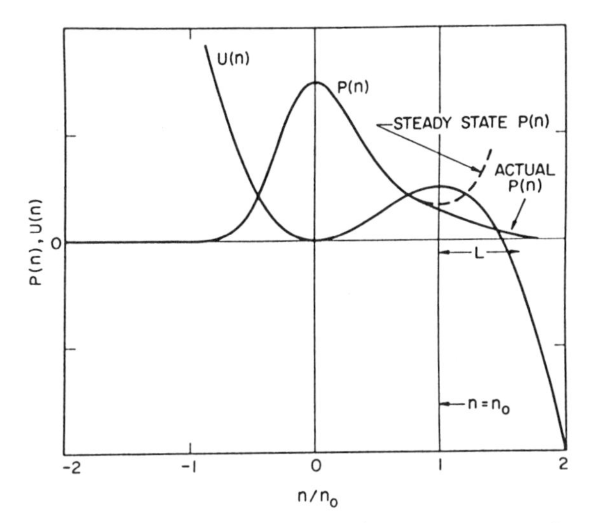

Fig. 3. Potential function $U(n)$ and probability function $P(n)$ as a function of n. For $n > n_0$, the actual time-dependent $P(n)$ goes to zero, while the unphysical steady state $P(n)$, shown dashed, increases. The distance $L = (D\gamma^{-1})^{1/2}$ is the diffusion length for leaving the barrier.

treatment involves solving the Fokker–Planck equation for the time dependence of $P(n)$. Instead, we will make an approximate analysis. For $n > n_0$, the distribution will decay in a diffusion length L. The rate t_I^{-1} is just the decay rate for the integral of $P(n)$. This can be found by integrating (25) from $n = -\infty$ to n_0. Since $\partial U/\partial n = 0$ at $n = n_0$, integration of (25) yields

$$\frac{1}{t_I} = -D\left(\frac{\partial P}{\partial n}\right)_{n0} \approx \frac{DP(n_0)}{L}. \tag{27}$$

The instability time t_I can be determined by substitution of (26) into (27). Since L also approximately determines the width of the distribution, the normalization constant $P(0)$ in (26) will be on the order of L^{-1}. Therefore,

$$t_I \approx \gamma^{-1} \exp\left(\frac{U(n_0)}{D}\right). \tag{28}$$

The exact prefactor (28) is not important since t_I is overwhelmingly determined by $U(n_0)/D$. This exponent can be evaluated from (17), (18), (22), and (24):

$$\frac{U(n_0)}{D} = \frac{8\left(1+\dfrac{\kappa}{\Omega^2 T}\right)^3 \kappa^3}{3\alpha^4 G_N G R}. \tag{29}$$

E. Comparison to Experiment

Equations (28) and (29) describing the exponential behavior of the instability time t_I are evaluated in the Appendix.

$$t_I = \frac{T}{\left(1 + \dfrac{4I}{I_1}\right)} \exp\left[3300\left(1 + \frac{I_1}{4I}\right)^3 \left(\frac{\Delta C}{C}\right)^3\right] \tag{30}$$

where $\Delta C/C$ is the fractional decrease in threshold current with coherent feedback, I is the light intensity, and I_1 is the light intensity at current ΔC above threshold in the

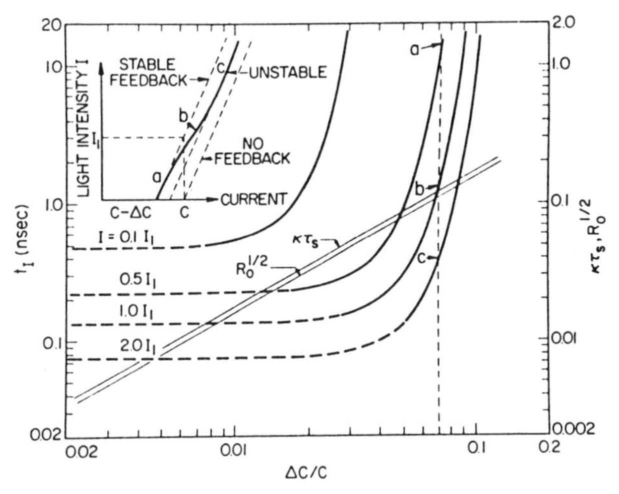

Fig. 4. Instability time t_I versus the fractional decrease in threshold current $\Delta C/C$. Also plotted are the feedback parameter $\kappa\tau_s$ and the square root of the external power reflectivity R_0. The set of curves for t_I are for different intensity ratios I/I_1. This ratio is shown in the inserted sketch, which also shows the nonlinear behavior of light versus intensity. The "kink" in this curve is attributed to going from nearly stable to unstable behavior as we go from a to c. The changes in t_I in going from a to c at fixed feedback of $\kappa\tau_s = 0.12$ are intersections with the vertical dashed line.

case of coherent feedback. These quantities are defined by the diagram inserted into Fig. 4. The numerical factor in the exponent in (30) is only approximately known to $x2$.

Fig. 4 shows that there are three regions of feedback depending on the value of $\kappa\tau_s$ where $\kappa\tau_s \approx 1.75\ \Delta C/C$. For low feedback $\kappa\tau_s \leq 0.05$, t_I is short and the laser is always unstable. For strong feedback $\kappa\tau_s \geq 0.2$, t_I becomes enormous and the laser becomes stable. For feedback in between these two limits, the laser is stable at low intensity and unstable at high intensity. The intermediate case results in a kink in the light intensity versus current curve sketched in Fig. 4. The curved lines in Fig. 4 are the calculated values of t_I for different values of light intensity. As the light intensity increases and we go from a to b to c, the laser changes from nearly stable to unstable operation. During unstable operation (c), the laser periodically builds up to the steady state of coherent feedback and then abruptly drops back to the intensity without feedback from which it begins to build up again. This results in an average intensity that is nearly midway between the light versus current curves for no feedback and for stable feedback.

The nonlinear relation, just described, between light intensity and current is sketched in Fig. 4. It corresponds precisely to that reported by Temkin *et al.* [14]. A light intensity versus current relation very similar to that observed by Temkin *et al.* [14], but with some additional structure, was reported by Fujiwara *et al.* [13] for a laser exhibiting low-frequency intensity fluctuations and having a mirror placed 2.4 cm from the laser. The similarity of these data with the data of Temkin *et al.* for distances of 15 cm to several meters implies that the phenomenon that we describe also applies to lasers in the presence of nearby reflectors and moderately high feedback.

Temkin *et al.* [14] did not observe the laser reach stable

operation, even at their highest levels of feedback ($\Delta C/C \approx 0.11$) in a laser with cleaved facets. However, they were able to observe stable operation at high feedback by using a laser with an antireflection (AR)-coated facet facing the external reflector (having $R = 0.02$). Under these conditions, greater values of $\Delta C/C$ could be achieved, and they found unstable behavior if the alignment was poor, but stable behavior if there is good coupling of the reflected light back into the laser cavity.

Our approach involves approximations that are only valid at sufficiently large $\kappa\tau_s$. The adiabatic elimination of ϕ (15) and the assumption of overdamped motion that allowed us to drop $\ddot{n}$ in (16) both require $\kappa > \gamma$. Using (A7), this condition is

$$\kappa\tau_s > \frac{\tau_s}{T}\left(1 + \frac{4I}{I_1}\right) \approx 0.01\left(1 + \frac{4I}{I_1}\right). \qquad (30)$$

The regions of the curves for small $\kappa\tau_s$, where this condition is not satisfied, are shown dashed in Fig. 4. We have not plotted τ_l in Fig. 4 for $I >> I_1$ because (30) is not satisfied for high optical intensity. The region where approximations are valid covers the most significant data of Temkin *et al.* [14].

III. Summary and Discussion

We have explained a puzzling instability occurring in continuously operating lasers in the presence of moderate feedback from distant reflectors. This instability occurs despite the fact that a linear analysis shows stability. Unlike other instabilities previously encountered in the description of the dynamic behavior of semiconductor lasers, this instability results from finite amplitude phase and carrier number changes caused by fluctuations in spontaneous emission. These fluctuations destroy the locking of the cavity field to the reflected field, which occurs in the steady state. The nature of this instability was described verbally in the Introduction and in terms of a barrier crossing in Fig. 3.

We find that at moderate levels of feedback, $\kappa\tau_s \approx 0.1$, the laser will be nearly stable at low light intensity, but unstable at high light intensity. This behavior enabled us to explain the shape of the light intensity versus current curves measured by Temkin *et al.* [14] and sketched in Fig. 4. The instability results from fluctuations that excite the system over a restraining barrier (Fig. 3). This is somewhat analogous to thermal ionization of a trapped electron. In this case, the fluctuations increase with light intensity rather than temperature [see (24) and (26)]. The barrier height also depends on light intensity, and the combined effects of barrier height and fluctuations (29) result in stability at low intensities and instability at high intensities.

At high feedback levels, the barrier height increases and the probability of a fluctuation over the barrier becomes negligible. This was observed by Temkin *et al.* [14] with a laser having one facet AR coated to increase external feedback. They found that the instability was present under conditions of poor optical alignment of the reflected field back into the laser cavity, but disappeared for good optical alignment.

Another puzzling feature of the experiment of Temkin *et al.* [14] is that the instability only occurs when the laser intensity builds up to a steady state. This behavior can be explained in the following way. The steady state corresponds to operation at the bottom of the ellipse in Fig. 2. The approach to the steady state is complicated, but probably involves traveling along the lower portion of the ellipse to the bottom as the cavity resonance changes and $\Delta\omega$ changes from nearly 0 to $-\alpha\kappa$. The motion along the lower portion of the ellipse corresponds to Φ changing from a negative angle to zero. The instability at $\Phi = 0$ arises from the ϕ^2 term in (13). The complete term for $\Phi \neq 0$ is

$$2 \sin \Phi\phi + \cos \Phi\phi^2.$$

We see that for negative values of Φ, there will be another term opposite in sign to the ϕ^2 term which increases the barrier height in Fig. 4 and provides stability until $\Phi \approx 0$ is reached. This increases stability for negative Φ was observed by Risch and Voumard [11], who could tune the point of steady-state operation by means of a reflecting grating.

The instability described in Section I results from a change in phase alignment of the cavity field and the reflected field (by ϕ in Fig. 1). The same argument carried out for nonzero Φ shows that a small change ϕ will grow for positive Φ, but not for negative Φ. Consequently, the laser which seeks to operate at the point of lowest threshold gain ($\Phi = 0$) becomes unstable just as the goal is reached.

Appendix A
Estimate of Parameters in (28) and (29)

The terms R and G_N in the denominator of (29) are both proportional to $G: R = n_{sp}G$ where $n_{sp} \approx 1.7$ is the spontaneous emission factor [22]. G_N can be expresses as

$$G_N = \frac{\delta G}{N} \qquad (A1)$$

where N is the carrier number (see Table I) and δ is a factor of order unity. For GaAs, $\delta \approx 4$ [23]. We achieved a better fit to the data of Temkin *et al.* [14] by using $\delta = 2$ for 1.55 μm InGaAsP lasers. If this deduction is correct, it implies that gain increases sublinearly with carrier density (the increase is nearly linear in GaAs [23]).

Another key parameter in (29) is the linewidth parameter α [19], which enters in the fourth power. Henry *et al.* [24] found $\alpha = 6 \pm 1$ from analysis of injection locking of 1.5 μm InGaAsP lasers. Recent linewidth measurements of Lee *et al.* [25] indicate $\alpha \approx 7$. We will take $\alpha \approx 6.5$ in (29).

With these substitutions, the exponent $U(n_0)/D$ in (29) depends on two parameters $(\kappa/G)^3$ and $(1 + \kappa/\Omega^2 T)^3$.

The ratio κ/G is related to $\Delta C/C$, the fractional decrease in threshold current C due to coherent feedback. When coherent feedback exists, the threshold gain G decreases by 2κ. This will be accompanied by a decrease in carrier number ΔN of

$$\Delta N = \frac{2\kappa}{G_N} = \frac{2\kappa N}{\delta G}. \tag{A2}$$

Suppose that the current increases as a power β of the carrier number

$$C \sim N^{\beta}. \tag{A3}$$

For radiative recombination, $\beta \approx 2$ and for Auger recombination, $\beta \approx 3$. For the lasers used in the experiment of Temkin *et al.*, the threshold current (32 mA) was typically four times greater than a broad area laser threshold. This increase is probably in part due to leakage and in part due to increases nonradiative recombination, making modeling very difficult. We will assume that half the current C goes into recombination S and half into leakage. We will also assume that the increase of both C and S with N is described by $\beta = 3$. In terms of these parameters, the fractional decrease in threshold current is

$$\frac{\Delta C}{C} = \beta \frac{\Delta N}{N} = \frac{2\beta}{\delta}\left(\frac{\kappa}{G}\right). \tag{A4}$$

The ratio $\kappa/\Omega^2 T$ in (29) decreases with light intensity because $\Omega^2 \sim I$. The rate $1/T = \partial S/\partial N$ is given by

$$\frac{1}{T} = \frac{\beta S}{N} = \frac{\beta}{2}\frac{C}{N}. \tag{A5}$$

Using (14), (A1), (A4), and (A5), we can express $\kappa/\Omega^2 T$ as

$$\frac{\kappa}{\Omega^2 T} = \frac{\Delta C}{4GI} = \frac{I_1}{4I} \tag{A6}$$

where $I_1 \equiv \Delta C/G$ is the intensity at a current ΔC above threshold when coherent feedback exists (see insert in Fig. 4). Relation (A6) is independent of the assumed values for δ and β.

Using (A6), we can express the characteristic time γ^{-1} given by (18) as a function of I:

$$\gamma^{-1} = \frac{T}{1 + \dfrac{\Omega^2 T}{\kappa}} = \frac{T}{1 + \dfrac{4I}{I_1}} \tag{A7}$$

where T is estimated in Table I. With these changes,

$$t_l = \frac{T}{\left(1 + \dfrac{4I}{I_1}\right)} \exp\left[\frac{\left(1 + \dfrac{I_1}{4I}\right)^3 N\delta^2}{3\alpha^4 n_{sp}\beta^3}\left(\frac{\Delta C}{C}\right)^3\right]. \tag{A8}$$

The carrier number N is easily estimated from the laser dimensions (see Table I). With the above estimates of parameters, (28) becomes

$$t_l = \frac{T}{\left(1 + \dfrac{4I}{I_1}\right)} \exp\left[3300\left(1 + \frac{I_1}{4I}\right)^3\left(\frac{\Delta C}{C}\right)^3\right] \tag{A9}$$

where, from evaluation in Table I, $T = 0.67$ ns.

Acknowledgment

We are indebted to H. Temkin and N. A. Olsson for furnishing us with their unpublished experimental results.

References

[1] R. Lang and K. Kobayashi, "External optical feedback effects on semiconductor injection laser properties," *IEEE J. Quantum Electron.*, vol. QE-16, pp. 347–355, Mar. 1980.

[2] R. O. Miles, A. Dandridge, A. B. Tveten, H. F. Taylor, and T. G. Giallorenzi, "Feedback-induced line broadening in cw channel-substrate planar laser diodes," *Appl. Phys. Lett.*, vol. 37, pp. 990–992, Dec. 1980.

[3] L. Goldberg, H. F. Taylor, A. Dandridge, J. F. Weller, and R. O. Miles, "Spectral characteristics of semiconductor lasers with optical feedback," *IEEE Trans. Microwave Theory Techn.*, vol. MTT-30, pp. 401–410, 1980.

[4] E. Patzak, H. Olesen, A. Sagimura, S. Saito, and T. Mukai, "Spectral linewidth reduction in semiconductor lasers by an external cavity with weak optical feedback," *Electron. Lett.*, vol. 19, pp. 938–949, Oct. 1983.

[5] G. A. Acket, D. Lenstra, A. J. denBoef, and B. H. Verbeek, "The influence of feedback intensity on longitudinal mode properties and optical noise in index-guided semiconductor lasers," *IEEE J. Quantum Electron.*, vol. QE-20, pp. 1163–1169, Oct. 1984.

[6] J. H. Osmundsen, B. Tromborg, and H. Olesen, "Experimental investigation of stability properties for a semiconductor laser with optical feedback," *Electron. Lett.*, vol. 19, pp. 1068–1070, 1984.

[7] Y. C. Chen, "Phase noise characteristics of single mode semiconductor lasers with optical feedback," *Appl. Phys. Lett.*, vol. 44, pp. 10–12, Jan. 1984.

[8] K. Kikuchi and T. Okoshi, "Simple formula giving spectrum-narrowing ratio of semiconductor-laser output obtained by optical feedback," *Electron. Lett.*, vol. 18, pp. 10–12, Jan. 1982.

[9] G. P. Agrawal, "Line narrowing in a single-mode injection laser due to external optical feedback," *IEEE J. Quantum Electron.*, vol. QE-20, pp. 468–471, May 1984.

[10] D. Lenstra, B. H. Verbeek, and A. J. den Boef, "Coherence collapse in single-mode semiconductor lasers due to optical feedback," *IEEE J. Quantum Electron.*, June 1985.

[11] Ch. Risch and C. Voumard, "Self-pulsation in the output intensity and spectrum of GaAs-AlGaAs cw diode lasers coupled to a frequency selective external optical cavity," *J. Appl. Phys.*, vol. 48, pp. 2083–2085, 1977.

[12] T. Morikawa, Y. Mitsuhashi, J. Shimoda, and Y. Kojima, "Return-beam-induced oscillations in self-coupled semiconductor lasers," *Electron. Lett.*, vol. 12, pp. 435–436, 1976.

[13] M. Fujiwara, K. Kubota, and R. Lang, "Low frequency intensity fluctuation in laser diodes with external optical feedback," *Appl. Phys. Lett.*, vol. 38, pp. 217–220, 1981.

[14] H. Temkin, N. A. Olsson, T. H. Abeles, R. A. Logan, and M. B. Panish, "Reflection noise in index guided InGaAsP lasers," this issue, pp. 294–301.

[15] R. Lang, "Injection locking properties of a semiconductor laser," *IEEE J. Quantum Electron.*, vol. QE-18, pp. 976–983, 1982.

[16] H. Kawaguchi and K. Otsuka, "A new class of instabilities in a diode laser with an external cavity," *Appl. Phys. Lett.*, vol. 45, pp. 934–936, 1984.

[17] Y. Cho and T. Umeda, "Chaos in laser oscillations with delayed feedback," *J. Opt. Soc.*, vol. 1, pp. 497–498, 1984.

[18] K. Otsuka and H. Iwarura, "Theory of optical multistability and chaos in a resonant-type semiconductor laser amplifier," *Phys. Rev. A*, vol. 28, pp. 3153–3155, 1983.

[19] C. H. Henry, "Theory of phase noise and power spectrum of a single mode semiconductor laser," *IEEE J. Quantum Electron.*, vol. QE-19, pp. 1391–1397, Sept. 1983.

[20] M. Lax, "Fluctuations from the nonequilibrium study state," *Rev. Mod. Phys.*, vol. 32, pp. 25–64, 1960.

[21] ——, "Classical noise III: Nonlinear Markoff processes," *Rev. Mod. Phys.*, vol. 38, pp. 359–379, 1966.
[22] C. H. Henry, R. A. Logan, H. Temkin, and F. R. Merritt, "Absorption emission and gain in 1.3 μm quaternary lasers," *IEEE J. Quantum Electron.*, vol. QE-19, pp. 941–946, 1983.
[23] C. H. Henry, R. A. Logan, and F. R. Merritt, "Measurement of gain and absorption in AlGaAs buried heterostructure lasers," *J. Appl. Phys.*, vol. 51, pp. 3042–3050, 1980.
[24] C. H. Henry, N. A. Olsson, and N. K. Dutta, "Locking range and stability of injection locked 1.54 micron InGaAsP semiconductor lasers," *IEEE J. Quantum Electron.* vol. QE-21, pp. 1152–1156, Aug. 1985.
[25] T. P. Lee, C. A. Burrus, K. Y. Liou, N. A. Olsson, and D. P. Wilt, "Measured spectral width of single-frequency injection lasers," *Electron. Lett.*, vol. 20, pp. 1011–1012, Nov. 1984.

450 Hz RELATIVE FREQUENCY STABILITY IN AN AlGaAs DIODE LASER

Y. C. CHUNG*
T. M. SHAY†
Department of Electrical Engineering
Utah State University
Logan, UT 84322, USA

4th August 1987

Indexing terms: Lasers and laser applications, Semiconductor lasers

A commercial AlGaAs diode laser is frequency-locked to a Fabry–Perot interferometer. The temperature stabilisation loop of the diode laser system maintains the relative stability within 11 kHz. When the frequency control loop is closed, the relative frequency stability is improved to 450 Hz.

Introduction: Frequency-stabilised diode lasers are practical sources for a wide variety of potential applications, including laser spectroscopy, optical frequency standards, coherent optical communication etc. This is due to the attractive features of diode lasers such as high reliability, compact size and low cost. In addition, unlike other lasers, diode lasers have no external optics. Therefore diode lasers are essentially impervious to mechanical vibrations and acoustic disturbances. On the other hand, since the operating frequencies of diode lasers are very sensitive to both junction temperature and injection current variations, standard diode laser systems under free-running operation have relatively poor frequency stability. Thus the first step in frequency-stabilising a diode laser consists of stabilising the junction temperature and injection current. Since Bykovskii *et al.*[1] reported a frequency-stabilised diode laser in 1970, there have been several reports of diode lasers stabi'ised to Fabry–Perot interference fringes, and atomic or molecular transition lines. Hori *et al.*[2] demonstrated 1 part in 10^{11} stability in an AlGaAs laser locked to the Cs-D_2 line. Nielsen and Jacobsen have demonstrated better than 6·6 parts in 10^{13} stability for an AlGaAs laser,[3] and Nielsen and Osmundsen improved this stability by 60% using a linewidth-narrowed diode laser.[4] However, the frequency of a laser with external optics is very sensitive to acoustic and mechanical disturbances, whereas solitary diode lasers themselves are insensitive to those disturbances. Thus, in principle a stabilised solitary diode laser should be insensitive to acoustic and mechanical disturbances. In this work we have stabilised the frequency of a solitary diode laser to a Fabry–Perot interference fringe.

Experiment: A schematic block diagram of our experimental set-up is shown in Fig. 1. A Hitachi HL-7801E AlGaAs laser and a thermistor were mounted on a copper heat sink. To minimise temperature variations due to air currents, the heat sink was completely covered with Styrofoam, leaving only the laser itself exposed to the air. The heat sink was in good thermal contact with a Peltier cooler. A thermistor was used to sense temperature drifts, and the temperature controller turned on the Peltier cooler when the temperature increased. The temperature stability of this active high-gain temperature control loop is estimated to be better than $\pm 3\,\mu$°C. This estimate is based on the measured maximum frequency fluctuations under free-running operation of the laser and the temperature tuning coefficient for this diode laser. The diode laser was excited by a high-accuracy ($< \pm 5\,\mu$A), stable current supply which utilises a 16-bit digital/analogue convertor. The diode laser current source also sums both the small sinusoidal current modulation (90 μA amplitude) at 1 kHz frequency and the error signal from the feedback loop. Single-mode oscillation of the laser was verified using a monochromator or a Fabry–Perot etalon. Between mode hops, temperature and injection current tuning coefficients were measured to be 20 GHz/°C and 3·5 GHz/mA, respectively. The output power was 4·3 mW at the injection current of 63 mA. The free spectral range and finesse of the Fabry–Perot etalon were 7·5 GHz and 32·5, respectively. The laser output radiation was collimated by a short-focal-length lens f_1, passed through the Fabry–Perot etalon (FP) and finally through a 1 m-focal-length lens f_2 to project a ring pattern on the pinhole located 1 m from the lens f_2. The pinhole transmitted a single interference fringe to the photodiode (PD). Some care in the optical set-up was necessary to avoid frequency jitter due to optical feedback.[5–7] To avoid optical feedback, since an optical isolator was not used in this experiment, the etalon had to be placed more than 50 cm from the diode laser and tilted slightly. An EG&G FND-100 PIN photodiode baised

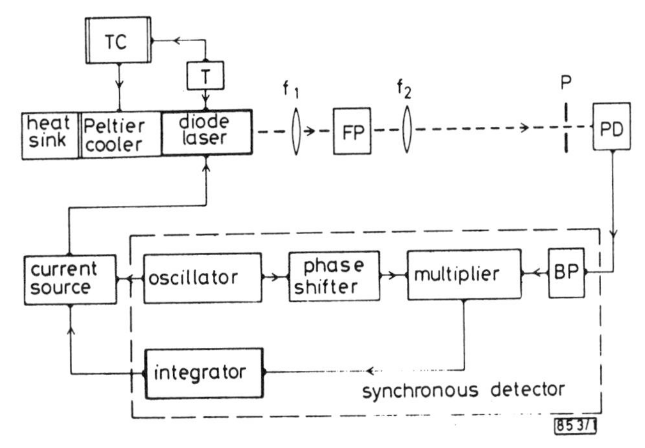

Fig. 1 *Schematic block diagram of diode laser frequency stabilisation experimental system*

f_1 is collimating lens, FP represents Fabry–Perot etalon, f_2 represents 1 m-focal-length lens which projects ring pattern on to pinhole aperture in front of photodiode (PD). Bandpass amplifier is represented by BP. The synchronous detector, which comprises the multiplier, oscillator and integrator, is inside the broken line

* Now with AT&T Bell Laboratories, Crawford Hill Laboratory, Lightwave Systems Research Department, PO Box 400, Holmdel, NJ 07733, USA
† Now with Los Alamos National Laboratory, PO Box 1663, CLS-5, MS/E535, Los Alamos, NM 87545, USA

Reprinted with permission from *Electron. Lett.*, vol. 23, no. 20, pp. 1044–1045, Sept. 24, 1987.

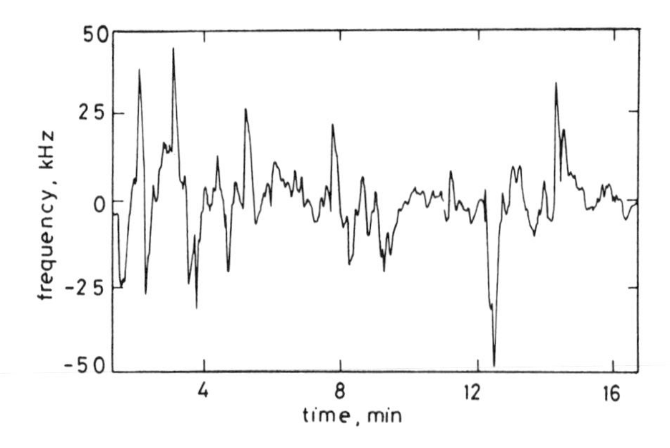

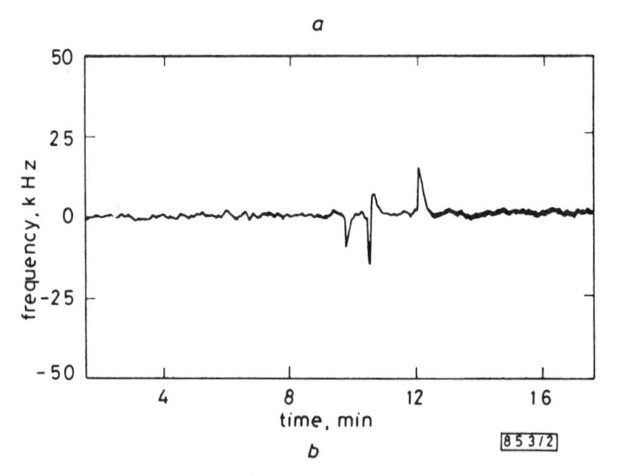

Fig. 2 *Trace of error signal (a) when first derivative feedback loop is open (i.e. only temperature control loop is operating) and (b) when first derivative feedback loop is also closed*

with a 90 V battery was used to detect the signal. The photodiode signal was amplified and sent to an active bandpass filter to isolate the portion of the photodiode signal which depends on the first derivative of the Fabry–Perot transmission curve, i.e. the frequency-discriminant signal. Next, the signal is synchronously detected (i.e. multiplied by the original modulation signal and integrated) to provide a DC error signal, proportional to the frequency-discriminant signal. The resulting error signal is subsequently summed in the current source to correct for frequency drifts. Finally, while the diode laser itself is insensitive to mechanical and acoustic disturbances, the Fabry–Perot etalon is very sensitive to such disturbances; therefore the entire system was mounted on a vibration isolation table.

Since the average frequency error is proportional to the amplitude of the frequency discriminant signal, a lock-in amplifier and strip chart recorder were used to measure the frequency stability of this system. Fig. 2 shows the measured open-loop (Fig. 2*a*) and closed-loop (Fig. 2*b*) frequency fluctuations of the laser centre frequency from the peak transmission frequency of the Fabry–Perot etalon. Note that the open-loop frequency fluctuations never exceeded ± 50 kHz over the 16 min time period shown here. This corresponds to an estimated Allan variance of $2{\cdot}9 \times 10^{-11}$, or 11 kHz for a 24 s averaging time. To our knowledge, this represents the best open-loop frequency stability reported yet. Note that the frequency and time scales are the same for Figs. 2*a* and *b*. When the first derivative feedback loop was closed, the frequency fluctuations were reduced by more than factor of 20; these residual fluctuations never exceed $\pm 2{\cdot}5$ kHz. For a 24 s averaging time an estimated Allan variance of $(1{\cdot}2 \pm 0{\cdot}5) \times 10^{-12}$ or 450 ± 190 Hz is measured.

One additional interesting feature of the locked frequency error measurements are the rather large error spikes between 9 and 12 min. These spikes are caused by vibrations of the optics, due solely to the acoustic noise transmitted through the air from one of the investigators speaking at a distance of more than 3 m from the apparatus. If we ignore the fact that the time constant of our lock-in amplifier is much longer than the duration of these acoustic disturbances, we can place an upper limit on the deflection of the laser beam relative to the Fabry–Perot of 20 nrad. This indicates that we may be able to measure very small angular deflections reliably using a stabilised diode laser-interferometer system such as this one.

Summary: The open-loop frequency stability of this diode laser system has been measured to be 11 kHz. This corresponds to a temperature stability of $\pm 3\,\mu$°C. When the frequency control loop is closed, the relative frequency stability is improved to 450 ± 190 Hz with an averaging time of 24 s. These results indicate that a simple temperature stabilisation loop could provide sufficient frequency stability for many applications, while active frequency stabilisation techniques could be used for those applications which requires very high frequency stability.

References

1 BYKOVSKII, Y. A., VELICHANSKII, V. L, GONCHAROV, I. G., and MASLOV, V. A.: 'Use of a Fabry–Perot resonator for the stabilization of the frequency of an injection laser', *Sov. Phys.-Semicond.*, 1970, **4**, pp. 580–583

2 HORI, H., KITAYAMA, Y., KITANO, M., YABUZAKI, T., and OGAWA, T.: 'Frequency stabilization of GaAlAs laser using Doppler-free spectrum of Cs-D_2 line', *IEEE J. Quantum Electron.*, 1983, **QE-19**, pp. 169–174

3 NIELSEN, C. J., and JACOBSEN, G.: 'Frequency stabilization of single mode semiconductor lasers at 830 nm and 1·3 μm', *J. Opt. Commun.*, 1983, **4**, pp. 122–125

4 NIELSEN, C. J., and OSMUNDSEN, J. H.: 'New approach towards frequency stabilisation of linewidth-narrowed semiconductor lasers', *Electron. Lett.*, 1983, **19**, pp. 644–646

5 OGASAWARA, N., ITO, R., KATO, M., and TAKAHASHI, Y.: 'Mode switching in injection laser induced by temperature variation and optical feedback', *Jpn. J. Appl. Phys.*, 1983, **22**, pp. 1684–1690

6 MILES, R. O., DANDRIDGE, A., TVETEN, A. B., TAYLOR, H. F., and GIALLORENZI, T. G.: 'Feedback-induced line broadening in cw channel-substrate planar laser diodes', *Appl. Phys. Lett.*, 1980, **37**, pp. 990–992

7 FAVRE, F., GUEN, D. L., and SIMON, J. C.: 'Optical feedback effects upon laser diode oscillation field spectrum', *IEEE J. Quantum Electron.*, 1982, **QE-18**, pp. 1712–1717

FREQUENCY STABILISATION OF A MODULATED SEMICONDUCTOR LASER

H. TSUCHIDA
Y. MITSUHASHI

Optoelectronics Section, Electrotechnical Laboratory
1-1-4, Umezono
Tsukuba Science City 305, Japan

28th August 1987

Indexing term: Semiconductor lasers

A method is described for stabilising the centre frequency of a directly modulated semiconductor laser. This method utilises the second derivative signal of the transmitted spectrum through a Fabry–Perot interferometer. The centre frequency fluctuation of a modulated AlGaAs laser with a maximum frequency deviation of 12 GHz is reduced to less than 15 MHz.

Frequency-stabilised semiconductor lasers[1,2] are very promising light sources for coherent optical communication systems, interferometric optical fibre sensors etc. Since direct modulation of the laser frequency through an injection current is usually employed in the above applications, frequency stabilisation and modulation should be achieved simultaneously in semiconductor lasers. Frequency stabilisation of a modulated laser with a small frequency deviation (< 1 GHz) was demonstrated using the modulation sidebands.[3]

In this letter we propose a method for stabilising the centre frequency of a modulated semiconductor laser with a large frequency deviation (> 10 GHz).

Fig. 1 shows the block diagram of the experimental set-up. An AlGaAs laser (Hitachi HLP-1400) with the lasing wavelength of 829 nm is used. The laser frequency is directly modulated by a symmetric sawtooth wave at low frequencies. This type of modulation is utilised to demodulate the output signals in interferometric optical sensors.[4] A piezoelectrically tunable Fabry–Perot interferometer (Burleigh TL-15) with a mirror spacing of 1·5 mm is used as a frequency reference. Since the laser has a large frequency deviation, relatively large free spectral range (100 GHz) is employed. The reflectivity of the two Fabry–Perot mirrors is 92% at 830 nm. The laser beam is detected by an Si avalanche photodiode (APD) after passing through the interferometer. The length of the interferometer is piezoelectrically modulated at a frequency of 800 Hz. The output signal from the APD is synchronously detected with a lock-in amplifier to obtain derivative curves of the transmitted spectrum.

Fig. 2 shows the transmitted spectrum obtained with the unmodulated laser. Figs. 2*a* and *b* represent the spectral profile and its first derivative curve, respectively. The observed full width at half-maximum is 6·8 GHz, which is limited by the resolution of the interferometer. Frequency stabilisation is usually achieved by using the first derivative curve, that is by locking the laser frequency at the zero-crossing point A in Fig. 2*b*. The slope at the point A is 4·7 mV/GHz.

Fig. 3 shows the transmitted spectrum obtained with the modulated laser. The modulation frequency and amplitude of the injection current are 5 kHz and 8 mA_{p-p}, respectively. The resulting maximum frequency deviation is about 12 GHz. Fig. 3*a* represents the spectral profile which is interpreted as dis-

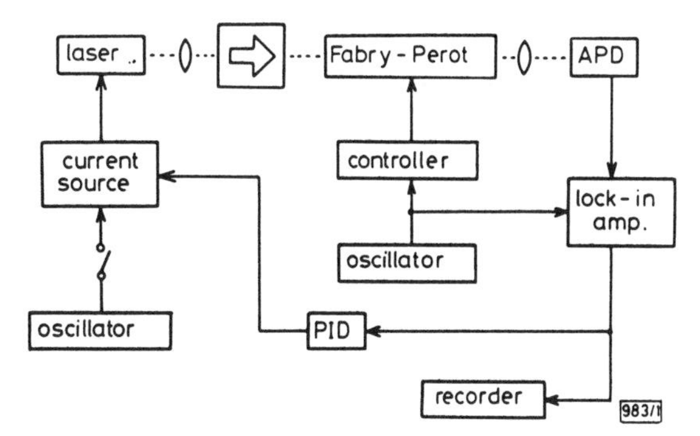

Fig. 1 *Block diagram of experimental set-up*

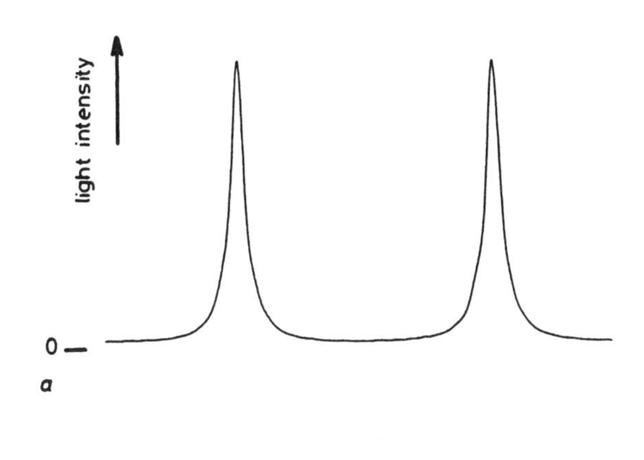

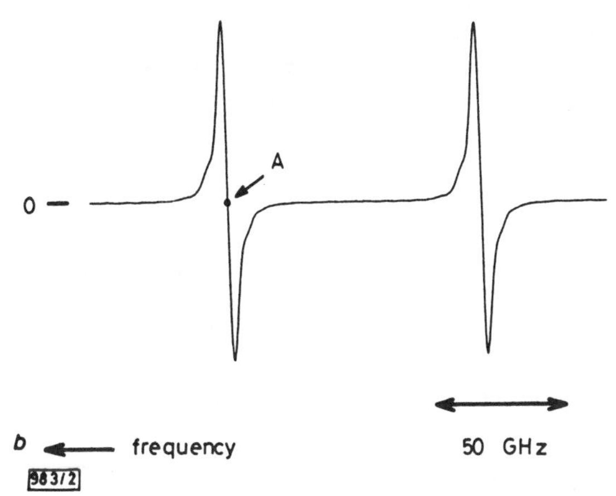

Fig. 2 *Transmitted spectrum through Fabry–Perot interferometer obtained with unmodulated laser*

a Spectral profile
b First derivative curve

Reprinted with permission from *Electron. Lett.*, vol. 23, no. 21, pp. 1147–1148, Oct. 8, 1987.

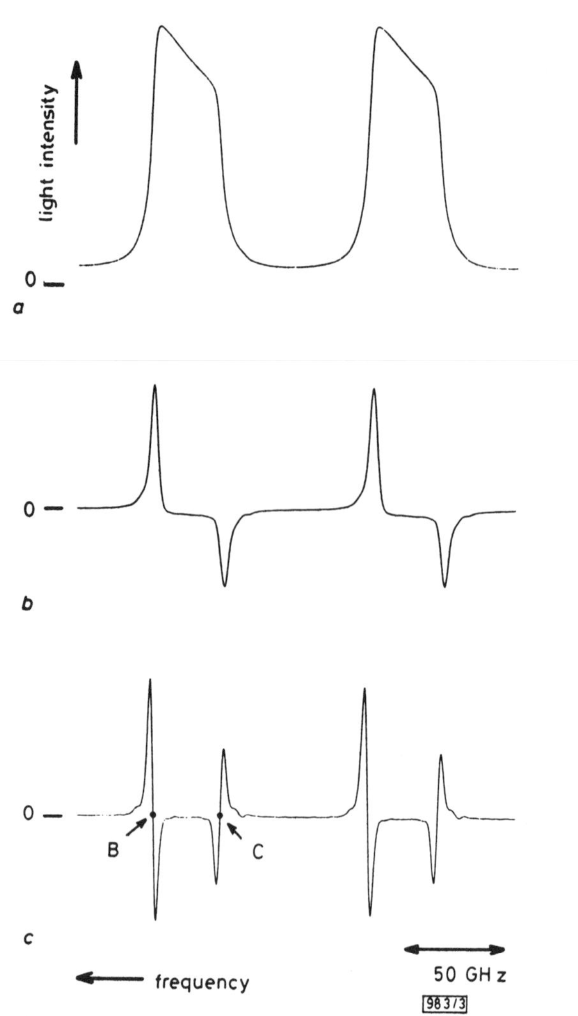

Fig. 3 *Transmitted spectrum through Fabry–Perot interferometer obtained with modulated laser*

a Spectral profile
b First derivative curve
c Second derivative curve

playing the broadened spectral envelope.[5] The observed full width at half-maximum is 33 GHz. The asymmetric sideband amplitudes result from a combined intensity and frequency modulation. Fig. 3*b* represents the first derivative curve, which displays two peaks with opposite polarity. This curve does not have frequency-discriminant characteristics like the curve Fig. 2*b*, and cannot be used for stabilisation. Fig. 3*c* represents the second derivative curve. It can be seen that the curve consists of two components and that each component has a frequency-discriminant characteristic similar to that in Fig. 2*b*. This curve can be used as a discriminator for stabilisation. The slopes at the zero-crossing points B and C are 0·22 mV/GHz and −0·13 mV/GHz, respectively.

Frequency stabilisation experiments are carried out by utilising the zero-crossing points A and B for the unmodulated and modulated lasers, respectively. The output signal from the lock-in amplifier is fed to the laser current source through a PID controller. The bandwidth of the feedback loop is about

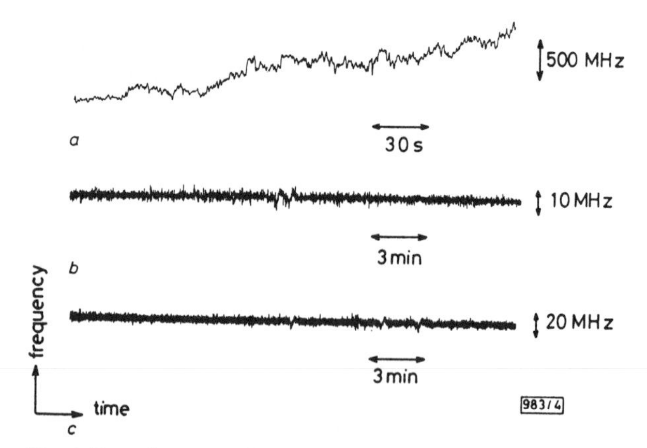

Fig. 4 *Recorder trace of frequency fluctuations*

a Free-running laser without modulation
b Stablised laser without modulation
c Stabilised laser with modulation

300 Hz. The laser frequency stability is estimated from the error signals of the feedback loop.

Fig. 4 shows the recorder traces of the laser frequency fluctuations. Fig. 4*a* corresponds to the free-running laser without modulation. The laser frequency varies by about 1·1 GHz during a period of 3 min, caused mainly by the temperature fluctuation. Fig. 4*b* corresponds to the stabilised laser without modulation. The residual frequency fluctuation is about 8 MHz, which is smaller than that of the free-running laser by two orders of magnitude. Fig. 4*c* corresponds to the stabilised laser with modulation. This trace is interpreted as representing the centre frequency fluctuation of the modulated laser. The residual frequency fluctuation is about 13 MHz, which is slightly larger than that of the stabilised laser without modulation. The difference may be attributed to the smaller slope of the second derivative curve.

In summary, a new method has been proposed for stabilising the frequency of a directly modulated semiconductor laser. The centre frequency of an AlGaAs laser with a maximum frequency deviation of 12 GHz is stabilised to within 13 MHz. Although the present experiment is carried out for sawtooth modulation, it can easily be applied to sinusoidal and square-wave modulations, and to a laser with a larger frequency deviation by properly setting the mirror spacing of the interferometer.

References

1 TSUCHIDA, H., MITSUHASHI, Y., and SUGIMURA, M.: 'Wideband frequency scanning of a stabilised semiconductor laser', *Electron. Lett.*, 1986, **22**, pp. 553–554

2 TSUCHIDA, H., OHTSU, M., TAKO, T., KURAMOCHI, N., and OURA, N.: 'Frequency stabilisation of AlGaAs semiconductor laser based on the ^{85}Rb-D$_2$ line', *Jpn. J. Appl. Phys.*, 1982, **21**, pp. L561–L563

3 NIELSEN, C. J., and JACOBSEN, G.: 'Frequency stabilisation of single-mode semiconductor lasers at 830 nm and 1·3 μm', *J. Opt. Commun.*, 1983, **4**, pp. 122–125

4 CORKE, M., KERSEY, A. D., JACKSON, D. A., and JONES, J. D. C.: 'All-fibre Michelson thermometer', *Electron. Lett.*, 1983, **19**, pp. 471–473

5 OLESEN, H., and JACOBSEN, G.: 'A theoretical and experimental analysis of modulated laser fields and power spectra', *IEEE J. Quantum Electron.*, 1982, **QE-18**, pp. 2069–2080

Narrow-linewidth, electro-optically tunable InGaAsP-Ti:LiNbO$_3$ extended cavity laser

F. Heismann, R. C. Alferness, L. L. Buhl, G. Eisenstein,[a] S. K. Korotky, J. J. Veselka, L. W. Stulz,[a] and C. A. Burrus[a]
AT&T Bell Laboratories, Holmdel, New Jersey 07733

(Received 15 April 1987; accepted for publication 19 May 1987)

We report an electro-optically tunable, single-frequency extended cavity laser with a linewidth of less than 60 kHz. The laser consists of a 1.5-μm InGaAsP gain medium and an electro-optically tunable, narrow-band Ti:LiNbO$_3$ wavelength filter ($\Delta\lambda \approx 12$ Å). Electro-optic tuning over at least 70 Å and single-frequency operation with output power of more than 1 mW have been demonstrated. The laser linewidth was measured by beating the laser against a 1.523-μm HeNe laser.

Wavelength tunable, single-frequency lasers with linewidths in the sub-MHz region are of great interest for applications in coherent optical communication systems and in optical sensors. Monolithic integrated semiconductor lasers, such as tunable distributed feedback (DFB) and distributed Bragg reflector (DBR) lasers,[1,2] are clearly advantageous in operation as well as in fabrication. Thus far, however, no monolithic integrated laser has been reported with a linewidth in the sub-MHz region. Such narrow linewidths can be obtained by using laser resonators of significantly higher Q factors, e.g., laser cavities of several cm length.[3] Several hybrid approaches of tunable semiconductor lasers with long external cavities have been proposed and demonstrated.[4-7] Single-frequency operation of such extended cavity lasers requires tunable, narrow-band wavelength selective elements inside the laser cavity. For example, a linewidth of ~10 kHz and continuous single-frequency tuning over more than 150 Å have been demonstrated with an extended cavity laser that employs a bulk-optic reflection grating as the intracavity wavelength filter.[6,8] Although this laser exhibits superb characteristics, it suffers from the fact that it employs bulk-optic components and that wavelength tuning requires mechanical rotation of the grating.

In this paper we report a narrow-linewidth, *electro-optically* tunable extended cavity laser (NEOTEC laser). The laser, shown in Fig. 1, consists of a 1.55-μm gain medium and an electro-optically tunable, integrated-optic bandpass filter as the wavelength selective element. The gain medium is a buried crescent InGaAsP Fabry–Perot laser with an antireflection (AR) coating on one facet.[9] The tunable bandpass filter employs a wavelength tunable TE$\leftrightarrow$TM polarization converter[10] and a passive polarization filter fabricated from a single-mode Ti:LiNbO$_3$ strip waveguide. The extended laser cavity is defined by the uncoated facet of the InGaAsP gain medium and a gold mirror on the far endface of the 3-cm-long LiNbO$_3$ crystal. Coupling between the Ti:LiNbO$_3$ waveguide and the gain medium is achieved via a 1.3-cm-long standard single-mode fiber having a microlens on one end. Thus, the overall length of the extended laser cavity is 4.3 cm, corresponding to an optical path length in air of ~8.5 cm.

The basic component of the tunable bandpass filter is the wavelength tunable TE$\leftrightarrow$TM polarization converter. The concept of electro-optically tunable polarization conversion in birefringent LiNbO$_3$ waveguides has been previously demonstrated[10] and will be reviewed here only briefly. Wavelength-dependent TE$\leftrightarrow$TM polarization conversion, or mode conversion (MC), in x-cut, y-propagation LiNbO$_3$ is electro-optically induced via the r_{51} electro-optic coefficient ($r_{51} \approx 28\times10^{-12}$ m/V) using interdigital finger electrodes of period Λ. Maximum TE$\leftrightarrow$TM mode conversion is obtained at a vacuum wavelength $\lambda_0 = |\Delta n_{ph}|\Lambda$, where Δn_{ph} is the difference of the effective phase indices of the quasi-TE and quasi-TM polarized modes ($\Delta n_{ph} \approx 0.072$). The wavelength of maximum mode conversion can be electro-optically tuned by means of periodically interleaved tuning electrodes that induce a change in the birefringence (Δn_{ph}) of the waveguide via the r_{33} and r_{13} electro-optic coefficients ($r_{33} \approx 30\times10^{-12}$ m/V; $r_{13} \approx 10\times10^{-12}$ m/V). The TE$\leftrightarrow$TM mode converter acts as a continuously tunable wavelength filter when linear polarized TM (or TE) input light is used and the output light of the mode converter is fed through a TE (or TM) pass polarizer.[10]

The optical bandwidth of the resulting filter is determined by the overall interaction length L of the mode converter, i.e., $\Delta\lambda/\lambda_0 \sim \Lambda/L$. In the present device the overall length of the mode converter is $L = 2$ cm and the period of the interdigital finger electrodes is $\Lambda = 21$ μm, yielding a filter bandwidth of 12 Å (FWHM).[11] In the absence of a tuning voltage ($V_T = 0$), complete TE$\leftrightarrow$TM mode conversion is obtained at a wavelength of 1.521 μm with $V_{MC} = 15$ V applied to the mode converter electrodes. The wavelength of maximum mode conversion can be continuously tuned at a rate of $\approx$0.5 Å/V by applying a common voltage V_T to all 70 interleaved tuning electrodes.[11]

A TE-pass polarization filter is integrated next to the polarization converter using a 0.1-μm-thick chrome-aluminum overlay directly deposited on the waveguide without an intermediate SiO$_2$ buffer layer, which is employed over the rest of the crystal. The 3-mm-long metal overlay strongly attenuates TM-polarized light (-5 dB single pass) while passing TE-polarized light without significant loss.[12] The wavelength-dependent TE$\leftrightarrow$TM polarization converter, together with the polarization filter and the polarization-dependent gain in the InGaAsP chip,[13] acts as a continuously tunable, narrow-band wavelength filter. The gain medium

[a] AT&T Bell Laboratories, Crawford Hill Laboratory, Holmdel, NJ 07733.

Reprinted with permission from *Appl. Phys. Lett.*, vol. 51, no. 3, pp. 164–166, July 20, 1987.

is oriented in such a way that it provides maximum gain for light that is TM-polarized light in the $LiNbO_3$ waveguide.

The NEOTEC laser operates as follows. Above threshold, the InGaAsP chip emits polarized light that is coupled as TM-polarized light into the $LiNbO_3$ waveguide via the lensed fiber. With $V_{MC} = 15$ V applied to the polarization converter electrodes, TM-polarized light at the center wavelength of the polarization converter is completely converted into TE-polarized light and passes the succeeding polarization filter without significant loss. It is then reflected by the gold mirror at the end of the waveguide and again passes the polarization filter as well as the polarization converter. Since this TE-polarized light already has the proper wavelength, it is converted back into TM-polarized light and returns to the gain medium with the same polarization as being emitted. Only this light provides significant feedback to the gain medium. TM-polarized light at other wavelengths is not completely converted into TE-polarized light and suffers high loss at the polarization filter. TE-polarized light which may be fed back from the $LiNbO_3$ waveguide experiences significantly lower gain in the InGaAsP chip.[13] TM-polarized input light at the center wavelength of the polarization converter thus experiences the lowest loss in the $LiNbO_3$ wavelength filter and the highest gain in the InGaAsP chip.

The feedback from the $LiNbO_3$ wavelength filter into the gain medium is estimated to about -17 dB, where the coupling efficiency between the gain medium and the lensed fiber is about -4 dB to -5 dB (one way), the insertion loss from the fiber into the $LiNbO_3$ waveguide is -3 dB (including propagation loss), and the reflectivity of the gold mirror is -2 dB. To avoid undesired reflections and feedback from the near endface of the $LiNbO_3$ crystal, we AR-coated this endface[14] before attaching the lensed fiber (see Fig. 1).

When driven above threshold, and with no voltage applied to the tuning electrodes, the NEOTEC laser emits a single laser line at 1.522 μm, corresponding well to the center wavelength of the untuned wavelength filter. Undesired side modes are suppressed by more than 20 dB. Coarse tuning of the laser wavelength is achieved by tuning the center wavelength of the polarization converter via the tuning voltage V_T. The laser can be tuned to shorter as well as to longer wavelengths, depending on the polarity of V_T. A total tuning range of 70 Å has been demonstrated, as shown in Fig. 2. The (averaged) tuning rate in Fig. 2 corresponds well to the tuning rate of the passive polarization converter. Of course, this coarse electro-optic tuning of the laser is not completely continuous in frequency, since the tunable wavelength filter only assists in *selecting* one of the closely spaced modes of the extended cavity ($\Delta f \approx 1.8$ GHz) by introducing wavelength-dependent loss, but does not provide tuning of the selected mode at the tuning rate of the polarization converter.

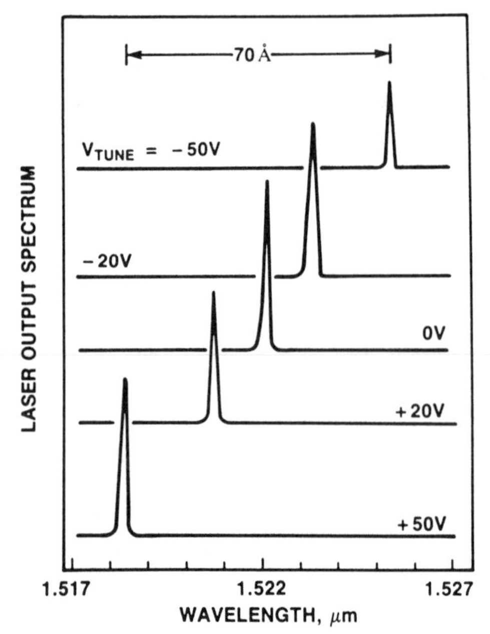

FIG. 2. Laser output spectra for five different tuning voltages, V_T, measured with a grating spectrometer.

In the present laser, the mode selection is further influenced by undesired Fabry–Perot modes of the InGaAsP gain medium ($\Delta\lambda \sim 12$–18 Å) that are present due to residual reflections at the AR-coated semiconductor facet. With AR coatings of less than -30 dB residual reflectivity[9] we were able to tune the NEOTEC laser over about 4-Å-wide bands around each residual Fabry–Perot mode of the gain medium, as demonstrated in Fig. 3. It is expected that these

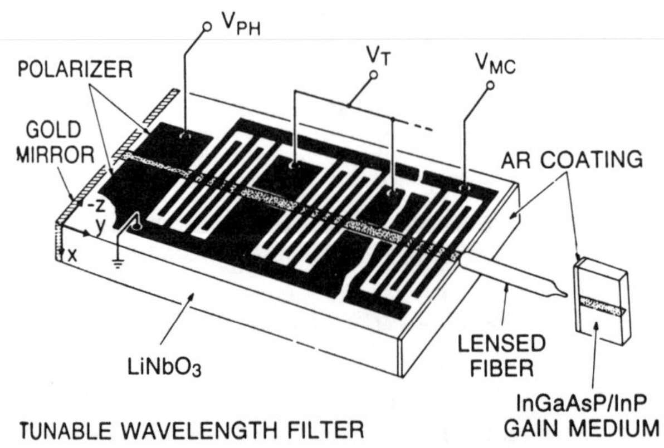

FIG. 1. Schematic diagram of the NEOTEC laser consisting of an InGaAsP gain medium and a $LiNbO_3$ tunable wavelength filter. V_{MC}, TE ↔ TM mode converter voltage; V_T, birefringence tuning voltage (for coarse tuning); V_{PH}, phase shifter voltage (for fine tuning). Only 3 of the total 70 interleaved birefringence tuning electrodes are shown here. The overall length of the laser is 4.3 cm.

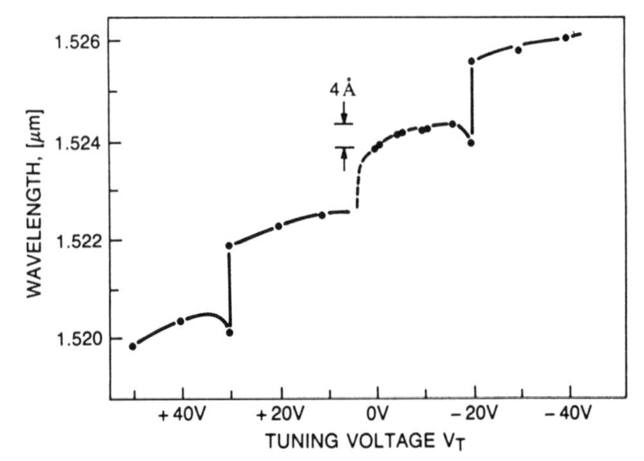

FIG. 3. Coarse tuning of laser frequency via V_T. The residual Fabry–Perot modes of the gain medium ($L = 160$ μm) are spaced here by ≈ 18 Å.

bands can be extended to cover the entire tuning range by improving the feedback from the $LiNbO_3$ wavelength filter and by using even better AR coatings.

A measurement of the laser spectrum with a high-resolution Fabry–Perot spectrum analyzer ($\Delta f \approx 10$ MHz) confirmed that the laser can be operated in a single longitudinal mode of the extended cavity. Single-frequency operation with output power of more than 1 mW emerging from the uncoated laser facet has been obtained at a laser current of about 60 mA ($T = 15$ °C). The threshold current observed with the extended cavity laser (25–35 mA) is typically two times the threshold current of the solitary InGaAsP laser chip before AR coating.

The linewidth of the lasing mode was measured by beating the NEOTEC laser against a 1.523-μm single-frequency HeNe laser. For this measurement we tuned the NEOTEC laser close to the frequency of the HeNe laser and mixed the outputs of the two free-running lasers in a fast InGaAs *p-i-n* photodiode. Isolators were used in the output beams of both lasers to avoid undesired external feedback into the lasers. Figure 4 displays the heterodyne beat spectrum of the two lasers measured with a rf spectrum analyzer at an output power of the NEOTEC laser of about 0.4 mW. The peak in this spectrum can be well described by a Lorentzian form with a width of ≈ 60 kHz (FWHM). The linewidth of the HeNe laser is well below 20 kHz,[6,7] indicating that the linewidth of the NEOTEC laser is less than 60 kHz.

Fine tuning of the lasing mode was achieved by changing the optical length of the laser cavity via an electro-optic phase shifter on the $LiNbO_3$ crystal. In the present device, we have introduced a gap in the TE-pass polarization filter to form a phase shifter electrode (see Fig. 1). By varying the voltage V_{PH} applied to the phase shifter electrode we could tune the single oscillating mode continuously over more than 1 GHz at a tuning rate of ≈ 100 MHz/V before mode hopping to neighboring modes occurred.

Electro-optic laser tuning offers the potential of high-speed frequency tuning as compared to the tuning speed obtained by mechanical rotation[6] or by current injection,[1,2] where slow temperature drifts can affect the tuning speed. The short phase shifter electrode ($L = 3$ mm) in the NEOTEC laser has a broad modulation bandwidth, thus allowing fast electro-optic frequency tuning. We have demonstrated frequency modulation of the laser by applying rf frequencies up to 250 MHz to the fine tuning electrode (V_{PH}). With rf voltages applied to the coarse tuning electrodes of the mode converter (V_T), which were not specifically designed for high-frequency operation, we have obtained frequency tuning over 4 Å at repetition rates up to ~ 10 MHz.

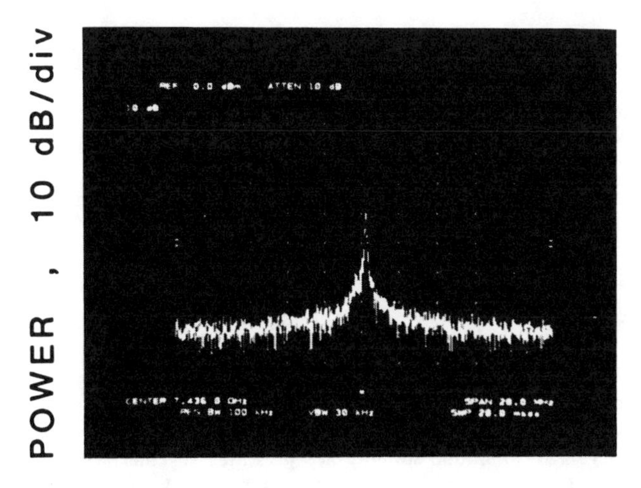

FIG. 4. Heterodyne beat spectrum of the NEOTEC laser with a 1.523-μm HeNe laser.

In summary, we have demonstrated an electro-optically tunable extended cavity laser with a linewidth of less than 60 kHz. The laser can be broadly tuned over a range of about 70 Å via a tunable, intracavity $LiNbO_3$ wavelength filter, and can be continuously fine tuned over more than 1 GHz via a high-speed electro-optic phase shifter.

We are grateful to C. D. Miller and P. J. Anthony for providing the laser diodes, to R. H. Bosworth for preparation of the electrode pattern, and to W. J. Minford for assistance with the mask design.

[1]Y. Tohmori, Y. Suematsu, H. Tsushima, and S. Arai, Electron. Lett. **19**, 656 (1983).
[2]M. Yamaguchi, M. Kitamura, S. Murata, I. Mito, and K. Kobayashi, Electron. Lett. **21**, 63 (1985).
[3]C. H. Henry, J. Lightwave Technol. **LT-4**, 298 (1986).
[4]C. L. Tang, V. G. Kreismanis, and J. M Ballantyne, Appl. Phys. Lett. **30**, 113 (1977).
[5]M. W. Fleming and A. Mooradian, IEEE J. Quantum Electron. **QE-17**, 44 (1981).
[6]R. Wyatt and J. Devlin, Electron. Lett. **19**, 110 (1983).
[7]S. K. Korotky, E. A. J. Marcatili, G. Eisenstein, J. J. Veselka, F. Heismann, and R. C. Alferness, Appl. Phys. Lett. **49**, 10 (1986).
[8]F. Favre, D. Le Guen, J. C. Simon, and B. Landousies, Electron. Lett. **22**, 795 (1986).
[9]G. Eisenstein, L. W. Stulz, and L. G. Van Uitert, J. Lightwave Technol. **LT-4**, 1373 (1986).
[10]R. C. Alferness and L. L. Buhl, Appl. Phys. Lett. **47**, 1137 (1985).
[11]F. Heismann, L. L. Buhl, and R. C. Alferness, Electron. Lett. **23**, 572 (1987).
[12]T. Findakly and C.-L. Chen, Appl. Opt. **17**, 469 (1978).
[13]G. Eisenstein, R. M. Jopson, R. A. Linke, C. A. Burrus, U. Koren, M. S. Whalen, and K. L. Hall, Electron. Lett. **21**, 1076 (1985).
[14]G. Eisenstein, S. K. Korotky, L. W. Stulz, J. J. Veselka, R. M. Jopson, and K. L. Hall, Electron. Lett. **21**, 363 (1985).

Performance Characteristics of 1.5-μm External Cavity Semiconductor Lasers for Coherent Optical Communication

N. A. OLSSON AND J. P. VAN DER ZIEL

***Abstract*—The performance characteristics of 1.5-μm external cavity semiconductor lasers have been investigated. Measurements of phase, frequency, and amplitude stability are presented together with the power and threshold characteristics. Amplitude shift keyed coherent receiver sensitivity measurements gave a receiver sensitivity of −55.7 dBm at 150 Mbit/s equivalent to 137 photon/bit as compared to previous amplitude shift keying results of 520 photon/bit and the shot-noise limit of 36 photon/bit.**

Introduction

MODE control of semiconductor lasers by means of an external cavity [1] is well known. Single frequency operation and tunability can be obtained by using a dispersive external cavity, for example with a grating [2], [3] or by an intracavity electrooptic element [4]. An important use for external cavity semiconductor lasers (ECL) is as a light source in coherent optical transmission systems [5]. For most coherent applications, the linewidth and frequency stability of regular single frequency lasers are not sufficient for acceptable system performance [6], [7]. External cavity lasers, however, have very narrow linewidth, excellent phase stability, and a wide tuning range [8], [9] making them near ideal sources for coherent communication systems.

In this paper we present a comprehensive study of the performance characteristics of an ECL. We have investigated the power, tuning, and linewidth characteristics under typical operation conditions. Also, the amplitude noise characteristics have been measured for the first time. The ECL performance has been verified by system experiments. A receiver sensitivity of −55.7 dBm was obtained for a 150-Mbit/s ASK heterodyne configuration.

The ECL's used in this study, shown in Fig. 1, were assembled from off-the-shelf standard optical components. The 1.5-μm channel substrate buried heterostructure lasers were mounted on a thermoelectric heat pump for temperature control and the laser facet facing the external cavity was coated with a quarter wave antireflection coating. The residual reflection of the facet is approximately 2 percent. The output from the laser is collimated and coupled to the external cavity with a 0.85-NA microscope objective. The back reflector of the external cavity is a 600 lines/mm grating. Its position can be varied to obtain cavity lengths between 5 and 20 cm. An etalon with a 1–2.5 Å free spectral range is usually placed in the external cavity for more stable single external cavity mode operation.

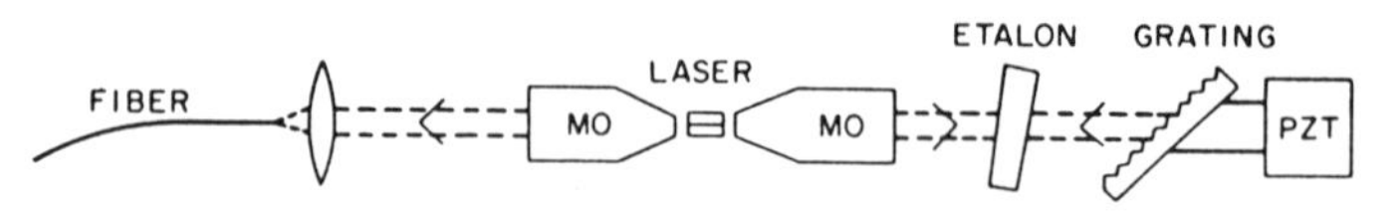

Fig. 1. Schematic of external cavity semiconductor laser.

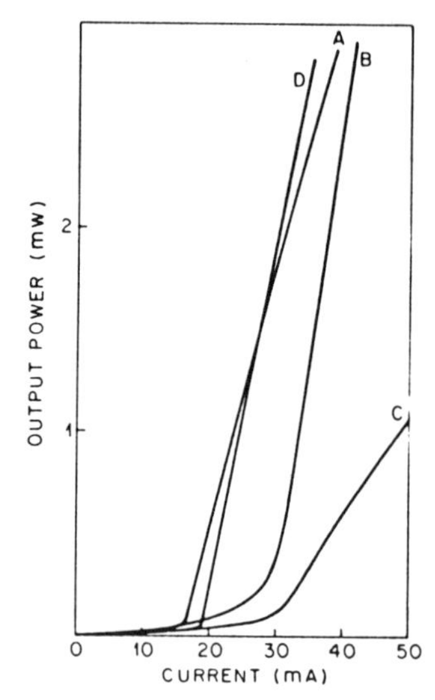

Fig. 2. Light versus current characteristics for, *A*: before AR coating, *B*: AR coated facet no optical feedback, *C*: uncoated facet no optical feedback, and *D*: uncoated facet with optical feedback.

Threshold and Power Characteristics

A typical light-current characteristic is shown in Fig. 2. Threshold current before AR coating was 16.5 mA and the slope efficiency was 0.13 mW/mA per facet. After AR coating, the threshold current increased to 32 mA and the slope efficiency changed to 0.24 mW/mA and 0.05 mW/mA for the coated and uncoated facet, respectively. With the external cavity tuned to the peak of the gain curve, the threshold current is reduced to 19 mA and the slope efficiency for the output facet (uncoated facet) increased to 0.17 mW/mA. Using bulk optics and with an

Manuscript received August 18, 1986.
The authors are with AT&T Bell Laboratories, Murray Hill, NJ 07974.
IEEE Log Number 8612959.

Reprinted from *J. Lightwave Tech.*, vol. LT-5, no. 4, pp. 510–515, April 1987.

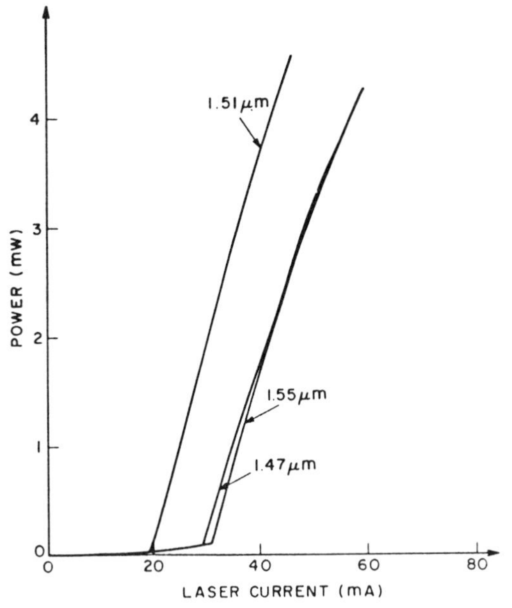

Fig. 3. Light versus current for optical feedback at 1.51, 1.47, and 1.55 μm.

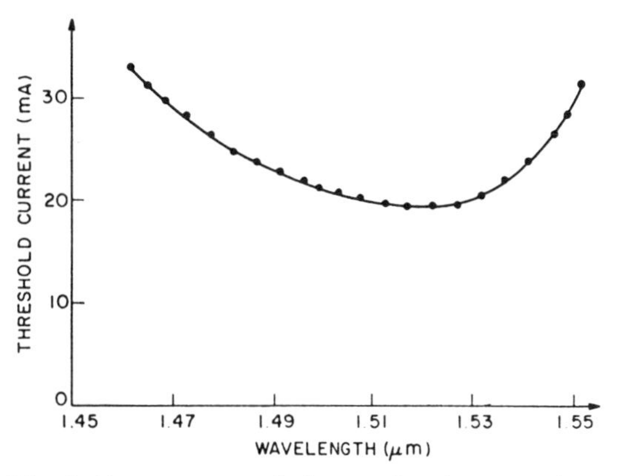

Fig. 4. Threshold current versus lasing wavelength measured at constant temperature.

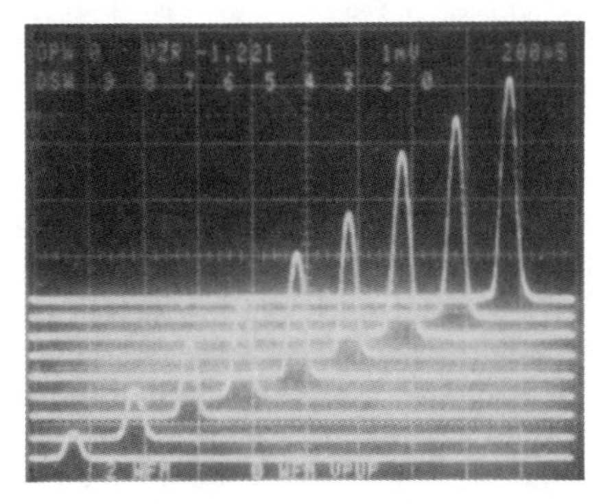

Fig. 5. Wavelength tuning between the internal longitudinal modes of the laser chip obtained by rotation of the grating and the etalon. The horizontal scale is 2 A/div.

optical isolator and polarization control optics in the beam path, typically 0 dBm of power can be coupled into a single-mode fiber at a laser current of 70 mA. In a separate experiment using a lensed fiber pigtail, +7 dBm of power at 150-mA drive current, was coupled into a single-mode fiber from a laser with AR coatings on both facets. This coupling scheme gives more power; however, the use of an isolator improves the stability of the laser. As the ECL is tuned away from the peak of the gain curve, the threshold current increases as shown in Fig. 3. However, the slope efficiency is essentially the same. The ECL can be tuned until the threshold current has increased to the threshold of the AR coated laser by itself at which point the laser emits multimode radiation at the peak of the gain curve independently of the external cavity.

Tuning Characteristics

The tuning of an external cavity laser can be divided into a coarse, medium, and fine tuning regime. Coarse tuning is obtained by rotating the grating reflector and selecting the internal mode which is closest to the desired wavelength. The internal mode is here the longitudinal modes of the solitary laser without the external cavity. These modes appear because of the nonperfect AR coating of the laser facet. The course tuning is illustrated in Fig. 4 where a tuning range in excess of 900 A is obtained. We note that with such a large tuning range, the entire low loss region of silica fibers can be covered with a single laser. The "medium" scale tuning is tuning of the laser in between its internal modes. Typically, the laser can be tuned over some 80 percent of the internal mode spacing. This tuning is achieved by adjusting the intracavity etalon in combination with a fine rotation of the grating. Fig. 5 shows an example of the intermode tuning where the laser is tuned 18 A out of the 22-A internal mode spacing. As seen in Fig. 5, this tuning is accompanied by a change in the output power. The output power increases when the laser is tuned towards longer wavelengths. The effect is a result of the carrier density dependence of the internal mode position in combination with the optical feedback dependence of the threshold carrier density. The effect has previously been described [10] and the net result is a sawtooth shaped variation of the output power as the laser is tuned between the internal modes. With moderate temperature tuning of the laser (~ 10 C), the wavelength for maximum power can be set to any point within the span of the internal modes.

Fine tuning, finally, is the adjustment of the laser frequency on a megahertz scale. This is done by fine adjustments to the external cavity length. An external cavity length change of a half wavelength shifts the external cavity mode position by one external cavity mode spacing. The grating reflector is mounted on a piezoelectric transducer to facilitate this adjustment. To illustrate the fine tuning, Fig. 6 shows scanning of the beat frequency between a fixed frequency and scanned external cavity laser. The beat frequency can continuously be adjusted from 0 Hz to 740 MHz without power variation or mode hops. The external cavity mode spacing was approximately 800 MHz. The small power variation seen in Fig. 6 arises from a cable resonance in the electronics. With a shorter external cavity, the fine tuning range can be extended to several gigahertz which may be desired in multichannel WDM coherent systems.

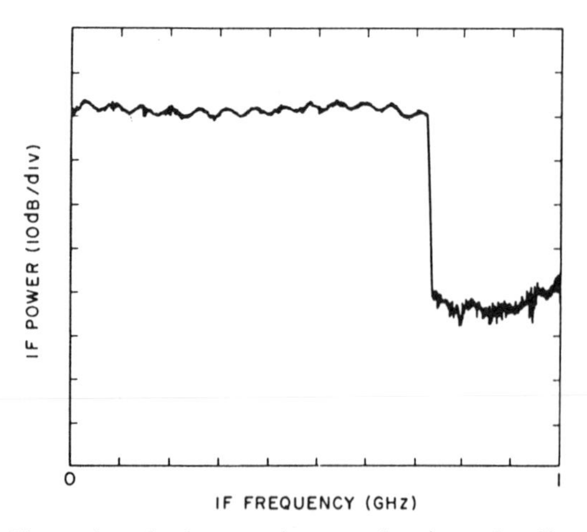

Fig. 6. Fine scale tuning between the external cavity modes. Shown is the beat frequency power between two ECL's while one laser is tuned 740 MHz of the 800-MHz external cavity mode spacing obtained by fine adjustments of the external cavity length.

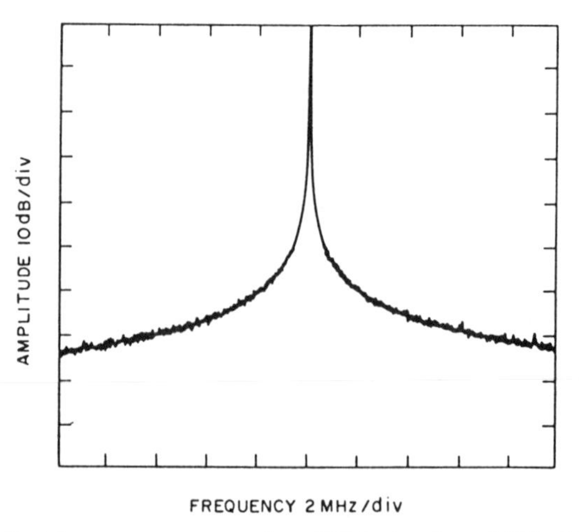

Fig. 7. Beat frequency spectrum of two ECL's showing a 4-MHz full width at the 60 dB down from the peak intensity point.

Linewidth Characteristics

An important property of the ECL is the emission linewidth. It is well known that the linewidth of ECL's is very narrow [8], [9] and with optimized AR coatings, subkilohertz linewidths have been achieved [11]. Coherent transmission systems require transmitter and local oscillator linewidths which are less than bit rate/100 for a ASK or FSK heterodyne system. Homodyne systems, on the other hand, requires linewidths of the order bit rate/1000. A 100-Mbit/s system would therefore require linewidths of the order 1 MHz to 100 kHz for ASK/FSK heterodyne and homodyne systems, respectively.

Measurements of the ECL linewidth under various operating conditions were made by heterodyning two identical external cavity lasers and observing the beat frequency on a RF spectrum analyzer. A typical beat frequency spectrum is shown in Fig. 7. At the 60-dB down point the beat frequency full width is 4 MHz. For a Lorentian line shape, the corresponding laser linewidth (FWHM) is 2 kHz. The measured beat frequency shape closely follows a Lorentian lineshape. The output power dependence of the linewidth is shown in Fig. 8. The linewidth is linearly dependent of the inverse output power in accordance with the Schawlow–Townes formula and the linewidth power product is 7.4 kHz · mW. For comparison, a solitary 1.5-μm semiconductor laser have a power linewidth product of approximately 100 MHz · mW. The ECL cavity length was 18 cm for this measurement. For proper functioning of a coherent transmission system, it is important that the linewidth remains narrow and does not vary significantly in width over the tuning of the laser, for example, when the local oscillator tracks the transmitter laser. We demonstrate a constant measured linewidth during IF tuning in Fig. 9. One laser was held at a fixed frequency, and the IF frequency was tuned from 0 to 700 MHz by adjusting the cavity length of the second laser. The tuning was done continuously without mode jumps and spanned 90 percent of the external cavity mode spacing. As seen in Fig. 9, the linewidth is independent of the tuning. The measurement was made at an output power of approximately 3 mW.

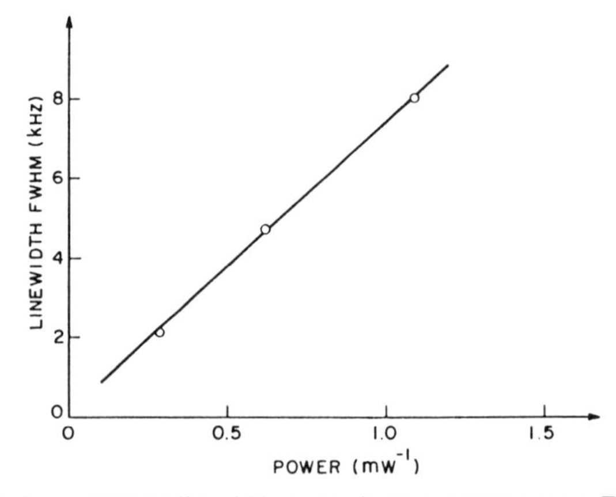

Fig. 8. Laser FWHM linewidth versus inverse output power. The linewidth power product is 7.4 kHz · mW.

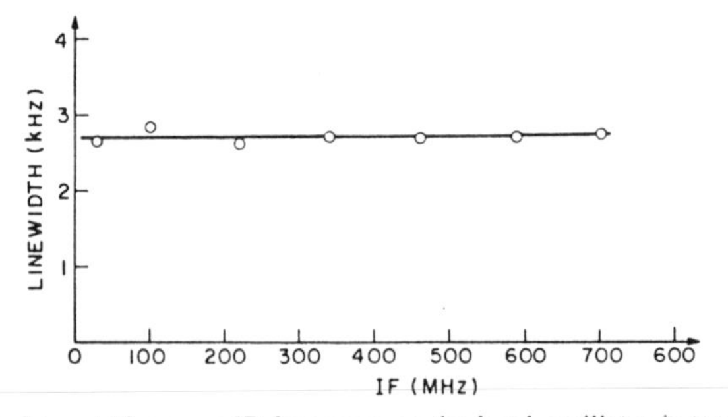

Fig. 9. Linewidth versus IF frequency as the local oscillator is tuned by changing its external cavity length.

Amplitude Stability

Coherent transmission systems require not only lasers with narrow linewidth, but also lasers with little excess amplitude noise in the frequency range of interest. Ideally, the lasers should be shot noise limited.

The amplitude noise characteristics of the ECL was measured by illuminating a p-i-n detector, followed by a low noise amplifier, with the CW light from an ECL. The noise from the p-i-n receiver was measured with a spec-

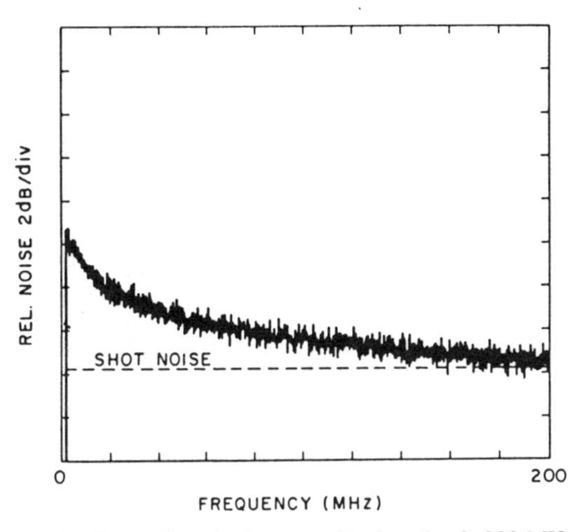

Fig. 10. External cavity laser amplitude noise 0–200 MHz.

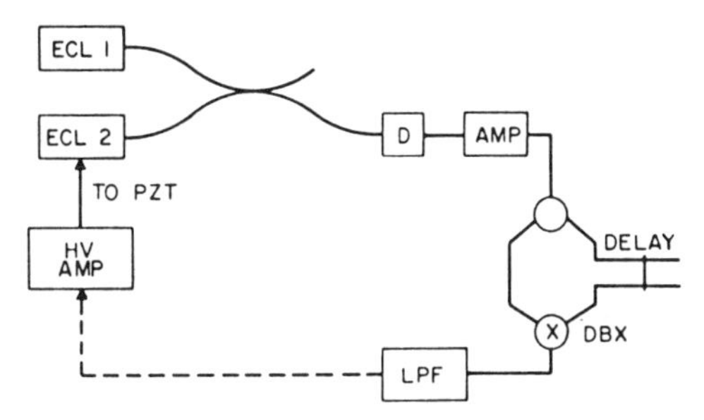

Fig. 11. Experimental setup for frequency stability measurements and IF frequency tracking. D: detector, AMP: amplifier, DBX: double balanced mixer, and LPF: low pass filter.

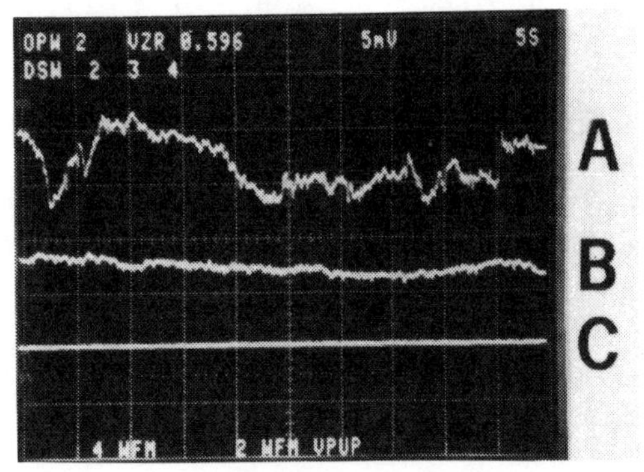

Fig. 12. IF frequency drift for *A*: ECL without enclosure, *B*: with plexiglas enclosure, and *C*: with feedback stabilization. The horizontal scale is 5 s/div and the vertical scale is 10 MHz/div.

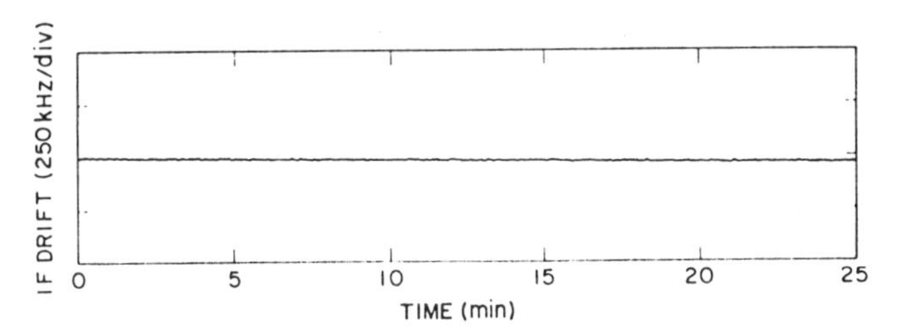

Fig. 13. IF long-term stability with feedback stabilization.

trum analyzer and the setup was calibrated by measuring the RF power when the laser was modulated with a known modulation depth. The ECL amplitude noise in the 0–200 MHz region is shown in Fig. 10. The noise has $1/f$ type of dependence and starts out at low frequency (1 MHz) 6 dB above the shot noise limit. At 40 MHz the noise is within 3 dB of the shot noise. From 200 MHz and up to the maximum measured, 2 GHz, the noise is indistinguishable from the shot noise. A small resonance, approximately 3 dB above the shot noise is seen at the external cavity roundtrip frequency. This resonance, however, is very narrow and contains very little power. For a poorly aligned laser or close to an external cavity mode jump, these peaks can, however, be substantial. Most coherent communication systems will operate with IF frequencies above 200 MHz where the ECL has no excess noise and shot noise limited system performance should be achievable. The origin of the observed low frequency excess noise is yet not fully understood.

Frequency Stability

The frequency stability of the ECL is mainly determined by its mechanical design. The lasers used in this study were designed to be used in a research environment where flexibility and use of off-the-shelf components are important features. Consequently, the rigidity and stability of the mechanical design was compromised to allow the flexibility afforded by using modular components. The frequency stability measurements presented next should be viewed with this in mind.

The frequency stability was measured by converting frequency variations in the beat frequency between two external cavity lasers to amplitude variations in a RF frequency discriminator. The setup, shown in Fig. 11, was also used to construct a simple feedback loop for IF stabilization. The measurements were done with the lasers mounted on an optical table with pneumatic isolation mounts. Fig. 12, trace *A*, shows the IF drift over a 50-s period with the lasers placed on the optical table. The frequency drift is approximately 15 MHz. When a Plexiglas enclosure is added to isolate the lasers from air currents, the frequency drift over the same time span is reduced to about 4 MHz as shown in Fig. 11 trace *B*. On a shorter time scale, 50 ms, the frequency variation is about 1 MHz and mainly caused by microphonics. We note here that a 1-MHz frequency deviation in the IF corresponds to a 5-A change in the cavity length of each of the external cavity lasers.

If long-term frequency stability of the IF frequency is required, for example for coherent transmission experiments, a feedback loop which enables tracking of one laser to the other can easily be constructed. The output from the RF frequency discriminator in Fig. 11 is connected to the piezoelectric transducer which controls the frequency of the local oscillator. In our experiments, we used a feedback loop with a 10-Hz bandwidth and the IF stability with the feedback loop closed is shown in Fig. 12 trace *C*. In Fig. 13 we show the long term stability of the IF with feedback control. Over the entire measurement time, 25 min, the lasers remain locked and the IF drift is less than 50 kHz. The observed small drift is caused by a dc

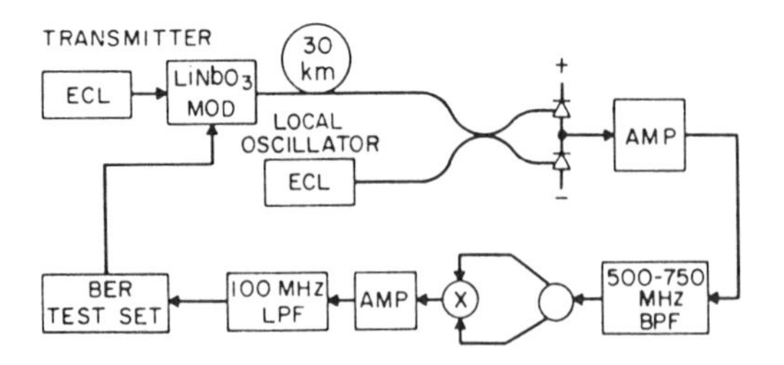

Fig. 14. Experimental setup for 150-Mbit/s receiver sensitivity measurements.

offset drift in the feedback amplifier and can easily be eliminated by more stable electronics. The bandwidth of the feedback loop is limited by mechanical resonances in the piezoelectric transducer. A higher bandwidth loop can be constructed by feeding back to the drive current of laser. The ECL frequency shifts approximately 2 MHz/mA of drive current and a feedback loop with megahertz bandwidth can be used. The drawback, however, is that this scheme introduces unwanted amplitude modulation in addition to the frequency modulation. An intracavity electrooptic modulator [4] may be the preferred means for frequency control of the external cavity semiconductor lasers.

Applications

External cavity semiconductor lasers have been used in a number of coherent transmission experiments [5], [7], [12], [13]. The particular lasers described in this paper were used in recent transmission experiments at 150 and 400 Mbit/s, and 1 Gbit/s using ASK and DPSK modulation [13]. As an example of the performance of the ECL's we will here give details of a 150-Mbit/s amplitude shift keying experiment.

The experimental setup for ASK receiver sensitivity measurements is shown in Fig. 14. The transmitter laser was amplitude modulated with a LiNbO3 amplitude modulator [14] at a data rate of 150 Mbit/s. The light is transmitted through a short section of fiber (30 km) and is mixed with the local oscillator in a 3-dB coupler. To utilize the full received power, we used a two detector receiver as shown in Fig. 14. The detectors are connected in a push–pull configuration and are loaded into the 50-Ω front end of a commercial high speed amplifier. The system was operated with 2×400 μW of local oscillator power and with an IF of 610 MHz. After amplification and filtering in a 500–750 MHz bandpass filter, the IF is envelope detected using a double balanced mixer. The IF spectrum and eye diagram are shown in Fig. 15 and Fig. 16, respectively. The bit-error-rate versus received power characteristics is shown in Fig. 17. The measured receiver sensitivity at 10-9 error rate is −55.7 dBm (both detectors) corresponding to 137 photon/bit. This compares to previous ASK sensitivity measurements of 520 photon/bit at 100 Mbit/s [15] and the theoretical limit for an ASK system of 36 photon/bit. The system margin in this experiment was 44 dB.

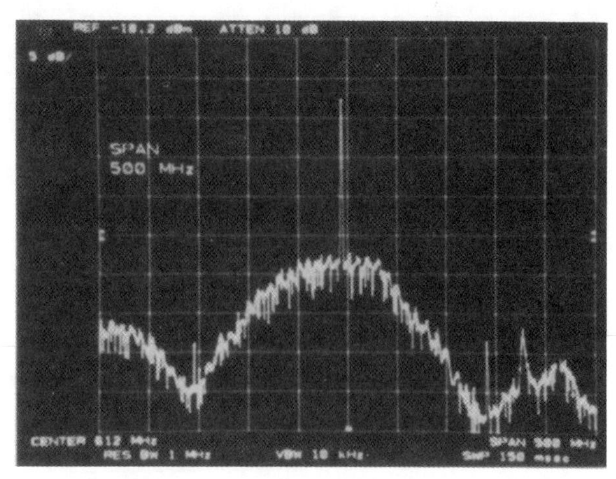

Fig. 15. IF frequency spectrum with 150-Mbit/s ASK modulation. The center frequency is 612 MHz and the horizontal scale is 50 MHz/div.

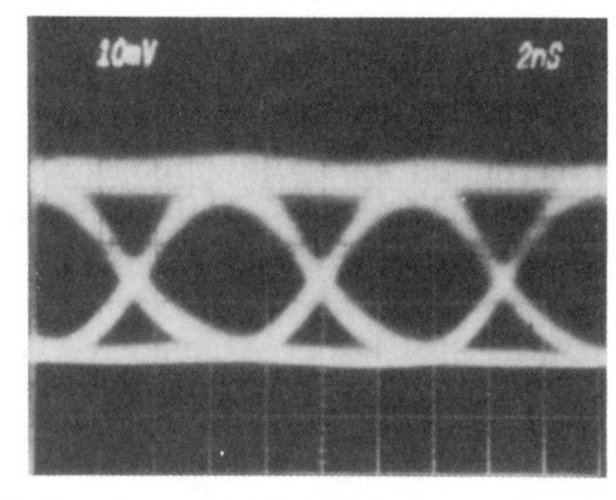

Fig. 16. Eye diagram of 150 Mbit/s after envelope detection.

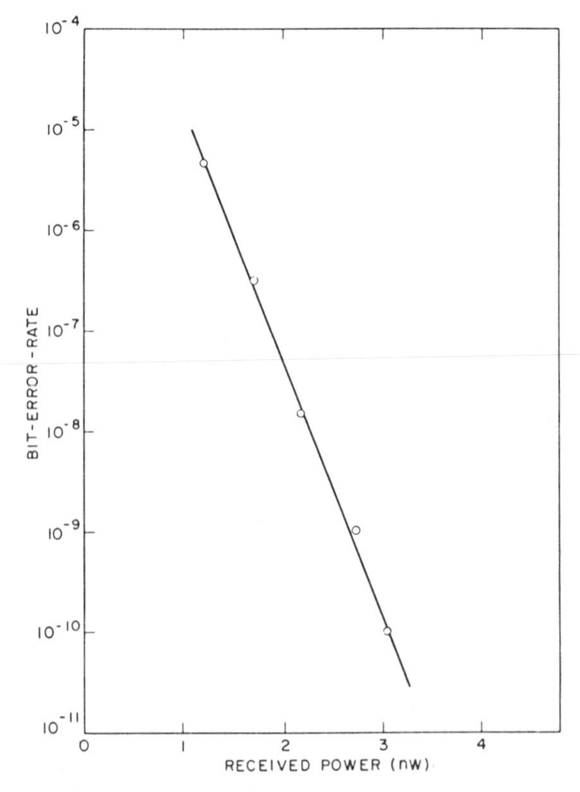

Fig. 17. Bit-error-rate versus received power. The power is total power received by both detectors.

Conclusions

The performance characteristics of 1.5-μm stabilized external cavity semiconductor lasers have been investigated. ECL's assembled from off-the-shelf modular components have a tuning range in excess of 900 A and a slope efficiency of 0.17 mW/mA. As much as 5 mW of power has been coupled into a single-mode fiber. The linewidth power product was 7.4 kHz · mW and the short term frequency stability 2 MHz. With a simple feedback loop for frequency tracking, the beat frequency between the two ECL's have a long-term stability better than 50 KHz/25 min. Above 40 MHz, the amplitude noise is within 3 dB of the shotnoise limit and the low frequency $1/f$ noise starts 6 dB above the shotnoise. The performance of the external cavities in coherent communication systems has been verified by 150 Mbit/s, 400 Mbit/s, and 1 Gbit/s system experiments. In a 150-Mbit/s ASK experiment, a receiver sensitivity of 137 photon/bit was achieved.

References

[1] E. M. Phillips-Rutz and H. D. Edmond, "Diffraction limited GaAs laser with external resonator," *Appl. Opt.*, pp. 1859–1863, 1969.

[2] R. Ludeke and E. P. Harris, "Tunable GaAs laser in an external dispersive cavity," *Appl. Phys. Lett.*, vol. 20, pp. 499–500, 1972.

[3] M. W. Fleming and A. Mooradian, "Spectral characteristics of external cavity controlled semiconductor lasers," *IEEE J. Quantum Electron.*, vol. QE-17, pp. 44–59, 1981.

[4] N. A. Olsson and C. L. Tang, "Electrooptically tuned CW semiconductor laser and FM optical communications," *IEEE J. Quantum Electron.*, vol. QE-15, pp. 1085–1088, 1979.

[5] R. Wyatt, D. W. Smith, R. A. Harmon, and W. J. Devlin, "140-Mbit/s optical FSK fiber heterodyne experiment at 1.54 μm," *Electron. Lett.*, vol. 20, pp. 912–913, 1984.

[6] S. Saito, Y. Yamamoto, and T. Kimura, "Optical FSK signal detection in a heterodyne system using semiconductor lasers," *Electron Lett.*, vol. 18, pp. 470–471, 1982.

[7] Y. K. Park, J-M. Delavaux, N. A. Olsson, T. V. Nguyen, R. W. Smith, S. K. Korotky, and M. Dixon, "Performance of ASK heterodyne detection for various laser linewidths," presented at OFC/IGWO '86, Atlanta, GA, 1986, pap. TuL6.

[8] A. Mooradian, D. Welford, and M. W. Fleming, "Linewidth characteristics of GaAlAs semiconductor laser diode," in *Proc. 5th Int. Conf. Laser Spectrosc.* New York: Springer-Verlag, 1981, pp. 67–71.

[9] R. Wyatt and W. J. Devlin, "10-kHz linewidth 1.5-μm InGaAsP external cavity laser with 55-nm tuning range," *Electron Lett.*, vol. 19, pp. 110–112, 1983.

[10] N. A. Olsson and C. L. Tang, "Injected carrier induced index change in semiconductor lasers," *Appl. Phys. Lett.*, vol. 39, pp. 24–26, 1981.

[11] R. Wyatt, "Spectral linewidth of external cavity semiconductor lasers with strong frequency selective feedback," *Electron Lett.*, vol. 21, pp. 658–659, 1985.

[12] R. Wyatt, T. G. Hodgkinson, and D. W. Smith, "1.52-μm PSK heterodyne experiment featuring an external cavity diode laser local oscillator," *Electron Lett.*, vol. 19, pp. 550–552, 1983.

[13] R. A. Linke, B. L. Kasper, N. A. Olsson, R. C. Alferness, L. L. Buhl, and A. R. McCormick, "Coherent lightwave transmission over 150-km fiber lengths at 400-Mbit/s and 1-Gbit/s data rates using DPSK modulation," *Electron. Lett.*, vol. 22, pp. 30–31, 1986.

[14] S. K. Korotky, G. Eisenstein, G. C. Alferness, J. J. Veselka, L. L. Buhl, G. T. Harvey, and P. H. Read, "Fully connecterized high speed Ti:LiNbO3 switch for time-division multiplexing and data encoding," *J. Lightwave Technol.*, vol. LT-3, pp. 1–6, 1985.

[15] M. Shikada *et al.*, "100-Mbit ASK heterodyne detection experiment using 1.3-μm DFB laser diodes," *Electron. Lett.*, vol. 20, pp. 164–165, 1984.

Part 3
Distributed Feedback and Distributed Bragg Reflectors

THE concepts of distributed feedback (DFB) and distributed Bragg reflectors (DBR) as employed in semiconductor lasers are of major importance in applications. Both DFB and DBR lasers incorporate periodic structures (gratings) either within the pumped length of the laser (DFB) or outside that length (DBR). In both cases the periodic nature of the grating provides integrated feedback and may serve as a surface emitter for output coupling as well. Although some differences in the two approaches exist, the similarities are more compelling. Thus this section is devoted to both.

Devices utilizing the principles of DFB and DBR lase in relatively stable, narrow, single longitudinal modes, whose wavelengths are less sensitive to temperature variations than most semiconductor lasers not exploiting their advantages. Moreover, there is some indication that the clever employment of periodic structures extends maximum modulation speeds, and, finally, the use of integrated reflectors should prove particularly convenient in integrated opto-electronic circuits.

The literature that describes the development of the field is particularly vast, and given the limited number of reprints that could be included in this volume, some significant works have been omitted. References quoted in the reprints will provide guidance to some of this literature; a list of other references grouped according to subject is included to furnish additional assistance to the reader.

As is noted in the introduction, our choices of papers are not to be interpreted as assigning priorities.

References

Dye Lasers

[1] Kaminow, I. P., H. P. Weber, and E. A. Chandross, "Polymethyl methacrylate dye laser with internal diffraction grating resonator," *Appl. Phys. Lett.*, vol. 18, p. 497, 1971.

[2] Zory, P., "Laser oscillation in leaky corrugated optical waveguides," *Appl. Phys. Lett.*, vol. 22, p. 125, 1973.

GaAs DFB and DBR Lasers

[3] Casey, H. C., Jr., S. Somekh, and Ilegems, "Room temperature operation of low threshold separate confinement heterostructure injection laser with distributed feedback," *Appl. Phys. Lett.*, vol. 27, p. 142, 1975.

[4] Kawanishi, H., Y. Suematsu, and K. Kishino, "GaAs-AlGaAs integrated twin-guide lasers with distributed Bragg reflectors," *IEEE J. Quantum Electron.*, vol. 13, p. 64, 1977.

DFB and DBR Theory

[5] Kogelnik, H., and C. V. Shank, "Coupled wave theory of distributed feedback lasers," *J. Appl. Phys.*, vol. 43, p. 2327, 1972.

[6] Nakamura, M., and A. Yariv, "Analysis of the threshold of double heterostructure GaAs-GaAlAs lasers with a corrugated interface," *Opt. Commun.*, vol. 11, p. 18, 1974.

[7] Kazarinov, R. F., Z. N. Sokolova, and R. A. Suris, "Planar distributed feedback optical resonator," *Sov. Phys. Technol. Phys.*, vol. 21, p. 130, 1976.

[8] Okuda, M., and K. Kubo, "Analysis of the distributed Bragg reflector laser of asymmetrical geometry," *Japan. J. Appl. Phys.*, vol. 14, p. 855, 1975.

Radiation from Gratings

Experiments

[9] Scifres, D. R., R. D. Burnham, and W. Streifer, "Highly collimated laser beams for electrically pumped SH GaAs/GaAlAs distributed feedback lasers," *Appl. Phys. Lett.*, vol. 26, p. 48, 1975.

[10] Scifres, D. R., R. D. Burnham, and W. Streifer, "Grating coupled GaAs single heterostructure ring laser," *Appl. Phys. Lett.*, vol. 28, p. 681, 1976.

[11] Kojima, K., S. Noda, K. Mitsunaga, K. Kyuma, and K. Hamanaka, "Continuous wave operation of a surface-emitting AlGaAs/GaAs multiquantum well distributed Bragg reflector laser," *Appl. Phys. Lett.*, vol. 50, p. 1705, 1987.

[12] Evans, G. A., N. W. Carlson, J. M. Hammer, M. Lurie, J. K. Butler, S. L. Palfrey, L. A. Carr, F. Z. Hawrylo, E. A. James, C. J. Kaiser, J. B. Kirk, and W. F. Reichert, "Efficient 30 mW grating surface-emitting lasers," *Appl. Phys. Lett.*, vol. 51, p. 1478, 1987.

Theory

[13] Handa, K., S. T. Peng, and T. Tamir, "Improved perturbation analysis of dielectric gratings," *Appl. Phys.*, vol. 5, p. 325, 1975.

[14] Tamir, T., *Beam and Waveguide Couplers*, vol. 7 in *Topics in Applied Physics*. Berlin: Springer-Verlag, 1975.

[15] Streifer, W., R. D. Burnham, and D. R. Scifres, "Analysis of grating coupled radiation in GaAs:GaAlAs lasers and waveguides - Part II," *IEEE J. Quantum Electron.*, vol. 12, p. 494, 1976.

[16] Yamamoto, Y., T. Kamiya, and H. Yanai, "Improved coupled mode analysis of corrugated waveguides and lasers," *IEEE J. Quantum Electron.*, vol. 14, p. 245, 1978.

[17] Yamamoto, Y., T. Kamiya, and H. Yanai, "Improved coupled mode analysis of corrugated waveguides and lasers-II TM mode," *IEEE J. Quantum. Electron.*, vol. 14, p. 620, 1978.

[18] Kazarinov, R. F., and C. H. Henry, "Second-order distributed feedback lasers with mode selection provided by first-order radiation losses," *IEEE J. Quantum Electron.*, vol. 21, p. 144, 1985.

[19] Henry, C. H., R. F. Kazarinov, R. A. Logan, and R. Yen, "Observation of destructive interference in the radiation loss of second-order distributed feedback lasers," *IEEE J. Quantum Electron.*, vol. 21, p. 151, 1985.

Spectral Linewidth

[20] Kojima, K., and K. Kyuma, "Analysis of spectral linewidth of distributed feedback laser diodes," *Electron. Lett.*, vol. 20, p. 869, 1984.

[21] Adams, M. J. and I. D. Henning, "Linewidth calculations for distributed feedback lasers," *IEE Proc.*, vol. 132, p. 136, 1985.

[22] Kojima, K., K. Kyuma, and T. Nakayama, "Analysis of spectral linewidth of distributed feedback laser diodes," *IEEE J. Lightwave Technol.*, vol. LT-3, p. 1048, 1985.

[23] Agrawal, G. P., N. K. Dutta, and P. J. Anthony, "Linewidth of distributed feedback lasers," *Appl. Phys. Lett.*, vol. 48, p. 457, 1986.

[24] Wang, J., N. Schunk, and K. Petermann, "Linewidth enhancement for DFB lasers due to longitudinal field dependence in the laser cavity," *Electron. Lett.*, vol. 23, p. 715, 1987.

[25] Soda, H., Y. Kotaki, H. Sudo, H. Ishikawa, S. Yamakoshi, and H. Imai, "Stability in single longitudinal mode operation in GaInAsP/InP phase-adjusted DFB lasers," *IEEE J. Quantum Electron.*, vol. 23, p. 804, 1987.

[26] Kikuchi, K., "Precise estimation of linewidth reduction in wavelength-detuned DFB semiconductor lasers," *Electron. Lett.*, vol. 24, p. 80, 1988.

External-Cavity Effects

[27] Lee, T. P., S. G. Menocal, and H. Matsumura, "Characteristics of linewidth narrowing of a 1.5 μm DFB laser with a short GRIN-rod external coupled cavity," *Electron. Lett.*, vol. 21, p. 655, 1985.

Multielectrode Lasers

[28] Yoshikuni, Y., K. Oe, G. Motosugi, and T. Matsuoka, "Broad wavelength tuning under single mode oscillation with a multielectrode distributed feedback laser," *Electron. Lett.*, vol. 22, p. 1153, 1986.

[29] Kotaki, Y., M. Matsuda, M. Yano, H. Ishikawa, and H. Imai, "1.55 μm wavelength tunable FBH–DBR laser," *Electron. Lett.*, vol. 23, p. 325, 1987.

[30] Yoshikuni, Y., and G. Motosugi, "Multielectrode distributed feedback laser for pure frequency modulation and chirping suppressed amplitude modulation," *IEEE J. Lightwave Technol.*, vol. LT-5, p. 516, 1987.

Grating Fabrication

[31] Johnson, L. F., and K. A. Ingersoll, "Interference gratings blazed by ion-beam erosion," *Appl. Phys. Lett.*, vol. 35, p. 500, 1979.

Quarter-Wave Shifted Gratings

[32] Utaka, K., S. Akiba, K. Sakai, and Y. Matsushima, "Analysis of quarter-wave shifted DFB laser," *Electron. Lett.*, vol. 20, p. 326, 1984.

Waveguide DBR Lasers

[33] Kobayashi, K., K. Utaka, Y. Abe, and Y. Suematsu, "CW operation of 1.5–1.6 μm wavelength GaInAsP/InP buried-heterostructure integrated twin-guide laser with distributed Bragg reflector," *Electron. Lett.*, vol. 17, p. 366, 1981.

[34] Tohmore, Y., K. Komori, S. Arai, and Y. Suematsu, "Low-threshold-current CW operation of 1.5 μm GaInAsP/InP bundle-integrated-guide distributed Bragg reflector (BIG–DBR) lasers," *Electron. Lett.*, vol. 21, p. 743, 1985.

Measurements of Coupling

[35] Iga, K., "On the use of effective refractive index in DFB laser mode separation," *Japan. J. Appl. Phys.*, vol. 22, p. 1630, 1983.

[36] Hirayama, Y., H. Okuda, H. Furuyama, J. Kinoshita, and M. Nakamura, "Determination of the coupling coefficient on DFB lasers by a newly proposed method," *Electron. Lett.*, vol. 23, p. 101, 1987.

Nonuniform Gratings

[37] Kogelnik, H., "Filter response of almost-periodic structures," *Bell Syst. Tech. J.*, vol. 55, p. 109, 1976.

STIMULATED EMISSION IN A PERIODIC STRUCTURE

H. Kogelnik and C. V. Shank
Bell Telephone Laboratories, Holmdel, New Jersey 07733
(Received 23 November 1970)

We have investigated laser oscillation in periodic structurès in which feedback is provided by backward Bragg scattering. These new laser devices are very compact and stable as the feedback mechanism is distributed throughout and integrated with the gain medium. Intrinsic to these structures is also a gratinglike spectral filtering action. We discuss periodic variations of the refractive index and of the gain and give the expression for threshold and bandwidth. Experimentally we have induced index periodicities in gelatin films into which rhodamine 6G was dissolved. The observed characteristics of laser action in these devices near 0.63 μm are reported.

Laser oscillators consist of a laser medium which provides gain and a resonator structure which provides the feedback necessary for the build-up of oscillation. The resonator is commonly formed by two (or more) end mirrors terminating the laser medium. In this paper we propose mirrorless laser devices in which the feedback mechanism is distributed throughout and integrated with the gain medium. In particular, the feedback mechanism is provided by Bragg scattering from a periodic spatial variation of the refractive index of the gain medium, or of the gain itself. Distributed feedback (DFB) lasers are very compact and have a mechanical stability which is intrinsic to integrated optical devices.[1,2] In addition, the gratinglike nature of the device provides a filter mechanism which restricts the oscillation to a narrow spectral range. The DFB approach appears applicable to such lasers as dye lasers, semiconductor lasers, and possibly parametric oscillators. In the following we will first discuss the general properties of DFB lasers including the conditions for threshold, and then describe experiments on DFB dye lasers which indicate a confirmation of our theoretical ideas.

One can produce a DFB structure by inducing a periodic spatial variation of the refractive index n or of the gain constant α of the laser medium such as

$$n(z) = n + n_1 \cos Kz \tag{1}$$

or

$$\alpha(z) = \alpha + \alpha_1 \cos Kz, \tag{2}$$

where z is measured along the optic axis and $K = 2\pi/\Lambda$. Here Λ is the period (or "fringe spacing") of the spatial modulation, and n_1 and α_1 are its amplitudes. A DFB structure of this kind will oscillate in the vicinity of a wavelength λ_0 given by the Bragg condition

$$\lambda_0/2n = \Lambda. \tag{3}$$

We have derived[3] expressions for the threshold and the spectral bandwidth of stimulated emission in such periodic structures from a simple coupled-wave analysis which is similar to that discussed in Ref. 4. The coupled-wave picture assumes that the field E in the device is of the form

$$E = R(z)e^{-jKz/2} + S(z)e^{jKz/2}, \tag{4}$$

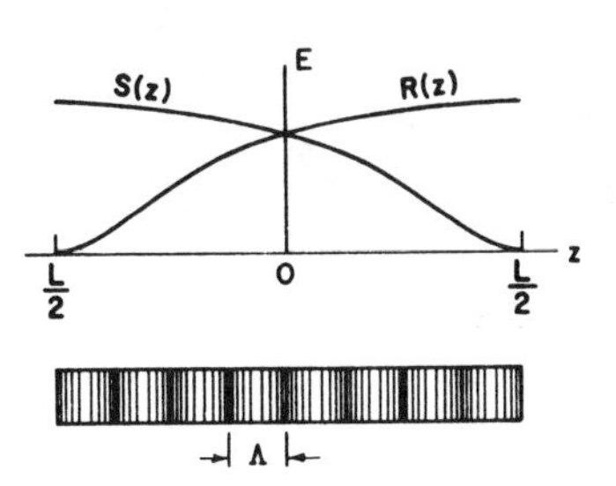

FIG. 1. Spatial dependence of the amplitudes of the two counterrunning waves $R(z)$ and $S(z)$.

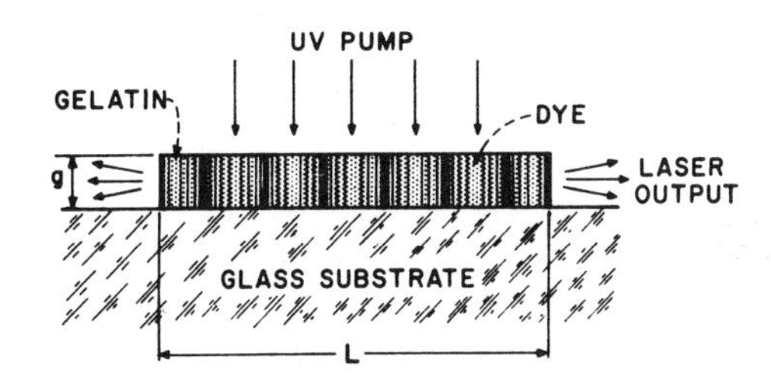

FIG. 2. Cross section of distributed feedback device consisting of dyed gelatin on a glass substrate.

consisting of two counterrunning waves with the complex amplitudes R and S. As indicated in Fig. 1 these waves grow in the presence of gain, and they feed energy into each other due to the spatial modulation of n or α. The boundary conditions for the wave amplitudes are

$$R(-L/2) = S(L/2) = 0, \tag{5}$$

where L is the length of the DFB laser. At the endpoints of the device a wave starts with zero amplitude receiving its initial energy through feedback from the other wave.

While nonlinear calculations are necessary to determine the final oscillation amplitudes, we can obtain the threshold conditions from a linear anal-

Reprinted with permission from *Appl. Phys. Lett.*, vol. 18, no. 4, pp. 152–154, Feb. 15, 1971.

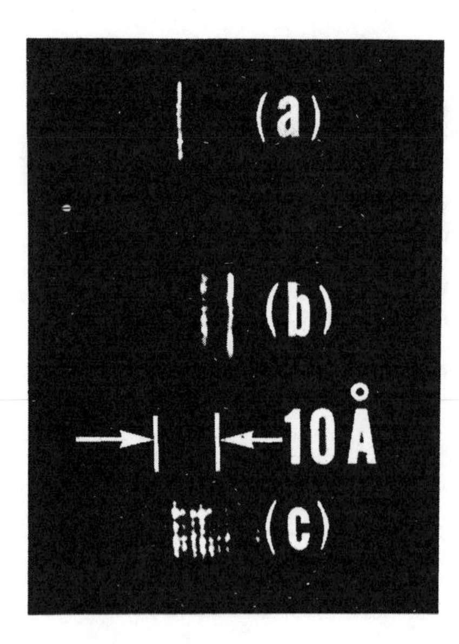

FIG. 3. Output spectra of (a) single mode of a 14-μ-thick DFB laser pumped just above threshold (wavelength is 6275 Å); (b) multiple film modes of a 14-μ-thick DFB laser pumped well above threshold; and (c) multiple film modes of a 45-μ-thick DFB laser.

ysis. We give its results in a simplified form, which is valid for large gain factors $G = \exp(2\alpha L)$. The start oscillation condition is

$$4\alpha^2 G = (\pi n_1/\lambda)^2 + \alpha_1^2/4. \tag{6}$$

If only the refractive index is modulated, the threshold condition becomes

$$n_1 = (\lambda_0/L)[\ln G/\pi(G)^{1/2}] \tag{7}$$

and for pure gain modulation we obtain

$$\alpha_1/\alpha = 4G^{-1/2}. \tag{8}$$

When the gain G exceeds the threshold value at center frequency by a factor of 2, the threshold is exceeded over a spectral bandwidth $\Delta\lambda$ approximately given by

$$\Delta\lambda/\lambda_0 = (\lambda_0/4\pi n L)\ \ln G. \tag{9}$$

Nonlinear effects will tend to further narrow the spectral width of the oscillator output. To illustrate the above relations let us assume a device with a length of $L = 10$ mm and a gain[5] of $G = 100$ operating at $\lambda_0 = 0.63\ \mu$m. Equation (7) indicates that oscillation will occur if $n_1 \gtrsim 10^{-5}$. This value is relatively easy to achieve by various methods. For the bandwidth of the device we obtain $\Delta\lambda \approx 0.1$ Å.

As a first test of the above ideas we have implemented and tested a DFB dye laser in a gelatin film. The laser was $L = 10$ mm long and about 0.1 mm wide. The film was deposited on a glass substrate as shown in Fig. 2. The gelatin was dichromated and exposed to the interference pattern produced by two coherent uv beams from a He-Cd laser. The fringe spacing (in the gelatin) was about 0.3 μm. After exposure the gelatin was developed using techniques which are well known in holography[6,7] and which result in a spatial modulation of the refractive index. The developed gelatin was soaked in a solution of rhodamine 6G to make the dye penetrate into the porous gelatin layer. After drying, the resulting DFB structure was transversely pumped with the uv radiation from a nitrogen laser as indicated in Fig. 2. At pump densities above 10^6 W/cm^2 we observed laser oscillations at a wavelength of about 0.63 μm. We analyzed the spectrum of the laser output using a spectrometer. We measured an output linewidth of less than 0.5 Å, which was the resolution limit of our instrumental technique. This should be compared to the stimulated fluorescence linewidth of rhodamine 6G in uniform gelatin under the same pumping conditions, which is approximately 50 Å and centered about 0.59 μm.[8] Considerable narrowing due to the distributed feedback is apparent.

We investigated devices of various gelatin thicknesses at various pumping levels. While it is possible to obtain single-line operation we have also observed simultaneous oscillation at several wavelengths. We have illustrated this in Figs. 3(a) and 3(b), which show the output spectrum obtained from a DFB laser with a gelatin thickness of $g = 14\ \mu$m, and in Fig. 3(c), which shows another DFB structure with $g = 45\ \mu$m. The line spacing of the multiline output of Fig. 3(b) is about 5 Å. We attribute the multiline nature of the output to oscillations of several modes of the gelatin film. These modes correspond to plane waves propagating in the film at discrete grazing angles which are reflected from the gelatin-air and gelatin-substrate interfaces. Their reflection losses are balanced by the gain in the medium. A film mode of mode number N will oscillate at a wavelength λ_N such that its propagation constant β_N obeys

$$K = 2\beta_N . \tag{10}$$

If $\lambda_0 \ll 2gn$ we can derive an approximate expression for the mode spacing $\lambda_N - \lambda_{N-1}$ which is

$$\frac{\lambda_N - \lambda_{N-1}}{\lambda_0} = -\frac{2N-1}{2}\left(\frac{\lambda_0}{2gn}\right)^2 . \tag{11}$$

The observed mode splitting corresponds to mode numbers of $N = 3$, 4, and 5. The lower orders are suppressed due to the finite (10 mm) length of the film.

The above observations clearly indicate DFB laser action which is due to the refractive-index modulation in the gelatin film. While this device was relatively easy to implement there are several other DFB structures which are promising possibilities. For example, one can employ the uv-induced index variations in poly(methylmethacrylate)[9] or the index damage in ferroelectrics which can be produced with a high spatial resolution.[10] Etched periodic deformations or loading of thin films offer further possibilities. Spatial variations of the current densities in semiconductor lasers are yet another means to achieve variations in the gain and the refractive index. The use of acoustic waves offers easy tunability. However, to satisfy the Bragg condition of Eq. (3) in the visible one needs acoustic frequencies of the order of 10 GHz, which poses technical problems. Finally, one can spatially modulate the pump intensity, and thereby the gain, by interfering two coherent pump beams at the proper angle. A change of the angle will then tune the oscillating wavelength. Further work is necessary to determine the advantages and disadvantages of the various DFB structures.

We would like to acknowledge, with thanks, the technical assistance of M.J. Madden.

[1]P.K. Tien, R. Ulrich, and R.J. Martin, Appl. Phys. Letters 14, 291 (1969).

[2]S.E. Miller, Bell System Tech. J. 48, 2059 (1969).

[3]H. Kogelnik and C.V. Shank (unpublished).

[4]H. Kogelnik, Bell System Tech. J. 48, 2909 (1969).

[5]C.V. Shank, A. Dienes, and W.T. Silfvast, Appl. Phys. Letters 17, 307 (1970).

[6]T.A. Shankoff, Appl. Opt. 7, 2101 (1968).

[7]L.H. Lin, Appl. Opt. 8, 963 (1969).

[8]T.W. Hansch, M. Pernier, and A.L. Schawlow, IEEE J. Quantum Electron. (to be published).

[9]W.J. Tomlinson, I.P. Kaminow, E. Chandross, R.L. Fork, and W.T. Silfvast, Appl. Phys. Letters 16, 486 (1970).

[10]F.S. Chen, J.T. LaMacchia, and D.B. Fraser, Appl. Phys. Letters 12, 223 (1968).

Distributed-feedback single heterojunction GaAs diode laser

D. R. Scifres, R. D. Burnham, and W. Streifer

Xerox Palo Alto Research Center, Palo Alto, California 94304
(Received 3 May 1974)

Laser operation utilizing distributed feedback (DFB) in single heterojunction (SH) GaAs/GaAlAs diodes is reported. Laser wavelengths ranging from 8430 to 8560 Å were observed in various samples depending on grating period. The threshold current densities required were comparable to those of normal SH diodes.

We report laser operation of single heterojunction (SH) GaAlAs/GaAs diode lasers utilizing a periodic structure within the gain medium of the device, to provide feedback and thus eliminate the need for cleaved end faces on individual devices. Although the feasibility of distributed-feedback (DFB) laser operation has been demonstrated in both optically pumped dye lasers[1] and in optically pumped GaAs lasers with corrugation feedback,[2,3] the demonstration of electrically pumped DFB diode lasers in conjunction with previously developed waveguides,[4,5] couplers,[6] and detectors[7] finally allows for practical integrated optical circuits.

The device structure used to obtain DFB laser operation consists of a GaAs n-type substrate, a GaAs p-type diffused layer, and a GaAlAs p-type grown layer. A corrugation with a spacing of $\Lambda = 3\lambda/2n$, where λ is the lasing wavelength of the diode and n is the refractive index of GaAs is provided at the interface between the substrate and the p-type GaAlAs grown layer. This corrugation produces the necessary feedback due to Bragg coupling of the forward and backward traveling waves of the laser. Since λ for GaAs is ~8500 Å and n ~3.6, the required spacing is roughly 3500 Å.

A transmission electron microscope photograph of a replica grating taken from a milled GaAs substrate is shown in Fig. 1. The light region corresponds to the GaAs substrate. The corrugation period was measured to be ~3550 Å.

The device was fabricated by spin coating a (100)-oriented GaAs (Si doped, $N_D \simeq 10^{18}$ cm^{-3}) substrate with Shipley AZ1350 photoresist and exposing it interferometrically with an Ar$^+$ laser. A standing wave pattern was then developed in the photoresist. This pattern was transferred into the GaAs substrate by ion milling through the photoresist mask. After removing the photoresist the milled substrate was placed into a liquid phase epitaxy growth furnace similar to those employed for fabrication of double heterojunction lasers and a GaAlAs Zn-doped layer was grown. (A portion of the unmilled substrate with no grating was grown simultaneously. This wafer provided a reference sample with which the DFB diodes could be compared.) The resulting $Ga_{1-x}Al_xAs$ grown layers were ~30 μm thick with x ~ 0.3 at the GaAs/GaAlAs interface. Both wafers were processed into various geometries so that they could be electrically excited.

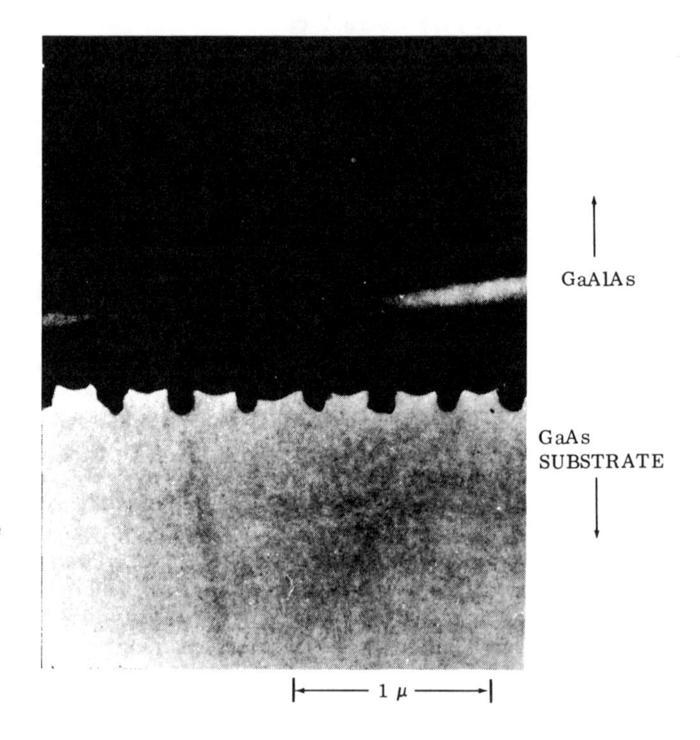

FIG. 1. TEM photograph of a cross section of a replica grating from an ion-milled GaAs substrate. The grating spacing is ~3560 Å and the corrugation height is ~1300 Å. The upper region would correspond to the GaAlAs grown layer, while the lower region would be the GaAs substrate in the laser diode.

All experimental results were obtained at liquid-nitrogen temperature. The diodes were excited with 0.5-μsec pulses. Emission spectra were observed with a Spex 1-m spectrometer whose resolution is better than 1 Å and a RCA C31034B photomultiplier with an InGaAs photocathode.

Typical results for a laser diode emitting at a wavelength of 8562 Å are shown in Fig. 2. This diode was ~250 μm wide and ~2.2 mm long and had a corrugation spacing 3560 Å. In order to minimize feedback from the diode walls, opposite faces were saw cut at ~10° angles. Laser operation at 8562 Å was observed at a threshold current of 7 A corresponding to a current density of ~1200 A/cm^2. This low value indicated that nonradiative recombination losses at the milled interface were minimal. Threshold current densities as low as 775

Reprinted with permission from *Appl. Phys. Lett.*, vol. 25, no. 4, pp. 203–206, Aug. 15, 1974.

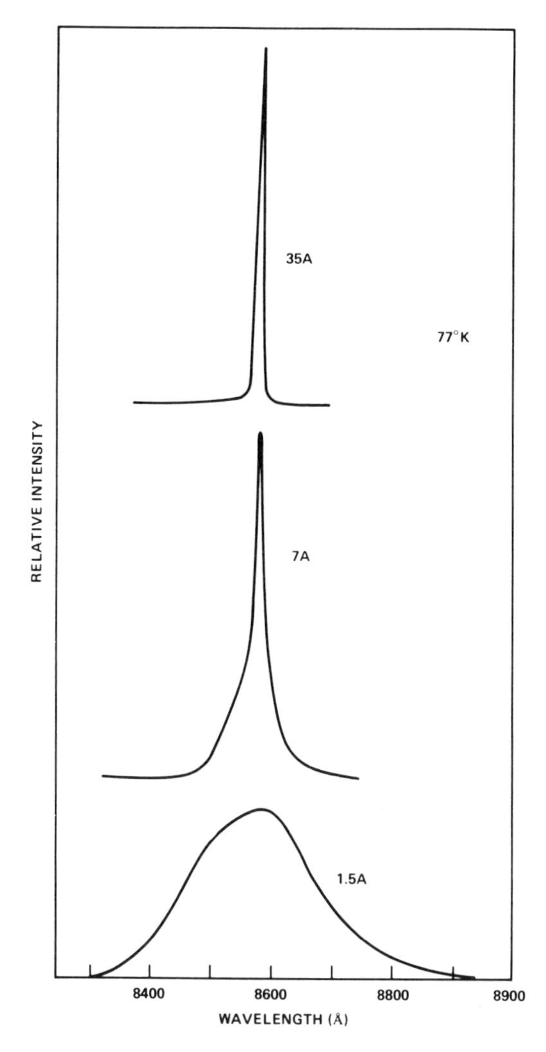

FIG. 2. Emission spectra of SH distributed-feedback diode 2.2 mm long and 250 μm wide with sawed end faces. Grating spacing is ~ 3560 A. Laser threshold is reached at 7 A and at higher currents the spectrum does not shift.

A/cm^2 were obtained from other DFB diodes with either saw-cut end faces or with faces polished to deflect light out of the junction plane. These threshold current densities were as low as those obtained from cleaved SH laser diodes taken from the control wafer (grown and processed simultaneously) which did not have a corrugation structure milled into the substrate. In addition, these reference diodes without corrugation feedback would not lase at all (currents as high as 50 A were applied) when they were fabricated with saw-cut and/or angle-polished end faces. However, the spectral output of these reference diodes did narrow to ~ 65 Å half-widths at high current densities, indicating the presence of superradiant gain.

The laser wavelength of the DFB diode shown in Fig. 2 was centered at 8562 Å; reference diodes with cleaved reflectors lased between 8480 and 8520 Å. Based on measurements of the grating spacing with an SEM and the laser wavelength of 8562 Å, the effective refractive index of the GaAs waveguide layer is 3.60 ± 0.02. This is in good agreement with the refractive index bulk measurements of p-type GaAs carried out by Marple.[8]

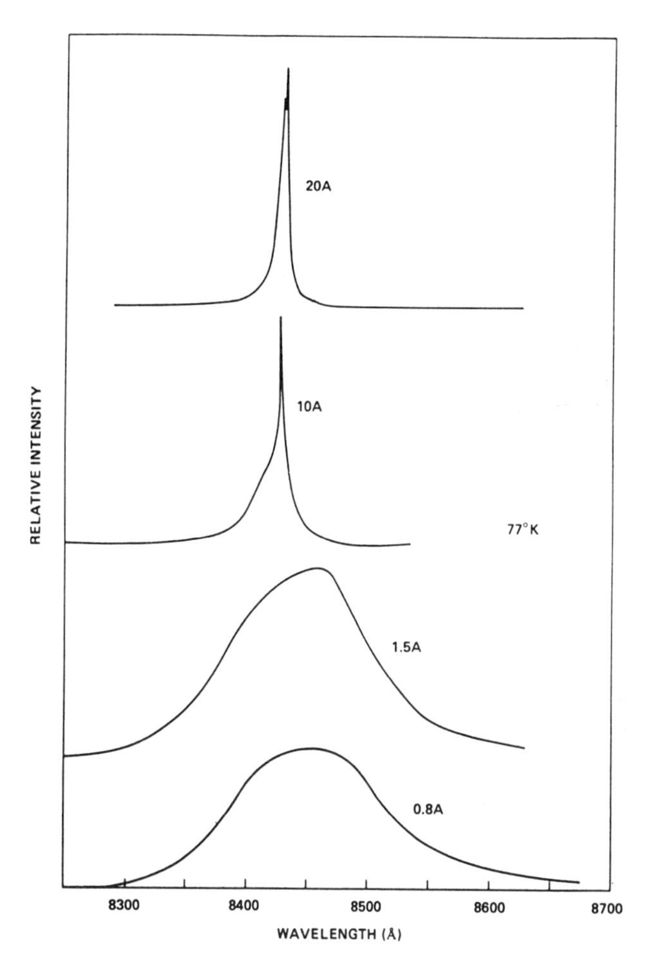

FIG. 3. Laser spectra of a saw-cut DFB diode structure 825 μm long and 250 μm wide. Below threshold the spontaneous emission peaks at ~ 8470 Å while the diode lases at higher energy (8430 Å) due to corrugation feedback.

Also as expected for a DFB device, the emission spectrum shifts very little in wavelength as a function of current density even up to 5 times threshold. This is in contrast to cleaved mirror lasers. In addition, most of the diodes fabricated from this particular growth showed uniformity in threshold wavelength independent of diode length, for lengths in excess of 750 μm. For DFB diodes less than 750 μm long made with cleaved mirrors, the mirror reflectivity dominates the distributed feedback and wavelengths ranging from 8470 to 8530 Å were observed. This behavior is in agreement with a calculation by Chinn[9] which predicts the interaction between cleaved mirrors and distributed feedback in GaAs lasers.

The half-width of the laser emission at 5 times threshold is ~ 5 Å and is not limited by spectrometer resolution. Many modes can be resolved within this linewidth and the spectra are similar to those observed by Yen *et al.*[3] for DFB laser operation of GaAs via optical pumping.

Several growth runs have been performed on gratings of various spacings. We have been able to observe laser operation at wavelengths ranging from 8430 to 8562 Å. Spectra from a saw-cut diode 33 mil long and 10 mil wide lasing at 8430 Å are shown in Fig. 3. These spec-

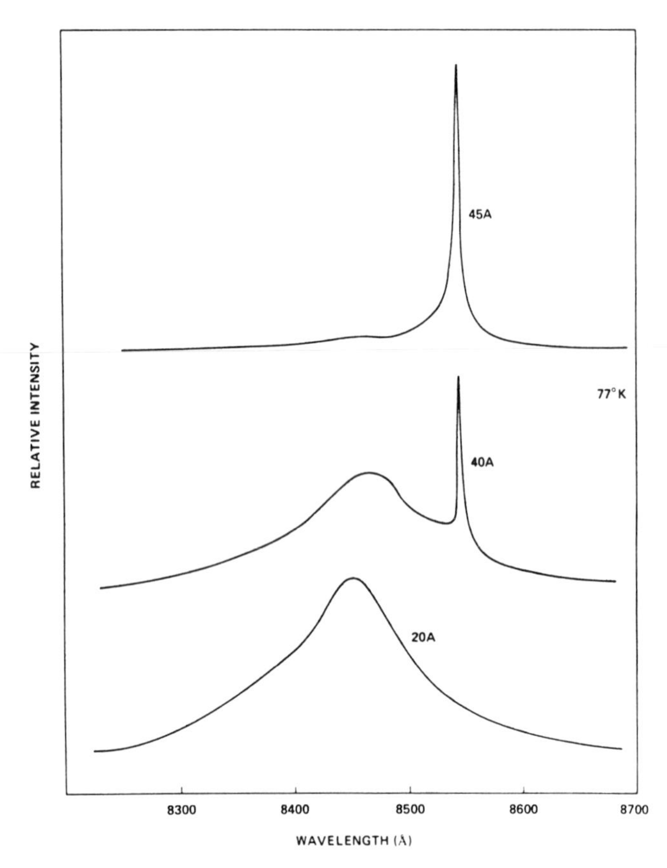

FIG. 4. DFB diode lasing on the long-wavelength side of the spontaneous emission peak.

tra are unlike those normally observed for cleaved SH diodes since the laser emission (8430 Å) occurs on the high-energy side of the spontaneous emission peak (8470 Å). Normally, the higher absorption coefficient at higher energies precludes laser operation at short wavelengths so that cleaved diodes lase more readily on the long-wavelength side of the spontaneous spectrum. However, in this case feedback only occurs at short wavelengths and is sufficient to overcome the higher absorption losses. Again, little shift in wavelength is observed when the diode is pulsed to several times the threshold current density, but the spectrum widens as several modes begin to oscillate. Spectra from another DFB laser diode with a larger corrugation spacing (~3550 Å) are shown in Fig. 4. In this case, the laser emission (8550 Å) is on the long-wavelength side of the spontaneous emission line (8470 Å). This is in contrast to the short-wavelength laser emission shown in Fig. 3 and indicates the effectiveness of the grating in determining the laser wavelength.

In conclusion we have been able to show it is possible to obtain DFB laser operation in a single heterojunction electrically pumped diode. We have found that saw-cut DFB diodes have threshold current densities as low as their cleaved counterparts. They exhibit good uniformity in laser wavelength between devices made on the same substrate, and their laser wavelength does not shift appreciably at currents several times threshold. This is in contrast to cleaved devices without gratings which were fabricated simultaneously with DFB diodes and showed a range of laser wavelengths as well as lasing at wavelengths closer to the spontaneous emission peak.

The authors would like to acknowledge J. Tramontana and A. Alimonda for their assistance in crystal growth and diode fabrication and R. Ewing, G. McKinley, and F. Walton for SEM and TEM measurements.

[1]H. Kogelnik and C.V. Shank, Appl. Phys. Lett. **18**, 152 (1971).
[2]M. Nakamura, A. Yariv, H.W. Yen, S. Somekh, and H.L. Garvin, Appl. Phys. Lett. **22**, 515 (1973).
[3]H.W. Yen, M. Nakamura, E. Garmire, S. Somekh, A. Yariv, and H.L. Garvin, Opt. Commun. **9**, 35 (1973).
[4]R.A. Logan and F.K. Reinhart, J. Appl. Phys. **44**, 4173 (1973).
[5]E. Garmire, H. Stoll, A. Yariv, and R.G. Hunsberger, Appl. Phys. Lett. **21**, 87 (1972).
[6]S. Somekh, E. Garmire, A. Yariv, H.L. Garvin, and R.G. Hunsberger, Appl. Opt. **13**, 327 (1974).
[7]H. Stoll, A. Yariv, R.G. Hunsberger, and G.L. Tangonan, Appl. Phys. Lett. **23**, 664 (1973).
[8]D.T.F. Marple, J. Appl. Phys. **35**, 1241 (1964).
[9]S.R. Chinn, J. Quantum Electron. **QE-9**, 574 (1973).

Semiconductor laser with extremely low divergence of radiation

Zh. I. Alferov, S. A. Gurevich, R. F. Kazarinov, M. N. Mizerov,
E. L. Portnoi, R. P. Seisyan, and R. A. Suris
A. F. Ioffe Physicotechnical Institute, Academy of Sciences of the USSR, Leningrad
(Submitted October 24, 1973)
Fiz. Tekh. Poluprovodn., 8, 832-833 (April 1974)

In a semiconductor laser coherent radiation is usually generated in a thin active layer, which also acts as a planar dielectric waveguide. The radiation emerges from the ends of this waveguide, which act as the Fabry–Perot resonator mirrors. The extremely narrow exit aperture gives rise to a large diffraction divergence amounting to several tens of degrees, which is a serious disadvantage of semiconductor lasers. This disadvantage can be avoided by extracting the radiation perpendicularly or at an angle to the active layer plane by allowing the waveguide mode to interact with periodic optical inhomogeneities.[1]

The present paper describes an experimental study of the possibility of extracting coherent radiation at an angle with respect to the waveguide plane. Our sample was an n-type gallium arsenide plate ($N_d = 2 \cdot 10^{17}$ cm^{-3}) oriented in the ⟨100⟩ plane. A diffraction grating was produced on the surface of this plate by the interference optical etching method.[2] The grating spacing a was selected from the condition

$$|\sin \alpha| = \left(n - \frac{\lambda_0}{a}\right), \quad (1)$$

which ensured that the radiation emerged in air at an angle α. Here n is the refractive index of gallium arsenide and λ_0 is the emission wavelength in vacuum. Since in our experiments the etching was produced by a helium–neon laser (λ = 0.6328 μ), the spacing amounting to half the wavelength of this radiation was ensured by employing a prism with a refractive index close to the refractive index of the etchant. In this way we prepared a high-quality grating with a spacing $a \approx 0.26$ μ.

A population inversion in a layer adjoining the grating was established at 80°K by optical pumping with nitrogen laser radiation (Fig. 1). A feedback was ensured by a Fabry–Perot resonator whose mirrors were the cleaved faces of the plate. We recorded the radiation emerging through the polished surface parallel to the waveguide plane. The angular distribution of this radiation in a plane perpendicular to the cleaved faces and to the diffraction grating was determined (Fig. 2). It consisted of two narrow peaks which were symmetric relative to the normal to the waveguide plane. The angles corresponding to the maxima of the peaks were in agreement with Eq. (1), provided we used the refractive index of gallium arsenide n = 3.59, the measured grating spacing a = 0.265 μ, and the emission wavelength λ_0 = 0.8365 μ. The half-width of each of the peaks $\Delta\alpha$ was ≈ 0.01 rad. This divergence was set by the multimode nature of the emission. The relationship between $\Delta\alpha$ and the half-width of the mode envelope $\Delta\lambda_0$ could be found by differentiating Eq. (1):

$$\Delta\alpha = \frac{\Delta\lambda_0}{a \cos \alpha}. \quad (2)$$

The value of $\Delta\alpha$ calculated from Eq. (2) using the measured half-width of the emission line $\Delta\lambda_0$ = 22 Å was $9.7 \cdot 10^{-3}$ rad, which was in agreement with the observed divergence (within the limits of the experimental error). The divergence expected from aperture considerations should be an order of magnitude smaller than that obtained (the aperture was 1.7 mm). However, this high directionality could only be achieved in the case of single-mode emission. Such emission could conveniently be obtained by feedback due to the Bragg reflections from the periodic inhomogeneities.

Single-mode emission from lasers with a distributed feedback in the case of a three-dimensional periodic inhomogeneity was reported in refs. 3 and 4.

In semiconductor lasers a distributed feedback can be achieved using a periodic surface inhomogeneity.[1,5] Thus, the diffraction grating used in our study to extract radiation can also act as a resonator if its spacing is a multiple of half the wavelength of the waveguide mode. In contrast to the Fabry–Perot resonator, single-frequency emission would be easy to achieve in such a grating resonator because of the strong dependence of the Q factor of the mode on its index.[1]

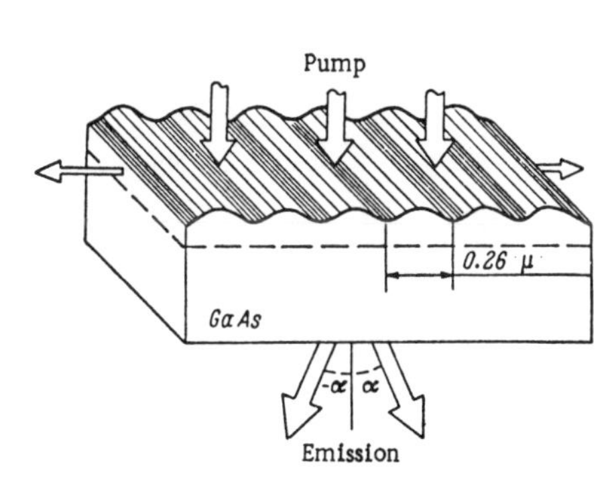

Fig. 1. Schematic representation of the investigated laser.

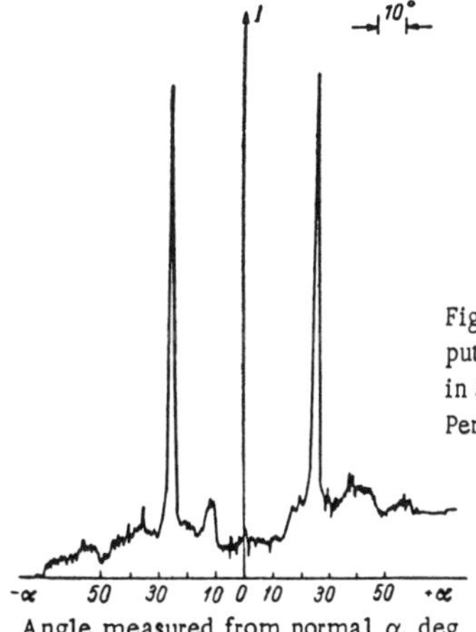

Fig. 2. Angular distribution of the output radiation of the investigated laser in a plane perpendicular to the Fabry–Perot resonator and the active layer.

Reprinted with permission from *Sov. Phys. Semicond.*, vol. 8, no. 4, pp. 541-542, Oct. 1974.

The authors are grateful to V. M. Tuchkevich and A. M. Prokhorov for their constant interest and encouragement. They are also grateful to N. V. Klepikova and G. N. Shelovanova for their help in the preparation of the samples.

[1]R. F. Kazarinov and R. A. Suris, Fiz. Tekh. Poluprovodn., 6, 1359 (1972) [Sov. Phys. – Semicond., 6, 1184 (1973)].
[2]L. V. Belyakov, D. N. Goryachev, M. N. Mizerov, and E. L. Portnoi, Zh. Tekh. Fiz. (in press).
[3]H. Kogelnik and C. V. Shank, Appl. Phys. Lett., 18, 152 (1971).
[4]A. A. Zlenko, A. M. Prokhorov, and V. A. Sychugov, ZhETF Pis. Red., 18, 156 (1973) [JETP Lett., 18, 91 (1973)].
[5]A. Yariv, IEEE J. Quantum Electron., QE-9, 919 (1973).

GaAs-$Ga_{1-x}Al_xAs$ double-heterostructure distributed-feedback diode lasers

M. Nakamura, K. Aiki, and Jun-ichi Umeda

Central Research Laboratory, Hitachi, Ltd., Kokubunji, Tokyo, Japan

A. Yariv, H. W. Yen, and T. Morikawa*

California Institute of Technology, Pasadena, California 91109
(Received 8 July 1974)

We report laser oscillation at 80–100 °K in electrically pumped GaAs-$Ga_{1-x}Al_xAs$ double-heterostructure distributed-feedback diode lasers. The feedback for laser oscillation was provided by a corrugated interface between the active GaAs layer and the p-$Ga_{1-x}Al_xAs$ layer. The lowest threshold current density was 2.5 kA/cm^2 in pulsed operation. The wavelength of laser emission was 8112 Å at 82 °K with a half-width of less than 0.3 Å. The temperature dependence of the laser wavelength was found to be smaller than that of the conventional Fabry-Perot laser.

An analysis of the performance of semiconductor injection lasers with a corrugated interface indicates the possibility of low-threshold operation as well as frequency and mode discrimination.[1] Such a laser is also expected to facilitate the problem of coupling to other monolithic integrated optical circuit components because of the freedom from cleaved mirrors.

Several workers, including the present authors, have reported on optically pumped GaAs and GaAs-GaAlAs waveguide lasers in which the feedback was provided by corrugating the GaAs surface.[2-5] In the present work, we have fabricated GaAs-$Ga_{1-x}Al_xAs$ double-heterostructure *diode* lasers with a corrugated interface and examined their lasing characteristics under injection pumping.[6]

The diode laser is illustrated schematically in Fig. 1. A n-$Ga_{0.7}Al_{0.3}As$ layer doped with Sn and a p-GaAs (active) layer doped with Ge were grown on a n-GaAs substrate by conventional liquid-phase epitaxy. The thickness of the layers was ~4 and ~1.5 μm, respectively. After reducing the thickness of the p-GaAs layer by chemical etching down to 0.5–1.3 μm, we fabricated surface corrugations on the p-GaAs layer by ion milling through a photoresist mask which was produced by holographic photolithography.[7] The period of the corrugation was ~0.34 μm so that the third-order coupling was used for laser oscillation. The depth of the corrugation was ~900 Å. Next a p-$Ga_{0.7}Al_{0.3}As$ layer (~3 μm thick) and a p-GaAs layer (~1 μm thick), both doped with Ge, were grown on the corrugated surface of the p-GaAs layer by liquid-phase epitaxy. Meltback of the corrugated surface during the epitaxial growth was avoided by growing the layers at relatively low temperatures (~700 °C) at a cooling rate of 5 °C/min. The details of the liquid-phase epitaxy were reported in Ref. 8.

The diode had a mesa-stripe geometry[9] so that the injection was limited to a rectangular region. The width of the stripe was ~50 μm. The metallic contacts to the diode were made by evaporating Cr and Au on the p side and Au-Ge-Ni on the n side. The length of the Cr-Au contact varied between 150 and 700 μm. A lossy unexcited waveguide with a length of 2.5–3 mm was contiguous to the current-excited section. This prevented optical feedback from the end surface. The output was obtained through the front cleaved surface as shown in Fig. 1.

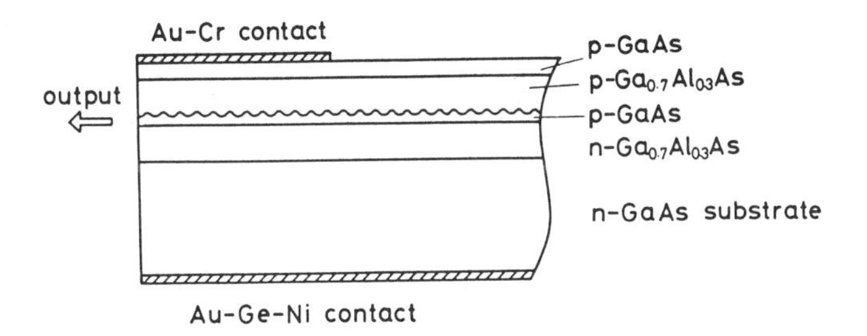

FIG. 1. Schematic cross section of the double-heterostructure distributed-feedback laser.

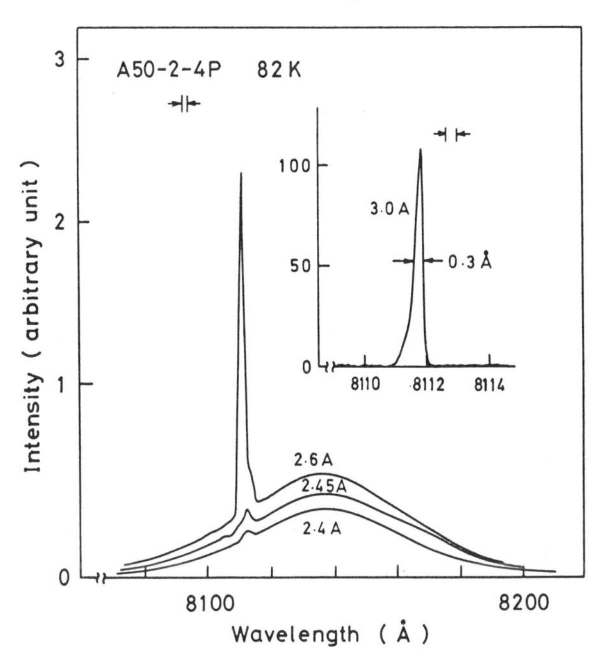

FIG. 2. Emission spectra of a double-heterostructure distributed-feedback laser. The length and the thickness of the active region were 630 and 1.3 μm, respectively. The depth of the corrugation was 900 Å, and the period was 3416 Å.

Reprinted with permission from *Appl. Phys. Lett.*, vol. 25, no. 9, pp. 487–488, Nov. 1, 1974.

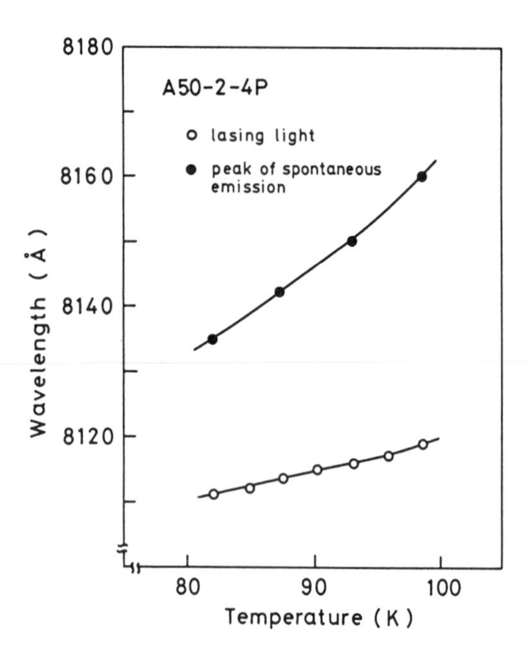

FIG. 3. Temperature dependence of the wavelength of the laser emission and the spontaneous emission.

Current pulses with a duration of 50 ns were applied to the diode, and the lasing characteristics were measured at 80–100 °K.

Figure 2 shows the emission spectra of a typical diode laser, where the corrugation period was 3416 Å and the threshold current density was 9 kA/cm^2. In this figure, the spontaneous emission has a broad peak centered at 8135 Å. Just above threshold (2.6 A), a narrow peak of stimulated emission appears at 8112 Å. The linewidth of the stimulated emission is 0.3 Å and is within the resolution of the spectrometer. The lasing light was polarized with the electric field vector parallel to the junction plane. The wavelength λ of the laser emission and the corrugation period Λ are related theoretically by

$$\Lambda = 3\lambda/2n_g \qquad (1)$$

for the third-order coupling, where n_g is the effective refractive index of the waveguide. From Eq. (1) and Fig. 2, the effective refractive index n_g is estimated to be 3.56, which is a reasonable value for the thin-slab waveguide structure.

The temperature dependence of the emission spectrum was investigated in the range 82–98 °K. In Fig. 3, the wavelength of the laser emission and the wavelength of the spontaneous emission peak are plotted as a function of temperature. The temperature dependence $d\lambda/dT$ of the wavelength of the stimulated emission is 0.5 Å/°K. This result is predicted from Eq. (1) if one accounts for the temperature dependence of the refractive index of GaAs.[10] The wavelength of the spontaneous emission peak, on the other hand, changes at a rate of 1.5 Å/°K, which reflects the shift of the band-gap energy with temperature. Cleaved Fabry-Perot lasers made from the same epitaxial wafer lased at wavelengths near the peak of the spontaneous emission, and had the same temperature dependence as that of the spontaneous emission peak. This clearly demonstrates the fact that the laser feedback is due predominantly to the periodic corrugation. The smaller temperature dependence of the wavelength of the laser emission may be attractive in the practical application of semiconductor lasers.

The lowest threshold current density of 2.5 kA/cm^2 was obtained at 80 °K in a sample with an excitation length of 480 μm, a corrugation depth of 850 Å, and an active layer thickness of 0.6 μm. The surface damage caused by the ion milling was found to severely reduce the recombination efficiency, thus increasing the threshold current density. This may be reduced by adopting a SCH structure with a corrugated interface as was proposed elsewhere.[11] The use of fundamental corrugations with a period of 0.12 μm will also reduce the threshold current density.

The authors would like to thank Dr. Y. Ohtomo and Dr. O. Nakada of Central Research Laboratory, Hitachi, Ltd., for their continuous encouragement; Y. Sasaki of the same laboratory for his help in fabricating the diodes; and A. Gover of California Institute of Technology for his helpful discussions.

*Present address: Electrotechnical Laboratory, Tanashi, Tokyo, Japan.

[1]M. Nakamura and A. Yariv, Opt. Commun. 11, 18 (1974).
[2]M. Nakamura, A Yariv, H.W. Yen, S. Somekh, and H.L. Garvin, Appl. Phys. Lett. 22, 515 (1973).
[3]M. Nakamura, H.W. Yen, A Yariv, E. Garmire, S. Somekh, and H.L. Garvin, Appl. Phys. Lett. 23, 224 (1973).
[4]H.W. Yen, M. Nakamura, E. Garmire, S. Somekh, A. Yariv, and H.L. Garvin, Opt. Commun. 9, 35 (1973).
[5]C.V. Shank and R. Schmidt, Digest of Technical Papers, Topical Meeting on Integrated Optics, New Orleans, 1974, Paper No. MB1-1 (unpublished). This paper discusses the results of optically pumped double-heterostructure GaAs-$Ga_{1-x}Al_xAs$ lasers.
[6]D.R. Scifres, R.D. Burnham, and W. Streifer, VIII International Quantum Electronics Conference, San Francisco, 1974, Paper No. R1 (unpublished). This is the first DFB injection laser reported in the literature.
[7]H.L. Garvin, E. Garmire, S. Somekh, H. Stoll, and A. Yariv, Appl. Opt. 12, 455 (1973).
[8]M. Nakamura, K. Aiki, J. Umeda, A. Yariv, H.W. Yen, and T. Morikawa, Appl. Phys. Lett. 24, 466 (1974).
[9]T. Tsukada, H. Nakashima, J. Umeda, S. Nakamura, N. Chinone, R. Ito, and O. Nakada, Appl. Phys. Lett. 20, 344 (1972).
[10]J. Zoroofchi and J.K. Butler, J. Appl. Phys. 44, 3697 (1973). (1973).
[11]M. Nakamura and A. Yariv, Digest of the 1974 Topical Meeting on Integrated Optics, Paper No. TuB9 (unpublished).

Effect of External Reflectors on Longitudinal Modes of Distributed Feedback Lasers

WILLIAM STREIFER, SENIOR MEMBER, IEEE, ROBERT D. BURNHAM, AND DONALD R. SCIFRES

Abstract—The effect of external reflectors on longitudinal modes of distributed feedback (DFB) lasers is analyzed. The general case of dissimilar reflectors arbitrarily located relative to the phase of the DFB structure is considered. An eigenvalue equation for the propagation constants is derived and solved numerically for a variety of practical cases. Longitudinal mode thresholds, wavelengths, separations, and field distributions are obtained for GaAs lasers and for DFB lasers with a single reflector. It is shown that these quantities are very sensitive not only to the relative strength of the discrete and DFB, but also to the relative phases. Quite asymmetric transmitted powers are shown to occur under a variety of circumstances.

I. Introduction

Longitudinal modes in a distributed feedback (DFB) laser with external reflectors are studied in this paper. In such devices, internal reflections are caused by a periodic DFB structure. External, as opposed to internal, reflectors may be purposely produced in GaAs diode lasers by cleaving along a crystallographic plane to produce flat parallel surfaces. External reflectors on other DFB lasers can be implemented in obvious ways. Among the reasons for studying such devices is that the combined action of the internal and external reflectors sometimes reduces the laser threshold. Often too, other optical elements, such as couplers, guides, or modulators, within an integrated optic circuit may produce reflections which interact with the DFB structure. Finally, it is frequently convenient to cleave one or both end faces of a DFB diode laser to facilitate the experimental study.

The periodic feedback itself may be effected by variations in refractive index and/or gain or by a physical corrugation in the vicinity of the gain region. Since the latter structure is equivalent to a periodic variation in index and/or gain for most purposes, it suffices to consider

$$n(z) = n + (\Delta n)\cos(2\pi z/\Lambda + \Omega) \tag{1a}$$

and

$$\alpha(z) = \alpha + (\Delta\alpha)\cos(2\pi z/\Lambda + \Omega) \tag{1b}$$

where $n(z)$ is the refractive index, $\alpha(z)$ is the gain, and z is measured along the laser from $-L/2$ to $L/2$. Furthermore, n and α are constants and Δn and $\Delta\alpha$ are the amplitude variations with spatial period Λ and phase Ω. For nonsinusoidal variations (1a) and (1b) include only the constant and fundamental terms of the Fourier expansion. Equations (1a) and (1b) are appropriate only for analyzing first-order Bragg scattering in the DFB structure. Often third-order Bragg scattering is employed in which case

$$n(z) = n + (\Delta n)\cos(6\pi z/\Lambda + \Omega) \tag{2a}$$

and

$$\alpha(z) = \alpha + (\Delta\alpha)\cos(6\pi z/\Lambda + \Omega) \tag{2b}$$

where Δn and $\Delta\alpha$ are the third-harmonic coefficients.

Previous analyses have considered the DFB structure without external reflectors (see Kogelnik and Shank [1]) and with identical external reflectors located exactly symmetric with respect to the grating (see Chinn [2]). The latter analysis is not general in that it does not cover most cases. Specifically, both the following requirements must be met if Chinn's derivation is to apply.

1) The reflectors must have identical reflectivity.
2) The reflectors must be located relative to the grating, such that $\Omega = 0$.

As will be shown, reflector position relative to the peaks and troughs of the grating greatly influences the longitudinal mode structure. Since physical control of the relative reflector-grating position is very difficult (because of the small physical period Λ for visible and near IR lasers), the general case must be considered.

In Section II of this paper the eigenvalue equation for longitudinal modes in a DFB laser with external reflectors is derived. Although the equation is generally applicable, it is solved numerically to yield net threshold gains and wavelengths for some important special cases in Section III, viz., GaAs DFB lasers with two cleaves and DFB lasers with one reflector. Longitudinal mode separations are also calculated and the variation of mode fields along the length of the laser are also determined in Section III. The latter computation yields the ratios of radiated power from each end of the device.

II. Derivation of the Equation

Following [1], [2] we seek solutions of

$$[\nabla^2 + k^2(z)]E(z) = 0 \tag{3}$$

where the time dependence of the electric field $E(z)$ is $e^{i\omega t}$ and

$$k^2(z) \approx \beta^2 + 2i\alpha\beta + 4\kappa\beta\cos(2\beta_0 z + \Omega). \tag{4}$$

Here

$$\beta_0 \triangleq \pi/\Lambda \tag{5a}$$

Manuscript received October 9, 1974.
The authors are with the Xerox Palo Alto Research Center, Palo Alto, Calif. 94304.

Reprinted from *IEEE J. Quantum Elect.*, vol. QE-11, no. 4, pp. 154–161, April 1975.

for first-order Bragg scattering ($3\pi/\Lambda$ for third order)

$$\beta \triangleq n\omega/c \quad (5b)^1$$

and κ is the coupling coefficient ($\kappa \ll \beta$) given by

$$\kappa = \left(\frac{\beta}{2}\right)\left(\frac{\Delta n}{n}\right) + \frac{i\Delta\alpha}{2}. \quad (5c)$$

The assumptions $\Delta n \ll n$, $\alpha \ll \beta$, and $\Delta\alpha \ll \beta$, were employed in deriving (4). Both β and α are determined by the analysis which follows. Values of α specify net gain at threshold for laser oscillation and those of β specify the allowable values of ω and thereby the free-space wavelength λ_0.

Without loss of generality we seek solutions in the form

$$E(z) = R(z)\, e^{-i\beta_0 z} + S(z)\, e^{i\beta_0 z} \quad (6)$$

where $R(z)$ and $S(z)$ are opposite going waves with $R(z)$ propagating in the direction of increasing z. These functions are assumed to change slowly so that $R''(z)$ and $S''(z)$ can be neglected compared with $\beta_0 R'(z)$ and $\beta_0 S'(z)$. Then upon substitution in (3) we obtain

$$\begin{aligned}&[-2\beta_0 R' - \beta_0^2 R + \beta^2 R + 2i\alpha\beta R]\, e^{-i\beta_0 z}\\ &\quad + [2\beta_0 S' - \beta_0^2 S + \beta^2 S + 2i\alpha\beta S]\, e^{i\beta_0 z}\\ &\quad + 2\kappa\beta\left(e^{i2\beta_0 z}\, e^{i\Omega} + e^{-i2\beta_0 z}\, e^{-i\Omega}\right)\\ &\quad \cdot \left(Re^{-i\beta_0 z} + Se^{i\beta_0 z}\right) = 0 \end{aligned} \quad (7)$$

and after isolating expressions with similar z dependence

$$-R' + (\alpha - i\delta)R = i\kappa e^{-i\Omega} S \quad (8a)$$

and

$$S' + (\alpha - i\delta)S = i\kappa e^{i\Omega} R \quad (8b)$$

where

$$\delta \triangleq \beta - \beta_0 \quad (9)$$

$|\delta| \ll \beta$ has been assumed, and terms which propagate as $e^{\pm i3\beta_0 z}$ have been dropped. Since (8a) and (8b) are constant coefficient linear differential equations they admit exponential solutions in the form

$$R(z) = r_1 e^{\gamma z} + r_2 e^{-\gamma z} \quad (10a)$$

and

$$S(z) = s_1 e^{\gamma z} + s_2 e^{-\gamma z} \quad (10b)$$

where r_1, r_2, s_1, and s_2 are constants. Without loss of generality Re $(\gamma) > 0$, so that r_1 and s_2 grow as they propagate. The combined effects of gain and coupling from opposite going waves ($s_1 \rightarrow r_1$ and $r_2 \rightarrow s_2$) cause the growth. Growing waves have propagation constants given by β_0 - Im (γ) [cf. (6)]. The waves multiplied by r_2 and s_1 decay as they propagate with constant given by β_0 + Im (γ).

The substitution of (10a) and (10b) in (8a) and (8b) results in four equations when terms with identical z dependence are collected

$$\hat{\Gamma} r_1 = i\kappa e^{-i\Omega} s_1 \quad (11a)$$

$$\Gamma r_2 = i\kappa e^{-i\Omega} s_2 \quad (11b)$$

$$\Gamma s_1 = i\kappa e^{i\Omega} r_1 \quad (11c)$$

$$\hat{\Gamma} s_2 = i\kappa e^{i\Omega} r_2 \quad (11d)$$

where

$$\hat{\Gamma} = -\gamma + \alpha - i\delta \quad (12a)$$

and

$$\Gamma = \gamma + \alpha - i\delta. \quad (12b)$$

These equations have nontrivial solutions if and only if γ satisfies the dispersion relation

$$\gamma^2 = (\alpha - i\delta)^2 + \kappa^2 \quad (13)$$

which, as expected, is independent of Ω.

The actual determination of γ, and thereafter α and δ, is achieved only after imposing the reflection conditions at $z = \pm L/2$. If the reflection coefficient at $z = -L/2$ is denoted by $\hat{\rho}_l$ and that at $z = L/2$ by $\hat{\rho}_r$, we obtain

$$(r_1 e^{-\gamma L/2} + r_2 e^{\gamma L/2})\, e^{i\beta_0 L/2} = \hat{\rho}_l (s_1 e^{-\gamma L/2} + s_2 e^{\gamma L/2})\, e^{-i\beta_0 L/2} \quad (14a)$$

and

$$(s_1 e^{\gamma L/2} + s_2 e^{-\gamma L/2})\, e^{i\beta_0 L/2} = \hat{\rho}_r (r_1 e^{\gamma L/2} + r_2 e^{-\gamma L/2})\, e^{-i\beta_0 L/2}. \quad (14b)$$

Next (11a) and (11d) are employed to eliminate r_2 and s_1 from (14a) and (14b). The latter equations are homogeneous in r_1 and s_2, so that nontrivial solutions exist only if

$$\frac{(1 - \rho_l \hat{\Gamma}/i\kappa)\, e^{-\gamma L}}{(\rho_l - \hat{\Gamma}/i\kappa)} = \frac{(\rho_r - \hat{\Gamma}/i\kappa)\, e^{\gamma L}}{(1 - \rho_r \hat{\Gamma}/i\kappa)} \quad (15)$$

where

$$\rho_l = \hat{\rho}_l e^{-i\beta_0 L}\, e^{i\Omega} \quad (16a)$$

and

$$\rho_r = \hat{\rho}_r e^{-i\beta_0 L}\, e^{-i\Omega}. \quad (16b)$$

Equation (15) can also be derived by setting the coefficient determinant of (11a), (11d), (14a), and (14b) equal to zero.

The phase functions in (16a) and (16b) are just those of the DFB structure at $z = \pm L/2$, i.e., at $z = -L/2$, which is the location of the left reflector, the index variation from (1a) is $\cos(-\beta_0 L + \Omega)$, where as in the preceding $\beta_0 = \pi/\Lambda$. Similarly, at the right reflector $z = L/2$ so that the index variation is $\cos(\beta_0 L + \Omega)$. Values of $-\beta_0 L + \Omega$ and $-\beta_0 L - \Omega$ are shown in Fig. 1(a) and (b), respectively, for various positions of the left and right reflectors in the case of a nonsinusoidal corrugation grating and first-order Bragg scattering. It should be noted that ρ_l and ρ_r also depend on the phase of $\hat{\rho}_l$ and $\hat{\rho}_r$, which are commonly π. In that case all phases in Fig. 1(a) and (b) are shifted by π to obtain those of ρ_l and ρ_r.

[1] A more complicated relation applies for waveguiding structures. In that case an equivalent index n_{eq} should be used in (5b).

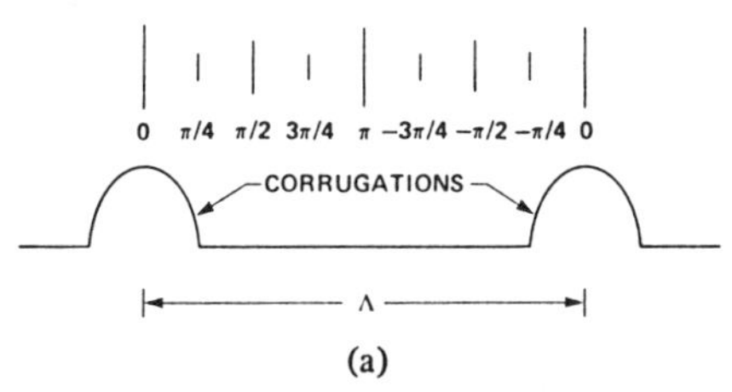

(a)

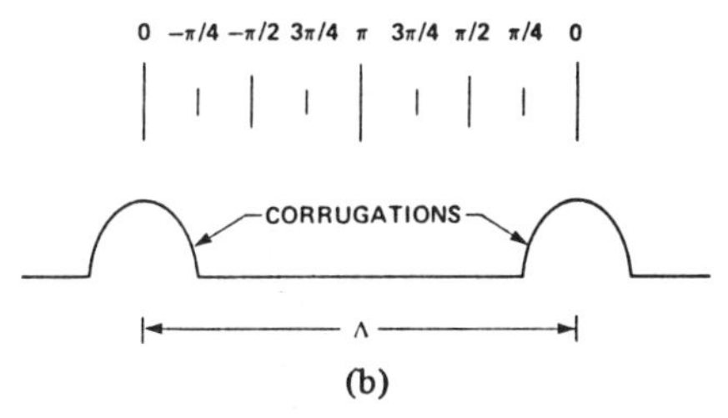

(b)

Fig. 1. Phases as a function of left- and right-reflector positions with first-order Bragg scattering.

By solving (15) for $\hat{\Gamma}/i\kappa$ and employing the relation

$$\gamma = \frac{-i\kappa}{2}\left(\frac{\hat{\Gamma}}{ik} - \frac{i\kappa}{\hat{\Gamma}}\right) \tag{17}$$

which follows from (11a), (11c), (12a), and (12b), we obtain (after substantial manipulation) the eigenvalue equation

$$\gamma L = \frac{-i\kappa L \sinh(\gamma L)}{\mathfrak{D}}\{(\rho_l + \rho_r)(1 - \rho^2)\cosh(\gamma L) \pm (1 + \rho^2)[(\rho_l - \rho_r)^2 \sinh^2 \gamma L + (1 - \rho^2)^2]^{1/2}\} \tag{18}$$

where

$$\mathfrak{D} = (1 + \rho^2)^2 - 4\rho^2 \cosh^2(\gamma L) \tag{19}$$

and

$$\rho^2 = \rho_l \rho_r = \hat{\rho}_l \hat{\rho}_r e^{-2i\beta_0 L}. \tag{20}$$

Values of γ found by solving (18) determine the propagation constants for the longitudinal modes. For each γ, (13) is used to calculate α, which is the net gain required at threshold for that mode to lase and δ, which gives the laser frequency

$$\omega = \frac{c\beta}{n} = \frac{c}{n}(\beta_0 + \delta)$$

of that mode.

For the special case considered by Chinn [2], $\rho_l = \rho_r$, i.e., $\Omega = 0$, (18) reduces to (22). With $\rho_l = \rho_r = 0$ the equation derived by Kogelnik and Shank [1] is recovered.

Equation (18) is in an inconvenient form for solution since it contains a square root, two possible signs, and because the numerator and $\mathfrak{D}$ contain a common factor $\mathfrak{D}^{1/2}$. These difficulties are overcome by rewriting (18) in the form

$$\gamma L\, \mathfrak{D} + i\kappa L(\rho_l + \rho_r)(1 - \rho^2)\sinh(\gamma L)\cosh(\gamma L) = \mp i\kappa L(1 + \rho^2)\sinh(\gamma L)[(\rho_l - \rho_r)^2 \sinh^2(\gamma L) + (1 - \rho^2)^2]^{1/2} \tag{21}$$

squaring (21), and combining terms to obtain

$$(\gamma L)^2\, \mathfrak{D} + (\kappa L)^2 \sinh^2(\gamma L)(1 - \rho_l^2)(1 - \rho_r^2) + 2i\kappa L(\rho_l + \rho_r)(1 - \rho^2)\gamma L \sinh(\gamma L)\cosh(\gamma L) = 0 \tag{22}$$

where the factor $\mathfrak{D}$ has been cancelled from the equation. No additional roots have been added by squaring (21) since both negative and positive signs precede the right-hand side.

Clearly, (22) and its solutions are unaffected by interchanging ρ_l and ρ_r. If $\rho_l \to -\rho_l^*$, $\rho_r \to -\rho_r^*$, and $\kappa \to \kappa^*$, then (22) is conjugated except for all functions depending on γL. Thus the solutions are conjugated; α is unchanged, but $\delta \to -\delta$. Conjugating κ is equivalent to shifting the gain variation by π; of course if $\Delta\alpha = 0$, $\kappa = \kappa^*$. An interesting special case occurs when one reflectance (say ρ_r) is zero. Then $\rho^2 = 0$, $\mathfrak{D} = 1$, and (22) becomes

$$(\gamma L)^2 + (\kappa L)^2 \sinh^2(\gamma L)(1 - \rho_l^2) + 2i\kappa L \rho_l \gamma L \sinh(\gamma L)\cosh(\gamma L) = 0. \tag{23}$$

With $\rho_l = \pm 1$

$$\gamma L \pm 2i\kappa L \sinh(\gamma L)\cosh(\gamma L) = 0 \tag{24}$$

and

$$(2\gamma L) \pm i(2\kappa L)\sinh(2\gamma L) = 0 \tag{25}$$

which is the eigenvalue equation for a DFB laser of length $2L$ without reflectors.

In the limit $\kappa L \to 0$, solutions of (22) are given by

$$\mathfrak{D} = (1 + \rho^2)^2 - 4\rho^2 \cosh^2(\gamma L) = 0 \tag{26}$$

from which it follows that

$$\rho^2 e^{2\gamma L} = \rho_l \rho_r e^{2\gamma L} = 1. \tag{27}$$

Equation (27) expresses the threshold and resonance conditions for a laser with conventional reflectors. For any fixed κL and large values of Im (δL) (far from the Bragg condition) solutions of (22) also approach those given by (26) since $(\gamma L)^2$ has the largest magnitude in (22).

To obtain numerical solutions for the eigenvalues we rewrite (22) symbolically

$$W(\gamma L) = U(\gamma L) + iV(\gamma L) = 0 \tag{28}$$

where U and V are, respectively, the real and imaginary parts of the analytic function $W(\gamma L)$ and

$$\gamma L = x + iy. \tag{29}$$

Thus

$$U(x, y) = 0 \tag{30a}$$

and

$$V(x, y) = 0 \tag{30b}$$

are to be solved simultaneously. Let (x_r, y_r) denote a solution of (30a) and (30b), which is to be determined. Then at any point (x, y) we have

$$U(x_r, y_r) = U(x, y) + \partial U/\partial x|_{x,y}(x_r - x) + \partial U/\partial y|_{x,y}(y_r - y) = 0 \tag{31a}$$

and

$$V(x_r, y_r) = V(x, y) + \partial V/\partial x|_{x,y}(x_r - x) + \partial V/\partial y|_{x,y}(y_r - y) = 0 \tag{31b}$$

where only first-order terms in the expansion about (x, y) have been retained. Equations (31a) and (31b) are now solved for (x_r, y_r), viz.,

$$x_r = x + \frac{V(x, y)\partial U/\partial y - U(x, y)\partial V/\partial y}{D} \tag{32a}$$

and

$$y_r = y + \frac{U(x, y)\partial V/\partial x - V(x, y)\partial U/\partial x}{D} \tag{32b}$$

where

$$D = \frac{\partial U}{\partial x}\frac{\partial V}{\partial y} - \frac{\partial U}{\partial y}\frac{\partial V}{\partial x}. \tag{33}$$

Since (31a) and (31b) are only approximations, so too are (32a) and (32b). The new estimates are then used as (x, y) in (31a) and (31b) and the procedure is continued until U and V are, simultaneously, less than a specified tolerance. In applying this method we also required that (x, y) change less than a tolerance for a point to be accepted as a root. All numerical results in this paper were obtained by the preceding procedure. Usually, depending on the initial values of (x, y), less than nine iterations were required to achieve accuracies of better than 10^{-5}. The calculation was facilitated by the analytic character of $W(\gamma L)$, i.e.,

$$\frac{dW}{d(\gamma L)} = \frac{\partial U}{\partial x} + \frac{i\partial V}{\partial x}$$

and

$$\frac{\partial U}{\partial x} = \frac{\partial V}{\partial y}, \quad \frac{\partial U}{\partial y} = -\frac{\partial V}{\partial x}$$

so that

$$D = \left(\frac{\partial U}{\partial x}\right)^2 + \left(\frac{\partial V}{\partial x}\right)^2.$$

The derivative itself is given by

$$\begin{aligned}\frac{dW}{d(\gamma L)} = {} & 2\gamma L\,\mathfrak{D} - 8(\gamma L)^2\rho^2 \sinh(\gamma L)\cosh(\gamma L) \\ & + 2(\kappa L)^2(1 - \rho_l^2)(1 - \rho_r^2)\sinh(\gamma L)\cosh(\gamma L) \\ & + 2i\kappa L(\rho_l + \rho_r)(1 - \rho^2)[\cosh(\gamma L)\sinh(\gamma L) \\ & + \gamma L \sinh^2(\gamma L) + \gamma L\cosh^2(\gamma L)].\end{aligned} \tag{34}$$

Occasionally, in applying the preceding method several starting points would converge to the same solution [say $x_r^{(1)}, y_r^{(1)}$]. To overcome this inconvenience $W(\gamma L)$ was divided by $\gamma L - x_r^{(1)} - iy_r^{(1)}$ to remove that root. Equation (34) for $dW/d(\gamma L)$ was then modified in an obvious fashion.

TABLE I

COMBINATIONS OF $\beta_0 L$ AND Ω ENCOMPASSED BY THE SAME PHASES. THE † DENOTES $(-\rho_l^*, -\rho_r^*) = (\rho_l, \rho_r)$ AND †† DENOTES $(-\rho_l^*, -\rho_r^*) = (\rho_r, \rho_l)$

PHASE		EQUIVALENCE		CASES ENCOMPASSED	
ρ_l	ρ_r	$-\rho_l^*$	$-\rho_r^*$	Ω	$\beta_0 L$
0	0	π	π	$0, \pi$	$0, \pi$
$\pi/4$	$-\pi/4$	$3\pi/4$	$-3\pi/4$	$\pm\pi/4, \pm3\pi/4$	$0, \pi$
$\pi/2$	$-\pi/2$	†	†	$\pm\pi/2$	$0, \pi$
$\pi/4$	$\pi/4$	$3\pi/4$	$3\pi/4$	0 π	$\pi/4, 3\pi/4$ $-\pi/4, -3\pi/4$
0	$\pi/2$	π	$\pi/2$	$\pm\pi/4$ $\pm3\pi/4$	$\pi/4, 3\pi/4$ $-\pi 4, -3\pi/4$
$\pi/4$	$-3\pi/4$	$3\pi/4$	$-\pi/4$	$\pm\pi/2$	$\pm\pi/4, \pm3\pi/4$
0	$-\pi/2$	π	$-\pi/2$	$\pm\pi/4$ $\pm3\pi/4$	$-\pi/4, -3\pi/4$ $\pi/4, 3\pi/4$
$\pi/2$	$\pi/2$	†	†	0 π	$\pi/2$ $-\pi/2$
$\pi/4$	$3\pi/4$	††	††	$\pm\pi/4$ $\pm3\pi/4$	$\pi/2$ $-\pi/2$
0	π	††	††	$\pm\pi/2$	$\pm\pi/2$
$-\pi/4$	$-3\pi/4$	††	††	$\pm\pi/4$ $\pm3\pi/4$	$-\pi/2$ $\pi/2$
$-\pi/2$	$-\pi/2$	†	†	0 π	$-\pi/2$ $\pi/2$
$-\pi/4$	$-\pi/4$	$-3\pi/4$	$-3\pi/4$	0 π	$-\pi/4, -3\pi/4$ $\pi/4, 3\pi/4$

III. THRESHOLDS, WAVELENGTHS, AND MODE FIELDS

The following subsection III-A contains results for longitudinal mode thresholds and frequencies of GaAs DFB lasers with two cleaved ends. In subsection III-B the case $\rho_r = 0.0$ is treated. Zero reflectivity can be achieved (or at least closely approximated) by antireflection coating a laser end surface or by matching an integrated laser to a guide. Various values of ρ_l are studied. Subsection III-C deals with longitudinal mode separation and III-D with fields and power distribution within the laser and transmitted through the end reflectors.

A. GaAs Lasers with Two Cleaved Faces

Since the refractive index ratio at the GaAs:air interface is 3.6, the electric field reflection coefficients are $(\hat{\rho}_l, \hat{\rho}_r) = (-0.565, -0.565)$. Consideration of all possible values of κL, $\beta_0 L$, and Ω is a virtual impossibility and so the discussion is restricted to real κL and values of $\beta_0 L$ which are multiples of $\pi/4$ in the range $-\pi < \beta_0 L \leqslant \pi$. With $-\pi < \Omega \leqslant \pi$ and increments of $\pi/4$ there are 64 possible geometries, but because the results are unchanged for $\rho_l \rightleftharpoons \rho_r$ and the eigenvalues are conjugated either if $(\rho_l, \rho_r) \to (-\rho_l^*, -\rho_r^*)$ or $(\rho_l, \rho_r) \to (-\rho_r^*, -\rho_l^*)$ only 13 cases need be treated. These are listed in Table I with their various equivalencies. In Table I the symbols † and †† denote $(-\rho_l^*, -\rho_r^*) = (\rho_l, \rho_r)$ and $(-\rho_l^*, -\rho_r^*) = (\rho_r, \rho_l)$, respectively, for these cases plots of αL versus δL are symmetric about $\delta L = 0$. Plots for $(\rho_l, \rho_r) = (0.565\, e^{i\pi/4}, 0.565\, e^{i\pi/4})$ and $(0.565, 0.565\, e^{i\pi})$ were presented in our earlier paper [3]. Here in Fig. 2, αL (the total net threshold gain) versus δL (which determines laser frequency) with κL (the coupling) as a parameter is shown for $(\rho_l, \rho_r) = (0.565\, e^{i\pi/2}, 0.565\, e^{i\pi/2})$, which is one of the geometries included in [2]. Six longitudinal modes are presented; it should be noted that high-threshold longitudinal modes exist near $\delta L = 0$, which are not shown in Fig. 3 of [2]. This mode, i.e., with minimum, positive δL, is plotted in Fig. 3 with $\hat{\rho}_l = \hat{\rho}_r = -0.565 = 0.565\, e^{i\pi}$, and $e^{-i\beta_0 L} = e^{-i\pi/2}$ for various values of Ω with κL as a parameter

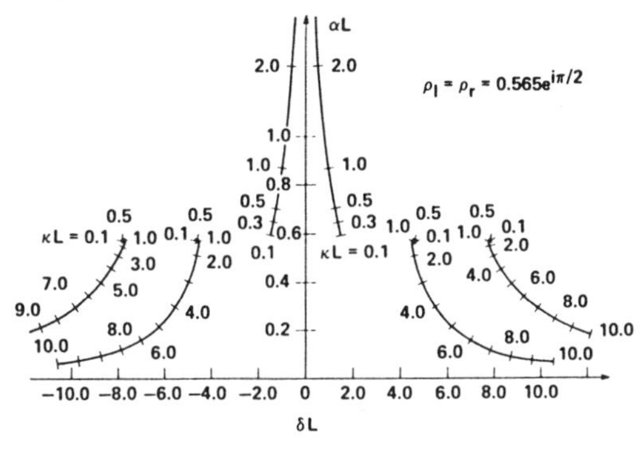

Fig. 2. Threshold and phase for longitudinal modes with κL as a parameter.

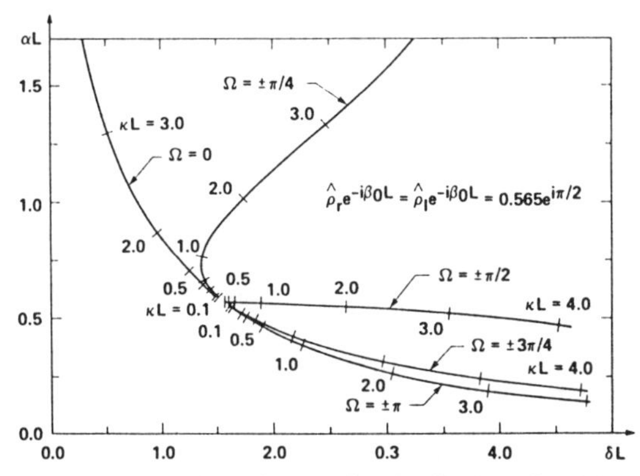

Fig. 3. Threshold and phase for one longitudinal mode with κL and Ω as parameters.

along each curve. Setting $e^{-i\beta_0 L} = e^{-i\pi/2}$ (or any other value) fixes the laser length. Then with $\Omega = 0$, the grating is symmetrically located. For first-order Bragg coupling, $\beta_0 = \pi/\Lambda$, and with $\Omega = +\pi/4$ the grating is shifted to the left relative to the reflectors by $\Lambda/8$ [cf. Fig. 1(a) and (b)]; with $\Omega = -\pi/4$ the grating is shifted to the right. Similarly, with $\Omega = \pm\pi/2$ it is shifted by $\Lambda/4$, etc. Note that shifts of $\Omega > \pi$ correspond to shifts of $\Omega < \pi$ and the plot depends only on $|\Omega|$ because of the eigenvalue equation symmetry properties. For third-order Bragg scattering, the third-harmonic refractive index variation is employed, i.e., $\beta_0 L = 3\pi/\Lambda$, and Ω is the phase of that harmonic. The situation for the third harmonic is illustrated in Fig. 4(a) and (b). Fig. 3 also gives values of αL and δL for the mode nearest $\delta L = 0$ with $\delta L < 0$, if every phase shown is changed according to the symmetry conditions discussed previously and listed in Table I. A plot similar to Fig. 2 is shown in Fig. 5 for $(\rho_l, \rho_r) = (0.565, 0.565\, e^{i\pi/2})$. From both figures it is evident, as noted in the previous section, that the thresholds approach those of a conventional cleaved mirror laser without DFB as $|\delta L|$ becomes large. The rate at which this occurs depends on κL.

B. DFB Lasers with One Reflector ($\hat{\rho}_r = 0.0$)

Fig. 6 illustrates αL versus δL for $\delta L > 0$ near the Bragg condition $\delta L = 0$, with $\kappa L = 1.0$, $\rho_r \equiv 0.0$, and ρ_l taking on various values. Once again results for $\delta L < 0$ can be deduced from symmetry considerations. On the solid curves $|\rho_l| =$ constant, whereas phase (ρ_l) = constant along the dashed curves. For $|\rho_l| = 0.0$, the phase is of no consequence and all dashed curves in Fig. 6 converge to $\alpha L = 1.75$, $\delta L = 2.67$, the

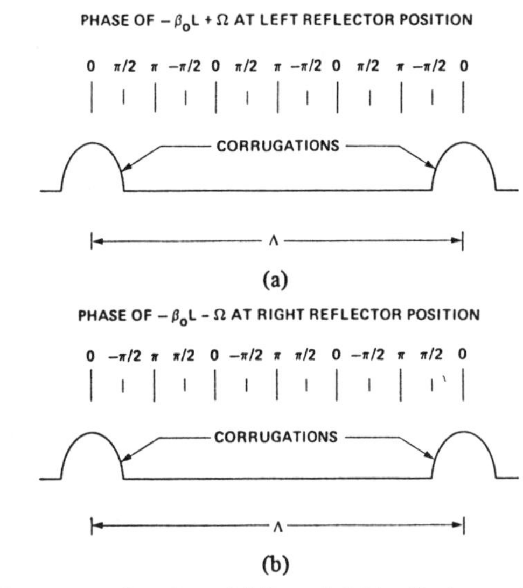

Fig. 4. Phases as a function of left- and right-reflector positions with third-order Bragg scattering.

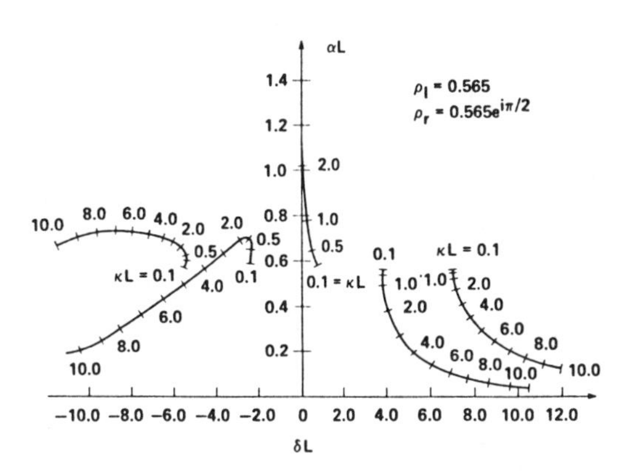

Fig. 5. Threshold and phase for longitudinal modes with κL as a parameter.

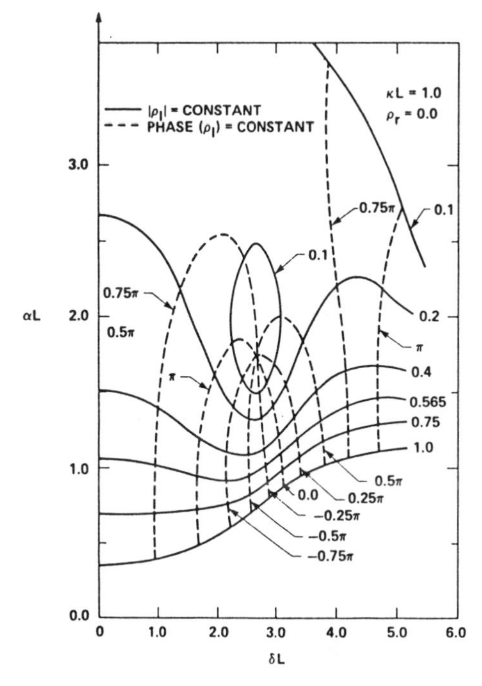

Fig. 6. Threshold and phase for longitudinal modes with $\rho_r = 0.0$ and $\kappa L = 1$. On the solid curves $|\rho_l|$ = constant and on the dashed curves phase (ρ_l) = constant.

point appropriate to a DFB laser without external reflectors [1]. For reflectivities $|\rho_l|$ greater than approximately 0.4 all thresholds regardless of phase are lower than $\alpha L = 1.75$. The phase (ρ_l), as noted after (16b), is just that of the grating structure at $z = -L/2$. For $\hat{\rho}_l = |\hat{\rho}_l| e^{i\pi}$ reflector positions relative to the grating are illustrated in Fig. 1(a) or Fig. 4(a) by adding π to the phases shown therein. Thus if $\rho_l = \pm 1.0$ the reflector images the grating such that it appears to be a DFB structure of length $2L$ without reflectors, a result which was derived analytically as (25) in the preceding. From Fig. 6, the solutions are $\alpha L = 0.429$, $\delta L = 1.69$ with $\rho_l = -1.0$ and $\alpha L = 0.885$, $\delta L = 3.15$ with $\rho_l = 1.0$. These values equal half those for the first and second longitudinal modes (numbering from $\delta L = 0$) of a DFB laser without reflectors and $\kappa L = 2.0$ (see [1]). The factor one-half occurs because (25) is for $2\gamma L$, whereas the equation for the single reflector geometry was solved for γL. Therefore κ, γ, α, and δ are identical in the two cases.

The minimum threshold as a function of phase occurs at $\pi/2$ for $|\rho_l|$ near 1.0 and quickly shifts to the vicinity of $-\pi/2$ as $|\rho_l|$ decreases. Perhaps this result is counterintuitive since placement at 0 or π may appear to optimally image the grating [see Fig. 1(a) and Fig. 4(a)]. It should be understood, however, that a grating length of $2L$ without reflectors and one of length L with one reflector are not identical even if $\rho_l = \pm 1.0$. This is the case because gratings continuously couple left and right going waves and the reflection interchanges directions and superimposes the wave differently. Furthermore, the threshold depends on the exact frequency of the waves (determined by δL) and their phases so that the preceding picture is overly simplistic.

Fig. 7 illustrates αL versus δL for six longitudinal modes with $\rho_r = 0.0$ and $\rho_l = 0.565\, e^{i\pi}$. For small κL, the reflector is relatively more important than the grating in determining device behavior, but as κL increases to overcoupled values the grating dominates. In fact, as shown in Fig. 8 for $\rho_l = 0.565\, e^{i3\pi/4}$, the mode with minimum $|\delta L|$, which does not exist in the pure DFB device, has an increasing threshold for $\kappa L \gtrsim 1.4$. For the other modes the threshold is generally lower with one reflector present rather than absent, although differences diminish with increasing κL.

C. Mode Separation

Longitudinal mode separation is obtained from differences in δL. If $\Delta(\delta L)$ is the difference between the ith and jth modes, then

$$\Delta(\delta L) = (\beta_i L - \beta_j L) = 2\pi L(n_{eq}^i/\lambda_i - n_{eq}^j/\lambda_j) \tag{35}$$

where λ_i, λ_j are the free-space wavelengths and n_{eq}^i, n_{eq}^j are the equivalent refractive indices, taking into account the laser waveguiding structure. As is customary we write

$$n_{eq}^j = n_{eq}^i + (dn_{eq}/d\lambda)_i(\lambda_j - \lambda_i)$$

substitute in (35) and solve for $\lambda_j - \lambda_i$ to obtain

$$\lambda_j - \lambda_i = \frac{\lambda_i\lambda_j\Delta(\delta L)}{2\pi n_{eq}^i L[1 - (dn_{eq}/d\lambda)_i(\lambda_i/n_{eq}^i)]}. \tag{36}$$

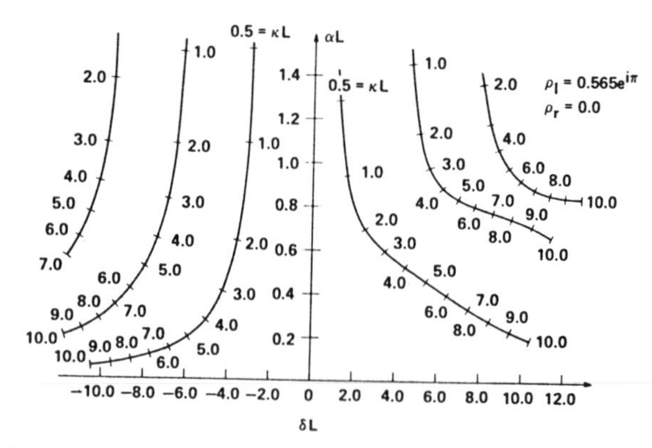

Fig. 7. Threshold and phase for longitudinal modes with κL as a parameter.

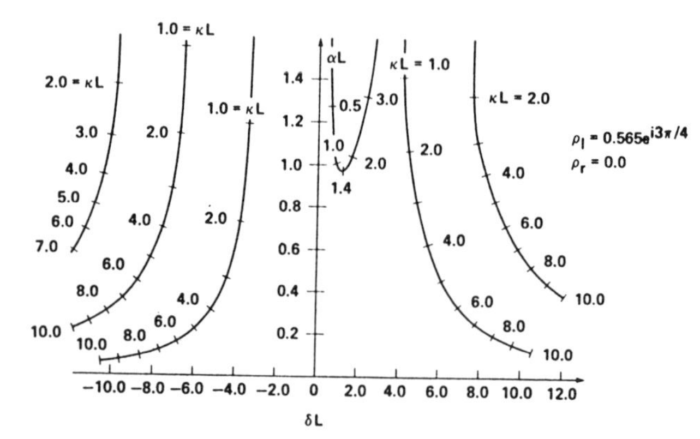

Fig. 8. Threshold and phase for longitudinal modes with κL as a parameter.

Often n_{eq} will approximate the active region index, $\lambda_i \approx \lambda_j$ (say λ), and $n_{eq}^i \approx n_{eq}^j$ (say n) so that

$$\lambda_j - \lambda_i = \frac{\lambda^2\Delta(\delta L)}{2\pi nL[1 - (dn/d\lambda)(\lambda/n)]}. \tag{37}$$

For $\Delta(\delta L) = \pi$, which is approximately correct for many of the longitudinal modes illustrated in this paper, this equation becomes

$$\lambda_j - \lambda_i = \frac{\lambda^2}{2nL[1 - (dn/d\lambda)(\lambda/n)]}. \tag{38}$$

This is the same result as for conventional lasers.

D. Mode Fields

Since saturation effects have not been considered the analysis applies only at threshold and absolute values of r_1, r_2, s_1, and s_2 in (10a) and (10b) cannot be determined. Instead, relative amplitudes, and thereby the energy distribution, within the DFB structure are computed as are the relative energies transmitted through the external reflectors.

From (11a) we have

$$r_1 = (i\kappa e^{-i\Omega}/\hat{\Gamma})s_1 \tag{39a}$$

and from (11d) and (14a)

$$r_2 = \frac{(1 - \rho_l\hat{\Gamma}/i\kappa)}{(\rho_l - \hat{\Gamma}/i\kappa)} e^{-i\Omega} e^{-\gamma L} s_1. \tag{39b}$$

In the special case $\rho_l = 0.0$

$$r_2 = -e^{-\gamma L} r_1 \tag{40}$$

so that

$$r_1 e^{\gamma z} + r_2 e^{-\gamma z} = 2r_1 e^{-\gamma L/2} \sinh [\gamma(z + L/2)] \tag{41}$$

in agreement with earlier results [1]. For $\rho_l = \pm 1.0$

$$r_2 = e^{-i\Omega} e^{-\gamma L} s_1. \tag{42}$$

From (39b) and (11d), we find

$$s_2 = \frac{i\kappa}{\hat{\Gamma}} \frac{(1 - \rho_l \hat{\Gamma}/i\kappa)}{(\rho_l - \hat{\Gamma}/i\kappa)} e^{-\gamma L} s_1 \tag{43}$$

which, by invoking (15), can be rewritten

$$s_2 = \frac{i\kappa}{\hat{\Gamma}} \frac{(\rho_r - \hat{\Gamma}/i\kappa)}{(1 - \rho_r \hat{\Gamma}/i\kappa)} e^{\gamma L} s_1. \tag{44}$$

Then with $\rho_r = 0.0$

$$s_2 = -e^{\gamma L} s_1 \tag{45}$$

so that

$$s_1 e^{\gamma z} + s_2 e^{-\gamma z} = 2s_1 e^{\gamma L/2} \sinh [\gamma(z - L/2)] \tag{46}$$

and with $\rho_r = \pm 1.0$

$$s_2 = \frac{i\kappa}{\hat{\Gamma}} e^{\gamma L} s_1 = e^{i\Omega} e^{\gamma L} r_1 \tag{47}$$

where (11a) has been employed.

The power in the wave $R(z)$ at any point in the DFB structure is

$$P_a(z) = c_1 |r_1 e^{\gamma z} + r_2 e^{-\gamma z}|^2 \tag{48a}$$

that in $S(z)$ is

$$P_b(z) = c_1 |s_1 e^{\gamma z} + s_2 e^{-\gamma z}|^2 \tag{48b}$$

where c_1 is a constant. The transmitted power through the right- and left-hand reflectors is

$$P_r = (1 - |\rho_r|^2) P_a(L/2) \tag{49a}$$

and

$$P_l = (1 - |\rho_l|^2) P_b(L/2) \tag{49b}$$

respectively. For $\rho_r = \rho_l$, $P_r = P_l$ for all modes as can be verified from the preceding formulas. Physically, this must be the case since the geometry is completely symmetric. However, if $\rho_l \neq \rho_r$, even if the magnitudes of the reflections are equal, $|\hat{\rho}_l| = |\hat{\rho}_r|$, P_r and P_l generally differ for each mode because of the phase difference. For the geometries marked † and †† in Table I, the modes and ratios P_r/P_l and P_l/P_r are symmetric about $\delta L = 0.0$. In Table II are listed values of αL, δL, and P_r/P_l for $(\rho_l, \rho_r) = (0.565, 0.565\, e^{i\pi/2})$ with $\kappa L = 1.0$. Note that the mode with maximum αL, i.e., minimum $|\delta L|$ also has the highest ratio $P_r/P_l = 5.0586$, all modes with $\delta L > 0$ have $P_r/P_l > 1.0$ and those with $\delta L < 0$ have $P_r/P_l < 1.0$. This is not a general characteristic, e.g., with $(\rho_l, \rho_r) = (0.565\, e^{-i\pi/4}, 0.565\, e^{i\pi/4})$, $P_r/P_l > 1.0$ for all modes. It is always true, however, that as $|\delta L|$ increases P_r/P_l approaches unity, since then the longitudinal modes are primarily determined by the external reflectors and not the DFB structure.

In Figs. 9 and 10 are plotted $|R(z)|$ and $|S(z)|$ for the two longitudinal modes with minimum $|\delta L|$ and $\delta L > 0$, $\delta L < 0$,

TABLE II
VALUES OF αL, δL, AND P_r/P_l, THE RATIO OF TRANSMITTED POWER THROUGH THE LEFT REFLECTOR TO THAT TRANSMITTED THROUGH THE RIGHT REFLECTOR FOR NINE LONGITUDINAL MODES WITH $\rho_l = 0.565$, $\rho_r = 0.565e^{i\pi/2}$ AND $\kappa L = 1.0$

αL	δL	P_r/P_l
0.5969	−11.775	0.9023
0.6066	−8.632	0.8676
0.6278	−5.490	0.7956
0.7013	−2.378	0.5878
0.7805	0.270	5.0586
0.4945	3.897	1.3053
0.5288	7.054	1.1678
0.5417	10.200	1.1157
0.5486	13.345	1.0882

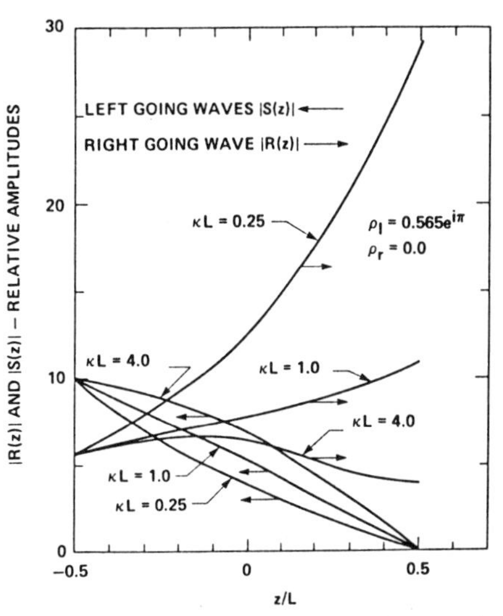

Fig. 9. Amplitudes of traveling waves for the first longitudinal mode (minimum $|\delta L|$) with $\delta L > 0$ and various κL.

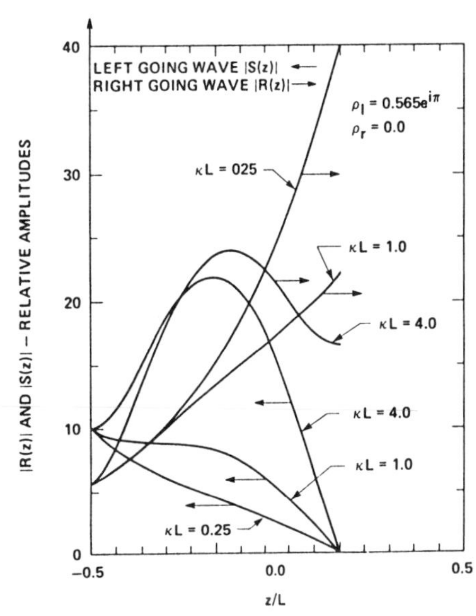

Fig. 10. Amplitudes of traveling waves for the first longitudinal mode (minimum $|\delta L|$) with $\delta L < 0$ and various κL.

respectively. Here $(\rho_l, \rho_r) = (0.565\, e^{i\pi}, 0.0)$ and $\kappa L = 0.25$, 1.0, 4.0. In the undercoupled case ($\kappa L = 0.25$) the fields are approximately given by a single exponential, viz., $R(z) \sim r_1 e^{\gamma z}$, $S(z) \sim s_2 e^{-\gamma z}$. With increasing coupling ($\kappa L = 1.0$) both exponential terms in $R(z)$ and $S(z)$ are nonnegligible and in the overcoupled case Re (γL) is so small that the exponentials are more nearly oscillating functions. Power flows are proportional to the squares of the plotted fields and it is interesting to compute the ratio of transmitted power from (49a) and (49b). We find, for $\kappa L = 0.25$ and $\delta L > 0$, $P_r/P_l \approx 125$ whereas with $\delta L < 0$, $P_r/P_l \approx 245$.

IV. Remarks

The results presented in this paper provide insight into the longitudinal mode behavior of DFB lasers with external reflectors. We have shown that the relative positions of the reflectors and grating are of critical importance in determining laser thresholds, frequencies, and relative transmitted powers, which can differ markedly. The results were obtained under various assumptions, viz., the reflectors are aligned with the grating κ, the absorption, and the pumping are uniform along the laser length, all nonlinear effects of saturation, pumping, and spontaneous emission are neglected as is scattering from the grating other than into the desired Bragg order. No doubt these phenomena will affect comparisons with experimental results.

References

[1] H. Kogelnik and C. V. Shank, "Coupled-wave theory of distributed feedback lasers," *J. Appl. Phys.*, vol. 43, pp. 2327–2335, 1972.
[2] S. R. Chinn, "Effects of minor reflectivity in a distributed-feedback laser," *IEEE J. Quantum Electron.*, vol. QE-9, pp. 574–580, June 1973.
[3] W. Streifer, D. R. Scifres, and R. D. Burnham, *Appl. Phys. Lett.*, to be published.

GaAs-$Al_xGa_{1-x}As$ injection lasers with distributed Bragg reflectors

F. K. Reinhart and R. A. Logan

Bell Laboratories, Murray Hill, New Jersey 07974

C. V. Shank

Bell Laboratories, Holmdel, New Jersey 07733
(Received 18 March 1975; in final form 28 April 1975)

Room-temperature operation of an optically integrated double heterostructure (DH) GaAs-$Al_xGa_{1-x}As$ injection laser with a distributed Bragg reflector (DBR), with threshold current densities of 5 kA/cm^2 is reported. The DBR was in the form of a third-order grating which was ion milled on a passive single heterostructure (SH) waveguide section with the latter taper coupled to the active DH section. The observed half-power spectral bandwidth was $\lesssim 1$ Å. A highly collimated beam output with a half-power divergence angle of $\lesssim 0.3°$ was also achieved by coupling the scattered light from the oil-immersed grating at the Bragg angle with a prism.

PACS numbers: 42.60.J, 42.82.

Distributed feedback (DFB) lasers which were first demonstrated in organic dyes[1] are very attractive in integrated optics, because the fabrication of DFB lasers is consistent with planar technology, and the DFB lasers are extremely frequency selective.[2,3] Optically pumped DFB lasers in GaAs[4,5] indicated that sufficiently smooth single heterostructure (SH) and double heterostructure (DH) GaAs-$Al_xGa_{1-x}As$ surfaces could be made. Injection lasers with DFB operated near 77 °K were finally demonstrated.[6,7] DFB injection lasers operating at room temperature have not been reported thus far, owing to interface recombination centers introduced in the regrowth on the grating in the laser cavity, where wetting problems are encountered.

Recent developments of liquid phase epitaxy (LPE) have led to the fabrication of the split composition lasers[8] and taper coupled lasers (TCL)[9–11] which permit the separation of functions such as generation and feedback. Gratings in the optical circuit can be applied to integrated SH passive waveguides and therefore the necessity of regrowth is eliminated altogether. This approach leads to a novel structure, the distributed Bragg reflection (DBR) laser[12] which can be completely integrated. In this letter we report the successful fabrication and some of the properties of TCL with DBR. The structures were grown by LPE such as described in detail in Ref. 11. Figure 1(a) shows a schematic of the layer cross section which also gives nominal dimensions and dopant levels. In a first set of structures a SH waveguide was formed by selectively etching the top layer in the region between the dashed lines of Fig. 1.[8] In a second set of structures the top layer was grown in segments similar to that used in forming the tapers. In the exposed SH waveguide section between the tapers, a third-order holographic grating with a periodicity Λ was formed by photolithography and ion milling,[5] which then resulted in the

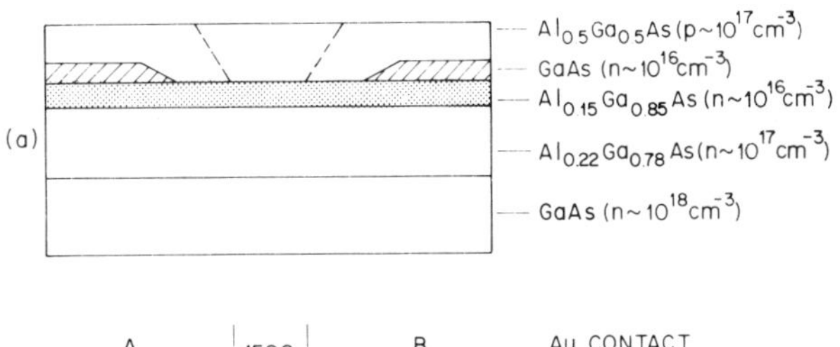

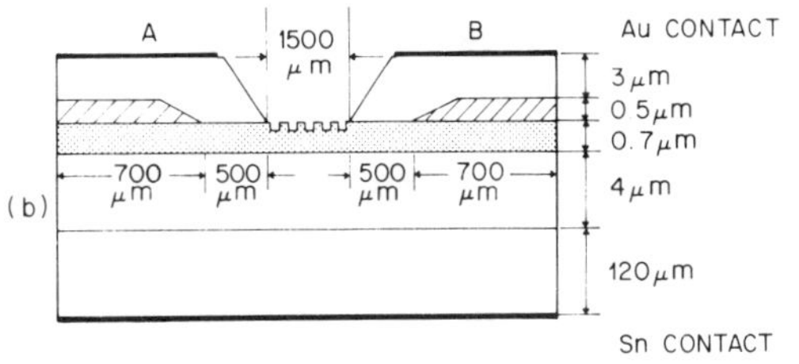

FIG. 1. The layer compositions of the taper-coupled device and the corresponding doping levels are shown in (a). A schematic cross section of the final device with typical dimensions is given in (b).

structure shown in Fig. 1(b). Ohmic contacts to the *p* and *n* side were formed in the standard fashion, except that during the evaporation of the Au on the top surface, the grating area was protected by a mask.

The laser structures were tested by applying current pulses of 100-ns duration to section A of the device shown in Fig. 1(b). The cavity is formed by the cleaved mirror and the grating. Section B simply served as an unpumped termination for the laser radiation and therefore suppresses reflected energy from the cleaved mirror section of B. No laser radiation was ever observed from this mirror. In principle, section B could be used in reverse bias as an integrated detector for the radiation.[13] The roles of A and B could also be interchanged. The laser radiation was generally observed from the cleaved mirror of the pumped section.

Reprinted with permission from *Appl. Phys. Lett.*, vol. 27, no. 1, pp. 45–48, July 1, 1975.

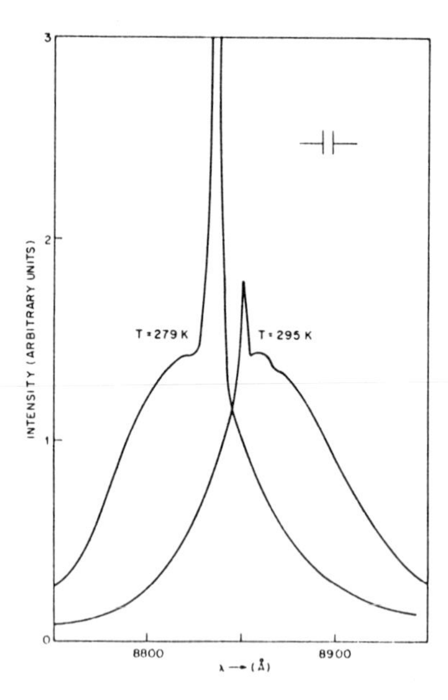

FIG. 2. Spectral light emission at $j \approx j_{th} \approx 5$ kA/cm² (296 °K) and at $j \approx 4.5$ kA/cm² (279 °K) with the resolution indicated by bars.

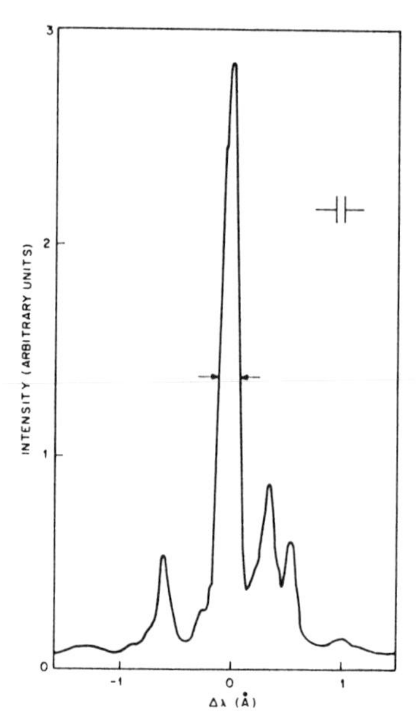

FIG. 3. High-resolution spectrum at 296 K centered at $\lambda(0) \approx 8850$ Å with $\lambda = \lambda(0) + \Delta\lambda$.

Typical low-resolution laser spectra for a laser with $\Lambda = 0.3865$ μm are shown in Fig. 2 for two different temperatures. The lasing emission changes from the low-wavelength (λ) side to the high-λ side of the spontaneous luminescence as the temperature is reduced. This temperature dependence is typical of DFB and DBR lasers and results from the usually smaller temperature dependence of the Bragg condition compared to that of the band gap. The room-temperature threshold current density, j_{th}, for a typical DBR is 5 kA/cm² for an active region thickness $2w = 0.5$ μm. This threshold current density is about a factor of 2 higher than expected on the basis of reduced current threshold densities, $j_0 \simeq 6$ kA/cm² μm measured for TCL.[10] Measurements on control lasers with and without taper-coupled guides from the same material indicated unusually high losses in the passive section, $\alpha \approx 20$ cm⁻¹, even for passive guide sections that possessed a p-type cladding layer. Losses in SH waveguide sections appear to be even larger. Since the effective passive sections are relatively long in all of the devices fabricated thus far, the increase in j_{th} is partially understood. This extra loss is also manifested by the low differential quantum efficiency η_d, which is estimated to be $10^{-3} < \eta_d < 10^{-2}$. Taper coupling efficiencies t are typically 0.7 ± 0.2.[11]

A high-resolution spectrum of a DBR laser at $T \simeq 296$ °K is shown in Fig. 3 at a current density $j = 1.2 j_{th}$. The spectral resolution is approximately 0.08 Å. The oscillation is distinctly multimode. The bandwidth of the dominant modes measured at the half-power points is ≈0.2 Å. The full bandwidth of the DBR laser, $\Delta\lambda_{BR}$, is shown to be $\Delta\lambda_{BR} \simeq 1$ Å. This value strongly depends on the coupling constant κ of the grating and the passive waveguide losses α_p.[12] Since $\Delta\lambda_{BR}$ increases with κ and α_p, we estimate from Wang's analysis[12] $\kappa \lesssim 10$ cm⁻¹. This is also in good agreement with estimates based on scanning electron microscope observations of the grating profile. A number of longitudinal modes separated by a wavelength difference $\Delta\lambda_l$ can, in principle, be accommodated within $\Delta\lambda_{BR}$. Using the relationships previously described[10] and the dimensions of our device, we estimate $\Delta\lambda_l$ to lie within $0.8 \lesssim \Delta\lambda_l \lesssim 0.9$ Å. The uncertainty arises primarily in the difficulty of localizing the actual grating boundary. It is therefore quite evident that we can have at most two TE and two TM modes within our experimentally established $\Delta\lambda_{BR}$. While we have not established the polarization of the individual modes, our tests indeed show the presence of both polarizations.

For a number of units tested thus far, either TE or TM modes dominate in a given unit. The high-resolution spectra indicate more than the expected maximum number of four modes. This is attributed to some stepwise variations of the waveguide thickness or of the index of refraction. For the nominal parameters given in Fig. 1(a) we expect for a 0.01-μm thickness variation, but constant index of refraction, a shift of the Bragg condition by 1.36 Å. Since the mode spacing is typically less than 0.45 Å we estimate the corresponding average thickness variation to be no more than 30 Å. When attempting to separate various filaments we indeed succeeded in suppressing certain modes. However, the mere existence of filamentary oscillation requires a more sophisticated mode count which can qualitatively also account for the observed number of modes. It was also observed that the mode distribution changed with increasing current. This is expected in a DFB laser, particularly for pulsed operation, since the round-trip phase is affected by slight temperature increases in the active region.[12] The passive section is not subjected to temperature changes during a 100-ns current pulse which leaves the Bragg condition and the corresponding $\Delta\lambda_{BR}$ unchanged.

In analogy with the grating coupler,[14,15] a highly collimated beam can be obtained from the DBR laser by attaching a small glass prism (index of refraction

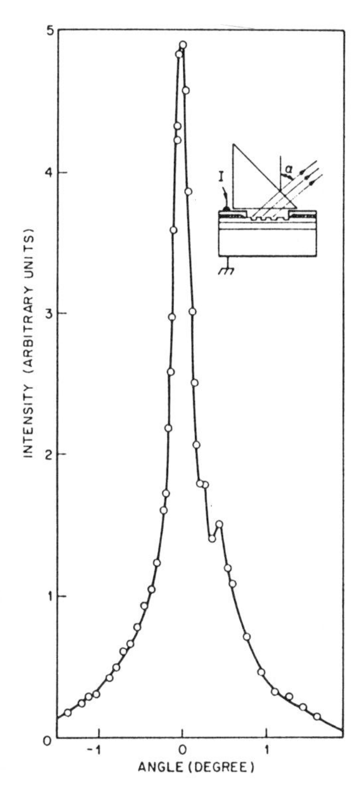

FIG. 4. Far-field pattern in the plane perpendicular to the junction plane. The inset shows the experimental device with the laser excited by current I. The abscissa denotes the measured deviation in degrees from the external determined Bragg angle α.

≈ 1.5) to the grating section as shown by the inset of Fig. 4. Optical contact between prism and grating is achieved by oil immersion. The beam angle towards the surface normal, α, is estimated from the Bragg (or phase-matching) condition and prism angle (45°) and amounts to approximately 51.2°. The degree of collimation is demonstrated by Fig. 4. The angular width of the radiation pattern between the half-power points perpendicular to the junction plane was determined to be 0.3°, whereas the corresponding value parallel to the junction plane was estimated at 6° due to diffraction limitation. The strong astigmatism of the beam and the low lasing and low coupling efficiency made it difficult to establish the actual angular resolution limitation of the slit arrangement used in the test set. The radiation appeared to originate from an effective grating length, $l_g \approx 450$ μm, that is defined as the length at which the scattered radiation intensity decays by a factor of $1/e^2$. Since the effective beam diameter in the prism is $l_g \cos\alpha \simeq 280$ μm, the divergence of the beam perpendicular to the junction plane will also be diffraction limited. Estimates of the diffraction limitation agree within a factor of 2 with the measured angle. By choosing a different grating order, [16] the need for a prism can be eliminated altogether.

It is a great pleasure to thank H.G. White for growing the LPE layers, M.J. Madden and L.L. Buhl for providing the third-order gratings, J.J. Schott for skillful assistance with the device fabrication and measurements, and J.L. Merz for helpful discussions.

[1]H. Kogelnik and C.V. Shank, Appl. Phys. Lett. 18, 152 (1971).
[2]C.V. Shank, J.E. Bjorkholm, and H. Kogelnik, Appl. Phys. Lett. 18, 395 (1971).
[3]H. Kogelnik and C.V. Shank, J. Appl. Phys. 43, 2327 (1972).
[4]M. Nakamura, H.W. Yen, A. Yariv, E. Garmire, and H.L. Garvin, Appl. Phys. Lett. 22, 515 (1973); 23, 224 (1973); H.M. Stoll and D.H. Seib, Appl. Opt. 13, 1981 (1974); D.B. Anderson, R.R. August, and J.E. Coker, *ibid.* 13, 2742 (1974).
[5]C.V. Shank, R.V. Schmidt, and B.I. Miller, Appl. Phys. Lett. 25, 200 (1974).
[6]D.R. Scifres, R.D. Burnham, and W. Streifer, Appl. Phys. Lett. 25, 203 (1974).
[7]M. Nakamura, K. Aiki, Jun-idi Umeda, A. Yariv, H.W. Yen, and T. Morikawa, Appl. Phys. Lett. 25, 487 (1974).
[8]F.K. Reinhart and R.A. Logan, Appl. Phys. Lett. 25, 622 (1974).
[9]J. L. Merz, R.A. Logan, H.C. Gossard, and W. Wiegmann, Appl. Phys. Lett. 26, 337 (1975).
[10]F.K. Reinhart and R.A. Logan, Appl. Phys. Lett. 26, 516 (1975).
[11]R.A. Logan and F.K. Reinhart, IEEE J. Quantum Electron. (to be published).
[12]Shy Wang, IEEE J. Quantum Electron. QE-10, 413 (1974).
[13]F.K. Reinhart, Appl. Phys. Lett. 22, 372 (1973).
[14]M.L. Dakss, L. Kuhn, P.F. Heidrich, and P.A. Scott, Appl. Phys. Lett. 16, 523 (1970).
[15]H. Kogelnik and T.P. Sosnowski, Bell Syst. Tech. J. 49, 1602 (1970).
[16]D.R. Scifres, R.D. Burnham, and W. Streifer, Appl. Phys. Lett. 26, 48 (1975).

cw operation of distributed-feedback GaAs-GaAlAs diode lasers at temperatures up to 300 K

M. Nakamura, K. Aiki, and J. Umeda

Central Research Laboratory, Hitachi Ltd., Kokubunji, Tokyo, Japan

A. Yariv

California Institute of Technology, Pasadena, California 91109

(Received 17 June 1975; in final form 22 July 1975)

Distributed-feedback GaAs-GaAlAs diode lasers with separate optical and carrier confinement have been successfully operated under dc bias up to room temperature. They lased in a single longitudinal mode with a threshold current density of 0.94 kA/cm² at 170 K and 3.5 kA/cm² at 300 K.

PACS numbers: 42.60.J

Semiconductor diode lasers with distributed feedback (DFB) are expected to find application as future light sources because of their integration capability as well as their inherent spectral and modal control.[1-4] A remarkable reduction of the threshold current density of DFB GaAs-GaAlAs lasers has been achieved by adopting a separate confinement hetero (SCH) structure, as has been reported previously.[5] In these lasers, the active layer has been separated from the corrugated interface to avoid nonradiative recombination of the injected carriers. The lasers have been operated at ~300 K under pulsed bias with a threshold current density of ~3 kA/cm².

In this correspondence, we describe the study of the SCH structure DFB laser, which is aimed at the achievement of cw operation. The diodes are mounted on diamond heat sinks and are operated successfully under dc bias at temperatures up to 300 K. To our knowledge, this is the first report of cw operation of DFB semiconductor lasers.

The structure of the diode laser is shown in Fig. 1. It has a mesa-stripe geometry so that the injection is limited to a rectangular region.[6] The width of the stripe was 50 μm and the length of the excited region was ~700 μm. The output was obtained from the front surface. An unexcited waveguide with a length of 2–3 mm was continuous to the excited region. This blocked the optical feedback from the end surface. The photograph in Fig. 1 shows a crosssection of the corrugated waveguide. The grating with a period of 0.36–0.38 μm was made by chemical etching through a photoresist mask produced by holographic photolithography.[7] In this structure, the injected electrons are confined to the active layer by the p-$Ga_{0.83}Al_{0.17}As$ layer, while the light extends from the active layer to the p-$Ga_{0.93}Al_{0.07}As$ layer.[5]

A similar structure was recently reported by Casey *et al.*, where the diodes were prepared by a hybrid liquid-phase-epitaxy and molecular-beam-epitaxy growth process.[8] In our experiment, we were able to grow all the layers by liquid-phase epitaxy by introducing the p-$Ga_{0.93}Al_{0.07}As$ layer.

From a theoretical analysis of the SCH structure DFB laser,[9] it was found necessary to reduce the thickness of the waveguide in order to achieve low-threshold operation. In this experiment, the thickness of the active layer was chosen to be ~0.2 μm and that of the p-$Ga_{0.83}Al_{0.17}As$ layer to be ~0.1 μm. The thickness of the p-$Ga_{0.93}Al_{0.07}As$ layer was ~0.15 μm and about the same as the height of the corrugation.

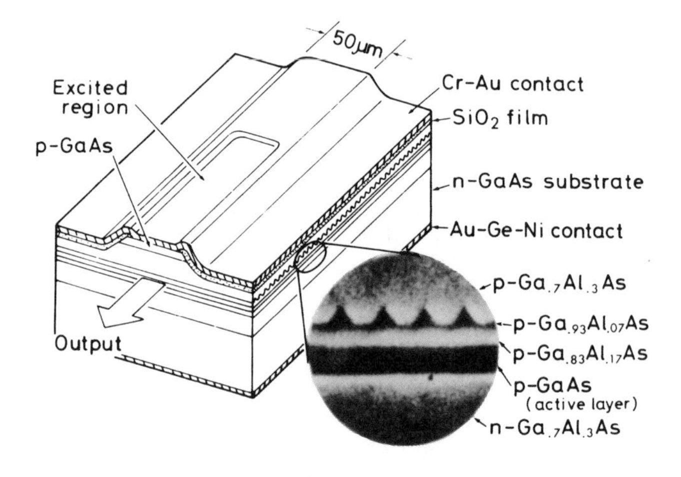

FIG. 1. Structure of the DFB laser with separate optical and carrier confinement.

Metallic contacts to the diode were made by evaporating Cr and Au on the p side and Au-Ge-Ni on the n side. The diode was bonded with the p side down onto a metallized diamond heat sink mounted on a copper block. The thermal resistance per unit area R_T was $\sim 3\times10^{-3}$ deg cm²/W.

The dependence of the threshold current density and the lasing wavelength on the junction temperature was investigated under pulsed operation, and typical results are shown in Fig. 2. The length of the excited region was 730 μm, and the period Λ was 3814 Å in the diode. For comparison, the results obtained in a Fabry-Perot (FP) type cleaved laser which was made from the same wafer are also plotted in Fig. 2. The length of the cleaved laser was 570 μm. The DFB laser showed two transverse modes perpendicular to the junction plane. At junction temperatures between 300 and 350 K, the

Reprinted with permission from *Appl. Phys. Lett.*, vol. 27, no. 7, pp. 403–405, Oct. 1, 1975.

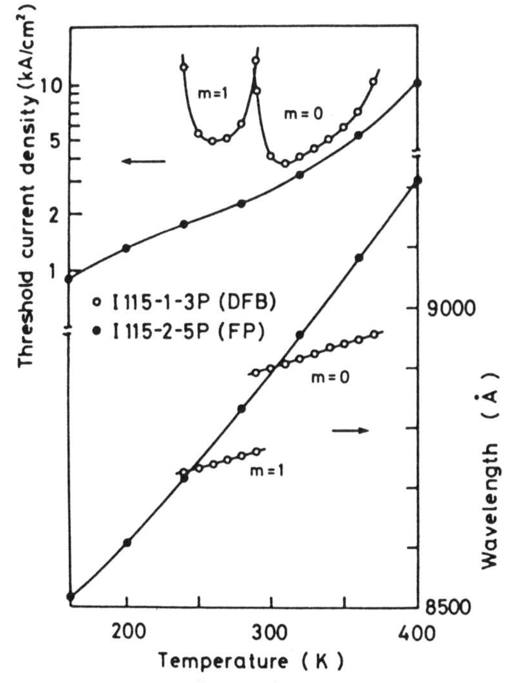

FIG. 2. Threshold current density and the lasing wavelength as a function of junction temperature. The period was 3814 Å in I115-1-3P. The results were obtained under pulsed operation.

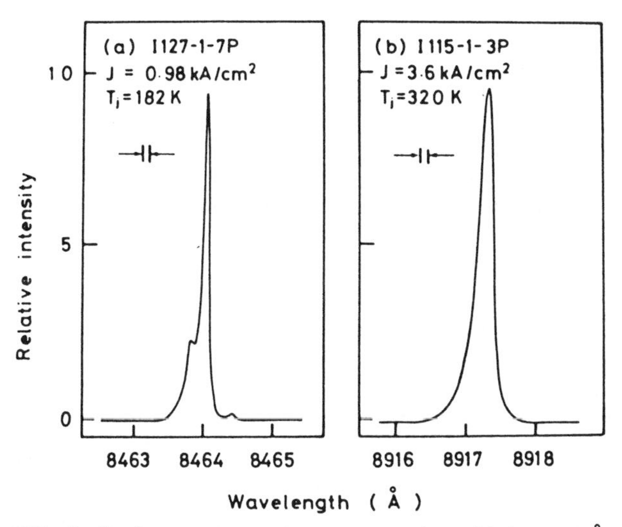

FIG. 3. Lasing spectra under cw operation. (a) $\Lambda = 3648$ Å, (b) $\Lambda = 3814$ Å.

diode lased in the lowest mode ($m = 0$) with a threshold current density of about 1.2 times that of the Fabry-Perot laser. The rapid increase of the threshold below 300 K and above 350 K was due to the mismatching between the period and the gain spectrum of GaAs. The intrinsic threshold gain of the $m = 0$ mode is estimated to be ~25 cm^{-1} from the reflection loss of the cleaved laser.

Figure 3 shows the lasing spectra obtained under cw operation. In Fig. 3(a), the period Λ was 3648 Å and the length of the excited region was 690 μm. At heat-sink temperature $T_H = 170$ K, the threshold current density J_{th} was 0.94 kA/cm^2. The junction temperature T_J was 182 K for the current density J of 0.96 kA/cm^2. Figure 3(b) shows the spectrum of the diode shown in Fig. 2, where $J_{th} = 3.4$ kA/cm^2 at $T_H = 280$ K. The junction temperature became 320 K for $J = 3.6$ kA/cm^2. These threshold current densities were the same as those obtained at the above mentioned junction temperatures under pulsed operation.

The lasing spectra in Fig. 3 show that the diodes lased in a single longitudinal mode. From the study of the far-field pattern, the subpeaks in Fig. 3(a) and the broadening of the spectrum in Fig. 3(b) were attributed to the multitransverse-mode oscillation parallel to the junction plane.

The lasing characteristics were investigated up to twice the threshold current density. Spectra similar to those in Fig. 3 were obtained in this range of excitation, and no indication of multilongitudinal-mode oscillation was recognized.

For the operation at $T_H = 300$ K, the junction temperature became ~340 K. In this case, the lowest threshold current density of 3.5 kA/cm^2 was obtained for $\Lambda = 3820$ Å. A dc output as high as 10 mW was obtained at 1.3 times the threshold current density. Further reduction of the threshold current density will be achieved by optimizing the structure parameters including the use of high-quality fundamental gratings. The thermal resistance will also be reduced by the reduction of the stripe width[10] and by the improvement of the bonding technique. Since the corrugation is separated from the active layer in the SCH structure, we expect that the life of the DFB laser is as long as that of conventional semiconductor lasers. Investigation on the degradation problem is being under way.

In conclusion, cw operation of DFB semiconductor lasers has been achieved at temperatures up to 300 K by a carefully designed SCH structure. The results obtained in this work are encouraging and prompt us to further explore the application of DFB lasers to optical communications and integrated optics.

The authors would like to thank Dr. Y. Otomo and Dr. O. Nakada of the Central Research Laboratory, Hitachi Ltd., for their support in this work. They are also grateful to S. Yamashita of the same laboratory for his extensive assistance in diode preparation and scanning microscope measurements.

[1]D.R. Scifres, R.D. Burnham, and W.Streifer, Appl. Phys. Lett. **25**, 203 (1974).
[2]H.M. Stoll and D.H. Seib, Appl. Opt. **13**, 1981 (1974).
[3]M. Nakamura, K. Aiki, J. Umeda, A. Yariv, H.W. Yen, and T. Morikawa, Appl. Phys. Lett. **25**, 487 (1974).
[4]D.B. Anderson, R.R. August, and J.E. Coker, Appl. Opt. **13**, 2742 (1974).
[5]K. Aiki, M. Nakamura, J. Umeda, A. Yariv, A. Katzir, and and H.W. Yen, Appl. Phys. Lett. **27**, 145 (1975).
[6]T. Tsukada, H. Nakashima, J. Umeda, S. Nakamura, N. Chinone, R. Ito, and O. Nakada, Appl. Phys. Lett. **20**, 344 (1972).
[7]M. Nakamura, K. Aiki, J. Umeda, A. Katzir, A. Yariv, and H.W. Yen, IEEE J. Quantum Electron. **QE-11**, 436 (1975).
[8]H.C. Casey, Jr., S. Somekh, and M. Ilegems, Appl. Phys. Lett. **27**, 142 (1975).
[9]M. Nakamura, K. Aiki, and J. Umeda (unpublished).
[10]T. Tsukada, J. Appl. Phys. **45**, 4899 (1974).

Coupling Coefficients for Distributed Feedback Single- and Double-Heterostructure Diode Lasers

WILLIAM STREIFER, SENIOR MEMBER, IEEE, DONALD R. SCIFRES, MEMBER, IEEE, AND ROBERT D. BURNHAM

***Abstract*—We compute coupling coefficients for TE modes as a function of tooth height, active layer thickness, and Bragg scattering order in single-heterostructure (SH) and double-heterostructure (DH) distributed feedback (DFB) diode lasers for a variety of corrugation shapes. In particular, equations for rectangular, sinusoidal, and triangular shapes are evaluated; the last both in the symmetric and sawtooth cases. It is shown that the coupling coefficient for rectangular and sawtooth gratings decreases much less rapidly with increasing Bragg order than do the sinusoidal and symmetric triangular.**

I. Introduction

Distributed feedback (DFB) lasers differ from conventional lasers in that feedback is provided by a distributed periodic spatial variation in gain, refractive index, and/or geometry, rather than by discrete reflectors. The analysis of these devices [1] has been carried out as a function of the coupling coefficient κ, which describes the degree to which oppositely going waves transfer energy. Generally, κ has been expressed in terms of refractive index and/or gain variations, but in many cases there exist instead periodic corrugations which perturb the light. To employ the results of Kogelnik and Shank [1] for thresholds and frequencies of pure DFB lasers or similar results for DFB lasers with external reflectors [2]-[4] to geometries which employ corrugations [5]-[7], one must relate the coupling coefficients to the corrugations. This task has been formally carried out by several authors [8]-[10] using a perturbation procedure in which modes of the unperturbed structure are examined in their interaction with the corrugation. To date no extensive evaluation of the resulting integrals has been carried out except for square shaped corrugations, and therefore, no detailed comparisons of different corrugation shapes exist in the literature. Furthermore, the unperturbed mode fields used in many previous calculations were not chosen optimally and the published results are somewhat inaccurate. It is our purpose, therefore, in writing this paper to present analytic and numerical results for TE-mode coupling coefficients for various tooth shapes and Bragg scattering orders m using a more accurate formulation. We consider rectangular, sinusoidal, triangular, and sawtooth shapes in detail, but the methods employed are shown to be valid for other shapes as well. The derived formulas apply to both GaAs and dye DFB lasers, but are evaluated herein only for GaAs/GaAlAs SH's and DH's.

Manuscript received January 13, 1975; revised July 9, 1975.
The authors are with the Xerox Palo Alto Research Center, Palo Alto, Calif. 94304.

II. Analytic Results

In three-layer laser structures, as illustrated in Fig. 1, there exist right and left going TE and TM modes coupled by the corrugations. A perturbation analysis is used to obtain an expression for the coupling coefficients produced by the corrugations and thereby permit one to predict thresholds and lasing wavelengths as described in [1]-[4]. The result of the perturbation analysis, as given in [10], for TE modes is

$$\kappa = \frac{k_0^2}{2\beta N^2} \int_{\text{corrugation}} \Delta\,[n^2(x,z)]\; \mathcal{E}^2(x)\,dx \tag{1}$$

where κ is the coupling coefficient, $k_0 = 2\pi/\lambda_0$ (the free-space wavenumber), β is the TE-mode propagation constant, $\mathcal{E}$ is the y component of the unperturbed E-field, and N^2 is a normalization constant given by

$$N^2 = \int_{-\infty}^{\infty} \mathcal{E}^2(x)\,dx. \tag{2}$$

As shown in the following only the negative spatial harmonic of $\Delta\,[n^2(x,z)]$ (which is the perturbation in refractive index of the corrugation) appropriate to the Bragg scattering is to be retained.

In [10] the full guide width t (see Fig. 1) was employed to compute the unperturbed mode field $\mathcal{E}$, but as shown in [11], this can lead to inaccurate excessively high coupling coefficients. The optimal unperturbed mode $\mathcal{E}$ is that of a related four-layer structure (see [11]); however, we have found that one can obtain adequate accuracy without excessive complexity by judiciously choosing the unperturbed guide boundary at $t' < t$. We choose t' such that the volume of n_1 material extending into region 2 just equals the volume of n_2 material extending into region 1. The symbol t' thus refers to the distance from the n_2-n_3 interface to the line

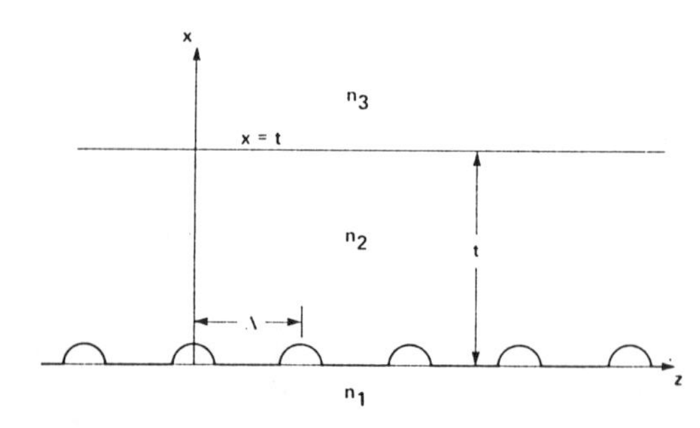

Fig. 1. Three-layer DFB laser structure.

Reprinted from *IEEE J. Quantum Electron.*, vol. QE-11, no. 11, pp. 867-873, Nov. 1975.

shown in Fig. 2. That line is positioned such that the areas labeled A and B are equal. It is not coincident with the base of the teeth as in [10], [12], [13]. The unperturbed mode $\mathcal{E}(x)$ is then

$$\mathcal{E}(x) = \begin{cases} \exp(qx), & x \le 0 \\ \cos(hx) + (q/h)\sin(hx), & 0 \le x \le t' \\ [\cos(ht') + (q/h)\sin(ht')]\exp[-p(x-t')], & t' \le x \end{cases} \quad (3)$$

where

$$q = \sqrt{\beta^2 - n_1^2 k^2} \quad (4a)$$
$$h = \sqrt{n_2^2 k^2 - \beta^2} \quad (4b)$$
$$p = \sqrt{\beta^2 - n_3^2 k^2} \quad (4c)$$

and where β is found by solving

$$\tan(ht') = \frac{h(q+p)}{h^2 - pq} \quad (5)$$

and

$$N^2 = \int_{-\infty}^{\infty} \mathcal{E}^2(x)\,dx = \frac{(h^2+q^2)(t'+q^{-1}+p^{-1})}{2h^2}. \quad (6)$$

Consider now a single corrugation as shown in Fig. 2. Here

$$\Delta[n^2(x,z)] = \begin{cases} n_1^2 - n_2^2, & \text{in area } A \\ n_2^2 - n_1^2, & \text{in area } B \end{cases} \quad (7)$$

and $w_i(x)$, $i = 1, 2, 3, 4$ describe the tooth boundary. If any of these functions are not single valued the tooth shape can be decomposed into two or more curves with single valued boundaries and the results superimposed.

Since $\Delta[n^2(x,z)]$ is periodic in z it is expanded in a Fourier series whose coefficients depend on x. After some manipulation we obtain

$$\Delta[n^2(x,z)] = \begin{cases} (n_1^2 - n_2^2)\left[\dfrac{w_2(x) - w_1(x)}{\Lambda} - \dfrac{i}{2\pi}\sum\limits_{m=-\infty}^{\infty}\dfrac{1}{m}\{\exp[i2\pi m w_2(x)/\Lambda] - \exp[i2\pi m w_1(x)/\Lambda]\} \cdot \exp(-i2\pi m z/\Lambda)\right], & x > 0 \\ (n_2^2 - n_1^2)\left[\dfrac{w_4(x) - w_3(x)}{\Lambda} - \dfrac{i}{2\pi}\sum\limits_{m=-\infty}^{\infty}\dfrac{1}{m}\{\exp[i2\pi m w_4(x)/\Lambda] - \exp[i2\pi m w_3(x)/\Lambda]\} \cdot \exp(-i2\pi m z/\Lambda)\right], & x < 0 \end{cases} \quad (8)$$

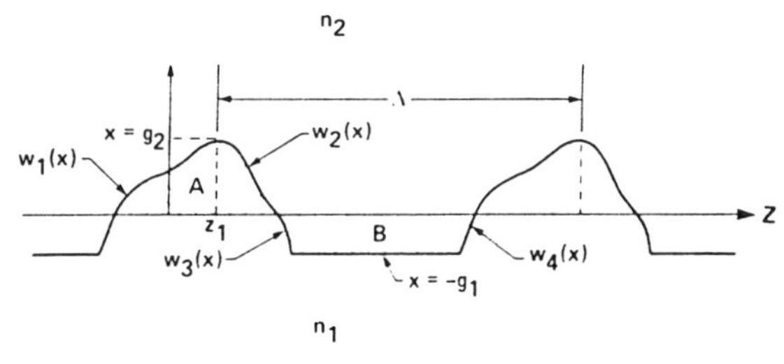

Fig. 2. Illustrating the functions defining tooth shape.

and so

$$\kappa = \frac{-ik_0^2(n_1^2 - n_2^2)}{4\pi\beta m N^2}\left\{\int_0^{g_2}\{\exp[i2\pi m w_2(x)/\Lambda] - \exp[i2\pi m w_1(x)/\Lambda]\}\,\mathcal{E}^2(x)\,dx - \int_{-g_1}^{0}\{\exp[i2\pi m w_4(x)/\Lambda] - \exp[i2\pi m w_3(x)/\Lambda]\}\,\mathcal{E}^2(x)\,dx\right\} \quad (9)$$

where, as shown in Fig. 2, g_1 and g_2 are the maximum tooth heights in media 1 and 2, respectively, and m is the Bragg scattering order.

Rectangular Grating

For rectangular teeth $w_2(x) = -w_1(x) = w/2$, $w_3(x) = w/2$, $w_4 = \Lambda - w/2$, and the area averaging conditions yields

$$g_1 = wg/\Lambda \quad (10)$$

and

$$g_2 = (1 - w/\Lambda)g \quad (11)$$

where g is the total tooth height. After integration (9) becomes

$$\kappa = \frac{k_0^2(n_1^2 - n_2^2)}{4\pi\beta m N^2}\sin\left(\frac{\pi m w}{\Lambda}\right)\left\{g_2 + \frac{\sin(2g_2 h)}{2h} + \frac{q}{h^2}\cdot[1 - \cos(2g_2 h)] + \frac{q^2}{h^2}\left[g_2 - \frac{\sin(2g_2 h)}{2h}\right] + \frac{1}{q}[1 - \exp(-2qg_1)]\right\} \quad (12)$$

where q, h, and p are defined by (4a)-(4c).

In (12) the quantities β, N^2, q, and h all depend on the unperturbed geometry, i.e., n_1, n_2, n_3, and $t' = t - g_1$ as well as the transverse mode number. The dependence on Bragg order m is completely represented by the multiplicative factor

$$\frac{\sin(\pi m w/\Lambda)}{m}. \quad (13)$$

Clearly, κ can be zero for integral values of mw/Λ, but generally it decreases as $1/m$. Finally, the dependence on tooth height is given by the bracketed expressions, which for $2g_1h$, $2g_2h \ll 1$ reduces to $2g_1 + 2g_2 = 2g$. The dependence of κ on the various parameters is discussed more completely in [14].

Sinusoidal Grating

The tooth profile for sinusoidal teeth is

$$x = (g/2)\cos(2\pi z/\Lambda) \tag{14}$$

and so

$$w_2(x) = -w_1(x) = \frac{\Lambda}{2\pi}\cos^{-1}\left(\frac{2x}{g}\right) \tag{15a}$$

and

$$[w_4(x) - \Lambda/2] = -[w_3(x) - \Lambda/2] = \frac{\Lambda}{2\pi}\cos^{-1}\left(-\frac{2x}{g}\right) \tag{15b}$$

where it is understood that

$$0 < \cos^{-1}(U) < \pi/2.$$

The boundary line for the unperturbed modes bisects the corrugation and (9) is then

$$\kappa = \frac{k_0^2(n_1^2 - n_2^2)}{2\pi\beta m N^2}\left\{\int_0^{g/2} \sin[m\cos^{-1}(2x/g)]\,\mathcal{E}^2\,dx - (-1)^m \int_{-g/2}^{0} \sin[m\cos^{-1}(2x/g)]\,\mathcal{E}^2\,dx\right\}. \tag{16}$$

The integrals in (16) can be evaluated numerically or analytically by using trigonometric identities for $\sin[m\cos^{-1}(2x/g)]$ and expanding $\mathcal{E}^2(x)$ in power series. Details of the latter procedure and evaluation of the integrals are too lengthy to be included herein. The results for $m = 1, 2, 3$, and 4 are in the form

$$\kappa = \frac{k_0^2(n_1^2 - n_2^2)}{\beta N^2}\begin{cases} \dfrac{g}{8}S_1 \\[2ex] \dfrac{g^2}{64}S_2 \\[2ex] \dfrac{g^2}{60\pi}S_3 \\[2ex] \dfrac{g^3}{420\pi}S_4 \end{cases} \tag{17}$$

where S_i, $i = 1, 2, 3, 4$ are summations whose first terms are $S_1 = 1, S_2 = S_3 = q$, and $S_4 = (q^2 - h^2)/2$.

Symmetric Triangular Grating

Consider next a symmetric triangular grating defined by

$$w_1(x) = w_4(x) - \Lambda = \frac{x\Lambda}{2g} - \frac{\Lambda}{4} \tag{18a}$$

and

$$w_2(x) = w_3(x) = \frac{x\Lambda}{2g} + \frac{\Lambda}{4}. \tag{18b}$$

The integrals which result upon substitution in (9) are in standard form and are easily evaluated to yield

$$\begin{aligned}\kappa = \frac{k_0^2(n_1^2 - n_2^2)}{4\pi\beta m N^2}\,g\Bigg\{&\left(1 + \frac{q^2}{h^2}\right)\frac{[1 - \cos(\pi m/2)]}{\pi m} \\ &+ \frac{q}{h}\frac{2}{[(2gh)^2 - (\pi m)^2]}[2gh\sin(\pi m/2) - \pi m\sin(gh)] \\ &- \left(1 - \frac{q^2}{h^2}\right)\frac{\pi m}{[(2gh)^2 - (\pi m)^2]}[\cos(gh) - \cos(\pi m/2)] \\ &- \frac{2(-1)^m}{[(2gq)^2 + (\pi m)^2]}[2gq\sin(\pi m/2) - \pi m\cos(\pi m/2) \\ &+ \pi m e^{-gq}]\Bigg\}.\end{aligned} \tag{19}$$

Since $\sin(\pi m/2) = 0$ for m even and $\cos(\pi m/2) = 0$ for m odd many terms in (19) vanish for particular Bragg diffraction orders. In general, however, $\kappa \to 1/m^2$ with increasing order.

Sawtooth Grating

The sawtooth grating is defined by

$$w_1(x) = w_4(x) = x\Lambda/g \tag{20a}$$

and

$$w_2(x) = -w_3(x) = \Lambda/2. \tag{20b}$$

The integral (9) again is in standard form, and we find

$$\begin{aligned}\kappa = \frac{k_0^2(n_1^2 - n_2^2)}{8\pi\beta m N^2}\Bigg\{&g\Bigg[\frac{(u-1)v_1}{2\pi m} + \frac{\pi m}{2d_1} \\ &\cdot\left\{v_2(1 - uC_1) - \frac{2uq}{h}S_1\right\} + \frac{\pi m}{d_2}(1 - uE_1)\Bigg] \\ &- i\Bigg[\frac{u}{2}\left\{v_1 g + \frac{2q}{h^2}(1 - C_1) + \frac{v_2}{h}S_1\right\} \\ &- \frac{g^2h}{2d_1}\left\{\frac{2q}{h}(1 - uC_1) + uv_2S_1\right\} \\ &- \frac{qg^2}{d_2}(1 - uE_1) + \frac{u}{q}(1 - E_1)\Bigg]\Bigg\}\end{aligned} \tag{21}$$

where

$$C_1 = \cos(gh), \quad S_1 = \sin(gh), \quad E_1 = \exp(-qg) \tag{22a}$$

$$v_1 = (1 + q^2/h^2), \quad v_2 = (1 - q^2/h^2) \tag{22b}$$

$$d_1 = (gh)^2 - (\pi m)^2, \quad d_2 = (gq)^2 + (\pi m)^2 \tag{22c}$$

and

$$u = (-1)^m. \tag{22d}$$

An examination of (21) reveals that $|\kappa| \to 1/m$ with increasing

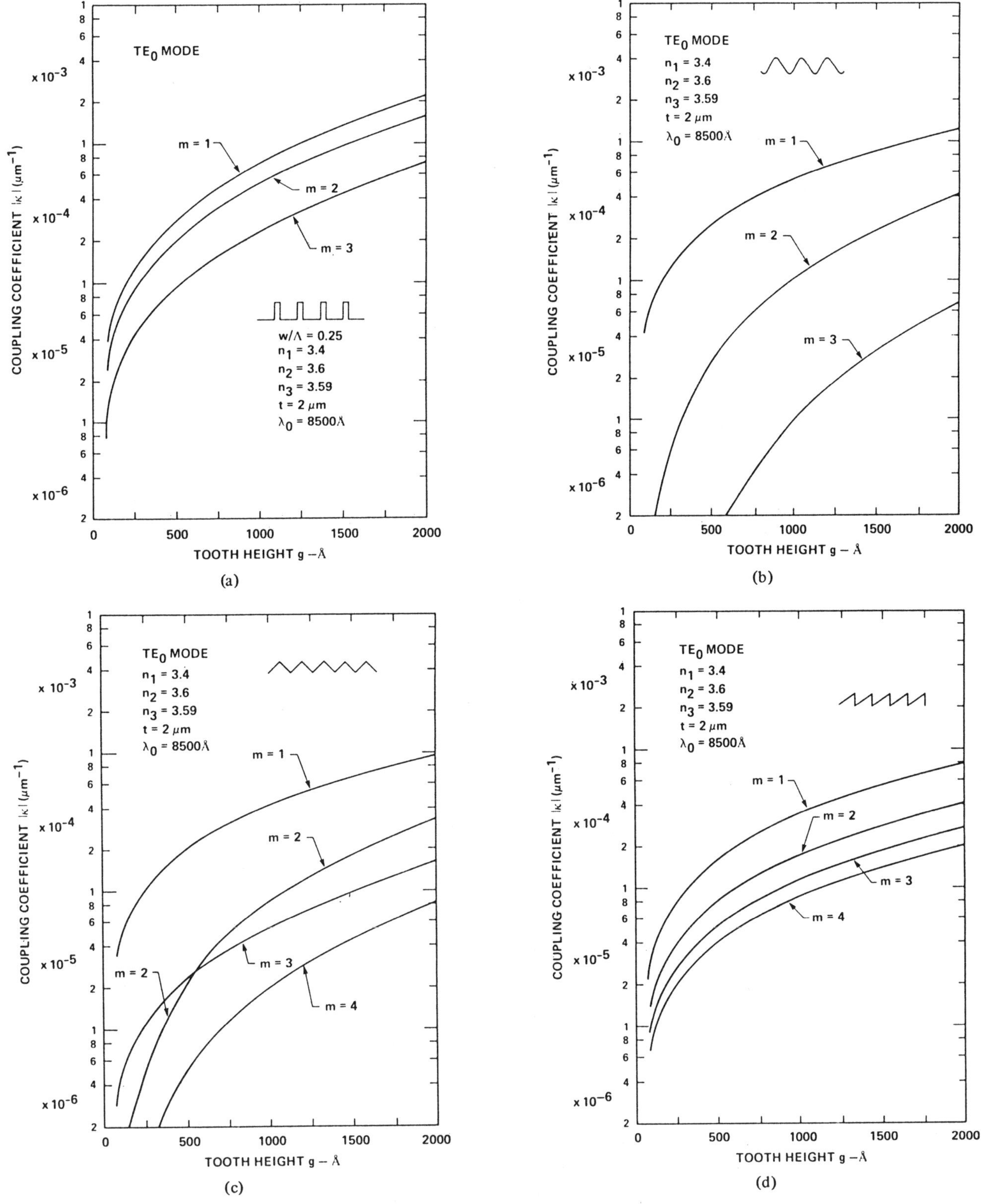

Fig. 3. Coupling coefficient versus tooth height with Bragg order as a parameter for TE_0 mode in a SH geometry. (a) Rectangular grating. (b) Sinusoidal grating. (c) Symmetric triangular grating. (d) Sawtooth grating.

m and for $gh, gq << 1$

$$|\kappa| \approx \frac{k_0^2(n_1^2 - n_2^2)}{8\pi\beta m N^2} g \tag{23}$$

where only the dominant inverse power of m has been retained.

III. Numerical Results

Fig. 3(a)-(d) are plots of coupling coefficient versus tooth height g in a SH GaAs DFB laser geometry for the four corrugation shapes discussed in the preceding. Interestingly enough, κ for $m = 1$ is not strongly dependent on tooth shape.

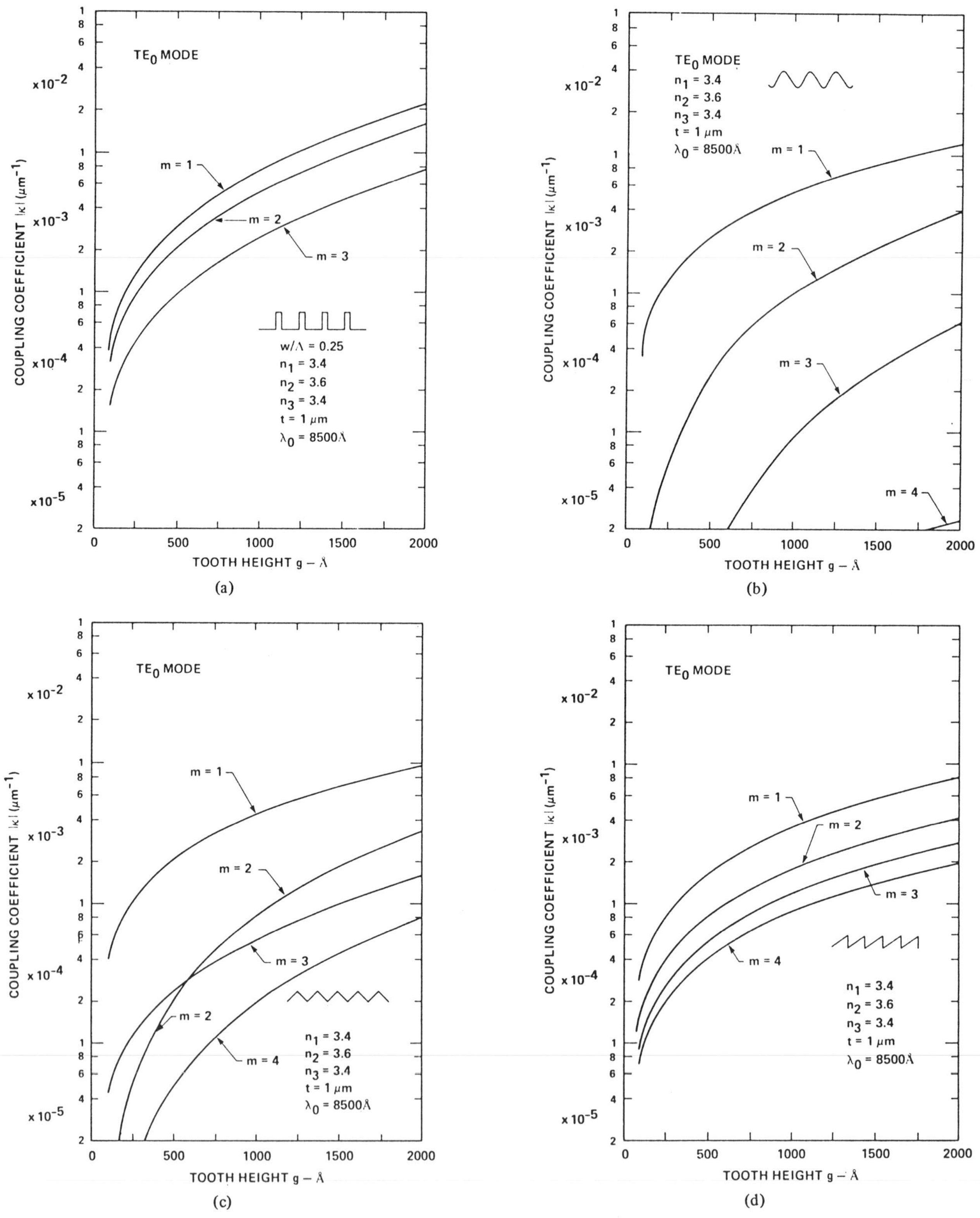

Fig. 4. Coupling coefficient versus tooth height with Bragg order as a parameter for TE_0 mode in a DH geometry. (a) Rectangular grating. (b) Sinusoidal grating. (c) Symmetric triangular grating. (d) Sawtooth grating.

With increasing m the coupling constants for rectangular ($w/\Lambda = 0.25$) and sawtooth gratings decrease at approximately the same rate and that decrease is much less rapid than those for the triangular and sinusoidal gratings. The coupling coefficient for rectangular teeth with $m = 4$ is zero because the factor (13) is zero. Physically, when mw/Λ is an integer, reflections from the parallel vertical tooth boundaries are exactly a half-wavelength out-of-phase and therefore cancel. It is likely that $|\kappa|$ for any tooth shape with discontinuities will decrease with Bragg order at approximately the same rate as the rectangular and sawtooth gratings. The coupling coefficient for sinusoidal teeth decreases most rapidly and for $m = 4$ values of $|\kappa|$ are all less than the lowest point on the graph. For symmetrical triangular teeth $|\kappa|$ also decreases quickly and exhibits other interesting behavior. In this case with m odd, $\kappa \propto g$ for small g, whereas with $m = 2$, $\kappa \propto g^2$ for small g; as g increases, however, the latter exceeds the former above approximately $g = 550$ Å.

Consider next the aspect ratios. Since it is often the period Λ which largely determines the maximum tooth height, one may well ask, given a fixed aspect ratio of tooth height to period, what Bragg order will maximize κ? Clearly, for rectangular and sawteeth dividing tooth height and period by m reduces κ by a greater factor. Thus, other considerations aside, one need not (in these cases) strive for lowest order Bragg scattering. Of course, this result is predicated on the assumption of constant aspect ratio, particular tooth shapes (since it is invalid in the other cases), and finally the neglect of other phenomena such as radiation losses to the lower order Bragg scattering modes.

In Fig. 4(a)-(d) we plot similar curves for the lowest order transverse mode TE_0 in a DH geometry ($n_1 = n_3 = 3.4$, $n_2 = 3.6$, and $t = 1.0$ μm). As a result of the stronger confinement and smaller thickness the coupling coefficients exceed those for the SH geometry by more than an order of magnitude. For the particular refractive indices and thickness given in the preceding the DH geometry will actually allow additional transverse electric modes to propagate, the TE_1 and TE_2. In Fig. 5(a) and (b) we plot $|\kappa|$ versus tooth height for the TE_1 mode with rectangular ($w/\Lambda = 0.25$) and symmetric triangular corrugations, respectively. Values of $|\kappa|$ are roughly a factor of 3 greater than for the TE_0 mode in the same geometry. It should be noted that the grating period Λ must be adjusted somewhat to resonate these higher order transverse modes [13]-[15]. Also as shown in [13] and [15], depending on t, $|\kappa|$ may continue to increase with transverse mode number.

DFB lasers have also been shown to produce highly collimated beams by radiation from the grating [16]-[19]. For single beam output [19] it is best to employ the grating in the 2nd Bragg order, i.e., $m = 2$ and optimum output coupling may well occur for symmetric triangular or sawtooth gratings [20]. With $m = 2$, $\Lambda \simeq 2300$ Å, and so $g = 1150$ Å and $g = 2300$ Å will give teeth with a 45° slope for symmetric triangular or sawtooth gratings, respectively. We plot $|\kappa|$ versus t for four transverse (TE) modes in a DH geometry with a symmetric triangular grating in Fig. 6. The TE_1, TE_2, and TE_3 modes all exhibit a more complex $|\kappa|$ versus t dependence then shown in Fig. 6. In Fig. 7 we plot $|\kappa|$ versus t for a small range of t just above cutoff for the TE_2 mode. The behavior illustrated can be explained mathematically by studying (19). As t increases the bracketed expression changes from positive to negative at which point $|\kappa|$ passes through zero. Physically, there is destructive interference from different parts of the tooth which exactly cancel for a particular value of t. This phenomenon is not of great significance since it is probably desirable to resonate the transverse modes well above cutoff.

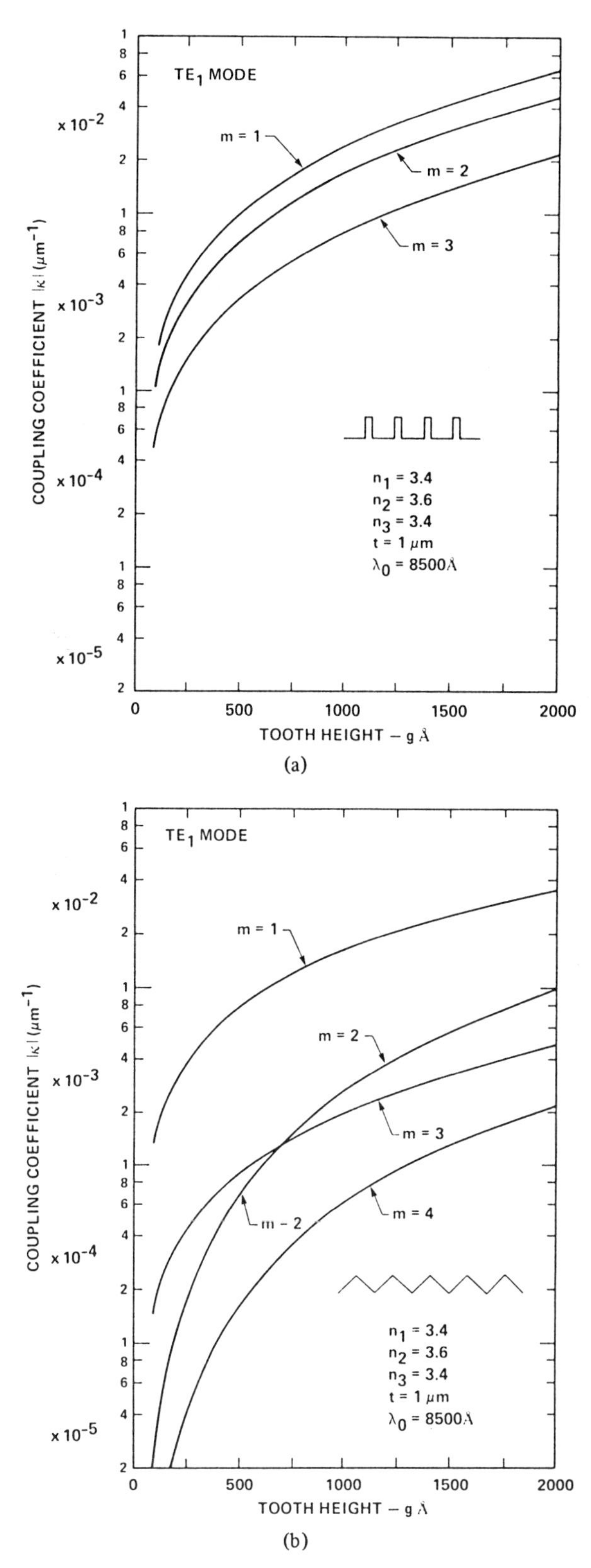

Fig. 5. Coupling coefficient versus tooth height with Bragg order as a parameter for the TE_1 mode in a DH geometry. (a) Rectangular grating. (b) Symmetric triangular grating.

IV. Remarks

The computed values of coupling coefficients for TE modes presented in the preceding for rectangular, sinusoidal, triangular, and sawtooth corrugation shapes in both SH and DH

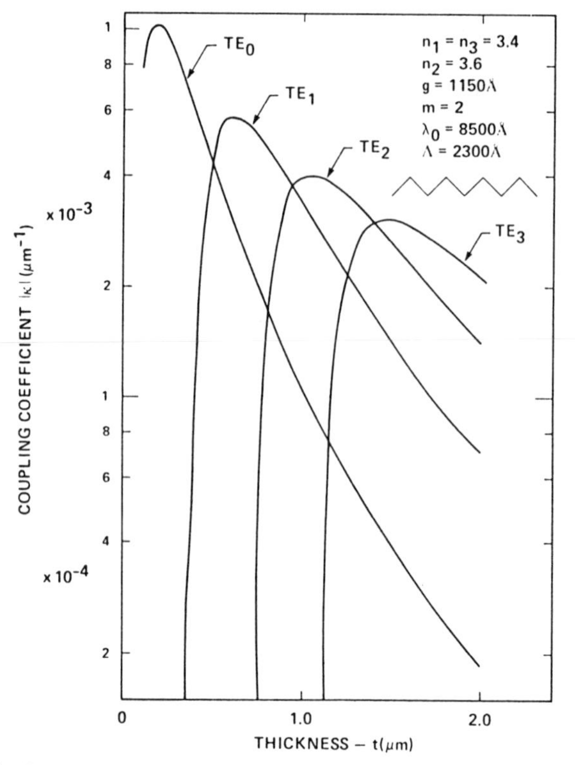

Fig. 6. Coupling coefficient versus thickness for transverse modes in a DH geometry with a symmetric triangular grating.

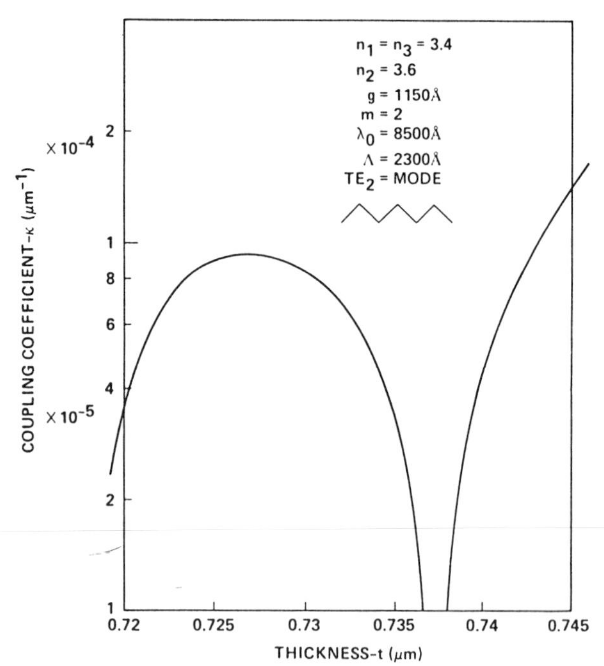

Fig. 7. Detail of the TE_2 mode shown in Fig. 6.

laser diodes are based on a perturbation analysis, which uses a more accurate unperturbed mode field than heretofore published.

REFERENCES

[1] H. Kogelnik and C. V. Shank, "Coupled mode theory of distributed feedback lasers," *J. Appl. Phys.*, vol. 43, pp. 2327–2335, 1972.

[2] S. R. Chinn, "Effects of mirror reflectivity in a distributed-feedback laser," *IEEE J. Quantum Electron.*, vol. QE-9, pp. 574–580, June 1973.

[3] W. Streifer, D. R. Scifres, and R. D. Burnham, "Longitudinal modes in distributed feedback lasers with external mirrors," *J. Appl. Phys.*, vol. 46, pp. 247–249, 1975.

[4] W. Streifer, R. D. Burnham, and D. R. Scifres, "Effect of external reflectors on longitudinal modes of distributed feedback lasers," *IEEE J. Quantum Electron.*, vol. QE-11, pp. 154–161, Apr. 1975.

[5] D. R. Scifres, R. D. Burnham, and W. Streifer, "Distributed-feedback single heterojunction GaAs diode laser," *Appl. Phys. Lett.*, vol. 25, pp. 203–206, 1974.

[6] M. Nakamura *et al.*, "GaAs-GaAlAs double-heterostructure distributed feedback diode lasers," *Appl. Phys. Lett.*, vol. 25, pp. 487 and 488, 1974.

[7] P. Zory, "Leaky wave thin film laser," in *Dig. Tech. Papers, Integrated Optics Topical Meeting of the Optical Society of America*, Feb. 1972, pp. ThA2-1–ThA2-2.

[8] D. Marcuse, "Mode conversion caused by surface imperfections of a dielectric slab waveguide," *Bell Syst. Tech. J.*, vol. 48, pp. 3187–3215, 1969.

[9] S. Wang, "Proposal of periodic layer waveguide structures for distributed lasers," *J. Appl. Phys.*, vol. 44, pp. 767–780, 1972.

[10] A. Yariv, "Coupled-mode theory for guided-wave optics," *IEEE J. Quantum Electron.*, vol. QE-9, pp. 919–933, Sept. 1973.

[11] K. Handa, S. T. Peng, and T. Tamir, "Improved perturbation analysis of dielectric gratings," *Appl. Phys.*, vol. 5, p. 325, 1975.

[12] H. Stoll and A. Yariv, "Coupled-mode analysis of periodic dielectric waveguides," *Opt. Commun.*, vol. 8, pp. 5–8, 1973.

[13] W. Streifer, R. D. Burnham, and D. R. Scifres, "Coupling coefficients and propagation constants in guided wave distributed feedback lasers," *J. Appl. Phys.*, vol. 46, pp. 946–948, 1975.

[14] R. D. Burnham, D. R. Scifres, and W. Streifer, "Single heterostructure distributed-feedback GaAs-diode lasers," *IEEE J. Quantum Electron.* (*Part II of Two Parts*), vol. QE-11, pp. 439–449, July 1975.

[15] J. E. Bjorkholm and C. V. Shank, "Distributed-feedback lasers in thin-film optical waveguides," *IEEE J. Quantum Electron.*, vol. QE-8, pp. 833–838, Nov. 1972.

[16] Zh. I. Alferov *et al.*, "Semiconductor laser with extremely low divergence of radiation" (in Russian), *Sov. Phys.–Semicond.*, vol. 8, pp. 832–833, 1974; also (in English), *Sov. Phys.–JETP*, pp. 541 and 542.

[17] P. Zory, "Laser oscillation in leaky corrugated optical waveguides," *Appl. Phys. Lett.*, vol. 22, pp. 125–128, 1973.

[18] K. O. Hill and A. Watanabe, "Passive-core corrugated-waveguide laser," *Appl. Opt.*, vol. 12, pp. 430–433, 1973.

[19] D. R. Scifres, R. D. Burnham, and W. Streifer, "Observation of highly collimated laser beams from electrically pumped SH GaAs/GaAlAs distributed feedback lasers," *Appl. Phys. Lett.*, vol. 26, pp. 48–50, 1975.

[20] S. T. Peng and T. Tamir, "Directional blazing of waves guided by asymmetric dielectric gratings," *Opt. Commun.*, vol. 11, pp. 405–409, 1974.

GaAs-GaAlAs distributed-feedback diode lasers with separate optical and carrier confinement

K. Aiki, M. Nakamura, and J. Umeda

Central Research Laboratory, Hitachi, Ltd., Kokubunji, Tokyo, Japan

A. Yariv,* A. Katzir,* and H. W. Yen*

California Institute of Technology, Pasadena, California 91125

(Received 21 April 1975; in final form 26 May 1975)

Remarkable reduction of the threshold current density is achieved in GaAs-GaAlAs distributed-feedback diode lasers by adopting a separate-confinement heterostructure. The diodes are lased successfully at temperatures up to 340°K under pulsed operation. The lowest threshold current density is 3 kA/cm^2 at 300°K.

PACS numbers: 42.60.J, 73.40.L

We have previously reported the operation of GaAs-GaAlAs double-heterostructure (DH) distributed-feedback (DFB) diode lasers in which the optical feedback was provided by a corrugated interface between the active layer and the outer p-GaAlAs layer.[1,2] Since the light and the carriers were confined to the active layer by the double heterojunction, the threshold current density at 80 °K was the lowest among those of the DFB diode lasers reported so far.[3-5] It was found, however, that the fabrication of a grating on the active layer caused the interface recombination centers which increased the threshold current density substantially at higher temperatures. For this reason, it was impossible to operate such lasers at around 300 °K at low current densities. Recombination centers existed even when the grating was made by chemical etching instead of by ion milling.

One of the solutions to this problem will be to use a separate optical and carrier confinement heterostructure (SCH). In the present work, we describe heterostructure lasers in which carriers are confined to the p-GaAs active layer while the light extends to the p-$Ga_{1-y}Al_yAs$ layer ($y \sim 0.17$) and the p-$Ga_{1-z}Al_zAs$ layer ($z \sim 0.07$) grown successively on the active layer. The grating is made on the p-$Ga_{1-z}Al_zAs$ layer to obtain the optical feedback. Since the active layer is separated from the corrugated interface, the threshold current density has been found to be low enough to operate the diode at higher temperatures. In this experiment lasers were operated successfully at room temperature.

In the fabrication of the DFB diode laser with separate confinement, an n-$Ga_{0.7}Al_{0.3}As$ layer (~ 2 μm thick), a p-GaAs active layer (~0.3 μm thick), a p-$Ga_{0.83}Al_{0.17}As$ layer (~0.1 μm thick), and a p-$Ga_{0.93}Al_{0.07}As$ layer (~0.2 μm thick) were grown successively by liquid phase epitaxy (LPE). The n layer was doped with Sn, and the p layers with Ge. Next, surface corrugations with a period of ~0.37 μm were made on the p-$Ga_{0.93}Al_{0.07}As$ layer by chemical etching through a photoresist mask produced by holographic photolithography. Finally, a p-$Ga_{0.7}Al_{0.3}As$ layer (~2 μm thick) and a p-GaAs layer (~1 μm thick), both doped with Ge, were grown on the corrugated surface by LPE. The SEM photograph of the corrugated waveguide with separate confinement is shown in Fig. 1, where the period Λ and the depth of the grating are 3700 Å and 1500 Å, respectively. In this figure, the injected electrons are confined to the p-GaAs active layer by the p-$Ga_{0.83}Al_{0.17}As$ layer. The p-$Ga_{0.93}Al_{0.07}As$ layer was necessary because it was difficult to grow GaAlAs uniformly on the exposed $Ga_{1-y}Al_yAs$ layer ($y > 0.1$) in the second LPE. The mole fraction of Al in the corrugated layer was chosen to be 0.07, so that the absorption of light could be reduced and the next p-$Ga_{0.7}Al_{0.3}As$ layer could be uniformly grown on it.

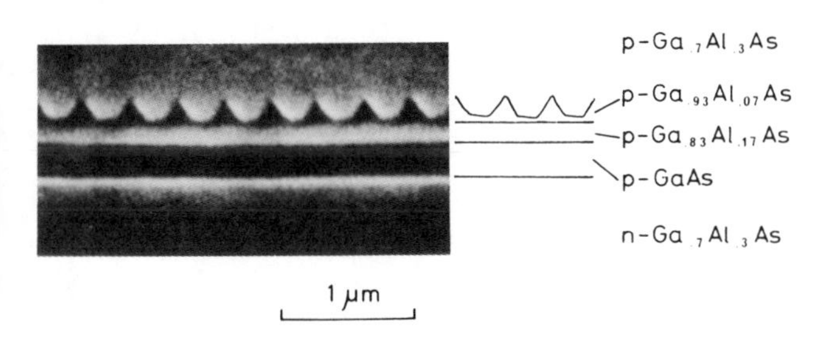

FIG. 1. SEM photograph of the SCH structure DFB laser. The period is 3700 Å.

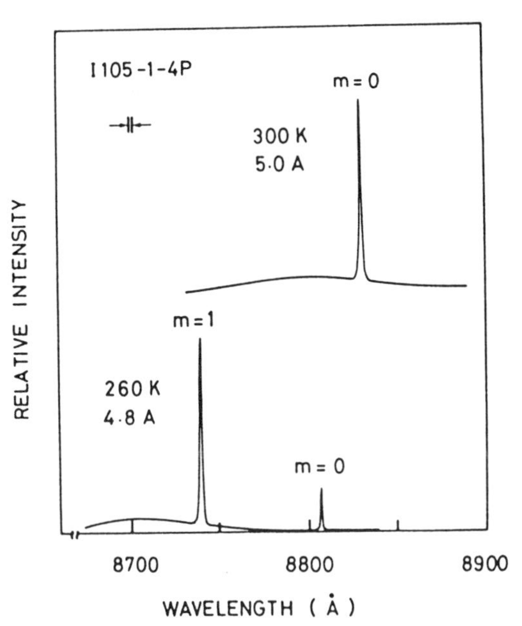

FIG. 2. Lasing spectra of a SCH structure DFB laser. m is the transverse mode number.

Reprinted with permission from *Appl. Phys. Lett.*, vol. 27, no. 3, pp. 145-146, Aug. 1, 1975.

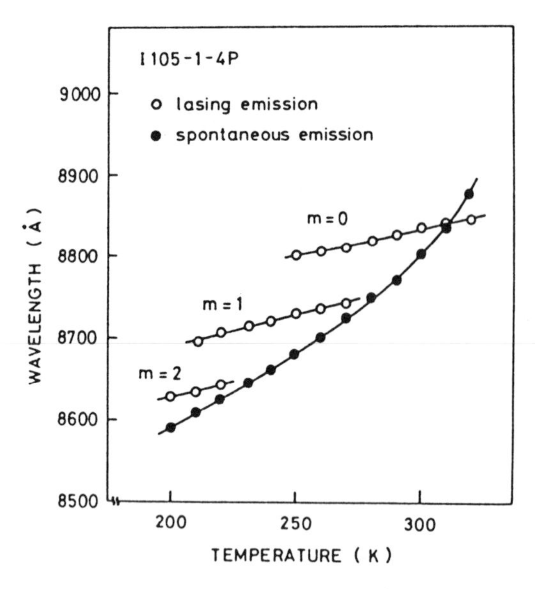

FIG. 3. Wavelength as a function of temperature. The open circles denote the lasing wavelength. The filled circles denote the peak wavelength of the spontaneous emission.

The diode had a mesa-stripe geometry so that the injection could be limited to a rectangular region. The width of the stripe was 50 μm. The length of the excited area, L, was 200–1000 μm. The details of the geometry are the same as those described before.[1,2] The lasing characteristics were investigated in a temperature range from 80 to 340 °K under pulsed operation. The duration and the repetition rate of current pulses were 50 ns and 100 Hz, respectively.

At 80 °K, the threshold current density J_{th} was ~500 A/cm^2 for $\Lambda = 3600$ Å and $L = 500$ μm. This is about the same as the J_{th}(80 °K) obtained in the DH structure DFB lasers. At 300 °K, the lowest threshold current density was 3 kA/cm^2 for $\Lambda = 3770$ Å and $L = 500$ μm. This is about 1/30 of the J_{th}(300 °K) of the DH structure DFB lasers.

The emission spectra of a typical SCH structure DFB laser are shown in Fig. 2, where $\Lambda = 3770$ Å and $L = 500$ μm. At 260 °K, we observed two peaks, the separation of which was 67 Å. These two peaks corresponded to the two transverse modes operating perpendicular to the junction plane, as was theoretically discussed in Refs. 6–8. From the study of the radiation pattern, the peak centered at 8807 Å was assigned to the lowest transverse mode ($m = 0$), and the peak centered at 8740 Å to the second transverse mode ($m = 1$). The threshold current density of the lowest transverse mode was higher than that of the second transverse mode at 260 °K. At 300 °K, the diode lased in the lowest transverse mode with a peak wavelength of 8829 Å.[9] As is shown in Fig. 2, the selectivity of the longitudinal mode was as remarkable in the SCH structure DFB laser as in the DH structure DFB lasers. The lasing wavelength of the diode is plotted as a function of the diode temperature in Fig. 3, where current pulses up to 10 A were applied to the diode. Three transverse modes were observed in total, and the wavelength of each mode had a temperature dependence of 0.6 Å/deg.

In some diodes an increase of the pumping current by a factor of 5 above threshold resulted in the appearance of two, or at most three, longitudinal modes. The peak room-temperature power was about 5 mW.

In conclusion, GaAs-GaAlAs DFB lasers with a SCH structure were operated at temperatures up to 340 °K under pulsed bias. cw operation will be possible in this structure by improving the heat sink of the diode.

The authors would like to thank Dr. Y. Otomo and Dr. O. Nakada of the Central Research Laboratory, Hitachi Ltd., for their continuous encouragement, S. Yamashita for his assistance in the experiment, and A. Gover of California Institute of Technology for helpful discussions.

*Work sponsored by the Office of Naval Research.
[1]M. Nakamura, K. Aiki, J. Umeda, A. Yariv, H.W. Yen, and T. Morikawa, Appl. Phys. Lett. 25, 487 (1974).
[2]M. Nakamura, K. Aiki, J. Umeda, A. Katzir, A. Yariv, and H.W. Yen, IEEE J. Quantum Electron. (to be published).
[3]H.M. Stoll and D.H. Seib, Appl. Opt. 13, 1981 (1974).
[4]D.R. Scifres, R.D. Burnham, and W. Streifer, Appl. Phys. Lett. 25, 203 (1974).
[5]D.B. Anderson, R.R. August, and J.E. Coker, Appl. Opt. 13, 2742 (1974).
[6]M. Nakamura and A. Yariv, Digest of the 1974 Topical Meeting on Integrated Optics, Paper No. TuB9 (unpublished).
[7]C.V. Shank and R.D. Schmidt, Appl. Phys. Lett. 25, 200 (1974).
[8]W. Streifer, R.D. Burnham, and D.R. Scifres (unpublished).
[9]It depends on the gain spectrum of the diode as well as on the coupling coefficient of each mode as to which transverse mode has the lowest threshold. The details will be discussed elsewhere.

Analysis of Grating-Coupled Radiation in GaAs:GaAlAs Lasers and Waveguides

WILLIAM STREIFER, SENIOR MEMBER, IEEE, DON R. SCIFRES, MEMBER, IEEE, AND ROBERT D. BURNHAM, MEMBER, IEEE

Abstract—Grating-coupled radiation in GaAs:GaAlAs lasers and waveguides is analyzed. A general formulation is developed for arbitrary-shaped gratings which need not be small in size. Two methods are used to solve the resulting equations in the case of rectangular-shaped gratings. The first is a perturbation technique and the second is iterative in nature. The iterative procedure converges to a numerical exact solution in many cases of practical interest and indicates that the perturbation results are quite accurate. Curves are presented for radiated power from traveling waves as a function of grating tooth height, tooth width, refractive index, waveguide thickness, and period for rectangular gratings in heterostructure waveguiding geometries. It is shown that radiation is not a monotonically increasing function of tooth height, but rather maxima occur when the teeth are half the optical wavelength in the material. Also, in particular geometries with an air:GaAs grating interface, radiated power of a mode can exceed 100 cm^{-1}.

I. Introduction

THE phenomenon of radiation from periodic structures in waveguides is utilized in couplers and lasers. In the former situation one generally deals with a structure which contains a wave propagating in one direction. Through its interaction with the periodic grating the propagating wave excites one or more radiating waves which provide the output coupling. If the grating period is approximately an integral multiple of half the propagating wavelength in the guide (the Bragg condition) then a strong coupling also exists between the propagating wave and an identical contradirectional wave. This is, of course, just the situation which exists in a distributed feedback (DFB) or Bragg reflection (DBR) laser [1]. If one of the latter devices functions such that the grating provides the feedback, two contradirectional propagating waves always exist and both simultaneously contribute to the radiation field. However, laser devices which contain gratings for output coupling, but obtain feedback away from the Bragg condition from external reflectors [2]-[5] (such as cleaved crystal facets) may be considered to radiate as two independent contradirectional waves in a waveguide.

In this paper we study analytically the radiation properties of gratings in GaAs:GaAlAs structures which are used either as waveguides or as lasers, where in the latter case the oscillation wavelength is not in the immediate vicinity of that determined by the Bragg condition. An exact formulation for arbitrary grating tooth shape is presented. The first-order solution of these equations in the case of rectangular-shaped corrugations corresponds to the perturbation technique given by Handa *et al.* [6]. Starting with the perturbation results, numerical iterations converge, in many cases of practical interest, to a more accurate solution. Specifically, we present results of radiated power as a function of grating tooth height, tooth width, refractive index, waveguide thickness, and period for rectangular gratings in heterostructure waveguiding geometries.

Manuscript received January 22, 1976; revised March 9, 1976.
The authors are with the Xerox Palo Alto Research Center, Palo Alto, CA 94304.

II. Formulation

Consider TE modes of the structure shown in Fig. 1. The E-field is in the y direction and satisfies

$$\frac{\partial^2 E_y}{\partial x^2} + \frac{\partial^2 E_y}{\partial z^2} + k_0^2 n^2(x,z) E_y = 0 \tag{1}$$

where a time dependence $\exp(-i\omega t)$ has been assumed, $k_0 = 2\pi/\lambda_0$, λ_0 is the free-space wavelength, and $n^2(x, z)$ is the squared refractive index which is equal to the relative dielectric constant. Next, we express the mode field E_y as an infinite summation of partial waves in a form dictated by Floquet's theorem,

$$E_y(x,z) = \sum_{m=-\infty}^{\infty} \mathcal{E}_m(x) \exp(i\beta_m z) \tag{2}$$

with

$$\beta_m = \beta_0 + \frac{2\pi m}{\Lambda} \tag{3}$$

where Λ is the grating period. If no grating were present, then all $\mathcal{E}_m(x)$ with $m \neq 0$ would be zero, whereas $\mathcal{E}_0(x)$ and β_0 are the mode pattern and propagation constant of that unperturbed waveguide structure.

Next we express $n^2(x, z)$ analytically as

$$n^2(x,z) = \begin{cases} n_1^2, & x<0 \\ \sum_{p=-\infty}^{\infty} [n_1^2\{u[z - w_1(x) - p\Lambda] - u[z - w_2(x) - p\Lambda]\} & \\ \quad + n_2^2\{u[z - w_2(x) - p\Lambda] & \\ \quad - u[z - w_1(x) - (p+1)\Lambda]\}], & 0<x<g \\ n_2^2, & g<x<t \\ n_3^2, & t<x \end{cases} \tag{4}$$

where the functions $w_1(x)$ and $w_2(x)$ express the tooth shape as shown in Fig. 1 and u is the unit step function. Then since $n^2(x, z)$ is periodic in z, we write

$$n^2(x,z) = n_0^2(x) + \sum_{\substack{q=-\infty \\ q\neq 0}}^{\infty} A_q(x) \exp(i2\pi qz/\Lambda) \tag{5}$$

Reprinted from *IEEE J. Quantum Electron.*, vol. QE-12, no. 7, pp. 422–428, July 1976.

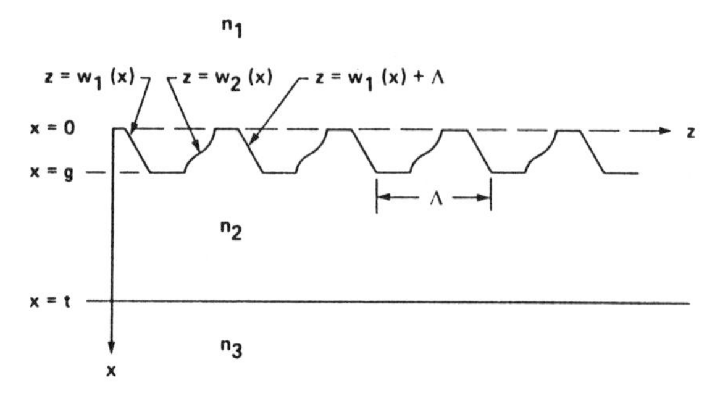

Fig. 1. A waveguide with a grating.

where

$$n_0^2(x) = \begin{cases} n_1^2, & x<0 \\ \{n_1^2[w_2(x)-w_1(x)] + n_2^2[\Lambda + w_1(x) - w_2(x)]\}/\Lambda, & 0<x<g \\ n_2^2, & g<x<t \\ n_3^2, & t<x. \end{cases} \tag{6}$$

This quantity just equals $n^2(x,z)$ outside the grating region, and inside that region it equals the Fourier series term with no z-dependence which would correspond to $A_0(x)$. Thus $A_0(x) \equiv 0$. The other Fourier coefficients ($q \neq 0$) are given by

$$A_q(x) = \begin{cases} 0, & x<0, g<x \\ \frac{1}{\Lambda}\int_{-\Lambda/2}^{\Lambda/2} n^2(x,z)\exp(-i2\pi qz/\Lambda)\,dz \\ = \frac{(n_2^2 - n_1^2)}{i2\pi q}\{\exp[-i2\pi q w_2(x)/\Lambda] \\ - \exp[-i2\pi q w_1(x)/\Lambda]\}, & 0<x<g. \end{cases} \tag{7}$$

Upon substituting (5) and (2) in the differential equation (1) and collecting all terms with the same z-dependence we obtain

$$\frac{d^2\mathcal{E}_m}{dx^2} + [k_0^2 n_0^2(x) - \beta_m^2]\,\mathcal{E}_m = -k_0^2 \sum_{\substack{q=-\infty \\ q\neq m}}^{\infty} A_{m-q}(x)\,\mathcal{E}_q(x), \;\forall m \tag{8}$$

where the $q = m$ term has been omitted from the summation since $A_0(x) \equiv 0$.

The system of (8), satisfied by $\mathcal{E}_m$, determines a single mode of the corrugated waveguide when summed according to (2). The solution of (8), subject to the boundary conditions of E_y and $H_z \propto \partial E_y/\partial z$ continuity at $x = 0$, g, and t, determines β_0 and through (3), β_m. (Note that E_y continuity ensures $H_x \propto \partial E_y/\partial x$ continuity.) Partial waves with $|\mathrm{Re}(\beta_m)| < \min(k_0 n_1, k_0 n_3)$ radiate power into both regions 1 and 3, whereas those with $|\mathrm{Re}(\beta_m)| > \max(k_0 n_1, k_0 n_3)$ exponentially decay in both regions [7]. For (say) $n_3 > n_1$, there may exist partial waves with $k_0 n_1 < |\mathrm{Re}(\beta_m)| < k_0 n_3$, which radiate into region 3 and not into region 1. If any radiation occurs, the mode loses power as it propagates and this loss is represented by a complex β_0:

$$\beta_0 = \beta_r + i\beta_i \tag{9a}$$

with

$$\mathrm{Im}(\beta_0) = \beta_i > 0. \tag{9b}$$

All the partial waves decay at the same rate since

$$\beta_m = \beta_r + \frac{2\pi m}{\Lambda} + i\beta_i. \tag{10}$$

Thus the mode power decay with propagation in z is given by $\exp(-\alpha z) = \exp(-2\beta_i z)$.

Next consider only the left side of (9) for $m = 0$,

$$\frac{d^2\mathcal{E}_0}{dx^2} + [k_0^2 n_0^2(x) - \beta_0^2]\,\mathcal{E}_0 = 0 \tag{11}$$

with $n_0^2(x)$ given by (7). Clearly $n_0^2(x)$ describes a four-layer waveguiding structure; outside the grating region for $x<0$ and $x<g$ this waveguide is identical to the original, for $g>x>0$, $n_0^2(x)$ is equal to $n^2(x,z)$ in the grating region averaged along z for each x. For example, $n_0^2(x)$ for rectangular teeth is a constant equal to the average of n^2 in the grating region (see [6] and [8]). For any trapezoidal- (including all triangular-) shaped teeth $n_0^2(x)$ varies linearly across the grating region.

If (11) is solved for $\mathcal{E}_0$ and β_0, and then only $\mathcal{E}_0$ is used to drive other $\mathcal{E}_m (m \neq 0)$ in the right side of (8), i.e.,

$$\frac{d^2\mathcal{E}_m}{dx^2} + [k_0^2 n_0^2(x) - \beta_m^2]\,\mathcal{E}_m = -k_0^2 A_m(x)\,\mathcal{E}_0(x) \tag{12}$$

we obtain a first-order perturbation solution for $\mathcal{E}_m$. This is just the technique carried out in [6] for rectangular-shaped gratings.

The value of β_0 determined by (11) alone is real and therefore does not reflect power lost through radiation. Instead, the time-averaged power lost by the partial wave $\mathcal{E}_m$ per unit length is found, using the Poynting vector, to be

$$P_m = \frac{1}{2\omega\mu_0}\mathrm{Re}\,\{\sqrt{k_0^2 n_1^2 - \beta_m^2}\,|\mathcal{E}_m(0)|^2 + \sqrt{k_0^2 n_3^2 - \beta_m^2}\,|\mathcal{E}_m(t)|^2\}. \tag{13}$$

Here the first and second bracketed terms are the parts radiated into regions 1 and 3, respectively, and if β_m^2 exceeds $k_0^2 n_1^2$ and/or $k_0^2 n_3^2$, imaginary terms occur in (13) which do not contribute to P_m. Thus $P_m = 0$ for all terms with $m \geq 0$ and with sufficiently large negative m, which could be $m = -1$ for small Λ. Since the radiated power is proportional to the guided power it is convenient to use the normalized measure of radiated power given by α, the exponential rate at which power is lost by the $\mathcal{E}_0$ wave. From (13)

$$\alpha = \sum_m P_m / \{(\beta_0/2\omega\mu_0)\int_{-\infty}^{\infty} |\mathcal{E}_0(x)|^2\,dx\}. \tag{14}$$

To solve (8) more accurately, we use the approximate solutions obtained in the perturbation technique above to evaluate the right side of (8) for $m = 0$ and thereby obtain more accurate solutions for $\mathcal{E}_0$ and β_0. Then (8) is solved for all other values of m using the current partial wave solutions to evaluate the right side. This process is continued until convergence. The above remarks are illustrated by calculations for rectangular gratings presented in the next section.

III. Results for Rectangular Gratings

Algebraic details of solutions for rectangular-shaped gratings are given in Appendix A and some comments concerning the numerical techniques employed are included in Appendix B. The results presented below for α in the form of continuous curves were obtained utilizing the perturbation technique and (13) and (14). This procedure yields accurate data in many cases of practical interest with little expenditure of computer time. Specific points computed by the numerical iteration technique using summations of the partial waves with $-8 \leq m \leq 5$ are also shown for comparison purposes. Here $\alpha = 2\,\mathrm{Im}\,(\beta)$. In all cases, iterations were continued to convergence as determined by changes in the Im (β) of less than 1 part in 10^4. This calculation requires a comparatively large amount of computer time, which explains the few "exact" points computed and plotted.

In the results w is the grating tooth width of n_1^2 material so that $\Lambda - w$ is the width of n_2^2 material. The refractive index squared in the grating region is

$$n_4^2 = [n_1^2 w + n_2^2 (\Lambda - w)]/\Lambda. \tag{15}$$

Fig. 2 is a plot of α for total radiated power versus grating tooth height, g, in a double-heterostructure waveguide or laser geometry with $n_1 = n_3 = 3.4$, $n_2 = 3.6$, and a 1.0-μm-thick guiding region as measured to the outside of the grating. The grating period is $\Lambda = 2100$ Å, $w/\Lambda = 0.25$, and the free-space wavelength is $\lambda_0 = 8800$ Å. With these values of λ_0 and Λ, only the $m = -1$ partial wave radiates and that wave radiates in a backward direction into both media 1 and 3. The radiation directions are equal in regions 1 and 3 only because $n_1 = n_3$. Since the waveguiding geometry as described by (6) in which the partial waves $\mathcal{E}_m(x)$ are determined varies with grating height, g, the propagation constants of the guided modes vary with g, and so too does the angle at which light is radiated. Specifically, the radiation in regions 1 and 3 makes angles of 100.3°-100.6°, 101.2°-101.7°, 102.6°-102.9° with the propagation direction in the waveguide for the TE_0, TE_1, and TE_2 modes, respectively, where the lower values apply in the limit $g = 0.0$ μm and the higher values apply for $g = 0.5$ μm. Of course, in passing through a GaAlAs (index 3.4): air interface the wave is refracted.

The calculation reveals that for this particular situation the powers radiated into regions 1 and 3 are approximately equal. Since the differences would be difficult to discern if plotted on the scale of Fig. 2, we have shown only α resulting from the sum of power radiated into 1 and 3.

Consider first the plot for the TE_0 mode. The radiated power is an increasing function of g with a superimposed oscillation, whose period is approximately equal to the wavelength of light in the material, λ. As expected, radiation is strongest for $g \approx \lambda/2$, $3\lambda/2$, and $5\lambda/2$. For $g \approx \lambda$ and 2λ, power is trapped in the grating region by resonance in the transverse direction. Radiated power generally increases with g because the overlap of $\mathcal{E}_0$ and the radiating partial wave $\mathcal{E}_{-1}$ increases. A comparison of the points obtained from the iterated solution and the perturbation solution curve leads to the perhaps surprising conclusion that the perturbation results are quite accurate even for gratings which are several λ in height. This

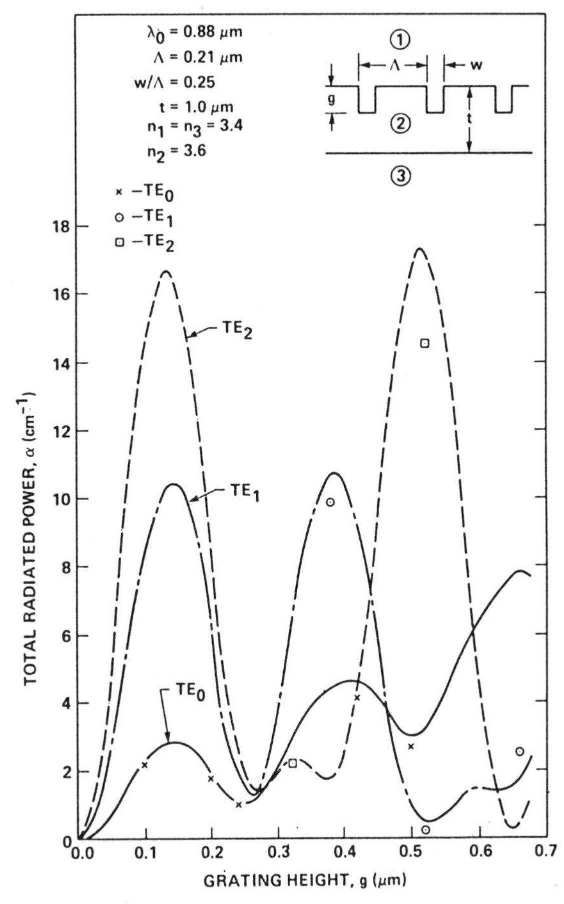

Fig. 2. Total radiated power versus tooth height for a rectangular grating. Discrete points are iterative solution results.

is the case when the index differential at the grating is not large as in this figure.

The TE_1 and TE_2 modes also exhibit oscillations in radiated power, but in addition there exist irregularities in these curves. These occur for $0.5 < g < 0.6$ for the TE_1 mode and for $0.3 < g < 0.4$ for the TE_2 mode. An examination of the TE_1 mode pattern of $\mathcal{E}_0$ reveals that the mode undergoes a 180° phase shift near the base of the teeth for $0.5 < g < 0.6$. Thus $\mathcal{E}_0$ exciting the TE radiating partial wave $\mathcal{E}_{-1}$ actually reduces its integrated driving effect just as the tooth height approaches $5\lambda/2$. The net effect of these competing phenomena is to produce the curve shape shown. The situation is identical for the TE_2 mode with $0.3 < g < 0.4$.

For small values of g the TE_2 radiated power exceeds that of the TE_1, which in turn exceeds that of the TE_0. This occurs because of the greater percentage of higher mode power in the grating vicinity. It is also important to note that even for relatively small grating heights, i.e., 1500 Å, α is comparable in value to mode decay produced by free-carrier absorption losses, e.g., 10 cm^{-1}.

In Fig. 3 we plot radiated power as a function of w for the same waveguide geometry as in Fig. 2 with $g = 0.2$ μm. All three modes have a radiation peak near $w/\Lambda = 0.5$ because the dependence of the dominant coefficient coupling $\mathcal{E}_0$ and $\mathcal{E}_{-1}$, i.e., A_{-1}, on w is given by $A_{-1} \propto \sin(\pi w/\Lambda)$ [see Appendix A]. However, the peak occurs just below $w/\Lambda = 0.5$ and the curves are not symmetric about that value. The asymmetry results

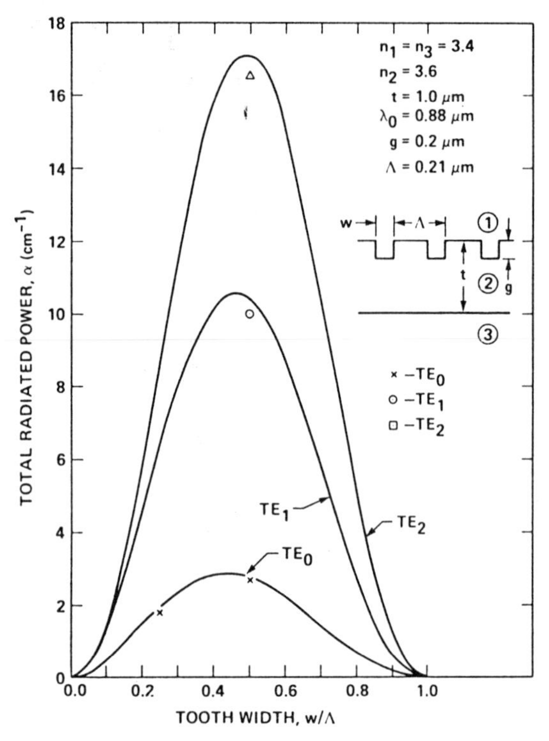

Fig. 3. Total radiated power versus tooth width for a rectangular grating. Discrete points are iterative solution results.

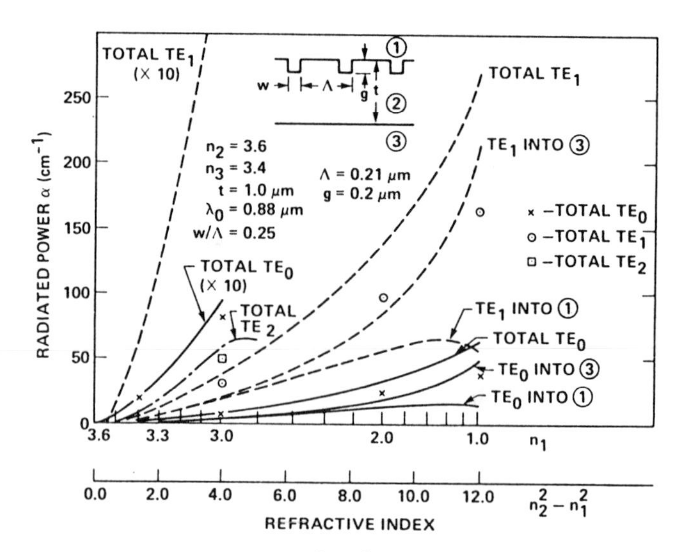

Fig. 4. Radiated power versus $n_2^2 - n_1^2$ for a rectangular grating. Discrete points are iterative solution results.

from the decreased penetration of $\mathcal{E}_0$ into the grating region with decreasing n_4^2 [increasing w according to (15)]. Furthermore, the higher order transverse modes are less sensitive to variations in w in this respect because their equivalent refractive indices as determined by their propagation constants are smaller.

Fig. 4 is a plot of radiated power versus the refractive index n_1 of the outer medium at the corrugated interface for the same waveguiding geometry as above with $w/\Lambda = 0.25$. The actual horizontal scale is in equal increments of $n_2^2 - n_1^2$, which is the difference in relative dielectric constant at the grating teeth and is the quantity occurring naturally in the analysis. Equally spaced increments in n_1 of 0.2 between 1.0 and 3.0, and of 0.1 between 3.0 and 3.6 are also shown on the abscissa. Values of n_1 between 3.6 and 2.9 may be obtained in practice by varying Al composition in $Ga_{1-x}Al_xAs$ from $x = 0.0$ to $x = 1.0$. The interesting and important result illustrated by this figure is the dramatic increase in radiated power with increasing $n_2^2 - n_1^2$. The continuous curves for total radiated power are approximately quadratic. This dependence occurs because the A_{-1} coefficient coupling $\mathcal{E}_0$ and $\mathcal{E}_{-1}$ [see (A1)] is proportional to $n_2^2 - n_1^2$ and the radiated power is proportional to $|\mathcal{E}_{-1}|^2$. Again we observe that for this rectangular grating radiated power divides approximately equally between regions 1 and 3 for smaller values of $n_2^2 - n_1^2$, but for increasing $n_2^2 - n_1^2$ more power is radiated into region 3, whose refractive index n_3 is significantly higher than n_1. The curve for the TE_2 mode exists only for $n_1 > 2.8$ since below that value this mode is beyond cutoff. It is also important to examine the accuracy of the perturbation calculation as a function of $n_2^2 - n_1^2$. Clearly since all coefficients A_q are proportional to $n_2^2 - n_1^2$, all partial waves are coupled more strongly with increases in this parameter. The perturbation technique used to compute the continuous curves in Fig. 5 includes only the first-order effect between $\mathcal{E}_0$ and $\mathcal{E}_{-1}$, which is proportional to $n_2^2 - n_1^2$ as noted above, whereas the points marking exact solutions contain all partial waves with $-8 \leqslant m \leqslant 5$ including coupling effects which depend on higher powers of $n_2^2 - n_1^2$. Thus the accuracy of the perturbation solution decreases significantly with increasing $n_2^2 - n_1^2$, but even for large differences, e.g., as occur with $n_1 = 1.0$, the perturbation technique yields results accurate to much better than an order of magnitude.

In Fig. 5 we plot radiated power versus the refractive index of region 3 for the TE_0 mode in the same waveguiding geometry as above with $n_1 = 3.4$. We observe that the total radiated power increases with decreasing n_3. For n_3 near 3.6 there is a rapid increase in radiated power as n_3 decreases because the mode then experiences a greater degree of confinement, i.e., the mode power in region 3 decreases rapidly as n_3 decreases. As n_3 continues to decrease (say, below 3.4) the mode penetrates the grating region more strongly since then n_3 is much less than n_4 and n_1. We note, too, that for larger values of n_3 power radiates approximately equally into regions 1 and 3, but for smaller values of n_3 more power is radiated into region 1.

Radiated power versus waveguide thickness t is plotted in Fig. 6 for the same geometry as studied above. The curve for each TE mode shows a rapid increase as t exceeds the value corresponding to mode cutoff. This increase occurs because the mode confinement improves rapidly above the cutoff thickness value. With continued increases in t there is a gradual decrease in radiated power resulting from the decreased field penetration into the grating region.

Fig. 7 is a plot of radiated power by each partial wave versus grating period for the TE_0 mode in the same waveguide as above with $t = 1.0\ \mu m$. The figure also contains broken curves of radiation angle versus Λ, where the angle is measured from the horizontal and is zero in the forward direction. The angle is computed from

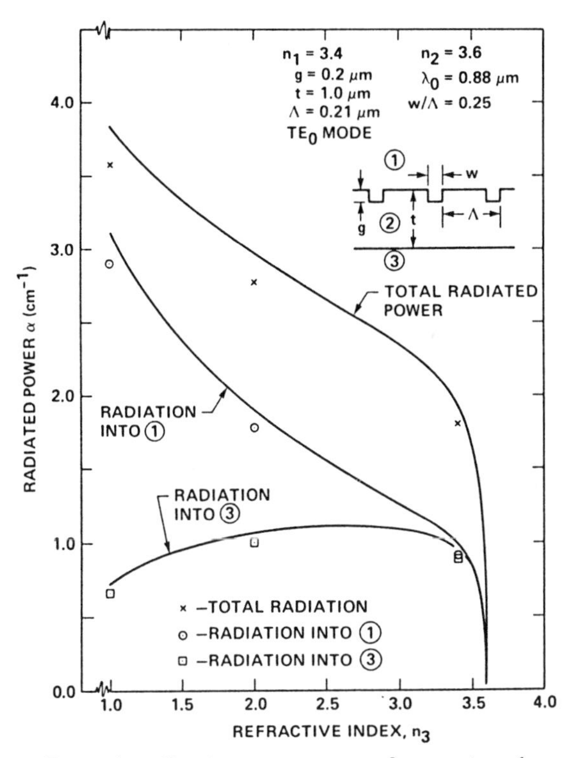

Fig. 5. TE_0 mode radiated power versus n_3 for a rectangular grating. Discrete points are iterative solution results.

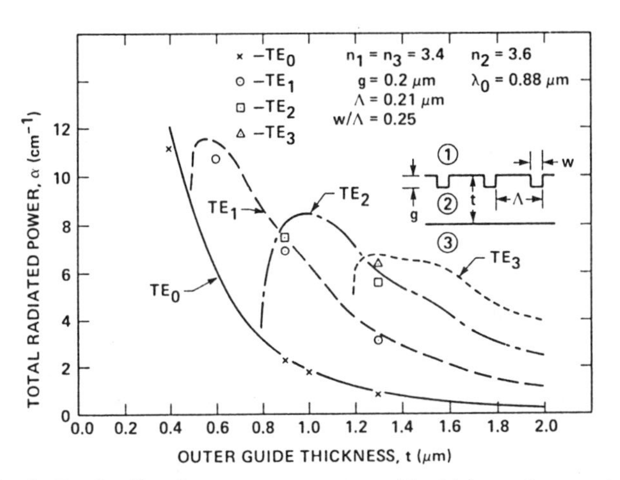

Fig. 6. Total radiated power versus outer guide thickness for a rectangular grating. Discrete points are iterative solution results.

$$\theta_i = \cos^{-1} [\beta_m/(2\pi n_i/\lambda_0)], \qquad i = 1,3 \tag{16}$$

where β_m is given by (3), λ_0 is the free-space wavelength, and n_i is the refractive index of media 1 or 3. In this plot, $n_1 = n_3 = 3.4$ so that the radiation angles are equal in the two media. For small values of Λ, all partial waves are trapped within the waveguide. At $\Lambda = 0.1229$ μm, $\beta_{-1} = -\beta_0$, and the grating functions to provide distributed feedback (DFB) in the first Bragg order. For very slightly larger Λ, $|\beta_{-1}| < \beta_0$, but since the equivalent refractive index, as given by

$$n_{eq} = \frac{\lambda_0 |\beta_{-1}|}{2\pi} \tag{17}$$

exceeds n_1, n_3 there exists no radiated partial wave; rather a guided wave propagating with β_{-1}. However, at $\Lambda = 0.1261$ μm, radiation begins to escape from the waveguide.

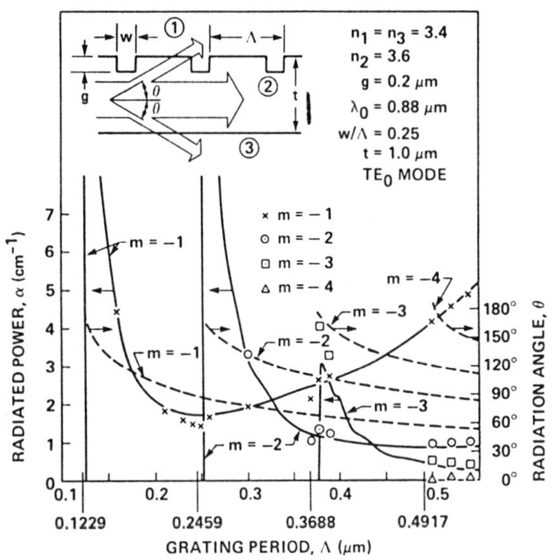

Fig. 7. TE_0 mode radiated power (solid curves) and radiation angle (broken curves) versus grating period for each partial wave. Discrete points are iterative solution results.

This value of Λ is obtained from (17) and (3) with $n_{eq} = 3.4$. At that value $\theta_1 = \theta_3 = 180°$. With continuing increases in Λ, the radiated power in the $m = -1$ partial wave rapidly peaks and then starts to decrease as the radiation angle moves toward the vertical ($\theta = 90°$). We note that as Λ approaches $\Lambda = 0.2459$ μm, at which value $\beta_{-2} = -\beta_0$, the accuracy of the perturbation technique decreases. At $\Lambda = 0.2459$ μm the grating functions in the second Bragg order to provide DFB, and the grating resonantly couples the partial traveling wave $\mathcal{E}_0$ to its oppositely traveling identical wave $\mathcal{E}_{-2}$. Since the perturbation theory used to obtain the curve does not take into account the coupling between $\mathcal{E}_{-2}$ and $\mathcal{E}_{-1}$, but only between $\mathcal{E}_0$ and $\mathcal{E}_{-1}$, it becomes inaccurate. For this Λ, $\beta_{-1} = 0.0$ and therefore, according to (16), the $m = -1$ radiating partial wave is emitted normally. This is also the region in which the $m = -1$ radiated power is a minimum.

At $\Lambda = 0.2522$ μm the $m = -2$ partial wave begins to radiate and with increasing Λ, the process continues. Third-order Bragg scattering to produce DFB occurs at $\Lambda = 0.3688$ μm, and the $m = -3$ partial wave begins to radiate at $\Lambda = 03783$ μm. The perturbation calculations are again inaccurate in this region. At $\Lambda = 0.4917$ μm, $\beta_{-4} = -\beta_0$ and $\beta_{-2} = 0.0$ so that the $m = -2$ partial wave radiates normally. Then at $\Lambda = 0.5044$ μm the $m = -4$ partial wave begins to radiate. For the particular tooth width $w/\Lambda = 0.25$, $A_{-4} = 0$, since $A_{-4} \propto \sin(4\pi w/\Lambda)$ [see Appendix A]. Thus the perturbation technique predicts no $m = -4$ partial wave and therefore no radiation. The iterative solution indicates that some small $m = -4$ partial wave does exist; it is produced by partial waves other than $\mathcal{E}_0$ coupling to $\mathcal{E}_{-4}$. Since all $\mathcal{E}_m$ ($m \neq 0$) are generally small compared to $\mathcal{E}_0$, the partial wave $\mathcal{E}_{-4}$ is very weak and radiates very little power.

IV. Concluding Remarks

We have employed an accurate perturbation technique and an iterative procedure to calculate radiation from gratings in waveguide geometries. The results indicate optimum parameter values to maximize radiation. In particular it was shown that there exist optimal tooth heights and that the index difference at a grating should be as large as possible to maximize radiated power. In a particular geometry with an air:GaAs interface at the grating, radiated power of a mode exceeds 100 cm^{-1}.

APPENDIX A

ANALYSIS FOR RECTANGULAR GRATINGS

Consider a rectangular grating with a tooth width w of n_1^2 material as shown in Fig. 8. For this grating $w_2(x) = -w_1(x) = w/2$ and from (7)

$$A_q(x) = \begin{cases} \dfrac{-(n_2^2 - n_1^2)}{\pi q} \sin(\pi q w/\Lambda), & 0<x<g \\ 0, & x<0,\ g<x \quad q \neq 0 \end{cases} \tag{A1}$$

and

$$n_0^2(x) = \begin{cases} n_1^2 \\ n_4^2 = [w n_1^2 + (\Lambda - w) n_2^2]/\Lambda, & 0<x<g \\ n_2^2, & g<x<t \\ n_3^2, & t<x. \end{cases} \tag{A2}$$

We next rewrite (8) in the form

$$\frac{d^2 \mathcal{E}_m}{dx^2} + k_n^2(x)\, \mathcal{E}_m = \mathcal{F}_m(x), \quad \forall_m \tag{A3}$$

where

$$\mathcal{F}_m(x) = \begin{cases} -k_0^2 \sum\limits_{\substack{q=-\infty \\ q \neq m}}^{\infty} A_{m-q}(x)\, \mathcal{E}_q(x), & 0<x<g \\ 0, & x<0,\ g<x, \end{cases} \tag{A4}$$

$$k_m^2(x) = k_0^2 n_0^2(x) - \beta_m^2 = k_{mj}^2, \quad j = 1,2,3,4, \tag{A5}$$

and the subscript j in (A5) for $j = 1,2,3$ refers to regions 1,2,3 whereas $j = 4$ refers to the grating region.

Each equation in (A3) is formally solved using variation of parameters. Then imposing continuity conditions on $\mathcal{E}_m$ and $d\mathcal{E}_m/dx$ at $x = 0$ and t, we obtain

$$\mathcal{E}_m(x) = \begin{cases} C_{m1} \exp(-ik_{m1} x), & x<0 \\ C_{m1} [\cos(k_{m4} x) - (ik_{m1}/k_{m4}) \sin(k_{m4} x)] + T_m(x), & 0<x<g \\ C_{m3}\{\cos[k_{m2}(t-x)] - (ik_{m3}/k_{m2}) \cdot \sin[k_{m2}(t-x)]\}, & g<x<t \\ C_{m3} \exp[ik_{m3}(x-t)], & t<x \end{cases} \tag{A6}$$

where

$$T_m(x) = \frac{1}{k_{m4}} \int_0^x \mathcal{F}_m(\xi) \sin[k_{m4}(x-\xi)]\, d\xi. \tag{A7}$$

Since $T_m(x)$ and its derivative are zero at $x = 0$, i.e., $T_m(0) = 0$,

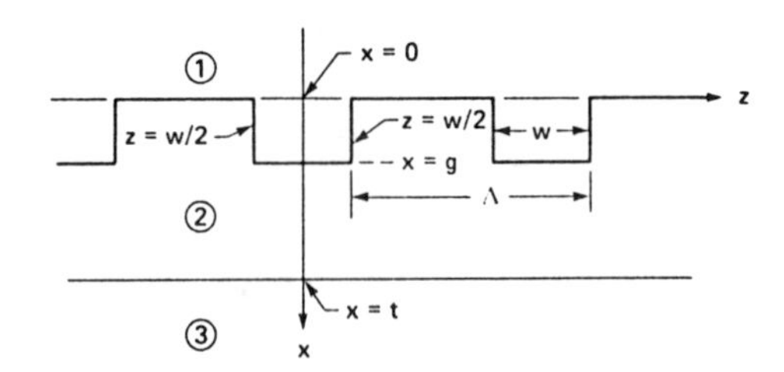

Fig. 8. Illustrating the geometry of a rectangular grating.

$dT_m/dx|_0 = 0$, the solution as given by (A6) is continuous and since T_m satisfies

$$\frac{d^2 T_m}{dx^2} + k_{m4}^2 T_m = \mathcal{F}_m, \quad 0<x<g \tag{A8}$$

(A6) also satisfies the differential equation (A3) with $\mathcal{F}_m$ given by (A4). In (A6) and (A7), k_{mj} as defined by (A5) is, in general, complex and thus also are the sine and cosine functions and the coefficients C_{m1} and C_{m3}. For $m = 0$, we set $C_{01} = 1$, solve for C_{03} by requiring continuity of $\mathcal{E}_0$ at $x = g$, and solve for β_0, which determines k_{0j}, by requiring continuity of $d\mathcal{E}_0/dx$ at $x = g$ [see Appendix B]. For $m \neq 0$, with k_{mj} assumed known, the coefficients are determined by requiring continuity of $\mathcal{E}_m$ and $d\mathcal{E}_m/dx$ at $x = g$. In both situations $T_m(g)$ is given by (A7) with $x = g$ and

$$\left.\frac{dT_m}{dx}\right|_g = \int_0^g \mathcal{F}_m(\xi) \cos[k_{m4}(g-\xi)]\, d\xi. \tag{A9}$$

It is necessary to clarify the calculation of k_{mj} as defined by (A5). The choice of sign is unimportant in the case of k_{m2} and k_{m4} since the expressions in (A6) apply if either sign is chosen. However, in the outer regions the partial wave fields must decay away from the waveguide if the partial wave is confined and must travel away from the guide if it radiates [9]. Specifically, from (A5) for a particular partial wave if

$$k_0^2 n_0^2 > \mathrm{Re}(\beta_m^2) = \mathrm{Re}\{(\beta_0 + 2\pi m/\Lambda)^2\} \tag{A10}$$

in either outer region, the partial wave radiates in that region; otherwise it decays there. Thus all partial waves with $m \geqslant 0$ decay in both outer regions, all partial waves with sufficiently negative m also decay outside the guide, and some partial waves with $m \leqslant -1$ radiate in one or both outer regions if (A10) is satisfied. The conditions on radiating waves imply that those which radiate in a forward direction actually increase in intensity along lines normal to the guide. In this case the partial wave at some distance from the guide was radiated by the mode before it decayed to its current value [10].

APPENDIX B

SOLUTION TECHNIQUE

It was demonstrated in Appendix A that knowledge of β_0 and $\mathcal{F}_m(x)$ enable one to compute all the partial waves, but $\mathcal{F}_m(x)$ itself depends on the partial waves and β_0 is also an unknown. The procedure used to resolve this problem is as follows.

First we set $\mathcal{F}_0(x) \equiv 0$ [and therefore $T_0(x) \equiv 0$] and calculate $\mathcal{E}_0(x)$ and β_0. Next this value of β_0 is used in (A5) to calculate k_{mj}, and $\mathcal{E}_0(x)$ is used to estimate $\mathcal{F}_m(x), m \neq 0$; all

$\mathcal{E}_m(x)$ other than $\mathcal{E}_0(x)$ are ignored in this calculation of $\mathcal{F}_m(x)$. With these estimates of k_{mj} and $\mathcal{F}_m(x)$, all $\mathcal{E}_m(x)$, $m \neq 0$ are determined. This constitutes the perturbation calculation of the partial wave fields and, together with (13) and (14), yields α.

To obtain more accurate solutions, all $\mathcal{E}_m(x)$ are employed to determine first $\mathcal{F}_0(x)$, and then, simultaneously, $\mathcal{E}_0(x)$ and β_0 (β_0 is computed numerically as described below). Next, β_0 and all the current estimates of the partial wave fields are used to determine $\mathcal{F}_m(x)$, noting that $\mathcal{F}_m(x)$ as given by (A4) does not depend on $\mathcal{E}_m(x)$. Finally all $\mathcal{E}_m(x)$, $m \neq 0$, are computed and used to obtain first $\mathcal{F}_0(x)$ and then, simultaneously, $\mathcal{E}_0(x)$ and β_0. This entire process, which is illustrated by the flow chart of Fig. 9, is repeated until convergence.

The solution for β_0 is as follows. After C_{01} is set equal to 1, we obtain

$$C_{03} = \frac{\cos(k_{04}g) - (ik_{01}/k_{04})\sin(k_{04}g) + T_0(g)}{\cos[k_{02}(t-g)] - (ik_{03}/k_{02})\sin[k_{02}(t-g)]} \quad \text{(B1)}$$

by requiring $\mathcal{E}_0$ to be continuous at $x = g$. Then $d\mathcal{E}_0/dx$ will be continuous at $x = g$ if

$$R(\beta_0) = k_{04}\sin(k_{04}g) + ik_{01}\cos(k_{04}g) - dT_0/dx|_g + C_{03}\{k_{02}\sin[k_{02}(t-g)] + ik_{03}\cos[k_{02}(t-g)]\} = 0 \quad \text{(B2)}$$

where C_{03} is given by (B1). It should be recalled that all k_{0j} and C_{03} are functions of β_0. To solve (B2), we expand $R(\beta_0)$ about the unknown solution value β_{0s}, i.e., $R(\beta_{0s}) = 0$, retain one term of the series, and solve for β_{0s},

$$\beta_{0s} = \beta_0 - R(\beta_0)/[dR/d\beta_0]. \quad \text{(B3)}$$

An estimate of β_0 is used in the right side of (B3), β_{0s} is calculated and this process is repeated until $|R(\beta_0)|$ is sufficiently small. For the first calculation, in which case $T_0(x) \equiv 0$, β_0 is real and the procedure presents no difficulties. For later calculations we employ the β_{0s} value from the previously determined partial waves as a starting point. Convergence occurred in almost all cases, except for very large grating teeth, i.e., $g = 0.66\ \mu$m in the geometry of Fig. 2. There, no solutions of (B2) for the TE_0 and TE_2 modes exist with the initially calculated values of $T_0(g)$ and $dT_0/dx|_g$. Of course the formulation still applies, but the iterative solution will not converge without modification.

The calculation of $T_m(x)$ according to (A7) requires numerical evaluation of the integral since after the first iteration $\mathcal{F}_m(x)$ is known only numerically. However, direct evaluation of (A7) proved to be quite inaccurate and wasteful of computer time for large values of $|m|$, in which case k_{m4} is a large complex number. Indeed, the sine function evaluation often produced floating point overflows in the computer. This situation was aggravated by the fact that $T_m(x)$ and $C_{m1}[\cos(k_{m4}x) - (ik_{m1}/k_{m4})\sin(k_{m4}x)]$ in (A6) were both large and added to yield a small difference. We therefore abandoned this approach and instead solved (A3) directly for $\mathcal{E}_m(x)$ with $0 < x < g$. This was accomplished by dividing the grating region into twenty segments and using

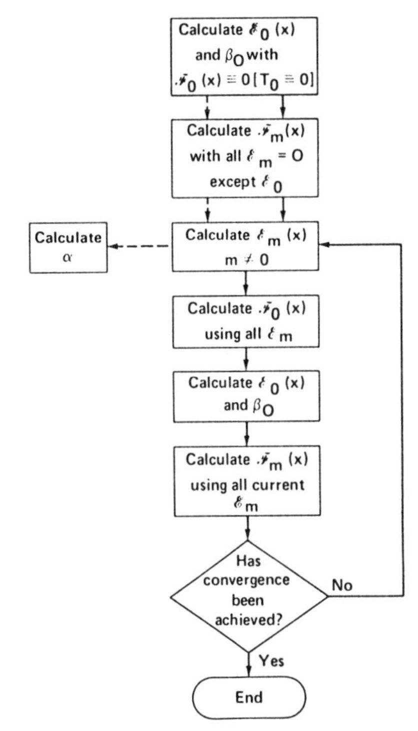

Fig. 9. Flow chart illustrating the solution procedure. The perturbation method follows the dashed path; the iterative technique follows the solid path.

difference methods to solve for the field at these points. Even here care had to be taken to avoid roundoff problems in solving the resultant matrix equation.

References

[1] H. Kogelnik and C. V. Shank, "Coupled mode theory of distributed feedback lasers," *J. Appl. Phys.*, vol. 43, pp. 2327-2335, 1972.

[2] Zh. I. Alferov *et al.*, "Semiconductor laser with extremely low divergence of radiation" (in Russian), *Sov. Phys.-Semicond.*, vol. 8, pp. 832-833, 1974; also (in English), *Sov. Phys.-JETP*, pp. 541-542, 1974.

[3] R. D. Burnham, D. R. Scifres, and W. Streifer, "Low divergence beams from grating coupled composite guide heterostructure GaAlAs diode lasers," *Appl. Phys. Lett.*, vol. 26, pp. 644-647, 1975.

[4] P. Zory and L. D. Comerford, "Grating-coupled double-heterostructure AlGaAs Diode Lasers," *IEEE J. Quant. Elect.*, vol. QE-11, pp. 451-457, 1975.

[5] D. R. Scifres, R. D. Burnham, and W. Streifer, "Output coupling and distributed feedback utilizing substrate corrugations in double-heterostructure GaAs lasers," *Appl. Phys. Lett.*, vol. 27, pp. 295-297, 1975.

[6] K. Handa, S. T. Peng, and T. Tamir, "Improved perturbation analysis of dielectric gratings," *Appl. Phys.*, vol. 5, pp. 325-328, 1975.

[7] T. Tamir, "Inhomogeneous wave types at planar interfaces:III-Leaky waves," *Optik*, vol. 38, pp. 269-297, 1973.

[8] W. Streifer, D. R. Scifres, and R. D. Burnham, "TM mode coupling coefficients in guided wave distributed feedback lasers," *IEEE J. Quant. Elect.*, vol. QE-12, pp. 74-78, Feb. 1976.

[9] A. Hessel, "General characteristics of traveling wave antennas," in *Antenna Theory-Part II*, R. E. Collin and F. J. Zucker, Ed. New York: McGraw-Hill, 1969, ch. 19, pp. 151-258 (particularly, p. 203 ff.).

[10] A. A. Oliner, "Leaky waves in electromagnetic phenomena," in *Electromagnetic Theory and Antennas, Part II*, E. C. Jordan, Ed. New York: Pergamon, 1963, pp. 837-856.

Frequency multiplexing light source with monolithically integrated distributed-feedback diode lasers

K. Aiki, M. Nakamura, and J. Umeda

Central Research Laboratory, Hitachi, Ltd., Kokubunji, Tokyo, Japan
(Received 29 June 1976)

A frequency multiplexing light source is realized by monolithically integrating GaAs-GaAlAs distributed-feedback diode lasers with different grating periods and passive waveguides on a GaAs substrate. The lasers with wavelength separation of ~20 Å are modulated independently, and the output beams are obtained from a common launching waveguide.

PACS numbers: 42.82.+n, 42.60.Jf, 84.40.Vt, 42.80.Sa

The successful performance of distributed-feedback (DFB) semiconductor lasers at room temperature reported previously[1-3] makes these new-type lasers more and more practical. Their promising features such as frequency selectivity and integration capability are expected to induce various applications in the future. This letter reports a frequency multiplexing light source with monolithically integrated DFB diode lasers. In the process, six DFB lasers with different grating periods are integrated with passive waveguides on a single chip, and individually modulated laser outputs with different frequencies are collected into a launching waveguide. This is, to our knowledge, the first demonstration of the realistic optical IC having the function of frequency multiplexing.

A schematic cross-sectional view of the waveguide coupled DFB lasers studied here is shown in Fig. 1. The DFB lasers incorporated are of a separate confinement hetero (SCH) structure,[4,5] which has been proved to be useful in reducing threshold current density.[2,6] The laser beam is guided from the DFB laser to a relatively thick $Ga_{0.9}Al_{0.1}As$ layer through a stepped coupling region as shown in Fig. 1. A top view of the optical IC fabricated here is shown in Fig. 2(a). In this experiment, six lasers were integrated with passive waveguides. The grating period of each laser was selected in such a way that the expected wavelength separation was ~20 Å. The waveguides having a mesa-stripe geometry with a 20 μm width were bent in such a way as to join into a single guide. The radius of the bend was ~4 mm.

The structure was fabricated as follows, a n-$Ga_{1-x}Al_xAs$ layer ($x=0.3$, ~1 μm thick), a p-GaAs active layer (~0.2 μm thick), a p-$Ga_{1-y}Al_yAs$ layer ($y=0.2$, ~0.1 μm thick), and a p-$Ga_{1-z}Al_zAs$ layer ($z=0.07$, ~0.2 μm thick) were successively grown on a n-GaAs substrate by conventional liquid-phase epitaxy (LPE). Third-order gratings were made on the surface by chemical etching through a mask produced by holographic photolithography. Six grating zones with different periods were formed by successive exposure through a sliding slit. The wafer was then chemically etched down to the substrate except for the region where the DFB lasers would be made. A p-$Ga_{1-x}Al_xAs$ layer

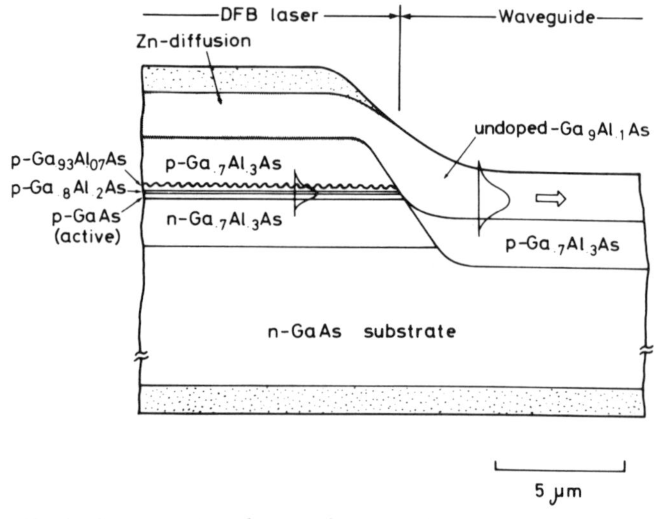

FIG. 1. Cross-sectional view of waveguide coupled DFB laser.

($x=0.3$, ~2 μm thick) and an undoped $Ga_{1-w}Al_wAs$ layer ($w=0.1$, ~2 μm thick) were regrown on the wafer by the LPE under relatively rapid growth condition.[7] The p-$Ga_{1-x}Al_xAs$ layer was grown within a 90-sec duration at ~700 °C with a cooling rate of 5 °C min. The p-$Ga_{1-x}Al_xAs$ layer grown under these conditions was split at the step as shown schematically in Fig. 1. This effectively guided the laser output to the undoped $Ga_{1-w}Al_wAs$ guiding layer. This layer was undoped in order to reduce free-carrier absorption loss. Zinc was selectively diffused in the DFB laser region as shown in Fig. 1. Ohmic contacts were provided by evaporating Cr and Au on the p side and Au-Ge-Ni on the n side.

The threshold current density of each DFB laser on a single chip ranged from 3 to 6 kA/cm² at room temperature. The lasing wavelength separation was 20 ± 5 Å, and the spectral width of each laser was ~0.3 Å. An infrared TV photograph of the device while two of the DFB lasers were excited is shown in Fig. 2(b). The lights emitted from the DFB lasers are successfully guided to the launching terminal with no significant leakage at the bends or the confluences. The DFB laser to waveguide coupling efficiency was estimated to be ~30%, and the waveguide loss was measured to be about 5 cm⁻¹. The over-all external quantum efficiency

Reprinted with permission from *Appl. Phys. Lett.*, vol. 29, no. 8, pp. 506–508, Oct. 15, 1976.

(a)

(b)

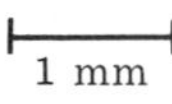

FIG. 2. Photographs of monolithically integrated frequency multiplexing light source. (a) Top view. (b) Scattered light pattern showing optical path when two DFB lasers are excited. Far-field pattern projected on a screen near the launching terminal is also shown.

measured at the launching terminal was ~0.3%, whereas that obtained from the direct DFB laser output was 7%. These characteristics can be improved by refinement of the device structures and fabrication techniques. Near-field and far-field patterns showed that the propagating light modes in the waveguides are multiple in the direction parallel to the junction plane, and mainly in the lowest order in the direction perpendicular to the junction plane.

An example of the multiplexing experiment, in which two DFB lasers were independently modulated by applying current pulses, is shown in Fig. 3. The multiplexed output from the launching terminal was demultiplexed by a monochrometer with a ~1-Å resolution. The spectra of the output beam, with diode a lasing at $\lambda_a = 8621.5$ Å and diode b at $\lambda_b = 8664.3$ Å, are shown in Fig. 3(a). The demultiplexed signal obtained at each wavelength appears in Fig. 3(b).

In summary, a frequency multiplexing light source has been realized by monolithically integrating DFB lasers with passive waveguides. In spite of the simple configu-

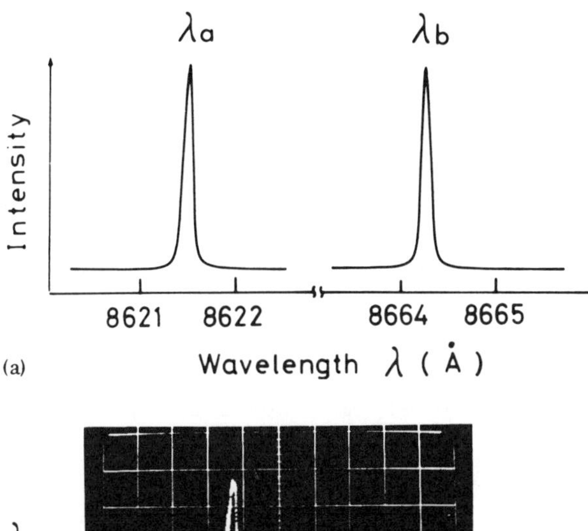

(a)

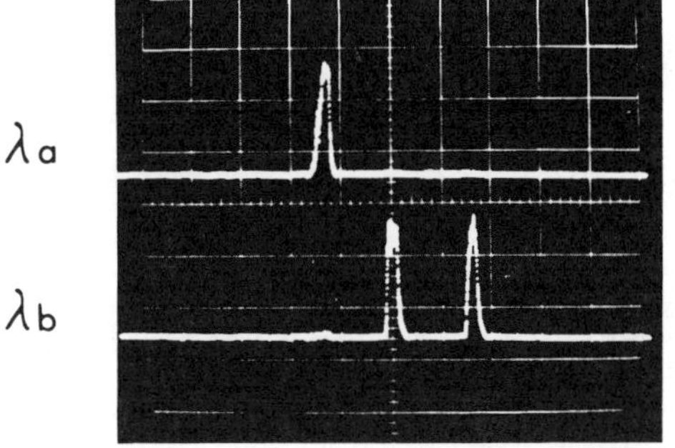

(b)

FIG. 3. Multiplexing and demultiplexing experiment. (a) Spectrum of multiplexed output when two lasers are excited. (b) Demultiplexed signals at wavelengths $\lambda_a = 8621.5$ Å and $\lambda_b = 8664.3$ Å.

ration, such an optical IC provides useful functions which have not been easily realized by conventional electro-optic devices. Work is now under way to improve the quantum efficiency and more precise control of the lasing wavelength of these devices. Such improved devices hold promise of finding practical utilization in future optical communication systems.

The authors thank Dr. Yasutsugu Takeda of the Central Research Laboratory, Hitachi Ltd., for his support in this work, and Shigeo Yamashita and Takao Kuroda of the same laboratory for their extensive assistance in device fabrication, SEM observation, and epitaxial growth. They are also grateful to Professor Amnon Yariv of the California Institute of Technology for his helpful discussions.

[1]M. Nakamura, K. Aiki, J. Umeda, and A. Yariv, Appl. Phys. Lett. 27, 403 (1975).
[2]H.C. Casey, Jr., S. Somekh, and M. Ilegems, Appl. Phys. Lett. 27, 142 (1975).
[3]F.K. Reinhart, R.A. Logan, and C.V. Shank, Appl. Phys. Lett. 27, 45 (1975).
[4]G.H.B. Tomson and P.A. Kirkby, Electron. Lett. 9, 295 (1973).
[5]M.B. Panish, H.C. Casey, Jr., S. Sumski, and P.W. Foy, Appl. Phys. Lett. 22, 590 (1973).
[6]K. Aiki, M. Nakamura, J. Umeda, A. Yariv, A. Katzir, and H.W. Yen, Appl. Phys. Lett. 27, 145 (1975).
[7]M. Nakamura, K. Aiki, J. Umeda, A. Yariv, H.W. Yen, and T. Morikawa, Appl. Phys. Lett. 24, 466 (1974).

Radiation Losses in Distributed Feedback Lasers and Longitudinal Mode Selection

W. STREIFER, R. D. BURNHAM, AND D. R. SCIFRES

Abstract—**We show that seemingly symmetric longitudinal modes in symmetrical distributed feedback (DFB) lasers utilizing higher order Bragg reflection actually have differing thresholds and resonant wavelength shifts from the Bragg condition as a result of power radiated by the grating.**

Distributed feedback (DFB) lasers with symmetrical-shaped gratings and symmetrical boundary conditions at their ends, $z = \pm L/2$, have been shown by calculation to have longitudinal modes which are symmetric in threshold and resonant wavelength, λ_0, about the Bragg wavelength λ_b [1]-[3]. Experimentally, this is not the case [4]. One cause of this experimentally observed asymmetry is that laser medium gain and index vary with wavelength. A second, previously unnoted, factor is that otherwise symmetric longitudinal modes of DFB lasers resonating in higher Bragg orders (not the first) radiate [5]-[8] different amounts of power. Formulation and calculation of DFB longitudinal mode thresholds and resonant wavelengths, taking into account radiation losses, are given below.

Radiation from corrugated waveguides in the nonresonant case is well understood [9], [10], but the resonant situation introduces complications. The two resonant contradirectional waves are coherent and therefore their relative phases along the length of the laser must be taken into account in computing radiated power. Furthermore, the radiation reacts on the resonant waves to change the threshold and λ_0, and the overall process is dependent on the longitudinal mode structure. To understand the interactions, recall first that in the nonresonant case, a wave traveling in the $+z$ direction propagates as $\exp(i\beta_0 z)$ [with $\exp(-i\omega t)$ suppressed]. This wave interacts with the grating (period Λ), whose Fourier representation is [9]

$$\sum_{\substack{-\infty \\ q\neq 0}}^{\infty} A_q(x) \exp i2\pi qz/\Lambda \tag{1}$$

to produce waves with

$$\beta_q = \beta_0 + 2\pi q/\Lambda. \tag{2}$$

DFB in pth Bragg order occurs if

$$\beta_p = -\beta_0 = \beta_0 + 2\pi p/\Lambda, \tag{3}$$

where $p < 0$. Waves with $p < q < 0$ generally radiate power away from the structure, whereas those with $q < p$ and $q > 0$ neither supply nor drain power directly.

In the resonant case, we let $\mathcal{E}_0(x)R(z)\exp(i\beta_0 z)$ be the TE wave traveling in the $+z$ direction and $\mathcal{E}_0(x)S(z)\exp(-i\beta_0 z)$ be the pth TE wave traveling in the $-z$ direction. $\mathcal{E}_0(x)$ is the transverse field variation and $R(z)$, $S(z)$ are the axial variations which can be shown to satisfy

$$R' + (-\alpha - i\delta - i\zeta_1)R = i(\kappa + \zeta_2)S, \tag{4a}$$

$$-S' + (-\alpha - i\delta - i\zeta_1)S = i(\kappa + \zeta_2)R, \tag{4b}$$

where κ is the coupling coefficient computed without regard to the radiating waves [9]. In (4a) and (4b), $\alpha > 0$ is the net threshold field gain,

$$\delta = \beta - \beta_0, \tag{5}$$

where $\beta = \beta(\lambda_0)$, so that δ is a measure of the shift from λ_b, i.e., $\beta_0 = \beta(\lambda_b)$, and ζ_1, ζ_2 are discussed below. Solving (4a) and (4b) subject to reflection boundary conditions at $z = \pm L/2$, determines α and δ; with no reflection $R(-L/2) = 0$ and $S(L/2) = 0$. The quantities ζ_1 and ζ_2 are zero when the effects of R and S in generating other waves ($q \neq 0, p$) are ignored. For definitiveness, R is used in the discussion. The term ζ_1 represents the first-order effect of R producing waves with $q \neq p$ and those waves reacting on R itself. Since some of the waves carry power away from the structure, they constitute a loss mechanism and so $\text{Im}(\zeta_1) < 0$. The quantity ζ_2 represents the first-order effect of R generating waves with $q \neq p$ and these waves acting on S. Thus, ζ_2 is, in effect, a coupling term. $\text{Re}(\zeta_2)$ acts as an index modulation whereas $\text{Im}(\zeta_2)$ acts as a gain/loss modulation. These may have either sign relative to κ depending on phase. Thus, $\text{Re}(\zeta_2)$ may in effect increase or decrease κ. In first Bragg order DFB, with $p = -1$, no radiating waves exist, and ζ_1, ζ_2 are both real. The calculation of ζ_1 and ζ_2 involves overlap integrals which are, in principle, similar to those for κ and α. This computation will be discussed elsewhere.

To solve (4a) and (4b) subject to the boundary conditions at $z = \pm L/2$, we write

$$R' + (-\hat{\alpha} - i\hat{\delta})R = i\hat{\kappa}S \tag{6a}$$

$$-S' + (-\hat{\alpha} - i\hat{\delta})S = i\hat{\kappa}R, \tag{6b}$$

where $\hat{\kappa} = \kappa + \zeta_2$ and

$$\alpha + i\delta = \hat{\alpha} + i\hat{\delta} - i\zeta_1. \tag{7}$$

Then we employ the methods of [3]. Generally, since ζ_2, and therefore $\hat{\kappa}$, are complex, the spectra are no longer symmetric about λ_b even if the boundary conditions are symmetric. Particular longitudinal mode thresholds may be larger or smaller than those computed with ζ_1, ζ_2 neglected. This is most evident for $|\kappa L| \gg 1$. Consider a conventional three-layer double-heterostructure GaAs:GaAlAs laser as shown in Fig. 1. With outer refractive indices of 3.4, active region thickness of $t = 1\ \mu\text{m}$, active region index 3.6, $\lambda_0 = 0.85\ \mu\text{m}$, $g = 1500$ Å, and $w = 0.15\ \Lambda$, $\Lambda = 4746$ Å for fourth-order Bragg DFB operation ($p = -4$), we find $\kappa = -43.45\ \text{cm}^{-1}$, $\zeta_1 = -2.468 + i\ 2.004\ \text{cm}^{-1}$, and $\zeta_2 = -3.1345 + i\ 1.928\ \text{cm}^{-1}$, where all q with $-8 \leqslant q \leqslant 4$ have been taken into account. This truncation yields results accurate to about 1 percent. For a 1-mm long laser with no end reflectors, we obtain the results shown in Table I. Recalling that αL is the total net field gain at threshold, the total net threshold power gain at threshold is $2\alpha L$, and the actual threshold power gain, $2\alpha_{th}$, is given by

$$2\alpha_{th} = 2\alpha + 2\alpha_{ab}, \tag{8}$$

where $2\alpha_{ab}$ is the power absorption. If $2\alpha_{ab} \approx 15\ \text{cm}^{-1}$ (free carrier absorption), then $2\alpha_{th} \approx 22\ \text{cm}^{-1}$ for the -1 longitudinal mode and $29\ \text{cm}^{-1}$ for the $+1$ longitudinal mode. Thus near threshold one would expect single longitudinal mode behavior. In the same geometry with $w = 0.85\ \Lambda$, we find $\kappa = 14.55\ \text{cm}^{-1}$, $\zeta_1 = -.8471 + i\ 0.7954\ \text{cm}^{-1}$, and $\zeta_2 = -1.0559 + i\ 0.7654\ \text{cm}^{-1}$, and now the longitudinal modes with $\delta L < 0$ have higher thresholds than their counterparts with $\delta L > 0$. Note that with $w/\Lambda = 0.85$, the resonant period is $\Lambda = 4750$ Å because the effective guide width is slightly decreased.

Manuscript received August 6, 1976.

The authors are with the Xerox Palo Alto Research Center, Palo Alto, CA 94304.

Reprinted from *IEEE J. Quantum Electron.*, vol. 12, pp. 737-739, Nov. 1976.

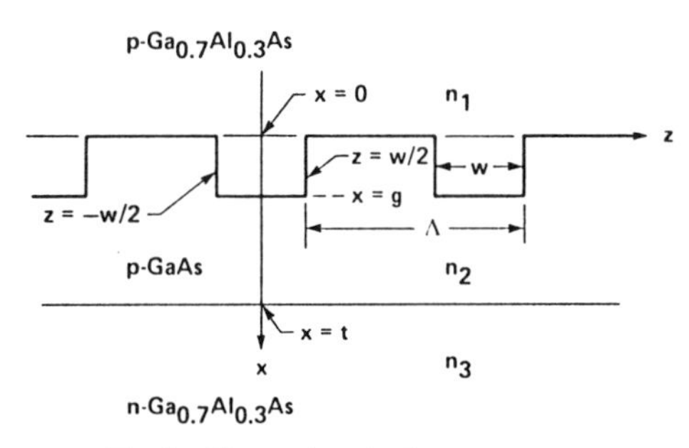

Fig. 1. Illustrating the laser geometry.

TABLE I
NET THRESHOLD GAIN AND RESONANT WAVELENGTH FOR LONGITUDINAL MODES WITH ($\zeta_1, \zeta_2 \neq 0$) AND WITHOUT ($\zeta_1, \zeta_2 = 0$) THE EFFECTS OF RADIATING WAVES

Longitudinal Mode Number	$\zeta_1, \zeta_2 = 0$ αL	δL	$\zeta_1, \zeta_2 \neq 0$ αL	δL
−3	1.372	−10.225	1.407	−10.077
−2	0.945	−7.485	0.954	−7.392
−1	0.374	−5.263	0.369	−5.265
+1	0.374	5.263	0.704	5.081
+2	0.945	7.485	1.199	7.965
+3	1.372	10.225	1.588	10.658

Generally, the effects described above increase with increasing Bragg order resonance as one would expect. For $p = -1$, there exists no radiating wave and ζ_1, ζ_2 are real. For the laser described above with $w = 0.15\ \Lambda$ and $\Lambda = 1186$ Å, the thresholds of modes on both sides of the Bragg wavelength increase identically, and with $w = 0.85\ \Lambda$ and $\Lambda = 1188$ Å, all thresholds decrease symmetrically. In both cases, the lasing wavelengths shift asymmetrically, but this shift and the threshold changes are quite small.

The results presented herein apply to any symmetrical tooth shape. If external reflectors are employed and are asymmetric, then the thresholds are asymmetric even if radiation is not taken into account [3]. The case of asymmetric tooth shapes with or without reflectors will be discussed elsewhere.

In conclusion, we have shown that radiative losses produced by low-order Bragg scattering introduce asymmetries in longitudinal mode thresholds in otherwise symmetric DFB lasers.

REFERENCES

[1] H. Kogelnik and C. V. Shank, "Coupled mode theory of distributed feedback lasers," *J. Appl. Phys.*, vol. 43, pp. 2327–2335, 1972.

[2] S. R. Chinn, "Effects of mirror reflectivity in a distributed-feedback laser," *IEEE J. Quantum Electron.*, vol. QE-9, pp. 574–580, June 1973.

[3] W. Streifer, R. D. Burnham, and D. R. Scifres, "Effect of external reflectors on longitudinal modes of distributed feedback lasers," *IEEE J. Quantum Electron.*, vol. QE-11, pp. 154–161, Apr. 1975.

[4] R. D. Burnham, D. R. Scifres, and W. Streifer, "Single heterostructure distributed-feedback GaAs-diode lasers," *IEEE J. Quantum Electron. (Part II of Two Parts)*, vol. QE-11, pp. 439–449, July 1975.

[5] Zh. I. Alferov *et al.*, "Semiconductor laser with extremely low divergence of radiation" (in Russian), *Sov. Phys.-Semicond.*, vol. 8, pp. 832–833, 1974; also (in English), *Sov. Phys.-JETP*, pp. 541, 542.

[6] P. Zory, "Laser oscillation in leaky corrugated optical waveguides," *Appl. Phys. Lett.*, vol. 22, pp. 125–128, 1973.

[7] D. R. Scifres, R. D. Burnham, and W. Streifer, "Observation of highly collimated laser beams from electrically pumped SH GaAs/GaAlAs distributed feedback lasers," *Appl. Phys. Lett.*, vol. 26, pp. 48–50, 1975.

[8] F. K. Reinhart, R. A. Logan, and C. V. Shank, "GaAs-$Al_xGa_{1-x}As$ injection lasers with distributed Bragg reflectors," *Appl. Phys. Lett.*, vol. 27, pp. 45–48, 1975.

[9] W. Streifer, D. R. Scifres, and R. D. Burnham, "Analysis of grating-coupled radiation in GaAs:GaAlAs lasers and waveguides," *IEEE J. Quantum Electron.*, vol. QE-12, pp. 422–428, July 1976.

[10] W. Streifer, R. D. Burnham, and D. R. Scifres, "Analysis of grating-coupled radiation in GaAs:GaAlAs lasers and waveguides–II: Blazing effects," *IEEE J. Quantum Electron.*, vol. QE-12, pp. 494–499, Aug. 1976.

GaInAsP/InP INTEGRATED LASER WITH BUTT-JOINTED BUILT-IN DISTRIBUTED-BRAGG-REFLECTION WAVEGUIDE

Y. ABE
K. KISHINO
Y. SUEMATSU
S. ARAI

Department of Physical Electronics
Tokyo Institute of Technology
2-12-1 O-okayama, Meguro-ku, Tokyo 152, Japan

27th October 1981

Indexing terms: Lasers and applications, Semiconductor lasers, Waveguides

A novel GaInAsP/InP integrated laser with butt-jointed built-in distributed-Bragg-reflection waveguide (BJB-DBR integrated laser for short) is proposed and demonstrated. In this structure, it is found theoretically that an efficient coupling of 98% between the active and butt-jointed external waveguides is available by matching the propagation constants and the field profiles of both waveguides, which gives relatively larger fabrication tolerance. Prototype BJB-DBR integrated lasers with emitting wavelength of 1·55 μm were fabricated, and single-longitudinal-mode operation was obtained at room temperature.

Monolithic integration of optical devices in the ultralow-loss 1·5–1·6 μm wavelength region[1] is very attractive for optical-fibre communication. Recently, a 1·5–1·6 μm wavelength GaInAsP/InP laser has been integrated with a distributed-Bragg-reflector (DBR) waveguide,[2] utilising the integrated twin-guide (ITG) structure.[3] A 1·58 μm DBR-ITG laser with pure dynamic spectral properties has been demonstrated to increase the transmission bandwidth of fibres.[4]

In this letter, room-temperature operation of a novel GaInAsP/InP integrated laser with a butt-jointed built-in distributed-Bragg-reflection waveguide (BJB-DBR integrated laser for short) is reported. The significance of this structure is that the coupling efficiency between the two butt-jointed waveguides, namely the active guide and the external guide, is significantly increased by matching the equivalent refractive indices and the field profiles of both waveguides.

The proposed BJB-DBR integrated laser consists of an active waveguide and a built-in external waveguide, butt-jointed to the active waveguide, as shown in Fig. 1, where (*a*) the equivalent refractive indices (or the propagation constants) of both waveguides are matched; $\beta_a \sim \beta_e$, and (*b*) the field profiles of both waveguides are matched; $E_a(y) \sim E_e(y)$, so as to reduce the joint loss of waveguides. Corrugation is formed on the surface of the external waveguide to form a distributed Bragg reflector.

An example of the calculated power coupling efficiency C_{out} between active and external waveguides is shown in Fig. 2 in relation to the displacement s. Parameters are thickness t, and bandgap wavelength λ_{ge} of the external waveguide, cladded by 0·1 μm-thick InP at the air side. The layer thickness and composition of the four-layer laser structure with antimeltback (AMB) layer, assumed in the calculation, are given in the Figure. When λ_{ge} and t are 1·40 μm and 0·51 μm, respectively, two waveguides are index matched ($\beta_a = \beta_e$), and maximum

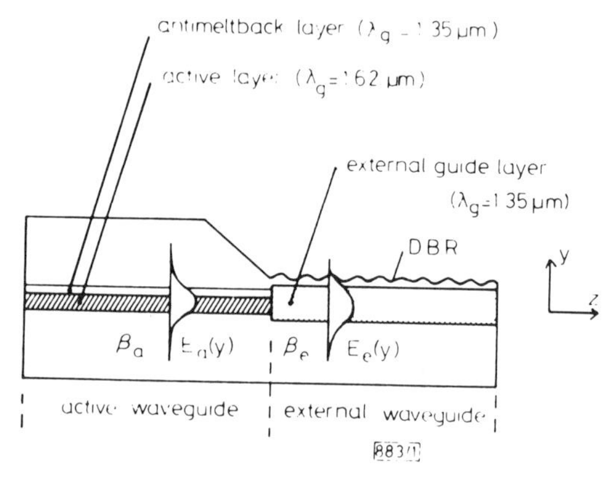

Fig. 1 *Schematic structure of 1·62 μm GaInAsP InP BJB-DBR integrated laser*

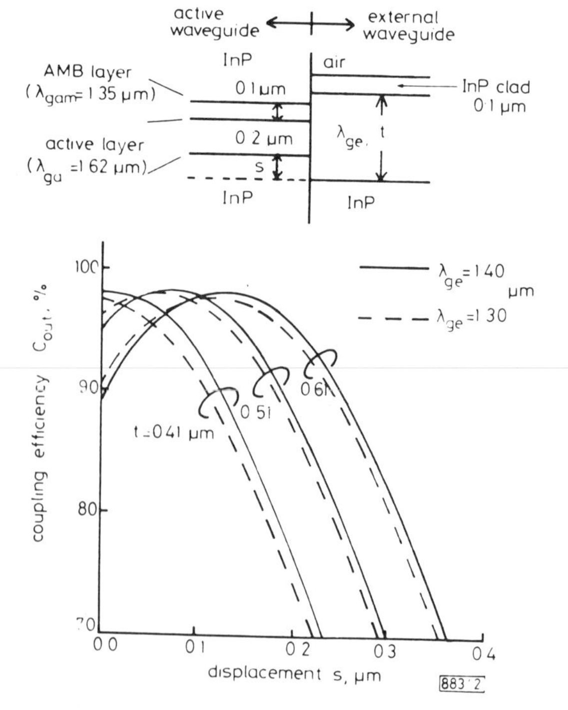

Fig. 2 *Power coupling efficiency against displacement between active and external waveguides*

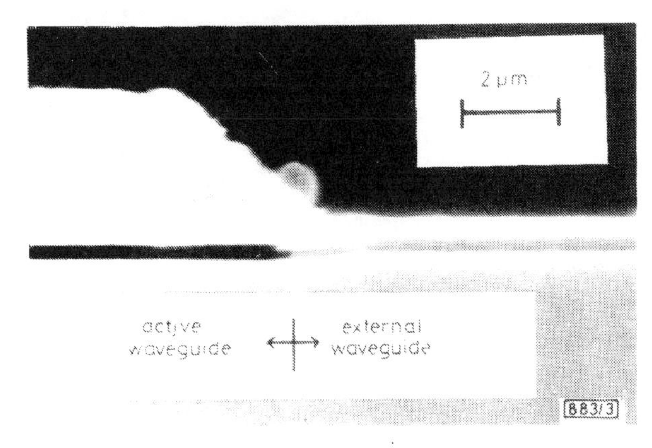

Fig. 3 *Cross-sectional view of butt-jointed place*

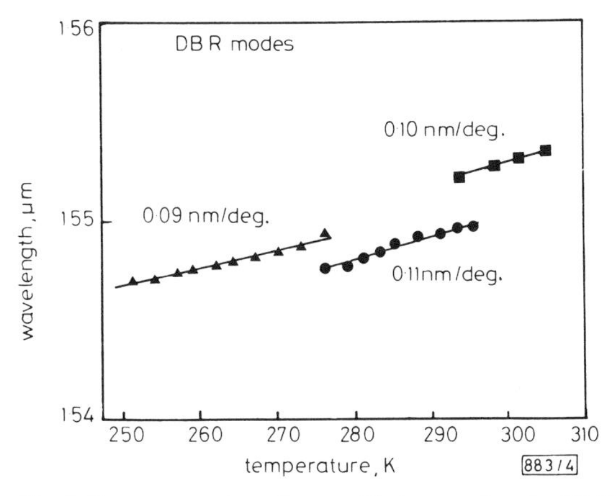

Fig. 4 *Temperature dependences of lasing wavelength of BJB-DBR integrated laser*

coupling efficiency of 98% is attained at $s \simeq 0.08$ μm. Note that the coupling efficiency approaches 100% more closely with increasing thickness of InP clad of the external waveguide. As can be seen, the fabrication tolerance of waveguide thickness is considerably relaxed to obtain high coupling efficiencies of more than 90%. In the calculation, radiation modes are not taken into account, but as is easily understood, this treatment never significantly affects the calculated results of coupling efficiency for the case of small joint loss concerned here.

The integrated laser was fabricated by a two-step two-phase-solution LPE growth technique. First, a conventional five-layer DH wafer with antimeltback layer,[5] partly shown in Fig. 1, was prepared. On the wafer, SiO_2 stripe masks of 400 μm width were formed along the 011 crystal axis. The exposed surface was preferentially etched down to the surface of the antimeltback layer by use of the etchants $3H_2SO_4:H_2O:H_2O_2$ and $4HCl:H_2O$ for GaInAsP and InP crystals, respectively, to form a mesa structure along the 011 crystal axis. A mesa side with low slope angle of 40° to the [100] surface was obtained. Such a structure is found to be very important for growing a uniform external waveguide in the area adjacent to the active layer.[6] After melting away the exposed antimeltback and active layers, preferentially by an unsaturated InP/In solution, an undoped GaInAsP external guide layer ($\lambda_{ge} = 1.35$ μm, 0.4 μm thick) and an undoped InP cladding layer (0.2 μm thick) were successively grown. An SEM view of the jointed place is shown, as an example, in Fig. 3. Two waveguides were jointed almost ideally except for the small amount of the displacement and invasion of external guide layer into the mesa. This kind of structure with external waveguide was reported for GaAs/AlGaAs lasers.[7-9] The wafer from which BJB-DBR integrated lasers were fabricated, i.e. a first-grown wafer, had worse jointed-place forms because the growth condition was not well confirmed. First-order corrugation with period of 239.8 nm was formed on the external waveguide. On the top of the mesa structure, a 25 μm-wide oxide-stripe window was opened. The final devices were fabricated by sawing and cleavage. Typical lengths of active and DBR waveguides were 200–400 μm and 400–600 μm, respectively.

The devices thus fabricated were operated at room temperature under pulsed condition. Single-longitudinal-mode operation was maintained at 1.5530 μm wavelength up to an injection current 1.38 times the threshold. At temperatures between 251 K and 305 K, single-longitudinal-mode operation was observed, as shown in Fig. 4, with temperature dependences of 0.09–0.11 nm/deg, which agreed with previously reported values for DBR-ITG and DFB GaInAsP/InP lasers.[2,10] The typical value of threshold current was 600 mA, which would be considerably reduced by optimising the fabrication conditions and introducing the stripe structure to suppress the spreading of current, such as a buried heterostructure. The maximum light output was 30 mW/facet.

In conclusion, a novel 1.5–1.6 μm GaInAsP/InP BJB-DBR integrated laser was proposed. In this structure, it was theoretically found that a high coupling efficiency between active and external waveguides is obtained by matching equivalent refractive indices and field profiles of both waveguides. A prototype BJB-DBR integrated laser with an oxide stripe was fabricated, and single-longitudinal-mode operation at 1.55 μm wavelength was demonstrated.

Acknowledgment: This work was supported by a scientific research grant-in-aid from the Ministry of Education, Science and Culture, Japan. The authors are grateful to T. Tanbun-ek and S. Tamura for their helpful assistance in experiments.

References

1 MIYA, T., TERUNUMA, Y., HOSAKA, T., and MIYASHITA, T.: 'Ultimate low-loss single-mode fiber at 1.55 μm', *Electron. Lett.*, 1979, **15**, pp. 106–108

2 UTAKA, K., KOBAYASHI, K., KISHINO, K., and SUEMATSU, Y.: '1.5–1.6 μm GaInAsP/InP integrated twin-guide lasers with first-order distributed Bragg reflectors', *ibid.*, 1980, **16**, pp. 455–456

3 SUEMATSU, Y., YAMADA, M., and HAYASHI, K.: 'A multihetero-AlGaAs laser with integrated twin-guide'. *Proc. IEEE*, 1975, **63**, p. 208

4 KOYAMA, F., ARAI, S., SUEMATSU, Y., and KISHINO, K.: 'Dynamic spectral width of rapidly modulated 1.58 μm GaInAsP/InP buried-heterostructure distributed-Bragg-reflector integrated-twin-guide lasers', *Electron. Lett.* (under consideration)

5 ITAYA, Y., ARAI, S., KISHINO, K., ASADA, M., and SUEMATSU, Y.: '1.6 μm wavelength GaInAsP/InP lasers prepared by two-phase solution technique', *IEEE J. Quantum Electron.*, 1981, **QE-17**, pp. 635–640

6 KISHINO, K., SUEMATSU, Y., and ITAYA, Y.: 'Mesa-substrate buried-heterostructure GaInAsP/InP injection lasers', *Electron. Lett.*, 1979, **15**, pp. 134–136

7 HURWITZ, C. E., ROSSI, J. A., HSIEH, J. J., and WOLFE, C. M.: 'Integrated GaAs-AlGaAs double-heterostructure lasers', *Appl. Phys. Lett.*, 1975, **27**, pp. 241–243

8 AIKI, K., NAKAMURA, M., and UMEDA, J.: 'Frequency multiplexing light source with monolithically integrated distributed-feedback diode lasers', *ibid.*, 1976, **29**, pp. 506–508

9 TAKAHASHI, S., KOBAYASHI, T., SAITO, H., and FURUKAWA, Y.: 'GaAs-AlGaAs DH lasers with buried facet', *Jpn. J. Appl. Phys.*, 1978, **17**, pp. 865–870

10 MIKAMI, O.: '1.55 μm GaInAsP/InP distributed feedback lasers', *ibid.*, 1981, **20**, pp. L488–L490

HIGH-QUALITY 1·3 μm GaInAsP/InP BH-DFB LASERS WITH FIRST-ORDER GRATINGS

H. OKUDA
Y. HIRAYAMA
J. KINOSHITA
H. FURUYAMA
Y. UEMATSU

Toshiba Research & Development Center
Toshiba Corporation
Komukai-Toshiba-cho, Saiwaiku, Kawasaki 210, Japan

26th September 1983

Indexing terms: Lasers and applications, Semiconductor lasers

High-quality 1·3 μm GaInAsP/InP BH-DFB lasers have been demonstrated. The threshold current was 16 mA and the differential quantum efficiency was 25% per facet. A stable single-longitudinal-mode oscillation was obtained, both up to four times the threshold current and up to 85°C. These results are comparable or superior to reported results of Fabry–Perot BH lasers.

Stable single-longitudinal-mode lasers, like distributed feedback (DFB) lasers or distributed Bragg reflector (DBR) lasers, are considered to be one of the promising light sources for long-distance and high-capacity optical fibre communication systems, or for frequency-multiplexing optical fibre communication systems. CW operation of 1·3 μm GaInAsP/InP BH-DFB lasers has been recently reported by the authors.[1] In the previous letter the threshold current of the DFB laser was relatively high, at 66 mA, and the CW operation temperature was only up to 52°C. This may be due to the relatively wide active width (about 4 μm), the small irregularity of the grating, with a 2000 Å period in each DFB laser, and the leakage current through the burying region.

This letter reports high-quality 1·3 μm GaInAsP/InP BH-DFB lasers with a lower threshold current, a higher differential quantum efficiency and a higher temperature CW operation in the *p*-side-up configuration, achieved by solving the problems previously mentioned. As a result, with respect to a threshold current, a DFB laser has been obtained with a 16 mA threshold current ($L = 330$ μm), which is as low as, or lower than, that for a conventional Fabry–Perot laser with the same BH structure.[2]

To obtain high-quality DFB lasers, key points are to fabricate uniform gratings, to grow uniform quaternary compositions, to fabricate a narrow active width and to decrease leakage current through the burying region. The DFB laser structure was shown in Fig. 1, which was the same as in the previous letter.[1] To fit the lasing wavelength to the spontaneous emission peak, the first-order grating period was $2000 \pm 0{\cdot}7$ Å, using a computer-controlled interferometer system.[3] The active-layer, InP buffer-layer and waveguide-layer thicknesses were designed to be 0·15, 0·05 and 0·2 μm, respectively. 1·3 μm BH-DFB lasers were fabricated by a two-step LPE process. To grow uniform quaternary (active and waveguide) compositions, the melt soaking temperature was raised to 610°C, which was 10 degrees higher than that mentioned in the previous letter.[1] For 1·3 μm DFB lasers, the refractive-index difference at the corrugated interface is about two-thirds that for 1·5 μm DFB lasers. Therefore, even a slight deterioration in the surface grating influences threshold current for a 1·3 μm DFB laser. It was found that the first-order grating, with a 2000 Å period, was uniformly preserved by covering a grating surface with a GaAs wafer during about 2 h of melt soaking.[4] In the second LPE process, burying layers were optimised to decrease leakage current. Based on calculated results for the first-order-mode cutoff condition for buried rectangular GaInAsP/InP SCH waveguides, the active-layer cutoff width is about 1 μm, when the active-layer and waveguide-layer thicknesses are 0·1 and 0·2 μm, respectively. This cutoff condition is much more severe than that for the conventional DH laser. So, in order to control the transverse mode as far as possible, the active layer width was designed to be about 1·5 to 2 μm.

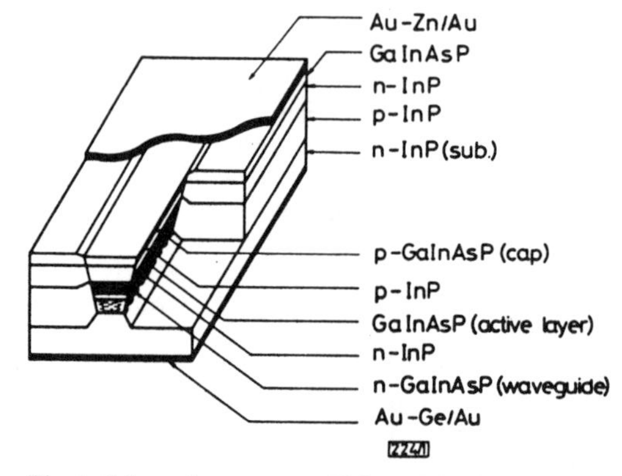

Fig. 1 *Schematic structure of 1·3 μm DFB laser*

Fig. 2 shows a typical output/current characteristic and lasing spectra for a DFB laser without an unexcited region. The threshold current was 16 mA ($J_{th} = 2{\cdot}4$ kA/cm^2) and the differential quantum efficiency was 17% per facet at 25°C. A stable single-longitudinal-mode oscillation was obtained, up to four times the threshold current. Fig. 3 shows a typical output/current characteristic and lasing spectra for a DFB laser with an unexcited region, fabricated from the same wafer as the DFB laser shown in Fig. 2. In this case, the threshold current and differential quantum efficiency were 27 mA and 25% per facet, respectively. In each DFB laser, the output power of more than 7 mW per facet was obtained without kinks. The threshold current for a DFB laser without an unexcited region was lower than that for a DFB laser with an unexcited region. The reflection from both cleaved mirrors may reduce the threshold current of the DFB laser. The threshold current of 16 mA is the lowest value and the differential quantum efficiency of 25% per facet is the highest value for all the DFB lasers that have ever been reported.[5,6] These results are comparable or superior to those of our Fabry–

Reprinted with permission from *Electron. Lett.*, vol. 19, no. 22, pp. 941–943, Oct. 27, 1983.

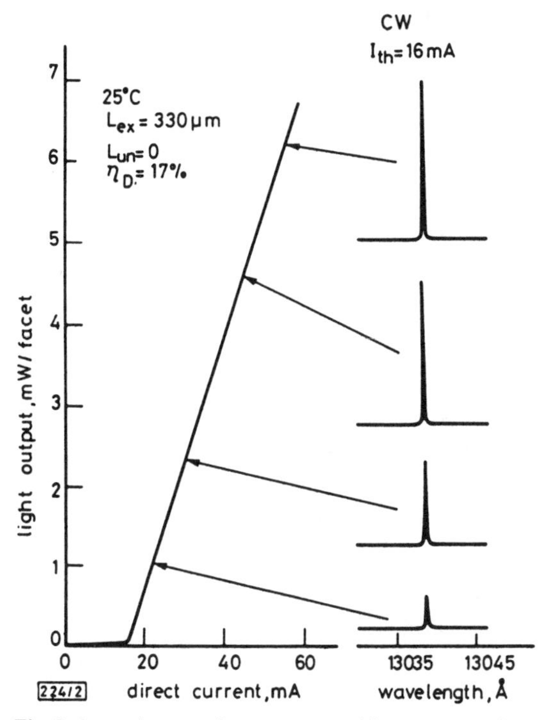

Fig. 2 *Output/current characteristic and lasing spectra for a DFB laser without an unexcited region*

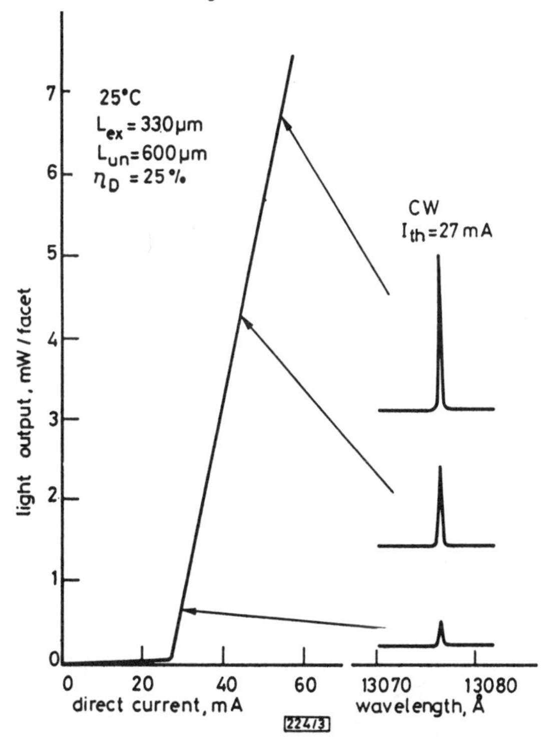

Fig. 3 *Output/current characteristics and lasing spectra for a DFB laser with an unexcited region*

Perot lasers fabricated from the same wafer and the reported results of Fabry–Perot lasers with the same BH structure. From the theoretical point of view, DFB lasers with first-order gratings should have lower threshold currents than Fabry–Perot lasers. To the authors' knowledge, this letter concerns the first performance of DFB lasers with lower threshold currents than those for Fabry–Perot lasers.

A temperature dependence of output/current curves is shown in Fig. 4. A stable single-longitudinal-mode oscillation was obtained up to 85°C atmospheric temperature. This DFB laser has two cleaved facets without an unexcited region.

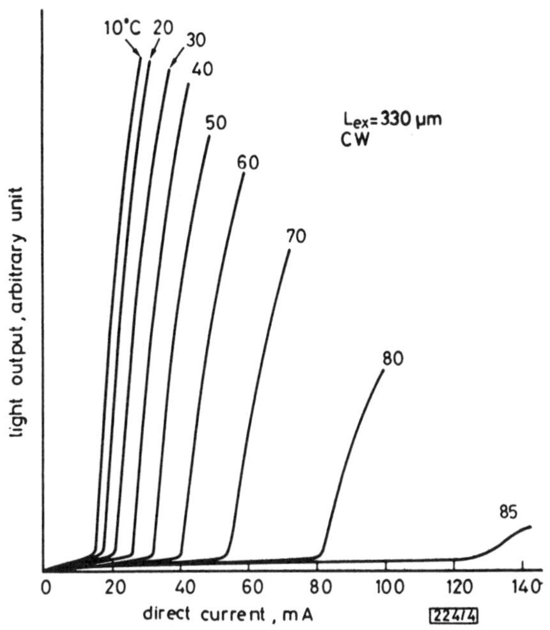

Fig. 4 *Temperature dependence of output/current curves for a DFB laser*

However, a Fabry–Perot mode oscillation was not observed at all over the measured temperature range. It was found that, even if a DFB laser has two cleaved facets without an unexcited region, only a stable DFB mode oscillation against both temperature and current injection was obtained. This means that a DFB laser with two cleaved facets can be used for optical communications. It has the merit of being able to monitor the output power from the rear facet.

In conclusion, high-quality 1·3 μm GaInAsP/InP BH-DFB lasers have been demonstrated in the *p*-side-up configuration. The threshold current was 16 mA, which was the lowest value for all the DFB lasers that have every been reported. The highest differential quantum efficiency was 25% per facet. A stable single-longitudinal-mode oscillation was obtained, both up to four times the threshold current and up to 85°C atmospheric temperature. It was found that, even if a DFB laser has two cleaved facets without an unexcited region, only a stable DFB mode oscillation was obtained. This is due to the effect of first-order gratings.

This work has been supported by the Agency of Industrial Science & Technology, Ministry of International Trade & Industry, Japan, in the Optical Measurement & Control System Project.

References

1 UEMATSU, Y., OKUDA, H., and KINOSHITA, J.: 'Room-temperature CW operation of 1·3 μm distributed-feedback GaInAsP/InP lasers', *Electron. Lett.*, 1982, **18**, pp. 857–858

2 HIRAO, M., TSUJI, S., MIZUISHI, K., DOI, A., and NAKAMURA, M.: 'Long wavelength InGaAsP/InP lasers for optical fiber communication systems', *J. Opt. Commun.*, 1980, **1**, pp. 10–14

3 OKUDA, H., KINOSHITA, J., and UEMATSU, Y.: 'Monolithically integrated GaInAsP/InP distributed feedback lasers'. IOOC, 1983, pp. 160–161

4 KINOSHITA, J., OKUDA, H., and UEMATSU, Y.: 'Preserving InP surface corrugations for 1·3 μm GaInAsP/InP DFB lasers from thermal deformation during LPE process', *Electron. Lett.*, 1983, **19**, pp. 215–216

5 MATSUOKA, T., NAGAI, H., ITAYA, Y., NOGUCHI, Y., SUZUKI, Y., and IKEGAMI, T.: 'CW operation of DFB-BH GaInAsP/InP lasers in 1·5 μm wavelength region', *ibid.*, 1982, **18**, pp. 27–28

6 AKIBA, S., UTAKA, K., SAKAI, K., and MATSUSHIMA, Y.: 'Low threshold-current distributed-feedback InGaAsP/InP CW lasers', *ibid.*, 1982, **18**, pp. 77–78

cw operation of 1.57-μm $Ga_xIn_{1-x}As_yP_{1-y}InP$ distributed feedback lasers grown by low-pressure metalorganic chemical vapor deposition

M. Razeghi, R. Blondeau, K. Kazmierski, M. Krakowski, B. de Cremoux, and J. P. Duchemin
Thomson–CSF, Laboratoire Central de Recherches, Domaine de Corbeville, BP N° 10, 91401 Orsay Cedex, France

J. C. Bouley
Centre National D'Etudes et Telecommunications, 196 Rue De Paris 92220 Bagneux, France

(Received 13 June 1984; accepted for publication 23 July 1984)

Continuous wave operation of 1.57-μm distributed feedback lasers fabricated on material grown by two-step low-pressure metalorganic chemical vapor deposition growth process is reported for the first time. Room-temperature continuous wave threshold currents as low as 60 mA have been measured for devices with cavity length of 300 μm and stripe width of 5 μm. Single longitudinal mode operation at fixed mode was obtained under the continuous wave condition, in the temperature range 9–90 °C, with the wavelength shift of 0.9 Å/°C. A stop band of 25 Å in which no resonance mode emission existed, was observed in the output spectrum of the distributed feedback laser.

Distributed feedback semiconductor injection lasers are very important for the wide-band single-mode fiber transmission in the lowest loss wavelength range of 1.5–1.6 μm.

$Ga_xIn_{1-x}As_yP_{1-y}/InP$ distributed feedback lasers have been studied using one-step, two-step, or three-step liquid phase epitaxy,[1] hybrid of molecular beam epitaxy and liquid phase epitaxy,[2] and hybrid of liquid phase epitaxy and metalorganic chemical vapor deposition.[3]

Many important problems exist in distributed feedback laser fabrication. Prominent among them is the phenomenon of surface deformation which occurs during the liquid phase epitaxy regrowth. The metalorgainc chemical vapor deposition growth technique can be used to overcome this problem and has produced structures after overgrowth without any deformation in corrugation depth.[4]

In a series of papers Razeghi *et al.*[5] showed that the low-pressure metalorganic chemical vapor deposition growth technique is promising for large scale production of high quality $Ga_xIn_{1-x}As_yP_{1-y}InP$ double heterostructure lasers emitting at 1.3 and 1.55 μm.[6]

The distributed feedback laser structure was manufactured in the following manner.

First a 1-μm-thick InP ($n = 1\times10^{18}$ cm^{-3}) confinement layer, a 0.2-μm-thick undoped GaInAsP active layer (1.55-μm wavelength composition), and a 0.2-μm-thick GaInAsP guiding layer (1.3-μm wavelength composition) were successively grown by low-pressure metalorganic chemical vapor deposition on a Sn-doped (100) 2° off or a (100) exact InP substrate. The growth temperature was 650 °C. The growth conditions for $Ga_xIn_{1-x}As_yP_{1-y}InP$ have been reported in detail in a previous publication.[7]

Next, second-order corrugation gratings with a period of $\Lambda = 4700$ Å ($\Lambda = \lambda_L/n_{eq}$, where λ_L is the lasing wavelength and n_{eq} is the equivalent refractive index), and a depth of 1000–1500 Å were formed in the top of the guiding (1.3 μm) layer by holographic photolithography followed by chemical etching, orientating the gratings along the (011) direction. The gratings were then covered with 2 μm of Zn-doped InP (confinement layer) and 0.5 μm Zn-doped GaInAsP (1.3-μm wavelength composition) $P = 2\times10^{18}$ cm^{-3} cap layer, grown by low pressure metalorganic chemical vapor deposition.

The device structure is shown in Fig. 1.

Figure 2 shows scanning electron microscope cross sections of the corrugated structure before and after low-pressure metalorganic chemical vapor deposition overgrowth. It appears from these photomicrographs that no significant surface deformation has occurred and the final depth of the corrugation is similar to the pregrowth height.

Significant advantages result from the use of this technique for distributed feedback lasers: (i) use of only one epitaxial growth technique, (ii) production of a large number of devices at the same time,[8] and (iii) avoiding the problem of melt back and grating deformation which are the major problems with the liquid phase epitaxy technique.

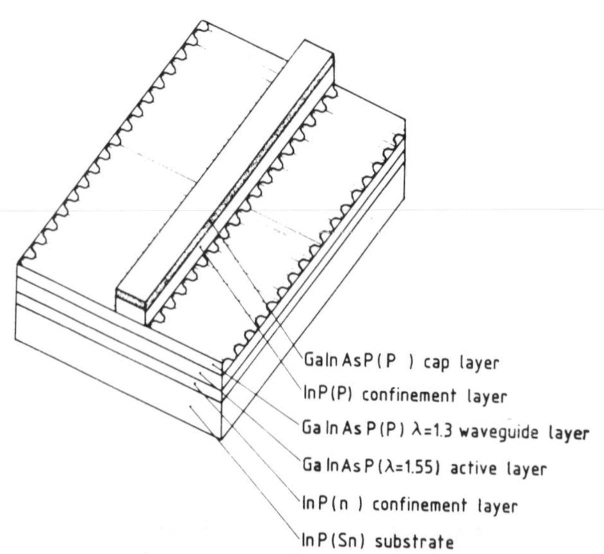

FIG. 1. Ridge-waveguide distributed feedback lasers with an asymmetric structure grown completely by low-pressure metalorganic chemical vapor deposition. The composition of the active layer is 1.55 μm and the composition of the waveguide layer is 1.3 μm.

Reprinted with permission from *Appl. Phys. Lett.*, vol. 45, no. 7, pp. 784–786, Oct. 1, 1984.

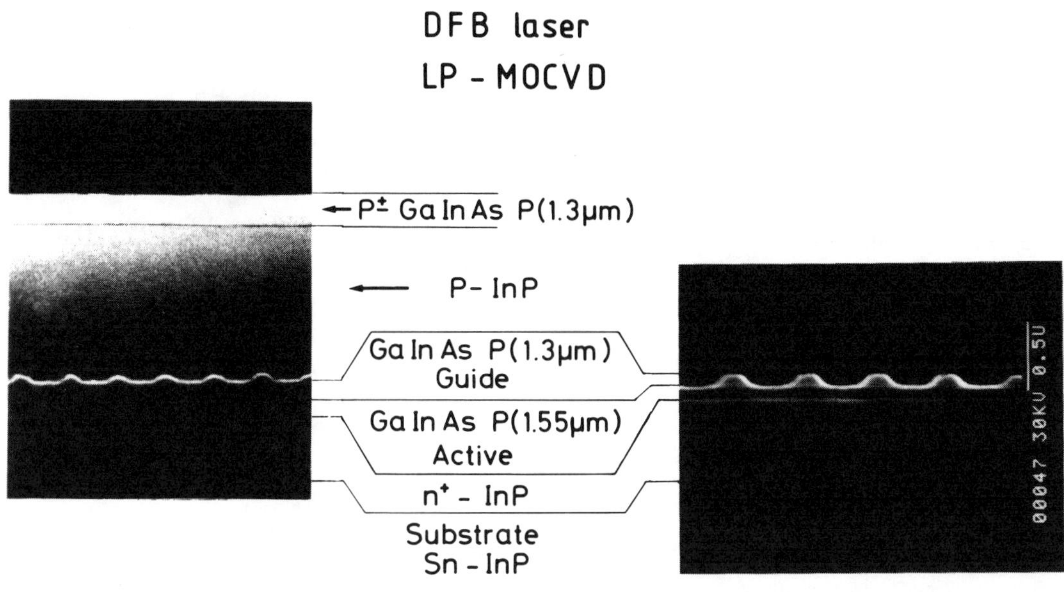

FIG. 2. Scanning electron microscope photograph of the cross section of a distributed feedback laser with second order corrugation grating before and after low-pressure metalorganic chemical vapor deposition overgrowth at 650 °C.

The ridge-waveguide structures developed by Kaminow *et al.*[4,9] have been fabricated (Fig. 1). The devices were separated by cleaving two facets and scribing the two other facets. The width of the ridge was 5 μm and the length of the cavity was about 300 μm. Individual diodes were bonded with In to an Ni-plated copper heat sink.

Typical single longitudinal mode spectrum of a distributed feedback laser with emission power characteristics is shown in Fig. 3(a). The ratio between the main distributed feedback mode and the adjacent mode is better than 30 dB.

The typical threshold current I_{th} of continuous wave operation was 66 mA and the best value was 60 mA at 20 °C. The external quantum efficiency was 15% per facet at 20 °C.

An cw output power of 6 mW/facet was measured. These results were improved with antireflective coating on the front facet. The distributed feedback lasers operated in a single longitudinal mode up to more than two times the threshold current. The lasing wavelength was 1.57 μm at 20 °C. Single longitudinal mode operation under high speed direct modulation at 1 GHz has been obtained with a bias current of 1.2 I_{th}. The temperature dependences of the threshold current I_{th} and the lasing wavelength under cw operation are shown in Fig. 4.

Stable single longitudinal mode operation was obtained in the temperature range 9–90 °C. The temperature coefficient of the lasing wavelength $d\lambda_L/dT$ was 0.9 Å/°C.

Kogelnik and Shank[10] predicted that periodic structures consisting of corrugation gratings have a stop band of frequencies in which propagation is forbidden.

A stop band of 25 Å on which no resonance mode emission existed was observed in the output spectrum of the distributed feedback laser. Details will be published at a later date.[11]

The characteristic temperature T_0 is 61 °C between 20 and 75 °C without break point.

The control and advantages of the low pressure metalorganic chemical vapor deposition growth technique should permit a more rapid exploitation of these useful devices and advance the prospect of practical optical integrated circuits.

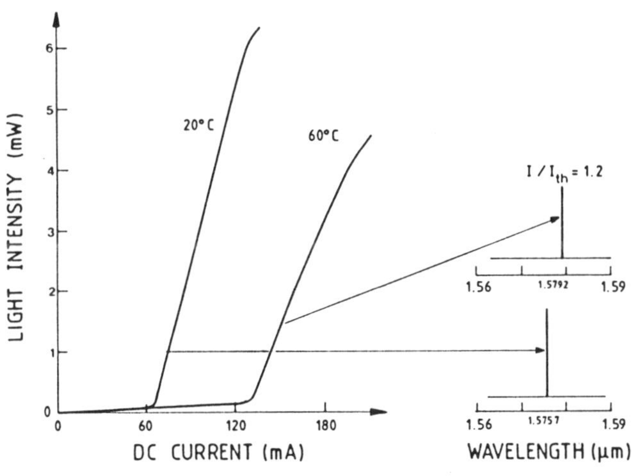

FIG. 3. Current-light output and current-spectrum characteristics of a distributed feedback laser under cw operation.

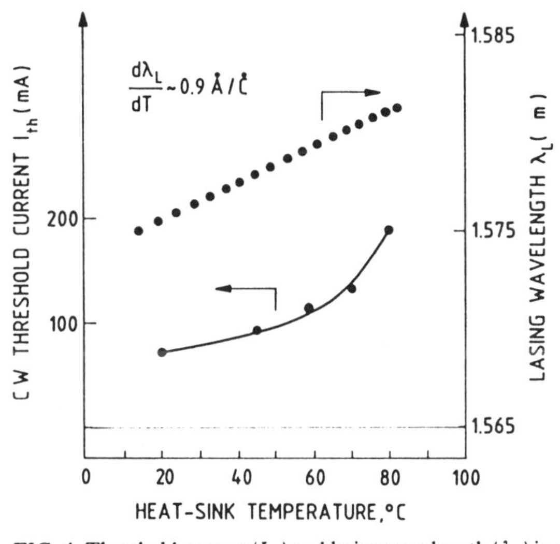

FIG. 4. Threshold current (I_{th}) and lasing wavelength (λ_L) in cw operation of a distributed feedback laser as function of heat sink temperature. Single longitudinal mode operation at the temperature range between 9 and 90 °C with the same mode has been obtained, under cw operation.

In conclusion, room-temperature cw operation of GaInAsP-InP distributed feedback lasers emitting at 1.57 μm, fabricated on material grown by two-stop low pressure metalorganic chemical vapor deposition was presented for the first time. Room-temperature cw threshold current as low as 60 mA at 20 °C has been measured.

Single longitudinal mode operation at fixed mode was obtained under the cw condition in the temperature range 9–90 °C. The temperature coefficient of the lasing wavelength was 0.9 Å/°C ($d\lambda_L/dT = 0.9$ Å/°C).

A stop band of 25 Å on which no resonance mode emission existed was observed in the output spectrum of the distributed feedback laser.

Single longitudinal mode operation under high speed direct modulation at 1 GHz has been obtained with a bias current of $1.2I_{th}$.

The authors wish to thank D. Leguen for technical assistance, G. Vilain, and L. Noël for device bonding, P. Hirtz, J. P. Pocholle, J. Charil, and B. Lent for useful discussion. They would also like to thank Dr. Noblenc for much encouragement.

[1]Osamu Mikami, Jpn. J. Appl. Phys. **20**, 1488 (1981).
[2]Y. Itaya, J. Matsuoka, Y. Nakano, Y. Suzuki, K. Kuroiwa, and T. Ikegami, J. Electron. Lett. **18**, 1006 (1982).
[3]L. D. Westbrock, A. W. Nelson, P. J. Fiddyment, and J. S. Evans, J. Electron. Lett. **20**, 225 (1984).
[4]A. W. Nelson, L. D. Westbrock, and J. S. Evans, J. Electron. Lett. **19**, 34 (1983).
[5]See for example, M. Razeghi, S. Hersee, P. Hirtz, R. Blondeau, B. de Cremoux, and J. P. Duchemin, J. Electron. Lett. **19**, 336 (1983).
[6]M. Razeghi, P. Hirtz, R. Blondeau, B. de Cremoux, and J. P. Duchemin, J. Electron. Lett. **18**, 481 (1983).
[7]M. Razeghi, B. de Cremoux, and J. P. Duchemin, J. Cryst. Growth (to be published).
[8]M. Razeghi, M. A. Poisson, J. P. Larivain, and J. P. Duchemin, J. Electron. Mater. **12**, 371 (1983).
[9]I. P. Kaminov, L. W. Stulz, J. S. Ku, B. Milles, R. D. Feldman, and M. A. Pollack, J. Electron. Lett. **19**, 877 (1983).
[10]H. Kogelnik and C. V. Shank, J. Appl. Phys. **43**, 2327 (1972).
[11]M. Razeghi, R. Blondeau, M. Krakowski, K. Kazmierski, B. de Cremoux, J. P. Duchemin, and J. C. Bouley, 9th International Semiconductor Laser Conference, Rio de Janeiro, Brazil, August 7–19, 1984, p. 18.

1·5 μm PHASE-SHIFTED DFB LASERS FOR SINGLE-MODE OPERATION

K. SEKARTEDJO*
N. EDA
K. FURUYA
Y. SUEMATSU
F. KOYAMA
T. TANBUN-EK

Tokyo Institute of Technology
Department of Physical Electronics
O-okayama, Meguro-ku, Tokyo 152, Japan

2nd December 1983

Indexing terms: Lasers and applications, Semiconductor lasers

Fabrication and single-mode laser oscillation were demonstrated for modified DFB lasers where the phase of the corrugations was shifted at the centre by a quarter guided-wavelength and which, in principle, provided a resonance at the Bragg wavelength and stable single-mode oscillation. Phase-shifted corrugations were fabricated using electron-beam lithography.

The distributed feedback (DFB) laser[1] is promising as the dynamic-single-mode (DSM) laser[2] for a light source in an optical communication system. However, in the conventional DFB laser, in principle, two longitudinal modes equidistant from the Bragg wavelength have equal chance to lase[1] causing problems, deviation and jump of the lasing wavelength.

Theoretically it was pointed out that the distributed Bragg reflector (DBR) laser and the DFB laser can oscillate in a single mode at the Bragg wavelength by arranging appropriate phase relations,[3] and by introduction of an antisymmetric taper,[4] or phase shift of the corrugations[5] in the DFB laser. Also asymmetry in the spectrum due to reflections at facets was studied.[6-8] For the DBR lasers, by combining tuning sections, single-mode oscillations at the Bragg wavelength were achieved experimentally.[9] However, a DFB laser with phase-shifted corrugations has never been demonstrated.

This letter is the first demonstration of the fabrication and single-mode operation of a phase-shifted DFB laser. Electron-beam lithography was applied to fabricate the corrugations on an InP substrate.[10]

First, we explain the reason why the conventional DFB laser does not oscillate at the Bragg wavelength. Considering division of a DFB laser, with the first-order sinusoidal modulation in equivalent refractive index n_e of the waveguide at the centre, in two sections, the right and left sections (Fig. 1*a*). Forward and backward waves, F_r and B_r, or F_l and B_l in Fig. 1*b*, make standing waves in each section. At the Bragg wavelength ($\lambda_B = 2n_e\Lambda$) all nodes of the standing wave are at points where the equivalent refractive index increases most rapidly in the direction of propagation of forward waves (Fig. 1*b*). Standing waves in the right and left sections do not connect smoothly at the centre (Fig. 1*b*) and therefore resonance does not occur at the Bragg wavelength (Fig. 1*c*).

On the other hand, an introduction of a phase shift into the centre of the corrugation by π as shown in Fig. 1*d* results in smooth connection of the standing wave (Fig. 1*e*) and therefore resonance at the Bragg wavelength (Fig. 1*f*).

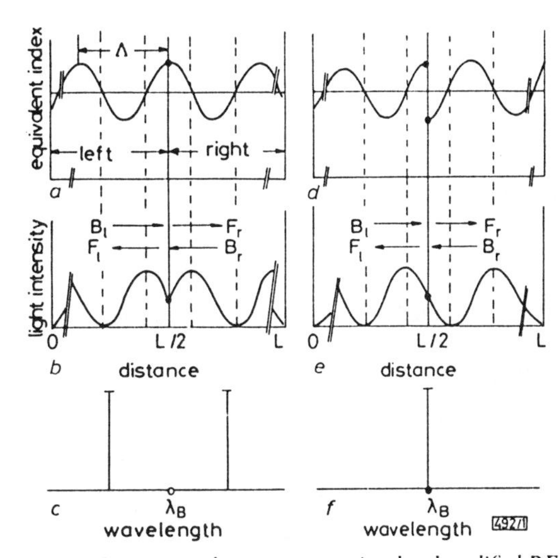

Fig. 1 *Comparison between conventional and modified DFB lasers*

(*a*) and (*d*) are equivalent refractive-index distributions, (*b*) and (*e*) are distributions of light intensity around centres of corrugations, and (*c*) and (*f*) are resonance spectra. L is the cavity length and λ_B the Bragg wavelength

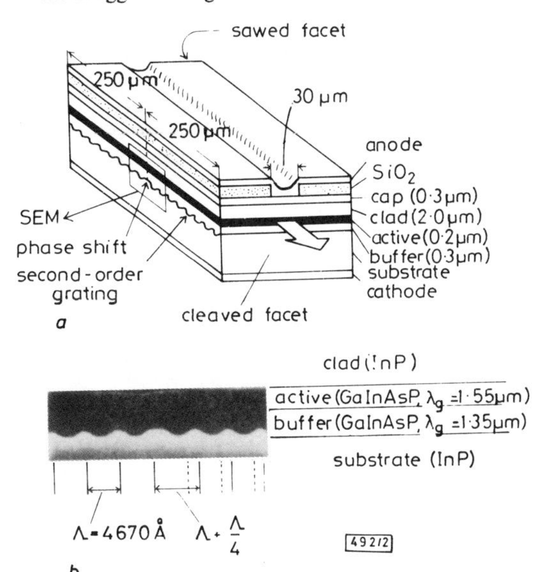

Fig. 2 *Phase-shifted DFB laser*

a Schematic representation of structure
b Cross-sectional SEM view of part where phase of corrugation is shifted

* On leave from Graduate School for Opto-Electrotechniques & Laser Application, University of Indonesia, Jakarta, Indonesia

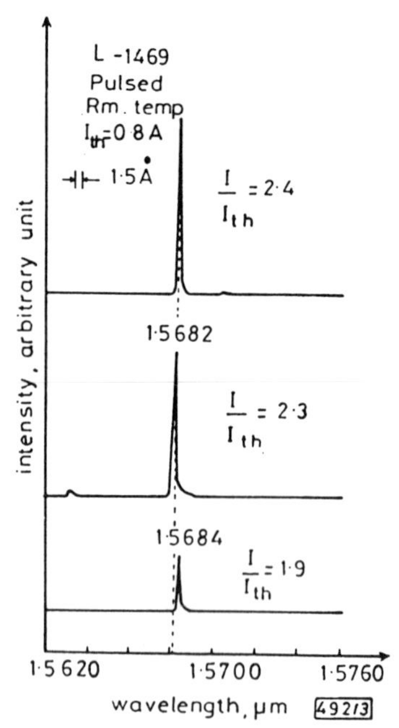

Fig. 3 *Output spectra of phase-shifted DFB laser*

We fabricated phase-shifted DFB lasers of the structure shown in Fig. 2*a*. The second-order corrugation was formed on the InP substrate using an electron-beam exposure system with a precise pitch controller,[11] where at the centre the phase of the corrugation was shifted by $\Lambda/4$, corresponding to a shift of π in the first-order space-harmonics (Fig. 2*b*). The corrugation was transcribed into InP substrate by etching with HBr + HNO_3 + $10H_2O$. The liquid-phase epitaxy was carried out to grow the *n*-GaInAsP ($\lambda_g = 1{\cdot}35$ μm) buffer, undoped GaInAsP ($\lambda_g = 1{\cdot}55$ μm) active, *p*-InP cladding and *p*-GaInAsP cap layers successively, where a GaAs cover was used to preserve the corrugated surface from thermal deformation[12] (Fig. 2*b*). Lasers with 30 μm oxide stripes were cut with sawed sides, and the cavity was formed by sawing at one end to suppress the Fabry–Perot modes and cleaving the other end to provide the output facet, so that the point of the phase shift is at the centre of the cavity.

The typical pulsed threshold current was 800 mA at room temperature, which will be reduced by device optimisation. Single-longitudinal-mode operation of several milliwatts was observed as shown in Fig. 3. The oscillating wavelength, 1·568 μm, coincided with the photoluminescence peak within 180 Å and agreed with the theoretical value of the Bragg wavelength, 1·564 μm and pitch 4670 Å by the equivalent refractive index 3·35.

The authors thank Prof. K. Iga, S. Suzaki and T. Watanabe for fruitful discussions, K. Yoshida for help in EBX, and Y. Tohmori for help with the measurements. This work was supported by a Scientific Research Grant-In-Aid from the Ministry of Education, Science & Culture, Japan, and partly by NTT and KDD.

References

1 KOGELNIK, H., and SHANK, C. V.: 'Coupled mode theory of distributed feedback lasers', *J. Appl. Phys.*, 1972, **43**, pp. 2327–2335
2 SUEMATSU, Y., ARAI, S., and KISHINO, K.: 'Dynamic-single-mode semiconductor lasers with a distributed reflector', *IEEE J. Lightwave Technol.*, 1983, **LT-1**, pp. 161–176
3 SUEMATSU, Y., and HAYASHI, K.: 'General analysis of distributed Bragg reflector and laser resonator using it'. National Convention Record, IECE, Japan, 1974, p. 1200
4 HAUS, H. A., and SHANK, C. V.: 'Antisymmetric taper of distributed feedback lasers', *IEEE J. Quantum Electron.*, 1976, **QE-12**, pp. 532–539
5 TADA, K., and SUZUKI, A.: 'Integrated lasers with intracavity distributed Bragg reflector and phase modulator'. Monthly Meeting of Microwave Group, IECE, Japan, 1977, MW 77-114
6 STREIFER, W., BURNHAM, R. D., and SCIFRES, D. R.: 'Effect of external reflectors on longitudinal mode of distributed feedback lasers', *IEEE J. Quantum Electron.*, 1975, **QE-11**, pp. 154–161
7 ITAYA, Y., MATSUOKA, T., KUROIWA, K., and IKEGAMI, T.: 'Longitudinal mode spectra of 1·5 μm GaInAsP/InP distributed feedback lasers'. 4th Integrated Optics and Optical Fiber Comm. Conf. (IOOC), Tokyo, 1983, 28B1-1
8 AKIBA, S., UTAKA, K., SAKAI, K., and MATSUSHIMA, Y.: 'Effect of mirror facet on lasing characteristics of InGaAsP/InP DFB lasers', *ibid.*, 1983, 28B1-2
9 TOHMORI, Y., SUEMATSU, Y., TSUSHIMA, H., and ARAI, S.: 'Wavelength tuning of GaInAsP/InP integrated laser with butt-jointed built-in distributed Bragg reflector', *ibid.*, 1983, 29B5-3
10 WESTBROOK, L. D., NELSON, A. W., and DIX, C.: 'High quality surface corrugations for 1·55 μm InGaAsP DFB lasers fabricated using electron-beam lithography', *Electron. Lett.*, 1982, **18**, pp. 863–865
11 FURUYA, K., YOSHIDA, K., HONJO, K., and SUEMATSU, Y.: 'Precise control of grating pitch by electron-beam exposure system for integrated optics', *Trans. IECE Jpn.*, 1983, **66**, pp. 561–562
12 KINOSHITA, J., OKUDA, H., and UEMATSU, Y.: 'Preserving InP surface corrugations for 1·3 μm GaInAsP/InP DFB lasers from thermal deformation during LPE process', *Electron. Lett.*, 1983, **19**, pp. 215–216

1·53 μm DFB LASERS BY MASS TRANSPORT

B. BROBERG*
F. KOYAMA
Y. TOHMORI
Y. SUEMATSU

Department of Physical Electronics
Tokyo Institute of Technology
1-12-2 Ookayama, Meguro-ku, Tokyo 152, Japan

10th July 1984

Indexing terms: Lasers and laser applications, Optical communication

DFB lasers emitting at $\lambda = 1{\cdot}53\ \mu m$ made by mass transport have been demonstrated. Output power exceeding 5 mW/facet was obtained when operated in CW at room temperature. Single-longitudinal-mode operation with a minimum threshold current of 26 mA was achieved. No degradation can be observed after aging at 5 mW continuous power at room temperature for more than 1000 h.

For high-performance fibre-optics communication systems operating in the minimum-loss 1·55 μm wavelength region dynamic-single-mode (DSM) lasers are essential.[1] Longitudinal-mode stabilisation can be achieved by integrated Bragg gratings, such as in the distributed Bragg reflector (DBR)[2] or the distributed feedback (DFB)[3–5] lasers, or by coupled cavities.[6] For transverse-mode control the waveguide has to be narrow and be buried in material of lower refractive index. The DSM lasers so far reported have the waveguide buried by regrowth of a reverse *pn*-junction, as in the conventional mesa-BH type,[3] the PBH,[4] the DC-PBH[5] or as in the buried crescent laser.[6]

An alternative to the regrowth is the novel mass transport process.[7–10,†] The narrow waveguides that are possible with this method may result in very low threshold currents and in complete transverse-mode control. The absence of large-area reverse *pn*-junctions may give low capacitance, which is important for high-speed modulation. The simplicity of the process is another attractive feature and may result in high yield in the fabrication.

Mass transport takes place when the sample is heated in a suitable atmosphere containing phosphorus. There are reports on mass transport in H_2 atmosphere when PH_3 is added[7] and when the phosphorus is provided by an InP cover wafer.[8] Some halogens are likely to work as a catalyst for the process.[10,†]

Some of the advantages of the mass transport process have already been experimentally demonstrated for Fabry–Perot-type lasers emitting at $\lambda = 1{\cdot}3\ \mu m$.[7,8,*] In this letter we report DFB lasers for $\lambda = 1{\cdot}53\ \mu m$, made using the mass transport process.

As a first step in the fabrication process first-order gratings with the period 235 nm were made directly on *n*-InP substrates using HeCd laser interference and $HBr:HNO_3:H_2O$ etching. A 0·15 μm-thick *n*-doped InGaAsP buffer layer ($\lambda_g = 1{\cdot}35\ \mu m$), a 0·15 μm undoped InGaAsP active layer ($\lambda_g = 1{\cdot}55\ \mu m$), a 1·5 μm *p*-type InP cladding and a 0·3 μm-thick *p*-InGaAsP ($\lambda_g = 1{\cdot}3\ \mu m$) cap layer were grown on the grating using LPE.

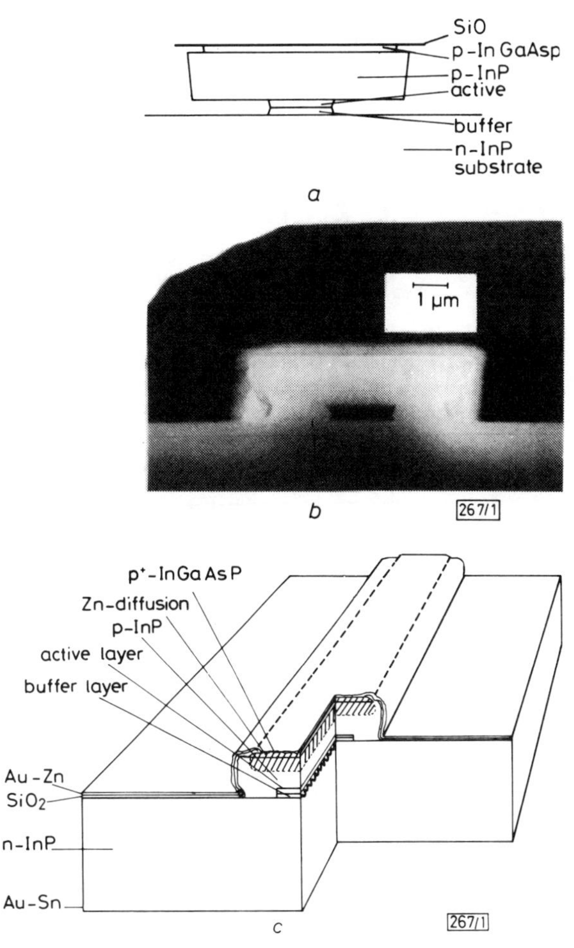

Fig. 1 *Cross-section of sample (a) before and (b) after mass transport, and (c) schematic structure of the mass transported DFB laser*

An etch mask consisting of 8 μm-wide stripes in the ⟨011⟩ direction, perpendicular to the grating corrugation, was formed using SiO_2 deposition, conventional photolithography and buffered HF etching. To minimise underetch, bromine methanol was used to remove the cap layer and partly the cladding layer. Using $HCl:H_2O$ etchant the remaining cladding layer was removed down to the active layer, which acts as a stop-etch layer. The active and buffer layers were etched by $H_2SO_4:H_2O_2:H_2O$ (3:1:1) at 30°C to undercut the mesas until a 1·5 μm-wide stripe remained.

* On leave from Institute of Microwave Technology, Box 70033, S-100 44, Stockholm, Sweden
† KIRKBY, P.: STL, England. Private communication.

Reprinted with permission from *Electron. Lett.*, vol. 20, no. 17, pp. 692–694, Aug. 16, 1984.

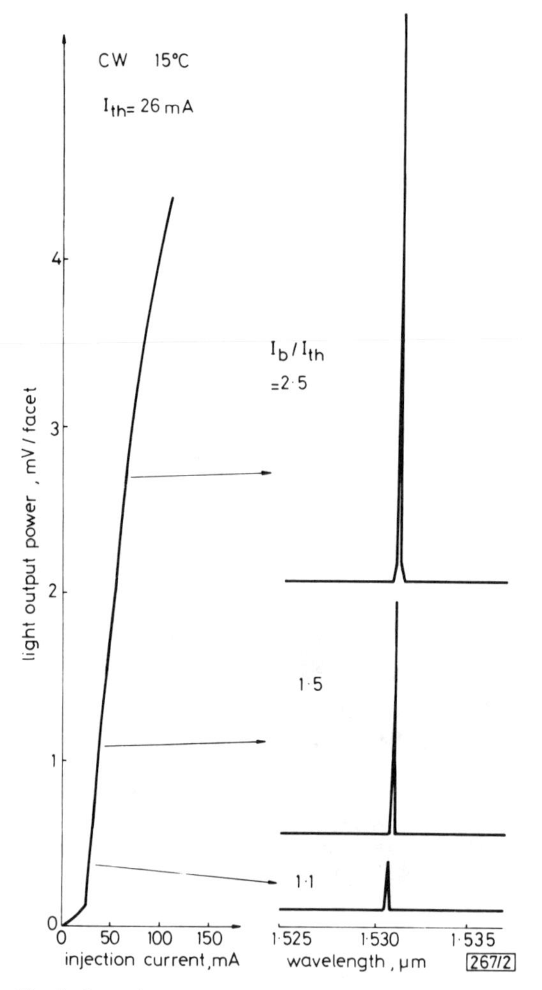

Fig. 2 *Optical output power against current and spectra at different injection levels*

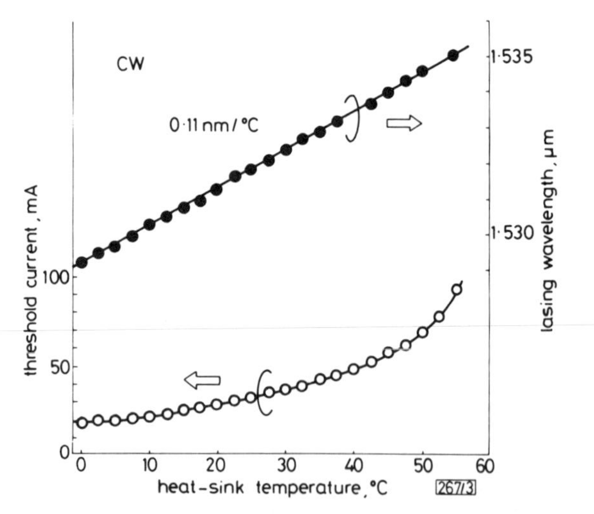

Fig. 3 *Temperature dependence of lasing wavelength and threshold current*

We used an LPE system for the mass transport. The sample was placed in a graphite boat and was covered by an unpolished InP cover wafer and a graphite lid. The mass transport was carried out at 700°C for 2 h in H_2 atmosphere. Cross-sections of the sample before and after mass transport are shown in Fig. 1. A contact mask of SiO_2 with openings on the mesa tops was made in the same way as the etch mask, and Zn was diffused through the openings to reduce the contact resistance. After lapping Au-Sn and Au-Zn contacts were evaporated and alloyed on the *n* and *p* sides, respectively. Laser chips with around 300 μm cavity length were made with both facets cleaved and were soldered using Sn *p*-side down to a heat sink.

The lasers operated in CW at room temperature. As can be seen in Fig. 2 a single longitudinal mode was obtained. The lowest threshold current was 26 mA. The differential quantum efficiency was about 10%/facet. The emission wavelength was 1·53 μm with a 0·11 nm/°C temperature dependence. T_0 was 36 K.

The maximum output power was well above 5 mW/facet for most of the DFB lasers. For some samples operating at Fabry–Perot mode more than 20 mW/facet output power, differential quantum efficiency of 17%/facet and CW operation up to 75°C were obtained. One of the lasers is operated at 5 mW continuous power in a room-temperature aging test. The test has presently continued for more than 1000 h. No degradation of threshold current or differential quantum efficiency can be observed.

In conclusion, we have demonstrated mass-transported 1·5 μm buried-heterostructure dynamic single-mode lasers with distributed reflectors. In this first experiment the laser performance is comparable to what can be achieved using the conventional regrowth process. Our results, together with the potential advantages of the mass-transport process such as complete transverse-mode control, low threshold current, low capacitance and high fabrication yield, are encouraging for further development of mass-transported DFB and DBR lasers.

Acknowledgment: Fruitful discussions with Assoc. Prof. K. Furuya are acknowledged. This work was supported by a Scientific Grant-In-Aid from the Ministry of Education, Science & Culture, Japan, the National Swedish Board for Technical Development, and partly by NTT and KDD.

References

1 SUEMATSU, Y., ARAI, S., and KISHINO, K.: 'Dynamic single-mode semiconductor lasers with a distributed reflector', *IEEE J. Lightwave Tech.*, 1983, **LT-1**, pp. 161–176

2 UTAKA, K., KOBAYASHI, K., KISHINO, K., and SUEMATSU, Y.: '1·5–1·6 μm GaInAsP/InP integrated twin-guide lasers with first-order distributed Bragg reflectors', *Electron. Lett.*, 1980, **16**, pp. 455–456

3 UTAKA, K., AKIBA, S., SAKAI, K., and MATSUSHIMA, Y.: 'Room-temperature CW operation of distributed-feedback buried-heterostructure InGaAsP/InP lasers emitting at 1·57 μm', *ibid.*, 1981, **17**, pp. 961–963

4 MATSUOKA, T., NAGAI, H., ITAYA, Y., NOGUCHI, Y., SUZUKI, U., and IKEGAMI, T.: 'CW operation of DFB-BH GaInAsP/InP lasers in the 1·5 μm region', *ibid.*, 1982, **18**, pp. 27–28

5 KITAMURA, M., SEKI, M., YAMAGUCHI, M., MITO, I., KOBAYASHI, KE., KOBAYASHI, KO., and MATSUOKA, T.: 'High-power single-longitudinal-mode operation of 1·3 μm DFB-DC-PBH LD', *ibid.*, 1983, **19**, pp. 840–841

6 TSANG, W. T., OLSSON, N. A., LINKE, R. A., and LOGAN, R. A.: '1·5 μm-wavelength GaInAsP C^3 laser single-frequency operation and wideband frequency tuning', *ibid.*, 1983, **19**, pp. 415–416

7 LIAU, Z. L., and WALPOLE, J. N.: 'A novel technique for GaInAsP/InP buried heterostructure laser fabrication', *Appl. Phys. Lett.*, 1982, **40**, pp. 568–570

8 CHEN, T. R., CHIU, L. C., YU, K. L., KOREN, U., HASSON, A., MARGALIT, S., and YARIV, A.: 'Low threshold InGaAsP terrace mass transport laser on semi-insulating substrate', *ibid.*, 1982, **41**, pp. 1115–1117

9 CHEN, T. R., CHIU, L. C., HASSON, A., YU, K. L., KOREN, U., MARGALIT, S., and YARIV, A.: 'Study and application of the mass transport phenomenon in InP', *J. Appl. Phys.*, 1983, **54**, pp. 2407–2412

10 HASSON, A., CHIU, L. C., CHEN, T. R., KOREN, U., RAV-NOY, Z., YU, K. L., MARGALIT, S., and YARIV, A.: 'Selective low-temperature mass transport in InGaAsP/InP lasers', *Appl. Phys. Lett.*, 1983, **43**, pp. 403–405

SINGLE-LONGITUDINAL-MODE CONDITION FOR DFB LASERS

G. MOTOSUGI
Y. YOSHIKUNI
T. IKEGAMI

Atsugi Electrical Communication Laboratory
Nippon Telgraph & Telephone Public Corporation
Ono, Atsugi-shi, Kanagawa 243-01, Japan

13th February 1985

Indexing terms: Lasers and laser applications, Semiconductor lasers

We show theoretically that the loss difference of about 10% is required between the main mode and the side mode for a semiconductor laser to oscillate in single-longitudinal mode. The DFB laser has been found to meet this requirement, and a side-mode suppression of more than 30 dB was observed under high-speed direct modulation.

A wavelength-selective optical feedback mechanism is indispensable for semiconductor lasers to oscillate in single-longitudinal mode under high-speed direct modulation. In distributed-feedback (DFB) lasers, the corrugation grating is responsible for the wavelength selectivity. On the wavelength selectivity, analyses have been mainly on the basis of so-called coupled-wave theory,[1] which reveals the existence of cavity loss difference between DFB modes. However, on the cavity loss difference, the amount required is not completely known for DFB lasers to oscillate in single-longitudinal mode under high-speed direct modulation. In this letter we present a theoretical and experimental study on the spectral dynamics of DFB lasers. We show theoretically that the loss difference of about 10% is required between the main mode and the side mode for a semiconductor laser to oscillate in single-longitudinal mode. DFB laser was found to meet this requirement, and the side-mode suppression of more than 30 dB was observed experimentally under high-speed direct modulation.

We have solved the multimode rate equations by assuming that there is a loss difference between the main mode and the side mode in the longitudinal modes.[2,3] In the analysis, a wavelength-independent gain spectrum near the main mode and a homogeneous spectral broadening were assumed, and the carrier diffusion effect was not taken into account. Fig. 1 shows numerical results for light energy ratio of the highest side mode to the main mode in one time slot for 1 Gbit/s return-to-zero (RZ) modulation as a function of loss difference between the two modes. We have defined the loss difference as $(\alpha_1 - \alpha_0)/\alpha_0$, where α_0 and α_1 are the lowest and the second-lowest cavity loss. As shown by the inset, the bias level is $0{\cdot}95I_{th}$ (I_{th} is the threshold current), and the peak current amplitude is $1{\cdot}5I_{th}$. In the calculation the photon lifetime of 1 ps, the spontaneous carrier lifetime of 1 ns, and the spontaneous emission factor β of 1×10^{-6} and 1×10^{-5} were assumed. The light energy of a semiconductor laser becomes concentrated in the main mode as the loss difference increases. Therefore it can be concluded that the loss difference governs the single-longitudinal-mode condition of semiconductor lasers. The light energy ratio is sensitive to the spontaneous emission factor. When the spontaneous emission factor is 1×10^{-5}, the loss difference of 8% is required for a semiconductor laser to oscillate with the side-mode suppression of 30 dB under high-speed direct modulation.

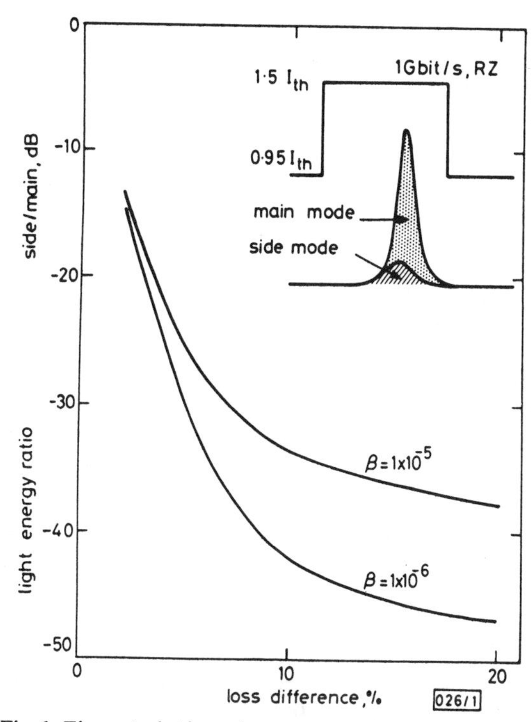

Fig. 1 *Theoretical side-mode suppression characteristics under 1 Gbit/s return-to-zero modulation*

Test devices were InGaAsP DFB lasers grown by liquid-phase epitaxy on *n*-InP substrates. The devices were of buried heterostructure and the corrugation grating was of second order. The threshold current was around 50 mA and the lasing wavelength was 1·3 μm. The typical cavity length was about 300 μm. The coupling coefficient was estimated around 40 cm^{-1} from the stopband width.[4] Two kinds of devices with different facet structures were examined; output cleaved/rear slanted, and output SiN-coated/rear cleaved. The reflectivity of SiN-coated facet was less than 1%. In the following experiments, similar longitudinal-mode-intensity characteristics were observed for both kinds of devices.

Fig. 2 shows the dependences of the main-mode intensity (open circles) and the highest-side-mode intensity (solid circles) on DC current. The facet structure is shown by the inset. The arrow indicates the threshold current. The side-mode intensity is almost saturated above the threshold, representing the carrier density clamping (contrary to the case of Reference 4). The light intensity ratio is about 30 dB at 2% above the

Reprinted with permission from *Electron. Lett.*, vol. 21, no. 8, pp. 352–353, Apr. 11, 1985.

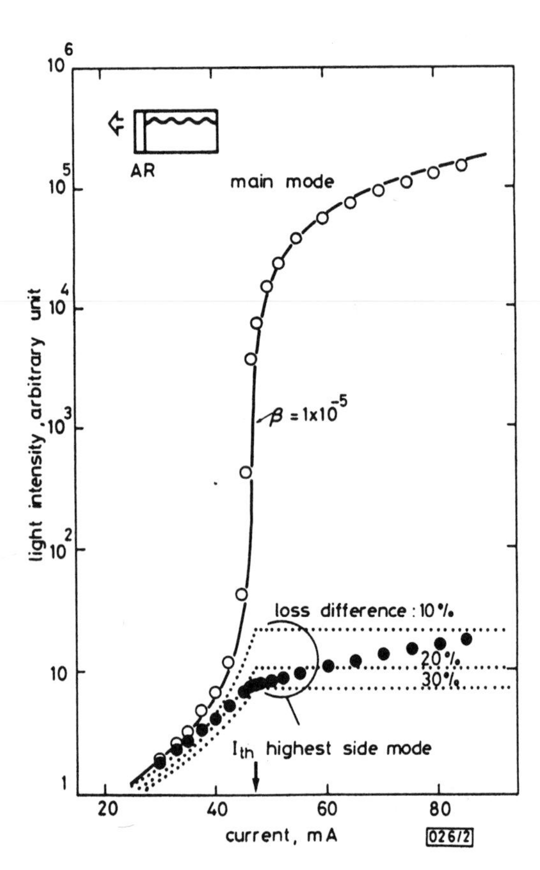

Fig. 2 *Mode-intensity characteristics of a DFB laser under DC operation*

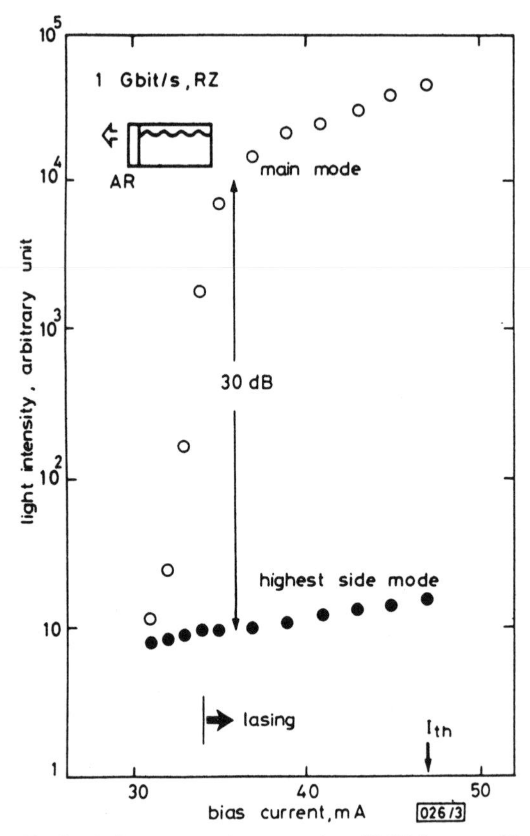

Fig. 3 *Mode-intensity characteristics of DFB laser used in Fig. 2, under 1 Gbit/s RZ modulation*

threshold and becomes as large as 38 dB at $1{\cdot}5I_{th}$. In Fig. 2, the solid curve is the best-fit theoretical main-mode intensity calculated from the steady-state rate equations. From the fitting we obtain $\beta = 1 \times 10^{-5}$. The dotted curves are the theoretical intensity for the highest side mode calculated for loss differences of 10, 20 and 30%. The Figure indicates that the loss difference of the device is around 20%, which predicts the side-mode suppression of 30 dB under high-speed direct modulation.

In Fig. 3, we show the mode-intensity characteristics of the DFB laser, which is the same device as used in Fig. 2, under 1 Gbit/s RZ modulation. The modulation current amplitude was fixed at 13 mA and the bias current was changed. In this experiment the spectrometer slit width was set to be larger than the chirped linewidth under modulation, but smaller than the mode spacing. As shown in the Figure, the side-mode suppression ratio is more than 30 dB just after lasing and becomes 35 dB when the bias current is increased. Therefore it can be concluded that the DFB laser meets the requirement of loss difference for single-longitudinal-mode oscillation.

In summary, an experimental and theoretical study on the spectral dynamics of DFB lasers has been presented. The single-longitudinal mode condition for DFB lasers was found to be a loss difference of about 10%. The side-mode suppression of more than 30 dB was predicted theoretically and confirmed experimentally.

Acknowledgments: The authors express their thanks to M. Fujimoto for his encouragement throughout this work. They thank K. Kurumada, H. Nagai and Y. Itaya for fruitful discussions. They also thank T. Matsuoka, Y. Suzuki and Y. Noguchi for device fabrication.

References

1 KOGELNIK, H., and SHANK, C. V.: 'Coupled-wave theory of distributed feedback lasers', *J. Appl. Phys.*, 1972, **43**, pp. 2327–2335

2 IKEGAMI, T., and MOTOSUGI, G.: 'Single longitudinal mode (SLM) lasers'. Proceedings of 9th European conference on optical communication, Geneva, 1983, pp. 31–34

3 KOYAMA, F., SUEMATSU, Y., KOMORI, K., and TAKAHASHI, S.: 'Dynamic single mode condition for semiconductor lasers'. Proceedings of 10th European conference on optical communication, Stuttgart, 1984, pp. 136–137

4 ITAYA, Y., MATSUOKA, T., KUROIWA, K., and IKEGAMI, T.: 'Longitudinal mode behaviours of 1·5 μm range GaInAsP/InP distributed feedback lasers', *IEEE J. Quantum Electron.*, 1984, **QE-20**, pp. 230–235

DESIGN OF DFB LASERS FOR HIGH-POWER SINGLE-MODE OPERATION

H. SODA
H. ISHIKAWA
H. IMAI

Fujitsu Laboratories Ltd.
10-1, Morinosato-wakamiya
Atsugi, Kanagawa 243-01, Japan

5th August 1986

Indexing term: Semiconductor lasers

The longitudinal-mode behaviour above threshold for DFB lasers has been analysed taking into account spatial hole burning along the laser axis. As a result, the single-longitudinal-mode operating condition up to high optical output power has been made clear.

Introduction: It has been reported that DFB lasers with one cleaved facet and one nonreflecting facet have better longitudinal mode selectivity than those with both nonreflecting facets.[1,2] Therefore such asymmetric-structure DFB lasers are promising as light sources for long-distance, high-bit-rate optical transmission systems. For this application, high optical output power operation in single longitudinal mode (SLM) is essential. In fact, some asymmetric-structure DFB lasers are able to operate up to about 10 mW. However, unexpectedly we often observe multilongitudinal-mode operation in these DFB lasers. The multilongitudinal-mode operation can be classified into two types. One is near threshold, which is due to a small threshold gain difference. To suppress this multilongitudinal-mode operation, we should avoid κL close to 1·4.[3] The other is above threshold. The mechanism of this multilongitudinal-mode operation is not clear because the conventional analysis is limited to the threshold condition.

In this letter we analyse a longitudinal-mode behaviour above threshold of asymmetric-structure DFB lasers. The occurrence of multilongitudinal-mode operation is well explained as a result of spatial hole burning along a laser axis. We show that there exists an optimum κL that gives the minimum effect of spatial hole burning and hence high yield of high-power SLM operation.

Analysis and results: Fig. 1 shows the analysed DFB laser model. We consider asymmetric-structure DFB lasers with one cleaved facet and one nonreflecting facet. Current is injected uniformly over a lasing region. An axial distribution of the refractive index affects the longitudinal-mode behaviour more seriously than that of the gain. So we have formulated a contribution of the axial distribution of the refractive index caused by the spatial hole burning to the longitudinal modes.[4] Above threshold the net carrier density profile along the laser axis is deformed by the stimulated recombination proportional to the light intensity distribution.[5] The deformed net carrier density profile $N_n(z)$ due to the spatial hole burning is expressed as

$$N_n(z) = \tau_s J_c/ed_1 - \xi\tau_s v_g g(z)P(z) \quad (1)$$

where τ_s is the carrier life time, J_c is the injection current

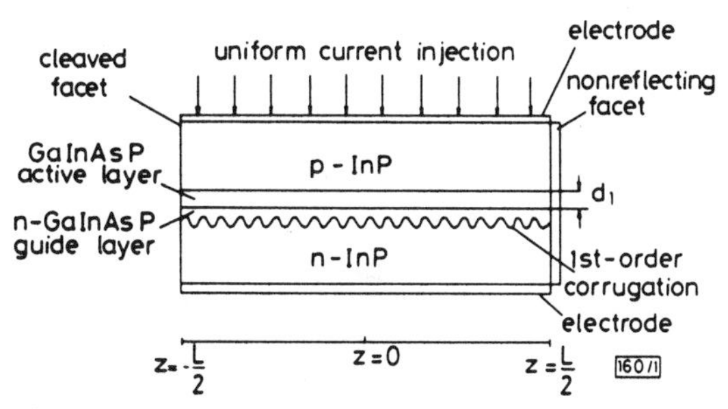

Fig. 1 *Analysed DFB laser model*

density, e is the electric charge, d_1 is the thickness of the active layer, ξ is the light confinement factor in the active layer, v_g is the light velocity in the laser, $g(z)$ is the gain and $P(z)$ is the photon density of the lowest longitudinal mode. Taking account of this deformed net carrier density profile, we obtain the effective refractive index profile $n_{eff}(z)$ above threshold:

$$n_{eff}(z) = n_{eff0} + \xi(dn/dN)N_{th}(J_c/J_{th} - 1) - \xi^2(dn/dN)\tau_s v_g g(z)P(z) \quad (2)$$

where n_{eff0} is the effective refractive index at threshold which is determined by the waveguide structure, and dn/dN is the coefficient of the carrier-induced refractive index change. Under lasing conditions the gain must be equal to the loss. Using this condition, $P(z)$ can now be found in terms of the normalised injection current:

$$-\xi(dn/dN)N_{th}(J_c/J_{th} - 1) = -\xi^2(dn/dN)\tau_s v_g g_0 \int_{cavity} P(z)/L\, dz \quad (3)$$

where we approximated $g(z)$ as g_0 (constant), because variation of $g(z)$ along the laser axis is much smaller than $P(z)$.

Combining eqns. 2 and 3 with the coupled-mode equations,[6] we calculated the longitudinal-mode behaviour above threshold. As it is difficult to solve the equations analytically, we performed numerical calculations. First, we assumed $P(z)$; next we gave $n_{eff}(z)$ by eqn. 2 and solved the coupled-mode equations. After this step we judged if $P(z)$ obtained as the solution is equal to the assumed $P(z)$. If not, we corrected the assumed $P(z)$ and repeated former steps until the solution $P(z)$ converged on the assumed $P(z)$. Then we calculated the threshold gain of higher-order longitudinal modes and the gain difference by using the determined $n_{eff}(z)$. Finally, by eqn. 3 we obtained the normalised injection current density. In the calculation we used 300 μm for the cavity length.

Figs. 2*a–c* show maps of the calculated gain difference

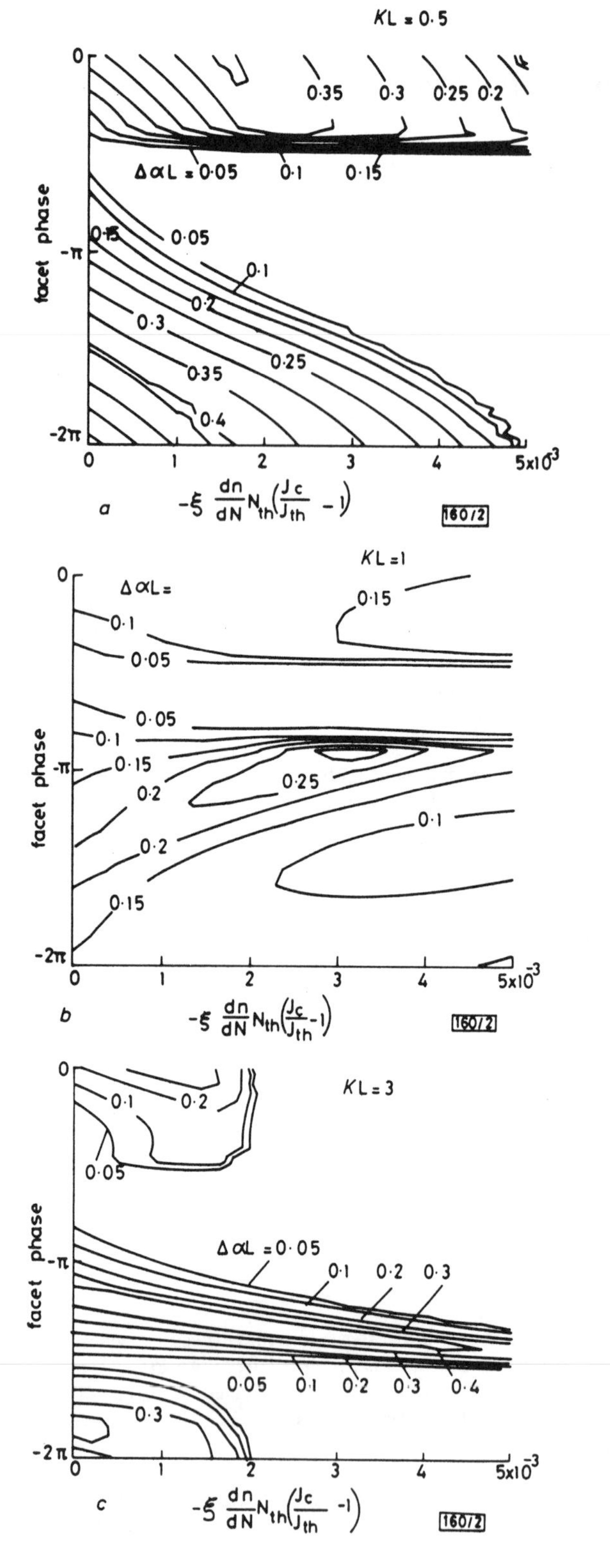

Fig. 2 *Map of normalised gain difference above threshold*
a For $\kappa L = 0{\cdot}5$
b For $\kappa L = 1{\cdot}0$
c For $\kappa L = 3{\cdot}0$

above threshold for $\kappa L = 0{\cdot}5$, 1 and 3. The vertical axis shows the facet phase at the cleaved facet. The horizontal axis shows the normalised injection current density. The magnitude of the normalised injection current density of 5×10^{-3} corresponds to J_c/J_{th} of about 1·7. In the case of strong coupling $\kappa L = 3$,

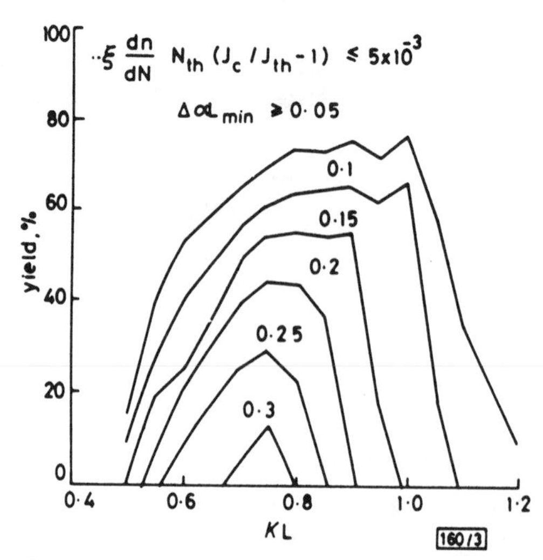

Fig. 3 *Yield of single-longitudinal-mode lasers above threshold*

the normalised gain difference reduces remarkably with increasing the normalised injection current except around $-1{\cdot}4\pi$ of the facet phase. As the facet phase cannot be controlled in the fabrication process, we can obtain only a finite yield of SLM operation. The yield is defined by the percentage of cases where the normalised gain difference exceeds a given value. Fig. 3 shows the SLM operating yield for the normalised injection current range $-\xi(dn/dN)N_{th}(J_c/J_{th} - 1) \leq 5 \times 10^{-3}$, for various normalised gain differences. It can be seen that high yield is obtained for $\kappa L = 0{\cdot}75$. This is because the light intensity is fairly flat over the cavity for κL of around 0·75. Such great κL dependence of the SLM yield is not predicted by conventional threshold theory.

Conclusion: We have analysed the longitudinal-mode behaviour above threshold for DFB lasers with one cleaved facet and one nonreflecting facet. As a result it was found that the spatial hole burning along the laser axis had a decisive effect on the SLM operation. The SLM yield depended largely on κL. Further, we found that κL near 0·75 gave a good SLM operation yield up to high optical output power.

Acknowledgment: The authors wish to thank T. Misugi and K. Dazai of Fujitsu Laboratories Ltd. for their encouragement.

References

1 STREIFER, W., BURNHAM, R. D., and SCIFRES, D. R.: 'Effect of external reflectors on longitudinal modes of distributed feedback lasers', *IEEE J. Quantum Electron.*, 1975, **QE-11**, pp. 154–161
2 UTAKA, K., AKIBA, S., SAKAI, K., and MATSUSIMA, Y.: 'Effect of mirror facets on lasing characteristics of distributed feedback InGaAsP/InP laser diodes at 1·5 μm range', *ibid.*, 1984, **QE-20**, pp. 236–246
3 BUUS, J.: 'Mode selectivity in DFB lasers with cleaved facet', *Electron. Lett.*, 1985, **21**, pp. 179–180
4 SODA, H., KOTAKI, Y., ISHIKAWA, H., and IMAI, H.: 'Mode analysis of λ/4 shifted GaInAsP/InP DFB lasers considering a refractive index change due to a spatial hole burning along a laser axis'. IECE of Japan, Tech. group meeting, 1986, OQE86-7, pp. 49–56
5 KIRKBY, P. A., GOODWIN, A. R., THOMPSON, G. H. B., and SELWAY, P. R.: 'Observations of self-focusing in stripe geometry semiconductor lasers and the development of a comprehensive model of their operation', *IEEE J. Quantum Electron.*, 1977, **QE-13**, pp. 705–719
6 KOGELNIK, H., and SHANK, C. V.: 'Coupled mode theory of distributed feedback lasers', *J. Appl. Phys.*, 1972, **43**, pp. 2327–2335

SPECTRAL LINEWIDTH OF AN AlGaAs/GaAs DFB-TJS EXTERNAL-CAVITY LASER WITH OPTICAL PHASE CONTROL LOOP

M. KAMEYA
S. TAI
K. MITSUNAGA
K. KYUMA
K. HAMANAKA
T. NAKAYAMA

Central Research Laboratory
Mitsubishi Electric Corporation
8-1-1 Tsukaguchi-honmachi
Amagasaki, Hyogo 661, Japan

22nd September 1986

Indexing term: Semiconductor lasers

A stable narrow spectral linewidth was obtained for an external-cavity laser consisting of an AlGaAs/GaAs distributed-feedback laser and a stabilised electro-optical feedback loop. The linewidth of 500 kHz with its fluctuation of less than ±5 kHz was achieved without any temperature control.

Introduction: Reducing the spectral linewidth of visible or near-infra-red AlGaAs/GaAs lasers is important for the application of fibre-optic sensor systems. As a method to obtain the narrow spectral linewidth stably, a stabilised external-cavity (E-C) laser where the phase of feedback light was adjusted automatically at the optimum point was reported by using a Fabry-Perot (F-P) laser.[1] However, instability was caused by mode hopping due to the fluctuation of the feedback light by the temperature change. Therefore, a stable single-mode laser with narrow linewidth was required.

Recently, AlGaAs/GaAs distributed-feedback (DFB) lasers with low threshold current were fabricated.[2,3] With the DFB laser in the E-C laser, it can be expected that mode hopping due to the fluctuation of the feedback light does not occur. Therefore, its linewidth can be narrowed stably even without temperature control. In this letter we report the linewidth stability of the E-C DFB transverse junction stripe (TJS) laser without temperature control.

Experiments and results: The schematic diagram of the laser structure is shown in Fig. 1. It was fabricated by two-step molecular beam epitaxy (MBE). The grating period was chosen so that the DFB resonant wavelength was close to the peak of the bulk gain at room temperature. Both facets were AR-coated (<0·02%) to suppress the F-P mode. The oscillation wavelength was 865·0 nm, and another DFB mode at the opposite side of the stopband, measured from the spontaneous emission spectrum, was 865·8 nm. The coupling coefficient was estimated to be $\kappa = 93\,cm^{-1}$ from the measured stopband width of 0·80 nm.[4] The threshold current at 20°C was 41 mA and the differential quantum efficiency of both facets was 37%.

The schematic diagram of the linewidth stabilisation system of the DFB-TJS E-C laser is shown in Fig. 2. The E-C laser was constructed of a variable neutral density (ND) filter and an external grating placed about 20 cm away from the laser. The linewidth of the E-C laser is minimised when the phase

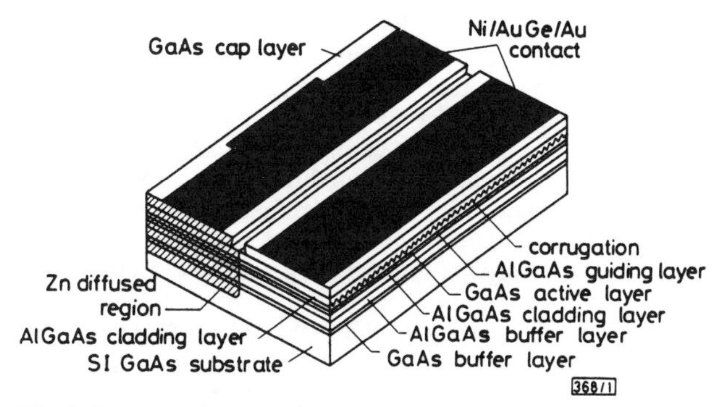

Fig. 1 *Schematic diagram of DFB-TJS laser*

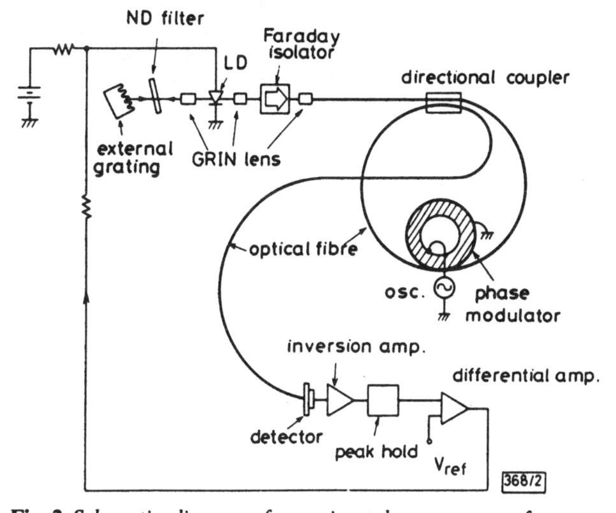

Fig. 2 *Schematic diagram of experimental arrangement for spectral linewidth stabilisation*

between the electric fields of the emitting and feedback lights at the laser facet is matched.[5] Therefore the fluctuation of the phase difference causes the change in the linewidth. To obtain the phase-matching condition, we used the automatic optical phase-control loop with a fibre-optic ring resonator (FORR),[6] where cavity length and finesse were 1 m and 60, respectively. A part of the fibre was wound around a piezoelectric cylinder to scan the phase of the light propagating in the fibre resonator. A triangular wave of 200 Hz was applied to this phase modulator. The resonant peaks of the FORR output signal

Reprinted with permission from *Electron. Lett.*, vol. 22, no. 23, pp. 1231–1232, Nov. 6, 1986.

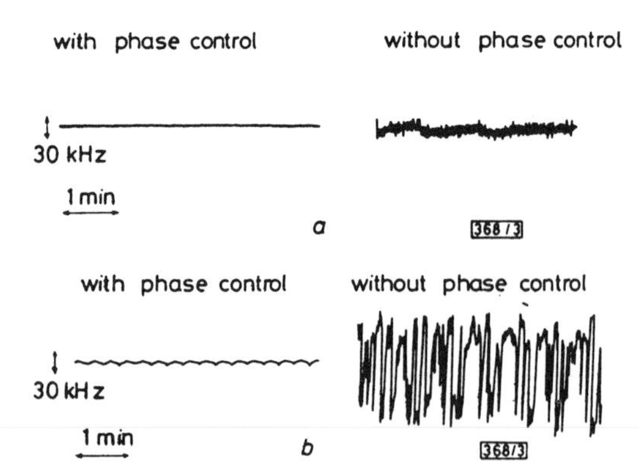

Fig. 3 ***Fluctuation of linewidth***
a **DFB-TJS laser**
b **CSP laser**

are strongly dependent on the linewidth of the laser, so that the FORR can be used for the linewidth discriminator.[7] To stabilise the linewidth, the peak voltage of the resonant signal was compared with the reference voltage V_{ref} by a differential amplifier. The error signal from the differential amplifier was added to the injection current to control the oscillation frequency so that the phase-matching condition was automatically satisfied. The bandwidth of this feedback circuit was 10 kHz. The fluctuation of the linewidth was estimated from the change of the resonance peak voltages of the FORR output signal.

To compare the DFB laser with the F-P laser, an AlGaAs/GaAs channelled-substrate planar (CSP) E-C laser was also fabricated and its spectral linewidth was measured. The fluctuations of the linewidth of the DFB and F-P E-C lasers are shown in Figs. 3*a* and *b*, respectively. These lasers were used without any temperature control. In both cases the stable linewidth of about 500 kHz was obtained when the feedback loop was switched on. However, the fluctuation of the linewidth ($< \pm 5$ kHz) of the DFB-TJS E-C laser was much smaller than that ($\simeq \pm 5$ kHz) of the F-P E-C laser, as shown in Figs. 3*a* and *b*. On the other hand, when the feedback loop was switched off, the stability for the DFB-TJS E-C laser was also much superior to that for the CSP E-C laser, since no mode-hopping occurs for the DFB laser. The fluctuations of linewidth for the DFB and F-P E-C lasers were less than ± 15 kHz and more than ± 60 kHz, respectively. In view of these results, the availability of the TJS-DFB laser in the external-cavity structure is confirmed.

Conclusion: The external-cavity lasers using the DFB-TJS laser and the F-P CSP laser were constructed. Comparing the linewidth stability of these lasers, it was demonstrated that the linewidth of the DFB E-C laser was more stable than that of the F-P E-C laser. In the case of the DFB-TJS E-C laser, a stable linewidth of 500 kHz with fluctuation less than ± 5 kHz was achieved.

References

1 TAI, T., KYUMA, K., and NAKAYAMA, T.: 'Spectral linewidth of an external-cavity laser diode stabilized by a fiber-optic ring resonator', *Appl. Phys. Lett.*, 1985, **47**, pp. 439–440
2 KOJIMA, K., NODA, S., MITSUNAGA, K., KYUMA, K., and NAKAYAMA, T.: 'Low threshold current AlGaAs/GaAs distributed feedback laser grown by two-step molecular beam epitaxy', *ibid.*, 1985, **47**, pp. 570–572
3 NODA, S., KOJIMA, K., MITSUNAGA, K., KYUMA, K., and NAKAYAMA, T.: 'Continuous wave operation of ridge waveguide AlGaAs/GaAs distributed feedback lasers with low threshold current', *ibid.*, 1986, **48**, pp. 4–6
4 IGA, K.: 'On the use of effective refractive index in DFB laser mode separation', *Jpn. J. Appl. Phys.*, 1983, **22**, p. 1630
5 KIKUCHI, K., and OKOSHI, T.: 'Simple formula giving spectrum-narrowing ratio of semiconductor laser output obtained by optical feedback', *Electron. Lett.*, 1982, **18**, pp. 10–11
6 STOKES, L. F., CHODOROW, M., and SHAW, H. J.: 'All-single-mode fiber resonator', *Opt. Lett.*, 1982, **7**, pp. 288–290
7 TAI, S., KYUMA, K., and NAKAYAMA, T.: 'Novel measuring method for spectral linewidth of laser diodes using fibre-optic ring resonator', *Electron. Lett.*, 1985, **21**, pp. 91–93

InGaAsP/InP Distributed Feedback Buried Heterostructure Lasers with Both Facets Cleaved Structure

HARUO NAGAI, TAKASHI MATSUOKA, MEMBER, IEEE, YOSHIO NOGUCHI, YOSHIO SUZUKI, AND YUZO YOSHIKUNI

Abstract—Feasibilities of InGaAsP/InP distributed feedback buried heterostructure lasers in the 1.3 and 1.5 μm wavelength regions with two cleaved facets are shown. Theoretical and experimental examinations show that the κL values ranging between 1 and 2 are sufficient for high-performance operation with the stable single longitudinal mode in a temperature range wider than 100 degrees. Distribution of lasing characteristics is investigated for 140 randomly chosen LD's from two wafers. Approximately 65 percent of the devices are found to be operable in the single longitudinal mode. A CW single longitudinal mode operation power of 20 mW at 25°C for a 1.5 μm device, and that of 40 mW (60 mW with AR coating) at 25°C for a 1.3 μm device with low threshold current are achieved. These characteristics are attained by both first- and second-order grating devices fabricated by the PH_3 addition LPE technique. The results of the aging test at 70°C and 110 mA in the automatic current control condition are also presented.

I. Introduction

REMARKABLE improvements have recently been made in the performance of InGaAsP/InP distributed feedback (DFB) laser diodes (LD's). The results of preliminary life tests [1] indicate that there are good prospects for their practical use in optical fiber communication systems. For the introduction of DFB LD's as a light source into communication systems, the yield of SLM operable devices is an essential problem. Ideal DFB LD's having no reflectors exhibit symmetric spectra. However, DFB LD's generally have one cleaved facet to facilitate easy coupling with optical components, while various structures such as a tilted facet, unexcited regions, window regions, and antireflection (AR) coating have been applied at the other end to suppress the Fabry–Perot (FP) mode. The cleaved facet acts as a reflector in the laser action, and this reflector can break the symmetric spectrum. This can make possible SLM operations as well as multimode operations, which depend on the phase of the light at the reflector. The authors have verified this effect by shifting the cleaved facet position of DFB LD's with a tilted rear facet using the ion beam etching technique [2]. The yield of an SLM device depends on the distribution of the cleaving location.

LD's with two cleaved facets, however, would be easier to fabricate. Another advantage of such LD's is that there is a sufficient coupling efficiency between the power monitoring detectors and the back facet. A theoretical analysis by Streifer [3] has shown that DFB LD's with two cleaved facets lower the required threshold gain as compared to those which have reflection free structures. The threshold value of DFB LD's with two cleaved facets depends on the coupling coefficient, matching between the corrugation pitch and gain peak, and the relative positions of the cleaved facet to the grating phase. There are several reports on SLM operation with low threshold current (I_{th}) values for this LD type in the 1.3 and 1.5 μm regions. Okuda *et al.* have reported [4] 1.3 μm DFB oscillation with I_{th} of 16 mA and light output of 7 mW at 25°C. SLM operation has been achieved in a temperature range of 10–85°C. Based on Streifer's model, Utaka *et al.* have analyzed [5] the theoretical possibility of SLM operation. They also achieved a 4 mW SLM oscillation in the 1.5 μm wavelength with a 24 mA I_{th}. Broberg *et al.* reported a 5 mW SLM power at 1.53 μm [6], while Kitamura *et al.* reported 60 mW at 1.3 μm and 36 mW at 1.565 μm [7]. Nelson *et al.* fabricated ridge-waveguide DFB lasers at 1.52 μm and observed 20 mW output [8]. DFB LD's grown by a MOCVD method emit 6 mW at 1.57 μm [9]. Buus discussed [10] the mode selectivity of this structure for various positions of the grating relative to the facets. The expected yield of single SLM lasers was calculated for several values of the coupling coefficient. However, discussions on the actual performance of this DFB LD type are insufficient. In addition, serious concerns exist relative to the SLM operable temperature range because competition is present between the FP and DFB modes.

This paper reports the feasibilities and characteristic distributions of DFB LD's with two cleaved facets in the 1.3 and 1.5 μm wavelength regions. High-performance SLM operation with low threshold current, high output power, and a wide temperature range has been achieved and analyzed.

II. Laser Diode Fabrication

LD's with two kinds of buried-heterostructures (BH) were examined. One is the conventional BH structure on n-type InP substrate and the other is doubly buried-het-

Manuscript received May 10, 1985; revised October 22, 1985.
The authors are with the NTT Atsugi Electrical Communication Laboratory, Atsugi-shi, Kanagawa, Japan.
IEEE Log Number 8406801.

Reprinted from *IEEE J. Quantum Electron.*, vol. QE-22, no. 3, pp. 450–457, Mar. 1986.

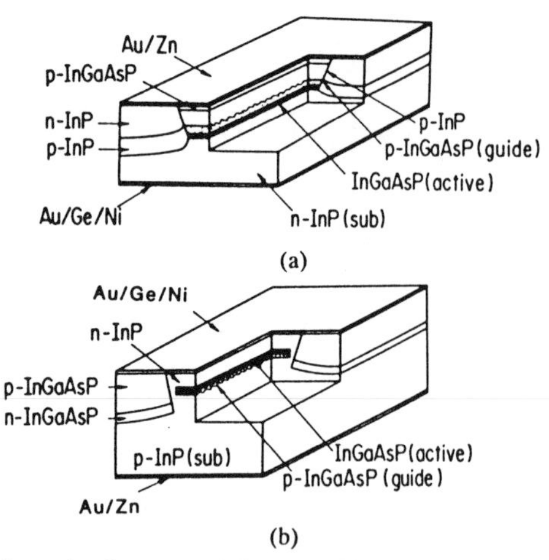

Fig. 1. Schematic diagrams of the two BH structures. (a) BH-DFB LD fabricated on n-type InP substrate with first-order grating on guide layer. (b) DBH-DFB LD fabricated on p-type substrate with second-order grating on substrate.

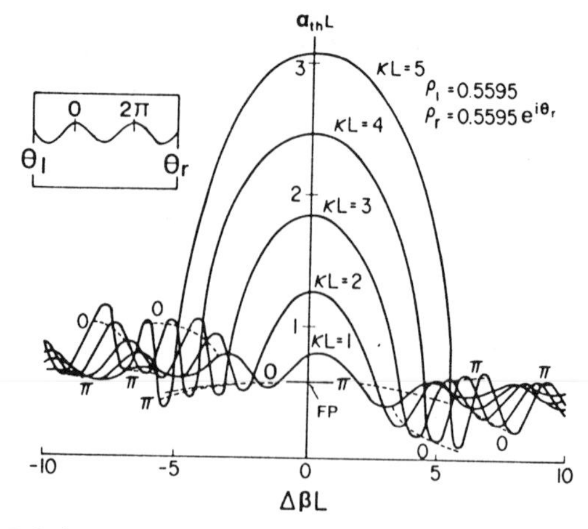

Fig. 2. Relation between $\alpha_{th}L$ and $\Delta\beta L$ for DFB lasers with two cleaved facets.

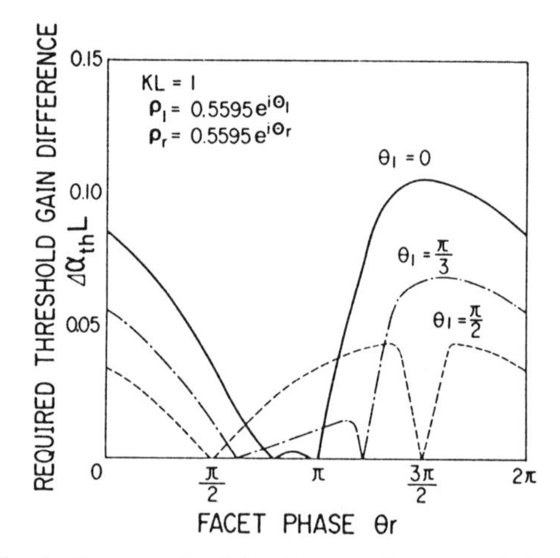

Fig. 3. An example of $\Delta\alpha_{th}L$ versus θ_l characteristics.

erostructure (DBH) on p-type InP substrate. Schematic diagrams of these two BH structures are shown in Fig. 1. Crystal growth and fabrication details have been presented in our previous reports [11], [12]. The first-order gratings were formed on an InP substrate surface, while the second-order gratings were formed both on an InGaAsP waveguide layer surface and on an InP substrate surface. These gratings were formed by a wet chemical etching technique through a photoresist mask formed by holographic lithography. The depth of the gratings after crystal growth was about 400-500 Å for the first order and about 1300 Å for the second order. The PH_3 addition LPE technique [11] was utilized during crystal growth to conserve the surface corrugations. LD cavity lengths were in the range of 200-300 μm. The LD chips were mounted on diamond heat sinks with the junctions down.

III. SLM Operable Grating Phase Conditions at the Facets

In the both-facets-cleaved structures, the DFB mode can oscillate when the required threshold gain (α_{th}) for the DFB mode is lower than that of the FP mode. The α_{th} value for the DFB mode depends on the coupling coefficient (κ) and the light phase on the facet. The situation is complicated since the two phases on both facets have to be considered. Fig. 2 shows examples of the relation between $\alpha_{th}L$ (L: cavity length) and $\Delta\beta L$ ($\Delta\beta$: the wavelength deviation from the Bragg condition). In this figure, the grating phase at the left facet is assumed to be 0, and the κL values are changed. The horizontal straight line at $\alpha_{th}L = 0.58$ indicates the value for the FP mode oscillation. In these cases the lowest threshold of the DFB modes are found to be lower than those of the FP modes. Calculations for other combinations of the facet phases also show that in most cases, the above-mentioned condition is satisfied. Therefore, if the Bragg wavelength coincides with the gain peak wavelength, the DFB mode can oscillate in the κL value of more than 1 as shown in Fig. 2. The forthcoming problem is the SLM oscillation probability. From the results of the discussion based on Streifer's model [3], it can be estimated that two modes have the same $\alpha_{th}L$ value in the following three cases: 1) $\theta_l = \pi/2$ or $3\pi/2$, $\theta_r = \pi/2$ or $3\pi/2$, 2) $\theta_l + \theta_r = n\pi$ ($n = 1$, 3 and $\theta_l \neq \pi/2, 3\pi/2$), and 3) the other combinations which depend on θ_l, θ_r, and the κL value. (Here θ_l denotes the grating phase at the left facet and θ_r denotes that at the right facet as shown in the inset of Fig. 2.) In the cases of 1) and 2), the two modes oscillate symmetrically on both sides of the stop band. In case 3), two modes exist at one side of the stop band or symmetrically on both sides of it. Fig. 3 shows an example of the $\Delta\alpha_{th}L$ versus θ_l characteristics. Here, $\Delta\alpha_{th}$ denotes the difference in the threshold gain between the two lowest DFB modes. In this example, θ_l is fixed at 0, $\pi/3$ and $\pi/2$, and $\Delta\alpha_{th}L$ value is plotted against θ_r. For $\theta_l = 0$, $\Delta\alpha_{th}L$ becomes 0 at $\theta_r = \pi$ and at about $4\pi/5$. The former corresponds to case 2) while the latter corresponds to case 3).

IV. SLM Operable Temperature Region

Generally, DFB LD's are designed for operation at room temperature. Therefore, the Bragg wavelength λ_B coincides with the gain peak wavelength λ_g at room temperature. The temperature coefficent of λ_g is larger than

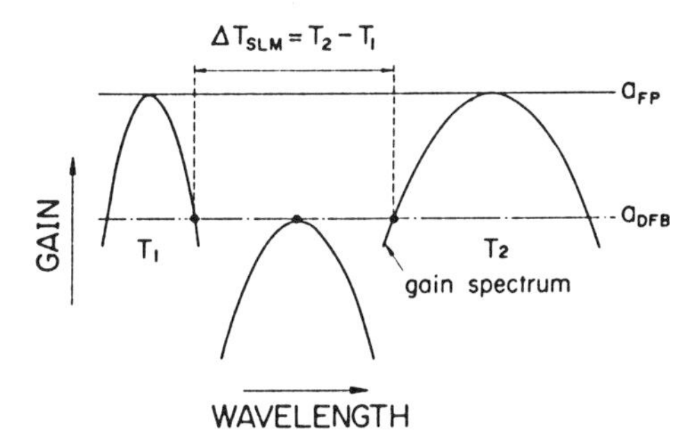

Fig. 4. Principle for estimation of SLM operable temperature regions.

that of λ_B. Therefore, the DFB mode operable temperature region is restricted as shown in Fig. 4. In the lower and higher temperature regions, FP mode oscillation occurs. This region width was estimated as the function of the κL value from the reported temperature characteristics of the gain curve for 1.6 μm wavelength InGaAsP/InP BH LD's [13]. Although the details of our analysis will be published elsewhere, the following three principal conclusions have been obtained.

1) There exist maximum and minimum values due to the facet grating phase effect.

2) κL values larger than 1 are sufficient to achieve a temperature range wider than 100 degrees under favorite grating phase combination conditions.

3) A lower temperature limit always exists. However, the upper temperature limit disappears in large κL devices due to gain spectrum broadening.

V. Experimental Results

A. Distribution of Lasing Characteristics

1) 1.5 μm LD with Second-Order Grating: One area of a wafer containing 40 devices was chosen, and they were mounted with junction side down. On this wafer, conventional BH structure DFB LD's were fabricated on n-type InP substrate, and second-order grating was fabricated on the quaternary waveguide layer (λ_{Eg} = 1.3 μm). The cavity length was 250 μm and all of the LD's lased with DFB modes. Due to the rather thick waveguide structure in the wafer, oscillation in one TE, one TM, and both TE/TM modes were observed. Fig. 5 shows the distribution of the CW threshold current. It ranged from 35 to 88 mA, averaging at 52 mA. The wavelength distribution at I_{th} is shown in Fig. 6. The average lasing wavelength was 1.5114 μm. Fig. 7 shows the distribution of spectral characteristics. Twenty seven LD's, 67 percent of the 40 LD's, exhibited stable SLM operation in the TE or TM mode. Among the other 13 LD's, the following causes were observed: 1) one TE and one TM mode, 2) two TE modes, 3) higher order transverse mode, as seen in Fig. 7. Fig. 8 shows the distribution of the limits of the driving level normalized by the threshold value to maintain the SLM operation. From observation of the stop band width and the calculation from the waveguide parameters, the coupling coefficient for these LD's was estimated to be about 40 cm^{-1}.

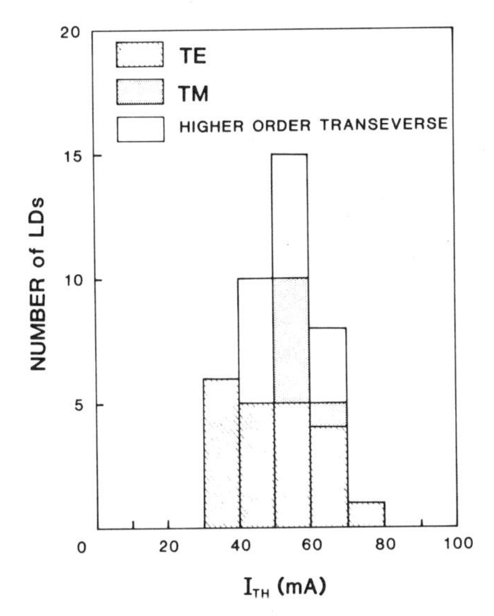

Fig. 5. Distribution of CW threshold current values of 1.5 μm BH-DFB LD's on n-type InP substrate with second-order grating on guide layer.

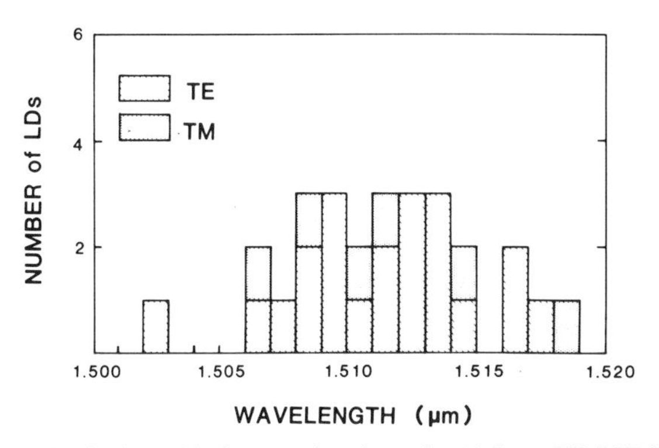

Fig. 6. Distribution of lasing wavelengths at I_{th}. (1.5 μm BH-DFB-LD's in n-type InP substrate.)

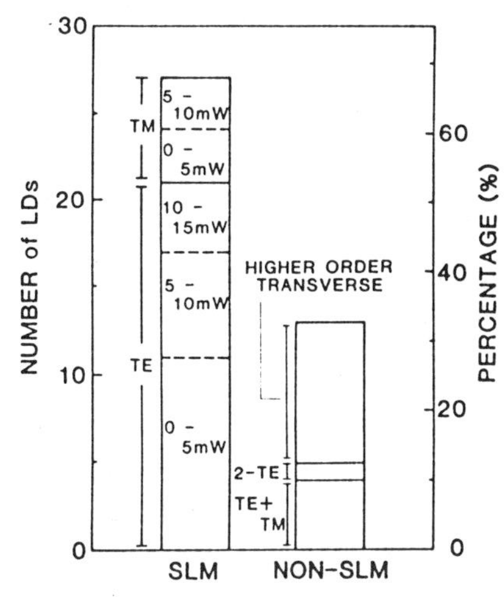

Fig. 7. Distribution of lasing spectral characteristics. (1.5 μm BH-DFB LD's on n-type InP substrate.)

2) 1.3 μm LD with Second-Order Grating: A random selection of 136 pellets of a 1.3 μm DBH-DFB LD was made from a 6 × 4.5 mm^2 wafer. In this wafer, the DBH structure was fabricated on p-type InP substrate. The cavity length was 300 μm. Thirty six LD's were purged be-

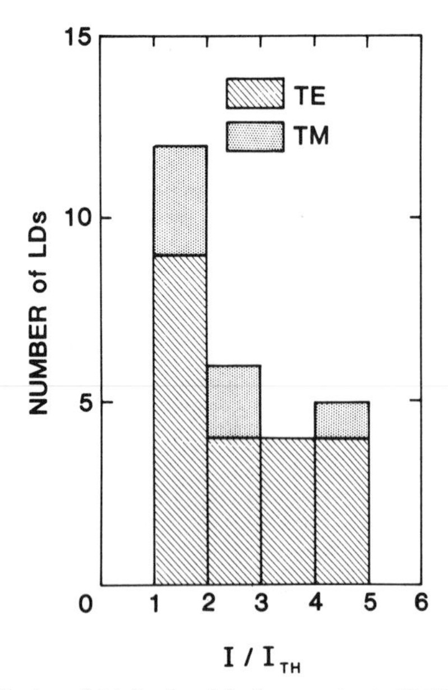

Fig. 8. Distribution of driving level limits to maintain SLM operation. (1.5 μm BH-DFB LD's on n-type InP substrate.)

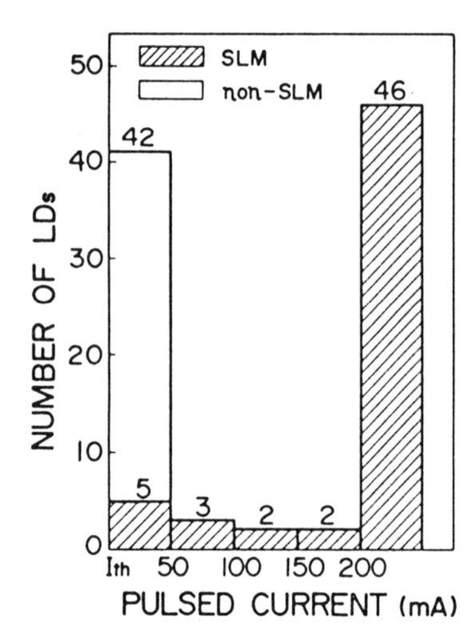

Fig. 9. Distribution of driving current limits to maintain the SLM operation for 1.3 μm DBH-DFB LD's with a second-order grating on p-type InP substrate.

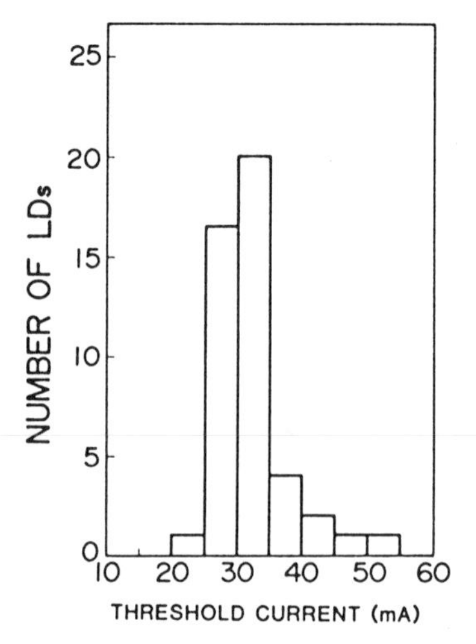

Fig. 10. Distribution of I_{th} of 46 LD's which are operable in SLM under current region greater than 200 mA. (1.3 μm DBH-DFB LD's on p-type substrate.)

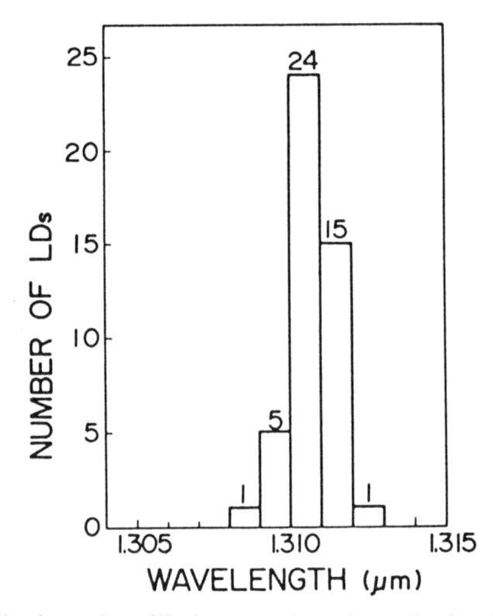

Fig. 11. Distribution of oscillation wavelengths at I_{th} for 46 LD's. (1.3 μm DBH-DFB LD's on p-type InP substrate.)

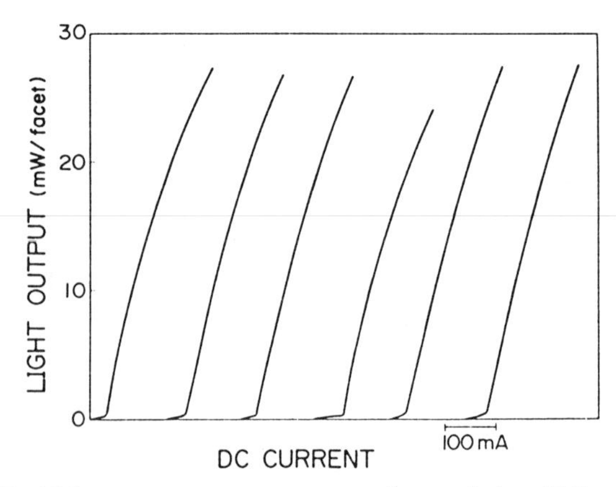

Fig. 12. Light output power versus current characteristics of 1.3 μm DBH-DFB LD's on p-type InP substrate.

cause of an extraordinarily high I_{th}, low external differential quantum efficiency, and a kink in the light output power versus current curves. For the remaining 100 LD pellets, characteristic distributions were investigated under pulsed operation (repetition of 1 kHz, width of 500 ns). Here, oscillation in the TM mode could not be seen. Fig. 9 shows the distribution of driving current limits necessary to maintain the SLM operation. Forty two LD's lased in the non-SLM state, and among the remaining 58 devices, 46 of them lased in SLM in wide current region from the I_{th} to larger than 200 mA. Figs. 10 and 11 show the distributions of the I_{th} and wavelength at the I_{th} for these 46 LD's. The average I_{th} value was 33 mA, and the oscillation wavelength ranged from 1.308 to 1.312 μm. These 46 LD's were mounted on diamond heat-sinks with the junction down. An average CW SLM light output of 24 mW at 25°C under the 200 mA current injection was achieved. Fig. 12 shows the light output power versus current curves for six mounted LD's. Three basic reasons for the non-SLM oscillation among the 42 LD's were analyzed to be: 1) the FP mode (35 LD's), 2) the higher order DFB mode (6 LD's), and 3) the higher order transverse

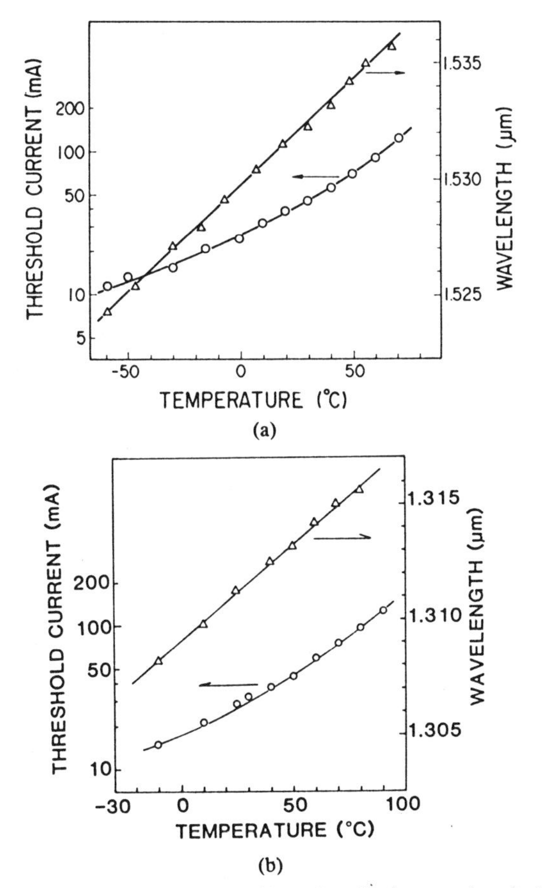

Fig. 13. Temperature dependence of I_{th} and oscillation wavelength. (a) 1.5 μm BH-DFB LD on n-type InP substrate (L: 250 μm). (b) 1.3 μm DBH-DFB LD on p-type InP substrate (L: 300 μm).

mode (1 LD). The coupling coefficient for the SLM LD's was estimated to be 40 cm^{-1}.

B. Temperature Region for SLM Oscillation

Examples of the temperature dependence of I_{th} and the oscillation wavelength for 1.5 and 1.3 μm LD's are shown in Fig. 13. In Fig. 13(a), a stable SLM mode lased in a 120 degree-wide temperature range from −50°C to the lasing limit of 70°C in a current range of more than 2 I_{th}. Even in the temperature range of −50°C to −85°C, the SLM operation was maintained in the 1–2 I_{th} current range. Higher order transverse mode oscillation was observed with a current increase in the low temperature range. This LD was fabricated from the wafer with first-order grating on InP substrate with the coupling coefficient estimated to be about 80 cm^{-1}. Measurements for other LD's from the same wafer showed about 100–140 degrees as the SLM temperature range. The LD of Fig. 13(b) was fabricated from the wafer with second-order grating on p-type InP substrate. The coupling coefficient was estimated to be about 40 cm^{-1}. The observed SLM temperature region was 100°C in this case, and this represents the typical value for the LD's from the same wafer.

C. High Power Operation

Stable high power operation is achieved in both the 1.3 and 1.5 μm wavelength regions. Fig. 14 shows an example of the temperature dependence of the light output power versus current characteristics for an 1.5 μm LD with the first-order grating on n-type substrate. The 20 mW maximum CW light output power was obtained under SLM operation at 25°C. The maximum CW SLM operable temperature was 70°C in this case, while the observed highest temperature for other devices was 85°C. Fig. 15 shows the case for a 1.3 μm DBH-DFB LD. This LD has second-order grating on Zn-doped p-type InP substrate. As can be seen, 40 mW at 25°C and 15 mW at 70°C were obtained. The highest CW SLM operable temperature was 95°C for these LD's.

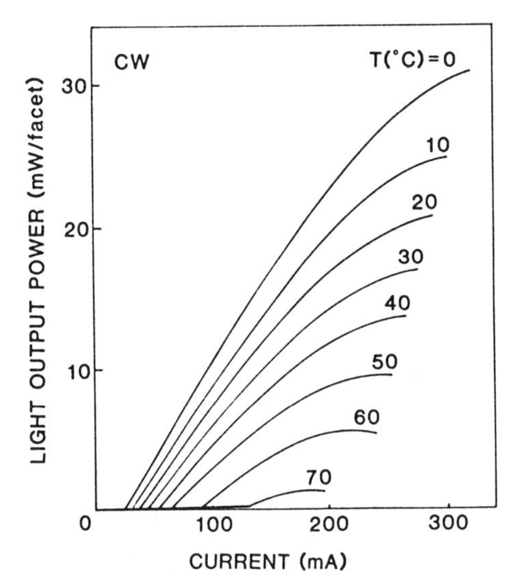

Fig. 14. Temperature dependence of the light output power versus current characteristics for a 1.5 μm LD with first-order grating on n-type InP substrate (L: 250 μm, and 80 cm^{-1}).

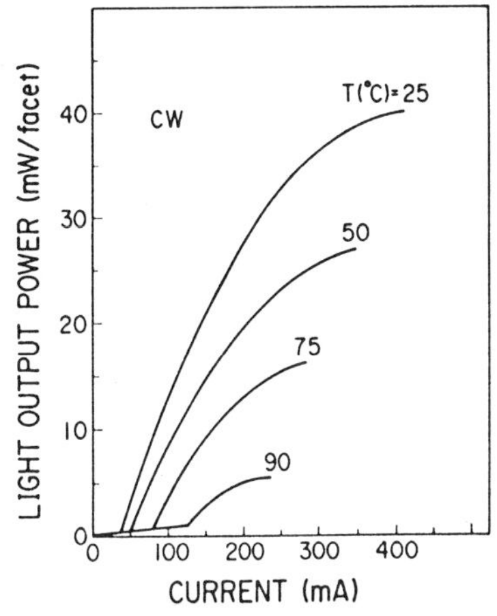

Fig. 15. Temperature dependence of light output power versus current characteristics for 1.3 μm DBH-DFB LD with a second-order grating on p-type InP substrate (L: 300 μm, and 40 cm^{-1}).

VI. Discussion

A. Probability of SLM Oscillation

In the DFB LD's with both facets cleaved structure, the oscillation mode is dominated by the combination of the grating phases of both facets. These combinations which lead to non-SLM oscillation have already been presented.

The width of the non-SLM region which spreads on both sides of these phases is thought to determine the SLM probability. This non-SLM region width depends on the curvature of $\alpha_{th}L$ versus the $\Delta\beta L$ spectrum near the non-SLM phase and the threshold gain difference between the lowest and second lowest modes which is necessary for oscillation in SLM. Therefore, it depends on the κL value. Here, the non-SLM region width was roughly estimated in the following manner. The region width was assumed to have the same value $\Delta\theta$ around each non-SLM phase. Then, assuming a perfect randomness for the corrugation phase at the cleaved facet, the non-SLM probabilities for the three cases mentioned in the previous section are presented as follows:

Case 1 $(2\Delta\theta/2\pi)^2$
Case 2 $\{(2\pi - 2\Delta\theta)/2\pi\} \times (\Delta\theta/2\pi)$
Case 3 $\{(2\pi - 2\Delta\theta)/2\pi\} \times (\Delta\theta/2\pi)$.

The sum of these three terms corresponds to the experimentally obtained non-SLM probability. The overall non-SLM probability reported in the previous section is about 30–40 percent. Here we tentatively assume the non-SLM probability P_{no} as follows:

$$P_{no} = (N_{HD} + N'_{SLM})/(N_{HD} + N_{SLM})$$

N_{HD}: number of LD's which show higher order DFB mode oscillation at I_{th}

N_{SLM}: number of all the LD's which show SLM oscillation at I_{th}.

N'_{SLM}: number of LD's which show SLM oscillation only in I_{th}–$2I_{th}$ current region.

From the investigated characteristic distribution, P_{no} is calculated to be $\frac{13}{28}$ (~50 percent) for the 1.5 μm device and $\frac{13}{64}$ (~20 percent) for the 1.3 μm device. The averaged non-SLM probability is 35 percent, which is the same as the observed overall non-SLM probability. Employing the value of 35 percent, $\Delta\theta$ becomes approximately 0.175π. The κL value in these LD's ranges between 1 and 1.2. According to Buus' analysis, the non-SLM device probability observed here indicates 0.04 to be the value of $\Delta\alpha_{th}L$, which is necessary to achieve SLM oscillation. For DFB LD's with κL value of 1–1.2, the $\alpha_{th}L$ value is estimated to be 0.3–0.4 as was shown in Fig. 1. Therefore, the $\Delta\alpha_{th}L/(\alpha_{th}L + \alpha_{loss})$ value for the SLM operation is estimated to be about 5 percent. This value roughly coincides with the estimation (7 percent) of Ikegami [14] for the SLM oscillation condition of DFB LD's.

A proposal has been made for a quarter-wave shifted DFB LD [15], [16] which can achieve a high SLM device yield. Even in such a structure, the effect of the grating phase at the cleaved facet is serious except for the large κL value range. Therefore, a detailed study of the non-SLM phase and the width of the non-SLM region around the phase is important for the future development of DFB LD's.

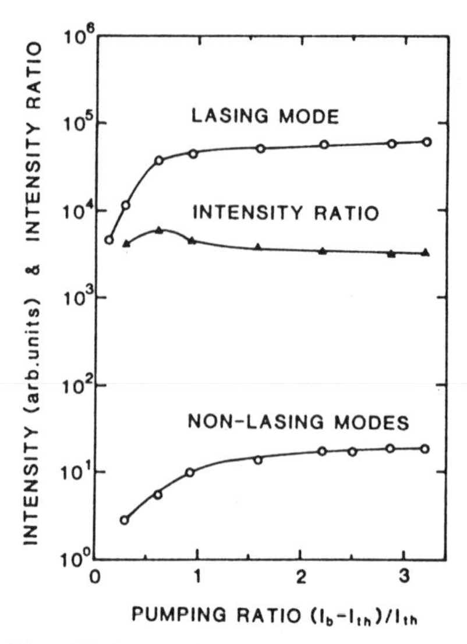

Fig. 16. Intensities of lasing mode and sum of nonlasing modes under 500 MHz sinusoidal modulation for a 1.5 μm BH-DFB LD on n-type InP substrate.

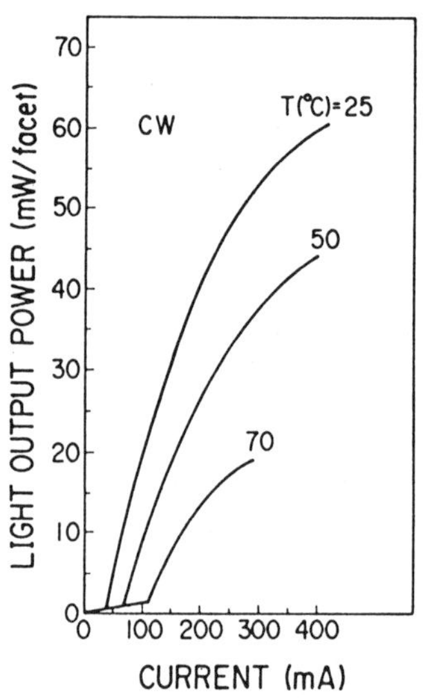

Fig. 17. Temperature dependence of light output power versus current characteristics for 1.3 μm DBH-DFB LD with second-order grating on p-type InP substrate (L: 300 μm, and 40 cm^{-1}). Front facet is AR coated (about 3 percent reflectivity).

B. Temperature Dependence of Lasing Characteristics

The observed SLM temperature regions are sufficiently wide for practical use. In the estimation given in Section IV, the effect of the scattering loss on the FP oscillation was neglected. Therefore, the actual required threshold gain difference between the DFB and FP modes is expected to become larger than the calculated value. This will lead to a wider SLM temperature region.

C. Additional Investigations

The intensity ratio between the lasing and the sum of the nonlasing side modes under high-speed modulation is an important factor for DFB LD's as light sources of communication systems. Fig. 16 shows an example of this ratio under the 500 MHz sinusoidal modulation as a function of the DC bias level, and the ratio was more than 30

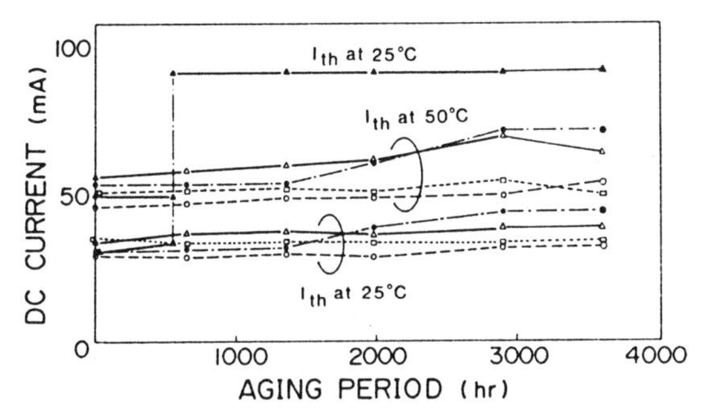

Fig. 18. Results of an aging test of 1.3 μm DBH-DFB LD's under ACC condition.

dB for the entire bias range. A 1.5 μm BH LD on n-type InP substrate with second-order grating on a quaternary guide layer was used for this measurement (I_{th}: 40 mA, L: 250 μm, and κ: 40 cm^{-1}). This value is comparable to that of the DFB LD's having a tilted rear facet or an AR coated front facet.

From the viewpoint of high power operation, structures having an AR coated front facet are superior to the both facets cleaved structure. Actually, through AR coating on the front facet, a 60 mW SLM output power has been achieved in a 1.3 μm DBH DFB LD with second-order grating on p-type InP substrate (L: 300 μm, and κ: 40 cm^{-1}). An example of this is shown in Fig. 17. This structure is expected to have a wider SLM temperature region than the devices which have both of their facets cleaved. However, the AR coated device has the problem of oscillation mode instability due to the external optical feedback. Investigations into the tradeoff between the effect of optical feedback and external quantum efficiency are important for the practical use of DFB LD's.

Discussions on the reliability of the DFB LD's are still in the initial stages. Several concerns arising from the corrugation near the active region need to be clarified. Fig. 18 shows the results of the aging test of randomly chosen 1.3 μm DBH-DFB LD's on p-type InP substrate (L: 300 μm, and κ: 40 cm^{-1}) using the ACC (automatic current control) method. The temperature is 70°C and the current is 110 mA, which corresponds to 3-5 mW of light output power. Five SLM LD's were examined with one LD showing a sudden large increase in I_{th} after 500 h of running time. This is thought to be caused by the formation of current paths in the burying layers. Among the other four LD's, two of them are stable following 3000 h of running, although a slight increase in threshold current was observed in two of them. A change in the mode behavior was observed in one of these two LD's which showed a threshold current increase. This change is shown in Fig. 19. The SLM operable characteristics of the other four LD's were maintained after 3000 h of aging. These results imply that the establishment of adequate screening conditions is essential for solving the reliability problems of DFB LD's of the future.

VII. Conclusion

A high performance of 1.3 and 1.5 μm InGaAsP/InP DFB-BH lasers with two cleaved facets has been demonstrated. DFB LD's with two kinds of buried-heterostructure which contain a first or a second-order grating were fabricated by the PH_3 addition LPE technique for the 1.3 and 1.5 μm wavelengths. SLM device probability as well as the SLM operable temperature region were discussed theoretically and experimentally.

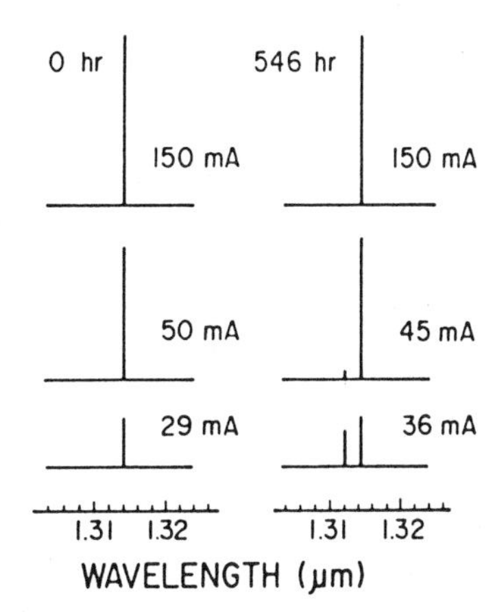

Fig. 19. Change in mode behavior after 546 h of aging. (1.3 μm DBH-DFB LD on p-type InP substrate.)

Experimental examinations showed that the κL values ranging between 1-2 are sufficient for high performance operation, with the stable single longitudinal mode in a temperature range wider than 100 degrees. The distribution of lasing characteristics was investigated for randomly chosen LD's, in which about 65 percent of these devices were found to be operable in the single longitudinal mode. A CW single longitudinal mode operation power of 20 mW at 25°C for the 1.5 μm devices and that of 40 mW at 25°C for the 1.3 μm devices having a low threshold has been achieved. Results of an aging test at 70°C and 110 mA in the ACC condition were also presented.

Acknowledgment

The authors would like to express their deep appreciation to M. Fujimoto for his valuable encouragement throughout this work. They also wish to thank T. Ikegami and K. Kurumada for their fruitful discussions and advice.

References

[1] Y. Nakano, G. Motosugi, Y. Yoshikuni, and T. Ikegami, "Aging characteristics of InGaAsP/InP DFB lasers," *Electron. Lett.*, vol. 19, pp. 437-438, June 1983.

[2] T. Matsuoka, H. Nagai, Y. Noguchi, Y. Suzuki, and Y. Kawaguchi, "Effect of the grating phase at the cleaved facet on DFB laser properties," *Japan J. Appl. Phys.*, vol. 23, pp. L138-L140, Mar. 1984.

[3] W. Streifer, R. D. Burnham, and D. R. Scifres, "Effect of external reflectors on longitudinal modes of distributed feedback lasers," *IEEE J. Quantum Electron.*, vol. QE-11, pp. 154-161, Apr. 1975.

[4] H. Okuda, Y. Hirayama, J. Kinoshita, H. Furuyama, and Y. Uematsu, "High-quality 1.3 μm GaInAsP/InP BH-DFB lasers with first-order gratings," *Electron. Lett.*, vol. 19, pp. 941-943, Oct. 1983.

[5] K. Utaka, S. Akiba, K. Sakai, and Y. Matsushima, "Effect of mirror facets on lasing characteristics of distributed feedback InGaAsP/InP laser diodes at 1.5 μm range," *IEEE J. Quantum Electron.*, vol. QE-20, pp. 236-245, Mar. 1984.

[6] B. Broberg, F. Koyama, Y. Tohmori, and Y. Suematsu, "1.53 μm DFB lasers by mass transport," *Electron. Lett.*, vol. 20, pp. 692-694, Aug. 1984.

[7] I. Mito, M. Yamaguchi, S. Murata, M. Kitamura, and K. Kobayashi, "High power operation of DFB-DC-PBH laser diode with a first order grating," in *Proc. 1985 Conf. Opt. Fiber Commun.*, San Diego, CA, Feb. 1985, post deadline paper PD9-1.
[8] A. W. Nelson, L. D. Westbrook, and P. J. Fiddyment, "Design and fabrication of 1.5 μm ridge waveguide distributed feedback lasers," *IEE Proc.*, vol. 132, pp. 12-19, Feb. 1985.
[9] M. Razeghi, R. Blondeau, K. Kazmierski, M. Krakowski, B. de Cremoux, and J. P. Duchemin, "CW operation of 1.57 μm GaInAsP/InP distributed feedback lasers grown by low-pressure metalorganic chemical vapor deposition," *Appl. Phys. Lett.*, vol. 45, pp. 784-786, Oct. 1984.
[10] J. Buus, "Mode selectivity in DFB lasers with cleaved facets," *Electron. Lett.*, vol. 21, pp. 179-180, Feb. 1985.
[11] H. Nagai, Y. Noguchi, T. Matsuoka, and Y. Suzuki, "Prevention of surface corrugation thermal deformation for InGaAsP/InP DFB lasers," *Japan J. Appl. Phys.*, vol. 22, pp. L291-L293, May 1983.
[12] Y. Suzuki, H. Nagai, Y. Noguchi, T. Matsuoka, and K. Kurumada, "High-power SLM operation of 1.3 μm InP/InGaAsP DFB LD with doubly buried heterostructure on p-type InP substrate," *Electron. Lett.*, vol. 20, pp. 881-882, Oct. 1984.
[13] K. Stubkjaer, M. Asada, S. Arai, and Y. Suematsu, "Spontaneous recombination, gain and refractive index variation for 1.6 μm wavelength InGaAsP/InP lasers," *Japan J. Appl. Phys.*, vol. 20, pp. 1499-1505, Aug. 1981.
[14] T. Ikegami and G. Motosugi, "Single longitudinal mode lasers," in *Proc. 9th European Conf. Opt. Commun.*, Geneva, Switzerland, pp. 31-34, Oct. 1983.
[15] H. A. Haus and C. V. Shank, "Antisymmetric taper of distributed feedback lasers," *IEEE J. Quantum Electron.*, vol. QE-11, pp. 154-161, 1975.
[16] K. Sekartedjo, N. Eda, K. Furuya, Y. Suematsu, F. Koyama, and T. Tanbun-ek, "1.5 μm Phase-shifted DFB lasers for single-mode operation," *Electron. Lett.*, vol. 20, pp. 80-81, Jan. 1984.

LINEWIDTH REDUCTION IN DFB LASER BY DETUNING EFFECT

S. OGITA
M. YANO
H. ISHIKAWA
H. IMAI

Fujitsu Laboratories Ltd.
10-1, Morinosato-Wakamiya
Atsugi, Kanagawa 243-01, Japan

3rd March 1987

Indexing terms: Lasers and laser applications, Semiconductor lasers

The detuning effect on the spectral linewidth in the DFB laser has been investigated. When we set the lasing wavelength of the DFB laser at the shorter side of the gain peak by 10 nm, a reduction in spectral linewidth of 50% was obtained experimentally. This result agreed with the theoretical prediction.

Introduction: In coherent optical communication systems, the narrow-spectral-linewidth laser diode is usually required as a light source. The linewidth enhancement factor is one of the most important parameters determining the spectral linewidth of a laser diode,[1,2] and there are many reports on the reduction of this linewidth enhancement factor.[3–5]

Recently, there has been a theoretical prediction that the linewidth enhancement factor decreases when we set the lasing wavelength on the shorter-wavelength side of the gain peak.[4,5] This is very easy for the DFB laser, in which the lasing wavelength is set independently against the gain peak. Therefore, we expect to obtain a narrower spectral linewidth when we set the lasing wavelength of the DFB laser at the shorter-wavelength side of the gain peak. In this letter we investigate experimentally how much the spectral linewidth is changed when the lasing wavelength of the DFB laser is moved in the gain profile, and compare the experimental results with the theoretical prediction.

Theory: The spectral linewidth of a single-longitudinal-mode laser diode is given by[1]

$$\Delta\nu = \frac{v_g(\alpha_{em} + \alpha_{int})^2 \eta_d h\nu n_{sp}(1 + \alpha^2)}{4\pi P \eta_i} \tag{1}$$

where v_g is the group velocity, $h\nu$ is the photon energy of the lasing mode, α_{em} is the equivalent mirror loss, α_{int} is the internal loss, η_d is the external differential quantum efficiency, η_i is the internal quantum efficiency, P is the optical output power, n_{sp} is the spontaneous emission factor and α is the linewidth enhancement factor. α_{em} and η_d/η_i depend on various parameters of the DFB laser structure such as the facet reflectivity, coupling coefficient, cavity length and corrugation phase at each facet. In this calculation, we assume that α_{em} and η_d/η_i are constant. α and n_{sp} are functions of the lasing wavelength λ and the threshold gain $g_{th} = \alpha_{em} + \alpha_{int}$. In conventional Fabry–Perot lasers, the peak gain value equals the threshold gain g_{th} and the lasing wavelength equals the gain peak wavelength under the lasing condition. Therefore, we cannot intentionally control α and n_{sp}. However, in the DFB laser the lasing wavelength λ_{DFB} is selected independently of the gain peak wavelength λ_{peak}. This gives us control of α and n_{sp}. The linewidth enhancement factor α is defined as[1,6]

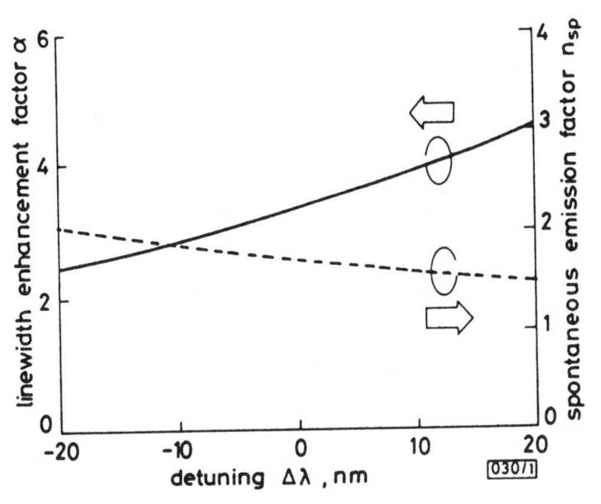

Fig. 1 *Calculated linewidth enhancement factor α (solid line) and spontaneous emission factor n_{sp} (broken line) as functions of wavelength difference $\Delta\lambda = \lambda_{DFB} - \lambda_{peak}$*

Threshold gain g_{th} of $85\,cm^{-1}$ and lasing wavelength λ_{DFB} of $1{\cdot}3\,\mu m$ were assumed

$$\Delta\nu = -\frac{d\chi_R(N, \lambda)}{dN} \bigg/ \frac{d\chi_I(N, \lambda)}{dN} \tag{2}$$

where $\chi_R(N, \lambda)$ is the real part of the complex susceptibility and $\chi_I(N, \lambda)$ is the imaginary part. We calculate $\chi_R(N, \lambda)$ and $\chi_I(N, \lambda)$ as functions of the lasing wavelength by using the theory which takes account of the intraband relaxation of electrons and holes.[5,7,8] Fig. 1 shows how α changes when the lasing wavelength is moved in the gain profile. The horizontal axis of this Figure shows the wavelength difference $\Delta\lambda = \lambda_{DFB} - \lambda_{peak}$. In this calculation, we take a $1{\cdot}3\,\mu m$ InGaAsP/InP laser and $g_{th} = 85\,cm^{-1}$, which is the theoretically calculated result using the coupled wave theory.[11–13] The intraband relaxation time is 0·1 ps.[8] We also calculate the spontaneous emission rate n_{sp} theoretically,[3] and show the result in this Figure as a broken line. When the lasing wavelength moves towards the left-hand side of this Figure, i.e. to the shorter-wavelength side of the gain peak, we obtain the smaller α value, and a slightly larger n_{sp} value. From these results it is theoretically estimated that about a 20% reduction in spectral linewidth is obtained when we set the lasing wavelength on the shorter-wavelength side of the gain peak by 10 nm, and the spectral linewidth calculated at this condition is about 4·3 MHz at 10 mW optical power.

Experiment and discussion: We examined the detuning effect on the spectral linewidth of DFB laser by measuring many

Reprinted with permission from *Electron. Lett.*, vol. 23, no. 8, pp. 393–394, Apr. 9, 1987.

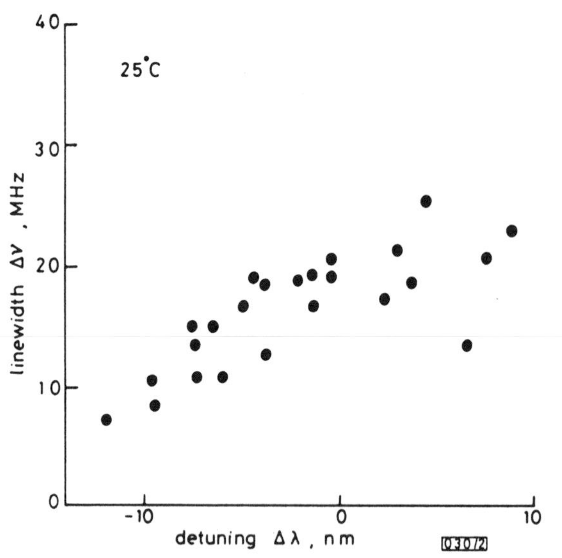

Fig. 2 *Measured spectral linewidth of 1·3 μm FBH-DFB laser at 10 mW optical output power when lasing wavelength was moved in gain profile*

lasers with different lasing wavelengths. The laser under test was an InGaAsP/InP FBH-DFB laser with the 1st-order corrugation emitting at 1·3 μm wavelength.[9] The width and thickness of the active layer were 1·0 μm and 0·1 μm, respectively, and the cavity length was 300 μm. The front facet was coated with the Al_2O_3 film to obtain the reflectivity of about 5%, and the rear facet was as cleaved.[13] The threshold current was 10–17 mA and the external differential efficiency of the front facet was 0·22–0·26 mW/mA at 25°C. The coupling coefficient was about 20–30 cm^{-1}. The side-mode suppression ratio of each laser at CW operation was more than 30 dB.

The spectral linewidth was measured using the delayed self-heterodyne method.[10] A 0·9 km single-mode fibre was used as a delay line and an acousto-optic modulator was used to obtain an 80 MHz frequency shift. The resolution of our system was about 80 kHz.

Fig. 2 shows the spectral linewidth at 10 mW optical output power when the lasing wavelength was moved in the gain profile. The horizontal axis shows the wavelength difference $\Delta\lambda$. In plotting Fig. 2, we assumed that the spontaneous emission peak wavelength equals the gain peak. The lasing wavelength was controlled by changing the corrugation period. As can be seen, a 20–50% improvement in spectral linewidth was obtained when we set the lasing wavelength on the shorter-wavelength side of the gain peak by 10 nm, and the minimum value obtained at this condition was about 7 MHz. This tendency agrees well with the theoretical prediction by considering that α_{em} and η_d/η_i are not constant because of the difference of the corrugation phase at each facet. However, the magnitude of the measured spectral linewidth is larger than the calculated value. To fit the theoretical value to the experimental value, α takes a value of about 6, which is larger than the theoretical value.[13] The reason for this difference in the α value is not clear, and some improvement in the theory is required. It was impossible to obtain a greater improvement in the spectral linewidth due to the detuning effect, because the laser shows multimode operation when the lasing wavelength was on the much shorter side of the gain peak.

Conclusion: We investigated theoretically and experimentally the effect of detuning on the spectral linewidth. The spectral linewidth was narrower when the lasing wavelength was set on the shorter-wavelength side of the gain peak. When we set the lasing wavelength of the DFB laser at the shorter-wavelength side of the gain peak by 10 nm, an improvement in the spectral linewidth of 50% was obtained experimentally. This result agreed with the theoretical prediction.

Acknowledgment: The authors wish to thank T. Misugi and K. Dazai for encouragement, and M. Hirano, H. Soda, K. Kamite and K. Kihara for useful discussions.

References

1 HENRY, C. H.: 'Theory of the linewidth of semiconductor lasers', *IEEE J. Quantum Electron.*, 1982, **QE-18**, pp. 259–264
2 AGRAWAL, G. P.: 'Line narrowing in a single-mode injection laser due to external optical feedback', *ibid.*, 1984, **QE-20**, pp. 468–471
3 ARAKAWA, Y., and YARIV, A.: 'Theory of gain, modulation response, and spectral linewidth in AlGaAs quantum well lasers', *ibid.*, 1985, **QE-21**, pp. 1666–1674
4 VAHALA, K., and YARIV, A.: 'Detuned loading in coupled cavity semiconductor lasers—effect on quantum noise and dynamics', *Appl. Phys. Lett.*, 1984, **45**, pp. 501–503
5 OGITA, S., YANO, M., and IMAI, H.: 'Theoretical calculation of the linewidth enhancement factor of DFB lasers', *Electron. Lett.*, 1986, **22**, pp. 580–581
6 VAHALA, K., CHIU, L. C., MARGALIT, S., and YARIV, A.: 'On the linewidth enhancement factor α in semiconductor injection lasers', *Appl. Phys. Lett.*, 1983, **42**, pp. 631–633
7 ASADA, M.: 'Theoretical linewidth enhancement factor α of GaInAsP/InP lasers', *Trans. IECE Jpn.*, 1985, **E68**, pp. 518–520
8 ASADA, M., and SUEMATSU, Y.: 'Density-matrix theory of semiconductor lasers with relaxation broadening model—gain and gain suppression in semiconductor lasers', *IEEE J. Quantum Electron.*, 1985, **QE-21**, pp. 434–442
9 ISHIKAWA, H., YAMAKOSHI, S., and ISOZUMI, S.: 'Distributed feedback laser emitting at 1·3 μm for high-bit-rate systems', *Fujitsu Sci. & Tech. J.*, 1986, **22**, pp. 451–460
10 OKOSHI, T., KIKUCHI, K., and NAKAYAMA, A.: 'Novel method for high resolution measurement of laser output spectrum', *Electron. Lett.*, 1980, **16**, pp. 630–631
11 KOGELNIK, H., and SHANK, C. V.: 'Coupled mode theory of distributed feedback lasers', *J. Appl. Phys.*, 1972, **43**, pp. 2327–2335
12 STREIFER, W., BURNHAM, R. D., and SCIFRES, D. R.: 'Effect of external reflectors on longitudinal modes of distributed feedback lasers', *IEEE J. Quantum Electron.*, 1975, **QE-11**, pp. 154–161
13 OGITA, S., HORANO, M., SODA, H., YANO, M., ISHIKAWA, H., and IMAI, H.: 'Dependence of spectral linewidth of DFB lasers on facet reflectivity', *Electron. Lett.*, 1987, **23**, pp. 347–349

Oscillation frequency tuning characteristics of fiber-extended-cavity distributed-feedback lasers

K.-Y. Liou
AT&T Bell Laboratories, Crawford Hill Laboratory, Holmdel, New Jersey 07733
R. T. Ku
AT&T Bell Laboratories, 2525 North 12th Street, Reading, Pennsylvania 19603-0856
T. M. Shen and P. J. Anthony
AT&T Bell Laboratories, 600 Mountain Avenue, Murray Hill, New Jersey 07974-2070

(Received 13 October 1986; accepted for publication 16 December 1986)

Stable narrow-linewidth (< 100 kHz) operation has been demonstrated for a fiber-extended-cavity distributed-feedback (EC DFB) laser emitting at 1.55 μm wavelength. We describe the observed oscillation frequency tuning characteristics of the laser obtained by controlling the temperature and injection current. The effects of distributed grating reflection and continuous frequency tuning schemes are examined for both the EC DFB laser and for the case of an EC DBR (distributed Bragg reflector) laser.

Stability and tunability of the center frequency of a single-mode injection laser as well as a narrow linewidth are important performance criteria for the laser to be used as the light source or local oscillator in coherent lightwave communication systems. We have reported previously the narrow-linewidth characteristics of a fiber-extended-cavity distributed-feedback (EC DFB) laser comprising an antireflection (AR) coated DFB laser chip coupled to a fiber resonator using a micropositioner.[1] A packaged device with the fiber attached to the DFB laser has been demonstrated. We present here the observed longitudinal mode behavior, frequency stability, and the characteristic of frequency tuning obtained by controlling the laser temperature and injection current. The effect of the distributed grating reflection is examined to study the possibility of wide-range continuous tuning of the center frequency.

The fiber-EC-DFB laser was similar to that reported recently.[1] Long-term mechanical stability, however, was significantly improved for the packaged device, which allowed detailed measurements of the laser output characteristics. The laser consisted of a 1.55-μm wavelength DFB laser chip optically coupled to a 5.5-cm single-mode fiber waveguide used as an extended cavity. The length of the DFB laser chip was 250 μm. The fiber had a microlens at one end for optical coupling to the DFB chip. The measured lens coupling efficiency was near 45%. The other end of the fiber was polished to within 1° perpendicular to the fiber axis then coated with a high reflective (> 95%) Au film. Controlling the orientation of the fiber end mirror is important since the effective reflectivity is reduced if the mirror is tilted relative to the fiber axis. The DFB laser was of the double-channel planar buried heterostructure (DC PBH) type and had a second order grating. The DFB facet adjacent to the fiber lens was AR coated (< 1% residual reflectivity) to achieve strong optical coupling to the fiber end mirror. A higher than 12% power feedback from the fiber section to the DFB chip was estimated from the change in the lasing threshold.[1] As a result of such a strong coupling, the laser operated with a stable narrow linewidth which was insensitive to spurious external reflection.[1,2] The output was taken from the uncoated DFB facet using a microscope objective lens in the experiment.

Linewidth narrowing by an extended cavity can be understood from the Schawlow–Townes formula modified for a composite cavity comprising an active gain medium and a passive resonator section.[3] A delayed self-heterodyne method[4] was used for linewidth measurements. Typical linewidths (full width at half-maximum) measured at 1 mW output for a 5.5-cm fiber length were about 70–80 kHz and the line shape was Lorentzian.

The frequency stability and the tuning characteristics were anlayzed using both a confocal and a planar Fabry–Perot interferometer with 150 MHz and 30 GHz free-spectral range, respectively. The fiber-EC-DFB device behaved as a long Fabry–Perot (FP) laser with one longitudinal mode stabilized by the intracavity DFB grating. The longitudinal mode spacing was 1.8 GHz for the cavity between the uncoated DFB facet and the fiber end mirror. A change in the heat sink temperature of the DFB chip resulted in a combination of slow frequency tuning of the lasing mode and abrupt mode hopping to successive FP modes. The series of interferometer output spectra in Fig. 1 shows single-mode oscillation tuned to successive FP modes as the heat sink temperature of the laser chip was increased. Similar mode behavior was observed when the injection current was increased as shown in Fig. 2(a). Figure 2(b) shows multimode operation and broadened linewidth that occurred at excessive output power. The observed output property can be characterized by the output light power (L) versus current (I) curve in Fig. 3. The laser operated with a single longitudinal mode of the long cavity up to an output power of L_c at I_c injection current. The spectrum became multimoded at output higher than L_c. The periodic undulation in the L-I curve as the current increased was due to mode hopping. The amplitude of undulation increased near I_c, indicating the transition from single-mode to multimode operation. The spectra in Figs. 2(a) and 2(b) were taken respectively with injection currents in regions (a) and (b) in Fig. 3. The single-mode output power level, L_c, increases with the DFB chip-to-fiber mirror coupling efficiency,

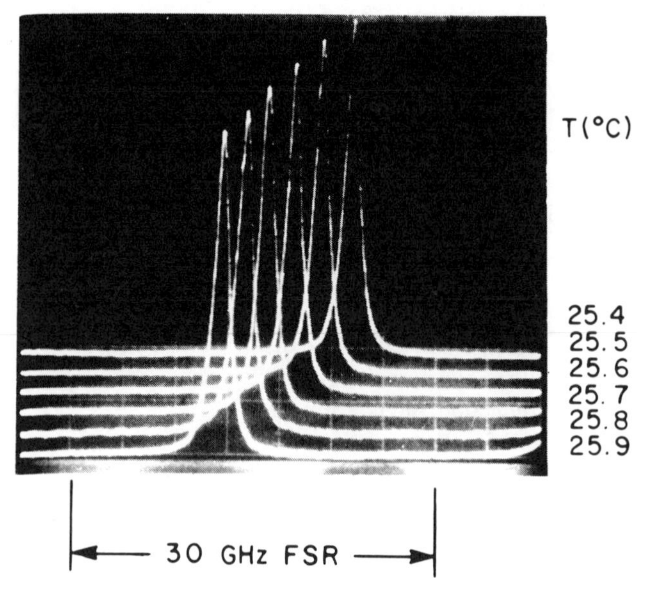

FIG. 1. Temperature tuning of the EC DFB laser output to successive longitudinal modes.

which is dependent on the effective reflectivity of the DFB grating and losses at the fiber lens and fiber end mirror.[1] Variation of L_c from 0.5 to 2.5 mW output has been observed for different DFB lasers upon addition of the fiber cavity.

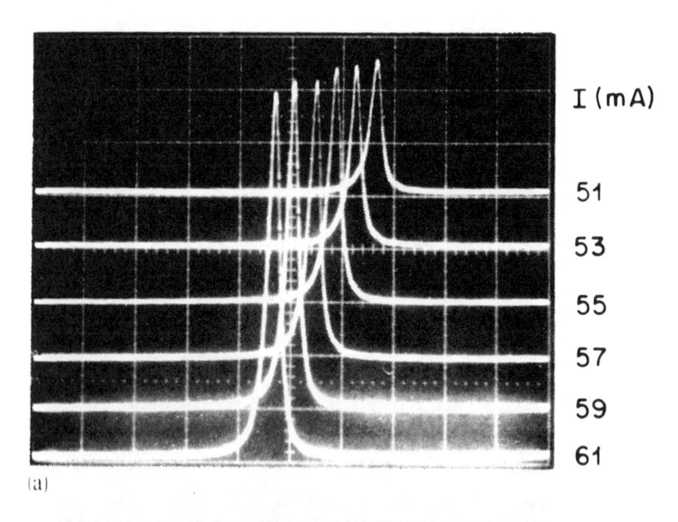

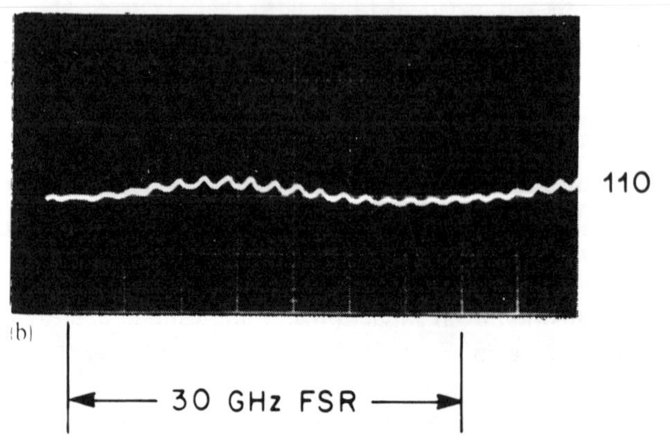

FIG. 2. (a) Current tuning of laser output to successive longitudinal modes and (b) multimode operation at high output power. (FSR = free-spectral range of interferometer.)

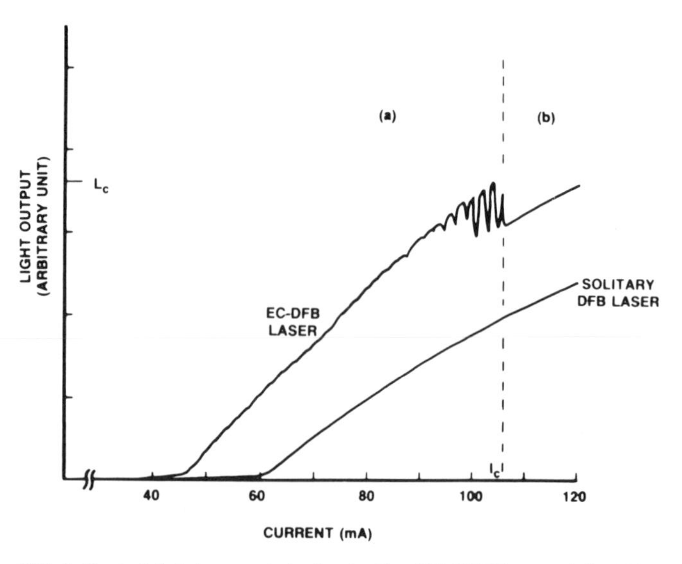

FIG. 3. Typical *L-I* characteristics for the fiber-EC-DFB laser and the AR-coated DFB laser without fiber. The EC DFB laser operated with a single mode up to an output power of L_c at I_c current. L_c varied from 0.5 to 2.5 mW for different lasers in the experiment.

The observed frequency tuning characteristics of the fiber-EC-DFB laser are plotted in Fig. 4. The tuning rates can be described by

$$df = -fL\,dn/(nL + n_e L_e)\,, \tag{1}$$

$$df_B = -f_B\,dn/n\,, \tag{2}$$

where f is the center frequency of the EC DFB laser and f_B is the Bragg frequency; nL and $n_e L_e$ are the optical length of the DFB chip and the extended cavity, respectively. The effective refractive index of the DFB laser, n, changes with temperature and the injection current.

The addition of a passive section in an extended FP cavity reduces the temperature coefficient (df/dT) and current coefficient (df/dI) for frequency shift by the ratio of the optical lengths of the active section and the extended cavity as can be seen from Eq. (1). The measured slow tuning rates of a single longitudinal mode were $df/dI \simeq 20$ MHz/mA and $df/dT \lesssim 300$ MHz/°C. Mode hopping occurred, however, due to the fast tuning rates of the Bragg frequency, which were measured from the solitary DFB laser to be 1.1 GHz/mA and 16 GHz/°C. The reduced df/dT stabilized the fluc-

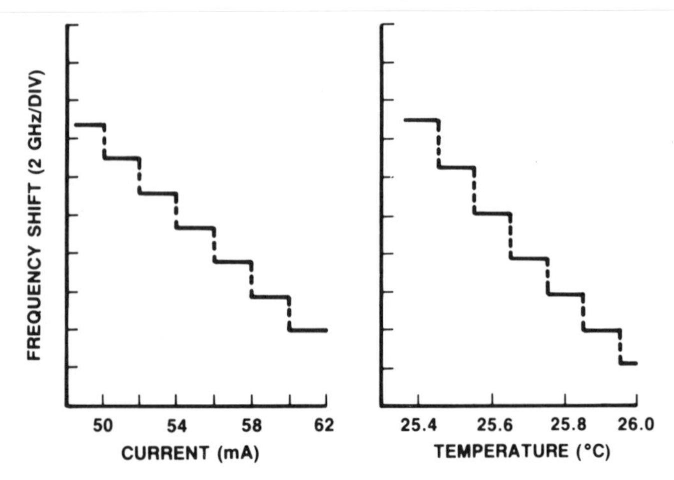

FIG. 4. Frequency tuning of the fiber-EC-DFB laser.

tuation of the center frequency to within a few MHz when the Cu heat sink temperature for the DFB chip was controlled to 0.01 °C. The acoustic noise induced frequency fluctuation, often observed for lasers with an air extended cavity, was also suppressed in this mechanically stable fiber-extended-cavity laser package. The total photon number in the lasing mode and the photon lifetime were both increased by the long extended cavity. As a result, the stability of single-mode oscillation under continuous wave operation was improved and the linewidth of the laser was observed to remain narrow ($\lesssim 100$ kHz at 1 mW output) except at abrupt mode hops.

The simple fiber-EC-DFB configuration allowed the laser to be packaged using conventional diode laser packaging technique. The narrow linewidth, stable center frequency, and a compact laser package with mechanical stability were obtained, however, at the expense of continuous frequency tuning. Since the laser oscillates at a FP longitudinal mode of the long cavity and mode switching is determined by the tuning rate of the Bragg wavelength, continuous frequency tuning is possible if the cavity length of the laser is adjusted to tune the FP modes at the same rate the Bragg wavelength is tuned. This can be achieved by either controlling the temperature of the fiber cavity using a peltier element or stressing the fiber using a piezoelectric element to change the optical length of the fiber.

The extended cavity approach can also be applied to distributed Bragg reflector (DBR) lasers. In a DBR laser, the passive grating section is separated from the active region; therefore, mode hopping due to current change is avoided for an EC DBR laser. The Bragg wavelength, however, is still tuned by the temperature of the laser chip. Continuous frequency tuning by temperature change is possible if the Bragg wavelength is tuned by a separate tuning current applied to the Bragg reflector region[5] to follow the frequency shift of the FP modes. If the undulation of the *L-I* curve, shown in Fig. 4, is used to monitor single-mode operation, conventional electrical feedback circuits (e.g., Ref. 6) can be used to stabilize the laser output automatically in a single mode while the frequency is tuned.

In conclusion, we have demonstrated that a narrow-linewidth (< 100 kHz) fiber-extended-cavity DFB laser can be packaged using existing diode laser packaging technique to achieve the mechanical stability required for a stable center oscillation frequency. A slow frequency tuning rate due to the long extended cavity and abrupt frequency switching tuned by the Bragg wavelength were observed. Continuous frequency tuning schemes by separate control of the Bragg wavelength or the extended cavity length are proposed. The frequency switching characteristic, however, may be attractive for frequency division multiplexing.

[1]K.-Y. Liou, Y. K. Jhee, G. Eisenstein, R. S. Tucker, R. T. Ku, T. M. Shen, U. K. Chakrabarti, and P. J. Anthony, Appl. Phys. Lett. **48**, 1039 (1986).

[2]A. R. Chraplyvy, K.-Y. Liou, R. W. Tkach, G. Eisenstein, Y. K. Jhee, T. L. Koch, P. J. Anthony, and U. K. Chakrabarti, Electron. Lett. **22**, 88 (1986).

[3]C. H. Henry, J. Lightwave Technol. **LT-4**, 298 (1986).

[4]T. Okoshi, K. Kikuchi, and A. Nakayama, Electron. Lett. **16**, 630 (1980).

[5]M. Yamaguchi, M. Kitamura, S. Murata, I. Mito, and K. Kobayashi, Electron. Lett. **21**, 63 (1985).

[6]K.-Y. Liou, C. A. Burrus, and F. Bosch, J. Lightwave Technol. **LT-3**, 985 (1985).

OVER 720 GHz (5·8 nm) FREQUENCY TUNING BY A 1·5 μm DBR LASER WITH PHASE AND BRAGG WAVELENGTH CONTROL REGIONS

S. MURATA
I. MITO
K. KOBAYASHI

Opto-Electronics Research Laboratories
NEC Corporation
4-1-1 Miyazaki, Miyamae-ku
Kawasaki-shi 213, Japan

11th February 1987

Indexing terms: Optical transmission, Frequency tuning

A 1·5 μm distributed Bragg reflector (DBR) laser with phase and Bragg wavelength control regions was newly developed. Over 720 GHz (5·8 nm) continuous frequency tuning with 2 mW light output were achieved for the first time.

Wavelength-tunable semiconductor lasers are attractive for future coherent and high-density WDM transmission systems. Among many kinds of wavelength-tunable semiconductor lasers, a wavelength-tunable distributed Bragg reflector (DBR) laser[1–8] is one of the most suitable light sources, because its tuning range is very large. However, only discrete tuning[2,3] or about 1 nm continuous tuning[4,5] were reported previously. In this letter a newly developed 1·5 μm wavelength-tunable DBR laser with both a phase control region and a Bragg wavelength control region is reported.[6] Tuning was performed by injecting currents into the PC and DBR regions. This changed the refractive index of the regions because of the plasma effect. Large-range continuous wavelength tuning was achieved by controlling the PC and DBR region currents simultaneously.[7,8]

The device structure is shown in Fig. 1. The structure was basically the same as that of the previously reported DBR laser,[5] which had no phase control region. The DBR laser consists of three current injection regions: a 190 μm-long active region, an 80 μm-long phase control (PC) region and a 700 μm-long DBR region. The waveguide layers of the PC and DBR regions, which were coupled to the active region optically, were transparent to laser light. For transverse mode control, the DC-PBH configuration was adopted for all regions. The three regions were electrically isolated from each other by 20 μm-wide etched grooves, which were formed on both sides of the centre mesa stripe area. A cross-section at the groove position is shown in the circle in Fig. 1. Isolation resistances were about 600 Ω. The sample was mounted on a silicon heat sink with a junction-up configuration.

Light output as a function of active region current I_a is shown in Fig. 2*a*, when currents are not injected into either the PC or DBR regions. The threshold current was 29 mA, and the external quantum efficiency was 19% per front facet at 20°C. Fig. 2*b* shows light output as a function of DBR region current I_d and of PC region current I_p. The active region current I_a was fixed. As the DBR region current increased, the light output changed periodically and the wavelength shifted toward a shorter wavelength with mode jumps, which was expected theoretically.[1,2] On the other hand, as the PC region current increased, the light output decreased almost monotonically and the wavelength dropped continuously towards a shorter wavelength, but occasionally shifted to longer wavelengths with mode jumps. This significant decrease in light output was due to an increase in threshold current, which increased from 29 mA to 75 mA, as the PC region current increased from 0 mA to 30 mA. The large increase in threshold current is probably due to absorption loss increase in the PC region, caused by free carrier density

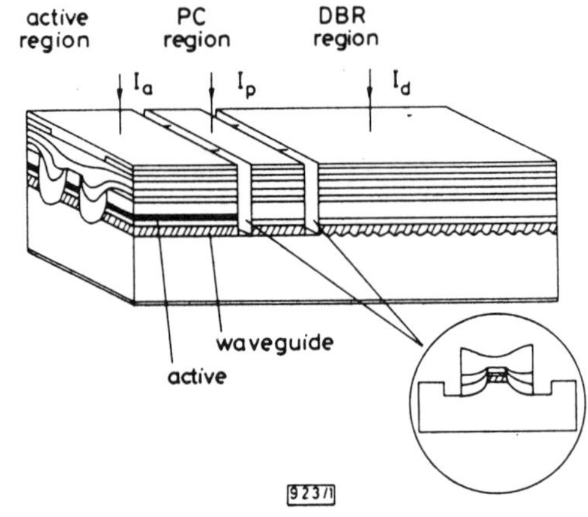

Fig. 1 *Wavelength-tunable DBR laser structure and cross-sectional view of groove position*

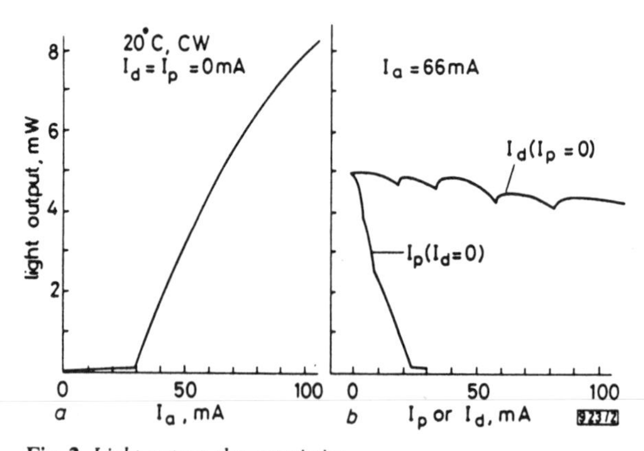

Fig. 2 *Light-output characteristics*

a Light output as a function of active region current I_a
b Light output as a function of DBR region current I_d and of PC region current I_p

Reprinted with permission from *Electron. Lett.*, vol. 23, no. 8, pp. 403–405, Apr. 9, 1987.

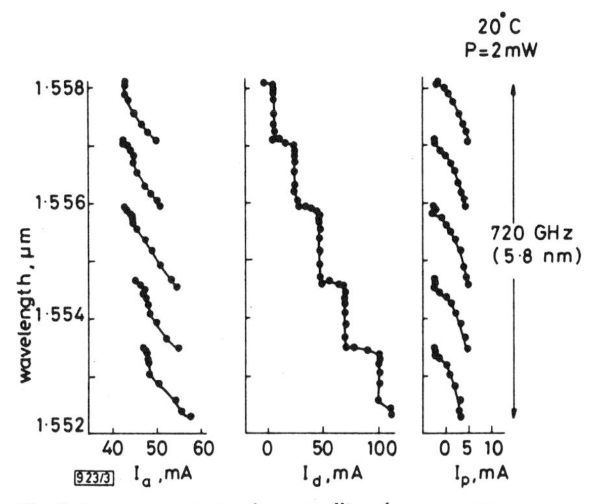

Fig. 3 *Large-range tuning by controlling three currents*

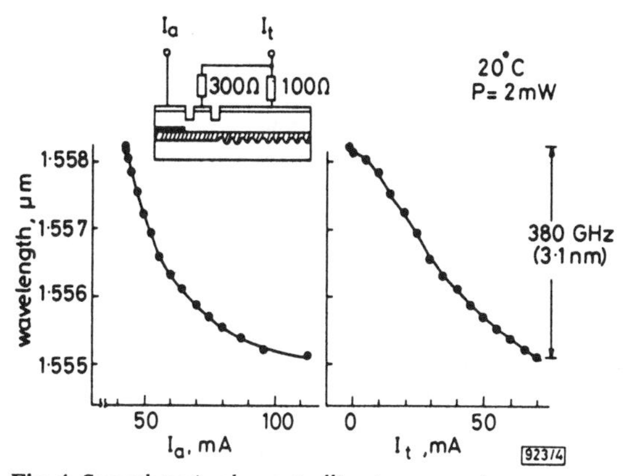

Fig. 4 *Smooth tuning by controlling two currents*

increase. Small negative values in I_d and I_p were due to the leakage currents between individual regions.

The tuning characteristics over a large wavelength range are shown in Fig. 3. Wavelengths are plotted as functions of the three currents. Large-range tuning was realised by the following procedures. First, the DBR region current I_d was increased when the PC region current I_p was not injected. The wavelength shifted slightly toward a shorter wavelength. More increase in I_d caused a mode jump. Therefore, before the mode jump occurred, I_p was increased when I_d was held constant. The wavelength shifted about 1 nm toward a shorter wavelength. After I_p was reset at zero the above procedures were repeated. In these processes the active-region current I_a was changed to maintain light output at 2 mW. Consequently, over 720 GHz (5·8 nm) continuous tuning was achieved by controlling the three currents simultaneously. At all data points, single-longitudinal-mode oscillations, with a submode suppression ratio of more than 30 dB, was maintained.

Fig. 4 shows a smooth wavelength tuning result for the same laser. In this case, tuning was performed by controlling only two currents. These were the active region current I_a and the tuning current I_t, which was the sum of the PC and DBR region currents. The current ratio of the PC and DBR regions I_d/I_p was kept nearly constant by using fixed load resistances of 100 Ω and 300 Ω for the DBR region and PC region, respectively, as shown in the Figure. The current ratio was about 3 to 1. The maximum tuning range was 380 GHz (3·1 nm) when the light output was kept constant at 2 mW. This range was restricted by an increase in threshold current, as mentioned previously. Nonetheless, it is very advantageous to be able to obtain both the desired wavelength and light output by controlling only two currents.

Spectral linewidth was also measured as a function of the wavelength by the delayed self-homodyne method. In a large-range tuning case (Fig. 3), the linewidth changed periodically between 23 MHz and 77 MHz, as the wavelength changed. The increase in linewidth corresponded to the increase in PC region current. As well as the threshold current increase, the linewidth increase was probably due to the absorption loss increase in the PC region. In a smooth tuning case (Fig. 4), the linewidth increased almost monotonically from 23 MHz to 100 MHz, as the wavelength decreased.

In summary, a newly developed 1·5 µm wavelength-tunable DBR laser with both a phase control region and a Bragg wavelength control region has been reported. A large-range tuning of over 720 GHz (5·8 nm) with 2 mW light output was achieved for the first time, by controlling three currents. Smooth tuning with a range of 380 GHz (3·1 nm) was also obtained by controlling two currents by the current ratio for the PC and DBR regions kept nearly constant. To suppress the increases in threshold current and linewidth, it is very important to suppress an absorption loss increase in the PC region during tuning.

The authors would like to thank M. Yamaguchi and M. Kitamura for their valuable comments and discussions. They are also grateful to M. Sakaguchi for his encouragement.

References

1 OKUDA, M., and ONAKA, K.: 'Tunability of distributed Bragg-reflector laser by modulating refractive index in corrugated waveguide', *Jpn. J. Appl. Phys.*, 1977, **16**, pp. 1501–1502

2 YAMAGUCHI, M., KITAMURA, M., MURATA, S., MITO, I., and KOBAYASHI, K.: 'Wide range wavelength tuning in 1·3 µm DBR-DC-PBH-LDs by current injection into the DBR region', *Electron. Lett.*, 1985, **21**, pp. 63–65

3 WESTBROOK, L. D., NELSON, A. W., FIDDYMENT, P. J., and COLLINS, J. V.: 'Monolithic 1·5 µm hybrid DFB/DBR lasers with 5 nm tuning range', *ibid.*, 1985, **20**, pp. 957–959

4 THOMORI, Y., KOMORI, K., ARAI, S., SUEMATSU, Y., and OOHASHI, H.: 'Wavelength tunable 1·5 µm GaInAsP/InP bundle-integrated-guide distributed Bragg reflector (BIG-DBR) lasers', *Trans. IECE Jpn.*, 1985, **E68**, pp. 788–790

5 MURATA, S., MITO, I., and KOBAYASHI, K.: 'Spectral characteristics of 1·5 µm DBR DC-PBH laser with frequency tuning region'. Proceedings of 10th semiconductor laser conference, 1986, Kanazawa, pp. 20–21

6 MURATA, S., MITO, I., and KOBAYASHI, K.: 'Over 5·8 nm continuous wavelength tuning of a 1·5 µm wavelength tunable DBR laser'. Technical digest of OFC/IOOC '87, Reno, 1987, WD3

7 THOMORI, Y., JIANG, X., and SUEMATSU, Y.: 'Wavelength tuning of semiconductor laser'. Paper of technical group meeting of IECE Japan, 1984, OQE84-81, pp. 47–54

8 KITAMURA, M., YAMAGUCHI, M., MURATA, S., MITO, I., and KOBAYASHI, K.: 'Wavelength tuning in three terminal DBR-LDs'. National convention record of IECE Japan (part 4), 1985, p. 304

OPTICAL FREQUENCY STABILISATION AND LINEWIDTH REDUCTION OF A MULTIELECTRODE DFB LASER WITH CURRENT FEEDBACK

H. YASAKA
Y. YOSHIKUNI
Y. NAKANO
K. OE

NTT Electrical Communications Laboratories
3-1 Morinosato, Wakamiya
Atsugi, Kanagawa 243-01, Japan

24th August 1987

Indexing term: Semiconductor lasers

Optical frequency stabilisation and linewidth reduction by the current feedback technique were studied with a multielectrode DFB laser. In the current feedback technique, phase rotation in the feedback loop, particularly induced by a laser, is the fundamental problem. This problem was resolved by using multielectrode DFB lasers without phase inversion. We simultaneously succeeded in optical frequency stabilisation and linewidth reduction with only one feedback electrical circuit. Optical frequency drift and spectral linewidth were reduced to 1/14 and 1/126, respectively, of those in the free-running state. The minimum spectral linewidth obtained was 95 kHz.

Introduction: There are many requirements for optical frequency-stabilised, linewidth-reduced semiconductor lasers. The spectral purity of a semiconductor laser is insufficient for coherent optical communications or coherent optical measurement applications in comparison with other light sources, for example gas lasers. Typically, optical frequency drift and spectral linewidth of semiconductor lasers in the free-running state are some hundreds of megahertz and several tens of megahertz, respectively.

The current feedback technique[1,2] is one promising candidate for realising frequency-stabilised and narrow-linewidth semiconductor laser light sources. With the current feedback technique, optical frequency drift is negated by negative electrical feedback to the injection current of a laser diode. This technique can also reduce the linewidth only by widening the feedback loop bandwidth, because the laser spectral linewidth is determined by rapid drift of the optical frequency. However, the direction of the optical frequency shifts due to current increase is inverted between the low- and high-frequency regions in conventional semiconductor lasers for its thermal and carrier effects.[3] For this reason, electrical oscillation occurs at the certain frequency where phase rotation in the feedback loop reaches 180 deg.[2] To overcome this problem, the feedback circuit was divided into two loops in conventional current feedback systems: one loop had a positive gain and the other a negative gain. However, this two-loop system was complicated and had to be adjusted to coincide with frequency modulation characteristics of individual laser diodes.

In our research we attempted to overcome phase inversion by using multielectrode DFB lasers,[4] which have flat and constant frequency modulation characteristics.[5] Optical frequency stabilisation and linewidth reduction were realised simultaneously with only one feedback circuit.

Experiments and results: The experimental set-up for optical frequency stabilisation and linewidth reduction of the multielectrode DFB laser is shown in Fig. 1. The total injection current to the multielectrode DFB laser was 90 mA ($4I_{th}$). The power of the laser was 7 mW, and the laser temperature was controlled to $20 \pm 0{\cdot}1$°C. The laser beam passed through two optical isolators and was divided into two beams by a half-mirror. One beam was used for observation of the laser spectral linewidth; the conventional delayed self-heterodyne method[6] was used for spectral linewidth measurement. The other beam passed through an optical frequency discriminator and was picked up by a detector. Optical frequency drift was converted into optical intensity change by optical frequency discriminators. In this letter a Fabry–Perot etalon was used as an optical frequency discriminator. The free spectral range and finesse of this Fabry–Perot etalon were about 5 GHz and 20, respectively. The detected signal was amplified by the feedback electrical circuit and was superimposed on the laser injection current to reduce optical frequency drift. Feedback loop gain and 3 dB down bandwidth were about 23 dB and 2 MHz, respectively. There is feedback loop gain up to 16 MHz because gain drops at the rate of 6 dB/octave. The characteristic of the feedback loop phase is determined by laser, time delay and feedback electrical circuits. According to the laser, multielectrode DFB lasers have flat and constant phase characteristics up to 200 MHz, and phase rotation due to laser can be neglected in the feedback frequency region. The feedback loop length was 60 cm and the time delay was estimated to be 2 ns. Phase inversion due to the time delay occurs at a frequency of 500 MHz. For this reason, phase rotation due to the time delay can be neglected in the feedback loop bandwidth. Phase rotation of the feedback loop and phase-inverted at a frequency of about 16 MHz.

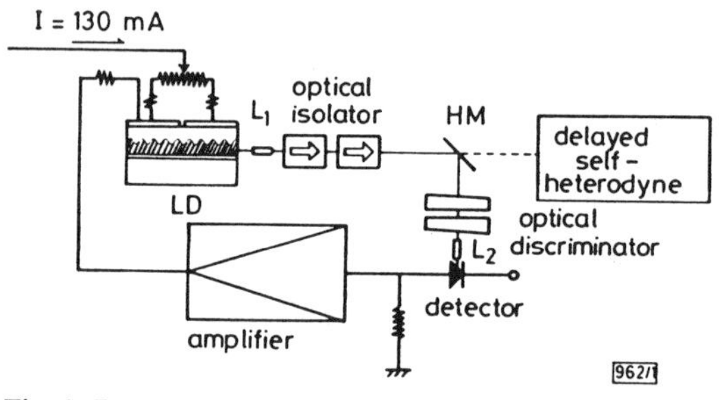

Fig. 1 *Experimental set-up for optical frequency stabilisation and linewidth reduction using a multielectrode DFB laser*

Spectra from the conventional delayed self-heterodyne system are shown in Fig. 2. Fig. 2*a* shows the beat signal of the laser beam in the free-running state, while Figs. 2*b* and *c* show the signal in stablised states. From these Figures the

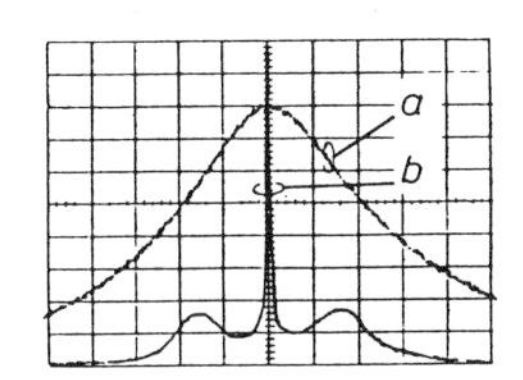

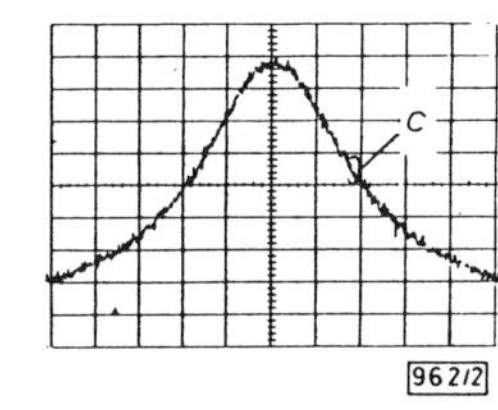

Fig. 2 *Power spectra of outputs from delay self-heterodyne system*

x-axis (left): 10 MHz/div, x-axis (right): 100 kHz/div, y-axis (left and right): 2 dB/div

a Free-running *b, c* Stabilised

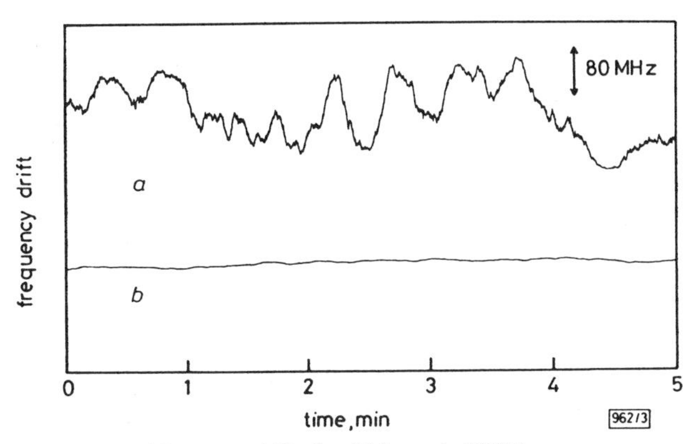

Fig. 3 *Optical frequency drift of multielectrode DFB laser*

a Free-running *b* Stablised

spectral linewidth of the free-running laser was estimated to be about 12 MHz, and was reduced to 1/126 (95 kHz) by controlling the injection current to the laser using the current feedback technique. In Fig. 2*b* the spectrum has the peaks symmetrical with regard to the main peak. This is because that feedback loop phase rotates by 180 deg at about 16 MHz and the feedback loop has a weak positive gain at this point. Therefore weak electrical oscillation occurs, and FM sidebands appear at this frequency. This frequency modulation was very weak, however, and the suppression ratio between main peak and sidebands was about 16 dB. This value can increase further by decreasing the phase rotation of the feedback electrical circuits.

The optical frequency drift of the laser was also measured by measuring the detected signal which was proportional to the optical frequency drift. Optical frequency drifts of the laser in the (*a*) free-running and (*b*) stabilised states are shown in Fig. 3. From this Figure the laser optical frequency drift in the free-running state was 200 MHz in 5 min; it became less than 15 MHz and laser stability increased by a factor of more than 14.

The loop gain of the current feedback loop was estimated to be 23 dB ($\times$ 200). This indicates that the optical frequency drift of the laser must become $1/\sqrt{200}$ and the laser spectral line width must become 1/200. The optical frequency drift of the stabilised laser is equal to the value observed in this study. On the other hand, the linewidth of the current feedback multielectrode DFB laser observed in this study was larger than the value expected from the loop gain of the current feedback loop. The expected value for the linewidth from the loop gain is 60 kHz, and is 2/3 of the observed spectral linewidth in this study, 95 kHz. The noise from the amplifier and detector is probably the cause of restricted linewidth reduction. By reducing the noise and increasing the loop gain of the feedback loop, the optical frequency drift and linewidth of the multielectrode DFB laser will be further reduced.

Conclusion: Using a multielectrode DFB with no phase rotation, optical frequency stabilisation and linewidth reduction were accomplished simultaneously using only one feedback electrical circuit. The optical frequency drift and linewidth of with those of the free-running laser. The minimum spectral linewidth obtained here was 95 kHz.

Acknowledgment: We are indebted to Dr. N. Tsuzuki for supplying the DFB laser and Dr. H. Kawaguchi for helpful discussions. We also thank Dr. K. Kurumada, Dr. T. Ikegami and Dr. M. Fujimoto for their encouragement throughout this work.

References

1 YAMAMOTO, Y., NILSSON, O., and SAITO, S.: 'Theory of a negative frequency feedback semiconductor laser', *IEEE J. Quantum Electron.*, 1985, **QE-21**, pp. 1919–1928

2 OHTSU, M., and KOTAJIMA, S.: 'Linewidth reduction of a semiconductor laser by electrical feedback', *ibid.*, 1985, **QE-21**, pp. 1905–1912

3 KOBAYASHI, S., YAMAMOTO, Y., ITO, M., and KIMURA, T.: 'Direct frequency modulation in AlGaAs semiconductor lasers', *ibid.*, 1982, **QE-18**, pp. 582–595

4 YOSHIKUNI, Y., and MOTOSUGI, G.: 'Independent modulation in amplitude and frequency regimes by a multielectrode distributed-feedback laser'. Optical fiber communication conference, 1986, Paper TUF1

5 YOSHIKUNI, Y., and MOTOSUGI, G.: 'Multi-electrode distributed feedback laser for pulse frequency modulation and chirping suppressed amplitude modulation', *J. Lightwave Technol.*, 1987, **LT-5**, pp. 516–522

6 OKOSHI, T., KIKUCHI, K., and NAKAYAMA, A.: 'Novel method for high resolution measurement of laser output spectrum', *Electron. Lett.*, 1980, **16**, pp. 630–631

Regimes of Feedback Effects in 1.5-μm Distributed Feedback Lasers

R. W. TKACH, MEMBER, IEEE, AND A. R. CHRAPLYVY

Abstract—**We have measured the effects of feedback on the spectra of 1.5-µm DFB lasers from feedback power ratios as low as −80 dB up to −8 dB. Five distinct regimes of effects are observed with well defined transitions between them. The dependence of these effects on the distance to the reflection is also investigated.**

I. Introduction

THE EFFECTS of reflections which feed light back into semiconductor lasers have been studied extensively. Recently, interest in this subject has intensified because of the growing emphasis on coherent optical communication systems, with their requirements for stable, narrow-linewidth sources. There are many different effects which can occur in semiconductor lasers subjected to external reflections, and there have been many observations and calculations of these effects. First noticed, was intensity noise in lasers subjected to relatively high feedback levels (0.1–10 percent) [1], [2]. Extreme line broadening was observed at these feedback levels [3]. Spectral effects, which occur at much lower feedback levels were subsequently seen [4]. Narrowing or broadening of the emission line were predicted and observed to occur at very low feedback levels (< −50 dB) [5]–[7]. For sufficiently high feedback, the laser spectrum becomes a multivalued function of the feedback phase [4]–[7]. Still higher feedback levels were seen to lead to intensity noise and line broadening [1]–[3]. However, if an antireflection coating is used to further increase the relative feedback strength, lasers with very strong external feedback operate stably in these extended cavities, with concomitantly narrowed linewidths. Such lasers have been constructed using AlGaAs diodes [8], and more recently, InGaAsP diodes [9]. While the line narrowing effects of external reflections are widely known, it is important to note that there are also many effects caused by feedback which are damaging to the performance of lasers to be used in coherent communications systems. In fact the results described here show that the useful range of feedback effects is restricted to a very narrow range of feedback levels, while all other levels of feedback produce deleterious effects.

Previous work, with the exception of [9]–[11], has been done with AlGaAs lasers. In this paper, we investigate the effects of feedback on the spectra of 1.5-μm distributed feedback lasers over 8 orders of magnitude variation in the feedback power ratio. We find that there are five distinct regimes of feedback effects, with well-defined transitions between them as a function of feedback power ratio. While there have been many previous observations of effects of reflections on the spectra of semiconductor lasers, earlier authors have typically concentrated on the effects within one or two feedback regimes. In this work the full range of feedback effects, from weak line narrowing at −80-dB feedback power ratio, to extended cavity operation at −8 dB, are described for the same experimental configuration, and with the same device.

The five regimes of feedback effects are:

Regime I: at the lowest levels of feedback, narrowing or broadening of the emission line is observed, depending on the phase of the feedback [5]. Effects on the linewidth of 30 percent are observable at −80-dB feedback power ratio, with an external reflector at a distance of 40 cm. For a 1-mW laser power, this corresponds to a feedback power of 10 pW.

Regime II: at a feedback level which depends on the distance to the external reflector, the broadening, which is observed at the lowest levels for out of phase feedback, changes to an apparent splitting of the emission line arising from rapid mode hopping. The magnitude of the splitting depends on the strength of the feedback, and on the distance to the reflector [11].

Regime III: as the feedback is increased further, at a level which does not depend on the distance to the reflection (approximately −45 dB), the mode hopping is suppressed, and the laser is observed to operate on a single narrow line. This regime occupies only a very small range of feedback power ratio, from −45 dB to −39 dB, and consequently the laser remains sensitive to other reflections of comparable or greater magnitude.

Regime IV: at a feedback level which does not depend on the distance to the reflection (approximately −40 dB), satellite modes, separated from the main mode by the relaxation oscillation frequency, appear [3]. These grow as the feedback increases and the laser line eventually broadens to as much as 50 GHz. This has been termed "coherence collapse" [12] because of the drastic reduction in the coherence length of the laser. The effects in this regime are independent of the feedback phase.

Regime V: extended cavity operation with a narrow

Manuscript received January 9, 1986; revised May 9, 1986.
The authors are with AT&T Bell Laboratories, Holmdel, NJ 07733.
IEEE Log Number 8610454.

Reprinted from *J. Lightwave Tech.*, vol. LT-4, no. 11, pp. 1655–1661, Nov. 1986.

linewidth is observed at the highest levels of feedback, usually greater than −10 dB; typically it is necessary to antireflection coat the laser facet to reach this regime [8]–[10]. In this regime the laser operates as a long cavity laser with a short active region. If there is sufficient frequency selectivity in the cavity, the laser operates on a single longitudinal mode with narrow linewidth for all phases of the feedback. In this regime of operation, the laser is relatively insensitive to additional external optical perturbations.

These five regimes of operation are experimentally very well defined and the transitions between them are easily identified. We report here measurements of all five regimes on a single type of device, vapor phase transport, InGaAsP, distributed feedback (DFB) lasers [13], operating at 1.5 μm. We also report measurements of the dependence of the feedback levels at which transitions between these regimes occur on the distance to the external reflection.

II. Theory

The analysis of feedback effects typically proceeds from the Van der Pol equation for the electric field of the laser with an additional source term corresponding to time delayed reinjection of the field [14], [15]. Neglecting noise terms, this can be written:

$$\frac{dE}{dt} = \left(-i\omega_0 + \frac{\Delta G}{2}(1 - i\alpha)\right)E(t) + \kappa E(t - \tau_e) \quad (1)$$

where ω_0 is the free running laser frequency, ΔG is the gain change due to the feedback, α is the linewidth enhancement factor [12], τ_e is the external round trip delay time, and

$$\kappa = \frac{1}{\tau_s}\frac{1 - R_s}{\sqrt{R_s}}\sqrt{R_e}$$

with τ_s the round trip time in the semiconductor chip, R_s the facet power reflectivity, and R_e the external power reflection coefficient, including coupling losses and attenuation. The field is assumed to have the form

$$E(t) = E_0 e^{-i\omega t}.$$

Equations for the change in steady state gain and oscillation frequency due to feedback can be derived:

$$\Delta G = -2\kappa \cos(\omega\tau_e) \quad (2)$$

and

$$\Delta\omega \equiv \omega - \omega_0 = -\kappa(\sin(\omega\tau_e) + \alpha\cos(\omega\tau_e)). \quad (3)$$

If the external delay time τ_e is less than the coherence time of the laser field, the effect of the feedback on the linewidth can be calculated [14]:

$$\delta f = \frac{\delta f_0}{[1 + \sqrt{1 + \alpha^2}\,\kappa\tau_e \cos(\omega\tau_e + \tan^{-1}\alpha)]^2} \quad (4)$$

where δf_0 is the linewidth of the laser without feedback.

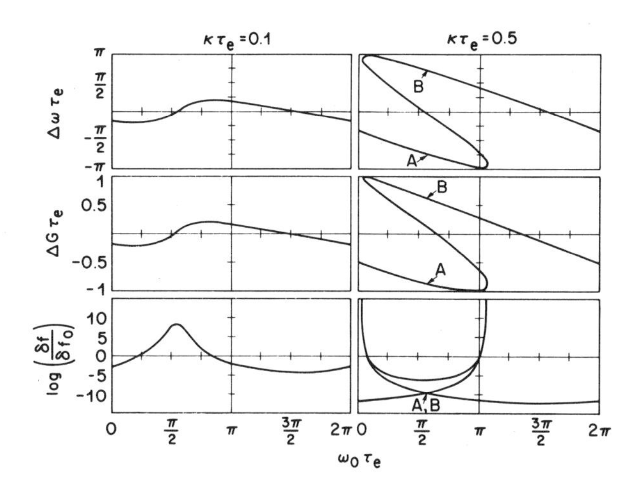

Fig. 1. Plots of change in laser frequency, threshold gain, and linewidth due to feedback as a function of feedback phase, for two values of $\kappa\tau_e$ with $\alpha = 6$.

Experimentally, the strength of the feedback, represented by κ, and the phase of the fed back light with respect to the laser field, represented by $\omega_0\tau_e$, can be varied. Solutions to these equations are obtained by setting these parameters and numerically solving (3). The values obtained for $\Delta\omega$ are then used to obtain the gain change and linewidth from (2) and (4). Fig. 1 shows plots of these results as a function of $\omega_0\tau_e$ for two values of κ. As can be seen, for sufficiently small feedback, there is only one solution, and the laser line is either narrowed or broadened, depending on the phase. For higher levels of feedback, specifically, when

$$\sqrt{1 + \alpha^2}\,\kappa\tau_e > 1$$

there are multiple solutions, and this leads to the rich variety of effects observed at the higher feedback levels.

III. Experiment

The experimental arrangement is shown in Fig. 2. The laser, a vapor-phase-transported distributed-feedback laser [13], is operated at approximately twice the threshold current. Light from the laser is collected with a 40× microscope objective and focused onto a mirror. The distance to the mirror can be varied from 20 cm to 400 cm. The maximum coupling efficiency to the laser mode is estimated to be 48 percent [11]. The variable attenuation can be set from 1 dB to 50 dB. The variable attenuator is tilted with respect to the optical axis by an angle of 30° to avoid any reflection from its surface. Reflections from the microscope objective were determined to be roughly −80 dB and thus could be neglected.

At the lowest feedback levels (Regime I), the laser line is observed to narrow or broaden, depending on the phase of the feedback. Fig. 3 shows laser spectra taken with a confocal Fabry–Perot interferometer with a free spectral range of 750 Mhz. The first trace is with no feedback, the second is with a feedback power level of −73 dB, with the phase adjusted for maximum narrowing, and in the third trace, the feedback phase is adjusted for maximum broadening. The transition to the second feedback regime

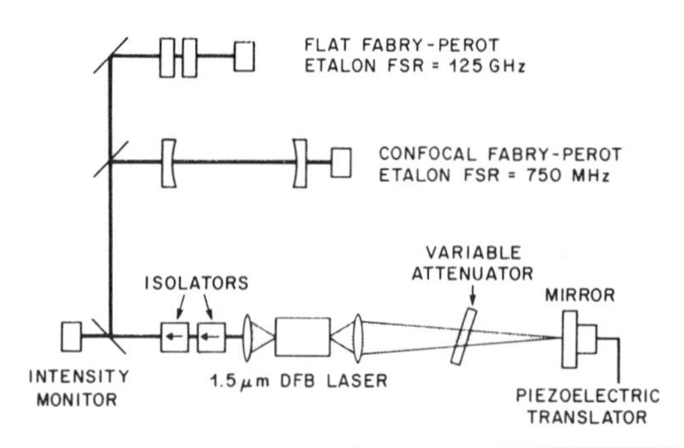

Fig. 2. Schematic of the experimental arrangement.

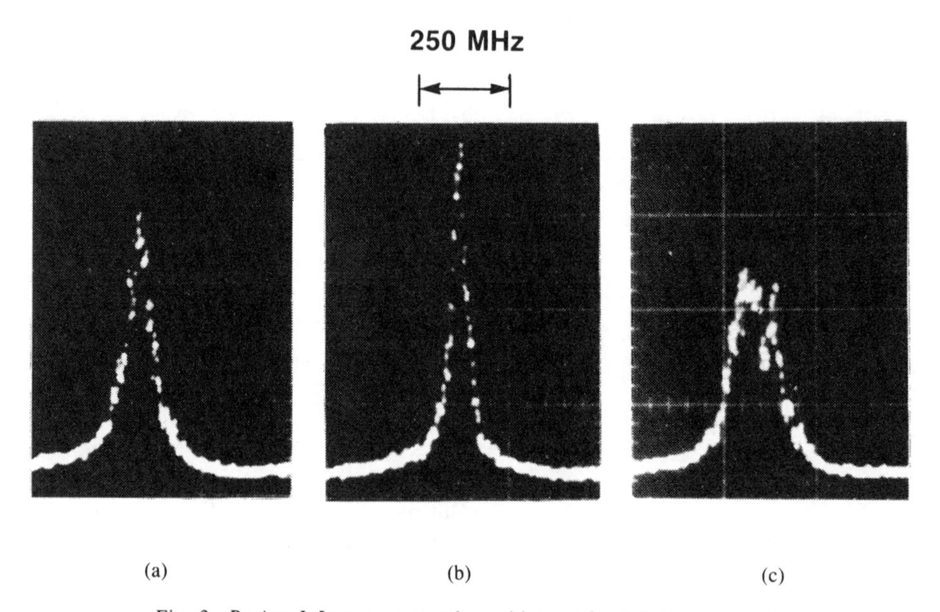

Fig. 3. *Regime I:* Laser spectra taken with a confocal Fabry–Perot etalon (a) no feedback, (b) feedback approximately −80 dB, in phase, (c) feedback out of phase. The distance to the external mirror was 40 cm.

occurs when the equation for the frequency shift induced by the feedback has multiple solutions, that is when

$$\sqrt{1 + \alpha^2}\, \kappa \tau_e > 1.$$

Experimentally this is evidenced by what appears to be a splitting of the emission line. This is shown in Fig. 4 for a feedback level of −62 dB corresponding to

$$\sqrt{1 + \alpha^2}\, \kappa \tau_e = 2.5.$$

the frequency separation of these two modes can be calculated from (3). When there are multiple solutions, the laser appears to operate at the frequency which results in the lowest linewidth. The line appears split when there are two solutions of lowest linewidth. This occurs when the feedback phase is adjusted so that

$$\omega_0 \tau_e = \pi - \tan^{-1} \alpha. \tag{5}$$

Fig. 5 shows a plot of the frequency separation of these modes as a function of feedback power ratio for an external cavity length of 40 cm. The solid line is calculated by solving for the possible oscillation frequencies with the feedback phase adjusted as in (5), and determining the frequency separation between the two solutions with the lowest linewidth. Those solutions are labeled in Fig. 1 as *A* and *B*. The parameters used in the calculation are: laser facet reflectivity = 36 percent, $\alpha = 6$, coupling efficiency to the laser = 48 percent. These last two parameters were chosen to fit the data, but are reasonable values. As can be seen from Fig. 5, the onset of this splitting is quite sharply defined both experimentally and theoretically. It provides a convenient bench mark for comparing lasers in terms of their sensitivity to feedback. The two modes observed do not exist simultaneously, the laser hops back and forth between them at a rate which depends on the feedback strength. For the case in Fig. 4 the rate of hopping is roughly 1 MHz. This frequency hopping is accompanied by changes in the intensity of the laser output arising from the different threshold gain associated with each of the two modes. This is shown in Fig. 6, the upper trace shows the frequency hopping, while the lower trace records the intensity fluctuations. It is important to note that the intensity difference between the two modes (approximately 2 percent) is on the order of the fluctuation in the number of photons in the semiconductor cavity (roughly 0.5 percent at 1-mW output power).

As the feedback, and hence the mode spacing, is increased, the dwell time at each mode increases. At a certain feedback level, approximately −45 dB, the hopping

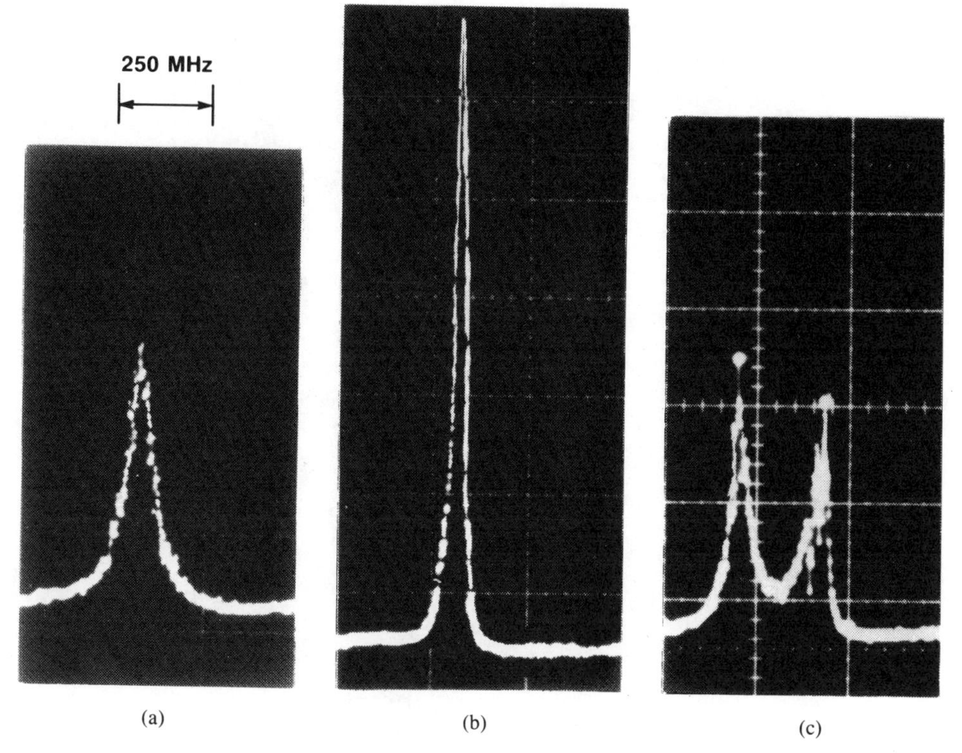

(a) (b) (c)

Fig. 4. *Regime II:* Spectra as in Fig. 2: (a) no feedback, (b) feedback approximately −62 dB in phase, (c) feedback out of phase.

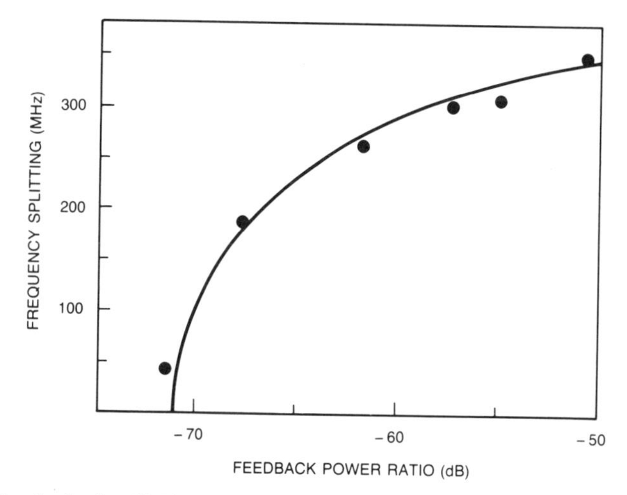

Fig. 5. *Regime II:* Plot of frequency separation of modes in Fig. 4(c) as a function of feedback power ratio. The solid line is calculated using (3).

ceases altogether; this is the transition to the third feedback regime. In this regime the laser line is narrowed for all phases of the feedback, and operates on a single frequency. The onset of this stable behavior seems to be related to the increase of the feedback induced gain difference between the split modes of the second regime. This stable regime is quite narrow however, as the feedback power ratio is increased 6 dB above the onset of stability there is a new effect: relaxation oscillation sidebands appear on the emission line.

As the feedback is increased these sidebands grow and broaden leading to ''coherence collapse'' [12]. Henry and Kazarinov [16], have recently analyzed this phenomenon and shown it to be an instability in the phase alignment between the feedback light and the laser mode. This unstable state is the fourth feedback regime. This regime occupies a range of over 30 dB of feedback power ratio beginning at approximately −40 dB. Fig. 7 shows traces taken with a 125-GHz free sprectral range Fabry–Perot interferometer for various stages of the ''coherence collapse''. Note that the line continues to broaden with increasing feedback intensity. Lines as broad as 100 GHz are observed. We define the transition to this regime as the feedback level at which the relaxation oscillation sidebands first appear (Fig. 7(a)).

The fifth regime of feedback effects is seen when the feedback finally dominates the field in the laser. To reach this regime experimentally it has been necessary to use an antireflection coating on the laser facet [8]–[10]. In this regime the laser is again stable. We have observed that for our antireflection coated DFB laser there is sufficient frequency selectivity provided by the DFB grating that the laser operates on a single longitudinal mode of the extended cavity [17]. The transition to this regime is theoretically explained in [16] as the onset of stability arising from an increasing barrier height against phase misalignment. Experimentally we observe that this stable regime of operation can only be achieved with an AR coating and careful alignment of the feedback, in agreement with the results of [8]–[10].

IV. Results and Discussion

The sharp transitions between these various regimes of feedback effects provides a convenient way of combining

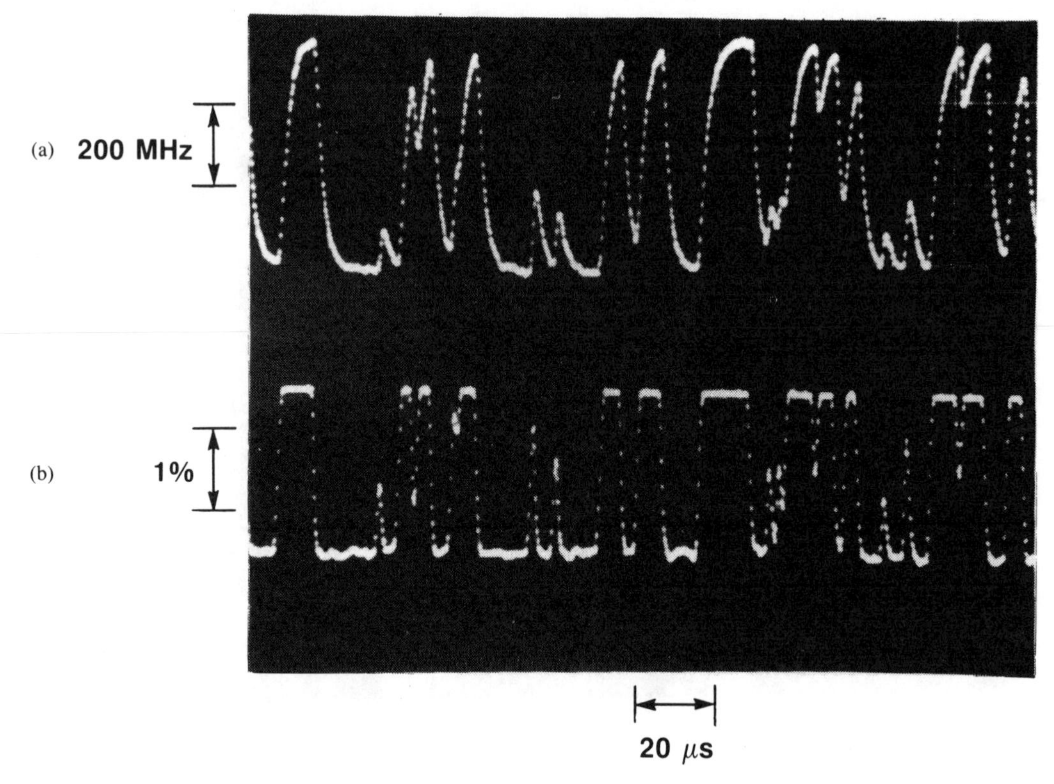

Fig. 6. *Regime II:* Evidence of frequency hopping: (a) frequency versus time, obtained by biasing the 125-GHz free spectral range Fabry–Perot interferometer at 70-percent transmission, (b) intensity versus time, the indicated vertical interval corresponds to a 1-percent change in intensity.

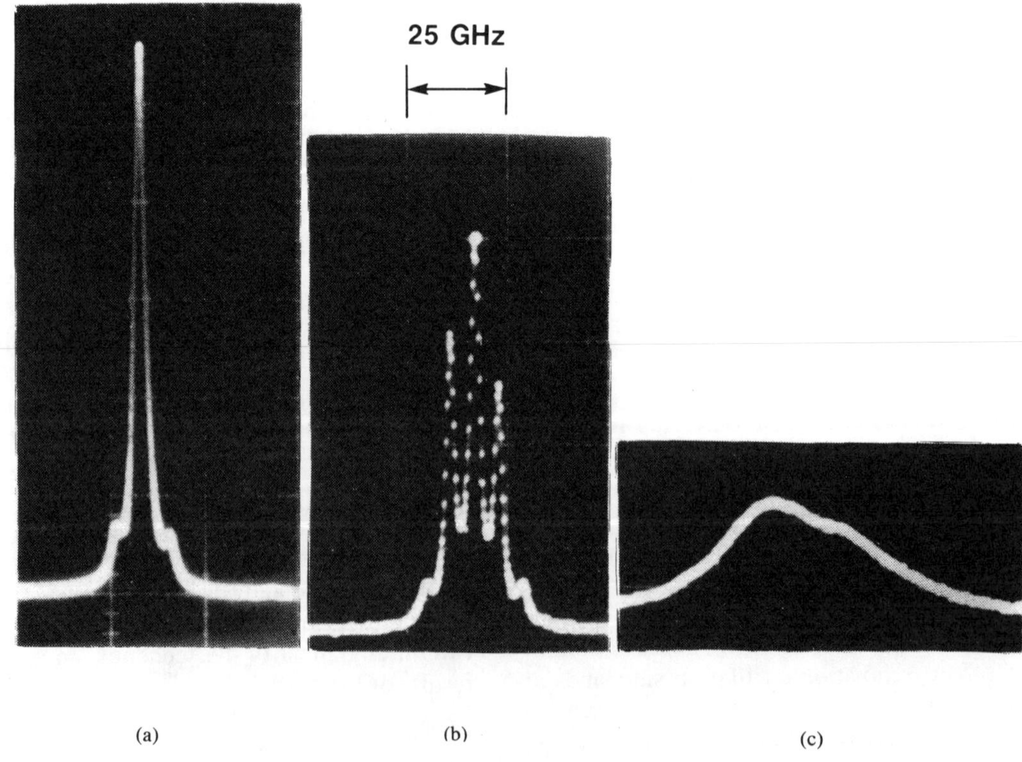

Fig. 7. *Regime IV:* Laser spectra taken with 125-GHz free spectral range Fabry–Perot: (a) approximately −40-dB feedback power ratio, (b) approximately −30-dB feedback, (c) −20-dB feedback.

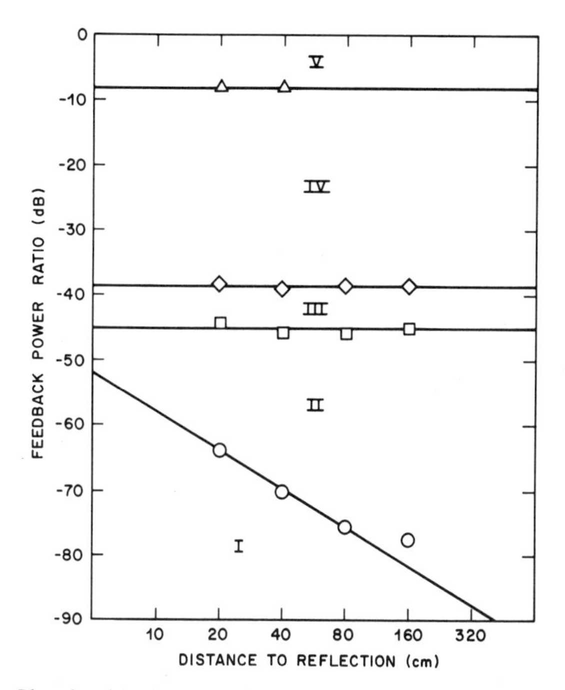

Fig. 8. Plot showing the power levels at which the transitions between regimes occur, as a function of distance to the reflection. Lines are drawn through the data points for clarity.

all these results onto a single plot. We have measured the feedback level where each transition occurs as a function of the distance to the external reflector. In Fig. 8 these results are displayed. The transition between regimes I and II, marked by the onset of frequency hopping or "splitting" of the laser line for out of phase feedback, is observed to scale with the length squared. This agrees with the theoretical description of this transition as the feedback level where

$$\sqrt{1 + \alpha^2}\, \kappa \tau_e = 1$$

since κ is proportional to the square root of the feedback power ratio.

As can be seen in Fig. 8, the transition between regimes II and III is relatively independent of the distance to the reflection. This indicates that the onset of stability which occurs at this transition is related to the difference in gain between the two lines, since the magnitude of

$$\Delta G = -2\kappa \cos (\omega \tau_e)$$

is independent of the gross distance to the reflection. Further, it is observed that the transition to regime III occurs at lower feedback levels when the laser is operated at higher powers. This lends support to the idea that the mode hopping observed in regime II is driven by photon number fluctuations in the semiconductor cavity. The transition to regime III occurs when the gain difference between the modes is great enough to select only one of them. The transition between regimes III and IV, which is the onset of coherence collapse, is again independent of the distance to the reflection. Henry and Kazarinov [16] have stated that this instability occurs when the coupling coefficient of the reflected light κ becomes comparable with the relaxation oscillation frequency. This is reasonable since the quantity

$$\sqrt{1 + \alpha^2}\, \kappa$$

sets the scale for frequency deviations induced by the reflections. On this basis, the transition to "coherence collapse" would be expected to be independent of distance to the reflection, as observed. Indeed the value of the feedback power ratio where this transition occurs is roughly consistent with this argument. This connection with the relaxation oscillations suggests that this transition should occur at higher feedback power ratios for higher laser powers since the relaxation oscillation frequency scales as the square root of power. This is also confirmed experimentally.

The transition from regime IV to V is also independent of the distance to the reflection. This is in agreement with the theory of [16] where the instability is shown to arise from spontaneous emission events which drive the laser out of synchronism with the external cavity. It is shown in [16] that this can be described as crossing a potential barrier. The height of this barrier scales with κ, and when κ is sufficiently large, the laser again becomes stable. The analysis in [16] also indicates that this transition will occur at lower feedback power ratio for higher laser power. Thus the "coherence collapse" regime is seen to become smaller for both ends as the laser power is increased. This can be qualitatively understood since the instability is driven by spontaneous emission and the effects of that noise are reduced when laser power increases, due to improved photon statistics. All the data in Fig. 7 was taken with two very similar Vapor Phase Transport distributed feedback lasers [13] from the same wafer. The data in regime five was taken using a laser with an antireflection coating $R = 5$ percent) on the side near the feedback mirror. The remaining points were taken using the same type of laser without the coating.

V. Conclusions

Perhaps the most surprising feature of these results is that while the experimental observations are rather complex, with many different types of effects, the behavior of the lasers can be neatly classified into these five regimes. The sharp demarcation between the various regimes is also quite unexpected. While all the observations reported here have been made with 1.5-μm distributed feedback lasers, these results are not peculiar to this type of laser. We have observed the same effects at essentially the same levels (within a few decibels) for Fabry–Perot and C^3 lasers. The important laser parameters affecting sensitivity to feedback are the stored energy in the cavity and the coupling of the laser mode to the external field.

It is important to note that feedback in general produces deleterious effects on semiconductor lasers, from the point of view of their use in optical communications systems. Only in Regimes III and V is the laser line always narrowed by the feedback, and these regimes occupy only a small fraction of the area of Fig. 8. In Regimes I and II, if the feedback phase is randomly varying, as it typically is for the reflection from, for example, a splice, the linewidths will be broadened some of the time or the frequency may hop back and forth between two modes. In Regime IV there is drastic line broadening (as much as 50 GHz) for all feedback phases. Regime III produces narrowing for all phases, but requires controlling the reflected power to be between −46 and −40 dB. This in turn results in extreme sensitivity to additional weak reflections. Only in Regime V is the laser narrowed for all feedback phases, and insensitive to additional reflections. This regime can only be attained for antireflection coated lasers. Thus, uncoated lasers operating without intentional external reflections, will in genral suffer degradation due to accidental reflections from splices and connectors in systems (typically −30 to −40 dB). Even with Faraday isolators with isolation of 30 dB [18], effects on the linewidth will be observable.

Acknowledgment

We are glad to acknowledge several helpful discussions with D. Marcuse, the use of the VPT-DFB lasers from T. L. Koch, and isolators from R. M. Jopson.

References

[1] R. F. Bloom, E. Mohn, C. Risch, and R. Salather, "Microwave self modulation of a diode laser coupled to an external cavity," *IEEE J. Quantum Electron.*, vol. QE-6, pp. 328-334, 1970.
T. Morikawa, Y. Mitsuhashi, and J. Shimada, "Return-beam-induced oscillations in self-coupled semiconductor lasers," *Electron. Lett.*, vol. 12, pp. 435-436, 1976.
[2] O. Hirota, and Y. Suematsu, "Noise properties of injection lasers due to reflected waves," *IEEE J. Quantum Electron.*, vol. QE-15, pp. 142-149, 1979.
[3] R. O. Miles, A. Dandridge, A. B. Tveten, H. F. Taylor, and T. G. Giallorenzi, "Feedback induced line broadening in CW channel-substrate planar laser diodes," *Appl. Phys. Lett.*, vol. 37, pp. 990-992, 1980.
[4] R. Lang and K. Kobayashi, "External optical feedback effects on semiconductor injection laser properties," *IEEE J. Quantum Electron.*, vol. QE-16, pp. 347-355, 1980.
[5] K. Kikuchi and T. Okoshi: "Simple formula giving spectrum-narrowing ratio of semiconductor-laser output obtained by optical feedback," *Electron. Lett.*, vol. 18, pp. 10-12, 1982.
[6] L. Goldberg, H. F. Taylor, A. Dandridge, J. F. Weller, and R. O. Miles, "Spectral characteristics of semiconductor lasers with optical feedback," *IEEE J. Quantum Electron.*, vol. QE-18, pp. 555-563, 1982.
[7] F. Favre, D. LeGuen, and J. C. Simon, "Optical feedback effects upon laser diode oscillation field spectrum," *IEEE J. Quantum Electron.*, vol. QE-18, pp. 1712-1717, 1982.
[8] M. W. Fleming and A. Mooradian, "Spectral characteristics of external-cavity controlled semiconductor lasers," *IEEE J. Quantum Electron.*, vol. QE-17, 1981.
[9] R. Wyatt and W. J. Devlin, "10 kHz linewidth 1.5-μm InGaAsP external cavity laser with 55 nm tuning range," *Electron. Lett.*, vol. 19, pp. 110-112, 1983.
[10] H. Temkin, N. A. Olsson, J. H. Abeles, R. A. Logan, and M. B. Panish, "Reflection noise in index guided InGaAsP lasers," *IEEE J. Quantum Electron.*, vol. QE-22, pp. 286-293, 1986.
[11] R. W. Tkach and A. R. Chraplyvy, "Line broadening and mode splitting due to weak feedback in single frequency 1.5-μm lasers," *Electron. Lett.*, vol. 21, pp. 1081-1083, 1985.
[12] D. Lenstra, B. H. Verbeek, and A. J. Den Boef, "Coherence collapse in single mode semiconductor lasers due to optical feedback," *IEEE J. Quantum Electron.*, vol. QE-21, pp. 674-679, 1985.
[13] T. L. Koch, T. J. Bridges, E. G. Burhhardt, P. J. Corvini, L. A. Coldren, R. A. Linke, W. T. Tsang, R. A. Logan, L. F. Johnson, R. F. Kazarinov, R. Yen, and D. P. Wilt, "1.55-μm InGaAsP distributed feedback vapor phase transported buried heterostructure lasers," *App. Phys. Lett.*, vol. 47, pp. 12-14, 1985.
[14] G. P. Agrawal, "Line narrowing in a single mode injection laser due to external optical feedback," *IEEE J. Quantum Electron.*, vol. QE-20, pp. 468-471, 1984.
[15] B. Tromborg, J. H. Osmundsen, and H. Olesen: "Stability analysis for a semiconductor laser in an external cavity," *IEEE J. Quantum Electron.*, vol. QE-20, pp. 1023-1032, 1984.
[16] C. Henry and R. F. Kazarinov, "Instability of semiconductor lasers due to optical feedback from distant reflectors," *IEEE J. Quantum Electron.*, vol. QE-22, pp. 295-301, 1986.
[17] A. R. Chraplyvy, K. Y. Liou, R. W. Tkach, G. Eisenstein, Y. K. Jhee, T. L. Koch, P. J. Anthony, and U. K. Chakrabarti, "A simple narrow-linewidth 1.5-μm InGaAsP DFB external cavity laser," *Electron. Lett.*, vol. 22, pp. 88-90, 1986.
[18] R. M. Jopson, G. Eisenstein, H. E. Earl, and K. L. Hall, "Bulk optical isolator tunable from 1.2 to 2 μm," *Electron. Lett.*, vol. 21, pp. 783-784, 1984.

HIGH EFFICIENCY SURFACE-EMITTING DISTRIBUTED BRAGG REFLECTOR LASER ARRAY

K. KOJIMA
M. KAMEYA
S. NODA
K. KYUMA

Central Research Laboratory
Mitsubishi Electric Corporation
1-1 Tsukaguchi-honmachi 8-chome
Amagasaki, Hyogo 661, Japan

4th January 1988

Indexing terms: Lasers and laser applications, Semiconductor lasers, Integrated optics

A surface-emitting distributed Bragg reflector laser array with three stripes were fabricated. The external differential quantum efficiency was 32% and the maximum output power was 500 mW.

There has been considerable interest in surface-emitting laser diodes, because they are potentially very important for one- and two-dimensional monolithic laser arrays. There are several approaches to the realisation of surface-emitting lasers, such as the vertical resonator cavity,[1,2] 45° mirror,[3] parabolic mirror,[4] and the grating-coupler.[5–9] Among these, grating-coupled lasers have the advantages of a narrow beam divergence and dynamic single mode operation. Although the quantum efficiencies of grating-coupled lasers were very low, there has been considerable progress recently in various aspects. Continuous wave operation in a distributed Bragg reflector (DBR) laser[7] and a distributed feedback (DFB) laser[8] were reported with differential quantum efficiencies of 9% and 8% respectively, and a differential quantum efficiency of 20% was obtained in a DBR laser under pulsed conditions.[9] Since grating-coupled surface-emitting lasers do not require cleaved facets, the ultimate maximum output power will be limited by internal heating, and very high output power is expected with one- and two-dimensional laser arrays. In this letter, we report a three-stripe surface-emitting multiquantum well (MQW) DBR laser array with a very high differential quantum efficiency of 32% and a high output power of 500 mW.

Fig. 1 shows the schematic diagram of a surface-emitting MQW-DBR laser array. The wafer consists of an *n*-GaAs buffer layer (0·2 μm), an *n*-$Al_{0.6}Ga_{0.4}As$ cladding layer (1·3 μm), an *n*-$Al_{0.2}Ga_{0.8}As$ guiding layer (0·25 μm), an undoped MQW layer (three 10 nm-thick GaAs well layers and two 5 nm-thick $Al_{0.2}Ga_{0.8}As$ barrier layers), a *p*-$Al_{0.2}Ga_{0.8}As$ guiding layer (0·15 μm), a *p*-$Al_{0.6}Ga_{0.4}As$ cladding layer (1·3 μm), and a *p*-GaAs contact layer (0·5 μm) on an *n*-GaAs substrate by molecular beam epitaxy. The main difference from previous work on a single stripe MQW-DBR laser[7] is that *n*- and *p*-guiding layers were introduced to form the separate confinement structure, and that the number of well layers was reduced from five to three. The optical power is mainly confined in the guiding layers, and the modal absorption loss in the unpumped MQW layer in the DBR section reduced. Moreover, the guiding layers increase the coupling efficiency between the active and the DBR sections, since the

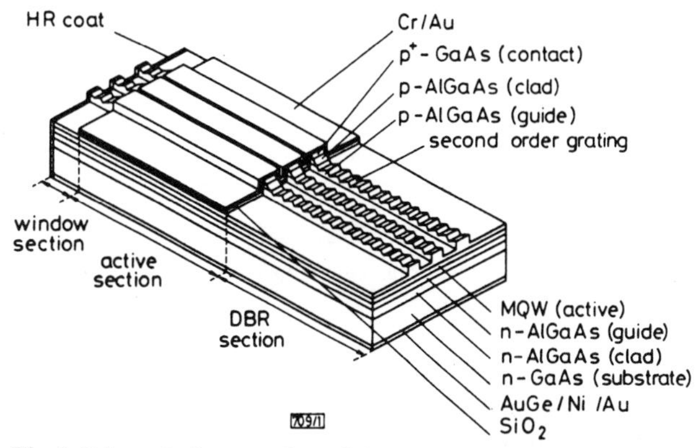

Fig. 1 *Schematic diagram of a surface-emitting MQW-DBR laser array*

vertical electric field distribution is less affected even though the *p*-guiding layer is deeply etched. The residual thickness of the *p*-guiding layer before grating formation was 0·05–0·1 μm, which is thinner than in the previous work and increases the diffraction efficiency. The stripes were formed by etching the *p*-guiding layer by about 0·05 μm. One chip consists of three stripes, and both the width and the separation of each stripe were 4 μm. The length of the DBR section, the active section, and the window section were 300, 300, and 17 μm, respectively. The window section was introduced to increase the catastrophic optical damage level. The facet of the window section was high reflection coated (86%) to increase the surface-emitting output, while the DBR section facet was scratched to suppress Fabry–Perot modes.

Fig. 2 shows the surface-emitting power/current characteristics at room temperature. The pulse width was 100 ns and the repetition frequency was 100 kHz, so the duty ratio was 1%. The threshold current was 105 mA and the maximum output power was 500 mW. The maximum differential quantum efficiency was as high as 32%, and the total quantum efficiency was 25%. This very high quantum efficiency is probably due to the introduction of the guiding layers and the reduction of the *p*-guiding layer thickness. The lasing wavelength was about 879 nm, and two or three modes were usually observed. The beam divergence in the direction normal to the grating lines was about 0·2°, although the beam pattern was slightly deformed when a multimode oscillation occurred.

In these laser arrays, phase locking has not been observed, and the measured beam divergence in the direction parallel to the grating lines was 18°. However, phase-locked operation

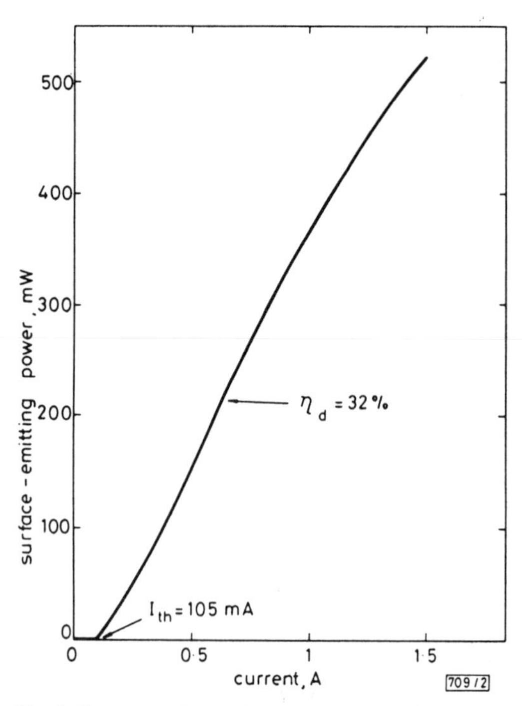

Fig. 2 *Current against surface-emitting power at room temperature*

with narrower beam divergence will be possible by increasing the optical coupling between the elements.

To conclude, we fabricated a surface-emitting MQW-DBR laser array with three stripes. The threshold current was 105 mA, and the maximum differential quantum efficiency and the output power were 32% and 500 mW, respectively. This shows that grating-coupled surface-emitting lasers offer great potential for high power laser arrays with narrow beam divergence.

The authors would like to thank T. Nakayama and K. Hamanaka for continuous encouragement.

References

1 IGA, K., KINOSHITA, S., and KOYAMA, F.: 'Microcavity GaAlAs/GaAs surface-emitting laser with I_{th} = 6 mA', *Electron. Lett.*, 1986, **23**, pp. 134–136

2 OGURA, M., HSIN, W., WU, M.-C., WANG, S., WHINNERY, J. R., WANG, S. C., and YANG, J. J.: 'Surface-emitting laser diode with vertical GaAs/GaAlAs quarter-wavelength multilayers and lateral buried heterostructure', *Appl. Phys. Lett.*, 1987, **51**, pp. 1655–1657

3 WINDHORN, T. H., and GOODHUE, W. D.: 'Monolithic GaAs/AlGaAs diode laser/deflector devices for light emission normal to the surface', *ibid.*, 1986, **48**, pp. 1675–1677

4 LIAU, Z. L., and WALPOLE, J. N.: 'Surface-emitting GaInAsP/InP laser with low threshold current and high efficiency', *ibid.*, 1985, **46**, pp. 115–117

5 REINHART, F. K., LOGAN, R. A., and SHANK, C. V.: 'Distributed-feedback single heterojunction GaAs diode laser', *ibid.*, 1985, **27**, pp. 45–48

6 KOJIMA, K., NODA, S., MITSUNAGA, K., KYUMA, K., HAMANAKA, K., and NAKAYAMA, T.: 'Edge- and surface-emitting distributed Bragg reflector laser with multiquantum well active/passive waveguides', *ibid.*, 1987, **50**, pp. 227–229

7 KOJIMA, K., NODA, S., MITSUNAGA, K., KYUMA, K., and HAMANAKA, K.: 'Continuous wave operation of a surface-emitting AlGaAs/GaAs multiquantum well distributed Bragg reflector laser', *ibid.*, 1987, **50**, pp. 1705–1707

8 MITSUNAGA, K., KAMEYA, M., KOJIMA, K., NODA, S., KYUMA, K., HAMANAKA, K., and NAKAYAMA, T.: 'cw surface-emitting grating-coupled GaAs/AlGaAs distributed feedback laser with very narrow beam divergence', *ibid.*, 1987, **50**, pp. 1788–1790

9 EVANS, G. A., CARLSON, N. W., HAMMER, J. M., LURIE, M., BUTLER, J. K., PALFREY, S. L., CARR, L. A., HAWRYLO, F. Z., JAMES, E. A., KAISER, C. J., KIRK, J. B., and REICHERT, W. F.: 'Efficient 30 mW grating surface-emitting lasers', *ibid.*, 1987, **51**, pp. 1478–1480

Efficient, high-power (> 150 mW) grating surface emitting lasers

G. A. Evans, N. W. Carlson, J. M. Hammer, M. Lurie, J. K. Butler, L. A. Carr, F. Z. Hawrylo, E. A. James, C. J. Kaiser, J. B. Kirk, and W. F. Reichert
David Sarnoff Research Center, CN 5300, Princeton, New Jersey 08543-5300

S. R. Chinn, J. R. Shealy, and P. S. Zory
General Electric Electronics Laboratory, Syracuse, New York 13221

(Received 2 December 1987; accepted for publication 1 February 1988)

Surface emitting AlGaAs second-order distributed Bragg reflector lasers using a superlattice graded-index separate confinement heterostructure with a single quantum well have been fabricated. The total peak power is emitted coherently from both gratings into a 0.06° full width half-power single lobe far field pattern. Peak powers are in excess of 150 mW. The external differential quantum efficiency is as high as 30%. Under severe current modulation conditions, the stable single longitudinal mode had 20–45 dB wavelength side mode rejection.

A recent paper[1] reported grating surface emitting lasers with peak powers in excess of 30 mW and an external differential quantum efficiency of 20%. The devices were fabricated using a conventional graded-index separate confinement heterostructure single quantum well (GRINSCH SQW) structure. The lasing cavity, defined by a distributed Bragg reflector (DBR) and a high reflect coated cleaved facet, had an index guided gain region with no lateral guiding in the DBR region. In this letter, we report on grating surface emitting DBR lasers that are index guided in both the gain regions and the DBR sections and have a lasing cavity defined by two DBR sections. The transverse structure of this surface emitting laser is a GRINSCH SQW geometry grown by organometallic vapor phase epitaxy (OMVPE) in a single step. These new devices are capable of coherently emitting more than 150 mW from two grating sections which are located on either end of the gain region. The far field pattern of the total emitted light from both grating sections is a single lobe with a 0.06° full width half-power beam divergence. The external differential quantum efficiencies are as high as 30%.

Several recent papers have shown that such grating surface emitting DBR lasers provide both dynamically stable single mode operation and a very narrow beam divergence.[1–4] Grating surface emitting lasers have already been used as elements in coherent[5–7] and incoherent[4] surface emitting arrays and are attractive components for optoelectronic integration. Although the concept for narrow beam grating surface emitting lasers was demonstrated[8–12] over ten years ago, only recently have such devices shown moderately high power (> 10 mW) and differential quantum efficiencies greater than about 1%. In the last year, grating surface emitting devices with differential quantum efficiencies approaching 10%[3,4] and as high as 20%[1] have been reported. The power and efficiency of single grating surface emitting lasers are now becoming comparable to those of single edge emitting semiconductor lasers.

Unlike the best performing single element grating surface emitters previously reported,[1,3,4] this surface emitting laser does not use a high reflecting cleaved facet at one end. Instead, the output and feedback for these new single devices are achieved solely from the built-in diffraction gratings as reported earlier for low-power single elements,[5] coherent linear arrays[5–7] of DBR surface emitters, and a recent distributed feedback device.[13]

As shown in Fig. 1, threshold currents for these devices were as low as 50 mA, and the external differential quantum efficiency is 30% for power levels below about 70 mW. At power levels above 70 mW, the mode spectra become increasingly multimode with corresponding nonlinearities in the power versus current curve. The optoelectronic properties of these devices were all obtained by simple probe testing of the lasers junction side up in wafer form with 50 ns current pulses, no dc bias, and a 2% duty cycle. Under these severe modulation conditions, the spectral output of the laser, shown in Fig. 2, was single wavelength up to 70 mW with 20–45 dB side mode rejection around the central peak located at 8500 Å. We believe that the narrow vertical spikes to

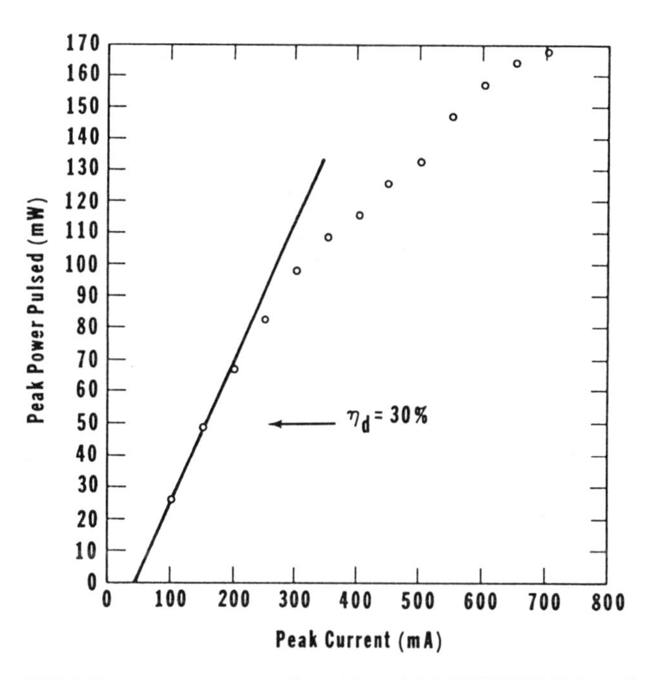

FIG. 1. Power vs current curve for a ridge-guided GRINSCH SQW surface emitting laser with a 200-μm-long gain section between 500-μm-long waveguide sections. The external differential quantum efficiency η_d is 30%.

Reprinted with permission from *Appl. Phys. Lett.*, vol. 52, no. 13, pp. 1037–1039, Mar. 28, 1988.

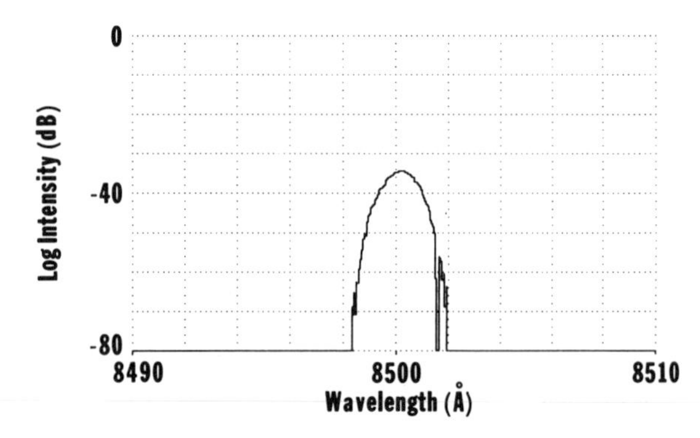

FIG. 2. Semilog plot of the surface emitted mode spectrum at an output power of 70 mW, showing 20–45 dB dynamic wavelength side mode rejection. Instrument resolution is 1 Å.

the right of the resolution limited central lobe in Fig. 2 are noise due to another mode appearing intermittently.

The laser wafers were grown by a multichamber OMVPE process.[14] The geometry of the grating surface emitting laser is shown in Fig. 3. The basic structure is a (GRINSCH) geometry with a SQW active region.[15] The GRINSCH SQW structure consists of an *n*-GaAs substrate, an *n*-graded buffer layer (0.1 μm), an *n*-$Al_{75}Ga_{25}As$ cladding layer (1.5 μm), a graded region from $Al_{75}Ga_{25}As$ to $Al_{25}Ga_{75}As$ (0.2 μm), a GaAs quantum well (100 Å), a second graded region from $Al_{25}Ga_{75}As$ to $Al_{75}Ga_{25}As$ (0.2 μm), a *p*-$Al_{75}Ga_{25}As$ cladding layer (1.0 μm), and a *p*-GaAs cap layer (0.1 μm). The cladding and graded-index regions consist of superlattices. The ratio of Al to Ga is varied in the graded regions by varying the thickness of the AlAs layers in a linear fashion from 3 to 30 Å while the thickness of the GaAs layer remains a constant 10 Å.

The devices were fabricated by performing a full surface Zn/In diffusion[16] followed by evaporating TiPtAu over the

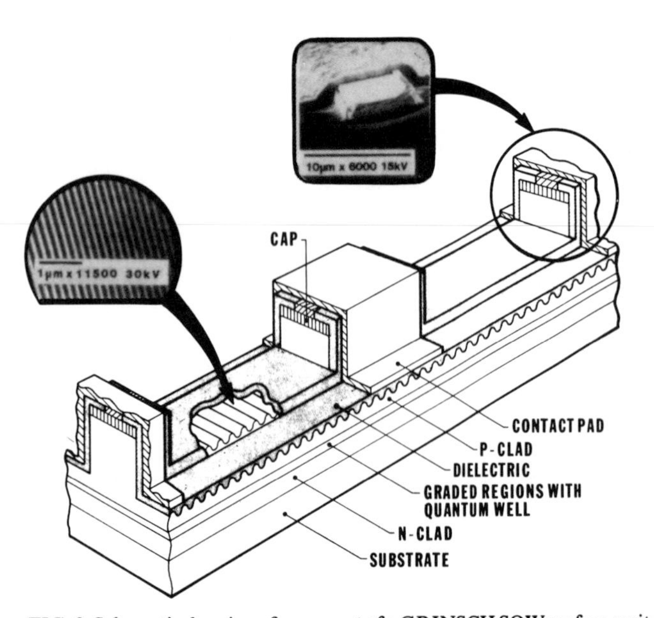

FIG. 3. Schematic drawing of a segment of a GRINSCH SQW surface emitting laser wafer. A single laser consists of a gain region (under the contact pad) between two grating sections. Insets show a scanning electron micrograph of (1) the transition between a gain region and a grating section and (2) the grating.

complete wafer. Next, an array of 5-μm-wide and 200-μm-long rectangles (on 300 μm centers laterally and separated by 500 μm longitudinally) are defined in photoresist to protect and define the gain sections while the metallization is removed elsewhere by ion beam etching. The cap layer and a portion of the *p*-clad layer are also removed by ion beam etching. For these devices, the thickness of the *p*-clad remaining above the graded region after the initial etching was about 1200 Å. To fabricate the grating (period = 2576 Å), photoresist is spun on the wafer, holographically exposed using the 3511 Å line of an argon ion laser, and then developed. The resulting photoresist grating is then replicated into the *p*-clad layer of the wafer by ion beam etching. The grating depth was approximately 800 Å. Next, ridges connecting the gain sections are defined in photoresist. An additional 300 Å of the *p*-clad layer is removed by chemical etching (using a 50:3:1 ratio of H_2O:H_3PO_4:H_2O_2) outside the ridge regions. After all the etch steps, we calculate that the effective index step for the ridge guide in the gain section is approximately 8×10^{-3} and for the ridge guide in the grating section, approximately 3×10^{-3}. The etching process is followed by plasma deposition of a 3000-Å-thick layer of Si_3N_4 over the complete wafer. Using standard photolithographic techniques, the Si_3N_4 is removed only on the top of the ridges in the gain sections, and the *p* surface is remetallized with Ti (500 Å) and Au (1000 Å) by electron beam evaporation. Gold contact pads are then plated to a thickness of about 1 μm over the gain sections through 180 μm$\times$200 μm openings in a photoresist layer. After photoresist removal, the thin layer of *p* metal connecting the plated contact pads is removed by ion beam etching to provide electrical isolation between devices. Finally, a Au/Ge/Ni/Au *n*-side contact is evaporated and sintered. The resulting devices have 200-μm-long gain sections separated by 500-μm-long passive ridge guides in the grating regions.

A schematic drawing of a series of devices is shown in Fig. 3. Since the lasers were probe tested at the wafer level, the two grating sections on either end of the central gain region are adjacent to a gain region of another element. A scanning electron micrograph of a transition between a gain region and a grating section is shown in one inset of Fig. 3. A second inset shows a scanning electron micrograph of the submicron grating. As reported earlier[1] for GRINSCH SQW grating surface emitting lasers, the mode transmission fraction K_x perpendicular to the junction between the laser and passive waveguide section is very high, ranging from 0.96 to 0.99 as the *p*-clad thickness varies from 500 to 2000 Å, resulting in very low reflection at the laser–waveguide transition. Kojima *et al.*[3] demonstrated that a multiquantum well structure could be used for both the laser and the passive waveguide sections of a DBR laser, achieving low losses in the passive waveguide due to the steplike density of states, band-gap shrinkage effects,[17] and saturation of the excitonic absorption.[18] This same concept has been shown to work equally well for GRINSCH SQW structures.[1] We calculate that the modal absorption is about 80–100 cm^{-1} near threshold and is quickly saturated to about 10 cm^{-1} for power levels above 3 mW.[19]

Because the gratings were relatively deep ($\cong$800 Å),

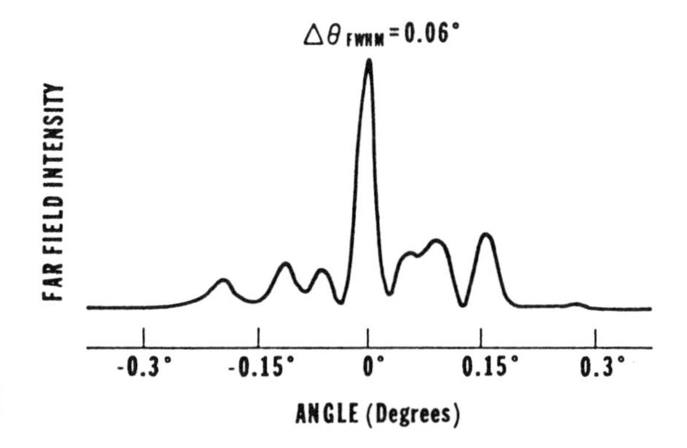

FIG. 4. Far field pattern of a ridge-guided GRINSCH SQW grating surface emitting laser in the direction normal to the grating lines.

very little light reached the adjacent gain sections, limiting the effective output aperture of each grating section to about 250 μm. The far field pattern perpendicular to the grating lines, shown in Fig. 4, has a full width half-power (FWHP) beam divergence of 0.06° which corresponds to the FWHP beam divergence from a diffraction limited source with a 700 μm aperture.

Further improvements in the performance of these devices are expected. Presently, about half of the grating deflected light is directed into the substrate. The use of either etched windows in the present substrate or an AlGaAs substrate (which would be transparent to the laser radiation) would therefore increase both efficiency and power while allowing junction side down mounting of the device. Finally, blazing the grating, using a dielectric stack or Au metallization over the grating could direct substantially all of the grating outcoupled light towards the substrate.

In conclusion, a GRINSCH SQW surface emitting laser has been fabricated with a differential quantum efficiency of 30% and a peak output power of 168 mW. Under severe current modulation conditions, the stable single longitudinal mode had 20–45 dB wavelength side mode rejection, and the 0.06° FWHP single lobe far field pattern, the narrowest to our knowledge for any single element semiconductor laser, was near diffraction limited.

The authors would like to thank J. Gillman, M. Harvey, D. Marinelli, J. Sprague, D. Tarangioli, and D. Truxal for excellent technical assistance and R. Bartolini, J. Connolly, M. Ettenberg, and S. Palfrey for many helpful discussions. This work was supported in part by the Department of the Air Force.

[1]G. A. Evans, N. W. Carlson, J. M. Hammer, M. Lurie, J. K. Butler, S. L. Palfrey, L. A. Carr, F. Z. Hawrylo, E. A. James, C. J. Kaiser, J. B. Kirk, and W. F. Reichert, Appl. Phys. Lett. **51**, 1478 (1987).
[2]G. A. Evans, J. M. Hammer, N. W. Carlson, F. R. Elia, E. A. James, and J. B. Kirk, Appl. Phys. Lett. **49**, 314 (1986).
[3]K. Kojima, S. Noda, K. Mitsunaga, and K. Kyuma, Appl. Phys. Lett. **50**, 227 (1987).
[4]K. Kojima, S. Noda, K. Mitsunaga, K. Kyuma, and K. Hamanaka, Appl. Phys. Lett. **50**, 1705 (1987).
[5]J. M. Hammer, N. W. Carlson, G. A. Evans, M. Lurie, S. L. Palfrey, C. J. Kaiser, M. G. Harvey, E. A. James, J. B. Kirk, and F. R. Elia, Appl. Phys. Lett. **50**, 659 (1987).
[6]N. W. Carlson, G. A. Evans, J. M. Hammer, M. Lurie, S. L. Palfrey, and A. Dholakia, Appl. Phys. Lett. **50**, 1301 (1987).
[7]N. W. Carlson, G. A. Evans, J. M. Hammer, M. Lurie, J. K. Butler, S. L. Palfrey, M. Ettenberg, L. A. Carr, F. Z. Hawrylo, E. A. James, C. J. Kaiser, J. B. Kirk, W. F. Reichert, J. R. Shealy, J. W. Sprague, S. R. Chinn, and P. S. Zory, Opt. Lett. (April, 1988); N. W. Carlson, G. A. Evans, J. M. Hammer, M. Lurie, L. A. Carr, F. Z. Hawrylo, E. A. James, C. J. Kaiser, J. B. Kirk, W. F. Reichert, D. A. Truxal, J. R. Shealy, S. R. Chinn, and P. S. Zory, Appl. Phys. Lett. **52**, 939 (1988).
[8]R. D. Burnham, D. R. Scifres, and W. Streifer, IEEE J. Quantum Electron. **QE-11**, 439 (1975).
[9]Zh. I. Alferov, V. M. Andreyev, S. A. Gurevich, R. F. Kazarinov, V. R. Larionov, M. N. Mizerov, and E. L. Portnoy, IEEE J. Quantum Electron. **QE-11**, 449 (1975).
[10]P. Zory and L. D. Comerford, IEEE J. Quantum Electron. **QE-11**, 451 (1975).
[11]F. K. Reinhart, R. A. Logan, and C. V. Shank, Appl. Phys. Lett. **27**, 45 (1975).
[12]W. Ng and A. Yariv, Appl. Phys. Lett. **31**, 613 (1977).
[13]S. H. Macomber, J. S. Mott, R. J. Noll, G. M. Gallatin, E. J. Gratrix, and S. L. O'Dwyer, Appl. Phys. Lett. **51**, 472 (1987).
[14]J. R. Shealy, Appl. Phys. Lett. **48**, 925 (1986).
[15]J. R. Shealy, Appl. Phys. Lett. **50**, 1634 (1987).
[16]J. R. Shealy, K. Kavanagh, and P. M. Enquist, Inst. Phys. Conf. Ser. No. 83, 251 (1987).
[17]S. Tarucha, Y. Horikoshi, and H. Okamoto, Jpn. J. Appl. Phys. **22**, **L482** (1983).
[18]D. A. B. Miller, D. S. Chemla, D. J. Eilenberger, P. W. Smith, A. C. Gossard, and W. T. Tsang, Appl. Phys. Lett. **41**, 679 (1982).
[19]J. K. Butler, S. R. Chinn, and G. A. Evans (unpublished).

High performance tunable 1.5 μm InGaAs/InGaAsP multiple quantum well distributed Bragg reflector lasers

T. L. Koch, U. Koren, and B. I. Miller
AT&T Bell Laboratories, Holmdel, New Jersey 07733

(Received 25 May 1988; accepted for publication 18 July 1988)

We describe the structure and performance of tunable four-quantum-well InGaAs/InGaAsP distributed Bragg reflector lasers. We observe total tuning range as large as 94 Å, differential efficiency of 32%/front facet, thresholds of 17 mA, low-chirp high-speed digital operation, and linewidths as low as 5.75 MHz at only 2 mW output.

Broadly tunable semiconductor lasers[1–4] are expected to play a major role in both high-speed direct detection wavelength division multiplexed (WDM) systems and coherent heterodyne detection systems, and may also find applications in new optical switching architectures. In this letter, we describe the structure and performance of tunable single longitudinal mode InGaAs/InGaAsP multiple quantum well (MQW) distributed Bragg reflector (DBR) lasers operating at 1.5 μm. These lasers display low threshold, excellent differential quantum efficiency, and large tuning range, with both low chirp under high-speed direct modulation and narrow linewidth under cw operation.

The longitudinal cross section cut through the laser waveguide is shown in Fig. 1. These devices are grown entirely by atmospheric pressure metalorganic chemical vapor deposition (MOCVD), and are based on the semi-insulating blocked planar buried heterostructure (SIPBH) geometry.[5] The low capacitance resulting from the Fe-doped InP current blocking layers allows high-speed operation with wide contacting mesas about the active region.

The active (gain) layer in these devices consists of four 80-Å-thick wells of InGaAs with 100-Å-thick barriers of 1.3 μm λ_{PL} (photoluminescence wavelength) InGaAsP. We have previously shown that 1.5 μm Fabry–Perot lasers based on this MQW sequence display low internal loss with excellent quantum efficiency and maximum power.[6]

In the DBR structure shown in Fig. 1, a 250-Å-thick InP etch-stop layer and a 2500-Å-thick passive 1.3 λ_{PL} InGaAsP guide layer are placed beneath the active MQW layers. The active layers are etched off in the guide region using a material selective InGaAs/InGaAsP etch, and a first-order ~2350 Å pitch grating is formed with conventional holographic means on the exposed surface of the passive guide only. Fabrication for the remaining steps is identical to the conventional SIPBH laser[5] except for additional etching of isolation grooves along the length to allow separate contacting of the gain and DBR sections. Typical Bragg region lengths are ~250 μm, and active lengths are in the range of 250–600 μm.

Figure 2 shows a cw 23 °C light-current characteristic of a 300 μm active length device with no current to the Bragg section. The differential efficiency is $\eta_d = 32\%$/front facet with no coatings applied, although some rollover occurs at higher powers. This is the highest value we know of for DBR lasers and indicates very good coupling into the Bragg region. Typical thresholds are 17–20 mA, with excellent device yield and uniformity permitting 10 mW output below 100 mA drive in the vast majority of devices.

Figure 3 shows a typical below threshold ($I \sim 0.9 I_{th}$) log-scale spectrum for the tunable MQW-DBR laser. The spectral width of the Bragg region for this wafer is ~40 Å, corresponding to a coupling constant of $\kappa \sim 140\ \mathrm{cm}^{-1}$ which is in reasonable agreement with the numerically evaluated value of $\kappa \sim 175\ \mathrm{cm}^{-1}$ based on the known layer indices and typical corrugation depths. Note that the spacing of the Fabry–Perot modes out of band is much closer than that of the Bragg band modes since the former corresponds to the entire cavity length. When run above threshold, these devices operate in a single longitudinal mode with side-mode suppression as high as 45 dB at high power. Most devices remain in the same single longitudinal mode over the entire operating range, although as expected some devices switch to an adjacent longitudinal mode within the Bragg band as power is increased.

The tuning characteristics for these devices are shown in Fig. 4. Results for both a 615 μm and a 298 μm active length

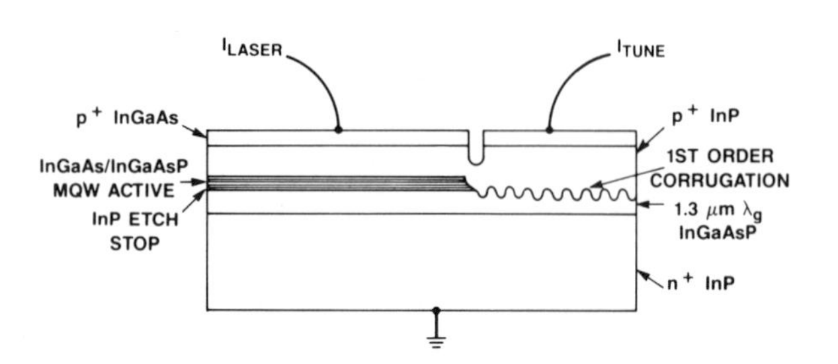

FIG. 1. Longitudinal structure of the tunable MQW SIPBH DBR laser.

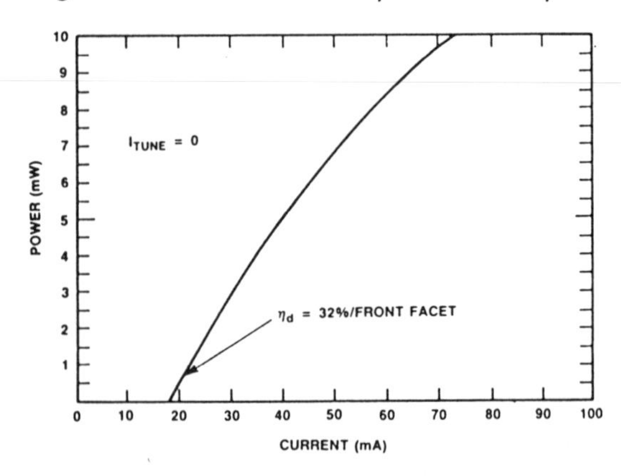

FIG. 2. cw light-current characteristic for a 300 μm active section length device at 23 °C with no current to the Bragg section.

Reprinted with permission from *Appl. Phys. Lett.*, vol. 53, no. 12, pp. 1036–1038, Sept. 19, 1988.

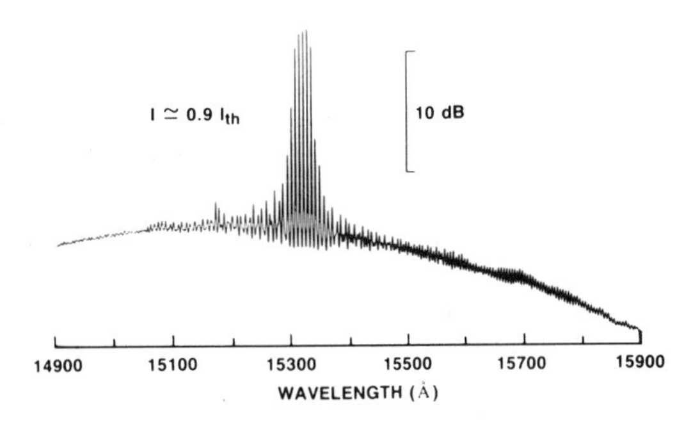

FIG. 3. Logarithmic scale spectrum of tunable MQW SIPBH DBR laser at $I \sim 0.9 I_{th}$. Above threshold, devices operate single longitudinal mode with side mode suppression in excess of 30 dB.

device are shown, and the maximum total tuning range obtained is 94 Å. The index change versus current is the same in both cases, and with a typical Bragg section confinement factor of $\Gamma \sim 0.4$ in the passive 1.3 μm λ_{PL} guide layer, it indicates a maximum index change under forward injection of $\sim 1.5\%$. Since we have not yet incorporated a separate phase tuning section,[1,2] the wavelength changes in discrete hops with a relatively small ($\sim$ 1–2 Å) continuous tuning between each hop. The longer device has 17 successive longitudinal modes which are accessible, while the shorter device has 9. The hopping behavior is uniform and reproducible, and a small amount of temperature tuning allows access to all wavelengths throughout the tuning range.

In wafers with strong gratings, there is little interplay between the tuning current and the laser output power. This is evident in Fig. 5, which shows the laser output power versus tuning current for three different laser-section drive levels. The curves are quite flat except for the discontinuity seen at each mode-hopping point as the device is tuned. Figure 5 also demonstrates that the various single longitudinal mode tuning current ranges are largely independent of the laser-section drive or output power. This manifests itself as the near-vertical mode-hopping boundaries as shown by the dotted lines in the figure.

A weak dependence of output power on tuning current will be obtained provided the loss γ induced by forward current injection in the passive guide is less than the grating coupling constant, $\gamma \lesssim \kappa$, since reflection then occurs in lengths shorter than the absorption depth in the guide. For

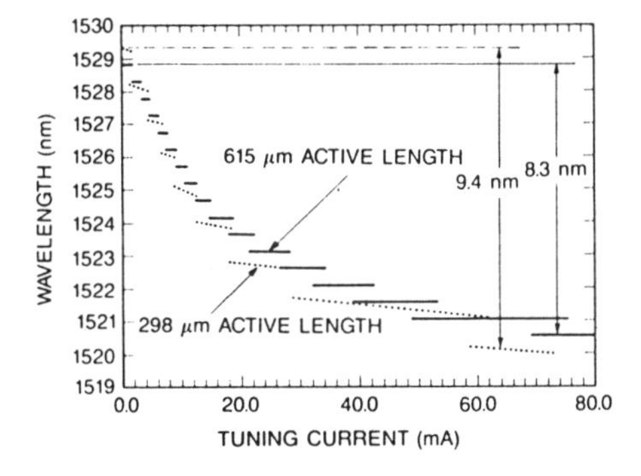

FIG. 4. Wavelength vs Bragg tuning current for two different active section length devices. For strong grating devices, continuous tuning between mode jumps is typically $\lesssim 20\%$ of the mode jump spacing.

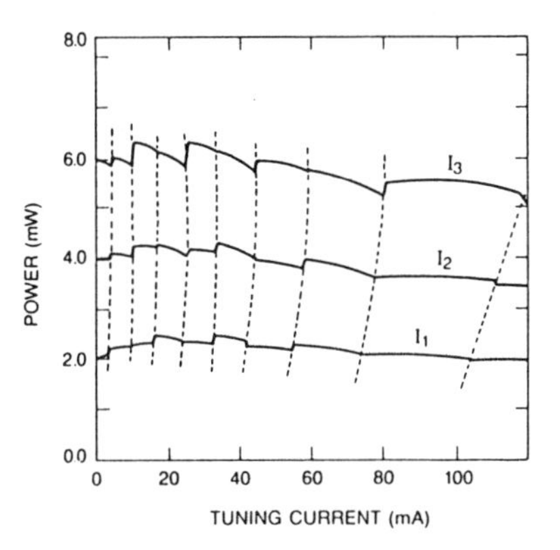

FIG. 5. Laser output power vs tuning-section current. Three curves are for the three laser section bias current levels corresponding to power levels of 2, 4, and 6 mW for an open-circuited tuning section. The dotted lines show the mode-hopping boundaries as the tuning current is varied.

weaker gratings ($\kappa \sim 70$ cm^{-1}), we have observed as much as a 50% reduction in power at the short wavelength end of the tuning range. Based on this behavior, we estimate the ratio of real index change to imaginary index change under forward injection in the passive Bragg region to be in excess of 10. This indicates that forward current injection, apart from its bandwidth limitations, provides a reasonably high performance mechanism for tuning.

At any particular current setting to the Bragg region, these devices provide excellent dynamic single-mode high-speed sources. Figure 6 shows a simultaneous measurement of the temporal intensity modulated (IM) waveform and the FM sideband spectrum of the single mode under 4.7 GHz sinusoidal modulation. At reasonably high frequencies, the ratio of the FM and IM indexes provides a measure[7,8] of the linewidth enhancement factor α, and Fig. 5 yields an unusually low value of $\alpha \sim -3.5$. We believe this low α value is partially due to the MQW active layer in these devices, but also due to the detuning of wavelengths shorter than the gain peak. This is evident in Fig. 3, where the gain peak is the location maximum Fabry–Perot fringe visibility. As expected, wafers detuned to the *longer* wavelength side of the gain peak displayed larger α values of ~ -6.

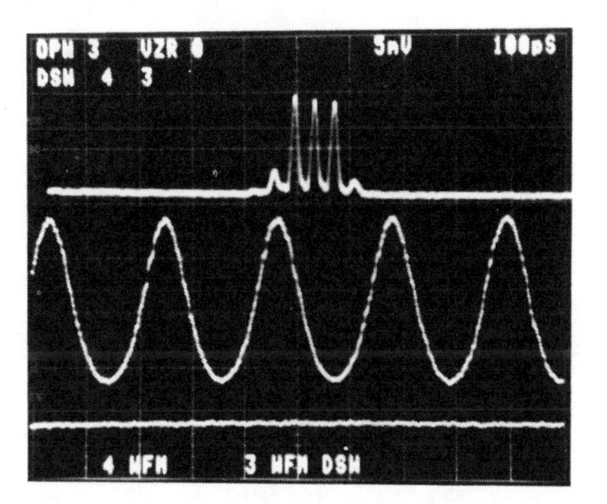

FIG. 6. Measurement of the linewidth enhancement factor α. Upper trace shows FM sideband spectrum resulting from the intensity modulated waveform shown in the lower trace under 4.7 GHz sinusoidal current modulation. Numerical simulation indicates that this ratio of FM to IM indices corresponds to $\alpha \sim -3.5$.

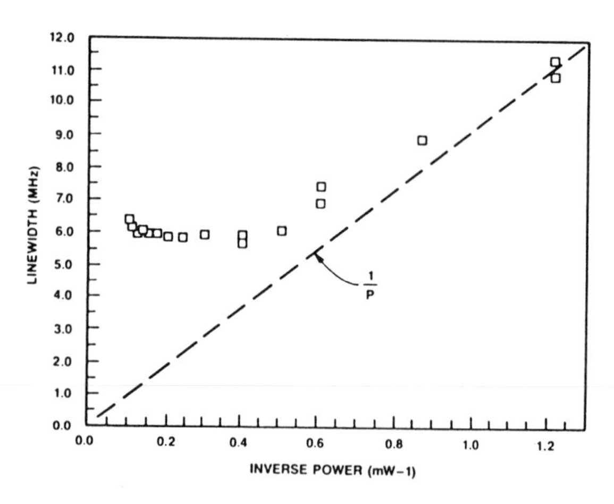

FIG. 7. cw linewidth vs inverse output power as measured by delayed self-heterodyne method.

One consequence of a small α is low chirping under large signal digital modulation. We have measured a spectral width of only 1.4 Å at the − 20 dB level under 5 Gb/s nonreturn to zero modulation with 5:1 extinction. Another consequence of a smaller α factor is reduced phase noise. Figure 7 shows the cw linewidth as measured by a delayed self-heterodyne apparatus plotted versus the inverse optical power from the laser. At relatively low output powers (~2 mW), the linewidth has reached a low value of ~6 MHz. This is qualitatively consistent with the α factor measured above. However, over the majority of the useful operating range of the laser the linewidth then remains constant, rather than decreasing with increasing optical power as expected. This behavior requires further investigation.

In summary, we have demonstrated a very large tuning range (94 Å) in a multiple quantum well InGaAs/InGaAsP distributed Bragg reflector laser. In addition to tunability, these lasers offer excellent operational characteristics for dynamic single-mode and narrow-line operation. We believe the prospects for application of this structure to high performance narrow-line continuously tunable sources are quite good.

[1]Y. Kotaki, M. Matsuda, M. Yano, H. Ishikawa, and H. Imai, Electron. Lett. **23**, 327 (1987).
[2]S. Murata, I. Mito, and K. Kobayashi, Electron. Lett. **23**, 405 (1987).
[3]B. Broberg and S. Nilsson, Appl. Phys. Lett. **52**, 1285 (1988).
[4]W. T. Tsang, N. A. Olsson, and R. A. Logan, Appl. Phys. Lett. **42**, 650 (1983).
[5]U. Koren, B. I. Miller, G. Eisenstein, R. S. Tucker, G. Raybon, and R. J. Capik, Electron. Lett. **24**, 138 (1988).
[6]U. Koren, B. I. Miller, Y. K. Su, T. L. Koch, and J. E. Bowers, Appl. Phys. Lett. **51**, 1744 (1987).
[7]Ch. Harder, K. Vahala, and A. Yariv, Appl. Phys. Lett. **42**, 328 (1983).
[8]T. L. Koch and J. E. Bowers, Electron. Lett. **20**, 1038 (1984).

Part 4
Quantum-Well Semiconductor Lasers

SEMICONDUCTOR lasers with active regions less than approximately 25 nm thick display desirable characteristics that are attributed to quantum mechanical effects. The properties of these devices differ from those with thicker active regions because the band structure of the thin active layer differs fundamentally from that of the bulk material.

Quantum-well lasers may contain one or more quantum-well layers; in the latter case they are generally referred to as multiple quantum-well devices, in contrast to single quantum-well lasers. Single quantum-well lasers almost invariably contain an optical waveguide bounding the single quantum well. Such lasers are variously called separate-confinement-heterostructure single-quantum-well (SCH SQW), or graded index (GRIN) SCH SQW lasers.

Papers on two other topics have also been included in this section. These are strained-layer lasers, in which strain is employed to modify the band structure of the active region. In addition we have selected a few reprints in the as yet unexploited field of quantum wire and dot structures. The concept in this area is to confine carriers in two or three dimensions (as opposed to one dimension in the quantum well). Modifications in the band structure caused either by strain or by increased dimensional confinement shift the lasing wavelength as well as the gain-current and other relations.

References

Quantum Wells

[1] Dingle, R., W. Wiegmann, and C. H. Henry, "Quantum states of confined carriers in very thin AlGaAs–GaAs–AlGaAs heterostructures," *Phys. Rev. Lett.*, vol. 33, p. 827, 1974.

[2] Holonyak, N., Jr., R. M. Kolbas, R. D. Dupuis, and P. D. Dapkus, "Quantum-well heterostructure lasers," *IEEE J. Quantum Electron.*, vol. 16, p. 170, 1980.

Multiple Quantum-Well Lasers

[3] Kobayashi, H., H. Iwamura, T. Saku, and K. Otsuka, "Polarization-dependent gain-current relationship in GaAs–AlGaAs MQW laser diodes," *Electron. Lett.*, vol. 19, p. 166, 1983.

Single Quantum-Well Lasers

[4] Dupuis, R. D., P. D. Dapkus, R. Chin, N. Holonyak, Jr., and S. W. Kirchoefer, "Continuous 300°K laser operation of single-quantum-well AlGaAs–GaAs heterostructure diodes grown by metalorganic chemical vapor deposition," *Appl. Phys. Lett.*, vol. 34, p. 265, 1979.

[5] Kasemset, D., C. S. Hong, N. B. Patel, and P. D. Dapkus, "Very narrow graded-barrier single-quantum-well lasers grown by metalorganic chemical vapor deposition," *Appl. Phys. Lett.*, vol. 41, p. 912, 1982.

[6] Hersee, S., M. Baldy, P. Assenat, B. De Cremoux, and J. P. Duchemin, "Low-threshold GRIN-SCH GaAs/GaAlAs laser structure grown by OM VPE," *Electron. Lett.*, vol. 18, p. 618, 1982.

[7] Welch, D. F., C. F. Schaus, and J. R. Shealy, "High external efficiency (36%) 5 μm mesa isolated GaAs quantum well laser by organometallic vapor phase epitaxy," *Appl. Phys. Lett.*, vol. 46, p. 121, 1985.

[8] Lau, K. Y., P. L. Derry, and A. Yariv, "Ultimate limit in low threshold quantum well GaAlAs semiconductor lasers," *Appl. Phys. Lett.*, vol. 52, p. 88, 1988.

[9] Chen, H. Z., A. Ghaffari, H. Morkoc, and A. Yariv, "Very low threshold current densities (under 100 A/cm^2) in AlGaAs/GaAs single-quantum-well GRINSCH lasers grown by molecular beam epitaxy," *Electron. Lett.*, vol. 23, p. 1334, 1987.

Strained-Layer Quantum-Well Lasers

[10] Biefeld, R. M., P. L. Gourley, I. J. Fritz, and G. C. Osbourn, "Independently variable band gaps and lattice constants in GaAsP strained-layer superlattices," *Appl. Phys. Lett.*, vol. 43, p. 759, 1983.

[11] Fekete, D., K. T. Chan, J. M. Ballantyne, and L. F. Eastman, "Graded-index separate-confinement InGaAs/GaAs strained-layer quantum well laser grown by metalorganic chemical vapor deposition," *Appl. Phys. Lett.*, vol. 49, p. 1659, 1986.

Quantum Wire and Dot Structures

[12] Arakawa, Y., K. Vahala, A. Yariv, and K. Lau, "Reduction of the spectral linewidth of semiconductor lasers with quantum wire effects—spectral properties of GaAlAs double heterostructure lasers in high magnetic fields," *Appl. Phys. Lett.*, vol. 48, p. 384, 1986.

[13] Kash, K., A. Scherer, J. M. Worlock, H. G. Craighead, and M. C. Tamargo, "Optical spectroscopy of ultrasmall structures etched from quantum wells," *Appl. Phys. Lett.*, vol. 49, p. 1043, 1986.

Continuous room-temperature multiple-quantum-well $Al_xGa_{1-x}As$-GaAs injection lasers grown by metalorganic chemical vapor deposition

R. D. Dupuis and P. D. Dapkus

Rockwell International, Electronic Devices Division, Electronics Research Center, Anaheim, California 92803

N. Holonyak, Jr. and R. M. Kolbas

Department of Electrical Engineering and Materials Research Laboratory, University of Illinois at Urbana-Champaign, Urbana, Illinois 61801

(Received 1 June 1979; accepted for publication 24 July 1979)

Room-temperature (~26 °C) continuous operation of $Al_xGa_{1-x}As$-GaAs multiple-quantum-well injection lasers has been achieved. These devices are grown by metalorganic chemical vapor deposition and employ active regions consisting of six GaAs quantum wells having a thickness $L_z \sim 120$ Å separated by five $Al_{0.30}Ga_{0.70}As$ barriers also ~120 Å thick. These laser diodes operate on LO-phonon-assisted confined-particle transitions and exhibit low threshold current densities ($J_{th} \sim 1660$ A/cm^2) and high total external differential quantum efficiencies ($\eta_{ext} \sim 85\%$).

PACS numbers: 42.55.Px, 81.15.Gh, 68.55. + b, 78.45. + h

Continuous-wave (cw) room-temperature single-quantum-well $Al_xGa_{1-x}As$-GaAs injection lasers have recently been reported.[1] These devices were grown by metalorganic chemical vapor deposition (MO-CVD),[2-4] and employed a conventional double heterostructure (DH) with an active region thickness L_z of about 200 Å. As a result of this extremely thin active region, quantum-size effects[5] dominate the electroluminescence and lasing spectra of these devices.[1,6,7] *Single-quantum-well* optically pumped and injection lasers have been observed to operate on allowed confined-particle electron-to-heavy-hole (e → hh), and electron-to-light-hole (e → lh) transition.[1,6,8-10] It has been shown, however, that *multiple-quantum-well* optically pumped lasers tend to operate at energies corresponding to one or more LO phonons ($E_{LO} \sim 36$ meV for GaAs)[11] from the allowed quantum-well electron-hole recombination transitions.[12-14] Laser radiation from phonon-assisted confined-particle transitions has been observed from a variety of optically pumped multiple-quantum-well $Al_xGa_{1-x}As$-GaAs heterostructures at 300, 77, and 4.2 °K. These results are expected from calculations of phonon scattering rates in such layered quantum-well structures.[14,15] Similar results have been obtained for Zn-diffused multiple-quantum-well injection lasers operated cw at 4.2 °K and pulsed at 77 °K.[16] This behavior has also been observed for optically pumped multiple-quantum-well InP-$In_{1-x}Ga_xP_{1-z}As_z$ lasers grown by liquid-phase epitaxy.[17,18]

We report here the cw room-temperature (~26 °C ambient) operation of multiple-quantum-well $Al_xGa_{l-x}As$-GaAs injection lasers that operate on phonon-assisted confined-particle transitions. These devices are grown by MO-CVD and exhibit low threshold current densities and high external differential quantum efficiencies.

The epitaxial structure used in the fabrication of these devices consists of fifteen layers grown sequentially on a (100)-oriented GaAs : Si ($n = 2\times10^{18}$ cm^{-3}) substrate. The metalorganic chemical vapor deposition materials technology used to produce these layers has been described previously.[2,3] The first layer grown is an ~0.3-μm GaAs : Se buffer layer. Then an $Al_{0.42}Ga_{0.58}As$: Se ~ 1.0-μm n-type confining layer is grown. The "active region" consists of six undoped GaAs quantum wells with a thickness $L_z \sim 120$ Å. These quantum wells are separated by five undoped $Al_{0.30}Ga_{0.70}As$ barriers that are also ~120 Å thick. The next layer is a p-type ~ 1.3-μm-thick $Al_{0.42}Ga_{0.58}As$: Zn confining layer. A p^+ GaAs : Zn cap layer ~ 1 μm thick completes the structure. The ~120 Å layer thicknesses of the GaAs quantum wells and the $Al_{0.30}Ga_{0.70}As$ barrier lay-

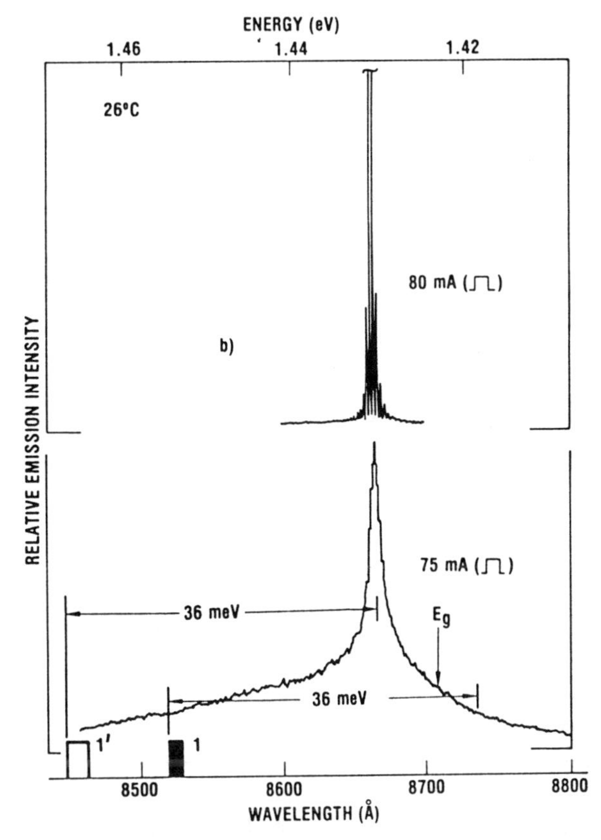

FIG. 1. Pulsed room-temperature (~26 °C ambient) electroluminescence spectra of a multiple-quantum-well $Al_xGa_{1-x}As$-GaAs laser (a) near and (b) above threshold. The laser operates on the first LO-phonon-assisted $n' = 1'$ e → lh transition. The diode length is 375 μm. The pulse width is 200 ns and the repetition rate is *l* kHz.

Reprinted with permission from *Appl. Phys. Lett.*, vol. 35, no. 7, pp. 487–489, Oct. 1, 1979.

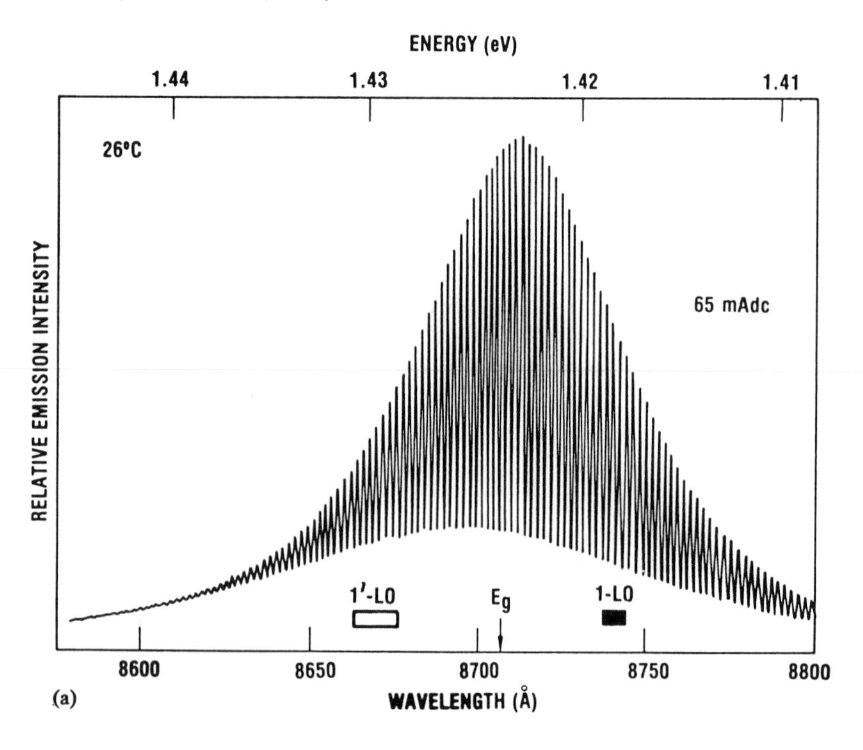

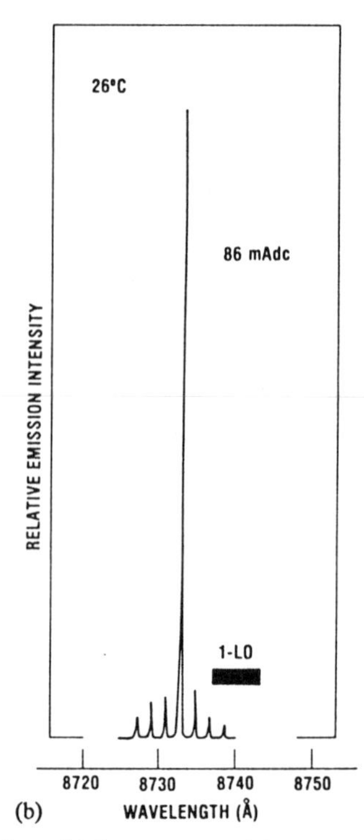

FIG. 2. (a) Room-temperature (26 °C ambient) cw electroluminescence spectrum of an $Al_xGa_{1-x}As$-GaAs multiple-quantum-well laser at threshold. The 65-mA threshold current corresponds to a value of $J_{th} \sim 1660$ A/cm^2 (laser length is $\sim 490\ \mu$m). The laser is operating on the LO-phonon-assisted lowest-energy confined-particle recombination transitions. (b) cw electroluminescence spectrum of the diode of Fig. 2(a) operating above threshold. The laser operates on phonon-assisted quantum-well transitions in a single longitudinal mode over a wide range of dc currents.

ers are estimated from Auger electron spectroscopy/ion sputter etching measurements taken on similar MO-CVD multiple-quantum-well structures.[4] These thicknesses agree well with the values expected from the growth time and with those estimated from $\sim 1°$ bevel cross sections taken on this wafer.[19]

Devices are fabricated by first photolithographically defining 8-μm-wide stripes and etching with 1 : 8 : 40 H_2SO_4 : H_2O_2(30%) : H_2O at 0 °C.[20] The mesas are etched into, but not through, the *p*-type $Al_{0.48}Ga_{0.52}As$ confining layers forming a low-mesa-stripe geometry[21] for current confinement. A 1000-Å SiO_2 layer is then sputtered over the top surface. Contact openings $\sim 4\ \mu$m wide are then opened in the SiO_2 on top of the mesa. Cr-Au is evaporated to form a contact for the *p*-type GaAs : Zn top layer Au-Ge-Ni is used for the *n*-type substrate contact. Bars $\sim$ 300–500 μm long are cleaved from the wafer and individual lasers are separated by sawing. The lasers are then mounted *p*-side down on Au-plated Kovar headers using In preforms. Ultrasonic Au wire bonds are made to the substrate side of the device.

The spectral output of the devices is measured at room temperature under pulsed and cw operating conditions. The cw light-output–vs–current characteristics are measured using a calibrated Si *p-i-n* photodiode detector. Typical pulsed electroluminescence spectra at and above laser threshold are shown in Fig. 1. At a peak current of 75 mA ($J \sim 2500$ A/cm^2) [Fig. 1(a)], the diode begins to lase at $\lambda \sim 8665$ Å, which is the location of the first LO-phonon replica of the $n' = 1'$ electron-to-light-hole (e $\rightarrow$ lh) confined-particle transition. At higher peak currents $\gtrsim 80$ mA [Fig. 1(b)], the longitudinal mode spectra of the laser is centered on this phonon-assisted e $\rightarrow$ lh transition.

Under cw excitation conditions, the laser emission typically shifts to slightly longer wavelength as shown in Fig. 2(a). (The device of Fig. 2 is not the same as that of Fig. 1.) At a dc current of 65 mA ($J \sim$ 1660 A/cm^2), the device is just above threshold. It is difficult to determine the specific phonon-assisted confined-particle transition involved since the spectrum is broadened and the exact junction temperature is unknown. It is also possible that both the LO-phonon-assisted $n' = 1'$ and $n = 1$ transitions are involved. However, the emission shown in Fig. 2(a) is probably not associated with the direct GaAs energy gap (labeled E_g), since cw lasers with a conventional DH structure and an undoped GaAs active region lase at wavelengths greater than 8800 Å.[22] At higher cw currents, these lasers operate in a single longitudinal mode, as shown in Fig. 2(b) for a drive current of 86 mA ($J \sim$ 2200 A/cm^2). As the current is increased further, the amplitude of the dominant mode increases relative to the other Fabry-Perot cavity modes. This behavior is characteristic of these multiple-quantum-well lasers and is also observed under pulsed conditions.

While the temperature dependence of the laser wavelength of these diodes has not been measured, results obtained on optically pumped multiple-quantum-well lasers and on multiple-quantum-well injection lasers operated at low temperatures (4.2 and 77 °K) indicate that the spectra should shift with the GaAs band edge.[10,12,13] The pulsed threshold current density of these multiple-quantum-well diode lasers varies with temperature as $J_{th}(T) \propto \exp(T/T_0)$ [23] with $T_0 \sim$ 220 °C, a value significantly larger than that observed for conventional $Al_xGa_{1-x}As$ DH lasers.[24]

The cw light-output–vs–current ($L - I$) characteristics

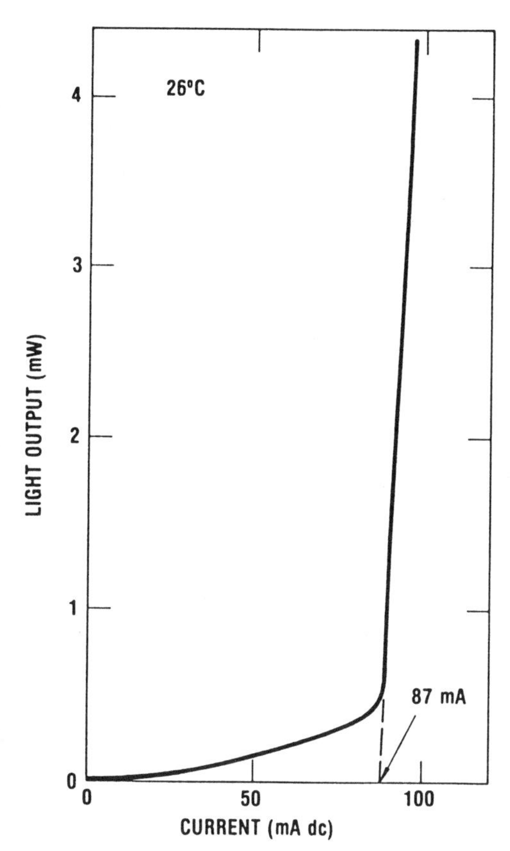

FIG. 3. Dependence of light output upon dc current for one facet of an $Al_xGa_{1-x}As$-GaAs multiple-quantum-well laser diode. The total external differential quantum efficiency is η_{ext} ~85%. The diode length is ~365 μm.

of these devices exhibit good linearity and high external differential quantum efficiencies in the range 60–85%. Shown in Fig. 3 is the cw *L-I* curve (one facet) of one of the multiple-quantum-well lasers. The cw threshold current is ~87 mA (J ~ 2980 A/cm^2) and η_{ext} ~85%. At a current of 95 mA dc, the single-mode amplitude ratio is greater than 180 : 1. Single-mode room-temperature (26 °C) cw operation of these multiple-quantum-well lasers *at constant current* has been demonstrated for operating times greater than 2500 h.[25]

In summary, $Al_xGa_{1-x}As$-GaAs multiple-quantum-well mesa-stripe-geometry injection lasers have been shown to operate cw at room temperature (~26 °C) with threshold current densities as low as J_{th} ~1660 A/cm^2 (diode length ~ 489 μm) and exhibit total external differential quantum efficiencies as high as η_{ext} ~85%. These devices operate on phonon-assisted confined-particle recombination transitions that are characteristic of the quantum-well heterostructures. In addition, they operate in a stable single mode over a wide current range and exhibit linear *L-I* curves. The cw lifetimes of these MO-CVD lasers indicate that there are no major problems related to the multiple $Al_xGa_{1-x}As$-GaAs heterojunction interfaces in the active region of these MO-CVD lasers.

We thank J.E. Cooper, N.L. Lind, L.A. Moudy, T.J. Raab, and J.J.J. Yang (Anaheim), and R. Chin, W.D. Laidig, B.A. Vojak, Yuri S. Moroz, R.T. Gladin, and B.L. Marshall (Urbana) for assistance in portions of this work. The authors are also grateful to M. Altarelli, J. Bardeen, and K. Hess for useful discussions. The work at Rockwell International has been partially supported by the Office of Naval Research under Contract N00014-78-C-0711. The work at the University of Illinois has been supported primarily by National Science Foundation Grant DMR 76-81432 and to a lesser extent by NSF Grant DMR 77-23999.

[1]R.D. Dupuis, P.D. Dapkus, R. Chin, N. Holonyak, Jr., and S.W. Kirchoefer, Appl. Phys. Lett. **34**, 265 (1979).
[2]R.D. Dupuis and P.D. Dapkus, Appl. Phys. Lett. **32**, 406 (1978).
[3]R.D. Dupuis and P.D. Dapkus, IEEE J. Quantum Electron. QE-**15**, 128 (1979).
[4]R.D. Dupuis, P.D. Dapkus, A.M. Garner, C.Y. Su, and W.E. Spicer, Appl. Phys. Lett. **34**, 335 (1979).
[5]For a recent review of quantum-size effects in $Al_xGa_{1-x}As$-GaAs heterostructures, see R. Dingle, in *Festkörperprobleme XV, Advances in Solid State Physics*, edited by H.J. Queisser (Pergamon Vieweg, Braunschweig, 1975), p. 21.
[6]N. Holonyak, Jr., R.M. Kolbas, R.D. Dupuis, and P.D. Dapkus, Appl. Phys. Lett. **33**, 73 (1978).
[7]R.D. Dupuis, P.D. Dapkus, N. Holonyak, Jr., E.A. Rezek, and R. Chin, Appl. Phys. Lett. **32**, 295 (1978).
[8]R.M. Kolbas, N. Holonyak, Jr., R.D. Dupuis, and P.D. Dapkus, Pis'ma Zh. Eksp. Teor. Fiz. **4**, 69 (1978) [Sov. Tech. Phys. Lett. **4**, 28 (1978)].
[9]N. Holonyak, Jr., R.M. Kolbas, E.A. Rezek, R. Chin, R.D. Dupuis, and P.D. Dapkus, J. Appl. Phys. **49**, 5392 (1978).
[10]R.D. Dupuis, P.D. Dapkus, R.M. Kolbas, and N. Holonyak, Jr., IEEE J. Quantum Electron. QE-**15** (to be published).
[11]E.W. Williams, Brit. J. Appl. Phys. **18**, 253 (1967). See also S.J. Fray, R.A. Johnson, J.E. Quarrington, and N. Williams, Proc. Phys. Soc. **77**, 215 (1961).
[12]N. Holonyak, Jr., R.M. Kolbas, W.D. Laidig, M. Altarelli, R.D. Dupuis, and P.D. Dapkus, Appl. Phys. Lett. **34**, 502 (1979).
[13]B.A. Vojak, S.W. Kirchoefer, N. Holonyak, Jr., R. Chin, R.D. Dupuis, and P.D. Dapkus, J. Appl. Phys. **50** (to be published).
[14]R.M. Kolbas, N. Holonyak, Jr., B.A. Vojak, K. Hess, M. Altarelli, R.D. Dupuis, and P.D. Dapkus, Solid State Commun. (to be published).
[15]K. Hess, Appl. Phys. Lett. **35** (to be published).
[16]B.A. Vojak, N. Holonyak, Jr., R. Chin, E.A. Rezek, R.D. Dupuis, and P.D. Dapkus, J. Appl. Phys. **50** (to be published).
[17]E.A. Rezek, R. Chin, N. Holonyak, Jr., S.W. Kirchoefer, and R.M. Kolbas, Appl. Phys. Lett. **35**, 45 (1979).
[18]E.A. Rezek, R. Chin, N. Holonyak, Jr., S.W. Kirchoefer, and R.M. Kolbas (unpublished).
[19]N. Holonyak, Jr., B.A. Vojak, R.M. Kolbas, R.D. Dupuis, and P.D. Dapkus, Solid State Electron. **22**, 431 (1979).
[20]W.T. Tsang and S. Wang, Appl. Phys. Letter **28**, 44 (1975).
[21]T. Tsukada, R. Ito, H. Nakashima, and O. Nakada, IEEE J. Quantum Electron. QE-**9**, 356 (1973).
[22]H. Kressel and H.F. Lockwood, Appl. Phys. Lett. **20**, 175 (1972).
[23]The threshold current density was measured over the temperature range − 30–30 °C using 400-ns-wide pulses at a repetition rate of 10 kHz.
[24]M. Ettenberg, C.J. Nuese, and H. Kressel, J. Appl. Phys. **50**, 2949 (1979).
[25]R.D. Dupuis, Appl. Phys. Lett. **35** (to be published).

A graded-index waveguide separate-confinement laser with very low threshold and a narrow Gaussian beam

W. T. Tsang
Bell Laboratories, Murray Hill, New Jersey 07974

(Received 2 February 1981; accepted for publication 28 April 1981)

A heterostructure semiconductor laser with graded-index waveguide and separate carrier and optical confinements prepared by molecular beam epitaxy is discussed. These lasers have very low broad-area threshold current densities J_{th} 500 A/cm^2 and support narrow beams of Gaussian distribution with far-field half-power full-width in the direction perpendicular to the junction plane $\theta_\perp \sim 20°–30°$. It is also shown that only when the active layer thickness is $\lesssim 700$ Å a significantly lower J_{th} is obtained by employing the symmetric laser structure instead of the regular double heterostructure.

PACS numbers: 42.55.Px, 42.80.Sa, 68.55. + b, 81.15.Ef

In semiconductor heterostructure lasers, thus far, the built-in waveguides in the direction perpendicular to the junction plane are limited to step profiles. In the present paper, we report a heterostructure semiconductor laser with parabolically graded-index waveguide and separate carrier and optical confinements (GRIN-SCH). Schematically the layer structure of such a GRIN-SCH laser is shown in Fig. 1(a) with the refractive index profiles of the optical cavity w given by Fig. 1(b), and one of the corresponding energy band diagram given in Fig. 1(c). The various index profiles given in Fig. 1(b) are the power law index profiles described by[1]

$$n(r) = n_y[1 - 2(2r/w)^g \Delta]^{1/2}, \quad |r| \leqslant w/2$$
$$= n_z, \quad |r| > w/2,$$

where r is the distance from the center of the waveguide, g is the exponent of the power law, $\Delta \approx (n_y - n_z)/n_y$, and n_y and n_z are the limits of the refractive indexes of the graded layer. In the limit of very large g, the refractive-index profile of the above laser structure approaches that of the regular symmetric SCH laser studied previously.[2–4] In contrast to the previously reported SCH or double-heterostructure (DH) lasers, the present lasers with parabolically graded-index waveguides support Hermite-Gaussians in the direction perpendicular to the junction plane and match those in the SELFOC optical fibers.[5]

As discussed previously in the case of regular SCH lasers,[4] by proper tailoring of the layer thicknesses and index profiles threshold currents lower than those obtained with equivalent regular DH lasers can also be obtained with the present GRIN-SCH laser. Compared with the regular symmetric SCH laser,[4] the present GRIN-SCH laser offers three main additional features: (i) Since the near field pattern has a significant effect on the shape and divergence of the far-field pattern,[7] the present graded-index waveguide laser offers the possibility of not only varying the wave propagation characteristics in the laser, but also the ability to control the far-field beam distributions to match the particular type of optical fiber in use or to suit the imaging optics in various optical systems. (ii) When the GRIN-SCH laser has a parabolically graded-index profile, the optical modes supported in the direction perpendicular to the junction plane are Hermite-Gaussians. By making the gain region (the active layer) very thin and locating it at the center of the waveguide, the mode gains (the optical overlap of the mode with the gain region) for the higher-order transverse modes are significantly smaller in these lasers than in regular SCH (or DH) lasers. This provides additional strong mode discrimination against higher-order transverse modes in these GRIN-SCH lasers. (It should be pointed out that for symmetric GRIN-SCH or regular SCH lasers, the very thin gain region is located exactly at the minima of the optical intensity distributions of all the odd-order transverse modes. As a result, all the odd-order transverse modes are completely suppressed irrespective of the width of the waveguide.) (iii) In the case of general GRIN-SCH lasers that have the active layer located asymetrically in the waveguide, Fig. 2 shows as a result of having smaller g, the cutoff thickness for the first-order

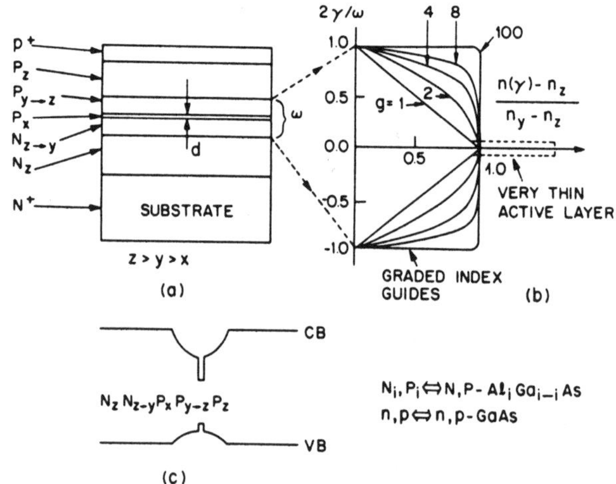

FIG. 1. (a) Shows schematically the layer structure of a graded-index waveguide SCH laser with (b) power law refractive index profiles and (c) one of the corresponding energy band diagram.

Reprinted with permission from *Electron. Lett.*, vol. 18, no. 25, pp. 1095–1097, Dec. 9, 1982.

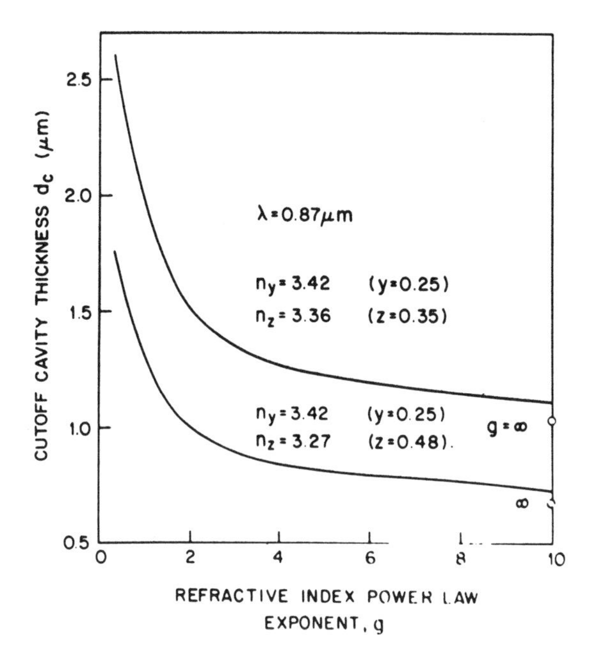

FIG. 2. The cutoff thickness for the first-order transverse mode in the direction perpendicular to the junction plane w_c plotted as a function of the refractive index power law exponent g for two different $\Delta n = n_y - n_z$.

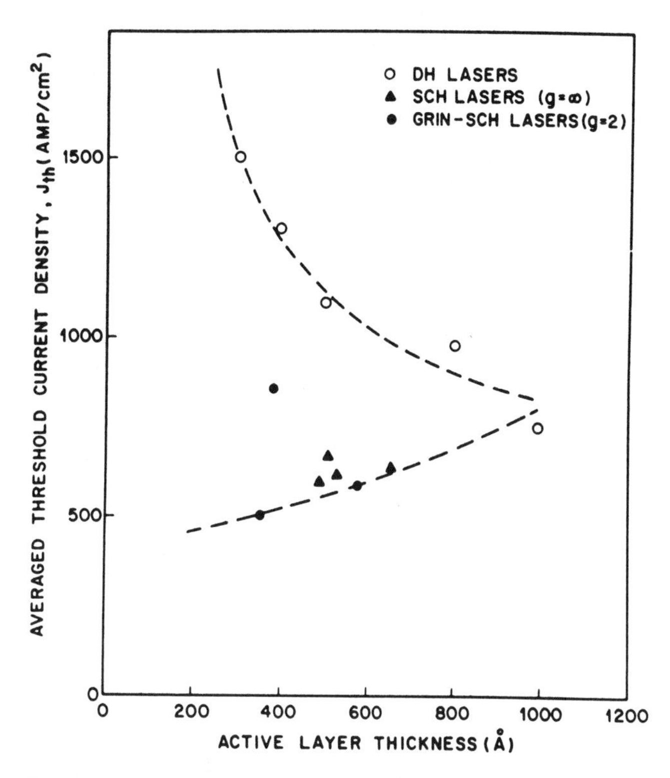

FIG. 3. A comparison of the averaged J_{th} of the GRIN-SCH lasers and the symmetric SCH lasers (Ref. 4) with the regular DH lasers in the very thin active-layer range.

transverse mode w_c (in the perpendicular direction) can still be increased quite significantly over that of the regular SCH ($g = \infty$). Features (ii) and (iii) are particularly important when lasers with high power output and very narrow beam divergence that operate in the fundamental mode are desired. The two curves shown in Fig. 2 are for two different refractive index differences ($\Delta n = n_y - n_z$) for the graded-index waveguides and are derived from the calculation given by Marcuse.[1]

For growing the graded-index waveguide SCH lasers, molecular beam epitaxy (MBE) proves to be particularly suitable because (i) grading of the index profile can be conveniently achieved by varying the Ga effusion cell temperature, so that the AlAs composition in the waveguide is varied accordingly and (ii) very thin and uniform layers having accurately controlled thicknesses as required in optimizing the symmetric SCH lasers can be grown reproducibly. In Table I, we summarize the various parameters of the layers and the results obtained with several symmetric parabolically GRIN-SCH laser wafers. For comparison, a regular DH laser wafer grown during the same period is also included. Averaged J_{th} as low as 500 A/cm^2 for broad-area Fabry–Perot lasers of 200×380 μm and with no reflective mirror coatings was obtained. In Fig. 3, a comparison of the averaged J_{th} of these symmetric GRIN-SCH lasers and the regular symmetric SCH lasers obtained previously[4] with the regular DH lasers[8] in this very thin active-layer range is shown. For an active-layer thickness $\lesssim 700$ Å, the J_{th} of the laser can be significantly lowered by employing the symmetric GRIN-SCH or the regular SCH laser structures. However, when the active layer thickness is $\gtrsim 800$ Å, the J_{th} approaches those of regular DH lasers. This is consistent with the fact that a significant increase in Γ is obtained in symmetric SCH lasers only when the active layer is thinner than typically $\lesssim 700$ Å. Detailed calculations and results have been given by Thompson *et al.*[9] and Casey, Jr., and Panish.[6] However, from the measured far-field half-power full-width in the direction perpendicular to the junction plane $\theta_\perp$, we estimated the beam width w_0 for the present GRIN-SCH lasers (see Table I). It is seen that lasers 2 SF and 3 SF which have narrower w_0 (larger optical confinement factor Γ) than laser 4 SF do indeed have lower threshold current densities.

For the present GRIN-SCH lasers, the half-power full-width in the direction perpendicular to the junction plane $\theta_\perp$ are 20°–30°. Figure 4(a) shows an example of the far-field distributions of a GRIN-SCH laser at various current levels up to $4 \times I_{th}$. The excellent agreement between the calculated Gaussian beam distribution and the measured far-field distribution shown in Fig. 4(b) indicates that the graded-index waveguide in the present laser is very close to being parabolic. However, if very precise determination of the index profile is desired, more complicated numerical fitting over approximately two decades of intensity is needed.[10] Also shown in Fig. 4(b) is the experimentally measured far-field distribution for a regular DH laser with $\theta_\perp$ normalized to the same value as the parabolically GRIN-SCH laser. It is seen that the DH laser has a wider "skirt." This is in agreement with the calculations of Kirkby and Thompson,[7] and Botez.[11]

For the regular MBE-grown DH lasers with GaAs active layers measured thus far, the coefficient T_0 in the temperature dependence of the threshold current is always $\lesssim 150$ °C in the temperature range of 25–120 °C. However, in the present GRIN-SCH and those regular symmetric SCH lasers reported previously,[4] *quite often but not always*

TABLE I. Layer structures and results.

Wafer No.	d (Å)	W (μm)	X	Y	Z	Ave. J_{th} (A/cm^2)	w_0 (μm)	$\theta_\perp$ (deg.)	T_0 (°C)
1 DH	1000	...	0.0	...	0.44	750	...	42	126
2 SF	580	0.25	0.0	0.22	0.44	597	0.61	30	188
3 SF	350	0.28	0.0	0.15	0.30	500	0.58	31	184
4 SF	385	0.19	0.1	0.26	0.36	872	0.88	21	153

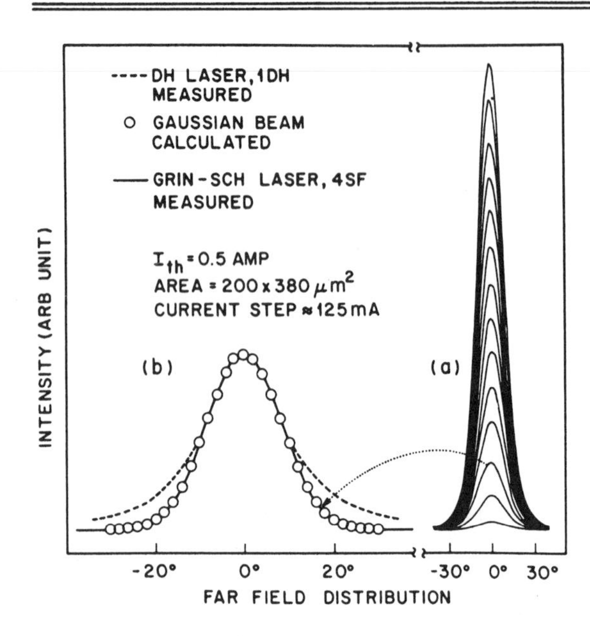

FIG. 4. (a) An example of the far-field distributions in the perpendicular direction to the junction plane of a SELFOC-SCH laser at various current levels up to $4\times I_{th}$. (b) Comparison of calculated Gaussian beam distribution and measured far-field distributions of a parabolically GRIN-SCH laser and a regular DH laser (with $\theta_\perp$ normalized to the same value as the GRIN-SCH laser).

(see for example, laser 4 SF which has 385 Å and yet $T_0 = 153$ °C) T_0 as high as 190 °C were obtained even though they also have GaAs active layers. The observation thus far is that generally (not without exception) the higher T_0 *appears* to be associated with the use of very thin gain region in the SCH lasers. This correlation seems to gain some support in that similarly high T_0's were also obtained with some MBE GaAs/$Al_xGa_{1-x}As$ multiquantum-well laser wafers,[12,13] where again the gain regions are also very thin (<200 Å). However, this does not seem to be a result of quantum-size effect because in some SCH lasers an active layer[4] as thick as 660 Å has been used. A better understanding of the gain saturation behavior and the effect of interfaces in these thin active-layered lasers is necessary and may prove to be important.

In summary, a symmetric separate-confinement heterostructure laser with a parabolically graded-index waveguide and an active layer $\lesssim 600$ Å has been prepared for the first time. Unlike the regular DH lasers, these GRIN-SCH lasers support Gaussian beams and have narrow beam divergence $\theta_\perp$ of 20°–30°. By making the active layer thinner than 600 Å the optical distribution can be independently designed for narrow beam and/or low threshold. With the graded-index waveguide SCH laser, it also offers the possibility to shape the far-field beam distribution to match the particular type of optical fiber in use or to suit the imaging optics in various optical systems. By having symmetric parabolically GRIN-SCH and very thin active layer, all the odd-order transverse mode (in the direction perpendicular to the junction plane) can be completely suppressed irrespective of the width of the waveguide, while all the even modes are strongly discriminated because of the very much reduced mode gain. We also show that only when the active-layer thickness is $\lesssim 700$ Å that a significantly lower J_{th} is obtained by employing the symmetric SCH laser structure instead of the regular double heterostructure. The present GRIN-SCH scheme can also be very useful in edge-emitting light emitting diodes (LED's)[14] when properly implemented.

I benefited significantly from discussions with F. K. Reinhart and is indebted to J. A. Ditzenberger for processing the laser diodes.

[1]D. Marcuse, J. Opt. Soc. Am. **68**, 103 (1978).
[2]G. H. B. Thompson and P. A. Kirkby, IEEE J. Quantum Electron. **QE-9**, 311 (1973).
[3]M. B. Panish, H. C. Casey, Jr., S. Sumski, and P. W. Foy, Appl. Phys. Lett. **22**, 590 (1973).
[4]W. T. Tsang, Electron. Lett. **16**, 939 (1980).
[5]T. Uehida, M. Furukawa, I. Kitano, K. Koizumi, and H. Matsumura, IEEE J. Quantum Electron. **QE-6**, 606 (1970).
[6]H. C. Casey, Jr., and M. B. Panish, *Heterostructure Lasers* (Academic, New York, 1978).
[7]P. A. Kirkby and G. H. B. Thompson, Opto-Electronics **4**, 323 (1972).
[8]W. T. Tsang, Appl. Phys. Lett. **36**, 11 (1980).
[9]G. H. B. Thompson, G. D. Henshall, J. E. A. Whiteaway, and P. A. Kirkby, J. Appl. Phys. (to be published).
[10]J. C. Shelton, F. K. Reinhart, and R. A. Logan, J. Appl. Phys. **50**, 6675 (1979).
[11]D. Botez, RCA Rev. **39**, 577 (1978).
[12]W. T. Tsang, C. Weisbuch, R. C. Miller, and R. Dingle, Appl. Phys. Lett. **35**, 673 (1979).
[13]W. T. Tsang and R. L. Hartman, Appl. Phys. Lett. **38**, 502 (1981).
[14]M. Ettenberg, H. Kressel, and J. P. Wittke, IEEE J. Quantum Electron. **QE-12**, 360 (1976).

Extremely low threshold (AlGa) As modified multiquantum well heterostructure lasers grown by molecular-beam epitaxy

W. T. Tsang
Bell Laboratories, Murray Hill, New Jersey 07974

(Received 2 July 1981; accepted for publication 19 August 1981)

It is shown that by modifying the layer structures of the conventional multiquantum well (MQW) lasers, extremely low J_{th} of 250 A/cm^2 (averaged value) for broad-area Fabry–Perot diodes of $200 \times 380\ \mu m$ was obtained. This was achieved as a result of utilizing the beneficial effects of the two-dimensional nature of the confined carriers, the improved injection efficiency of the carriers into the GaAs wells, and an increased optical confinement factor in these modified MQW lasers. It was also determined that for low threshold operation the optimal AlAs composition x in the $Al_xGA_{1-x}As$ barrier layers is about 0.19 when GaAs wells are used and for barrier and well thicknesses > 30 and 100 Å, respectively.

PACS numbers: 42.55.Px, 42.80.Sa, 68.55. + b, 81.15.Ef

Recently, a study has been made on the device characteristics of multiquantum well (MQW) lasers grown by molecular-beam epitaxy (MBE).[1,2] The results show that the device characteristics of the MQW lasers depend quite significantly on the detailed designs of the multilayer structure that composes the active region. In that study, an averaged threshold current density J_{th} as low as the lowest J_{th} (800 A/cm) obtained for standard double-heterostructure (DH) lasers with approximately the same AlAs composition in the cladding layers was obtained. This is obtained in spite of the reduced optical confinement factor Γ and a reduced injection efficiency of carriers into the various wells due to the presence of the interleaving $Al_xGa_{1-x}As$ ($x \geqslant 0.3$) barrier layers. Such low J_{th} suggests that the gain-current relation in the MQW lasers may indeed be favorably modified as a result of the modification of the density of states.[3] In this paper, we show that by modifying the structure of the conventional MQW lasers, extremely low threshold current density (250 A/cm^2) can be obtained.

Of the MQW lasers studied thus far, all have the AlAs composition in the $Al_xGa_{1-x}As$ barrier layers the $\gtrsim 0.3$ (Refs. 1, 2, 4–6). With regard to reducing the J_{th} of the MQW lasers, this is believed to pose two possible problems. (1) Though the detailed mechanism(s) by which the carriers are injected into the various GaAs wells that are separated by $Al_xGa_{1-x}As$ barrier layers of energy barriers $\Delta E > 380$ meV and thickness typically between 100 and 200 Å (Ref. 1) has not been well understood at present, it is believed that the presence of these barriers will hinder the effectiveness of the carrier injection irrespective of what process is involved. This belief appears to gain some support with the recent observation[7] of anomalous characteristics of the first and second derivatives (dV/dI and d^2V/dI^2) of the current-voltage (I-V) characteristics of these MQW stripe-geometry lasers when compared with those of regular DH stripe-geometry lasers also grown by MBE. A detailed description of these results will be reported separately.[7] (2) Since the effective refractive index of the alternating GaAs and $Al_xGa_{1-x}As$ layers can be approximated by a spatial average of the GaAs/$Al_xGa_{1-x}As$ layers,[8] the refractive index step at the MQW-cladding layer interface is reduced if the cladding layers have the same AlAs composition. Though this reduces the beam divergence, it at the same time reduces the Γ and hence leads to increased J_{th}.[1]

Very recently, it has been shown that the hetero-interface smoothness in the optimally grown MBE QW structures is within one atomic layer as determined by the excitation spectrum linewidth.[9–11] Also, as confirmed by photoluminescence and excitation spectra no alloy clusters were observed in these MQW structures even for $Al_xGa_{1-x}As$ barrier layers as thin as 16 Å.[11] This is evidenced and acertained by the fact that the various experimentally observed confined-particle transitions agree closely with those values calculated basing on the assumption that the potential barriers produced by the $Al_xGa_{1-x}As$ barrier layers are indeed ideal even for barriers as thin as 16 Å. Such hetero-interface perfection results in DH lasers having averaged J_{th} as low as 810 A/cm^2 even when the active layer is only 200 Å and the AlAs composition step Δx is 0.3 (Ref. 12). The above results together with the fact that this J_{th} agrees closely with the value calculated from first principles without adjustable parameters in the thin active layer regime[13] show that the hetero-interfaces grown by MBE under optimal conditions are of extremely high quality and should not cause any increase in J_{th} even though the MQW lasers contain more interfaces. Thus, the J_{th} of the MQW lasers should be able to be further reduced at least by simply increasing the carrier injection efficiency and the Γ if indeed they have been posing problems in the MQW lasers studied thus far.[1,2,4]

As shown in Fig. 1, these can be achieved as follows: (1) By reducing the $Al_xGa_{1-x}As$ barrier height so that it will not hinder the effectiveness of carrier injection in the various

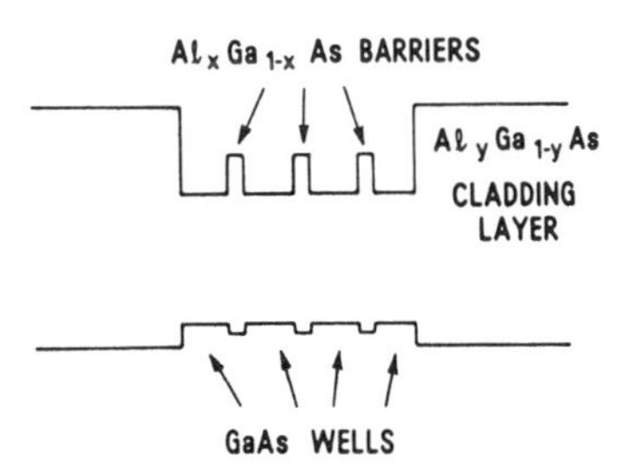

FIG. 1. Schematic energy band diagram from the modified multiquantum well laser.

Reprinted with permission from *Appl. Phys. Lett.*, vol. 39, no. 10, pp. 786–788, Nov. 15, 1981.

TABLE I. Layer structures and results for 8-well modified MQW lasers.

Wafer No.	Total MQW thickness (Å)	GaAs well thickness (Å)	Barrier thickness (Å)	Cladding layer y	Barrier layer x	Ave. J_{th} (A/cm^2)	$\theta_\perp$ (deg.)	T_0 (°C)
H1	1700	160	60	0.35	0.35	1200	43	143
H2	1500	142	52	0.36	0.26	680	44	188
H3	1600	156	50	0.36	0.15	627	44	178
H4	1700	167	52	0.32	0.12	797	45	170
H5	1600	159	47	0.30	0.08	1130	45	195

GaAs wells. This, at the same time, reduces the averaged refractive index of the multi-layer structure that composes the active region and hence results in larger Γ. (2) By using higher AlAs composition y in the $Al_yGa_{1-y}As$ cladding layers and larger well-to-barrier thickness ratio,[1] the optical confinement factor is increased. This, however, has the tradeoff of resulting in wider beam divergence.

In order to determine the optimal barrier height of the $Al_xGa_{1-x}As$ barrier layers for obtaining low J_{th}, a series of 8-well MQW laser wafers shown in Table I were grown. In this series, all the layer structures were maintained approximately the same while only the AlAs composition x in the $Al_xGa_{1-x}As$ barrier layers was varied. Broad-area Fabry–Perot laser diodes of $200\times380\ \mu m$ were fabricated from each wafer and the averaged J_{th} measured under pulsed operation. The layer structures and various results including the far-field beam divergence $\theta_\perp$ (half-power full-width) in the direction perpendicular to the junction plane and the temperature coefficient T_0 in the threshold-temperature dependence [$I_{th} \propto \exp(T/T_0)$] are summaries in Table I. The well and barrier thicknesses are estimated from growth rates. It is seen that indeed the averaged J_{th} does vary with the barrier height of the $Al_xGa_{1-x}As$ barrier layers as also shown in Fig. 2, in which the averaged J_{th} of each wafer is plotted against the AlAs composition x (and the barrier height) of the $Al_xGa_{1-x}As$ barrier layers of that wafer. As the AlAs composition x increases from 0.08, the J_{th} decreases first significantly to a minimum at about $x = 0.19$ (the cross point of the two dashed lines), and then increases with increasing x for x greater than ~ 0.19. Such behavior can be understood in the following manner. The J_{th} decreases with increasing x first because of two possible reasons. (1) As the barrier height of the $Al_xGa_{1-x}As$ barrier layers increases, the modification of the density of state becomes increasingly significant.[14] Specifically, the density of states increases with increasing depth of the wells. This increased density of states leads to a corresponding lowering of the threshold needed for achieving population inversion.[3] This effect is expected to continue for all x but gradually saturates for large x. (2) As oberved recently by Petroff,[15] in contrast to a regular double-heterostructure, the MQW structure shows that the dislocations are not behaving as nonradiative centers. This effect is believed to be related to the two dimensional nature of the confined carriers.[15] If indeed this is so, our present data can also be interpreted as a first experimental support to this belief. As the well depth is increased by increasing x, the increased two dimensionality due to carrier confinement decreases the effectiveness of any dislocations present as nonradiative centers. This in turn lowers the J_{th} of the MQW lasers. This effect is expected to saturate when the well is beyond certain depth. Both above models predict that the decrease of J_{th} with increasing x should initially be fast and gradually slow down after a certain x but continue to decrease. However, the present results show a turn over at a x of about 0.19. The increase of J_{th} with increasing x beyond 0.19 can be understood as follows. (1) As the barrier height becomes too high, the carriers become increasingly difficult to pass over the barriers and be injected into the next well. This decreasing carrier injection efficiency with increasing x results in increasing J_{th}. It is interesting and important to note that the turn-over point occurs at $x \sim 0.19$, a lower limit of AlAs composition in the cladding layers above which serious carrier leakage over the barrier into the cladding layer also can be avoided in regular DH lasers when operating near room temperature.[16] This observation provides strong support to the above described model. (2) Even though an increased x in the $Al_xGa_{1-x}As$ barrier layers increases the averaged refractive index of the multilayers and hence reduces Γ, thus, causing an increase in J_{th}, its effect is not significant in these wafers because the well-to-barrier thickness ratios are made large ~ 3. This is evidenced by the fact that the measured $\theta_\perp$ for all the wafers are very close to each other implying that the Γ's are also

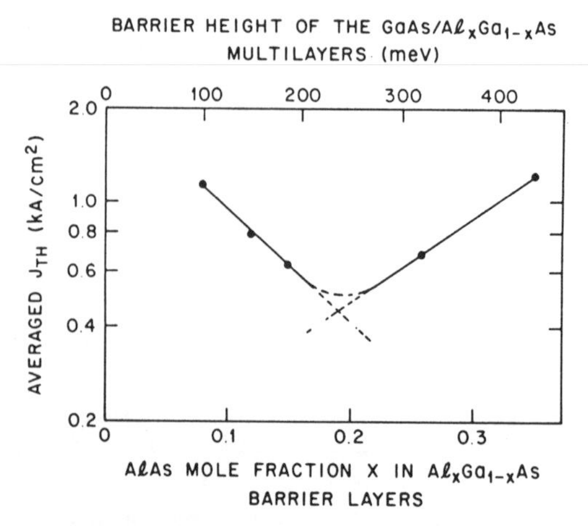

FIG. 2. Shows the variation of the averaged J_{th} of the various wafers given in Table I as a function of their respective AlAs composition x (and barrier height) in the $Al_xGa_{1-x}As$ barrier layers.

TABLE II. Layer structures and results of 5-well modified MQW lasers.

Sample No.	Total multilayer (Å)	Well thickness (Å)	Barrier thickness (Å)	Well barrier γ	Cladding layer y	Barrier layer x	Ave. J_{th} (A/cm²)	$\theta_\perp$ (deg.)
T1	1200	150	112	1.33	0.4	0.2	753	55
T2	1000	140	75	1.87	0.44	0.2	474	49
T3	740	120	35	3.43	0.44	0.2	253	42
T4	560	100	15	6.67	0.46	0.2	380	46
T5	1060	208	76	2.74	0.42	0.2	450	51

about the same. Therefore, we can conclude that the increase in J_{th} with increasing x beyond 0.19 is due mostly to decreasing carrier injection efficiency with increasing barrier height.

Next, a second series of 5-well MQW laser wafers with the optimal value of $x \sim 0.2$ in the $Al_xGa_{1-x}As$ barrier layers, and $y \sim 0.44$ in the $Al_yGa_{1-y}As$ cladding layers, and having different barrier thicknesses and well-to-barrier thickness ratio γ were grown. The layer structures and results are summarized in Table II. Figures 3(a) show the averaged J_{th} as a function of the barrier thickness (solid curve) and total multilayer thickness (dashed curve), while Fig. 3(b) plots the J_{th} as a function of γ. It is seen that extremely low averaged J_{th} of 250 A/cm² was obtained when the 5-well MQW laser has a barrier thickness of ~ 35 Å and a total multilayer thickness of ~ 740 Å. Note that wafer T4 should have lower J_{th}, instead of larger, than wafer T3 because T4 has a larger γ.[1] One possible reason is that when the barrier thickness is as thin as 15 Å, the strong coupling of the wells reduces the two-dimensional nature of the confined carriers.

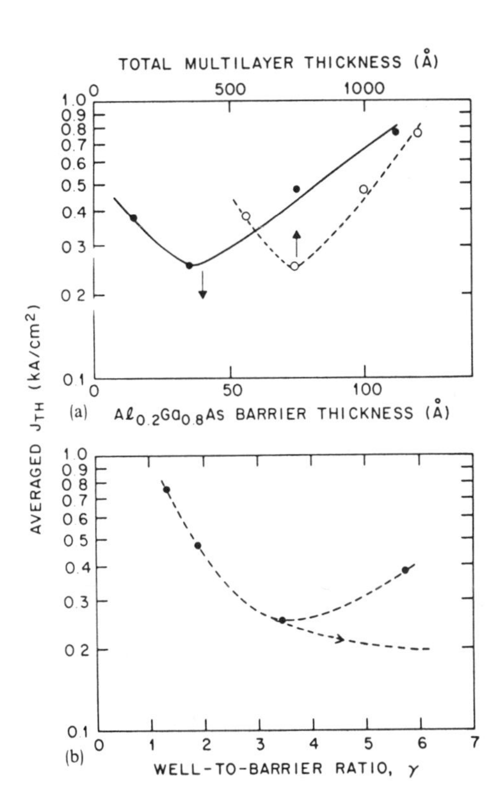

FIG. 3. (a) Shows the averaged J_{th} as a function of the barrier thickness (solid curve) and the total multilayer thickness (dashed curve). (b) Plots the J_{th} as a function of the well-to-barrier thickness ratio γ.

The resulting effect is equivalent to having very low barriers discussed above. As discussed above and in Ref. 11, alloy clustering cannot be the cause for this increase in J_{th} for it is independently checked that no alloy clusters were present even when the $Al_xGa_{1-x}As$ barriers were as than as 16 Å. To decrease this strong coupling when very thin barriers are used, one can use larger x[5] provided that it does not reduce the carrier injection efficiency discussed above. Thus, the value of $x \sim 0.19$ is optimal for low threshold operation MQW structures with barrier and well thicknesses $\gtrsim 30$ and 100 Å, respectively. The use of larger AlAs composition y in the cladding layers also results in better optical confinement in the present MQW lasers as evidenced by the larger $\theta_\perp$.

Included in Table II is also a 4-well MQW laser (T5) having about the same total multilayer thickness or total well thickness as wafer T1 but different γ. The lower J_{th} for T5 further supports that the use of larger γ results in lower J_{th}. Finally, comparing wafer T5 with those 4-well conventional MQW lasers studied previously,[1] it is evident that the use of the optimized barrier height ($x \sim 0.2$) results in significantly lower J_{th} (450 A/cm² versus $\sim$1,200 A/cm²).

The author would like to thank F. K. Rienhart, C. Wiesbuch, R. C. Miller, and P. M. Petroff for many valuable and helpful discussions, and J. A. Ditzenberger for processing these laser diodes.

[1] W. T. Tsang, Appl. Phys. Lett. **38**, 204 (1981).
[2] W. T. Tsang and R. L. Hartman, Appl. Phys. Lett. **38**, 502 (1981).
[3] R. Dingle and C. H. Henry, U. S. Patent No. 3982207, 21, September, 1976.
[4] W. T. Tsang, C. Weisbuch, R. C. Miller, and R. Dingle, Appl. Phys. Lett. **35**, 673 (1979).
[5] J. J. Coleman, P. D. Dapkus, W. D. Laidig, B. A. Vojak, and N. Holonyak, Jr., Appl. Phys. Lett **38**, 63 (1981).
[6] N. Holonyak, Jr., R. M. Kolbas, R. D. Dupuis, and P. D. Dapkus, IEEE J. Quantum Electron **QE-16**, 170 (1980).
[7] P. J. Anthony, J. R. Pawlik, R. L. Hartman, and W. T. Tsang (unpublished).
[8] N. Streifer, D. R. Scifres, and R. D. Burnham, Appl. Opt. **18**, 3547 (1979).
[9] R. C. Miller, D. A. Kleinman, W. T. Tsang, and A. C. Gossard, Phys. Rev. B **24**, xxx (1981).
[10] C. Weisbuch, R. C. Miller, R. Dingle, and A. C. Gossard, Solid State Commun. **37**, 219 (1981).
[11] R. C. Miller and W. T. Tsang Appl. Phys. Lett. **39**, 334 (1981).
[12] W. T. Tsang and J. A. Ditzenberger, Appl. Phys. Lett. **39**, 193 (1981).
[13] H. C. Casey, Jr., J. Appl. Phys. **49**, 3684 (1978).
[14] R. Dingle, Festkoper probleme XV, Advances in Solid-State Physics (1975), p. 21–47.
[15] P. M. Petroff, *Defects in Semiconductors*, edited by J. Narayan and T. Tan (North-Holland, Amsterdam, 1981), p. 457.
[16] D. L. Rode, J. Appl. Phys. **45**, 3887 (1974).

The dynamics of electron-hole collection in quantum well heterostructures

J. Y. Tang and K. Hess
Department of Electrical Engineering and Coordinated Science Laboratory, University of Illinois, Urbana, Illinois 61801

N. Holonyak, Jr. and J. J. Coleman
Electrical Engineering Research Laboratory and Materials Research Laboratory, University of Illinois, Urbana, Illinois 61801

P. D. Dapkus
Microelectronics Research and Development Center, Rockwell International, Thousand Oaks, California 91360

(Received 26 March 1982; accepted for publication 13 May 1982)

The dynamics of carrier collection in quantum-well heterostructures are studied by photoemission experiments and Monte Carlo simulations. It is shown that carrier scattering decreases rapidly for well sizes $L_z \lesssim 100$ Å. The collection mechanism depends sensitively on details of the band structure. The energy distribution function of the carriers after collection exhibits significant structure with respect to multiples of the phonon energy. This feature is also reflected by the experimental results.

PACS numbers: 42.55.Px, 71.38. + i, 78.55.Ds, 63.20.Kr

I. INTRODUCTION

If excess carriers are photogenerated or injected in the confining layers of a single quantum-well heterostructure within a diffusion length of the narrower gap active region, the carriers will diffuse to the quantum well, be collected and recombine in the well (GaAs) if it is large enough.[1] The process of excess carrier collection by single and multiple quantum-well heterostructures (QWH) has been studied experimentally and theoretically[2] by means of Fermi's age theory. The main goal of this theory has been to explain the experimentally observed cutoff of confined-particle recombination for single-well sizes $L_z \lesssim 80$ Å.

It is the purpose of this paper to present a more refined theory of the dynamics of carrier collection in quantum wells, which includes details of the band structure and the electron-phonon interaction, and to compare this theory with experimental results. We use a Monte Carlo simulation of the electrons percolating down in energy in a QWH by phonon emission. This simulation gives a detailed account of the history of the electrons in the Γ, X, and L valleys and shows that the cutoff features for confined-particle recombination depend sensitively on the valley type in which the electron resides when approaching and traversing the quantum well. The transient energy distribution reflects also characteristic structure with respect to the phonon energy which can be related to similar structure in the QWH laser spectrum. The theory is not complete, however, since effects of size quantization are not included in the simulation. The effects of a subband structure become increasingly important at low energy, i.e., when the electron has cascaded down a substantial fraction of the QW. At higher energies, however, size quantization plays a minor role, because of the small deBroglie wavelength, and we have to account only for the quantum mechanical transmission probability from the wider-gap confining layers to the GaAs well. Therefore, our numerical model is three dimensional with respect to the scattering and transport of electrons in the GaAs. We assume that the electrons transmitted into the GaAs stay in the valley type in which they started and simply gain kinetic energy in the amount of the band edge discontinuity ΔE_c. This assumption is supported by investigations of the quantum mechanical transmission coefficient by Osbourn and Smith.[3]

II. NUMERICAL RESULTS

The Monte Carlo program used for the computations is a revised version of that described in previous papers.[4] Without going into details of the Monte Carlo model, we would like to emphasize the importance of the inclusion of the realistic band structure in this problem because the electrons are injected into the GaAs with a significant amount of kinetic energy (ΔE_c). They are scattered initially high up in the GaAs conduction band where a simple effective mass approximation no longer holds. Therefore, the inclusion of the band structure is absolutely necessary. We use ~ 7000 mesh points and interpolations between these points. The $E(\mathbf{k})$ relation is calculated by the empirical pseudopotential method. The band structure is not simulated too well by this model at very low energies (few points only), and the results at low energies are therefore estimated to be in error by $\pm 20\%$. Within the model assumptions, our formalism (which is equivalent to the semiclassical Boltzmann formalism) is valid in the considered range of energies and scattering rates even if very strict criteria are applied.

The percentage of electrons scattered according to this model at a certain distance in the GaAs is shown in Fig. 1. This percentage does not directly reflect the percentage of electrons captured in the quantum well because of possible multiple electron reflection at the well boundaries and the possibility of phonon absorption and electron re-emission. Phonon absorption contributes only a few percent to the results at room temperature and is entirely negligible at low temperatures.

The influence of multiple reflection is displayed by the

Reprinted with permission from *J. Appl. Phys.*, vol. 53, no. 9, pp. 6043–6046, Sept. 1982.

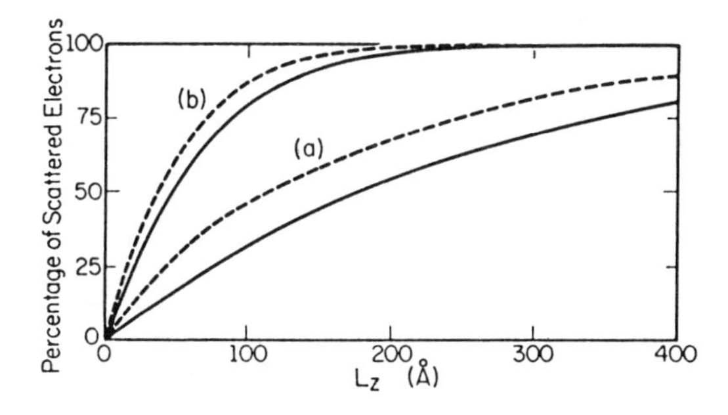

FIG. 1. Percentage of electrons scattered into a single GaAs quantum well from two $Al_xGa_{1-x}As$ confining layers by phonon emission. The solid lines are calculated for one transit and the dashed lines include multiple reflections by the well boundaries. Curves (a) are calculated for electrons at Γ and curves (b) for electrons at X in both the $Al_xGa_{1-x}As$ confining layers and the GaAs quantum well.

dashed curves in Fig. 1 which includes reflections assuming a transmission coefficient of 70% at each interface. The striking result shown by Fig. 1 is that electrons starting in the X valleys are scattered with a much higher probability than electrons in the Γ valley. The physical reason for this behavior is the low velocity of electrons in the X valleys, i.e., an electron needs a much longer time (factor ~ 10) to traverse the quantum well if it is in the X valley and the scattering probability increases exponentially during this time. This also explains the fact that holes (large mass, low velocity) are collected more easily than electrons, as has been shown before experimentally.[2]

The development of the energy distribution of the electrons after they are captured is shown in Fig. 2 for $T = 300$ K. The parameter identifying each curve is the width L_z of the well. The same type of curve obtained for the case of $L_z \sim 200$ Å would be obtained by injecting electrons into a 100-Å well and letting the carriers be reflected four times by the well boundaries as they percolate down. The curves for various L_z therefore represent also the initial transient development of the energy distribution function of the electrons. The electrons above ΔE_c (the injection energy) represent the fraction of the population that is re-emitted by phonon absorption. At 77 K this fraction would be negligible.

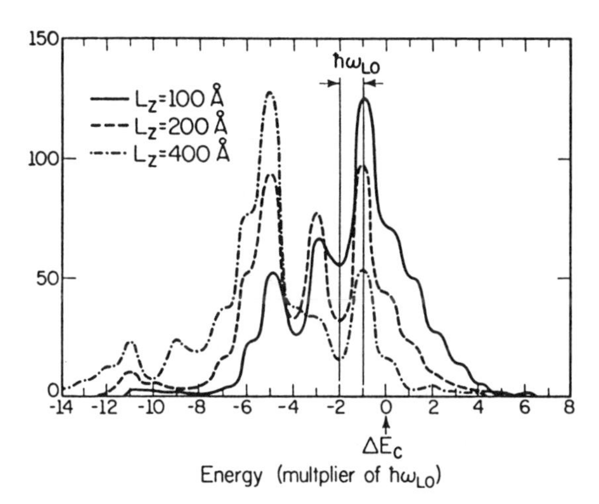

FIG. 2. Energy distribution of quantum-well electrons vs energy (in multiples of $\hbar\omega_{LO}$) for well sizes $L_z = 100$, 200, and 400 Å. $\Delta E_c \sim 0.53$ eV is the injection energy. ($T = 300$ K).

It is interesting that the carrier distributions display structure at multiples of the phonon energy, i.e., bumps spaced at one, two, or more phonons appear in the distributions. This structure persists down to very low energies as shown in Fig. 2. Notice, however, that the calculation is for the transient case and does not include size quantization effects which become significant at low energies (low scattering rate, large deBroglie wavelength). Thus, electrons can not cascade down below the lowest confined-particle state.

It has been outlined previously that also the steady-state distribution function can display distinct phonon structure if the electron-electron interaction is not too strong. Below we show that all of these theoretical aspects are qualitatively consistent with experimental results.

III. EXPERIMENTAL DATA

First we show in Fig. 3 the significance of a quantum-well size change from large size [(a), $L_z \sim 200$ Å] to small size [(b), $L_z \sim 80$ Å]. For the large well [curve (a)], a small number of the carriers photogenerated in the thick confining layers

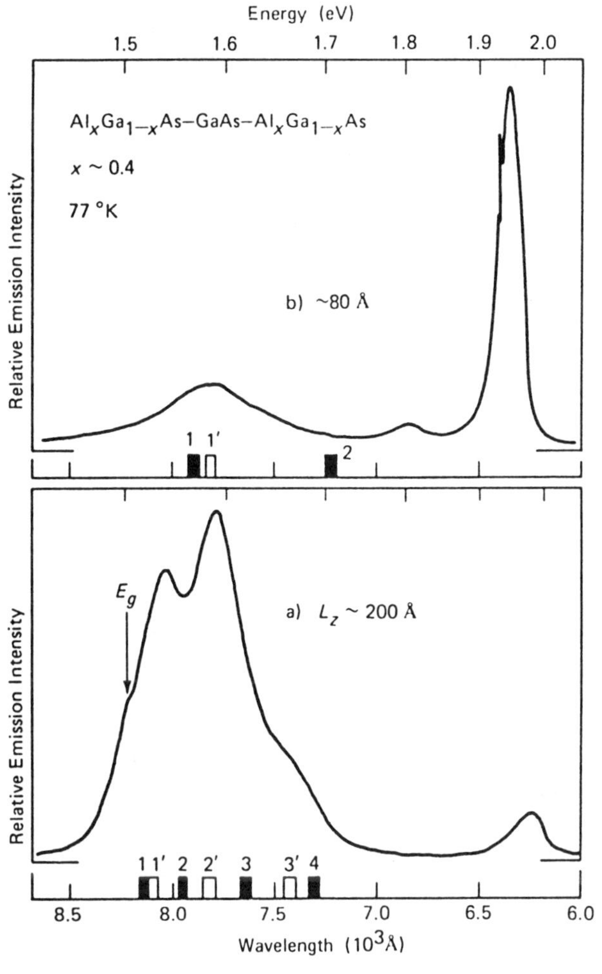

FIG. 3. Comparison of photoluminescence spectra of a large-size single quantum well [(a), $L_z \sim 200$ Å] with a small-size single quantum well [(b), $L_z \sim 80$ Å]. For the case of the larger well [curve (a)] most of the recombination occurs in the well, giving the greatest emission intensity in the lower gap region of the confined-particle transitions. In the case of the smaller well, most of the recombination (and emission intensity) occurs outside of the well (i.e., at higher energy).

recombine outside of the well (6400–6200 Å) compared to the large number that are collected and that recombine in the well. That is, in Fig. 3 [curve (a)] the emission intensity appearing on the confined-particle transitions $n = 1 - 4$ (electron-to-heavy-hole, $e \rightarrow hh$) and $n' = 1' - 3'$ (electron-to-light-hole, $e \rightarrow lh$) in the range 8500–7000 Å is much larger than the higher energy emission outside of the well (in the range 6400–6200 Å, $\Delta E_c \sim 440$ meV). In contrast to the case for curve (a) of Fig. 3, curve (b) $[L_z \sim 80$ Å$]$ shows that very little recombination occurs in the quantum well compared to the much larger confining-layer recombination (and emission) occurring at ~6350 Å. These results (see also Refs. 1 and 2) agree with the curves of Fig. 1, particularly the X-valley curves showing that the carrier scattering decreases rapidly for well sizes $L_z \lesssim 100$ Å. It is therefore clear why a single undoped[5] GaAs quantum well ceases to be an effective active layer for laser operation for $L_z < 100$ Å. Of course, this problem can be overcome with multiple GaAs quantum wells.[1]

As already indicated above, for a single GaAs quantum well of size $100 < L_z < 400$ Å the carrier scattering is efficient within the well (see Fig. 1) and insures that carriers arrive (in energy) and recombine from near the bottom of the well. At a significant excitation level, say a QWH sample photoexcited in the range 10^3–10^5 W/cm^2 (Ar^+ laser pumping[1]), it is possible to observe continuous 300 K laser operation at also much higher energy, e.g., to wavelengths as short as the $n' = 3'(e \rightarrow lh)$ transition or $\lambda \sim 7800$ Å in Fig. 4. As shown in Fig. 4 for an $Al_xGa_{1-x}As$-GaAs-$Al_xGa_{1-x}As$ sample of thickness of dimensions 1.0-0.02-0.1 μm, the QWH photoemission has a camel-back appearance with pronounced lower energy and pronounced higher energy shoulders. The higher energy shoulder, and pulsed laser operation, near $\lambda \sim 7800$ Å is typical and lies $m\hbar\omega_{LO} \sim 4\hbar\omega_{LO}$ below the L band edge of the GaAs well. This is for the case of recombination with $\Delta n \neq 0$; for recombination with $\Delta n = 0$ (n-electron, n-hole) $m\hbar\omega_{LO} \sim 5\ \hbar\omega_{LO}$, which agrees with the -5 peak in Fig. 2.

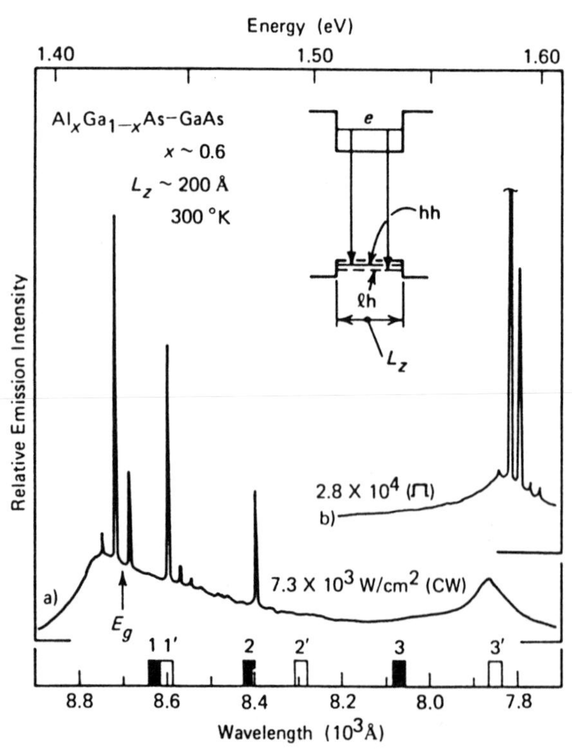

FIG. 4. Laser spectra (300 K) of a photopumped single 200-Å quantum well showing a typical camel-back emission profile. The lower energy emission results from carriers recombining near the bottom of the well. The higher energy shoulder is caused by carrier scattering $m\hbar\omega_{LO} \sim 5\ \hbar\omega_{LO}$ down from the L conduction band minima.

Figure 1 indicates clearly that carrier scattering in a GaAs quantum well, and subsequent energy loss, proceeds more efficiently in the indirect minima. In the case of the 200-Å single quantum-well sample of Fig. 4 (300 K) this behavior would tend to transport the carriers to the region (energy) of the L band edge, and there scatter and start the downward cascade process in the Γ energy band. Then according to Fig. 2, a peak in the carrier distribution and the recombination-radiation spectrum would tend to form a certain number of phonon multiples ($m\hbar\omega_{LO}$) below the L band edge as in Fig. 4. (Note that m is smaller at lower temperatures and larger at higher temperatures.)

Another example of some interest is shown in Fig. 5 (77 K), which is for the case of two $L_z \sim 50$-Å GaAs quantum wells coupled by one $x \sim 0.3$ $Al_xGa_{1-x}As$ barrier and confined with two $x \sim 0.4$ $Al_xGa_{1-x}As$ layers (of thickness 1 and 0.3 μm). In other words, the first quarter or so in energy-band discontinuity of the QWH (~120 meV is the conduction band) is an $L_z \sim 150$-Å single-well QWH. As the carriers scatter downward sufficiently in the QWH, then the double-well structure is fully manifest, and in this case the coupling barrier, if anything, increases the scattering. Of course, the barrier has an effect even when the carriers initially enter the active region at high energy (i.e., at the band edge energies of

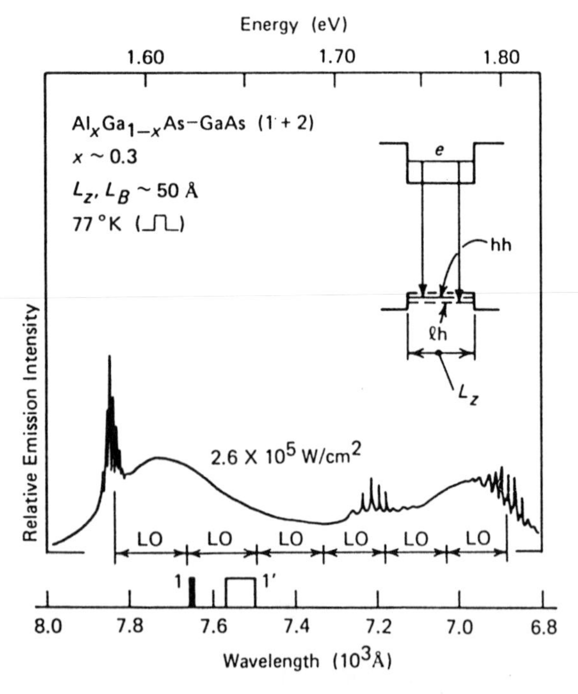

FIG. 5. Laser spectra (77 K) for two $L_z \sim 50$ Å GaAs quantum wells coupled by a single $L_B \sim 50$ Å $Al_xGa_{1-x}As$ ($x \sim 0.30$) barrier. The confining layers are $x \sim 0.40$ $Al_xGa_{1-x}As$. Notice that the coupling of the wells enhances the scattering and the collection efficiency substantially.

the confining layers). As for the single-well case of Fig. 4, the scattering to the L band edge is efficient and then permits scattering and efficient recombination (with large emission) to occur in the Γ (direct-gap) energy band. This is the region (i.e., high in Γ) in which the highest energy modes 7000–6800 Å (1.77–1.82 eV) occur in Fig. 5. As is expected from Fig. 2, in the region $m'\hbar\omega_{LO}$ still lower in energy more modes, generated by recombination of "scattered-down" carriers, might appear. In Fig. 5 these are the modes at $\lambda \sim 7200$ Å (~ 1.72 eV). Note that no steps in confined-particle transitions (subband steps) exist in this region, and the higher energy modes in Fig. 5 and their spacing ($m'\hbar\omega_{LO} = 2\,\hbar\omega_{LO}$) is a scattering and recombination effect involving $\hbar\omega_{LO}$ increments of energy.

We remark that the lower energy modes appearing $\hbar\omega_{LO}$ below the $n = 1$ confined-particle transitions in Fig. 4 have been discussed extensively elsewhere[6,7] and are not of special interest here, except to emphasize, of course, that carrier scattering to lower energy in this two-well QWH is efficient. We mention that these low-energy modes are supported by phonon-assisted recombination[8,9] involving virtual final states or possibly cluster-induced actual states (assuming clustering and thus increased coupling of the two 50-Å GaAs wells).[10]

ACKNOWLEDGMENTS

The authors are grateful to various of their colleagues for help with this work. The work of the Illinois group has been supported by the Army Research Office Contract DAAG 29-82-K-0059, the Office of Naval Research Contract N00014-76-C-0708, and by NSF Grant DMR 80-20250. The work of the Rockwell group has been partially supported by ONR Contract N00014-78-C-0711.

[1] N. Holonyak, Jr., R. M. Kolbas, R. D. Dupuis, and P. D. Dapkus, IEEE J. Quantum Electron. **QE-16**, 170 (1980).
[2] H. Shichijo, R. M. Kolbas, N. Holonyak, Jr., R. D. Dupuis, and P. D. Dapkus, Solid State Commun. **27**, 1029 (1978).
[3] G. C. Osbourn and D. L. Smith, Phys. Rev. B **19**, 2124 (1979).
[4] H. Shichijo and K. Hess, Phys. Rev. B **23**, 4197 (1981).
[5] See N. Holonyak, Jr., B. A. Vojak, H. Morkoc, T. J. Drummond, and K. Hess, Appl. Phys. Lett. **40**, 658 (1982), for a discussion of carrier collection in a doped quantum well.
[6] N. Holonyak, Jr., R. M. Kolbas, W. D. Laidig, B. A. Vojak, K. Hess, R. D. Dupuis, and P. D. Dapkus, J. Appl. Phys. **51**, 1328 (1980).
[7] K. Hess and N. Holonyak, Jr., Comments Solid State Phys. **10**, 67 (1981).
[8] N. Holonyak, Jr., R. M. Kolbas, W. D. Laidig, M. Altarelli, R. D. Dupuis, and P. D. Dapkus, Appl. Phys. Lett. **34**, 502 (1979).
[9] J. J. Coleman, P. D. Dapkus, B. A. Vojak, W. D. Laidig, N. Holonyak, Jr., and K. Hess, Appl. Phys. Lett. **37**, 15 (1980).
[10] N. Holonyak, Jr., W. D. Laidig, B. A. Vojak, K. Hess, J. J. Coleman, P. D. Dapkus, and J. Bardeen, Phys. Rev. Lett. **45**, 1703 (1980).

LOW-THRESHOLD SINGLE QUANTUM WELL (60 Å) GaAlAs LASERS GROWN BY MO-CVD WITH Mg AS p-TYPE DOPANT

R. D. BURNHAM
W. STREIFER
D. R. SCIFRES
C. LINDSTRÖM
T. L. PAOLI

Xerox Palo Alto Research Centers
Palo Alto, California 94304, USA

N. HOLONYAK

Department of Electrical Engineering & Materials Research Laboratory
University of Illinois at Urbana-Champaign
Urbana, Illinois 61801, USA

9th November 1982

Indexing terms: Semiconductor devices and materials, Semiconductor lasers

The letter reports low-threshold MO-CVD GaAlAs DH (~7730 Å) lasers containing Mg as the p-type dopant. The structure consists of symmetric stepped index cladding layers on both sides of a thin single quantum well (~60 Å) active region. Broad-area threshold current densities of 460 A cm^{-2} and 270 A cm^{-2} are achieved for cavity lengths of 250 and 500 μm, respectively. Broad-area room-temperature lasers without facet coatings emit in excess of 400 mW/facet CW output power.

We report low-threshold operation of a quantum well diode laser, whose p-side cladding regions and active region are magnesium-doped. Mg is expected to be more attractive than Zn as a p-type dopant in GaAs and related III-V compounds because the diffusion coefficient of Mg is about 10^4 times lower than that of Zn in GaAs.[1] Zn has been shown[2] to migrate in $Ga_{1-x}Al_xAs$ at low temperature and produce compositional disorder at a $Ga_{1-x}Al_xAs$-GaAs interface. Mukai *et al.*[3] showed that Mg can be incorporated as an acceptor in liquid phase epitaxy (LPE) grown $Ga_{1-x}Al_xAs$ and that the resistivity of $Ga_{1-x}Al_xAs$ doped with Mg exhibits a low temperature dependence. Wolf *et al.*[4] reported very low degradation (about 10^{-5} h^{-1} at 100–120°C) GaAlAs DH (8800 Å) oxide stripe lasers grown by liquid phase epitaxy using Mg as the p-type dopant in the cladding layer. Recently, a metalorganic compound bis(cyclopentadienyl) magnesium $(C_5H_5)_2Mg$ was reported to yield excellent results as a source of Mg in MO-CVD growth.[5] However, diode lasers grown by MO-CVD with Mg as a p-type dopant have not been reported.

Tsang[6,7] and Hersee *et al.*[8] have used a graded aluminium fraction (x) in the $Ga_{1-x}Al_xAs$ optical cavity cladding a quantum well active region[9,10] to substantially reduce the broad-area lasing threshold compared with a conventional double heterostructure laser. The lasers were grown by MBE[6,7] with undoped active and graded cladding regions and by low-pressure MO-CVD with Zn as a p-type dopant. Using atmospheric pressure MO-CVD in a vertical reactor,[11-13] we too have grown and characterised broad-area lasers with a similar structure.† These devices contain a symmetric step index in the cladding regions (in contrast to graded index layers[6,8]) bounding a single quantum well that is not intentionally doped. Threshold current densities below 300 A cm^2 were measured for various well thicknesses between 60 and 200 Å. All these devices utilised Zn as the p-type dopant.

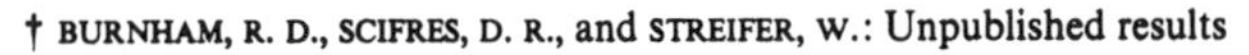

† BURNHAM, R. D., SCIFRES, D. R., and STREIFER, W.: Unpublished results

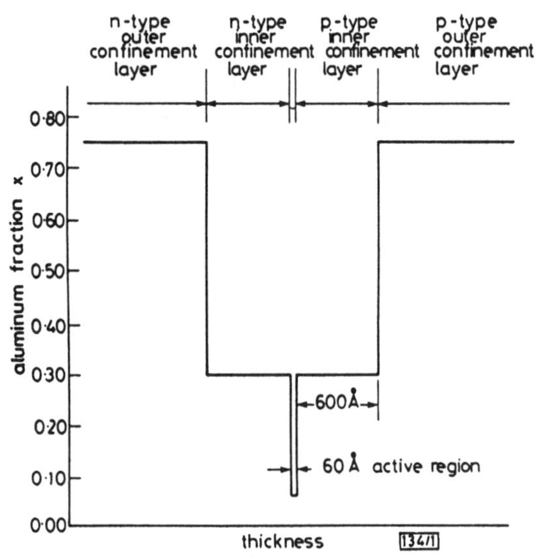

Fig. 1 *Illustrating the variation of aluminium fraction x with layer thickness for the laser*

Our purpose in this letter is to describe a similar laser with the same reduction in broad-area threshold current density, but employing Mg as the p-type dopant in both the cladding and active layers. The structure, layer compositions and thicknesses are shown in Fig. 1. The active region contains ~5% Al and is 60 Å thick; the inner claddings are composed of ~30% Al and are 600 Å thick; the outer regions contain ~75% Al.

Fig. 2 shows typical broad-area light-output/pulsed-current (L/I) characteristics at 300 K for two different cavity lengths. For a laser 250 μm long and 216 μm wide, $J_{th} \simeq 460$ A cm^{-2}, whereas 500 μm-long lasers of the same width have thresholds of $J_{th} \simeq 270$ A cm^{-2}. Although the Al constituted only 5% of the active layer, the 500 μm- and 250 μm-long devices lased simultaneously in several longitudinal modes centred at 7718 Å and 7755 Å, respectively; the difference in photon energy between the lasers and the bandgap of $Ga_{0.95}Al_{0.05}As$ is ≃ 120 meV, which results from the quantum size effect.[9,10,14] In

Reprinted with permission from *Electron. Lett.*, vol. 18, no. 25, pp. 1095–1097, Dec. 9, 1982.

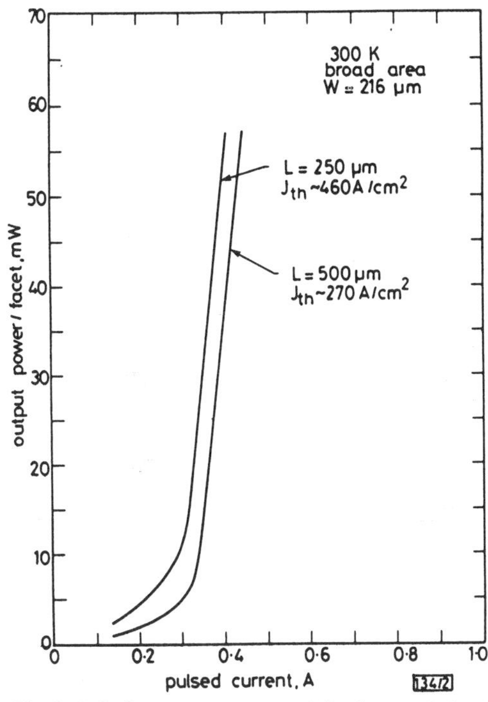

Fig. 2 *Pulsed room-temperature L/I characteristics for a symmetric step index $Ga_{1-x}Al_xAs$ single quantum well heterostructure laser diode with 250 µm- and 500 µm-long cavity lengths*

particular, this energy is in good agreement with the lowest confined carrier transition. The theoretical lasing wavelength for a transition from an $n = 1$ electron and a light hole, in a 55–60 Å quantum well with a barrier height of 310 meV, is 7775–7845 Å. This indicates efficient carrier scattering into the well, enhanced by the particular symmetric stepped index cladding layers. Moreover, the wavelength difference with laser length arises because the peak gain of the quantum well laser may shift slightly with active region charge density. We also note that the differential efficiencies of the 250 µm and 500 µm length lasers are approximately equal. This result, which is similar to that reported by Tsang,[7] indicates that either the internal losses are negligible compared with the facet transmission losses and/or the internal efficiency η_i decreases with increasing active region charge density (corresponding to reduced laser length). Indeed the internal losses may well be small, but we believe it more likely that carrier leakage effects[15] are responsible for a decrease in the apparent internal efficiency. It is also possible that circulating modes[16] are present and act to reduce η_i.

Fig. 3 compares the light-output/current (*L/I*) characteristic for the laser with a 250 µm-long cavity and a 216 µm-width under pulsed and CW operation. Under pulsed conditions, $I_{th} \simeq 300$ mA and the differential quantum efficiency is $\simeq$ 67%. For CW operation $I_{th} \simeq 350$ mA and the differential quantum efficiency is $\simeq$ 57%. The reduced differential quantum efficiency under CW conditions is probably a consequence of laser heating. Laser threshold increases with temperature and the resulting higher active region charge density likely decreases the effective internal efficiency.[15] For both pulsed and CW operation, the maximum output power exceeds 400 mW. These high CW output power levels are comparable with those reported by Scifres *et al.*[17,18]

In conclusion, we have reported operation of a *p-n* junction laser grown by MO-CVD with Mg *p*-type doping. The device combines a thin single quantum well $\simeq$ 60 Å active region and symmetric step index cladding regions. Threshold current densities as low as 270 A cm^{-2} were observed for a 500 µm-long broad-area device. CW broad-area output powers exceeding 400 mW/facet were also achieved. These results indicate that

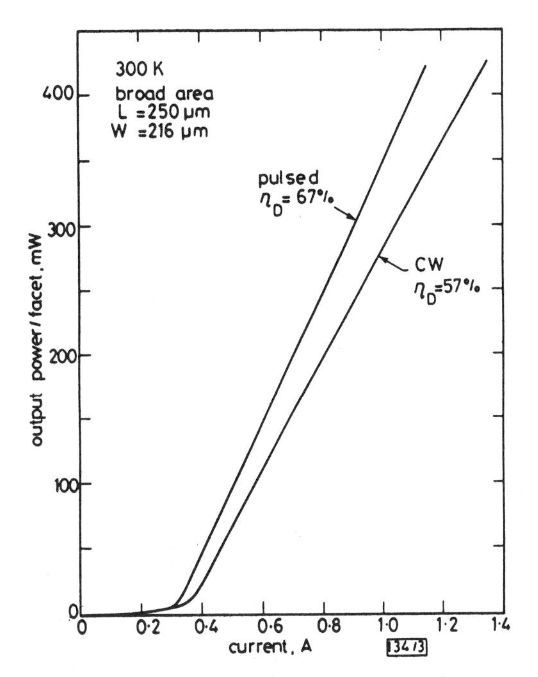

Fig. 3 *Pulsed and CW room-temperature L/I characteristics for a symmetric step index $Ga_{1-x}Al_xAs$ single quantum well broad-area heterostructure laser diode of length 250 µm*

Mg is an attractive *p*-type dopant in the MO-CVD growth system.

The authors wish to thank H. Chung, M. Bernstein, F. Endicott, J. Walker, R. D. Yingling, Jun., W. Mosby, J. Tramontana, G. L. Harnagel, P. Tihanyi, A. Alimonda and R. Ridder for their technical assistance. The work of one of us (NH) has been partially supported by National Science Foundation grant ECS-82-00517 and Army Research Office contract DAAG-29-82-K-0059.

References

1 WURST, E. C.: 'Final report on research and development of high temperature semiconductor devices'. Dept. of the Navy, NO-77532 and NO-85424, March 1963

2 LAIDIG, W. D., HOLONYAK, N., JUN., CAMRAS, M. D., HESS, K., COLEMAN, J. J., DAPKUS, P. D., and BARDEEN, J.: 'Disorder of an AlAs-GaAs superlattice by impurity diffusion', *Appl. Phys. Lett.*, 1981, **38**, pp. 776–778

3 MUKAI, S., MAKITA, Y., and GONDA, S.: 'Doping and electrical properties of Mg in LPE $Al_xGa_{1-x}As$', *J. Appl. Phys.*, 1979, **50**, pp. 1304–1307

4 WOLF, H. D., METTLER, K., and ZSCHAUER, K. H.: 'High performance 880 nm (GaAl)As/GaAs oxide stripe lasers with very low degradation rates at temperatures up to 120°C', *Jpn. J. Appl. Phys.*, 1981, **20**, pp. L693–L696

5 LEWIS, C. R., DIETZE, W. T., and LUDOWISE, M. J.: 'OM-VPE growth of Mg-doped GaAs', *Electron. Lett.*, 1982, **18**, pp. 569–570

6 TSANG, W. T.: 'A graded-index waveguide separate-confinement laser with very low threshold and a narrow Gaussian beam', *Appl. Phys. Lett.*, 1981, **39**, pp. 134–137

7 TSANG, W. T.: 'Extremely low threshold (AlGa)As graded-index waveguide separate-confinement heterostructure lasers grown by molecular beam epitaxy', *ibid.*, 1982, **40**, pp. 217–219

8 HERSEE, S., BALDY, M., ASSENAT, P., DECREMOUX, B., and DUCHEMIN, J. P.: 'Low-threshold GRIN-SCH, GaAs/GaAlAs laser structure grown by OM-VPE', *Electron. Lett.*, 1982, **18**, pp. 857–858

9 HOLONYAK, N., JUN., KOLBAS, R. M., DUPUIS, R. D., and DAPKUS, P. D.: 'Quantum-well heterostructure lasers', *IEEE J. Quantum Electron.*, 1980, **QE-16**, pp. 170–186

10 CAMRAS, M. D., HOLONYAK, N., JUN., HESS, K., COLEMAN, J. J., BURNHAM, R. D., and SCIFRES, D. R.: 'High energy $Al_xGa_{1-x}As$ ($0 \leq x \leq 0{\cdot}1$) quantum well heterostructure laser operation', *Appl. Phys. Lett.*, 1982, **42**, pp. 314–319

11 MANASEVIT, H. M.: 'The use of metal-organics in the preparation of semiconductor materials', *J. Electrochem. Soc.*, 1971, **118**, pp. 647–650

12 DUPUIS, R. D., MOUDY, L. A., and DAPKUS, P. D.: 'Proc. 7th Internat'l Symp. on GaAs and Related Compounds', WOLFE, C. M., Ed., (Inst. Phys. London, 1979), pp. 1–9

13 BURNHAM, R. D., SCIFRES, D. R., and STREIFER, W.: 'Low threshold, high efficiency $Ga_{1-x}Al_xAs$ single quantum well visible diode lasers grown by metalorganic chemical vapor deposition', *Appl. Phys. Lett.*, 1982, **41**, pp. 228–230

14 LINDSTRÖM, C., HALIDO, D., SCIFRES, D. R., and BURNHAM, R. D.: 'CW longitudinal mode spectra of multiple quantum well stripe lasers', *Electron. Lett.*, 1982, **18**, pp. 876–878

15 ANTHONY, P. J., and SCHUMAKER, N. E.: 'Temperature dependence of the lasing threshold current of double heterostructure injection lasers due to drift current loss', *J. Appl. Phys.*, 1980, **51**, pp. 5038–5040

16 HENSHALL, G. D.: 'Suppression of internally circulating modes in (GaAl)As/GaAs heterostructure lasers and their effect on catastrophic degradation and efficiency', *Appl. Phys. Lett.*, 1977, **31**, pp. 205–207

17 SCIFRES, D. R., BURNHAM, R. D., and STREIFER, W.: 'Lateral grating array high power CW visible semiconductor laser', *Electron. Lett.*, 1982, **18**, pp. 549–550

18 SCIFRES, D. R., BURNHAM, R. D., and STREIFER, W.: 'High power coupled multiple stripe quantum well injection lasers', *Appl. Phys. Lett.*, 1982, **41**, pp. 118–120

Spontaneous Emission Characteristics of Quantum Well Lasers in Strong Magnetic Fields —An Approach to Quantum-Well-Box Light Source—

Yasuhiko ARAKAWA,* Hiroyuki SAKAKI,* Masao NISHIOKA,*
Hiroshi OKAMOTO** and Noboru MIURA***

*Institute of Industrial Science, University of Tokyo, 7-22-1 Roppongi, Minato-ku, Tokyo, 106
**Musashino Electrical Communication Laboratory, NTT, 3-9-11 Midori-cho, Musashino-shi, Tokyo 180
***Institute for Solid State Physics, University of Tokyo, 7-22-1 Roppongi, Minato-ku, Tokyo 106

(Received October 12, 1983; accepted for publication November 26, 1983)

Characteristics of a GaAs/AlGaAs quantum well (QW) laser diode are studied for the first time under strong magnetic fields up to 30 Tesla. When field normal to QW plane is increased, the spontaneous emission spectrum is found to shift toward the higher photon energy, following the shift $\hbar\omega_c/2$ of the lowest Landau level in the region of strong magnetic fields. Moreover, the emission spectrum is shown to be very little affected when magnetic fields are applied parallel to the QW plane. These results give evidence of light emission from a fully-quantized zero-dimensional carrier system in GaAs QW structures with strong magnetic fields normal to the QW plane.

The confinement of carriers in GaAs quantum wells (QW) has provided a number of unique features to the characteristics of QW lasers.[1,2] The reduction of the laser threshold current Jth[3,4] as well as its lasing wavelength controllability are typical examples. Such improvements are mainly due to the two-dimensional nature of carrier motions in QW potentials.[5] It has recently been suggested by the authors[6] that these improvements can be substantially enhanced if carriers are confined two or three-dimensionally by QW wires or QW boxes. As a first step toward QW box lasers, we study here the spontaeneous emission characteristics of GaAs/AlGaAs QW lasers in strong magnetic fields up to 30 Tesla.

As is well known, carrier motions in QWs are quantized in the direction (//z) normal to the QW planes. If strong magnetic fields B are applied in parallel with the z-axis (B ⊥QW plane) as shown in Fig. 1, carrier motions in the QW active layers are quantized not only in z-direction but also in the two transverse directions (x, y). Hence, the application of magnetic fields to QW lasers quantizes the carrier motion completely, and results in the zero-dimensional carrier state. The energy levels of such electrons are completely discrete and given as

$$\varepsilon_{ln} = (l+1/2)\hbar\omega_c + \hbar^2(n+1)^2/2m_e^*(\pi/L_z^*)^2 \tag{1}$$

where $\hbar$ is Planck's constant divided by 2π, m_e^* is the effective mass of electrons, ω_c is the cyclotron angular frequency of electrons ($=eB/m_e^*$), L_z^* is the effective thickness of QWs and, l and n are quantum numbers. Corresponding expressions for holes can be obtained by replacing m_e^* with the effective mass m_h^* of holes. Note that the energy levels in actual situations have finite widths Γ_B for three different reasons: firstly, electrons are subject to scattering effects which disturb the completion of cyclotron motions; secondly, the system may have inhomogeneity; and, thirdly, the inter-well coupling of electrons in multiwell structures leads to the band formation. Equation (1) indicates that the effective energy gap E_g^* between the ground levels ($l=n=0$) of electrons and holes is given by

$$E_g^* = E_g + \frac{1}{2}\hbar eB(1/m_e^* + 1/m_h^*) + \frac{\hbar^2}{2}(\pi/L_z^*)^2(1/m_e^* + 1/m_h^*) \tag{2}$$

where E_g is the energy gap of GaAs.

In contrast, when magnetic fields are applied in parallel with the QW plane ($B//x$ or y) the cyclotron motion of carriers is generally interrupted by the QW (as long as L_z^* is smaller than the cyclotron diameter). Hence, practically all the features of two-dimensional electron gas (2DEG) will be preserved. The effective energy gap E_g^* in this case is equal to that of the ordinary 2DEG except that some correction term is added due to the shrinkage of the wavefunction. We discuss this effect more in detail later.

Since the formation of the zero-dimensional carrier gas (0-DCG) in GaAs/AlGaAs quantum wells leads to the prescribed change in the effective energy gap (eq. (2)) and affects the form of the density of states, one should be able to demonstrate it by studying the light emission characteristics of QW lasers in the strong magnetic field. For this purpose, we have operated a multiquantum well (MQW) laser in the pulsed magnetic field and studied the spontaneous emission characteristics using the experimental setup of Fig. 2.

Pulsed magnetic fields up to 30 Tesla are generated by feeding a current from a 16 mF capacitor into a copper coil

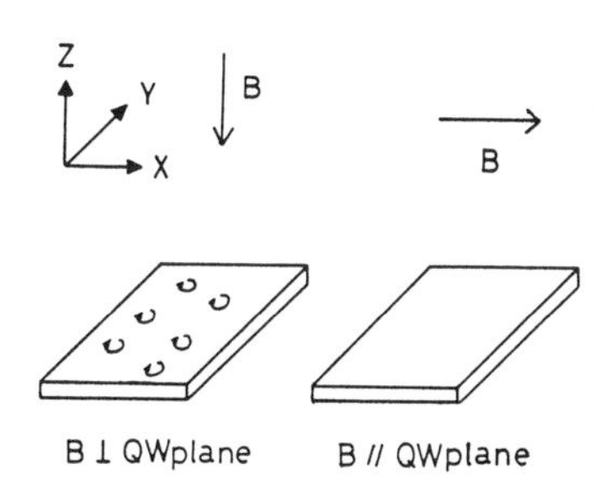

Fig. 1. Schematics of carrier motions in quantum well (QW) structures under strong magnetic fields B for two different field directions (a) QW plane ⊥ B, (b) QW plane //B.

Reprinted with permission from *Japan. J. Appl. Phys.*, vol. 22, no. 12, pp. L804–L806, Dec. 1983.

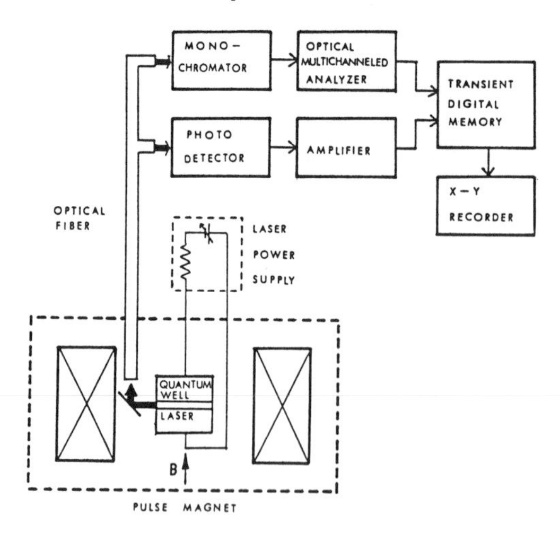

Fig. 2. A schematic drawing of the experimental setup.

immersed in liquid nitrogen. The pulse has a waveform of the half-sinusoid $B_{max}\sin(\pi t/T)$ with the width T of about 10 msec. Lasers are operated for the time interval of 1 msec at the top of the pulse, where the magnetic field is almost constant. The light output from the laser is first reflected by a micro mirror and then transmitted through an optical fiber bundle to the outside of the cryostat. One part of the light output is fed to a 25 cm grating monochromator with 1200 lines/mm and its spectrum is detected by an optical multichanneled analyzer (OMA2 SYSTEM). The other portion of light output is fed directly to the photo-detector for the measurement of integrated intensity at the top of magnetic fields.

Multiquantum well (MQW) lasers used in this study are grown by molecular beam epitaxy on Si-doped GaAs(100) substrate at 760°C. Following the growth of a 0.42 μm n^+ GaAs buffer layer and 1.93 μm thick Sn-doped n^+-$Al_yGa_{1-y}As$ ($y=0.28$) cladding layer, the MQW active layer was formed, which consists of 16 layers of 100 Å-thick undoped GaAs quantum well separated by the 28 Å-thick undoped $Al_xGa_{1-x}As$ ($x=0.18$) barrier layers. Then, a 1.92 μm thick Be-doped p-$Al_yGa_{1-y}As$ cladding layer and an uppermost p^+ GaAs contact layer were grown. Using wafers thus grown, 10 μm-wide stripe-geometry lasers are fabricated with the cavity length of 200 μm by forming p-contacts with (Cr–Au) and n^+-contact with (Au–Ge–Ni). The threshold current is typically 150 mA at room temperature.

The spontaneous emission spectrum of MQW lasers was measured at 130 K with injected current 40 mA. Figure 3 shows the observed emission spectrum with and without the magnetic field B of 30 Tesla. Note that the spectral peak shifts clearly to the shorter wavelength by above 50 Å when the magnetic field is applied perpendicularly to QW planes (B ⊥QW). Contrastingly, the spectral peak is found to shift no more than 12 Å when B is applied parallel to QW planes (B//QW). To investigate the spectral peak shifts $\Delta\lambda$ in more shown in Fig. 4. One notices immediately that the peak shifts for the normal magnetic field (triangles) has much greater amount than those for the parallel magnetic field (circles), demonstrating clearly the anisotropy of QW potentials.

As for the magnitude of the shift $\Delta\lambda$ under the normal

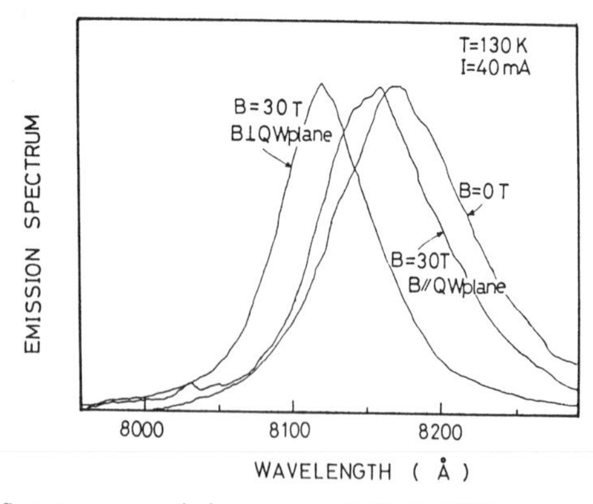

Fig. 3. Spontaneous emission spectra of a GaAs QW laser operated with and without magnetic fields $B=30$ Tesla. The field directions are perpendicular to or parallel with QW planes.

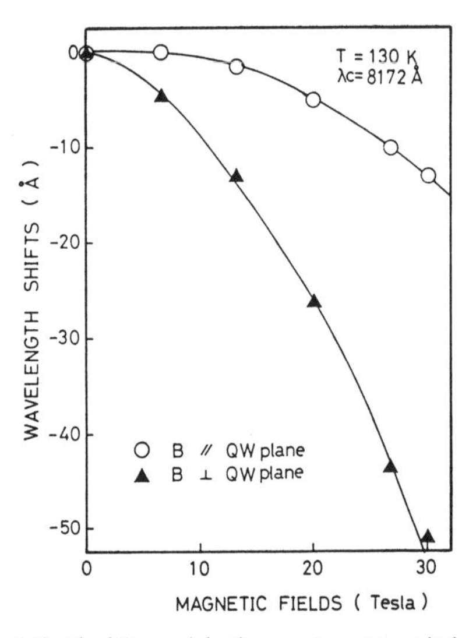

Fig. 4. The shift $\Delta\lambda$ of the peak in the spontaneous emission spectrum of QW lasers at 130 K plotted as a function of magnetic field B for the two different field directions. The wavelength λ_c of the peak without magnetic fields is 8172 Å.

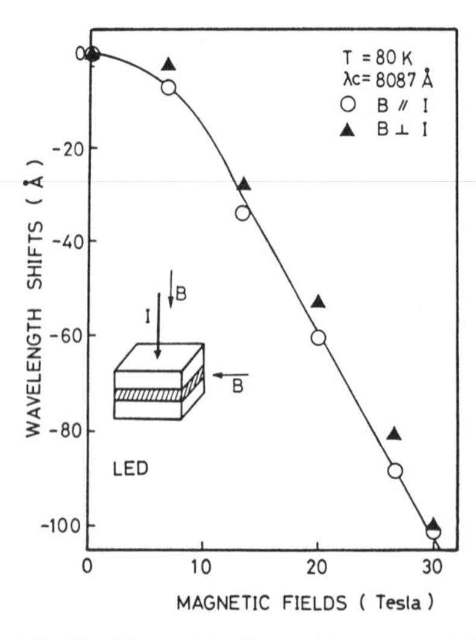

Fig. 5. The shift $\Delta\lambda$ of the peak in the spontaneous emission spectrum of a GaAs LED at 80 K as a function of magnetic field B for two different field directions. The wavelength λ_c of the peak without magnetic fields is 8087 Å. Note that the scale of the vertical axis is different from that of Fig. 4.

magnetic field, $\Delta\lambda$ in the range of low magnetic fields is far smaller than the shift of the ground Landau level $\hbar\omega_c/2$. This is due to the incompleteness of cyclotron motion ($\omega_c\tau \lesssim 1$). In the region of high magnetic fields, however, one notices in Fig. 4 that the incremental shift of spectrum $\Delta\lambda/\Delta B$ increases as B increases, and becomes as large as 3 Å/Tesla. This slope comes close to what is expected from the shift of the lowest Landau level. This indicates that carrier motions in quantum well planes are nearly quantized by the magnetic fields, and demonstrates the formation of the 0-DCG.

Another evidence of the formation of the O-DCG in QWs can be given by observing the anisotropy of the spontaneous emission spectrum with the magnetic field direction varied. Figure 4 shows clearly that the spectrum shift for the parallel field (B//QW plane) is very small up to 10 Tesla. This is because the cyclotron motion, whose diameter is 160 Å at 10 Tesla is interrupted by the quantum well potential, as discussed before. However, when B exceeds 15 T, the spontaneous emission spectrum shifts appreciably toward the shorter wavelength. This shift can be ascribed to the effect of an additional harmonic potential term $\alpha B_y(z-z_0)^2$, which appears in Hamiltonian in the presence of parallel magnetic field B_y.

Note that such a harmonic potential reduces the average extension of the carier wavefunction $\varphi(z)$ and results in the increase of energy eigenvalues of carriers. When the parallel magnetic field becomes extremely strong, this harmonic potential may well dominate the potential energy of Hamiltonian. In such a case, the carriers can complete the cyclotron motion within the well, since the cyclotron diameter becomes smaller than the thickness of the quantum well. The energy levels in such situations become entirelly identical with the usual Landau levels and the shift of emission spectrum is expected to be independent of the magnetic field directions. Note that the observation of this anisotropy is also evidence of the formation of the QW structure.

In order to further clarify the anisotropy of the spontaneous emission from a QW structure, we also measured, for comparison, emission characteristics of a GaAs light emitting diode, in which carriers are free to move in all three directions. Figure 5 shows the observed spectrum shift of the GaAs LED placed in magnetic fields of two different directions. One readily sees that the shift is almost independent of the field directions. Hence we can conclude that the observed anisotropy of spectrum shift in QW lasers is indeed evidence of anisotropic carrier states in QW structures. Note here also that the spectrum shift of the LED is almost identical with the predicted shift of the lowest Landau levels (eq. (2)) and proves the high quality of the LED active layer.

Lastly, a few remarks should be made on the full-width at half-maximum (FWHM) of the emission spectrum. Figure 3 shows that FWHM is reduced from 110 Å to 75 Å when the normal magnetic field is raised from zero to 30 Tesla. Such a reduction is most likely to result from the change of state density function from the original step-like form to the quasi-delta function form by the application of magnetic fields. Such an interpretation is supported by the fact that the reduction of FWHM under the parallel magnetic field is much smaller as shown in Fig. 3. Regarding this point, consideration should be given to the possible contribution of exciton states,[7,8] because the emission spectrum from exciton states is narrow even in the absence of magnetic fields. We think, however, that the contribution of exciton states is likely to be small in our experimental situations, since the QW laser was operated at medium current level.

In conclusion, we have demonstrated that the spontaneous emission spectrum of GaAs QW lasers shifts toward the shorter wavelength, when operated in high magnetic fields, with medium current level. The amount of such a shift and its marked dependence on magnetic field directions have given evidence of injection emission from fully quantized carrier states in semiconductors.

The authors wish to express their sincere gratitude to Professor J. Hamasaki and Professor Y. Fujii, University of Tokyo, for their support and encouragement. Thanks are also due to Dr. Y. Horikoshi, Mr. H. Iwamura, and Mr. S. Tarucha of Musashino Electrical Communication Laboratory, NTT, for useful discussions and support on experiments. This work was partly supported by a Grant-in-Aid from the Ministry of Education, Science, and Culture of Japan.

References

1) J. P. van der Ziel, R. Dingle, R. C. Miller, W. Wiegmann and W. A. Nordland, Jr.: Appl. Phys. Lett. **26** (1975) 463.
2) N. Holonyak, Jr., R. M. Kolbas, R. D. Dupuis and P. D. Dapkus: IEEE J. Quantum Electron. **QE-16** (1980) 170.
3) W. T. Tsang: Appl. Phys. Lett. **39** (1981) 786.
4) R. Chin, N. Holonyak, Jr. and B. A. Vojak: Appl. Phys. Lett. **36** (1980) 19.
5) K. Hess, B. A. Vojak, N. Holonyak, Jr., R. Chin and P. O. Dapkus: Solid State Electron. **23** (1980) 517.
6) Y. Arakawa and H. Sakaki: Appl. Phys. Lett. **40** (1982) 939.
7) T. Ishibashi, S. Tarucha and H. Okamoto: *Proc. of International Symposium on Gallium Arsenide and Related Compounds 1981* (1982) 587.
8) C. Weisbuch, R. C. Miller, R. Dingle, A. C. Gossard and W. Wiegmann: Solid State Commun. **37** (1981) 219.

Strained-layer quantum-well injection laser

W. D. Laidig, P. J. Caldwell, Y. F. Lin, and C. K. Peng
Department of Electrical and Computer Engineering, North Carolina State University, Raleigh, North Carolina 27695-7911

(Received 19 December 1983; accepted for publication 16 January 1984)

Data are presented demonstrating room-temperature operation of a strained-layer quantum-well injection laser. The laser structure, grown by molecular beam epitaxy, consists of an active region with three $In_xGa_{1-x}As$ ($x\sim0.35$) quantum wells ($L_Z\sim40$ Å) separated by two GaAs barriers ($L_B\sim30$ Å). These layers are centered in a larger GaAs collection/confinement region ($L_Z\sim1600$ Å) bounded by $Al_yGa_{1-y}As$ ($y\sim0.45$) cladding layers. The lasers operate at $\lambda\sim1.0\,\mu$m with greater than 4-mW optical power output/facet under pulsed conditions at 300 K. Threshold current densities between 1000 and 2000 A/cm^2 are obtained.

PACS numbers: 42.55.Px, 78.45. + h, 85.30. − z, 68.55. + b

Although semiconductor devices which incorporate lattice-mismatched materials are not new, interest in these devices has dwindled due to the problems associated with the effects of dislocations and defects resulting from the relaxation of misfit strain.[1,2] Recently a renewed effort in lattice-mismatched materials has developed, not because the effects of misfit dislocations are any less detrimental than in the past, but because it might be possible, with the use of quantum-well structures, to avoid the formation of such dislocations.[3-7] The slow growth rates, layer uniformity, and interfacial abruptness currently available with molecular beam epitaxy (MBE) and organometallic chemical vapor deposition have allowed the investigation of strained-layer or pseudomorphic materials. These structures consist of one or more thin epitaxial layers which in bulk form have a lattice constant different than that of the substrate but due to the extremely small layer thickness are strained to match the substrate lattice constant. These structures are potentially of significant practical importance since the restraints imposed by requiring the use of lattice-matched systems are loosened, thus providing another degree of freedom for device design.[1] Pseudomorphic materials have operated as photoexcited lasers[8-10] and have been used for light-emitting diodes[11,12] and photodetectors.[13] In this letter we demonstrate that strained-layer structures can be operated as current-injection lasers.

The laser structure was grown by MBE. Fluxes were set to maintain an As-stable surface condition and a GaAs growth rate of 1 μm/h. A schematic cross section of the device is shown in Fig. 1. After a 0.5-μm GaAs:Sn ($n\sim2\times10^{18}$ cm^{-3}) buffer layer, a 2.0-μm $Al_{0.45}Ga_{0.55}As$:Si ($n\sim5\times10^{16}$ cm^{-3}) cladding layer is grown. Next an $L_Z\sim1600$-Å undoped collection/confinement region is grown. This region consists of GaAs except for three $In_{0.35}Ga_{0.65}As$ wells ($L_Z\sim40$ Å) separated by two GaAs barriers ($L_B\sim30$ Å). The final layers include a 2.0-μm $Al_{0.45}Ga_{0.55}As$:Be ($p\sim5\times10^{16}$ cm^{-3}) cladding layer and a 0.5-μm GaAs:Be ($p\sim1\times10^{19}$ cm^{-3}) cap layer. Substrate temperature during growth was 630 °C for the GaAs buffer and cap layer, 670 °C for the $Al_{0.45}Ga_{0.55}As$ cladding layers, 600 °C for the GaAs confinement/collection region, and 525 °C for the thin layers of $In_{0.35}Ga_{0.65}As$ and GaAs in the active region. The metallization and fabrication of broad area laser diodes follow the procedure described elsewhere.[14]

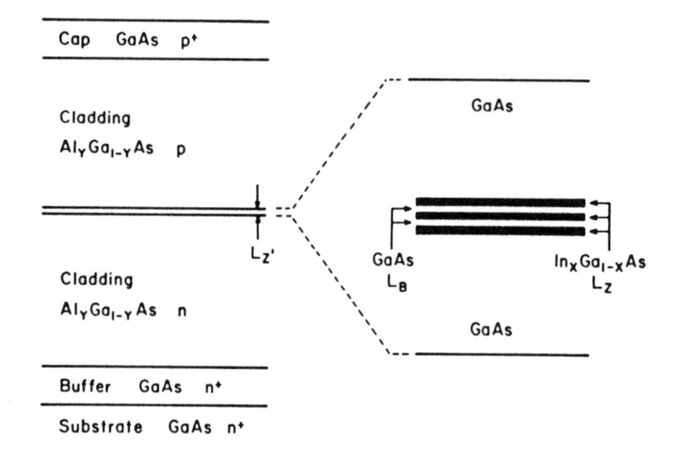

FIG. 1. Schematic diagram of strained-layer quantum-well laser diode structure. The undoped active region consists of three $L_Z\sim40$-Å $In_{0.35}Ga_{0.65}As$ quantum wells separated by two $L_B\sim30$-Å GaAs barriers.

Typical spectra from one of these strained-layer quantum-well lasers are shown in Fig. 2. The lasers were operated at room temperature under pulsed conditions with a 1-μs pulse at 1 kHz. Threshold current densities are between 1 and 2 kA/cm^2. The lasers operate at a wavelength $\lambda\sim1.0$ μm ($\hbar\omega\sim1.24$ eV). Since the energy band gap of bulk $In_{0.35}Ga_{0.65}As$ is ~0.94 eV at 300 K, this amounts to an increase of ~0.3 eV in the emission of the $L_Z\sim40$ Å strained quantum wells. The increase arises both from quantum size effects due to carrier confinement and from strain-induced band-gap alteration. For this structure the compression of the $In_{0.35}Ga_{0.65}As$ to match the GaAs lattice constant results in a strain of $\Delta a/a\sim2.5\%$. With this strain the 40-Å quantum-well thickness is sufficiently below the critical thickness to ensure a high integrity of the layered structure.[7]

Reprinted with permission from *Appl. Phys. Lett.*, vol. 44, no. 7, pp. 653–655, Apr. 1, 1984.

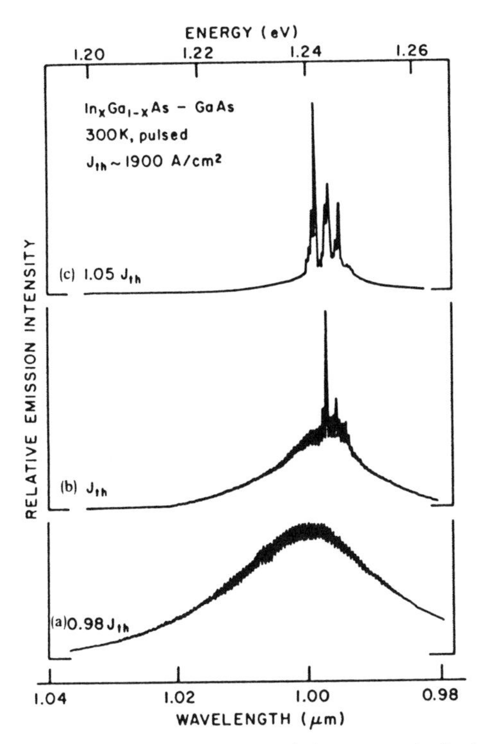

FIG. 2. Room-temperature emission spectra (pulsed operation) of a broad area laser diode ($110\times270\ \mu m^2$) fabricated from the material shown schematically in Fig. 1.

The optical power output per facet as a function of drive current (1-μs pulse at 1 kHz) is shown in Fig. 3. The threshold of this device is ~ 1.2 kA/cm^2. Peak powers of ~ 5 mW/facet are easily achieved. These results were obtained using a calibrated Si *p-i-n* detector.

Degradation and lifetime measurements of these lasers are critical to their evaluation, especially in view of the short lifetimes reported for cw photoexcited strained-layer quantum-well structures.[9-10] While these experiments are only in the preliminary stages, initial results are somewhat encouraging. One diode has been tested for degradation and a 10% increase in the threshold current has been observed in the first 25 hours of operation. More extensive evaluation will be the subject of future investigation.

In summary, the capability of strained-layer quantum-well diodes to operate as current injection 300-K lasers has been demonstrated. Three coupled 40-Å $In_{0.35}Ga_{0.65}As$ layers with $\sim 2.5\%$ strain exhibit laser emission near $\lambda \sim 1.0$ μm with $\sim$5-mW/facet pulsed power output.

The authors are grateful to Dr. M. A. Littlejohn and Dr. G. N. Maracas for their support and helpful discussions and to K. Julian for technical assistance. This work was supported by the National Science Foundation.

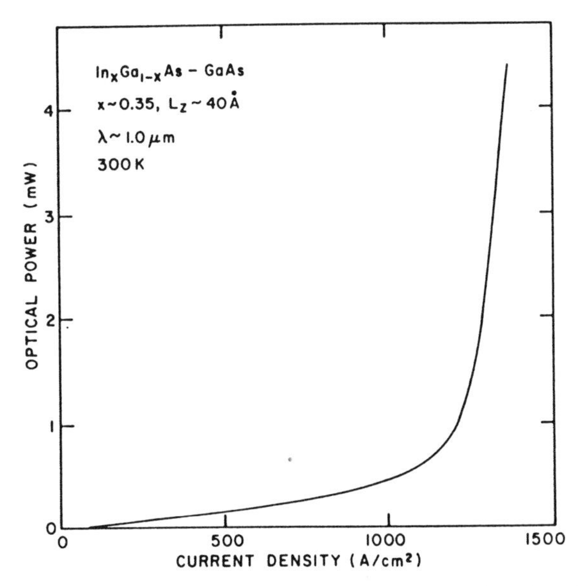

FIG. 3. Optical output power per facet (pulsed operation) for a diode laser with a threshold current density of ~ 1.2 kA/cm^2.

[1]J. W. Matthews and A. E. Blakeslee, J. Cryst. Growth **27**, 118 (1974).
[2]G. H. Olsen and M. Ettenberg, in *Crystal Growth*, edited by C. H. L. Goodman (Plenum, New York, 1978), Vol. 2, pp. 1–56.
[3]P. L. Gourley and R. M. Biefeld, J. Vac. Sci. Technol. B **1**, 383 (1983).
[4]G. C. Osbourn, J. Vac. Sci. Technol. B **1**, 379 (1983).
[5]M. J. Ludowise, W. T. Dietze, C. R. Lewis, N. Holonyak, Jr., and M. D. Camras, Electronic Materials Conference, Burlington, VT, June 1983.
[6]I. J. Fritz, L. R. Dawson, and T. E. Zipperian, J. Vac. Sci. Technol. B **1**, 387 (1983).
[7]W. D. Laidig, C. K. Peng, and Y. F. Lin, 5th Molecular Beam Epitaxy Workshop, Atlanta, GA, October 1983 (to be published).
[8]M. J. Ludowise, W. T. Dietze, C. R. Lewis, N. Holonyak, Jr., K. Hess, M. D. Camras, and M. A. Nixon, Appl. Phys. Lett. **42**, 257 (1983).
[9]M. J. Lüdowise, W. T. Dietze, C. R. Lewis, M. D. Camras, N. Holonyak, Jr., B. K. Fuller, and M. A. Nixon, Appl. Phys. Lett. **42**, 487 (1983).
[10]N. Holonyak, Jr., M. D. Camras, J. M. Brown, M. J. Ludowise, W. T. Dietze, and C. R. Lewis, Device Research Conference, Burlington, VT, June, 1983.
[11]L. R. Dawson, G. C. Osbourn, T. E. Zipperian, J. J. Wiczer, L. E. Barnes, I. J. Fritz, and R. M. Biefeld, 5th Molecular Beam Epitaxy Workshop, Atlanta, GA, October 1983.
[12]M. L. Timmons, T. Katsuyama, R. Sillmon, and S. M. Bedair, 1983 International Electron Devices Meeting Technical Digest, p. 692.
[13]D. R. Myers, T. E. Zipperian, R. M. Biefeld, and J. J. Wiczer, 1983 International Electron Devices Meeting Technical Digest, p. 700.
[14]W. D. Laidig, P. J. Caldwell, K. Kim, and J. W. Lee, IEEE Electron Devices Lett. **EDL-4**, 212 (1983).

Threshold current of single quantum well lasers: The role of the confining layers

J. Nagle, S. Hersee, M. Krakowski, T. Weil, and C. Weisbuch
Thomson–CSF, Laboratoire Central de Recherches, Domaine de Corbeville, BP 10, F-91401, Orsay, France

(Received 13 August 1986; accepted for publication 23 September 1986)

The threshold current density of single quantum well (SQW) GaAs/GaAlAs lasers is calculated, taking into account the carrier populations of the confining layer. We find that these populations are significant when compared to those of the quantum well. This effect explains the better performance of the graded-index separate confinement SQW laser when compared to the separate confinement heterostructure laser, as well as the T_0 performance of such lasers.

The excellent properties of single quantum well lasers have now been extensively described in several review papers.[1-6] A number of theoretical models have been developed in order to describe various aspects of the operating characteristics of quantum well lasers.[7-17] However, a few key issues remain unsatisfactorily answered such as (i) the performance improvement when going from a separate confinement heterostructure quantum well laser (SCH QW) to a graded-index SCH QW laser (GRIN SCH QW)[18,19]; (ii) what should the optimum cladding layer composition be for optimal threshold current and/or T_0?

Conditions for laser action in quantum wells can be fruitfully compared to that of double-heterostructure (DH) lasers.[20] Two opposing effects need to be considered. (i) The reduction in allowed quantum states for carriers in the active volume leads to the reduction of states which need to be inverted to reach threshold. (ii) The optical confinement factor Γ is strongly decreased. In order to obtain usable Γ's one has to use multiple quantum well structures or separate confinement heterostructures such as the SCH[21] or GRIN SCH,[18] where the active layer is a single quantum well but where the optical confinement is provided by additional layers surrounding the active layer (Fig. 1).

The two effects, i.e., reduced density of states (DOS) and reduced optical confinement, tend to balance each other. One has therefore to perform a complete two-dimensional (2D) calculation in order to ascertain QW laser properties.

Previous calculations have focused on one or several aspects of laser action in quantum wells. Dutta[8] has calculated laser threshold for single quantum well (SQW) laser taking into account the fundamental state of the quantum well. Various other authors have taken into account the quantum well excited states.[10-15] The optimization of SQW versus multiple quantum well (MQW) lasers has also been discussed.[15-17] Evaluations of the effect of Auger recombination on threshold conditions and its influence on quantum well structure optimization have also been performed.[12,22-24]

In this letter we go beyond the previous analyses by taking into account the whole heterostructure in the derivation of the gain coefficient of the active material. In particular, for the SCH and GRIN SCH QW lasers, the importance of the confining layer is crucial to the calculation of carrier populations near threshold.

The ingredients of the present calculation are as follows:

(i) Energy level calculations: the confined energy levels E_n in the quantum wells are calculated using the envelope function model. We use a 62% conduction-band offset. We use a first-order correction for the electron effective mass variation with energy. We use for holes the simplest approximation of uncoupled heavy- and light-hole bands. For the GRIN SCH energy levels we calculate the energy levels of the whole structure, matching Airy wave functions in the triangular potential regions with harmonic functions for the square-potential central region.

(ii) Band filling is calculated in the following way. We use the electron density in the quantum well n_{2D} as the input parameter for the whole calculation. From the known quantum well energy levels, we then calculate the quasi-Fermi level for electrons, then the electron population in the SCH or GRIN SCH confining layer n_{3D}. Assuming neutral equilibrium in the undoped regions, $n_{2D} + n_{3D} = P_{2D} + P_{3D}$, we evaluate the hole populations and quasi-Fermi level. In the hole density of states, we use as transverse hole masses the uncoupled hole masses deduced from the Luttinger

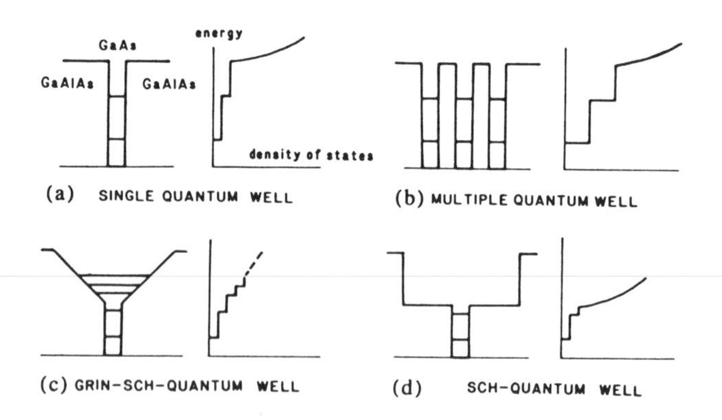

FIG. 1. Various quantum well laser structures schematically depicted by their conduction-band-edge space variation (left side of each figure) and their 2D density of states (DOS) (right side). (a) Single quantum well: Each quantized well state introduces a 2D DOS equal to $m^*/\pi\hbar^2$, while the onset of 3D states at the top of the well introduces a much larger DOS. (b) Multiple quantum well (MQW): Each quantized state introduces a 2D DOS equal to $Nm^*/\pi\hbar^2$, N being the number of wells. (c) Graded-index separate confinement heterostructure (GRIN SCH) laser: Note the ladder of quantum states in the graded region. (d) Separate confinement heterostructure (SCH) laser: The intermediate-composition layers introduce a large DOS.

Reprinted with permission from *Appl. Phys. Lett.*, vol. 49, no. 20, pp. 1325–1327, Nov. 17, 1986.

Hamiltonian.[25,26] Strong nonparabolicity and state mixing do exist in the quantum well valence band,[27] but inclusion of such effects would lead to strenuous complications without altering the basic conclusions of the present letter. We use the usual transition probabilities calculated at the Brillouin zone center, i.e., the transitions from the conduction band to the heavy-hole band have probabilities 1.5 (TE polarization) and the transitions to the light-hole band have probabilities 0.5 (TE polarization) and 2 (TM polarization).

(iii) Gain is calculated using the standard transition probability.[20] We use a k-conservation selection rule, as we can explain our gain spectral curves with such a model, using reasonable broadening coefficients. Under the same approximations we calculate the spontaneous radiative rate R_{sp} which appears as a function of n_{2D} and T.

(iv) The threshold current is then calculated using the confinement factor Γ of the structure. The threshold gain g_{th} is defined by[20]

$$\Gamma g_{th} = \alpha + (1/L)\ln(1/R),$$

where α is the laser medium loss, L the laser cavity length, and R the facet reflectivity. From this value of g_{th}, we deduce the corresponding electron density n_{2D} and radiative current injection J_{rad} from the value of R_{sp} for that n_{2D}.

If we consider that there is no other source of recombination (i.e., injection quantum efficiency is 1), the calculated J_{rad} is the threshold current density J_{th}. If there are other recombination paths such as Auger recombination, they give rise to an injection current J_{NR} which has to be calculated at the same value of the parameter n_{2D}.

We first can explain the wide spectral gain curves from the excited quantum state populations. Such broad curves have been considered quite surprising as simple nonquantitative arguments predict that the square 2D DOS should

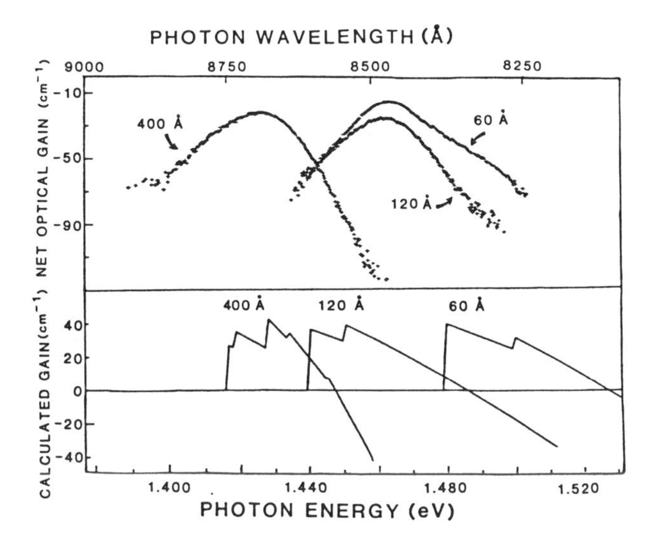

FIG. 2. Measured net optical gain curves $[\Gamma g(E) - \alpha(E) - (1/L)\ln(1/R)]$ along the method of Hakki and Paoli (see Ref. 28) (top) and corresponding calculated curves for modal gain (Γg). The low-energy side of the gain curve is not treated in the theory as no band tailing is included (see, for instance, Ref. 20). The high-energy slope of the gain curve is well represented by the calculations. The peak positions are shifted relatively to the calculated ones because of the presence of some Al in the active region due to memory effects in the MOCVD reactor.

lead to a gain curve narrower than in 3D. Figure 2 shows gain measurements along the method by Hakki and Paoli[28] in 400, 120, and 60 Å GRIN SCH quantum wells together with gain calculations, assuming the same loss factor (40 cm^{-1}) and confining factors of 0.1123, 0.0336, and 0.0164, respectively. Besides the sharp edges of the calculated curves, which should be smoothed out by introducing a phenomenological broadening parameter in order to take into account carrier collisions, we see that the main features can be well explained. The broadening of gain curves, in some analysis thought to be due to k nonconservation rules,[29] is rather due to higher quantum states populations in the wide wells. For narrower wells, the increase in linewidth is due to the very high band filling required to obtain enough gain because of the smaller confinement factor. The same gain calculations have been performed for the corresponding SCH structures. Results are summarized in Table I. The most remarkable feature is the large carrier population at threshold in the confining layers when the well becomes small. For GRIN SCH structures this population is smaller due to the slowly increasing density of states. Beyond the small change in total electron density at threshold, this 3D population translates into a larger threshold current of the SCH structure because of the usually nonunity quantum efficiency of GaAlAs confining layers. If we use a reasonable carrier lifetime of 1 ns in the confining layer material, we expect in the case of 60 Å SCH laser an additional current of 2 kA/cm^2 due to the recombination of carriers in the 5000-Å-wide optical cavity. We believe that there lies the improvement of the GRIN SCH structure as compared to the SCH structure. The often evoked "funnel effect"[19] of the GRIN SCH structure, which should lead to efficient capture by the active quantum well layer, was recently theoretically shown to be negligible[30] as the capture time, both in SCH and GRIN SCH structures, is always well below 100 ps. Our conclusion is that the GRIN SCH structure is always the better one, at variance with the conclusions of McIlroy *et*

TABLE I. Calculated operating features for SCH and GRIN SCH structures. The SCH confining layer width is adjusted at 5000 Å in order to yield the same confinement factor Γ as in the GRIN SCH lasers.

GRIN-SCH Structure: Al Grading 18–40% Width at top 4400 Å			
Quantum well width L_z (Å)	400	120	60
Confinement factor	0.122	0.0336	0.0164
n_{well} (threshold) (10^{12} cm^{-2})	5.1	2.3	1.7
n_{cavity} (threshold) (10^{12} cm^{-2})	0.12	0.37	0.82
Gain width (meV)	30	45.5	48
Lasing energy (meV)	1438	1459	1488
(transition type)	$(E_2 - HH_2)$	$(E_1 - LH_1)$	$(E_1 - HH_1)$

SCH Structure: Al confining layer contents: 18 and 40% Confining layer width: 5000 Å			
Quantum well width L_z (Å)	400	120	60
n_{well} (threshold) (10^{12} cm^{-2})	6.3	3.2	2.1
n_{cavity} (threshold) (10^{12} cm^{-2})	1.5	5.5	12

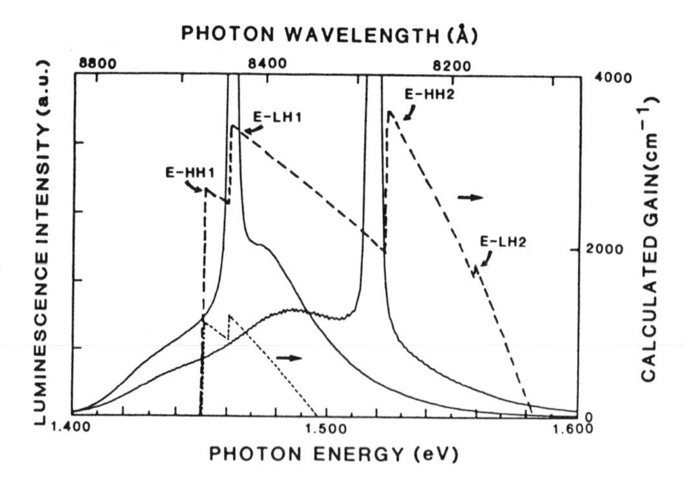

FIG. 3. Lasing emissions (full curves) recorded for two GRIN SCH lasers from the same wafer with cavity lengths of 366 and 100 μm. The respective losses are 40 and 120 cm^{-1}. Spectra are recorded in the TM mode in order to diminish the amount of laser light incoming on the detector to record simultaneously the spontaneous emission ($I = 1.5 I_{th}$). Both lasers lase in the TE mode. Calculated threshold gain in that mode (dashed lines) is shown, corresponding to $n_{2D} = 2.3\times10^{12}$ cm^{-2} and $n_{2D} = 5\times10^{12}$ cm^{-2} for $L = 366$ μm and $L = 100$ μm, respectively.

al.,[16] who neglected confining layer states. The smaller density of states in the confining layers of the GRIN SCH structures is at the origin of the larger T_0 of that laser as compared to the SCH's. However, such GRIN SCH lasers have quite often worse T_0 than DH lasers and certainly never as good as MQW lasers, due to the available cavity quantum states near the lasing states.

Finally, we have studied short cavity lasers for a 120-Å QW GRIN SCH structure, in order to increase the threshold gain. We observe (Fig. 3) a shift of the lasing emission to the $n = 2$ quantum well level at shorter wavelengths, as was recently independently reported by several authors.[31-33] We have made a calculation of the new threshold carrier density, which shows that one actually requires to populate the $n = 2$ quantized level to reach enough gain to obtain lasing. In the short cavity (100 μm) the well and cavity electron populations are 5.0×10^{12} cm^{-2} and 2.8×10^{12} cm^{-2} compared to 2.3×10^{12} cm^{-2} and 3.7×10^{11} cm^{-2} in the long cavity case (366 μm). This explains the much higher threshold current required as well as the poor temperature behavior (small T_0) of such short lasers.

In conclusion, we have shown that populations of quantum well excited states and confining layer states play a significant role in the threshold characteristics of SCH and GRIN SCH quantum well lasers. The superiority of the GRIN SCH structure stems from its low density of states in the confining region. In all cases, extremely large band filling occurs in the electron quantum states.

The authors acknowledge useful discussions on quantum well lasers with B. de Cremoux and M. Razeghi. Expert technical assistance was provided by R. Blondeau and R. Cordeau.

[1]W. T. Tsang, IEEE J. Quantum Electron. **QE-20**, 1119 (1984).
[2]L. J. Van Ruyven, J. Lumin. **29**, 123 (1984).
[3]R. D. Burnham, W. Streifer, and T. L. Paoli, J. Cryst. Growth **68**, 370 (1984).
[4]N. Holonyak, Jr., R. M. Kolbas, R. D. Dupuis, and P. D. Dapkus, IEEE J. Quantum Electron. **QE-16**, 170 (1980).
[5]B. de Cremoux, in *Proceedings of the European Solid State Device Research Conference (ESSDERC) 85*, Solid State Devices 85, edited by P. Balk and O. G. Folberth (Elsevier, Amsterdam, 1986), p. 83.
[6]W. T. Tsang, in *Semiconductors and Semimetals*, edited by R. K. Willardson and A. C. Beer (Academic, New York, 1985), Vol. 22A, p. 95.
[7]K. Hess, B. A. Vojak, N. Holonyak, Jr., R. Chin, and P. D. Dapkus, Solid State Electron. **23**, 585 (1980).
[8]N. K. Dutta, J. Appl. Phys. **53**, 7211 (1982).
[9]M. G. Burt, Electron. Lett. **19**, 210 (1983).
[10]D. Kasemset, Chi-Shain Hong, N. B. Patel, and P. D. Dapkus, IEEE J. Quantum Electron. **QE-19**, 1025 (1983).
[11]A. Sugimura, IEEE J. Quantum Electron. **QE-20**, 336 (1984).
[12]M. Asada, A. Kameyama, and Y. Suematsu, IEEE J. Quantum Electron. **QE-20**, 745 (1984).
[13]T. Ohtoshi, K. Uomi, N. Chinone, T. Kajimura, and Y. Murayama, J. Appl. Phys. **57**, 992 (1985).
[14]M. Yamada, S. Ogita, M. Yamagishi, and K. Tabata, IEEE J. Quantum Electron. **QE-21**, 640 (1985).
[15]Y. Arakawa and A. Yariv, IEEE J. Quantum Electron. **QE-21**, 1666 (1985).
[16]P. W. A. McIlroy, A. Kurobe, and Y. Uematsu, IEEE J. Quantum Electron. **QE-21**, 1958 (1985).
[17]B. Saint-Cricq, F. Lozes-Dupuy, and G.Vassilieff, IEEE J. Quantum Electron. **QE-22**, 625 (1986).
[18]W. T. Tsang, Appl. Phys. Lett. **39**, 134 (1981).
[19]S. D. Hersee, M. Baldy, P. Assenat, and B. de Cremoux, Electron. Lett. **18**, 870 (1982); see also M. Baldy, S.D.Hersee, and P. Assenat, Rev. Tech. Thomson CSF **15**, 5 (1983).
[20]See, e.g., the description of laser action in DH Lasers in H. C. Casey, Jr. and M. B. Panish, *Heterostructure Lasers* (Academic, New York, 1978).
[21]W. T. Tsang, Electron. Lett. **16**, 939 (1980).
[22]N. K. Dutta, J. Appl. Phys. **54**, 1236 (1983).
[23]A. Sugimura, IEEE J. Quantum Electron. **QE-19**, 932 (1983).
[24]C. Smith, R. A. Abram, and M. G. Burt, Superlattices and Microstructures **1**, 119 (1985).
[25]J. M. Luttinger, Phys. Rev. **102**, 1030 (1956).
[26]D. S. Chemla, Helv. Phys. Acta **56**, 607 (1983).
[27]See, e.g., D. A. Broido and L. S. Sham, Phys. Rev. B **31**, 888 (1985).
[28]B. Hakki and T. L. Paoli, J. Appl. Phys. **44**, 4113 (1973).
[29]P. T. Landsberg, M. S. Abrahams, and M. Osinsky, IEEE J. Quantum Electron. **QE-21**, 24 (1985).
[30]J. A. Brum, T. Weil, J. Nagle, and B. Vinter, Phys. Rev. B **34**, 2381 (1986).
[31]J. Nagle, T. Weil, M. Razeghi, S. Hersee, M. Krakowski, R. Blondeau, P. Hirtz, and C. Weisbuch, International Quantum Electronics Conference, San Francisco, June 1986 (unpublished).
[32]M. Mittelstein, Y. Arakawa, A. Larsson, and A. Yariv, International Quantum Electronics Conference, San Francisco, June 1986, post-deadline paper (unpublished).
[33]P. S. Sory, A. R. Reisinger, R. G. Waters, L. J. Mawst, C. A. Zmudzinski, M. A. Emanuel, M. E. Givers, and J. J. Coleman, Appl. Phys. Lett. **49**, 16 (1986).

Quantum Well Lasers—Gain, Spectra, Dynamics

Y. ARAKAWA, MEMBER, IEEE, AND A. YARIV, FELLOW, IEEE

(Invited Paper)

Abstract—**We discuss a number of theoretical and experimental issues in quantum well lasers with emphasis on the basic behavior of the gain, the field spectrum, and the modulation dynamics. It is revealed that the use of quantum well structures results in improvement of these properties and brings several new concepts to optical semiconductor devices.**

I. Introduction

THE ability to fabricate single quantum well (SQW) and multiple quantum well (MQW) devices has given rise to new optical and electronic devices as well as to new physical phenomena [1]. Since the first investigation of optical properties in quantum wells by Dingle *et al.*, [2] the application of quantum well structures to semiconductor laser diodes [3], [4] has received considerable attention because of physical interest as well as its superior characteristics, such as low threshold current density [5], [6], low temperature dependence of threshold current [7]–[9], lasing wavelength tunability, and excellent dynamic properties [10]–[12]. By controlling the width of the quantum wells, one can modify the electron and hole wavefunctions, which leads to the modification of material parameters. This results in improvements of the laser characteristics, as well as introduction of new concepts to semiconductor optical devices.

In this paper, we describe the basic properties of the quantum well laser with emphasis on its dynamic and spectral properties as well as gain characteristics. We also discuss new device concepts including a Q-switched quantum well laser [13] and a quantum wire laser [9], [10].

II. Gain and Threshold Current

A. Density of States

In a quantum well (QW) structure, a series of energy levels and associated subbands are formed due to the quantization of electrons in the direction of the QW thickness. The density of states (per unit energy and area) of such confined electrons in a SQW structure is given by

$$\rho_c(E) = \sum_{n=1}^{\infty} \frac{m_c}{\pi \hbar^2} H[E - \epsilon_n] \tag{1}$$

where $H[x]$, m_c, $\hbar$, and ϵ_n are the Heaviside function, the effective mass of electrons, Planck's constant (h) divided by 2π, and the quantized energy level of electrons in the nth subband of the QW, respectively. When the barriers are sufficiently high and the barrier thickness is sufficiently large, ϵ_n is equal to

$$\epsilon_n = \frac{(n\pi\hbar)^2}{2m_c L_z^2} \tag{2}$$

where L_z is the thickness of the QW.

If we use a MQW structure instead of the SQW, the density of states is modified. When barrier layers between wells are thick enough, each well is independent. In this case, the density of states is just N times density of states of electrons in an SQW.

$$\rho_c(E) = N \sum_{n=1}^{\infty} \frac{m_c}{\pi \hbar^2} H[E - \epsilon_n] \tag{3}$$

where N is the number of QW's. On the other hand, if the barrier is sufficiently thin or its barrier height is small enough so that coupling between adjacent wells is substantial, the quantized energy levels are no longer degenerate, and each single well level splits into N different energy levels. In this case, the density of states (per unit energy and area) is expressed by

$$\rho_c(E) = \sum_{n=1}^{\infty} \sum_{k=1}^{N} \frac{m_c}{\pi \hbar^2} H[E - \epsilon_{nk}] \tag{4}$$

where ϵ_{nk} ($k = 1, \cdots, N$) are the energy levels which split from a single well energy level. Kroemer *et al.* [14] and Yariv *et al.* [15] analytically estimated the energy broadening due to this coupling. The coupling is important for obtaining a uniform carrier distribution in the MQW structure. However, strong coupling leads to the smearing of the configuration of the density of states and a resulting reduction in the two-dimensional character of the wells. We can characterize the smearing due to coupling by ΔE ($\equiv$ max ϵ_{nk} − min ϵ_{nk}). This ΔE corresponds to the degree to which the smearing in the density of states occurs. Since the tunneling time τ_t of electrons through a barrier is on the order of $\hbar/\Delta E$, the following relations

Manuscript received January 5, 1986; revised April 11, 1986. This work was supported by the U.S. Air Force Office of Scientific Research, the U.S. Office of Naval Research, the I.T.T. Corporation, and the Japan Society for the Promotion of Science.

Y. Arakawa is with the California Institute of Technology, Pasadena, CA 91125, on leave from the Institute of Industrial Science, University of Tokyo, Minato-ku, Tokyo 106, Japan.

A. Yariv is with the California Institute of Technology, Pasadena, CA 91125.

IEEE Log Number 8609366.

Reprinted from *IEEE J. Quantum Electron.*, vol. QE-22, no. 9, pp. 1887–1899, Sept. 1986.

are required for obtaining good uniformity of carrier concentration and maintaining the two-dimensional properties [14]:

$$\hbar/\tau_r \ll \Delta E(=\hbar/\tau_t) \ll \hbar/\tau_{\text{in}} \quad (5)$$

where τ_r is the carrier recombination time at lasing and τ_{in} is the intraband relaxation time (i.e., T_2 time). The first inequality indicates that the tunneling time for uniform carrier distribution should be much smaller than the recombination time. The second one implies that the smearing due to the coupling should be much smaller than the smearing due to the carrier relaxation effects. A localization effect in two slightly asymmetric wells is also discussed by Lang *et al.* [16] and Yariv *et al.* [15]. In order to simplify the discussion in this paper, we assume that the coupling in an MQW is weak enough that the density of states can be described by (3).

B. Linear Gain

The gain properties in QW lasers have been investigated using different theoretical treatments [17]–[23]. The main features of the gain properties in QW lasers are the gain flattening effect, dependence on the number and the thickness of the QW's and the anisotropy of the momentum matrix element. When the recombination is dominated by the band-to-band radiative process [24], [25], the linear bulk gain derived under k-selection rule is given by [26]

$$g(E, n) = \frac{\omega}{n_r^2} \chi_I(E, n) \quad (6)$$

$$\chi_I(E, n) = \int \sum_{n=0}^{\infty} \sum_{j=l,h} \rho^j_{\text{red}_n}(\epsilon)(f_c(E_{c_n}) - f_v(E_{v_n}))\, \hat{\chi}_I^{n,j}(E, \epsilon)\, d\epsilon. \quad (7)$$

The bulk gain is the gain exercised by an electromagnetic field if it were completely confined to the QW (i.e., a confinement factor of unity). E is the photon energy, j designates either light holes (l) or heavy holes (h), $\rho^j_{\text{red}_n}$ is the reduced density of states which is defined by $\rho^j_{\text{red}_n} = ((\rho_{c_n})^{-1} + (\rho^j_{v_n})^{-1})^{-1}$, $\rho^j_{v_n}$ is the density of states of light holes ($j = l$) or heavy holes ($j = h$), and f_c (f_v) is the quasi Fermi–Dirac distribution function for electrons (holes) in the conduction band (the valence band) with the Fermi-energy ϵ_{f_c} (ϵ_{f_v}). E_{c_n} and $E^j_{v_n}$ are equal to $(m_c\epsilon^j_{v_n} + m^j_v E + m^j_v \epsilon_{cn})/(m_c + m^j_v)$ and $(m_c\epsilon^j_{v_n} - m_c E + m^j_v\epsilon_{cn})/(m_c + m^j_v)$, respectively, where m^j_v and $\epsilon^j_{v_n}$ are the effective mass and the energy level of the nth subband of light holes ($j = l$) or heavy holes ($j = h$). $\chi_I(E, n)$ is the imaginary part of the susceptibility and $\hat{\chi}_I^{n,j}(E, \epsilon)$ is the susceptibility of each electron–heavy hole pair (or electron–light hole pair) in the nth subband and is given by

$$\hat{\chi}_I^{n,j}(E, \epsilon) = \frac{\pi e^2 h}{m_0^2 c n_r E_g} |M_{n,j}(\epsilon)|^2_{\text{ave}} \frac{\hbar/\tau_{\text{in}}}{(E - \epsilon)^2 + (\hbar/\tau_{\text{in}})^2} \quad (8)$$

where n_r is the refractive index of the active layer, e is the electron charge, m_0 is the mass electrons, c is the light velocity, and E_g is the bandgap. Although the possibility of the transition with no k-selection rule [19] and a violation of the $\Delta n = 0$ selection rule have been discussed, we will adopt the formula with k-selection rule with $\Delta n = 0$ selection rule.

In QW structures, it was observed by Kobayashi *et al.* [27] that the internal gain depends on the polarization of the light. Asada *et al.* [28] and Yamanishi *et al.* [29] discussed this phenomenon using the $\boldsymbol{k} \cdot \boldsymbol{p}$ perturbation method developed by Kane [30]. For instance, $|M_{n,j}|^2_{\text{ave}}$ for the TE mode (polarized parallel to the layers) due to an electron–heavy hole transition is given by

$$|M_{n,h}|^{2\text{TE}}_{\text{ave}} = |M_0|^2_{\text{ave}}\,(1 + E/(\epsilon_{c_n} - \epsilon^h_{v_n})) \quad (8)$$

where $|M_0|^2_{\text{ave}}$ is the square of the dipole matrix element of conventional double heterostructure (DH) lasers and is approximately equal to $1.33\, m_0 E_g$. For more precise discussion on this matrix element, nonparabolicity and anisotropy of valence band should be considered, which is discussed elsewhere. The calculated results shown below are, however, on the basis of the above simple model.

The quasi-Fermi energy levels ϵ_{F_c} and ϵ_{F_v} in a laser are determined by both the charge neutrality condition and the condition that the modal gain $g_{\text{mod}}(E) = \Gamma_g(E)$ where Γ is the optical confinement factor) at the photon energy E_l for the laser oscillation is equal to the total losses α_{total} as follows:

$$g_{\text{mod}}(E_l) = \Gamma_g(E) = \alpha_{\text{total}} = \Gamma\alpha_{\text{ac}} + (1 - \Gamma)\,\alpha_{\text{ex}} + L^{-1}\ln(1/R) \quad (9)$$

where α_{ac}, α_{ex}, R, and L are the loss in the active region, the loss in the cladding layers, the reflectivity, and the cavity length, respectively.

Once the Fermi energy levels are fixed, the injected current density J is determined by the following equation:

$$J = eN\left(\iint \frac{8\pi n_r^2 E_g^2}{c^2 h} \sum_{n=0}^{\infty} \sum_{j=l,h} \rho_{\text{red}_j}(\epsilon)\, f_c(E_{c_n}) \cdot (1 - f_v(E_{c_n}))\, \hat{\chi}_I^{n,j}(E, \epsilon)\, d\epsilon\, dE\right). \quad (10)$$

The optical confinement factor Γ depends strongly on the structure. If we use the separate confinement structure, Γ can be expressed approximately by the following simple formulas [11]:

$$\Gamma = 0.3N \frac{L_z}{L_0} \quad (11)$$

where N is the number of QW's, L_0 is equal to 1000 Å, and the following structure is assumed; the MQW laser has $Ga_{0.75}Al_{0.25}As$ barriers and $Ga_{0.75}Al_{0.25}As$ waveguide layers, and the dimension of the waveguide layers is determined so that the total thickness, including QW's, barriers, and waveguide layers, is equal to 2000 Å. The cladding layers are made of p-$Ga_{0.6}Al_{0.4}As$ and n-$Ga_{0.6}Al_{0.4}As$. In the following calculation, we will ignore

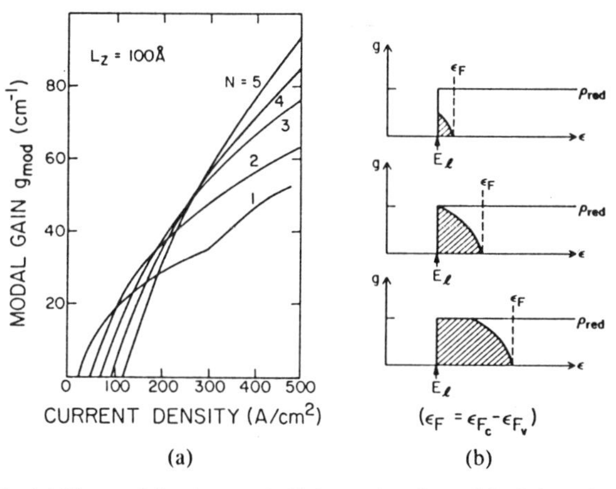

Fig. 1. (a) The modal gain g_{mod} $(=\Gamma g)$ as a function of the injected current density with various number of quantum wells N. The thickness of each quantum well is assumed to be 100 Å. (b) An illustration which explains how the gain flattening effect occurs with the increase of the Fermi energy levels.

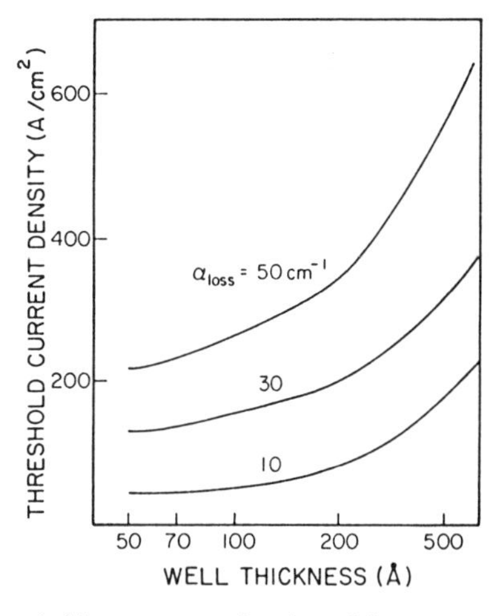

Fig. 2. The threshold current as a function of the quantum well thickness with various total loss α loss. The number of quantum wells is optimized so that the threshold current is minimum.

nonradiative effects such as the Auger recombination and the intervalence band effect [31]–[34].

If the carrier density, hence the quasi-Fermi energy level, in each QW is the same, the modal gain with N QW's, $g_{mod}^{N}(E_l)$, is given by

$$g_{mod}^{N}(E_l) = Ng_{mod}^{(N=1)}(E_l) \tag{12}$$

where E_l is the lasing photon energy. But, this, of course, happens at

$$J^N = NJ^{(N=1)} \tag{13}$$

or, stated in words, the modal gain available from N QW's is N times that of an SQW and is obtained at a current density which is N times that of an SQW laser. Fig. 1(a) shows the calculated modal gain $g_{mod}^{N}(E_l)$ as a function of the injected current density in a QW laser with N QW's on the basis of (12) and (13). We notice a very marked flattening (''saturation'') of the gain at high injected currents, especially in an SQW ($N = 1$). This gain flattening effect is due to the step-like shape of the density of states functions, and the fact that once the quasi-Fermi energy levels penetrate into the conduction band and valence band, which happens at high injected currents, the product $\rho_{red}(\epsilon)(f_c - f_v)$, which determines the gain, becomes a constant and no longer increases with the current. This is illustrated in Fig. 1(b). This flattening effect was evidenced recently by Arakawa *et al.* [35] in a systematic measurement of the threshold current of high-quality GRIN–SCH (graded index waveguide–separate confinement heterostructure) SQW lasers of different cavity length. They observed the jump of the lasing wavelength with the decrease of the cavity length from the wavelength corresponding to $n = 1$ transition to the wavelength corresponding to $n = 2$ transition, which demonstrates the existence of discrete quantized energy levels.

Owing to this gain flattening effect, there exits an optimum number of QW's for minimizing the threshold current for a given total loss α_{total}. From Fig. 1(a), we see that, for low losses, the injected threshold current is minimum with $N = 1$. On the other hand, if $\alpha_{total} = 20$ cm^{-1}, the threshold current with $N = 1$ is larger than that of $N = 2$. At higher values of α_{total} which call for larger laser modal gain, a larger number of wells is needed. When α_{total} is 50 cm^{-1}, a five-well structure ($N = 5$) will have the lowest threshold current.

Fig. 2 shows the threshold current as a function of the QW thickness for various α_{total}. In this calculation, the number of QW's is optimized for each QE thickness so that the threshold current is minimum. The results indicate that the threshold current of thinner QW lasers (L_z = 50–100 Å) is much lower than that of thicker QW lasers. We also notice that the threshold current is minimized with $L_z \approx 60$ Å when α_{loss} is low (α_{loss} = 10–30 cm^{-1}). This is mainly due to the fact that the current for transparency (gain equals to zero) is minimized at the thickness of $L_z \approx 60$ Å in the case of $N = 1$ and also due to the fact that the optimum N in QW lasers with each thickness is 1 in the case of low α_{total} for thin QW structures.

C. Experiment

Many experiments on GaAs/GaAlAs QW laser [5], [7], [36]–[43], InGaAsP/InP QW lasers [44]–[47], InGaAlAs QW lasers [48], and AlGaSb QW lasers [49] have been reported. Fuji *et al.* [5] reported a very low threshold current density as low as 175 A/cm^2 with 480 μm cavity length in a GaAs/AlGaAs GRIN-SCH SQW laser. This demonstrates the realization of high gain with lower spontaneous emission rate owing to the step-like density of states.

sulting in a red shift of the excitonic absorption energy. The band discontinuities prevent the ionization of the exciton, allowing excitonic resonances to be observed at room temperature with large applied fields ($> 10^5$ V/cm).

The concept of the size effect modulation proposed by Yamanishi *et al.* [74] also utilizes the application of electric field. This causes the spatial of the electron distribution and hole distribution in a well, which leads to the modulation of the matrix elements.

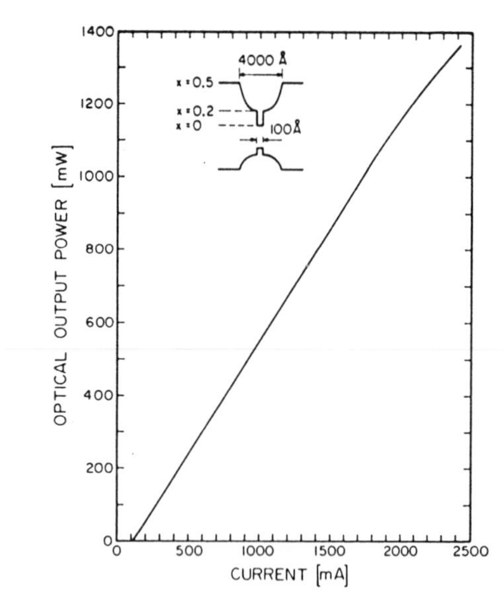

Fig. 3. The light output power versus injection current under pulsed condition of a 100 μm wide and 480 μm broad area GaAs/AlGaAs GRIN-SCH laser (400 ns, 25 Hz).

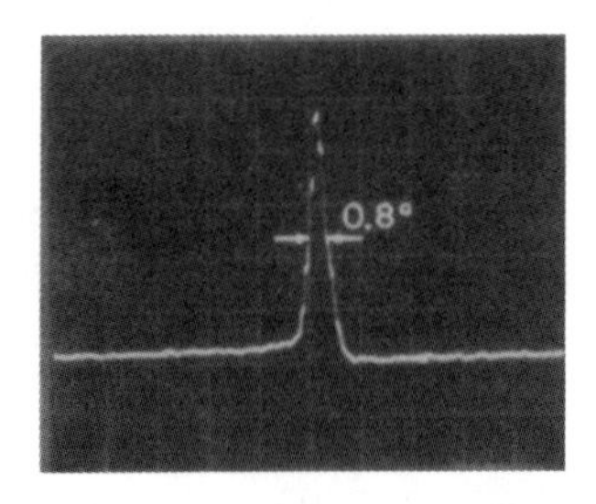

Fig. 4. The far-field pattern parallel to the injection plane of a 100 μm wide broad area GaAs/AlGaAs GRIN-SCH laser at $I = 1.2I_{th}$. The measured full width at half maximum is 0.8° which is quite close to the diffraction limit of 0.4°.

Recently, in MBE-grown broad area GaAs/AlGaAs GRIN-SCH SQW lasers, a quantum efficiency around 70 percent with a single far-field lobe as narrow as 0.8° has been achieved by Larsson *et al.* [50]. Fig. 3 shows the measured light output power versus injection current under pulsed condition (400 ns, 25 Hz) using calibrated Si photodiodes and filters. The threshold current is 110 mA, which corresponds to a threshold current density of 230 A/cm^2. The maximum output power of 1.35 W from one mirror was limited by the available current from current source. The high external quantum efficiency is a combined result of the low threshold current density and the high differential quantum efficiency of 84 percent. This can be explained in terms of the step-like density of states associated with the quasi-two-dimensional structure of the SQW, enhanced carrier and optical confinement in the GRIN region, and optimized growth conditions. The internal loss estimated by measuring the differential quantum efficiency of the lasers with various cavity length is as low as 1.8 cm^{-1}. Fig. 4 shows the far-field pattern parallel to the junction plane for a 100 μm wide laser at $I = 1.2I_{th}$ where I_{th} is the threshold current. The measured full width at half maximum (FWHM) is 0.8°, to be compared to the diffraction limit of 0.4°. This extremely narrow far field is a result of increased lateral coherence produced by uniformly distributed and phase-locked filaments.

III. Differential Gain and Modulation Bandwidth

A. Relaxation Oscillation Frequency and Differential Gain

The direct modulation of a semiconductor laser has been a subject of active research for the past 20 years [51]–[55]. Experiments have shown the existence of a resonance peak in the modulation response. In the early stage of the semiconductor laser development, the principal concern was in optimizing structures for realizing low threshold currents and high quantum efficiencies. With the increasing sophistication of the laser and the maturing of the technology, their high-speed dynamic characteristics became a subject of increasing importance. Many efforts have been devoted to realizing a wide bandwidth in conventional DH semiconductor lasers by changing the laser geometry. Another approach is to modify the basic material properties through the use of QW structures. In this section, we discuss the possibility of the improvement of these characteristics.

The relaxation oscillation corner frequency f_r gives the useful direct modulation bandwidth of a semiconductor laser. The simple rate equation for laser dynamics can be described as follows:

$$\frac{dn}{dt} = \frac{J(t)}{eL_z} - \frac{n_r}{c} g(n, E_l) P - \frac{n}{\tau_s} \tag{14}$$

$$\frac{dP}{dt} = \Gamma \frac{n_r}{c} g(n, E_l) P + \beta \frac{n}{\tau_s} - \frac{P}{\tau_p} \tag{15}$$

where P is the photon density, β is the spontaneous emission coefficient into the lasing mode, τ_s is the carrier lifetime, $J(t)$ (cm^{-2}) is the injected current density, n is the carrier concentration, and $g(n, E_l)$ (cm^{-2}) is the bulk gain, while $\Gamma g(n, E_l)$ is the modal gain as a function of the carrier density n at the lasing photon energy E_l. To emphasize the dependence of the gain on carrier concentration, we denote the gain as $g(E, n)$ hereafter. When we discuss the carrier density in QW structures, we usually use the two-dimensional density (per cm^2). However, the proper "bookkeeping" of photons and carriers requires that n stand for carrier density per unit volume. The relaxation resonance frequency f_r is determined by a small-signal analysis of (14) and (15). The result can simply be expressed by [53]

$$f_r = \frac{1}{2\pi} \sqrt{\frac{n_r g'(E_l, n)}{c} \frac{P_0}{\tau_p}} \tag{16}$$

where P_0 is the stationary photon density in the cavity and $g'(E_l, n)$ is the differential gain (i.e., $g'(E, n) = \partial g(E, n)/\partial n$). This result suggests several ways to improve f_r: larger $g'(E_l, n)$, smaller τ_p, and larger P_0. The reduction of τ_p and the increase of P_0 are realized with the use of short cavity lasers [53] and window-type lasers [54]. To

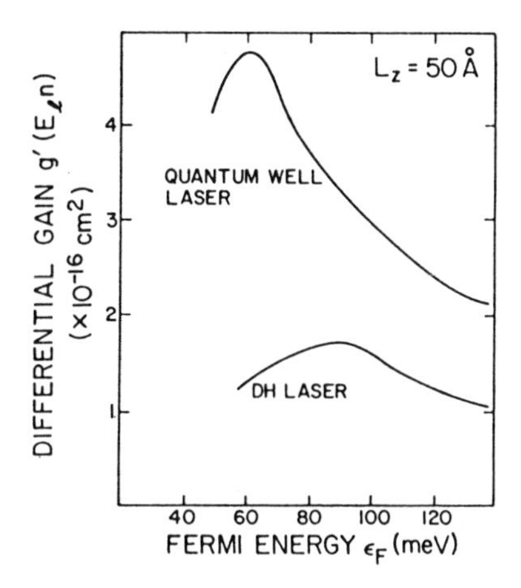

Fig. 5. The differential gain as a function of the conduction band quasi-Fermi energy level in a conventional double heterostructure laser and a quantum well laser with 50 Å well thickness.

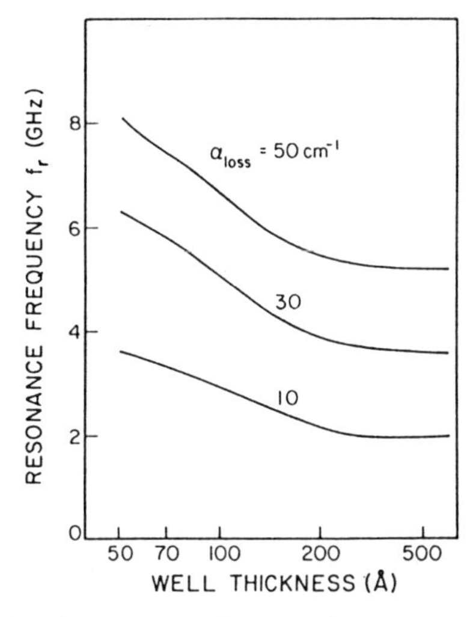

Fig. 6. The relaxation resonance frequency in a quantum well laser as a function of the well thickness. The number of quantum wells and quantum wires is optimized for each quantum well thickness.

increase $g'(E_l, n)$, operation at low temperatures [55] and the use of coupled cavity lasers [56] have been considered.

The basic quantum mechanical expression for $g'(E, n)$ suggests yet another way to increase $g'(E, n)$: changing the electron density of states with the use of QW's [10], [11]. Since the gain $g(E, n)$ is proportional to the imaginary part $\chi_I(E, n)$, as shown in (6), $g'(E, n)$ can be expressed by the following equation:

$$g'(E, n) = \frac{\partial}{\partial n}\left(\frac{\omega}{n_r^2}\chi_I(E, n)\right). \tag{17}$$

It is easily seen from this equation that the density of states plays an important role in determining the properties of $g'(E, n)$ as well as $g(E, n)$. The step-like density of states narrows the gain spectrum compared to that in the bulk material, which leads to an increase of $g'(E, n)$.

Fig. 5 shows the calculated differential gain $g'(E_l, n(\epsilon_{F_c}))$ for a conventional DH laser and a QW laser as a function of the conduction band quasi-Fermi energy level ϵ_{F_c} (measured from the lowest subband energy level). The thickness of the QW structures is equal to 50 Å. The quasi-Fermi energy level for the holes is determined by the charge neutrality condition. The result predicts an enhancement of $g'(E, n)$ for the QW active layer. Note that since $g'(E_l, n)$ is a bulk parameter, it is independent of the number of QW's.

This figure also shows that $g'(E_l, n)$ depends strongly on ϵ_{F_c} (i.e., necessary excitation for laser oscillation). The Fermi energy dependence of $g'(E_l, n)$ implies that there is an optimum number N of QW's in a laser structure which causes the largest enhancement of f_r. To see this, consider, again, the threshold condition for lasing in (9). For simplicity, we ignore the dependence of α_{total} on the structure. Since the gain is a monotonically increasing function of ϵ_{F_c}, the required ϵ_{F_c} for laser oscillation decreases monotonically with the increase of N. Consequently, there exits an optimum N for realizing $\epsilon_{F_c}^{\max}$, defined to yield the maximum $g'(E_l, n)$. It is easily shown that the ϵ_{F_c} at lasing threshold for $N = 1$ is much larger than $\epsilon_{F_c}^{\max}$. Therefore, the largest $g'(E_l, n)$ and the fastest modulation speeds are achieved for the MQW cases ($N \geq 2$). Fig. 6 shows the calculated f_r as a function of L_z (the QW width); α_{total} is assumed to be 50 cm^{-1}. At each L_z, the number of wells is optimized and f_r is normalized by f_r of a conventional DH laser (i.e., $L_z \rightarrow \infty$). The results suggest that by optimizing N, f_r can be enhanced by a factor of two in thin QW lasers.

B. *Experiment*

The enhancement of f_r was experimentally demonstrated by Uomi *et al.* [57]. They used an MQW laser with a self-aligned structure grown by MOCVD and measured the relaxation oscillation observed in the transient characteristics without dc bias at room temperature. f_r was measured as a function of (P/P_c) where P is the output power and P_c is the power for catastrophic optical damage. It was found that f_r of the MQW laser is about twice as large as that of a DH laser with the same structure. They estimated the modulation frequency to be 11 GHz near the catastrophic optical damage limit. This experimental result supports the above theoretical calculations. Iwamura *et al.* [58] measured the longitudinal mode behavior in MQW lasers under modulation, and they obtained a result which suggest that the narrower gain spectrum of an MQW laser causes fewer longitudinal modes under modulation.

IV. Spectral Noise Properties

A. *Spectral Linewidth*

Recently, the subject of semiconductor laser noise has received considerable attention. The deviation of conventional DH laser noise characteristics from well-established norms was demonstrated by Fleming *et al.* [59]. They found that the linewidth varies inversely with output power, as predicted by the modified Schawlow–Townes formula. The coefficient of the power dependence, however, was significantly larger than predicted by the formula. This discrepancy was explained physically by

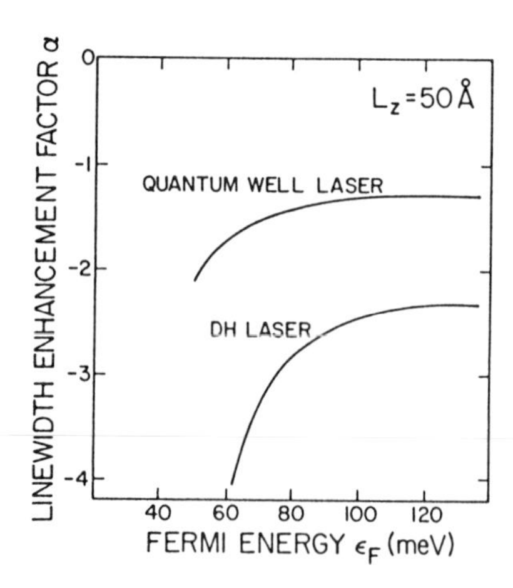

Fig. 7. The linewidth enhancement factor α as a function of the conduction band quasi-Fermi energy level in a conventional double heterostructure laser and a quantum well laser with 50 Å well thickness.

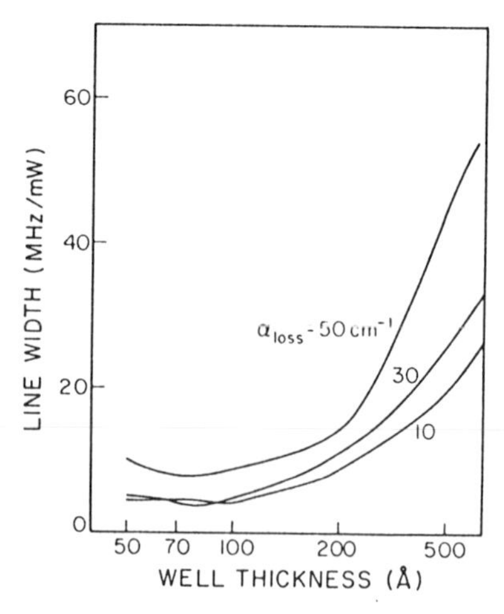

Fig. 8. The spectral linewidth in a quantum well laser as a function of the well thickness. The number of quantum wells is optimized for each quantum well thickness.

Henry [60], and a new theory was developed by Vahala *et al.* [61], [62]. They showed that the expected broadening enhancement is a factor $(1 + \alpha^2)$ where α is named the linewidth enhancement factor. The basic explanation is that phase fluctuations can result from index variations during relaxation oscillations after a spontaneous event, as well as by direct spontaneous emission events. For reducing the linewidth, the use of an external mirror, coupled cavity laser, and distributed feedback laser have been investigated. Another approach for reducing the linewidth is to modify the density of states. In this section, we indicate how the linewidth (or α) is reduced through the use of QW structures [10]–[12], [63].

The spectral linewidth $\Delta\nu$ can be expressed by [60], [61], [64]

$$\Delta\nu = \frac{v_g h\nu \Gamma_g R_m n_{sp}}{\pi P}(1 + \alpha^2) \tag{18}$$

$$\alpha = \frac{\partial \chi_R(E_l, n)/\partial n}{\partial \chi_I(E_l, n)/\partial n}. \tag{19}$$

R_m, v_g, $h\nu$, Γ, g, n_{sp}, and P are the mirror loss, the group velocity of light, the photon energy, the optical confinement factor, the bulk gain at threshold, the spontaneous emission factor, and the laser output power, respectively. $\chi_R(E, n)$ is the real part of the complex susceptibility and

$$\chi_R(E, n) = \int \sum_{n=0}^{\infty} \sum_{j=l,h} \rho^j_{\text{red}_n}(\epsilon)\,(f_c(E_{c_n}) - f_v(E_{v_n}))\, \hat{\chi}_R^{n,j}(E, \epsilon)\, d\epsilon$$

$$\hat{\chi}_R^{n,j}(E, \epsilon) = \frac{\pi e^2 h}{m_0^2 c n_r E_g} |M_{n,j}(\epsilon)|^2_{\text{ave}} \frac{E - \epsilon}{(E - \epsilon)^2 + (\hbar/\tau_{\text{in}})^2}. \tag{21}$$

α reflects the strong amplitude-phase coupling of the lasing field in a semiconductor laser resulting from the highly detuned optical gain spectrum. Equation (18) indicates that $\Delta\nu$ depends on the electronic density of states through α and n_{sp}.

The denominator of (19) is proportional to $g'(E_l, n)$. Therefore, from the results of the previous section, an increase of the denominator can be expected with the use of QW's. The numerator in (19), however, is also enhanced in QW structures. Therefore, it is difficult to predict the behavior of α in these structures without numerical calculations. Fig. 7 gives a calculation of α as a function of ϵ_{F_c} for conventional DH lasers and QW lasers. In this figure, the thickness of the QW's is equal to 50 Å. These calculation indicate first that α depends strongly on ϵ_{F_c} (or equivalently, on the level of injection which is determined by optical gain required for laser oscillation), its magnitude decreasing for larger ϵ_{F_c}. (This result has been observed experimentally for conventional DH lasers [65].) Second, this reduction of $|\alpha|$ with increasing excitation is larger in QW lasers than in conventional DH lasers. Therefore, a smaller number of QW's leads to a smaller value of $|\alpha|$ because a laser with a smaller number of QW's requires higher Fermi energy levels for a given modal gain.

The linewidth $\Delta\nu$ also contains the spontaneous emission factor n_{sp} which decreases monotonically with the increase of ϵ_{F_c} and converges to 1. This n_{sp} is the ratio of the spontaneous emission rate into the lasing mode to the stimulated emission rate and is given by

$$n_{sp} = \frac{\int \sum_{n=0}^{\infty} \sum_{j=l,h} \rho^j_{\text{red}_n}(\epsilon)\, f_c(E_{c_n})(1 - f_v(E_{v_n}))\, \hat{\chi}_I^{n,j}(E, \epsilon)\, d\epsilon}{\int \sum_{n=0}^{\infty} \sum_{j=l,h} \rho^j_{\text{red}_n}(\epsilon)\, (f_c(E_{c_n}) - f_v(E_{v_n}))\, \hat{\chi}_I^{n,j}(E, \epsilon)\, d\epsilon}. \tag{22}$$

If the energy broadening due to the intraband relaxation is extremely small, we can approximate n_{sp} at the photon energy E_l by

$$n_{sp} \approx \frac{1}{1 - \exp((E_l - \epsilon_{F_c} + \epsilon_{F_v})/kT)}. \tag{23}$$

As shown in this equation, n_{sp} is a monotonically decreasing function of ϵ_{F_c}. Therefore, for a fixed loss (i.e., Γ_g is constant), it is advantageous to operate with a high ϵ_{F_c} to attain a reduction in $\Delta\nu$. With regard to the number of QW's, this means that, in contrast to f_r, the SQW active layer is the optimum choice for phase noise reduction. Fig. 8 gives the minimum attainable $\Delta\nu$ as a function of L_z with various α_{loss}. We notice that $\Delta\nu$ is reduced greatly for a thin active layer. $\Delta\nu$ is minimum around $L_z = 80$ Å because there is the current region in which α of $L_z = 80$ Å is smaller than that of $L_z = 50$ Å in the case of $\alpha_{\text{loss}} = 10\ \text{cm}^{-1}$. Since the value $\Delta\nu$ for a DH laser (0.1 μm active layer) is calculated to be 60 MHz/mW with $\alpha_{\text{total}} = 30\ \text{cm}^{-1}$, $\Delta\nu$ can be substantially reduced with a thin QW structure by a factor of $\frac{1}{10}$ compared to $\Delta\nu$ for DH lasers. For all L_z, $\Delta\nu$ increases monotonically when the number of QW's increases.

B. Experiments

Recently, Ogasawara *et al.* [66] measured the α parameter of MQW lasers experimentally. The active layer consisted of four 40 Å thick GaAs wells and four 50 Å thick $Al_{0.3}Ga_{0.7}As$ barriers. They measured the change in $\partial\chi_R(E_l, n)/\partial n$ and $\partial\chi_I(E_l, n)/\partial n$ separately. $\partial\chi_R(E_l, n)/\partial n$ is measured from the wavelength shift of a Fabry–Perot mode with pulsed current injection below threshold and $\partial\chi_I(E_l, n)/\partial n$ is measured from the depth of modulation in the spontaneous emission intensity. Although their measurement is not a direct measurement and the measured α is obtained below threshold, their result supports our prediction. Their experiment suggests that α of a QW laser is smaller by a factor of $\frac{1}{2}$ compared to that of a conventional DH laser with the same carrier concentration.

V. New Optical Devices Using Quantum Wells

A. New Optical Devices Using QW Structures

As discussed above, the QW laser is a promising light source for various applications, and considerable effort has been devoted to developing high-quality QW lasers. In addition, other new optical devices based on QW structures have been proposed and demonstrated. These include optical modulators [67], [68], optical bistable devices [69], tunable p-i-n QW photodetectors [70], [71], size effect modulation light sources [74], Q-switching laser light sources [9], and modulation-doped detectors [72], [73]. The first three devices utilize the quantum-confined Stark effects [84], [85] described as follows. The room-temperature absorption spectrum of MQW displays enhanced absorption at the band edge, with a double-peaked structure caused by excitons whose binding energy is enhanced by the two-dimensional confinement. When an electric field is applied to the QW's perpendicular to the layers, the exciton absorption peak shifts to lower energy. This effect is much larger than the Franz–Keldysh effect seen in bulk materials. The dominant mechanism is the decrease in confinement energies, resulting in a red shift of the excitonic absorption energy.

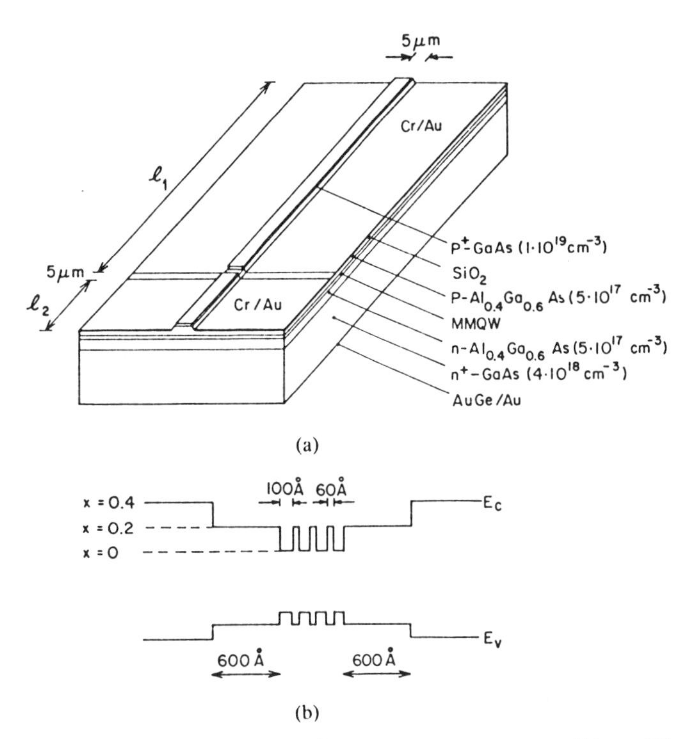

Fig. 9. (a) Perspective view of the two-segment quantum well laser. The lengths of the amplifier section l_1 and the modulator section l_2 were 250 and 50 μm, respectively. (b) The associated energy band diagram of the active layer.

The band discontinuities prevent the ionization of the exciton, allowing excitonic resonances to be observed at room temperature with large applied fields (> 10^5 V/cm).

The concept of the size effect modulation proposed by Yamanishi *et al.* [74] also utilizes the application of electric field. This causes the spatial displacement of the electron distribution and hole distribution in a well, which leads to the modulation of the matrix elements.

B. Q Switching in an MQW Laser with an Internal Loss Modulation

Picosecond pulse generation technology in semiconductor laser diodes is important for high-speed optical communication systems [75]–[83]. In Q-switching lasers, in contrast to mode-locked lasers, no external mirror is needed [80], [81] and lower modulation power is required compared to gain switching systems [82], [83]. Recently, effective active Q switching was successfully demonstrated by Arakawa *et al.* [13] in a GaAs/AlGaAs MQW laser with an intracavity monolithic electroabsorption loss modulator. The physical phenomena utilized are the quantum confined Stark effect in the modulation section and the enhanced carrier-induced band shrinkage effect [86] in the optical amplifier section. Optical pulses as narrow as 18.6 ps full width at half maximum (FWHM), assuming a Gaussian waveform, are generated.

Fig. 9(a) illustrates the two-segment MQW laser consisting of an optical amplifier section and an electroabsorption loss modulator section. The device structure was grown by molecular beam epitaxy. The associated energy band diagram is shown in Fig. 9(b). A 5 μm wide sepa-

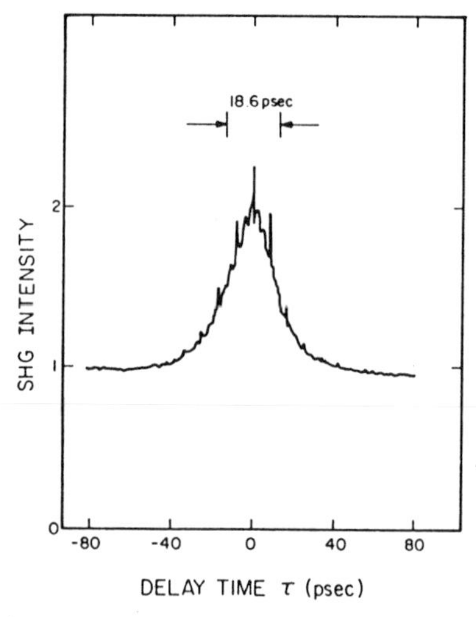

Fig. 10. Intensity autocorelation trace obtained from second harmonic generation widht 1.5 GHz modulation frequency and 0 V bias. The current injected into the optical amplifier section is 170 mA.

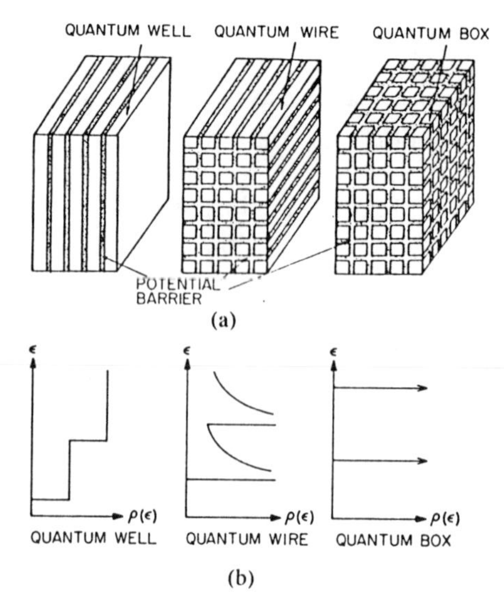

Fig. 11. (a) Illustration of the active layer with a multiquantum well structure, a multiquantum wire structure, and a multiquantum box structure. (b) Density of states of electrons in a DH structure, a multiquantum well structure, a multiquantum wire structure, and a multiquantum box structure.

ration was selectively etched in the p^+-GaAs between the two segments for electrical isolation. The lengths of the amplifier section l_1 and the modulator section l_2 were 250 and 50 μm, respectively.

In the amplifier section, the carrier-induced band shift occurs. This effect is enhanced in MQW lasers compared to conventional DH lasers, resulting in a decrease of the lasing photon energy by about 17 meV [86] compared to the absorption edge. Therefore, with no electronic field, the absorption loss is small at the lasing photon energy, which results in extremely large loss changes induced by the application of an electrical field with the quantum-confined Stark effects to the modulation section.

Q switching was obtained by applying both a dc bias voltage V_b and a microwave signal to the modulator. Fig. 10 shows an intensity autocorrelation trace obtained from the second harmonic generation under the condition of 1.5 GHz modulation frequency and $V_b = 0$. The autocorrelation FWHM is 26.3 ps, which corresponds to a pulse full width at half maximum $\Delta\tau_{1/2}$ of 18.6 ps if a Gaussian waveform is assumed.

The efficient Q switching in the two-segment MQW laser results from the following mechanisms. In the Q-switching regime, a large loss change and a high differential gain (the derivative of the gain with respect to carrier concentration) will lead to a narrow pulse width. In this device, a large loss change is realized with the quantum-confined Stark effect in the modulator section and the band shrinkage effect in the optical amplifier section. On the other hand, a high differential gain is also expected in the quasi-two-dimensional electronic system in an MQW structure [10], [11]. Thus, by the use of an MQW structure, the two-segment laser satisfies both requirements for the generation of narrow optical pulses.

The modulation frequency response (i.e., repetition rate) of the laser was also measured. We observed the fundamental spectrum as well as harmonic spectrum lines in the spectrum analyzer display. At the present stage, the maximum repetition rate which still leads to regular pulse generation is 5.2 GHz.

VI. Quantum Wire and Quantum Box Lasers and Their Experimental Demonstration

A. Concepts of Quantum Wire Laser and Quantum Box Laser

The QW structure has proved to be very promising for application to semiconductor lasers, which is due mainly to the two-dimensional properties of the carriers [9]. Arakawa *et al.* [9] proposed the concept of quantum wire lasers or quantum box lasers with, respectively, a one-dimensional or/and a zero-dimensional electronic system. They predicted a reduction in the temperature dependence of the threshold current due to the peaked structure of the density of states. In addition, the gain characteristics [87] and the dynamic properties were also investigated [10]. Although Petroff tried to fabricate quantum wire structures [88], no satisfactory quantum wire structure has been fabricated for optical devices or electronic devices [89] to date. Another approach for realizing the one- or two-dimensional effects experimentally is the use of magnetic fields [9], [90]–[95]. One-dimensional electronic systems can be formed by placing a conventional DH laser in a high magnetic field. If we place a quantum well laser in a high magnetic field so that the quantum well plane is perpendicular to the field, a zero-dimensional electronic system is realized. In this section, we discuss the possible properties obtained in quantum wire lasers and quantum box lasers theoretically and then demonstrate these effects in high magnetic field experiments.

Fig. 11(a) shows simple illustrations of the active layer in multiquantum well, multiquantum wire, and multiquantum box lasers. By making such multidimensional microstructures, the freedom of the carrier motion is re-

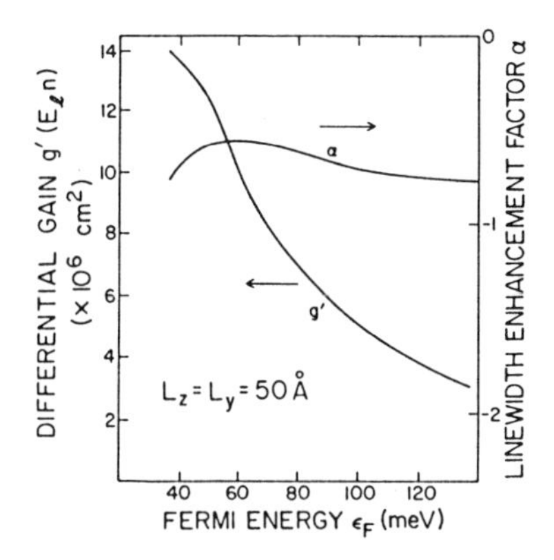

Fig. 12. The differential gain and α as a function of the conduction band quasi-Fermi energy level in a quantum wire laser with 50 Å quantum dimensions.

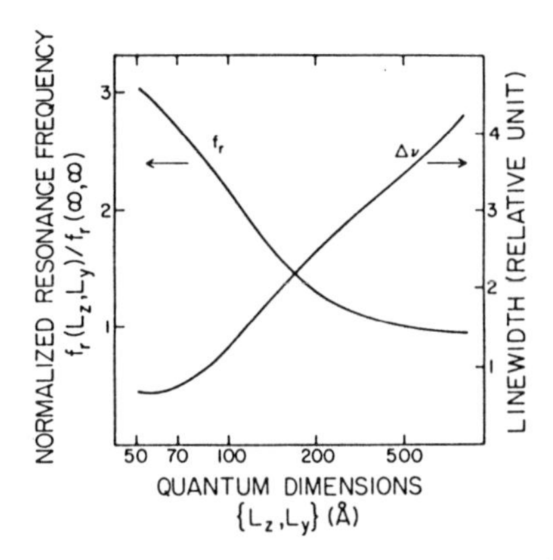

Fig. 13. The relaxation resonance frequency and the linewidth in a quantum wire laser as a function of the wire thickness. The number of quantum wells and quantum wires is optimized at each quantum well thickness.

duced to one or zero. The density of states of electrons in these structures is expressed as

$$\rho_c^{\text{wire}}(\epsilon) = \left(\frac{m_c}{2\hbar^2\pi^2}\right)^{1/2} \sum_{l,m} \frac{1}{\sqrt{\epsilon - \epsilon_l - \epsilon_m}}$$

for the quantum wire laser (24)

$$\rho_c^{\text{box}}(\epsilon) = \sum_{l,m,k} \delta(\epsilon - \epsilon_l - \epsilon_m \epsilon_k)$$

for the quantum box laser (25)

where ϵ_l, ϵ_m, and ϵ_k are the quantized energy levels of a quantum wire laser and a quantum box laser. As shown in Fig. 11(b), the density of states has a more peaked structure with the decrease of the dimensionality. This leads to a change in the gain profile, a reduction of threshold current density, and a reduction of the temperature dependence of the threshold current. Furthermore, improvements of the dynamic properties are also expected.

The narrower gain profile due to the peaked density of states leads to a high differential gain. One curve in Fig. 12 shows the differential gain as a function of the Fermi energy level for quantum wire lasers. A comparison of this figure to Fig. 5 reveals two important results. One is that a higher differential gain can be obtained with the use of quantum wire structures. The second one is that the dependence of the differential gain on the Fermi energy level is enhanced for quantum wire lasers compared to quantum well lasers. A higher differential gain, therefore, is obtained in a quantum wire laser with a large number of quantum wires, and the sensitivity of the differential gain to the number is more enhanced for quantum wire lasers compared to the quantum well lasers.

One curve in Fig. 13 shows the f_r as a function of the dimension of the quantum wires. In this calculation, it is assumed that the two quantum dimensions are equal and that the number of quantum wires is optimized for each quantum dimension. This result indicates that f_r is enhanced by a factor of 3 with the use of thin quantum wires compared to the conventional DH. The spectral properties of the quantum wire laser are also improved. The second curve in Fig. 12 shows the dependence of α on the Fermi energy level. As shown in this figure, the dependence of α in a quantum wire laser is not as enhanced and is almost constant in the whole range. The second curve in Fig. 13 shows $\Delta\nu$ as a function of the thickness of the quantum wells. This indicates that α is reduced with the decrease of the thickness.

The α parameter of quantum box lasers should be noted. If we can ignore higher subbands' effect, the density of states is a δ function-like. Therefore, the photon energy with the maximum gain coincides with the energy levels, which leads to the disappearance of the detuning and the real part of the complex susceptibility becomes zero. Consequently, α is expected to be extremely small in a quantum box laser with a simultaneous improvement of f_r.

B. Magnetic Field Experiment

A quasi-quantum wire effect in a semiconductor laser can be realized through the use of high magnetic fields [8], [9], in which case electrons can move freely only in the direction of the magnetic field. The motion of such electrons is quantized in the two transverse directions (x, y), forming a series of Landau energy subbands. The density of states for the system $\rho_c(\epsilon)$ can be expressed as

$$\rho_c(\epsilon) = (\hbar\omega_c)\left(\frac{2m_c}{\hbar^2}\right)^{3/2} \sum_{j=0}^{\infty} \frac{1}{\sqrt{\epsilon - (j + \frac{1}{2})\,\hbar\omega_c}} \tag{26}$$

where ω_c and m_c are the cyclotron corner frequency and the effective mass of electrons. When $\hbar\omega_c$ is large enough (i.e., the B field is large enough), only the first Landau subband is occupied, resulting in a true one-dimensional electronic system. In the actual system, the carrier relaxation effect should also be considered.

Fig. 14 shows the measured spectral linewidth at 190 K for various magnetic fields (B = 0, 11, 16, 19 tesla) as a function of the reciprocal mode power $1/P$ [94]. A GaAlAs buried heterostructure laser grown by liquid phase epitaxy was operated in a stationary magnetic field of up to 19 tesla at 190 K. The test laser (an ORTEL Corporation experimental model) has a 0.15 μm active region thickness, 3 μm stripe width, and was 300 μm long. As

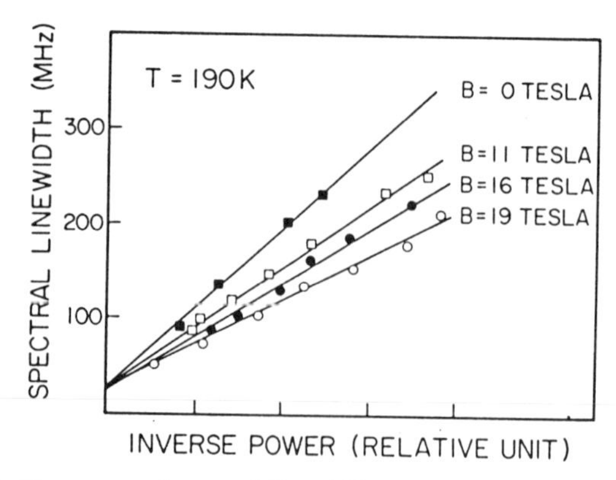

Fig. 14. The measured spectral linewidth as a function of the reciprocal of output power (in relative units) for magnetic fields of $B = 0$, 11, 16, and 19 tesla at 190 K.

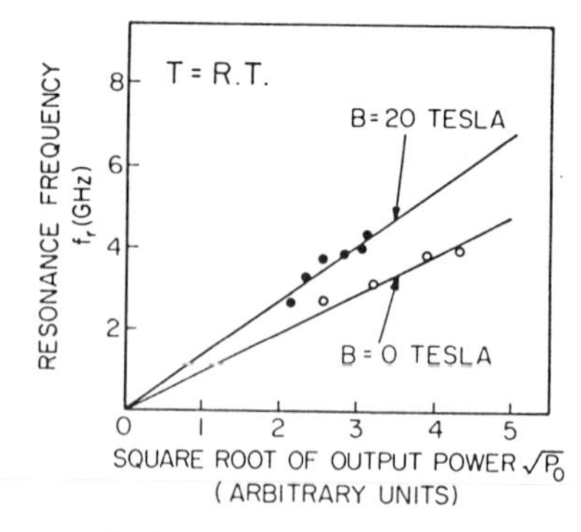

Fig. 15. The measured relaxation resonance frequency as a function of the square root of output power (in relative units) for magnetic fields of $B = 0$, 20 tesla at room temperature.

shown in the figure, the measured linewidth for each magnetic field varies linearly with the reciprocal mode power. Such a variation indicates that the linewidth results from quantum broadening (spontaneous emission). The experimental results indicate that this power-dependent linewidth is substantially reduced with the increase of the magnetic field. At 19 tesla, the linewidth decreases by a factor of 0.6 compared to the linewidth without a magnetic field. This improvement of the power-dependent linewidth is believed to be due mainly to quantum wire effects through the formation of a quasi-one-dimensional electronic system as discussed above.

One important difference between "true" quantum wire structures and the quasi-quantum wires due to magnetic fields is that the optical confinement factor for true quantum wire structures can be controlled by varying the number of quantum wires. Theoretical predictions indicate that a higher Fermi energy level for laser oscillation leads to lower α and n_{sp} [7]. Therefore, in the true quantum wire case, it should be possible to decrease n_{sp} and α by reducing the number of quantum wires while maintaining the one-dimensional electronic properties. This would allow one to reap the benefits of quantum wires in terms of smaller α's without paying a penalty in n_{sp}. The overall reduction of linewidth $\Delta\nu$ would then be much larger than demonstrated here.

f_r was also measured at room temperature [93]. Fig. 15 shows the measured f_r with and without a magnetic field of 20 tesla as a function of the square root of the output power P_0. Open circles ($B = 0$) and closed circle ($B =$ 20 tesla) indicate the measured f_r. The straight lines in the figure are drawn by the least square error method. Since, as shown in (16), f_r is proportional to $\sqrt{P_0}$, f_r should lie on a straight line. The variation of the slope of this line will mainly reflect the change in differential gain g' which has resulted from the applications of the magnetic field. We notice that f_r with $B = 20$ tesla is enhanced 1.4 times compared to f_r with $B = 0$. From this change, we can estimate that g' ($B = 20$ tesla) is 1.9 times larger than g' ($B = 0$).

Quantum box effects (i.e., full quantization) were also investigated by Arakawa *et al.* [95] by placing a GaAs/GaAlAs quantum well laser in a high magnetic field. If a magnetic field is applied perpendicular to the quantum well plane as shown in Fig. 16(a), electrons are confined by the quantum well potential as well as the Lorentzian force, being in zero-dimensional electronic states. In this case, the density of states is described by the following formula:

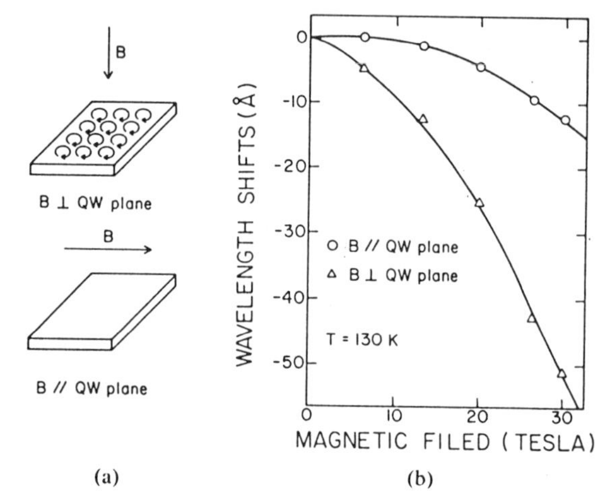

Fig. 16. (a) Electron motions confined by the quantum well potential as well as Lorentzian force, being in zero-dimensional electronic states. (b) Experimental results of the wavelength shift of the spontaneous emission spectrum as a function of the pulsed magnetic field up to 30 tesla.

$$\rho_c(\epsilon) = (\hbar\omega_c)\left(\frac{2m_c}{\hbar^2}\right) \sum_{k=0}^{\infty} \sum_{j=l,h} \sum_{n=1}^{\infty} \cdot \delta\left(\epsilon - \epsilon_{Cn}^j - \left(k + \frac{1}{2}\right)\hbar\omega_c\right). \quad (27)$$

The evidence of the formation of the full quantized effects was obtained by measuring anistropic properties of the spectral shift with the increase of the magnetic field. If a magnetic field is applied parallel to the QW plane, the cyclotron motion is interrupted by the QW potentials. Therefore, as long as the magnetic field is not extremely strong, the spectral peak shift is suppressed. On the other hand, with the perpendicular magnetic field, the spectral peak shift occurs towards a shorter wavelength through the increase of the Landau energy level. Fig. 16(b) is the experimental results of the wavelength shift of the spontaneous emission spectrum as a function of the pulsed magnetic field up to 30 tesla. The results clearly indicate the anisotropic properties, which is the evidence of the formation of the zero-dimensional electron states.

VII. Conclusions

We have discussed a number of interesting theoretical and experimental results of quantum well lasers with emphasis on the basic physical phenomena involved in the gain, the spectral fields, and the modulation response. The results reveal that an optimized use of the quantum well structure can lead to substantial improvement in most of the important properties of these devices.

References

[1] L. Esaki and R. Tsu, "Superlattice and negative differential conductivity in semiconductor lasers," *IBM. J. Res. Develop.*, vol. 14, pp. 61-68, 1970.

[2] R. Dingle, A. C. Gossard, and W. Wiegmann, "Direct observation of super lattice formation in a semiconductor heterostructure," *Phys. Rev. Lett.*, vol. 34, pp. 1327-1330, 1975.

[3] J. P. van der Ziel, R. Dingle, R. C. Miller, W. Wiegmann, and W. A. Nordland Jr., "Laser oscillation from quantum well states in very thin GaAl-$Al_{0.2}Ga_{0.8}As$ multilayer structures," *Appl. Phys. Lett.*, vol. 26, pp. 463-465, 1975.

[4] N. Holonyak, Jr., R. M. Kolbas, R. D. Dupuis, and P. D. Dapkus, "Quantum-well heterostructure lasers," *IEEE J. Quantum Electron.*, pp. 170-181, 1980.

[5] W. T. Tsang, "Extremely low threshold (AlGa)As modified multiquantum well heterostructure lasers grown by molecular beam epitaxy," *Appl. Phys. Lett.*, vol. 39, pp. 786-788, 1981.

[6] T. Fujji, S. Yamakoshi, K. Nanbu, O. Wada, and S. Hiyamizu, "MBE growth of extremely high-quality GaAs-AlGaAs GRIN-SCH lasers with a superlattice buffer layer," *J. Vac. Sci. Technol.*, vol. 2, pp. 259-261, 1984.

[7] R. Chin, N. Holonyak, Jr., B. A. Bojak, K. Hess, R. D. Dupuis, , and P. D. Dapkus, "Temperature dependence of threshold current for quantum well $Al_xGa_{1-x}As$-GaAs heterostructure laser diodes," *Appl. Phys. Lett.*, vol. 36, pp. 19-21, 1979.

[8] K. Hess, B. A. Bojak, N. Holonyak, Jr., R. Chin, and P. D. Dapkus, "Temperature dependence of threshold current for a quantum-well heterostructure laser," *Solid-State Electron.*, vol. 23, pp. 585-589, 1980.

[9] Y. Arakawa and H. Sakaki, "Multiquantum well laser and its temperature dependence of the threshold current," *Appl. Phys. Lett.*, vol. 40, pp. 939-941, 1982.

[10] Y. Arakawa, K. Vahala, and A. Yariv, "Quantum noise and dynamics in quantum well and quantum wire lasers," *Appl. Phys. Lett.*, vol. 45, pp. 950-952, 1984.

[11] Y. Arakawa, and A. Yariv, "Theory of gain, modulation response, and spectral linewidth in AlGaAs quantum well lasers," *IEEE J. Quantum Electron.*, vol. QE-21, pp. 1666-1674, 1985.

[12] Y. Arakawa, K. Vahala, and A. Yariv, "Dynamic and spectral properties in semiconductor lasers with quantum well and wire effects," presented at the 2nd Int. Conf. Modulated Semiconductor Structures, Kyoto, Japan, 1985.

[13] Y. Arakawa, A. Larsson, J. Paslaski, and A. Yariv, "Active *Q*-switching in a multiquantum well laser with an internal loss modulation," submitted to *Appl. Phys. Lett.*

[14] H. Kromer and H. Okamoto, "Some design consideration for multiquantum-well lasers," *Japan. J. Appl. Phys.*, vol. 23, pp. 970-972, 1984.

[15] A. Yariv, C. Lindsey, and U. Sivan, "Approximate analytic solution for electronic wave function and energies in coupled quantum wells," *J. Appl. Phys.*, vol. 58, pp. 3669-3671, 1985.

[16] R. Lang and K. Nishi, "Electronic localization in a semiconductor superlattice,," *Appl. Phys. Lett.*, vol. 45, pp. 98-100, 1984.

[17] D. Kasemset, C. S. Hong, N. B. Patel, and D. Dapkus, "Graded barrier single quantum well lasers—Theory and experiment," *IEEE J. Quantum Electron.*, vol. QE-19, pp. 1025-1030, 1983.

[18] A. Sugimura, "Threshold current for AlGaAs quantum well lasers," *IEEE J. Quantum Electron.*, vol. QE-20, pp. 336-343, 1984.

[19] P. T. Landsberg. M. S. Abrahams, and M. Olsinski, "Evidence of no k-selection in gain spectra of quantum well AlGaAs laser diodes," *IEEE J. Quantum Electron.*, vol. QE-21, pp. 24-28, 1985.

[20] N. K. Dutta, "Calculated threshold current of GaAs quantum well lasers," *J. Appl. Phys.*, vol. 53, pp. 7211-7214, 1982.

[21] ——, "Current injection in multiquantum well lasers," *IEEE J. Quantum Electron.*, vol. QE-19, pp. 794-797, 1983.

[22] M. Yamada, S. Ogita, M. Yamagishi, and K. Tabata, "Anisotropy and broadening of optical gain in a GaAs/AlGaAs multiquantum-well laser," *IEEE J. Quantum Electron.*, vol. QE-21, pp. 640-645, 1985.

[23] M. Yamada, K. Tabata, S. Ogita, and M. Yamagishi, "Calculation of lasing gain and threshold current in GaAsAlGaAs mutiquantum well lasers," *Trans. IECE Japan*, vol. E68, pp. 102-108, 1984.

[24] Y. Arakawa, H. Sakaki, M. Nishioka, J. Yoshino, and T. Kamiya," Recombination lifetime of carriers in GaAs-GaAlAs quantum wells near room temperature," *Appl. Phys. Lett.*, vol. 46k, pp. 519-521, 1985.

[25] N. K. Dutta, R. L. Hartman, and W. T. Tsang, "Gain and carrier lifetime measurement in AlGaAs single quantum well lasers," *IEEE J. Quantum Electron.*, vol. QE-19, pp. 1243-1246, 1983.

[26] Casey and Panish, *Heterostructure Lasers, Part A*. New York: Academic, 1978.

[27] H. Kobayaski, H. Iwamura, T. Saku, and K. Otsuka, "Polarization dependent gain-current relationship in GaAs-AlGaAs MQW laser diodes," *Electron. Lett.*, vol. 19, pp. 166-168, 1983.

[28] M. Asada, A. Kameyama, and Y. Suematsu, "Gain and intervalenceband absorption in quantum-well lasers," *IEEE J. Quantum Electron.*, vol. QE-20, pp. 745-753, 1984.

[29] M. Yamanishi and I. Suemune, "Comments on polarization dependent momentum matrix elements in quantum well lasers," *Japan. J. Appl. Phys.*, vol. 23, pp. L35-L36, 1984.

[30] E. O. Kane, "Band structure of indium antimonide," *J. Phys. Chem. Solids*, pp. 249-269, 1957.

[31] A. Sugimura, "Auger recombination effect on threshold current of InGaAsP quantum well lasers," *IEEE J. Quantum Electron.*, vol. QE-19, pp. 932-941, 1983.

[32] N. K. Dutta, "Calculation of Auger rates in a quantum well structure and its application to InGaAsP quantum well lasers," *J. Appl. Phys.*, vol. 54, pp. 1236-1245, 1983.

[33] L. C. Chiu and A. Yariv, "Auger recombination in quantum-well InGaAsP heterostructure lasers," *IEEE J. Quantum Electron.*, vol. QE-18, pp. 1406-1409, 1982.

[34] C. Smith, R. A. Abram, and M. G. Burt, "Auger recombination in long wavelength quantum-well lasers," *Electron. Lett.*, 1984.

[35] Y. Arakawa, A. Larsson, M. Mittelstein, and A. Yariv," Observation of gain flattening and second subband laser oscillation in a single quantum well laser," unpublished.

[36] R. D. Dupis, P. D. Dapkus, N. Holonyak, Jr., E. A. Rezek, and R. Chin, "Room-temperature laser operation of quantum well $Ga_{1-x}Al_xAs$-GaAs laser diodes by metal organic chemical vapor deposition," *Appl. Phys. Lett.*, vol. 32, pp. 292-297, 1978.

[37] W. T. Tsang, C. Weisbuch, R. C. Miller, and R. Dingle, "Curent injection GaAS-$Al_xGa_{1-x}As$ multiquantum well heterostructure lasers prepared by molecular beam epitaxy," *Appl. Phys. Lett.*, vol. 35, pp. 673-675, 1979.

[38] W. T. Tsang, "A graded-index waveguide separate-confinement laser with very low threshold and a narrow Gaussian beam," *Appl. Phys. Lett.*, vol. 39, pp. 134-136, 1981.

[39] P. Blood, E. D. Fletcher, and K. Woodbridge, "Dependence of threshold current on the number of wells in AlGaAs-GaAs quantum well lasers," *Appl. Phys. Lett.*, vol. 47, pp. 193-195, 1985.

[40] S. D. Harsee, M. Baldy, P. Assenat, B. de Cremoux, and J. P. Duchemin," Very low threshold GRIN-SCH GaAs/AlGaAs laser structure grown by OM-VPE," *Electron. Lett.*, vol. 18, pp. 1095-1097, 1982.

[41] D. R. Scifres, R. D. Burham, and W. Streifer, "High power coupled multiple strip quantum well injection lasers," *Appl. Phys. Lett.*, pp. 118-120, 1982.

[42] J. P. van der Ziel, H. Temkin, and R. D. Dupis, "High-power picosecond pulse generation in GaAs multiquantum well phase-locked laser arrays using pulsed current injection," *IEEE J. Quantum Electron.*, vol. QE-20, pp. 1236-1242, 1984.

[43] O. Wada, T. Sanada, M. Kuno, and T. Fujii, "Very low threshold current ridge-waveguide AlGaAs/GaAs single-quantum-well lasers," *Electron. Lett.*, 1985.

[44] E. A. Rezek, N. Holonyak, Jr., and B. K. Fuller, "Temperature dependence of threshold current for coupled multiple quantum well $In_{1-x}Ga_xP_{1-z}As_z$-InP heterostructure laser diodes," *J. Appl. Phys.*,

vol. 51, pp. 2402–2405, 1980.

[45] H. Temkin, K. Alavi, W. R. Wagner, T. P. Pearsall, and A. Y. Cho," 1.5-16 μm $Ga_{0.47}In_{0.53}As/Al_{0.48}$ multiquantum well laser grown by molecular beam epitaxy," *Appl. Phys. Lett.*, vol. 42, pp. 845–847, 1983.

[46] T. Yanase, Y. Kato, I. Mito, M. Yamaguchi, K. Nishi, K. Kobayashi, and R. Lang, "1.3 μm InGaAsP/InP multiquantum-well laser grown by vapour-phase epitaxy," *Electron. Lett.*, vol. 19, pp. 700–701, 1983.

[47] N. K. Dutta, T. Wessel, N. A. Olsson, R. A. Logan, R. Yen, and P. J. Anthony," Fabrication and performance characteristics of In-GaAsP ridge-guide distributed-feedback multiquantum-well lasers," *Electron Lett.*, vol. 21, pp. 571–573, 1985.

[48] Y. Kawamura, H. Asahi, and K. Wakita, "InGaAs/InGaAlAs/In-AlAs/InP SCH-MQW laser diodes grown by molecular beam epitaxy," *Electron Lett.*, vol. 20, pp. 459–460, 1984.

[49] Y. Ohmori, Y. Suzuki, and H. Okamoto, "Room temperature CW operation of GaSb/AlGaSb MQW laser diodes grown by MBE," *Japan. J. Appl. Phys.*, vol. 24, pp. L657–659, 1985.

[50] A. Larsson, M. Mittelstein, Y. Arakawa, and A. Yariv," High efficiency broad area single quantum well laser with narrow single-lobed far-field patterns prepared by molecular beam epitaxy," *Electron. Lett.*, vol. 22, pp. 79–81, 1986.

[51] T. Ikegami and Y. Suematsu, "Direct modulation semiconductor junction lasers," *Electron. Commun. Japan*, vol. B51, pp. 51–58, 1968.

[52] T. P. Paoli and J. E. Ripper, "Direct modulation of semiconductor lasers," *Proc. IEEE*, vol. 58, p. 1457, 1970.

[53] K. Y. Lau, N. Bar-Chaim, I. Ury, C. Harder, and A. Yariv, "Direct amplitude modulation of short cavity lasers up to *X*-band frequency," *Appl. Phys. Lett.*, vol. 43, pp. 1-3, 1983.

[54] K.Y. Lau, N. Bar-Chaim, I. Ury, and A. Yariv, "An 11 GHz direct modulation bandwidth GaAlAs window laser on semi-insulating substrate operating at room temperature," *Appl. Phys. Lett.*, vol. 45, pp. 345–347, 1984.

[55] K. Y. Lau and A. Yariv, "Ultra-high speed semiconductor lasers," *IEEE J. Quantum Electron.*, vol. QE-21, p. 121, 1985.

[56] K. Vahala and A. Yariv, "Detuned loading in couple cavity semiconductor lasers—Effects on quantum noise and dynamics," *Appl. Phys. Lett.*, vol. 45, pp. 501–503, 1984.

[57] K. Uomi, N. Chinone, T. Ohyoshi, and T. Kajimura, "High relaxation oscillation freqeuncy (beyond 10 GHz) of GaAlAs multiquantum well lasers," *Japan. J. Appl. Phys.*, vol. 24, pp. L539–L541, 1985.

[58] K. Kobayashi, H. Iwamura, T. Saku, K. Otsuka, and H. Okamoto," Dynamic behavior of a GaAs-AlGaAs MQW laser diode," *Electron. Lett.*, vol. 19, pp. 166–167, 1983.

[59] M. W. Fleming and A. Mooradian, "Fundamental line broadening of single mode (GaAl)As diode lasers," *Appl. Phys. Lett.*, vol. 38, pp. 511–513, 1981.

[60] C. Henry, "Theory of the linewidth of semiconductor," *IEEE J. Quantum Electron.*, vol. QE-18, pp. 259–264, 1982.

[61] K. Vahala and A. Yariv, "Semiclassical theory of noise in semiconductor lasers—Part I," *IEEE J. Quantum Electron.*, vol. QE-18, pp. 1096, 1101, 1982.

[62] ——, "Semiclassical theory of noise in semiconductor lasers—Part II, "*IEEE J. Quantum Electron.*, vol. QE-18, pp. 1102–1109, 1982.

[63] M. G. Burt, "Linewidth enhancement factor for quantum well laser," *Electron. Lett.*, vol. 20 pp. 27–28, 1984.

[64] K. Vahala, L. C. Chiu, S. Margalit, and A. Yariv," On the linewidth enchancement factor α in semiconductor injection lasers," *Appl Phys. Lett.*, vol. 42, pp. 531–633, 1983.

[65] Y. Arakawa and A. Yariv, "Fermi energy dependence of linewidth enhancement factor," *Appl. Phys. Lett.*, vol. 47, pp. 905-907, 1985.

[66] N. Ogasawara, R. Itoh, and R. Morita, "Linewidth enhancement factor in GaAs/AlGaAs multiquantum well lasers," *Japan. J. Appl. Phys.*, vol. 24, pp. L519–L521, 1985.

[67] T. H. Wood, C. A. Burrus, D. A. B. Miller, D. S. Chemla, T. C. Damen, A. C. Gossard, and W. Wiegmann," High-speed optical modulation with GaAs/GaAlAs quantum wells in a p-i-n diode structure," *Appl Phys. Lett.*, vol. 44, pp. 16–18, 1984.

[68] T. H. Wood, C. A. Burrus, R. S. Tucker, J. S. Weiner, D. A. B. Miller, D. S. Chemla, T. C. Damen. A. C. Gossard, and W. Wiegmann, *Electron. Lett.*, vol. 21, pp. 693–695, 1985.

[69] D. A. B. Miller, D. S. Chemla, T. C. Damen, A. C. Gossard, W. Wiegmann, T. H. Wood, and C. A. Burrus," Novel hybrid optically bistable switch: The quantum well self-optic effect device," *Appl. Phys. Lett.*, vol. 45, pp. 13–15, 1984.

[70] T. H. Wood, C. A. Burrus, A. H. Gnauck, J. M. Wiesenfeld, D. A. B. Miller, D. S. Chemla, and T. C. Damen," *Appl. Phys. Lett.*, vol. 47, pp. 190–192, 1985.

[71] A. Larsson, A. Yariv, R. Tell, J. Maserjian, and S. T. Eng, "Spectral and temporal characterisitcs of AlGaAs/GaAs superlattice p-i-n photodetectors," *Appl. Phys. Lett.*, vol. 47, pp. 866–868, 1985.

[72] C. Y. Chen, "New minority hole sinked photoconductive detector," *Appl. Phys. Lett.*, vol. 43, pp. 1115–1117, 1983.

[73] K. Kaede, Y. Arakawa, P. Derry, J. Papaslaski, and A. Yariv," High speed GaAs/AlGaAs photoconductive detector using a p-modulation doped superlattice," *Appl. Phys. Lett.*, vol. 48, pp. 1096–1097, 1986.

[74] M. Yamanishi and M. Suemune, "Quantum mechanical size effect modulation light source—A new field effect semiconductor laseror light emitting diode," *Japan. J. Appl. Phys.*, vol. 22, p. L22, 1983.

[75] K. Tsukada and C. L. Tang, "*Q*-switching of semiconductor lasers," *IEEE J. Quantum Electron.*, vol. QE-13, pp. 37–43, 1977.

[76] M. Yamanishi, K. Ishii, M. Ameda, and T. Kawamura, "High speed repetitive *Q*-switching in acoustic distributed feedback lasers," *Japan. J. Appl. Phys.*, suppl. 17, pp. 359–363, 1978.

[77] D. Z. Tsang, J. N. Walpole, S. H. Groves, J. J. Hsieh, and J. P. Donnelly, "Intracavity loss modulation of GaInAsP diode lasers," *Appl. Phys. Lett.*, vol. 38, p. 120, 1981.

[78] D. Z. Tsang and J. N. Walpole, "*Q*-switched semiconductor diode lasers," *IEEE J. Quantum Electron.*, vol. QE-19, p. 145, 1983.

[79] D. Z. Tsang, J. N. Walpole, Z. L. Liau, S. H. Groves, and V. Diadiuk, "*Q* switching of low threshold buried heterostructure diode laser at 10 GHz," *Appl. Phys. Lett.*, vol. 45, p. 204, 1984.

[80] P. T. Ho. L. A. Glasser, E. P. Ippen, and H. A. Haus, "Picosecond pulse generation with a CW GaAlAs laser diodes," *Appl. Phys. Lett.*, vol. 33, pp. 241–242, 1978.

[81] J. P. van der Ziel, R. A. Logan, and R. M. Mikulyak, "Generation of subpicosecond pulse from an actively mode locked GaAs laser in an external ring cavity," *Appl. Phys. Lett.*, vol. 39, pp. 867–869, 1981.

[82] H. Ito, H. Yokoyama, S. Murata, and H. Inaba, "Picosecond optical pulse generation from r.f. modulated AlGaAs DH diode laser," *Electron. Lett.*, vol. 15, p. 738, 1979.

[83] G. J. Aspin, J. E. Carrol, and R. G. Plumb," The effect of cavity length on picosecond pulse generation with high rf modulated AlGaAs double heterostructure lasers," *Appl. Phys. Lett.*, vol. 39, p. 860, 1981.

[84] D. A. B. Miller, D. S. Chemla, T. C. Damen, A. C. Gossard, W. Wiegmann, T. H. Wood, and C. A. Burrus," Bandedge electroabsorption in quantum well structure: The quantum confined Stark effect," *Phys. Rev. Lett.*, vol. 53, pp. 2173–2177, 1984.

[85] J. S. Weiner, D. A. B. Miller, D. S. Chemla, T. C. Damen, C. A. Burrus, T. H. Wood, A. C. Gossard, and W. Wiegman, *Appl. Phys. Lett.*, vol. 47, p. 1148, 1985.

[86] S. Tarucha, H. Kobayashi, Y. Horikoshi, and X. Okamoto, "Carrier induced energy-gap shrinkage in current injection GaAs/AlGaAs MQW heterostructures," *Japan. J. Appl. Phys.*, vol. 23, pp. 874–881, 1984.

[87] Asada and Suematsu, *Japan. J. Appl. Phys.*, vol. 24, pp. L93–L95, 1985.

[88] Petroff, "Toward quantum well wires: Fabrication and optical properties," vol. 41, pp. 635–637, 1982.

[89] H. Sakaki, "Scattering suppression and high mobility effect of single quantum electrons in ultrafine semiconductor wire structure," *Japan. J. Appl. Phys.*, vol. 20, pp. L91–L93, 1981.

[90] Y. Arakawa, H. Sakaki, M. Nishioka, and N. Miura, "Two dimensional quantum-mechanical confinement of electrons in semiconductor lasers by strong magnetic fields," *IEEE J. Quantum Electron.*, vol. QE-18, pp. 10–17, 1983.

[91] ——, "Two-dimensional quantum-mechanical confinement of electrons in light emitting diodes by strong magnetic fields," *IEEE Trans. Electron Devices*, vol. ED-30, pp. 330–338, Apr. 1983.

[92] H. J. A. Bluyssen and L. J. van Ruyven, "Operation of a double heterojunction GaAs/AlGaAs injection laser with a p-type active layer in a strong magnetic field," *IEEE J. Quantum Electron.*, vol. QE-16, pp. 29–33, 1983.

[93] Y. Arakawa, K. Vahala, A. Yariv, and K. Lau, "Enhanced modulation bandwidth of GaAlAs double heterostructure lasers in high magnetic fields: Dynamic response with quantum wire effects," *Appl. Phys. Lett.*, vol. 47, pp. 1142–1144, 1985.

[94] ——, "Reduction of the spectral linewidth of semiconductor lasers

with quantum wire effects—Spectral properties of GaAlAs double heterostructure lasers," *Appl. Phys. Lett.*, vol. 48, pp. 384-386, 1986.

[95] Y. Arakawa, H. Sakaki, M. N. Nishioka, H. Okamoto, and N. Miura, "Spontaneous emission characteristics of quantum well lasers in strong magnetic fields—An approach to quantum box light source," *Japan. J. Appl. Phys.*, vol. 22, pp. L804-L806, 1985.

Gain and the Threshold of Three-Dimensional Quantum-Box Lasers

MASAHIRO ASADA, YASUYUKI MIYAMOTO, AND YASUHARU SUEMATSU, FELLOW, IEEE

***Abstract*—Gain and threshold current density are analyzed for quantum-box lasers where electrons are confined in quantum well three-dimensionally, based on the density-matrix theory of semiconductor lasers with relaxation broadening.**

The electronic dipole moment and its polarization dependence are first analyzed, and it is shown that the gain becomes maximum when the electric field of light is parallel to the longest side of the quantum box. Calculated gain is about 10 times that of bulk crystal for 100 Å × 100 Å × 100 Å $GaAs/Ga_{0.8}Al_{0.2}As$ quantum box, and 15 times for $Ga_{0.47}In_{0.53}As/InP$ quantum box with the same size, respectively. The threshold current density are 45 A/cm^2 and 62 A/cm^2 for GRIN-SCH $GaAs/(Ga_{0.8}Al_{0.2}As$-$Ga_{0.4}Al_{0.6}As)$ and $Ga_{0.47}In_{0.53}As/(Ga_{0.28}In_{0.72}As_{0.6}P_{0.4}$-InP), respectively, where for the GaInAs/GaInAsP/InP system the intervalence band absorption and nonradiative recombinations have been assumed to be the same as those obtained for bulk crystals experimentally. These results show the possibility of remarkable reduction in the laser threshold by the quantum-box structures.

I. Introduction

CONSIDERABLE attention has been paid to the quantum-well lasers with ultrathin active layers [1], [2], since they have superior characteristics, such as extremely low threshold current [3]-[6], less temperature dependence [7], narrow gain spectrum [8], etc., compared to conventional double heterostructure lasers. These merits are expected to become more remarkable as the dimension of the quantization is increased. Experimentally, fabrication of the two-dimensional quantum-wire structure has been reported [9]. Theoretically, the improvement in the temperature dependence of the threshold current by multidimensional quantum-well structures has been pointed out [10], and the increase of gain in quantum-wire lasers has also been discussed [11]. However, gain and the laser threshold in three-dimensional quantum-box structures, where electrons are three-dimensionally confined, has not yet been discussed theoretically until now.

In this paper, we analyze gain and the laser threshold of the three-dimensional quantum-box lasers, based on the density-matrix theory of semiconductor lasers with relaxation broadening [12], [13]. First, the electronic dipole moment which gives the magnitude of the optical transition probability is analyzed, and its dependence on the electric-field polarization is shown. Next, gain and the laser threshold are analyzed. Results are compared with those of conventional, quantum-film, and quantum-wire lasers. It is shown that remarkable reduction in the laser threshold is expected by the quantum-box structures.

Manuscript received November 28, 1985; revised March 3, 1986. This work was supported by a Scientific Grant-in-Aid from the Ministry of Education, Science, and Culture, Japan. This paper was presented at the Technical Group Meeting on Optical and Quantum Electronics of IECE of Japan, Tokyo, Japan, September 1985 (in Japanese).

The authors are with the Department of Physical Electronics, Tokyo Institute of Technology, Meguro-Ku, Tokyo 152, Japan.

IEEE Log Number 8608753.

II. Gain in Quantum-Box Lasers

A. Dipole Moment

The optical transition probability of electrons is proportional to the square of the matrix element of the dipole moment formed between an electron and a hole. This matrix element is calculated using the electron and hole wave functions. The electron wave function confined in a quantum-box is approximately written as follows when the size of the box is much larger than the lattice period, as in the case of conventional quantum-well (quantum-film) structures [14]:

$$\Psi_{cnml} = u_c(r)\, \Phi_{cxn}(x)\, \Phi_{cym}(y)\, \Phi_{czl}(z), \tag{1}$$

where the subscript c (or h) denotes the conduction band (or heavy-hole band), n, m, and l denote the label of the quantized energy levels in the box, $u_c(r)$ is the periodic part of the bulk Bloch function, and Φ_{cxn}, Φ_{cym}, and Φ_{czl} are the envelope functions along the x-, y-, and z-directions, respectively, as shown in Fig. 1 (see the Appendix).

Each of the envelope functions in (1) is a standing wave which is composed of two propagating waves with opposite directions to each other. The components of the wave vector (k_x, k_y, and k_z) of these propagating waves are determined by the quantum numbers (n, m, and l) as discrete values, as shown in the Appendix. Consequently, the wave function given in (1) is composed of eight propagating waves, i.e., eight bulk Bloch functions. As a result, the matrix element of the dipole moment of the quantum-box structures is given as follows, calculated by the same way as in the quantum-film structures [14]:

$$\begin{aligned} R_{ch} &= \langle \Psi_{cnml} | er | \Psi_{hn'm'l'} \rangle \\ &\simeq \delta_{nn'} \delta_{mm'} \delta_{ll'} \sum_k \langle u_c | er | u_h \rangle, \end{aligned} \tag{2}$$

where $\langle u_c | er | u_h \rangle$ is the bulk dipole moment at fixed wave vector $\boldsymbol{k}(=\boldsymbol{k}_c=\boldsymbol{k}_h)$, the summation is made with respect

Reprinted from *IEEE J. Quantum Electron.*, vol. QE-22, no. 9, pp. 1915–1921, Sept. 1986.

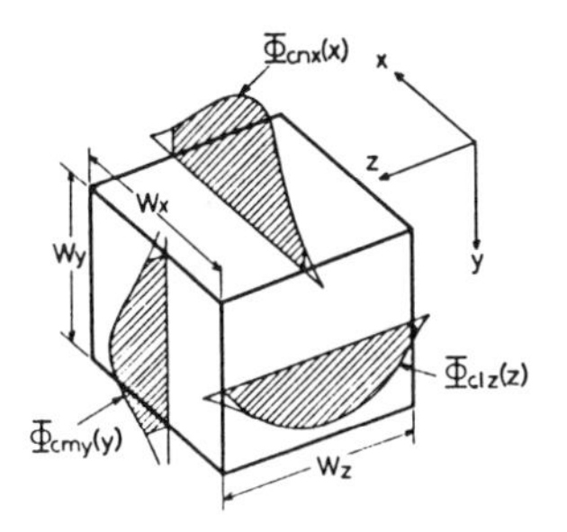

Fig. 1. Envelope functions of an electron confined into quantum box along the x-, y-, and z-axes.

to $\boldsymbol{k}$ of the eight propagating waves mentioned above, e is the electron charge, and $\boldsymbol{r}$ is the position operator. We have neglected the light-hole band in (2), because the quantized energy levels of light hole are much deeper than those of heavy hole.

The dipole moment of bulk crystal at fixed $\boldsymbol{k}$, $\langle u_c|er|u_h\rangle$ in (2), has been calculated by the $\boldsymbol{k} \cdot \boldsymbol{p}$ method [13]. It has been shown that this dipole moment is rotating in the plane perpendicular to the wave vector $\boldsymbol{k}$. Representing the latitude and longitude of the wave vector $\boldsymbol{k}$ by θ and ϕ ($\theta = 0$ at the y-axis, and $\phi = 0$ at the z-axis), each component of $\langle u_c|er|u_h\rangle$ is given by [14]

$$R(\cos\theta \sin\phi + j\cos\phi), \quad \text{(for } x\text{-direction)} \tag{3a}$$

$$-R\sin\theta, \quad \text{(for } y\text{-direction)} \tag{3b}$$

$$R(\cos\theta\cos\phi - j\sin\phi), \quad \text{(for } z\text{-direction)} \tag{3c}$$

where the magnitude of the dipole moment R is given by [13], [14]

$$R^2 = \left(\frac{e\hbar}{2E_{ch}}\right)^2 \frac{E_g(E_g + \Delta_0)}{(E_g + 2\Delta_0/3)m_c} \tag{4}$$

where E_{ch} is the transition energy between an electron and a heavy hole, E_g is the bulk band gap energy, Δ_0 is the spin-orbit splitting, and m_c is the condition effective mass.

The interaction between the dipole moment $\boldsymbol{R}_{ch}$ and the electric field of light, $\boldsymbol{E}$, is given by $\boldsymbol{R}_{ch} \cdot \boldsymbol{E}$. For bulk crystals, $\boldsymbol{k}$ distributes over all directions, and so does the dipole moment. Therefore, the effective dipole moment is obtained by averaging the component of the dipole moment parallel to $\boldsymbol{E}$ (one of (3a)-(3c), for example) over all directions of $\boldsymbol{k}$ [13].

For quantum-box structures, as discussed above, the effective dipole moment is calculated by averaging dipole moments corresponding to the eight directions of $\boldsymbol{k}(\pm k_x, \pm k_y, \pm k_z)$. Due to this quantization of $\boldsymbol{k}$, which is of the same origin as that in quantum-film and quantum-wire structures [14], [15], [11], the magnitude of the interaction $\boldsymbol{R}_{ch} \cdot \boldsymbol{E}$ is dependent on the polarization direction of $\boldsymbol{E}$. By the same calculation as for the quantum-wire structures [11], it is found that $\boldsymbol{R}_{ch} \cdot \boldsymbol{E}$ becomes maximum when $\boldsymbol{E}$ is parallel to the longest side of the quantum box. For a cubic quantum box, $\boldsymbol{R}_{ch} \cdot \boldsymbol{E}$ is isotropic. Assuming that the side of the quantum box along the x-direction is the longest in Fig. 1, and that $\boldsymbol{E}$ is parallel to the x-direction, the square of the effective dipole moment is given by averaging (3a) over the eight fixed directions of $\boldsymbol{k}$ as

$$\begin{aligned}\langle \boldsymbol{R}_{ch}^2\rangle &= R^2(\cos^2\theta\sin^2\phi + \cos^2\phi)\delta_{ll'}\delta_{mm'}\delta_{nn'} \\ &= R^2(k_y^2 + k_z^2)/k^2 \cdot \delta_{ll'}\delta_{mm'}\delta_{nn'},\end{aligned} \tag{5}$$

where θ and ϕ in this case are the latitude and longitude of any one of the eight fixed $\boldsymbol{k}$'s, respectively, and the relation between these angles and the quantized energy levels is given in the Appendix. Since the angles θ and ϕ depend on the quantized energy levels, and therefore, on the shape of the quantum box, $\langle \boldsymbol{R}_{ch}^2\rangle$ in (5) is dependent on the shape of the quantum box. $\langle \boldsymbol{R}_{ch}^2\rangle$ is less than R^2 for any shape of the quantum box, and is $(2/3)R^2$ for a cubic quantum box where $k_x^2 = k_y^2 = k_z^2$, which is the same value as that of bulk crystal [13].

Together with the results on the quantum-film and quantum-wire structures [14], [15], [11], it is concluded for the polarization dependence of the dipole moment in quantum-well structures that the interaction energy $\boldsymbol{R}_{ch} \cdot \boldsymbol{E}$ becomes maximum when the electric field $\boldsymbol{E}$ is parallel to the longest side of the interface of the quantum-well structures.

B. Linear Gain

Using the density-matrix theory with relaxation broadening [12], [13], the linear gain $\alpha^{(1)}$ of the quantum-box lasers is given by

$$\alpha^{(1)}(\omega) = \frac{\omega}{n_r}\sqrt{\frac{\mu_0}{\epsilon_0}} \sum_{lmn} \int_{Eg}^{\infty} \langle \boldsymbol{R}_{ch}^2\rangle \cdot \frac{g_{ch}(f_c - f_v)\hbar/\tau_{in}}{(E_{ch} - \hbar\omega)^2 + (\hbar/\tau_{in})^2}\, dE_{ch}, \tag{6}$$

where the summation is made with respect to quantized energy levels, ω is the angular frequency of light, ϵ_0 and μ_0 are the dielectric constant and permeability of the vacuum, n_r is the refractive index of the quantum box, f_c and f_v are the Fermi functions [12]-[14], the quasi-Fermi levels of which (E_{fc} and E_{fv}) are determined by the injected carrier density as shown below. τ_{in} is the intraband relaxation time [12], and g_{ch} is the density-of-states of electron-hole pairs with same quantized energy levels with each other given by

$$g_{ch}(E_{ch}) = 2\delta(E_{ch} - E_{cnml} - E_{hnml} - E_g)/w_x w_y w_z, \tag{7}$$

where w_x, w_y, and w_z are the well widths along the x-, y-, and z-directions, respectively, $\delta(E)$ is the delta function, and E_{cmnl} and E_{hnml} are the quantized energy levels given in the Appendix.

Electron density N and hole density $P(\simeq N)$ in the quantum box are related to the quasi-Fermi levels (E_{fc} and E_{fv}) as

$$N = \sum_{lmn} \frac{2}{\left[1 + \exp\left(\dfrac{E_{cmnl} - E_{fc}}{kT}\right)\right] w_x w_y w_z}, \tag{8a}$$

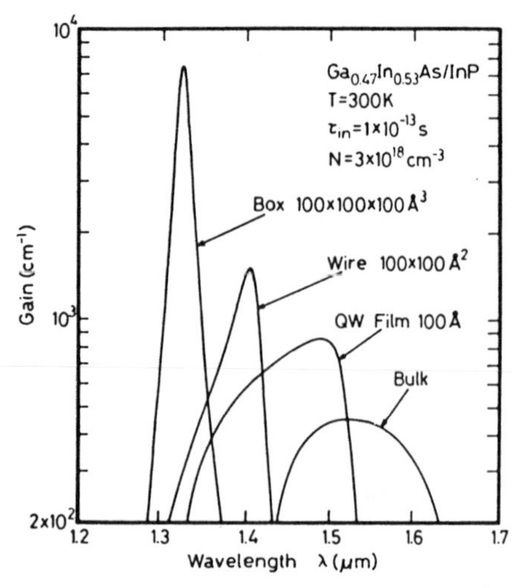

Fig. 2. Gain spectra calculated for $Ga_{0.47}In_{0.53}As/InP$ 100 Å × 100 Å × 100 Å cubic quantum box, 100 Å × 100 Å quantum wire, 100 Å thick quantum film, and bulk crystal at T = 300 K.

$$P \simeq N = \sum_{lmn} \frac{2}{\left[1 + \exp\left(\dfrac{E_{fv} - E_{hmnl}}{kT}\right)\right] w_x w_y w_z}, \quad \text{(8b)}$$

where the origin of the energy levels is at the bottom of the conduction band.

Fig. 2 shows the gain spectra calculated for 100 Å × 100 Å × 100 Å cubic $Ga_{0.47}In_{0.53}As/InP$ quantum box compared with 100 Å × 100 Å quantum wire [11], 100 Å thick quantum film [14], and bulk crystal [13]. The direction of electric-field polarization has been chosen so that gain becomes maximum for all of the quantum wells, according to the above discussion of the dipole moment. The intraband relaxation time τ_{in} has been assumed to be same as the bulk value, 1×10^{-13} s, for all quantum wells in order to obtain the effect of the change in density-of-states on the gain spectra, although detailed physical consideration will be necessary for the intraband relaxation process in quantum well structures, which has not yet been established. As can be seen, the shape of spectrum becomes sharper with increasing quantization dimension. This is due to the variation of the density-of-states [10] which is shown in Fig. 3. The width of gain spectrum is determined only by the relaxation broadening for quantum box, since the density-of-states is given by the delta function, while for other quantum wells it is determined by all of the shapes of the density-of-states, the relaxation broadening, and the thermal distribution of carriers. Fig. 4(a) and (b) show the peak gain as a function of carrier density N for $Ga_{0.47}In_{0.53}As/InP$ and $GaAs/Ga_{0.8}Al_{0.2}As$ bulk and quantum wells with various quantization dimensions. Gain increases with increasing quantization dimension. For GaAs/GaAlAs, gain of quantum box is about ten times that of bulk crystal at carrier density above about 3.5×10^{18} cm^{-3}, and, for GaInAs/InP, about 15 times that of bulk crystal above about 2×10^{18} cm^{-3}.

In the present theory, we have neglected the following three effects: i) excitonic effect, ii) band warping at high energy in the conduction band, and iii) change in the intraband relaxation time from the bulk value. For i), the Coulomb interaction between electrons and holes may be stronger than the case of bulk crystals, since electrons are perfectly confined, and thus, this effect may influence the gain even at high injection. The strength of the dipole moment becomes larger than the value calculated above due to this effect, as in the bulk case [22]. For ii), due to the band warping which makes the effective mass large at high energy, the quantized levels become lower than the value obtained in the Appendix. Therefore, carrier den-

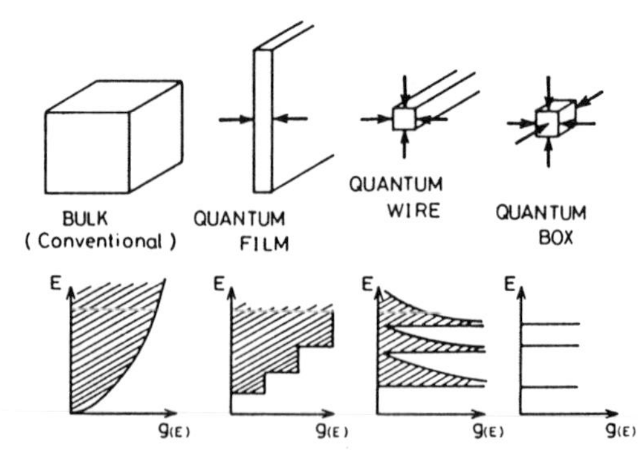

Fig. 3. Variation of density-of-states of electrons with the increase of the quantization dimension in quantum-well structures.

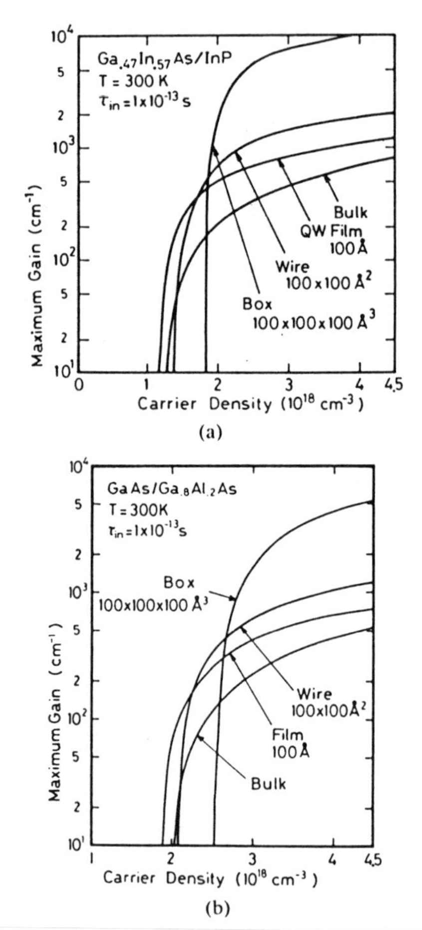

Fig. 4. Maximum gain as a function of carrier density calculated for (a) $Ga_{0.47}In_{0.53}As/InP$ and (b) $GaAs/Ga_{0.8}Al_{0.2}As$ quantum boxes, quantum wires, quantum films, and bulk crystals.

sity at these levels determined by the Fermi function becomes larger, which results in higher gain. For iii), since the scattering probability of electrons may be small in quantum-box structure due to the reduction of the density-of-states, the gain may become larger. Moreover, as pointed out recently [23], the approximation of the intraband relaxation effect by the Lorentz shape in (6) becomes unexact as the photon energy goes away from the center of the Lorentz shape. This effect also makes the gain larger [23]. Consequently, the three effects listed above make the gain larger, and thus, the gain magnitudes calculated here may give the lowest limit.

III. Threshold Current Density

We assume here that quantum boxes are arrayed in the plane perpendicular to the injection current as shown in Fig. 5. The broadening of the quantized energy levels due to the interaction between the boxes is neglected, assuming that the well potential is deep enough. This assumption is satisifed for well depth and well width larger than about 0.1 eV and 100 Å, respectively [14]. Current is assumed to be injected only into the surface of quantum boxes due to the potential difference between the box region and the separation region. Carrier density in the quantum boxes is related to injection current as

$$J = \eta n w_y eN/\tau_s, \tag{9}$$

where J expresses the average current density which is the total current, assumed to be injected entirely into the quantum boxes, divided by the whole area including both of the surfaces of quantum boxes and separation region. We use this definition for current density because a layer of quantum-box array including the separation region is regarded as a homogeneous artificial semiconductor layer. η is the rate of the surface area of quantum boxes included in the whole area. $\eta = 0.25$ for the array shown in Fig. 5, where the intervals between boxes along the x- and z-directions are equal to the well widths w_x and w_z, respectively, and moreover, $w_x = w_z$. The effect of optical confinement into the quantum-box region is discussed below [see (12)]. n is the number of the layers of quantum-box array, and τ_s is the carrier lifetime, which consists of the radiative and nonradiative recombination times (τ_r and τ_{nr}) as

$$1/\tau_s = 1/\tau_r + 1/\tau_{nr}. \tag{10}$$

Radiative lifetime τ_r is obtained from the spontaneous emission rate by the same way as that of bulk crystal [16] as

$$\tau_r = N\Big/\left[\mu_0^{3/2}\,\epsilon_0^{1/2} n_r\Big/\pi\hbar^{-4}\sum_{nml}\int_{E_g}^{\infty}\cdot\langle R_{ch}^2\rangle_{\text{bulk}}\,E_{ch}^3 f_c(1-f_v)g_{ch}dE_{ch}\right], \tag{11}$$

where the summation is made with respect to quantized energy levels, and the square of the dipole moment used in this equation is approximated as being the same as that

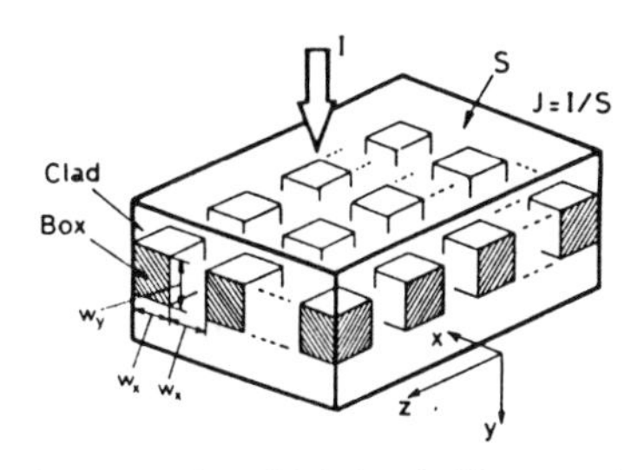

Fig. 5. Quantum-box array for which threshold current is calculated in the text.

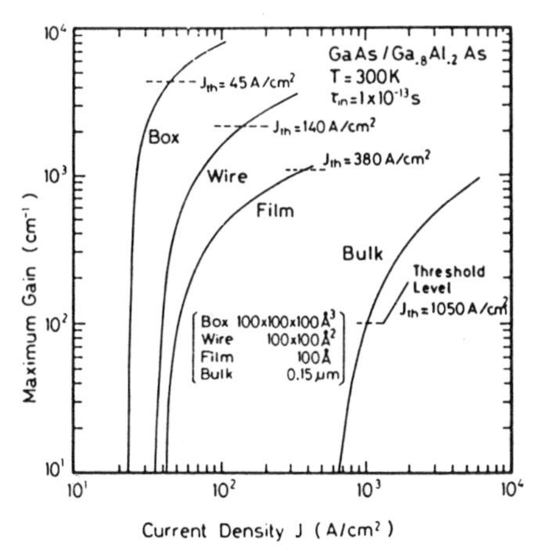

Fig. 6. Maximum gain as a function of injection current density calculated for GaAs/$Ga_{0.8}Al_{0.2}As$ quantum box, quantum wire, quantum film, and bulk crystal (conventional double heterostructure). Dashed line on each curve is the level of gain required for the laser threshold.

of bulk crystal, since the dipole moment is averaged over all modes of spontaneous emission which distribute over all directions.

For short wavelength (wide bandgap) semiconductors such as GaAs/GaAlAs, the rate of nonradiative recombinations such as the Auger effect is much smaller than that of radiative recombination, and thus, the carrier lifetime τ_s is approximately equal to the radiative recombination time τ_r. In this case, the gain is related to the current density using (6), (9), and (11). Fig. 6 shows the maximum gain as a function of current density calculated for GaAs/$Ga_{0.8}Al_{0.2}As$ bulk (conventional double heterostructure) and quantum wells with various quantization dimensions. The following assumptions have been made in Fig. 6: the thickness for bulk crystal is 0.15 μm, for the quantum wire wires are arrayed with the separation length equal to the wire width, and for the quantum box cubic boxes are arrayed in the structure shown in Fig. 5. The layer number n in (9) is one for all cases. The increases of gain with the quantization dimension is observed in Fig. 6.

The threshold condition is expressed using the linear gain as

$$\alpha^{(1)} = \alpha_{\text{th}} = \alpha_{ac} + (1 - \xi_x\xi_y\xi_z)\alpha_{ex}/(\xi_x\xi_y\xi_z) + \ln(1/R)/(\xi_x\xi_y\xi_z L), \tag{12}$$

where α_{th} is the threshold gain, the laser resonator is formed along the z-direction in Fig. 5, α_{ac} and α_{ex} are the loss coefficients in the quantum boxes and other regions, respectively, ξ_x, ξ_y, and ξ_z are the optical confinement factors in the quantum boxes along the x-, y-, and z-directions, respectively, L is the resonator length, and R is the reflectivity of the end mirrors. $\xi_x = \xi_z = 0.5$ for the box array in Fig. 5, assuming that the width of the laser waveguide along the x-direction is large enough compared to the wavelength of light. $\xi_x = 1$ and $\xi_z = 0.5$ for a quantum-wire array perpendicular to the resonator direction, with the direction of wires chosen so that the gain becomes maximum [11]. $\xi_x = \xi_z = 1$ for quantum film and bulk.

The threshold current density is obtained by putting the threshold gain α_{th} calculated by (11) into Fig. 6. We assume in the calculation $\alpha_{ac} = \alpha_{ex} = 10\ cm^{-1}$, which is the same as the bulk value around $N = 10^{18}\ cm^{-3}$ [17], $\ln(1/R)/L = 30\ cm^{-1}$, $\xi_y = 0.4$ for bulk (conventional double heterostructure) and 0.037 for quantum wells, which is the value calculated for GRIN-SCH [3] GaAs/($Ga_{0.8}Al_{0.2}As$-$Ga_{0.4}Al_{0.6}As$) with the active layer thickness of 100 Å and the cladding layer thickness optimized to obtain maximum ξ_y. The threshold gains thus calculated are shown in Fig. 6 by the dashed lines for bulk and all the quantum wells. From these threshold gains in Fig. 6, the threshold current densities are obtained for GaAs/GaAlAs, to be 1050 A/cm^2 for bulk (conventional double heterostructure), 380 A/cm^2 for quantum film, 140 A/cm^2 for quantum wire, and 45 A/cm^2 for quantum box. These threshold current densities can be reduced further by optimizing the well thicknesses.

For GaInAsP/InP systems, nonradiative recombination processes, such as the Auger effect and carrier leakage, and the intervalence band absorption must be taken into account in τ_{nr} in (10) and α_{ac} in (12), respectively, in the estimation of the threshold current density. These effects have not yet been estimated for quantum-well structures. For $Ga_{0.47}In_{0.53}As$/InP conventional double heterostructures, the carrier density dependences of the intervalence band absorption and the carrier lifetime including nonradiative recombinations are expressed experimentally as $\alpha_{ac} = K_0 N$ with $K_0 \simeq 4 \times 10^{-17}\ cm^2$ and $1/\tau_s \simeq B_{eff}N^{\gamma}$ with $B_{eff} \simeq 1.5 \times 10^{-10}\ cm^3/s$ and $\gamma \simeq 2$ [18]–[20]. If we use these expressions for quantum box for the moment, the threshold current density is estimated to be 62 A/cm^2 for GRIN-SCH $Ga_{0.47}In_{0.53}As$/($Ga_{0.28}In_{0.72}As_{0.6}P_{0.4}$-InP) quantum-box array lasers ($\xi_y = 0.02$) which is the same structure as that of GaAs/GaAlAs mentioned above.

IV. Conclusion

Gain and threshold current density have been analyzed for quantum-box laser where electrons are confined in quantum wells three-dimensionally, based on the density-matrix theory of semiconductor lasers with relaxation broadening.

The electronic dipole moment has first been analyzed, and it has been shown that the gain becomes maximum when the electric field of light is parallel to the longest side of the quantum box.

The linear gain has been calculated and shown to be about ten times and 15 times those of bulk crystals for 100 Å × 100 Å × 100 Å GaAs/$Ga_{0.8}Al_{0.2}As$ and $Ga_{0.47}In_{0.53}As$/InP quantum boxes, respectively, at fixed carrier density.

The threshold current density has been calculated to be 45 A/cm^2 and 62 A/cm^2 for GRIN-SCH GaAs/($Ga_{0.8}Al_{0.2}As$-$Ga_{0.4}Al_{0.6}As$) and $Ga_{0.47}In_{0.53}As$/($Ga_{0.28}In_{0.72}As_{0.6}P_{0.4}$-InP) quantum-box array lasers, respectively, where for the GaInAs/GaInAsP/InP system the intervalence band absorption and nonradiative recombinations have been assumed to be same as those obtained for bulk crystals experimentally. Although the quantum-box structure has not yet been realized, these results show the possibility of remarkable reduction in the laser threshold by this structure.

Appendix
Wave Functions and Quantized Energy Levels

Here we calculate the wave functions and the quantized energy levels in quantum-box structures. The method we use is that corresponding to the equivalent refractive index method used in the optical waveguide theory [21]. This method is a good approximation when $w_x >> w_y >> w_z$, where w_x, w_y, and w_z are the well widths of the quantum box along the x-, y-, and z-directions, respectively, or when the well depth is much larger than the resulting quantized energy levels measured from the bottom of the well.

The calculation process is schematically shown in Fig. 7. First, we obtain the envelope function and the energy level of the conduction band along the z-axis (Φ_{czl} in (1) and E_{czl}) by the following equation:

$$[-(\hbar/2m_c)\partial^2/\partial z^2 + V_{cz}(z)]\Phi_{czl}(z) = E_{czl}\Phi_{czl}(z) \quad \text{(A-1)}$$

with the potential given by

$$V_{cz}(z) = \begin{cases} 0 & (|z| \leq w_z/2\text{: inside the well}), \\ \Delta E_c & (|z| \geq w_z/2\text{: outside the well}), \end{cases} \quad \text{(A-2)}$$

where the origin of the energies is at the bottom of the conduction band, and ΔE_c is the well depth which has been calculated by the method of linear combination of atomic orbitals [14]. By the same calculation as that in conventional quantum films, the envelope function Φ_{czl} is given by

$$\Phi_{czl} = A \begin{pmatrix} \cos \\ \sin \end{pmatrix} [(2m_{c1}E_{czl})^{1/2}z/\hbar], \begin{pmatrix} l\text{: even} \\ l\text{: odd} \end{pmatrix}$$

$$(|z| \leq w_z/2) \quad \text{(A-3)}$$

$$\Phi_{czl} = B \exp[-\{2m_{c2}(\Delta E_c - E_{czl})\}^{1/2}|z|/\hbar],$$

$$(|z| \geq w_z/2) \quad \text{(A-4)}$$

where m_{c1} and m_{c2} are the effective masses of the conduction bands inside and outside the well, respectively. The energy level E_{czl} is obtained from the following equation:

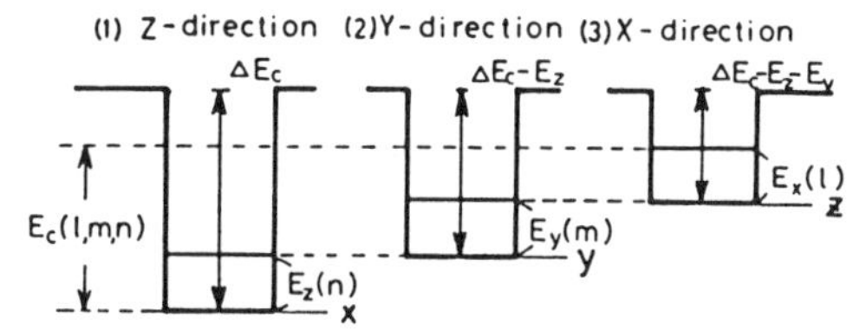

Fig. 7. Calculation process of the quantized energy levels in quantum box, which is corresponding to the equivalent refractive index method in optical waveguide theory. Calculation is processed from (1) to (3).

$$[(m_{c1}/m_{c2})(\Delta E_c - E_{czl})/E_{czl}]^{1/2} = \begin{pmatrix} \tan \\ -\cot \end{pmatrix} [w_z(2m_{c1}E_{czl})^{1/2}/\hbar] \begin{pmatrix} l:\text{even} \\ l:\text{odd} \end{pmatrix}. \quad \text{(A-5)}$$

Second, we obtain the envelope function and the energy level along the y-axis (Φ_{cym} in (1) and E_{cym}) by the equation obtained by exchanging z and the label l by y and m, respectively, with potential $V_{cy}(y)$ given by

$$V_{cy}(y) = \begin{cases} 0 & (|y| \leq w_y/2) \\ \Delta E_c - E_{czl} & (|y| \geq w_y/2) \end{cases}. \quad \text{(A-6)}$$

Equations for E_{cym} and Φ_{cym} are obtained similarly to (A-3)-(A-5).

Finally, we obtain the envelope function and the energy level along the x-axis (Φ_{cxn} in (1) and E_{cxn}) by the equation obtained by exchanging y and the label m by x and n, respectively, with the potential $V_{cx}(x)$ given by

$$V_{cx}(x) = \begin{cases} 0 & (|x| \leq w_x/2) \\ \Delta E_c - E_{czl} - E_{cym} & (|x| \geq w_x/2) \end{cases}. \quad \text{(A-7)}$$

By this process, quantized energy level in the conduction band of the quantum box is obtained by

$$E_{cnml} = E_{czl} + E_{cym} + E_{cxn}, \quad \text{(A-8)}$$

and the total wave function in the quantum box is given by (1).

Quantized energy levels in the valence band are calculated by the same process. The emission wavelength corresponding to the transition between the quantized energy levels of the conduction and valence bands with the same quantization number is given by

$$\lambda(\mu\text{m}) = 1.24/(E_g + E_{cnml} + E_{hnml})(\text{eV}). \quad \text{(A-9)}$$

This emission wavelength calculated for $Ga_{0.47}In_{0.53}As$/InP cubic quantum box is shown in Fig. 8 as a function of box size.

The wave function given by (A-3) is a standing wave in the well, which is divided into two propagating waves as

$$\Phi_{czl} = A[\exp(jk_z z) \pm \exp(-jk_z z)], \quad \text{(A-10)}$$

where

$$k_z = (2m_{c1}E_{czl})^{1/2}/\hbar. \quad \text{(A-11)}$$

The wave number k_z is quantized due to the quantization of E_{czl}. Envelope functions along the y- and x-axes are

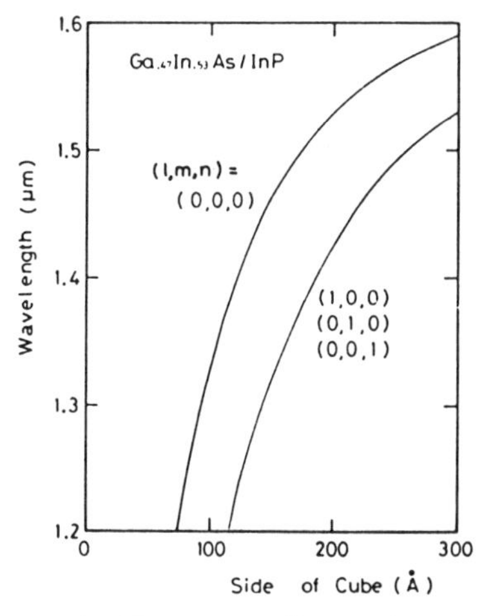

Fig. 8. Emission wavelength corresponding to the transition between quantized energy levels of electron and hole in cubic quantum box, as a function of length of side of cube.

expressed similarly to (A-10) and (A-11), and thus, the total wave function given by (1) is divided into eight propagating wave functions. Each component of the wave vector of these propagating waves is quantized due to the quantization of E_{czl}, E_{cym}, and E_{cxn}. Representing the longitude and latitude of one of the fixed eight wave vectors by θ and ϕ ($\theta = 0$ at the y-axis and $\phi = 0$ at the z-axis), the eight directions of $\boldsymbol{k}$ are given by $(\theta, \pm\phi)$, $(\theta, \pi \pm \phi)$, $(\pi - \theta, \pm\phi)$, and $(\pi - \theta, \pi \pm \phi)$. We have the following relations:

$$\cos^2\theta = k_y^2/k^2 = E_{cym}/E_{cnml} \quad \text{(A-12)}$$

$$\cos^2\phi = k_z^2/(k^2 - k_y^2) = E_{czl}/(E_{cnml} - E_{cym}). \quad \text{(A-13)}$$

The dipole moment in (5) is calculated by these equations.

Acknowledgment

The authors would like to thank Prof. K. Iga and Assoc. Profs. K. Furuya and M. Yamada for many discussions.

References

[1] R. Dingle, "Confined carrier quantum states in ultrathin semiconductor heterostructures," in *Festkoerperprobleme XV*, H. J. Queisser, Ed. New York: Pergamon, 1975, pp. 21-48.

[2] N. Holonyak, Jr., R. M. Kolbas, R. D. Dupuis, and P. D. Dapkus, "Quantum-well heterostructure lasers," *IEEE J. Quantum Electron.*, vol. QE-16, pp. 170-186, Feb. 1980.

[3] W. T. Tsang, "Extremely low threshold (AlGa)As graded-index waveguide separate-confinement heterostructure lasers grown by molecular beam epitaxy," *Appl. Phys. Lett.*, vol. 40, pp. 217-219, Feb. 1982.

[4] S. D. Hersee, M. Baldy, P. Assenat, B. de Cremoux, and J. P. Duchemin, "Very low threshold GRIN-SCH GaAs/GaAlAs laser structure grown by OM-VPE," *Electron. Lett.*, vol. 18, pp. 870-871, Sept. 1982.

[5] R. D. Burnham, W. Streifer, D. R. Scifres, C. Lindstroem, T. L. Paoli, and N. Holonyak, Jr., "Low-threshold single quantum well (60Å) GaAlAs lasers grown by MO-CVD with Mg as *p*-type dopant," *Electron. Lett.*, vol. 18, pp. 1095-1097, Dec. 1982.

[6] T. Fujii, S. Yamakoshi, O. Wada, and S. Hiyamizu, "Fabrication of low threshold GaAs-GaAlAs GRIN-SCH laser with superlattice buffer layer grown by MBE," *Nat. Conv. Rec.*, Japan. Appl. Phys. Soc., No. 14p-R-15, Oct. 1984 (in Japanese).

[7] R. Chin. N. Holonyak, Jr., B. A. Vojak, K. Hess, R. D. Dupuis, and P. D. Dapkus, "Temperature dependence of threshold current for quantum-well $Al_xGa_{1-x}As$-GaAs heterostructure laser diodes," *Appl. Phys. Lett.*, vol. 36, pp. 19-21, Jan. 1980.

[8] H. Iwamura, T. Saku, T. Ishibashi, K. Otsuka, and Y. Horikoshi, "Dynamic behaviour of a GaAs-GaAlAs MQW laser diode," *Electron. Lett.*, vol. 19, pp. 180-181, Mar. 1983.

[9] P. M. Petroff, A. C. Gossard, R. A. Logan, and W. Wiegmann, "Toward quantum well wires: Fabrication and optical properties," *Appl. Phys. Lett.*, vol. 41, pp. 635-638, Oct. 1982.

[10] Y. Arakawa and H. Sakaki, "Multidimensional quantum well laser and temperature dependence of its threshold current," *Appl. Phys. Lett.*, vol. 40, pp. 939-941, June 1982.

[11] M. Asada, Y. Miyamoto, and Y. Suematsu, "Theoretical gain of quantum-well wire lasers," *Japan. J. Appl. Phys.*, vol. 24, pp. L95-L97, Feb. 1985.

[12] M. Yamada and Y. Suematsu, "Analysis of gain suppression in undoped injection lasers," *J. Appl. Phys.*, vol. 52, pp. 2653-2664, Apr. 1981.

[13] M. Asada and Y. Suematsu, "Density-matrix theory of semiconductor lasers with relaxation broadening model—Gain and gain-suppression in semiconductor lasers," *IEEE J. Quantum Electron.*, vol. QE-21, pp. 434-442, May 1985.

[14] M. Asada, A. Kameyama, and Y. Suematsu, "Gain and intervalence band absorption in quantum-well lasers," *IEEE J. Quantum Electron.*, vol. QE-20, pp. 745-753, July 1984.

[15] M. Yamanishi and I. Suemune, "Comment on polarization dependent momentum matrix elements in quantum well lasers," *Japan. J. Appl. Phys.*, vol. 23, pp. L35-L36, Jan. 1984.

[16] M. Yamada and H. Ishiguro, "Gain calculation of undoped GaAs injection laser taking account of electronic intra-band relaxation," *Japan. J. Appl. Phys.*, vol. 20, pp. 1279-1288, July 1981.

[17] E. Pinkas, B. I. Miller, I. Hayashi, and P. W. Foy, "Additional data on the effect of doping on the lasing characteristics of GaAs-$Al_xGa_{1-x}As$ double heterostructure lasers," *IEEE J. Quantum Electron.*, vol. QE-9, pp. 281-282, Feb. 1973.

[18] A. R. Adams, M. Asada, Y. Suematsu, and S. Arai, "The temperature dependence of the efficiency and threshold current of $In_{1-x}Ga_xAs_yP_{1-y}$ lasers related to intervalence band absorption," *Japan. J. Appl. Phys.*, vol. 19, pp. L621-L624, Oct. 1980.

[19] M. Asada, A. R. Adams, K. E. Stubkjaer, Y. Suematsu, Y. Itaya, and S. Arai, "The temperature dependence of the threshold current of GaInAsP/InP DH lasers," *IEEE J. Quantum Electron.*, vol. QE-17, pp. 611-619, May 1981.

[20] K. Stubkjaer, M. Asada, S. Arai, and Y. Suematsu, "Spontaneous recombination, gain, and refractive index variation for 1.6 μm wavelength InGaAsP/InP lasers," *Japan. J. Appl. Phys.*, vol. 20, pp. 1499-1505, Aug. 1981.

[21] R. Ulrich and R. J. Martin, "Geometrical optics in thin film light guides," *Appl. Opt.*, vol. 10, pp. 2077-2085, Sept. 1971.

[22] J. O. Dimmock, "Introduction to the theory of exciton states in semiconductors," in *Semiconductors and Semimetals*, vol. 3, R. K. Willardson and A. C. Beer, Eds. New York: Academic, 1967, pp. 287-299.

[23] M. Yamanishi, Y. Lee, and Y. Osaka, "Theoretical discussion on the line shape function of semiconductor lasers," *Nat. Conv. Rec.*, Japan. Appl. Phys. Soc., no. 4a-N-2, Oct. 1985 (in Japanese).

Low-temperature photoluminescence from InGaAs/InP quantum wires and boxes

H. Temkin, G. J. Dolan, M. B. Panish, and S. N. G. Chu
AT&T Bell Laboratories, Murray Hill, New Jersey 07974

(Received 24 October 1986; accepted for publication 15 December 1986)

InGaAs/InP quantum well layers grown by gas source molecular beam epitaxy have been used to fabricate quantum wires and boxes with transverse dimensions as small as ~300 Å. These artificial structures exhibit intense low-temperature photoluminescence and show exciton shifts of 8–14 meV expected of low dimensional confinement. Low surface recombination velocity characteristic of InP and its alloys should allow luminescence studies of features as small as ~30 Å under moderate excitation intensities.

Effects of small size and reduced dimensionality alter many properties of semiconductors and semiconductor based devices. Many interesting effects have been studied in quasi-two-dimensional structures, for which modern epitaxial growth techniques are capable of preparing quantum wells with thicknesses of a few lattice constants and interfaces sharp on a monolayer scale. In principle, systems of lower dimensionality can be formed from such two-dimensional structures by lithographically patterning the layer to a transverse dimension comparable to the carrier wavelength. This dimension is typically ~0.02 μm which is near the present limits of electron beam lithography. However, the patterning must not degrade the layer's electronic integrity which may occur as a result of processing induced defects and enhanced recombination rate expected at layer sidewalls. In very small structures any increase in the surface recombination rate will dominate the structure's behavior since the surface to volume ratio becomes very large.

The physical reason for changes in optical and electrical characteristics of low dimensional structures lies in the markedly different nature of their density of states. It is well known that upon a reduction from three to two dimensions (D) the density of states $\rho(E)$ changes from a continuous $\rho(E) \sim E^{1/2}$ to a steplike dependence, shown in Fig. 1. This gives rise to a characteristic steplike absorption and a greatly enhanced exciton intensity in quantum well superlattices.[1] Elementary considerations[2] show that a 1-D (quantum wire) density of states is characterized by a single step followed by a $\rho(E) \sim E^{-1/2}$ decay and in a 0-D case (quantum box or quantum dot) $\rho(E)$ is reduced to a delta function. The resulting optical properties have been studied experimentally in CuCl and CdS microcrystals suspended in glass matrices,[3,4] where large increases in the absorption edge energy due to three-dimensional confinement have been observed. Very large absorption coefficients, inversely proportional to the square of the box's radius, have been predicted recently.[5] Significant improvement in the performance of quantum wire semiconductor lasers was also recently predicted as a consequence of a factor of two increase in the gain.[6] Earlier transport studies have also been made on very small Si structures.[7]

With III-V compounds, research in this field has been concentrated on GaAs/AlGaAs. Quantum wires and boxes with dimensions upward of 500 Å have been fabricated by a number of techniques and studied by low-temperature cathodoluminescence[8,9] and photoluminescence (PL).[10] The GaAs system, however, suffers from a relatively large surface recombination velocity and in order to fabricate structures with efficient PL, very sophisticated processes must be employed.[9] In Ref. 9 in particular, confinement was observed by quantum well disordering and hence without the vacuum interface. This more complex process is intrinsically limited to features larger than ~0.05 μm and produces a process related size dependence in the position of the energy levels. In contrast, the InGaAs/InP material system, also of interest for many optoelectronic applications, offers a stable surface with recombination velocity reduced by a factor of ~100,[11,12] and consequently very high luminescence efficiency.

Recent progress in gas source molecular beam epitaxy (GSMBE) of the InP compounds has resulted in quantum wells and superlattices of very high quality.[13–16] In this work we report the optical properties of GSMBE grown InGaAs/InP quantum wires and boxes with dimensions of ~300 Å. The results represent the observation of reduced dimensionality in the smallest objects yet fabricated and they also imply that features a factor of 10 smaller could be made and studied in InP.

Wafers were grown by GSMBE on (100) oriented InP using previously described procedures.[15] The epitaxial

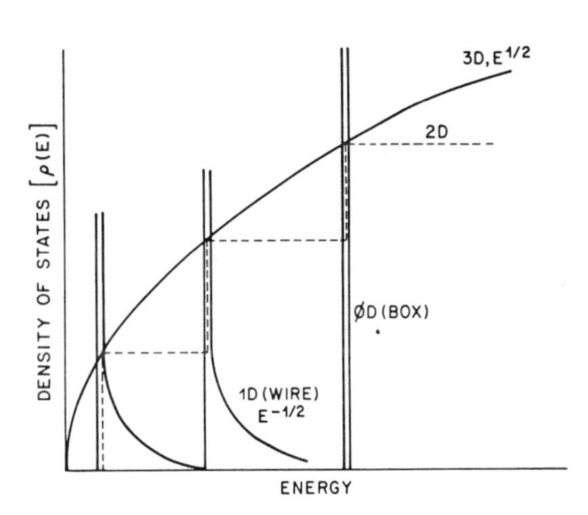

FIG. 1. Schematic representation of the density of states for low dimensional quantum confined structures.

Reprinted with permission from *Appl. Phys. Lett.*, vol. 50, no. 7, pp. 413–415, Feb. 16, 1987.

growth consisted of a ~1-μm-thick InP buffer layer, a single 50-Å-thick $In_{0.53}Ga_{0.47}As$ quantum well, and a 100-Å-thick InP cap (barrier) layer, indicated in a schematic cross section shown in the inset of Fig. 3. The layers were not intentionally doped, resulting in a n-type background carrier concentration at the mid 10^{15} cm^{-3} level.

Wires and round boxes were carved from the quantum well using electron beam lithography and argon ion milling. The JEOL JBX-5D electron beam writing instrument used is capable of creating openings as small as 0.02 μm (200 Å). For such a pattern, a composite polymethyl methacrylate/metal film stencil described previously[17,18] was made to form metal wires and dots by the "lift-off" technique. The metal patterns, of either chrome or titanium, were then used as masks for ion milling in a mixture of argon and oxygen. The ion milling removed ~30–50 nm from unmasked regions of the sample leaving the desired lines and dots of material. Cr is superior to Ti as a milling mask but cannot be easily removed after completion of the fabrication. The Cr masks, used for both wires and boxes, are believed to be removed (eroded) by the ion milling. Similar Cr mask was also evaporated and removed from a part of the control sample. The size and shape of the islands of material finally obtained depend on all of the fabrication elements, including the resist openings, the grain structure of the masking metal, and the erosive properties of the ion milling process with the mask used. All of these factors involve uncertainties and nonuniformities at the 50–100 Å level so that the size of the boxes, for example, is expected to vary by such amounts.

The transmission electron microscope image of the quantum box region is shown in Fig. 2. The micrograph shows a top view of the (100) surface with the rows of boxes aligned parallel to the cleavage directions. Under high magnification the boxes appear as round spots of somewhat different shapes with the average diameter of 300 ($\pm$50) Å. Since the ion milling transfer does not produce undercutting, this image reveals the true size of the quantum boxes. With the average box separation of ~2000 Å about 1.7% of the surface area (filling factor) is taken by the boxes. Quantum wires of similar dimensions, down to a width of 300 Å, have been fabricated with a filling factor of 15%. We believe these to be the smallest quantum wires and boxes prepared thus far. To put these sizes in perspective, each box is estimated to contain only 1.4×10^5 atoms.

Low-temperature (down to 6 K) photoluminescence (PL) experiments were carried out with wafers mounted on a conduction finger of a He flow cryostat. Conventional lock-in techniques were used in conjunction with a N_2-cooled Ge detector. A low power, < 1 mW, unpolarized HeNe laser operating at 6328 Å has been used as an excitation source. The exciting photon energy is larger than the band gap of InP and PL is expected to result from the capture of photocarriers generated in InP by the smaller band-gap InGaAs wells. This capture process is very efficient and luminescence from the InP barriers is not observed.[15] The sample areas covered with quantum wires, which form efficient diffraction gratings, were found by observing white light diffraction.

The resulting PL spectra are shown in Fig. 3. The upper trace shows a spectrum characteristic of the unprocessed quantum well structure. No changes were observed in the part of the control sample previously covered by the Cr mask. The lower two traces show the spectra of wires and boxes. The PL efficiency is high and the spectra of wires and dots could be observed at temperatures up to 60 K. All three traces were obtained at the same incident power and angle of incidence. The exciton wavelength of 1.37 μm is consistent with the 50 Å well width. The PL spectra of the wires and dots are found shifted to shorter energies by as much as 14 meV. The linewidth increase, particularly in the case of quantum boxes, is expected in view of a fairly large distribu-

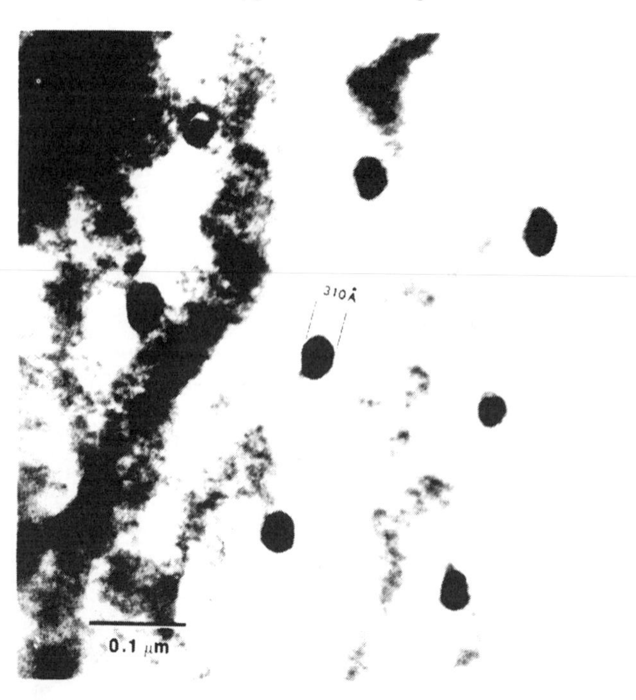

FIG. 2. Transmission electron micrograph of the InGaAs/InP quantum boxes fabricated by direct electron beam writing and ion beam milling. The average box diameter is 300 Å.

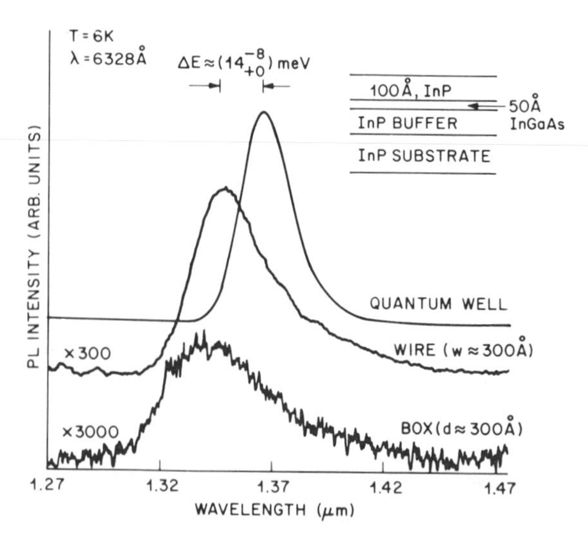

FIG. 3. Low-temperature (6 K) photoluminescence of the control quantum well sample, with the well thickness of 50 Å (upper trace) and the artificial low dimensional structures (lower traces). Inset shows a schematic diagram of the as-grown quantum well structure.

tion of sizes shown in Fig. 2, although we cannot exclude other causes. Prior to processing, the PL response of the quantum well sample was carefully mapped. Neither the exciton wavelength nor its linewidth and intensity were found to vary from position to position over the 1 cm^2 sample. Significant changes in the PL spectrum were found only as a function of the incident power, as expected from band-filling effects. Attenuation of the incident power by a factor of 4×10^3 results in the exciton peak shifting towards longer wavelength by nearly 8 meV. Since the interaction between the incident light and the features fabricated on the surface is not understood in detail, it may not be correct to assume a constant incident power. Thus as much as 8 meV of the observed energy up-shift may have to be attributed to band filling and not to low dimensional confinement. The lateral confinement in our structures is formed by an infinitely deep square potential well, and not, for instance, a rather shallow 60 meV well formed in lattice disordered GaAs/GaAlAs structures.[9] While the latter results in a number of closely spaced exciton levels observed by Cibert *et al.*,[9] the higher order exciton levels are effectively depopulated in the present structure and only a single exciton peak is expected in the PL spectrum. Using the InGaAs effective mass of $m_e^* = 0.041 m_e$ an energy shift of 10 meV is expected for the 300-Å-wide quantum wire. In view of the experimental uncertainties discussed above, the agreement with the observed exciton shift is excellent. Such low dimensional quantum confinement shifts can be seen because of very small dimensions achieved in our structures.

Another feature of the PL spectra of control sample, quantum wires, and dots shown in Fig. 3 is the luminescence efficiency which does not scale with the surface filling factors. This could be attributed either to nonradiative recombination at the sidewall of small structures fabricated by ion beam milling or to shadowing effects of the incompletely removed metal mask used in the fabrication process. The two effects can be distinguished by the measurement of the luminescence efficiency as a function of the incident laser power, as shown in Fig. 4. Reduction of the incident intensity by as much as a factor of 4000, from the full power of only ~1 mW, results in a smooth decrease in the integrated luminescence efficiency of the quantum well sample. In particular the saturation of the PL efficiency due to nonradiative centers was not observed down to the lowest laser intensities. The PL efficiency of the wires, for which fairly complete data could be obtained, was found to track the data obtained on the unprocessed control sample. The intensity ratio for wires compared to dots is furthermore close to that implied by the filling factors, but does not agree with the filling factor when compared to the control sample, suggesting shadowing effects of the metal mask. These results tend, in our opinion, to suggest negligible sidewall recombination. In this sense the integrity of the original material appears to be maintained in the patterning of InP, making it a particularly favorable material for a wide variety of experiments on ultrasmall samples. A significant increase in the PL efficiency, by perhaps as much as a factor of 10, could be realized by improved processing and in particular, by the complete removal of the metal mask residue. In addition, the incident intensity could be readily increased by at least a factor of 10. This should make features as small as 30 Å accessible to low-temperature PL studies.

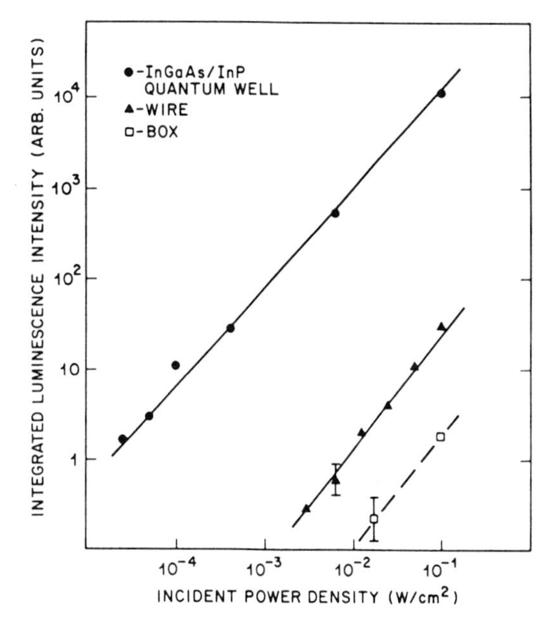

FIG. 4. Photoluminescence efficiency plotted as a function of the incident laser intensity. No indication of significant nonradiative surface or defect recombination, such as lower efficiency at very low incident powers, has been found.

[1] R. Dingle, W. Wiegmann, and C. H. Henry, Phys. Rev. Lett. **33**, 827 (1974).
[2] *Electronic States and Optical Transitions in Solids*, edited by F. Bassani (Pergamon, Oxford, 1975), p. 149.
[3] A. I. Ekimov and A. A. Onushchenko, Sov. Phys. Semicond. **16**, 775 (1982).
[4] L. Brus, IEEE J. Quantum Electron. **QE-22**, 1909 (1986).
[5] Al. L. Efros and A. L. Efros, Sov. Phys. Semicond. **16**, 772 (1982).
[6] M. Asada, Y. Miyamoto, and Y. Suematsu, Jpn. J. Appl. Phys. **24**, L95 (1985).
[7] W. J. Skocpol, L. D. Jackel, E. L. Hu, R. E. Howard, and L. A. Fetter, Phys. Rev. Lett. **49**, 951 (1982).
[8] P. M. Petroff, A. C. Gossard, R. A. Logan, and W. Wiegmann, Appl. Phys. Lett. **41**, 635 (1982).
[9] J. Cibert, P. M. Petroff, G. J. Dolan, S. J. Pearton, A. C. Gossard, and J. H. English, Second International Conference on Superlattices, Microstructures and Microdevices, 17–20 August 1986, Goteberg.
[10] M. A. Reed, R. T. Bate, K. Bradshaw, W. M. Duncan, W. R. Frensley, J. W. Lee, and H. D. Shih, J. Vac. Sci. Technol. B **4**, 358 (1986).
[11] H. C. Casey and E. Buehler, Appl. Phys. Lett. **30**, 247 (1977).
[12] R. Nottenburg, H. Temkin, and M. B. Panish, Appl. Phys. Lett. **49**, 1112 (1986).
[13] M. B. Panish, J. Electrochem. Soc. **127**, 2729 (1980).
[14] H. Temkin, M. B. Panish, P. M. Petroff, R. A. Hamm, J. M. Vandenberg, and S. Sumski, Appl. Phys. Lett. **47**, 394 (1985).
[15] M. B. Panish, H. Temkin, R. A. Hamm, and S. N. G. Chu, Appl. Phys. Lett. **49**, 164 (1986).
[16] J. M. Vandenberg, R. A. Hamm, A. T. Macrander, M. B. Panish, and H. Temkin, Appl. Phys. Lett **48**, 1153 (1986).
[17] G. J. Dolan and T. A. Fulton, IEEE Electron Device Lett. **EDL-4**, 178 (1983).
[18] D. J. Bishop, J. C. Licini, and G. J. Dolan, Appl. Phys. Lett. **46**, 1000 (1985).

Ridge waveguide injection laser with a GaInAs strained-layer quantum well ($\lambda = 1\ \mu m$)

S. E. Fischer, D. Fekete,[a] G. B. Feak, and J. M. Ballantyne
School of Electrical Engineering and Field of Applied Physics, Cornell University, Ithaca, New York 14853

(Received 17 October 1986; accepted for publication 12 January 1987)

Ridge waveguide lasers emitting near 1 μm have been made on a GaAs substrate using a single GaInAs strained-layer quantum well in a GaAs/AlGaAs graded-index separate confinement heterostructure. The epitaxial layers were grown by low-pressure metalorganic chemical vapor deposition, and the ridge waveguide was fabricated by chemically assisted ion beam etching. The lasers have threshold currents near 17 mA with fundamental lateral mode operation to five times this value. These are the first reported strained-layer current-injection lasers to run cw at room temperature; they operate, without bonding, to greater than 24 mW/facet (100 mA dc), and have 18 mW/facet (80 mA dc) lifetimes in excess of 144 h.

Strained-layer quantum well heterostructures used in optoelectronic devices permit band-gap tuning somewhat independently of the lattice constant. Strained-layer material stability, and the related question of device lifetime, are key issues with respect to the utilization of strained epitaxial layers in practical devices. Several strained-layer optoelectronic devices have been reported including photodetectors, light-emitting diodes, photopumped lasers, and current-injection lasers.[1-6] Of these, lasers are the most susceptible to accelerated degradation due to initial defects or built-in strain. Therefore, the production of high-quality strained-layer lasers and associated lifetime tests are significant measures of strained-layer material stability.

In this letter, we report the fabrication and characterization of a ridge waveguide laser designed with a graded-index separate confinement heterostructure (GRIN SCH) using a single strained-layer $Ga_{0.63}In_{0.37}As$ quantum well. The ridge waveguide was fabricated using chemically assisted ion beam etching (CAIBE). Separate papers deal with the material growth and broad-area laser testing[6] and the ridge waveguide fabrication process[7] in more detail.

The material used here was grown by low-pressure metalorganic chemical vapor deposition. The following epitaxial layers were grown sequentially on an n^+ substrate: (1) an $\sim$0.5 μm GaAs buffer layer graded to an $\sim$1.5 μm $Ga_{0.6}Al_{0.4}As$ lower cladding layer (both n doped $\sim 2\times10^{18}$ cm^{-3}), (2) the strained-layer GRIN SCH active region (unintentionally n doped $\sim 10^{16}$ cm^{-3}), and (3) an $\sim$1.5 μm $Ga_{0.6}Al_{0.4}As$ upper cladding layer graded to an $\sim$0.1 μm cap layer (both p doped $\sim 8\times10^{18}$ cm^{-3}). The GRIN SCH is symmetric about a single 40 Å $Ga_{0.63}In_{0.37}As$ quantum well. On each side of the quantum well is a 100-Å-thick GaAs shoulder, followed by a graded region in which the aluminum concentration increases to 40% over a distance of $\sim$0.2 μm. Broad-area lasers previously made with this material emitted near 1 μm, and had minimum threshold current densities as low as 152 A/cm^2 (layer 967, 146×527 μm cavity).[6]

The processing steps consist of (1) a shallow zinc diffusion, (2) a titanium-masked CAIBE ridge etch, (3) SiO_2 deposition and patterning, (4) TiPtAu p metallization, (5) substrate thinning, (6) AuGeNi n metallization, (7) alloying, and (8) cleaving. The resulting device is shown schematically in Fig. 1. The lasers are nominally 300 μm in length.

The ridge etch step is critical with respect to lateral mode control in the resulting laser. Using published data for the refractive index values of GaAs and AlGaAs at 1.24 eV (3.505 for undoped GaAs, 3.280 for undoped $Al_{0.4}Ga_{0.6}As$, 3.265 for 8×10^{18} cm^{-3} p-doped $Al_{0.4}Ga_{0.6}As$, and 3.270 for 2×10^{18} cm^{-3} n-doped $Al_{0.4}Ga_{0.6}As$),[8,9] along with a semianalytic effective-index method mode calculation program (Airy function solutions in the graded regions), we determined that we could etch to within 0.12 μm of the graded-index region and still support only the fundamental lateral mode. This figure was used to calculate the ridge etch time using scanning electron microscope data on the layer thicknesses.

The resulting diodes have a series resistance of about 4 Ω. The reverse breakdown voltage is about 14 V and the reverse saturation current is less than 1 μA. The cw light output versus current curve for a typical (unbonded) device is shown in Fig. 2 (solid curve). The threshold current is about 17 mA and the external differential quantum efficiency is 25% per facet. The curves are typically kink-free to greater than 90 mA.

The pulsed lateral near- and far-field characteristics for a device with a 2.5-μm-wide ridge are shown in Figs. 3(a) and 3(b), respectively. Figure 3(c) is the transverse far-field characteristic for the same device. The output beam is anas-

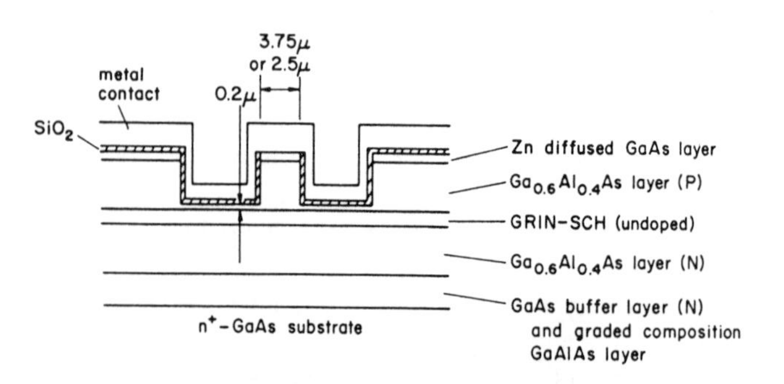

FIG. 1. Schematic drawing of the ridge waveguide laser.

[a] On leave from the Department of Physics and Solid State Institute, Technion, Haifa, Israel.

Reprinted with permission from *Appl. Phys. Lett.*, vol. 50, no. 12, pp. 714–716, Mar. 23, 1987.

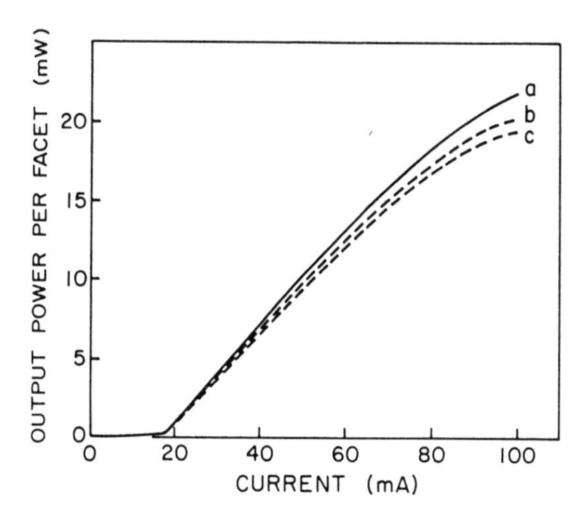

FIG. 2. Several cw (unbonded, ambient laboratory temperature) output power vs current curves: (a) prior to lifetime test ($I_{th} = 17$ mA, $\eta_d = 25\%$), (b) after 24 h of 80 mA cw operation, (c) after 48 h of 80 mA cw operation.

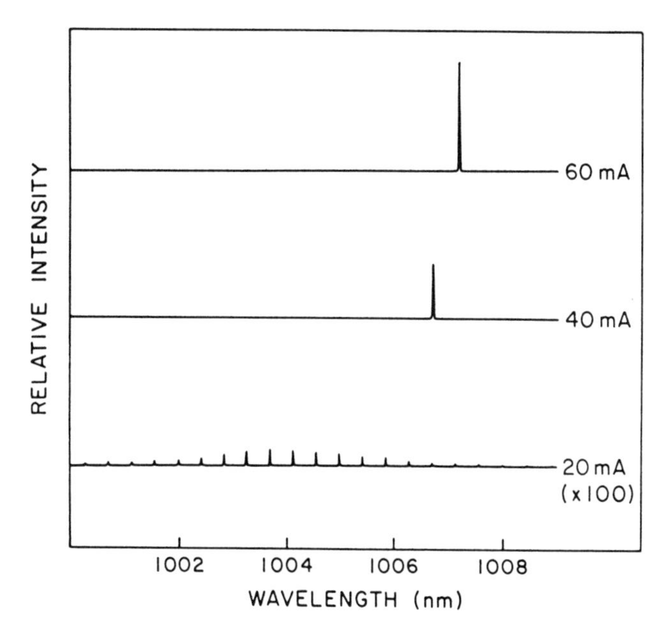

FIG. 4. Several cw stimulated emission spectra taken at various pump currents.

tigmatic and has constant far-field full-angle half-maximum for a wide range of pump currents, indicating real index guiding in the lateral direction. The consistent shape of the lateral curves for the various pump currents implies single lateral mode operation at up to 100 mA for this device.

The cw stimulated emission spectrum is shown in Fig. 4. As expected for cw operation, heating effects are dominant in controlling the lasing wavelength shift with increasing pump current.

A preliminary lifetime test was performed on a randomly selected device. The device was run cw (ambient laboratory temperature, unbonded) at 80 mA (18–14 mW/facet, $J \sim 10$ kA/cm^2) for 144 h. The test was interrupted at 24 h intervals in order to obtain a power versus current curve for the device; the first three such curves are shown in Fig. 2. During the first 94 h of the test, the threshold current rose from 17 to 20 mA and the differential quantum efficiency degraded from 25 to 23%. There was no significant change in the power versus current characteristic during the last 50 h of the test. Although differing test conditions make the results difficult to compare accurately, this seems to be at least a factor of 100 better lifetime performance than has been previously reported for any strained-layer laser.[1,4]

In summary, we have fabricated and tested GRIN SCH ridge waveguide lasers with $Ga_{0.63}In_{0.37}As$ strained-layer single quantum wells emitting near 1 μm. The room-temperature cw threshold current was typically 17 mA, and the unbonded devices produced as much as 20 mW/facet cw at 80 mA dc. A preliminary lifetime test produced encouraging results. Future work will include more conventional accelerated lifetime tests on bonded devices.

The authors would like to thank R. J. Davis and A. Perera for processing assistance, K. T. Chan for assistance with the material growth, and D. K. Wagner for waveguide calculations. This work was supported by the Air Force Office of Scientific Research under contract F49620-80-C-

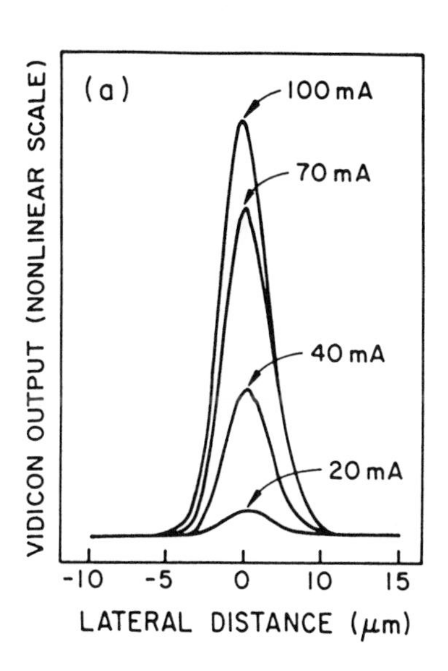

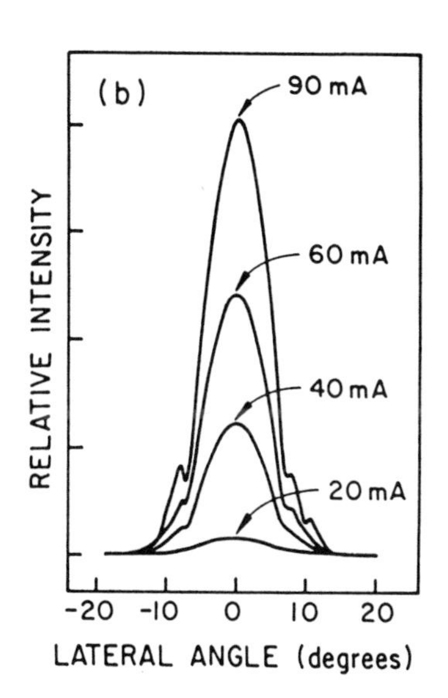

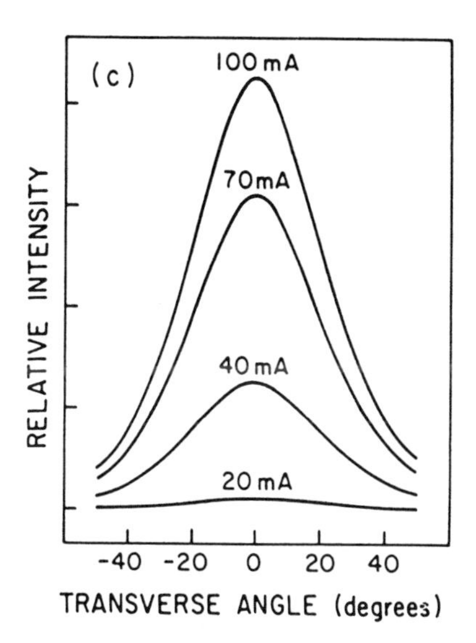

FIG. 3. Intensity distributions for the laser: (a) lateral near field, (b) lateral far field, and (c) transverse far field.

0060 and by a grant from the Emerson Electric Corporation. Work was performed in part at the National Research and Resource Facility for Submicron Structures which is supported in part by the National Science Foundation under grant ECS-8200312.

[1]M. D. Camras, J. M. Brown, N. Holonyak, Jr., M. A. Nixon, and R. W. Kaliski, M. J. Ludowise, W. T. Dietze, and C. R. Lewis, J. Appl. Phys. **54**, 6183 (1983).

[2]W. D. Laidig, P. J. Caldwell, Y. F. Lin, and C. K. Peng, Appl. Phys. Lett. **44**, 653 (1984).

[3]T. E. Zipperian, L. R. Dawson, C. E. Barnes, J. J. Wiczer, and G. C. Osbourn, presented at the International Electron Devices Meeting, Dec. 1984, San Francisco.

[4]W. D. Laidig, Y. F. Lin, and P. J. Caldwell, J. Appl. Phys. **57**, 33 (1985).

[5]P. L. Gourley, J. P. Hohimer, and R. M. Biefeld, Appl. Phys. Lett. **47**, 552 (1985).

[6]D. Fekete, K. T. Chan, J. M. Ballantyne, and L. F. Eastman, Appl. Phys. Lett. **49**, 1659 (1986).

[7]G. B. Feak, L. D. Zhu, R. J. Davis, and J. M. Ballantyne, IEEE J. Quantum Electron. (to be published).

[8]D. D. Sell, H. C. Casey, Jr., and K. W. Wecht, J. Appl. Phys. **45**, 2650 (1974).

[9]H. C. Casey, Jr., D. D. Sell, and M. B. Panish, Appl. Phys. Lett. **24**, 63 (1974).

Ultralow-threshold graded-index separate-confinement single quantum well buried heterostructure (Al,Ga)As lasers with high reflectivity coatings

Pamela L. Derry and Amnon Yariv
California Institute of Technology, Pasadena, California 91125

Kam Y. Lau, Nadav Bar-Chaim, Kevin Lee, and Jan Rosenberg
ORTEL Corporation, 2015 West Chestnut Street, Alhambra, California 91803

(Received 3 April 1987; accepted for publication 27 April 1987)

Unlike conventional semiconductor lasers, single quantum well lasers with high reflectively coatings have dramatically reduced threshold currents as a result of the smaller volume of the (active) quantum well region. A cw threshold current of 0.95 mA was obtained for a buried graded-index separate-confinement heterostructure single quantum well laser with facet reflectivities of ~70%, a cavity length of 250 μm, and an active region stripe width of 1 μm.

Future generations of supercomputers will rely on monolithic semiconductor lasers for their internal communication. The number of lasers involved is so large that a major premium is placed on a reduction of the threshold current of such lasers. To date the lowest threshold currents (~2.5 mA) have been obtained with buried heterostructure (BH) quantum well (QW) lasers.[1,2] The potential of QW lasers for much lower threshold operation has been pointed out by Sugimura[3] and by Arakawa and Yariv.[4] In this letter we recast the arguments of Refs. 3 and 4 in a form which employs more familiar semiconductor terminology and report on the first demonstration of a major reduction in the threshold current of a QW laser.

The exponential bulk gain constant of a QW layer of thickness L_z due to the lowest quantized states transition is given by[4]

$$g_{\rm QW}^{\rm bulk}(\omega) = \frac{2\pi\mu^2 m_r}{\lambda_0 \epsilon_0 n_r \hbar^2 L_z}[f_c(\omega) - f_v(\omega)] \times H(\hbar\omega - E_g - E_{1c} - E_{1v}). \quad (1)$$

Here $g_{\rm QW}^{\rm bulk}$ is the gain experienced by a wave at ω which is totally confined to the QW medium, μ is the transition matrix element, n_r is the refractive index, ϵ_0 is the dielectric constant in free space, λ_0 is the wavelength in free space, f_c and f_v are the Fermi functions at the transition energy, m_r is the reduced effective mass, E_g is the energy band gap, $H(x)$ is the Heaviside function and

$$E_{1c} = \hbar^2\pi^2/(2m_c L_z^2) \text{ and } E_{1v} = \hbar^2\pi^2/(2m_v L_z^2)$$

are the first quantized carrier energies in the limit of an infinite well depth. We can use (1) to calculate the bulk gain at any carrier density.[4] The unknown parameter involved in this calculation is the dipole transition matrix element μ. This dipole element also figures (with a slight modification due to spatial averaging) in the expression for the bulk absorption coefficient of GaAs. Using the appropriate effective mass data and the bulk absorption data of GaAs[5] we obtain $\mu \simeq 5.1\times10^{-29}$ (mks). As a check on this important parameter we used it to determine the maximum gain per quantized level which is given by (1) with $f_c = 1, f_v = 0$. The results agree closely with the value determined experimentally by measurements on very short QW lasers.[6] We can summarize our results near the transparency condition as

$$g_{\rm QW}^{\rm bulk} = B_{\rm QW}(N - 2\times10^{18}), \quad (2)$$

where $g_{\rm QW}^{\rm bulk}$ is in cm^{-1} and N is the carrier density in cm^{-3}. A result which at first seems surprising is that the transparency density ($N_0 = 2\times10^{18}$ cm^{-3}) is nearly the same as that for a conventional double heterostructure (DH) which has been estimated and measured at values near 1.6×10^{18} cm^{-3}:

$$g_{\rm DH}^{\rm bulk} = B_{\rm DH}(N - 1.6\times10^{18}). \quad (3)$$

To express the bulk gain in terms of injection current density J (A/cm^2) we use $J = Nde/\tau$ where d is the active region thickness ($d = L_z$ in a QW laser), τ is the effective recombination time at $N \simeq N_0$, and e is the absolute value of the electron charge. Using for simplicity $(N_0)_{\rm QW} = (N_0)_{\rm DH} = 1.6\times10^{18}$ cm^{-3} and the following data: $d_{\rm DH} = 0.1$ μm, $L_z = 100$ Å, $\tau \sim 4\times10^{-9}$, we obtain transparency current densities: $(J_0)_{\rm QW} \simeq 50$ A/cm^2, $(J_0)_{\rm DH} \simeq 800$ A/cm^2 so that

$$g_{\rm QW}^{\rm bulk} = \frac{B_{\rm QW}\tau}{L_z e}(J_{\rm QW} - 50), \quad (4)$$

$$g_{\rm DH}^{\rm bulk} = \frac{B_{\rm DH}\tau}{de}(J_{\rm DH} - 800). \quad (5)$$

The more than order of magnitude difference in the transparency current densities of QW and DH lasers reflects mostly the fact that at nearly equal transparency densities the thinner QW contains fewer carriers than the much thicker DH active region.

In laser oscillators we are concerned with the modal gains ($g_{\rm QW}^{\rm mode}$ and $g_{\rm DH}^{\rm mode}$), i.e., the gain constants experienced by the traveling laser mode. These are obtained by multiplying (4) and (5) by the respective confinement factors ($\Gamma_{\rm QW}$ and $\Gamma_{\rm DH}$) which are calculated as 0.03 for our typical QW laser and 0.5 for a typical DH laser. Equating total modal gains to the sum of the losses, we obtain the threshold conditions:

$$g_{\rm QW}^{\rm mode} = \frac{B_{\rm QW}\tau\Gamma_{\rm QW}}{L_z e}(J_{\rm th}^{\rm QW} - 50) = \alpha_{\rm QW}\Gamma_{\rm QW} + \alpha_{\rm QW}^{\omega} + \frac{1}{2L}\ln\frac{1}{R_1R_2}, \quad (6)$$

Reprinted with permission from *Appl. Phys. Lett.*, vol. 50, no. 25, pp. 1773–1775, June 22, 1987.

$$g_{\mathrm{DH}}^{\mathrm{mode}} = \frac{B_{\mathrm{DH}}\tau\Gamma_{\mathrm{DH}}}{de}(J_{\mathrm{th}}^{\mathrm{DH}} - 800)$$
$$= \alpha_{\mathrm{DH}}\Gamma_{\mathrm{DH}} + \alpha_{\mathrm{DH}}^{\omega} + \frac{1}{2L}\ln\frac{1}{R_1R_2}, \quad (7)$$

where α_{QW}, α_{DH} are the active region losses (mostly free-carrier absorption), $\alpha_{\mathrm{QW}}^{\omega}$, $\alpha_{\mathrm{DH}}^{\omega}$ represent losses due primarily to waveguide imperfections, L is the laser cavity length, and R_1 and R_2 are the end facet reflectivities. Since $\Gamma_{\mathrm{QW}} \simeq 0.03$, the active region losses are insignificantly low in the QW case and will be neglected. In the DH case we will use the accepted value of $\alpha_{\mathrm{DH}} \sim 15\ \mathrm{cm}^{-1}$.[7] The factors $(B\tau\Gamma/de) \equiv A$ multiplying the left sides of (6) and (7) are the so called differential gain coefficients which determine the frequency response of the laser.[8] Their numerical values have been the subject of considerable investigation. They can also be estimated reasonably closely from their relationship (given above) to the other basic parameters. Reasonable values in our case are: $A_{\mathrm{QW}} \simeq 0.7\ \mathrm{A}^{-1}\ \mathrm{cm}$, $A_{\mathrm{DH}} \simeq 0.4\ \mathrm{A}^{-1}\ \mathrm{cm}$ leading to

$$J_{\mathrm{th}}^{\mathrm{QW}}(\mathrm{A/cm^2}) \simeq 50 + \frac{\alpha_{\mathrm{QW}}^{\omega}}{0.7} + \frac{1}{1.4L}\ln\frac{1}{R_1R_2}, \quad (8)$$

$$J_{\mathrm{th}}^{\mathrm{DH}}(\mathrm{A/cm^2}) \simeq 800 + 19 + \frac{\alpha_{\mathrm{DH}}^{\omega}}{0.4} + \frac{1}{0.8L}\ln\frac{1}{R_1R_2}. \quad (9)$$

Equation (8) shows that in the case of a QW laser the threshold current may be determined largely by the losses and not by the transparency condition. In the case of an uncoated laser ($R = 31\%$), 250 μm long with $\alpha_{\mathrm{QW}}^{\omega} = 15\ \mathrm{cm}^{-1}$ (experimentally observed value for BH lasers described below), the sum of the two terms furthest on the right side of Eq. (8) is $\sim 88\ (\mathrm{A/cm^2})$ so that increasing the reflectivity and reducing the waveguide losses is expected to yield major reductions in threshold current densities. This is not the case in the DH laser where the transparency current ($J_0 = 800\ \mathrm{A/cm^2}$ in our example) dominates. The dramatic effect of increased facet reflectivity on threshold current calculated for a BH single QW laser for various cavity lengths is plotted in Fig. 1. These plots were generated using Eq. (6) for the relationship of modal gain to losses and using the gain versus current relationship calculated by Arakawa and Yariv.[4]

To check the conclusions of the reasoning described above we fabricated BH graded-index separate-confinement heterostructure (GRIN SCH)[9-11] single QW lasers. The laser structure was grown in a two-step growth process. The first growth took place in a Riber 2300 R&D molecular beam epitaxy (MBE) system with a substrate temperature of ~720 °C. The following layers (Fig. 2) were grown on an n^+-GaAs substrate: a 0.5 μm n^+-GaAs buffer layer, a 0.1 μm superlattice buffer layer (five periods of 100 Å GaAs and 100 Å $Al_{0.5}Ga_{0.5}As$), a 1.5 μm n-$Al_{0.5}Ga_{0.5}As$ cladding layer, a 0.2 μm graded n^--$Al_xGa_{1-x}As$ layer ($x = 0.5$–0.2), a 100 Å undoped GaAs QW, a 0.2 μm graded undoped $Al_xGa_{1-x}As$ layer ($x = 0.2$–0.5), and a 1.5 μm p-$Al_{0.5}Ga_{0.5}As$ cladding layer. The superlattice buffer layer was included to improve the quality of the lower interface of the QW.[12] Broad area lasers 450 μm long fabricated from this material had threshold current densities of ~450 A/cm².

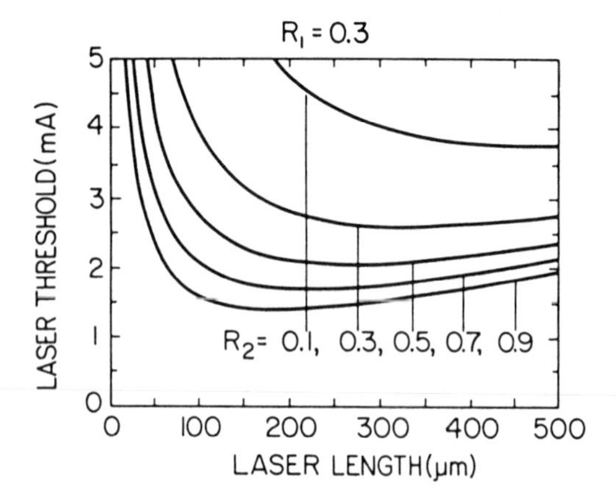

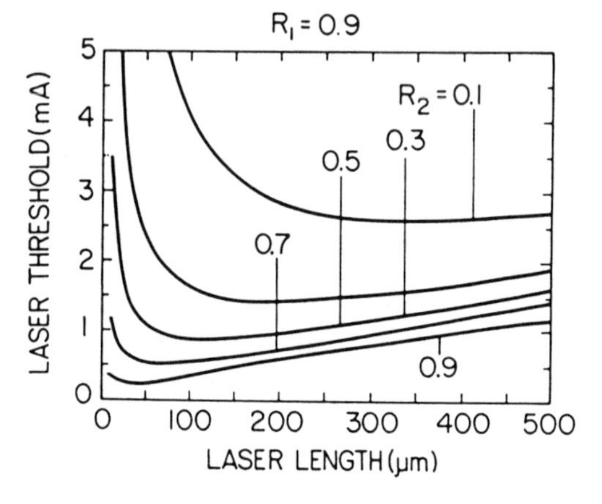

FIG. 1. Calculated threshold current for a buried GRIN SCH single QW laser with various cavity lengths and facet reflectivities.

Mesas 2 μm wide were etched through the MBE layers down to the substrate. A 1 μm p-$Al_{0.3}Ga_{0.7}As$ layer and a 3 μm n-$Al_{0.3}Ga_{0.7}As$ layer were grown by liquid phase epitaxy (LPE) to provide current confinement. A shallow Zn diffusion was performed to facilitate an ohmic contact on the p side of the device and ohmic contacts were applied. Finished devices had an active layer stripe width of 1 μm and were cleaved to a length of 250 μm.

A representative laser [Fig. 3(b)] with uncoated facets

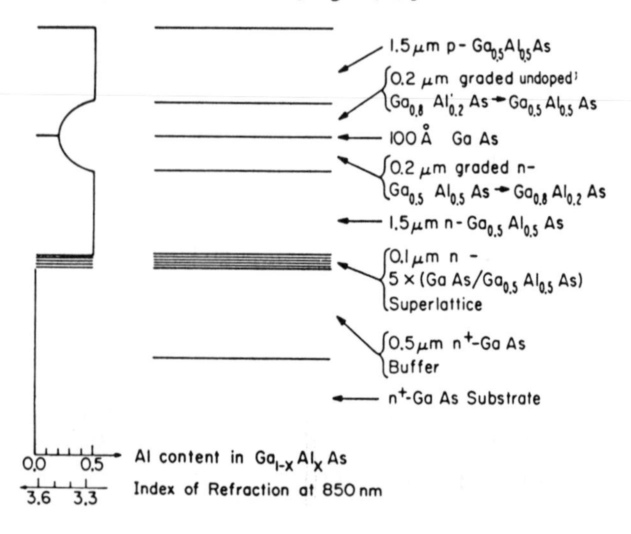

FIG. 2. Schematic diagram of a GRIN SCH single QW laser showing layers and their indexes of refraction.

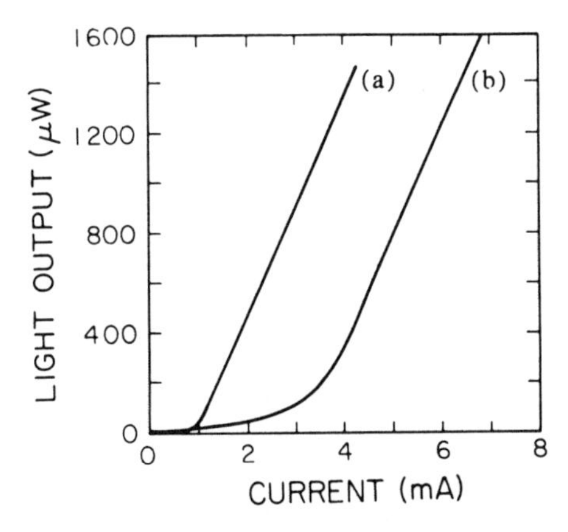

FIG. 3. Light output vs current curve for a 250-μm-long buried GRIN SCH single QW laser with: (a) high reflectivity dielectric coated cleaved facets and (b) uncoated cleaved facets. Both curves are for the *same* laser.

had a cw threshold current of 3.3 mA. Dielectric coatings (1/4 λ Si, 1/4 λ Al_2O_3) were subsequently evaporated on the cleaved facets of this laser. The facet reflectivity with coatings was 67% at the front facet and 71% at the rear facet The light versus current curve of the front facet is shown in Fig. 3(a). The cw threshold current was reduced from 3.3 to 0.95 mA. This is believed to be the lowest threshold current reported so far for any semiconductor laser at room temperature.

In conclusion, unlike conventional DH lasers, enhancement of the facet reflectivity of a QW leads to dramatic reduction of the threshold current. This is due to the fundamentally lower current density needed to render the thin active layer transparent. We have demonstrated threshold currents less than 1 mA. We anticipate that with higher reflectivities, shorter cavity lengths, and with better material (our best QW material, which was not used in this investigation, results in broad area lasers with $J_{th} \sim 140$ A/cm^2) threshold currents as low as ~0.2 mA should be realizable.

The Caltech portion of this work was supported by the National Science Foundation, the Office of Naval Research, and the Air Force Office of Scientific Research. The ORTEL effort was supported by the Defense Advanced Research Projects Agency under the Optical Computing Program and Naval Research Laboratories.

[1]W. T. Tsang, R. A. Logan, and J. A. Ditzenberger, Electron. Lett. **18**, 845 (1982).

[2]A. Kurobe, H. Furuyama, S. Naritsuka, Y. Kokubun, and M. Nakamura, Electron. Lett. **22**, 1117 (1986).

[3]A. Sugimura, IEEE J. Quantum Electron. **QE-20**, 336 (1984).

[4]Y. Arakawa and A. Yariv, IEEE J. Quantum Electron. **QE-21**, 1666 (1985).

[5]W. P. Dumke, Phys. Rev. **127**, 1559 (1962).

[6]M. Mittelstein, A. Larsson, and A. Yariv (unpublished results).

[7]H. Kressel and J. K. Butler, *Semiconductor Lasers and Heterojunction LEDs* (Academic, New York, 1977), p. 263.

[8]K. Y. Lau, C. Harder, and A. Yariv, Opt. Commun. **36**, 472 (1981).

[9]W. T. Tsang, Appl. Phys. Lett. **39**, 134 (1981).

[10]W. T. Tsang, Appl. Phys. Lett. **40**, 217 (1982).

[11]A. Larsson, M. Mittelstein, Y. Arakawa, and A. Yariv, Electron. Lett. **22**, 79 (1986).

[12]T. Fujii, S. Hiyamizu, S. Yamakoshi, and T. Ishikawa, J. Vac. Sci. Technol. B **3**, 776 (1985).

High-power conversion efficiency quantum well diode lasers

R. G. Waters, D. K. Wagner, D. S. Hill, P. L. Tihanyi, and B. J. Vollmer
McDonnell Douglas Astronautics Company, Opto-Electronics Center, 350 Executive Boulevard, Elmsford, New York 10523

(Received 13 July 1987; accepted for publication 28 August 1987)

cw power conversion efficiencies of 57% have been obtained on uncoated diode lasers emitting nearly 300 mW per facet. This performance is achieved by using a low-resistance graded index separate confinement single quantum well AlGaAs/GaAs structure with high (84%) differential quantum efficiency and low threshold current.

Lasers with high cw power conversion efficiencies are important for applications such as satellite communication. Present state-of-the-art conversion efficiencies fall well below 50%. For example, a value of 43% has been recently reported for a multiple quantum well array,[1] and 36% has been reported for a narrow stripe graded index separate confinement single quantum well (GRINSCH SQW) device.[2] In this letter we report measurement of 57% power conversion efficiency on a wide stripe AlGaAs GRINSCH SQW device and conclude that higher values should be attainable, provided that catastrophic facet damage does not prematurely limit output power.

Conversion efficiency in semiconductor lasers is limited by ohmic losses, loss of photons due to spontaneous emission, and by passive optical losses in the laser structure. In the absence of heating, conversion efficiency will increase with drive current, attain a peak value, and decrease thereafter due to the quadratic dependence of ohmic losses on current. The peak efficiency η_c^{peak} is a function of the external differential quantum efficiency η_e and the dimensionless parameter $x = h\nu/qI_{\text{th}}R_s$ as shown in Fig. 1. I_{th} is the threshold current, R_s is the diode series resistance, and $h\nu$ is the photon energy. The curve is a result[3] of determining the maximum of

$$\eta_c = \frac{(h\nu/q)\eta_e(I - I_{\text{th}})}{I(IR_s + h\nu/q)}, \tag{1}$$

and plotting the resulting expression for η_c^{peak}

$$\frac{\eta_c^{\text{peak}}}{\eta_e} = \frac{x\sqrt{1+x}}{(1+\sqrt{1+x})(1+x+\sqrt{1+x})}, \tag{2}$$

which occurs at a current

$$I^{\text{peak}} = I_{\text{th}}(1+\sqrt{1+x}). \tag{3}$$

The peak efficiency asymptotically approaches η_e at high values of x, but in practical devices catastrophic facet damage always sets an upper limit on the current. If P_1 is the optical power at which facet failure occurs, then the accessible range of x is

$$0 < x < \left(\frac{qP_1}{h\nu\eta_e I_{\text{th}}}\right)^2 - 1. \tag{4}$$

Lasers used in this study were grown by metalorganic chemical vapor deposition (MOCVD) and had separate confinement regions graded from 30 to 60% aluminum mole fraction. The GaAs quantum well was 50 nm thick and was the lowest threshold structure of a series grown to optimize the laser structure for performance.[4] The measured external quantum efficiency on uncoated devices (both facets) is 84% and corresponds to an internal quantum efficiency of 97% and a passive mode loss of 4 cm^{-1}. Series resistance was minimized by using high doping concentrations in all but the graded and quantum well regions. The resistance was measured to be 0.5 Ω. Lasers were processed with 60-μm-wide, oxide-defined stripes using Au/Ge/Ni (Ti/Pt/Au) for the *n*-side (*p*-side) metallization, followed by cleaving into 300-μm-long cavities and bonding junction-side down to a copper heat sink.

Optical power measurements were made with a silicon photodiode and integrating sphere calibrated at the emission wavelength, and the total power was obtained by doubling the single-facet power. Voltage was measured as close to the device as possible, but actually includes a contribution from the fixturing resistance. Voltage, laser current, and photocurrent measurements all employed calibrated multimeters. Finally, power conversion efficiency was simply taken as the ratio of total optical power to the current-voltage product.

Measured cw power conversion efficiency as a function of current is shown in Fig. 2. A maximum value of 57% was attained with a drive current of 552 mA and with 292 mW optical power per facet. The light-current characteristic, also given, shows no evidence of thermal rollover. It is also noteworthy that the peak efficiency in the device occurs at an optical power well below the catastrophic limit (500–700

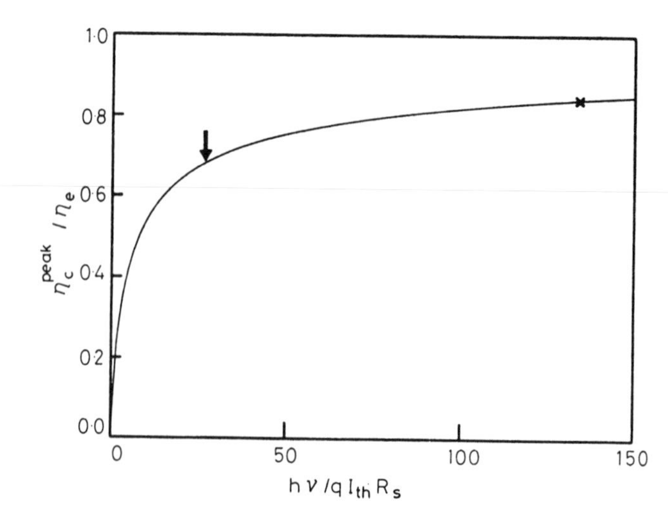

FIG. 1. Calculated peak power conversion efficiency normalized to external quantum efficiency as a function of the reciprocal resistance-threshold current product. The arrow indicates the operating point of the laser and the × indicates the highest peak efficiency that can be achieved before catastrophic facet failure.

Reprinted with permission from *Appl. Phys. Lett.*, vol. 51, no. 17, pp. 1318–1319, Oct. 26, 1987.

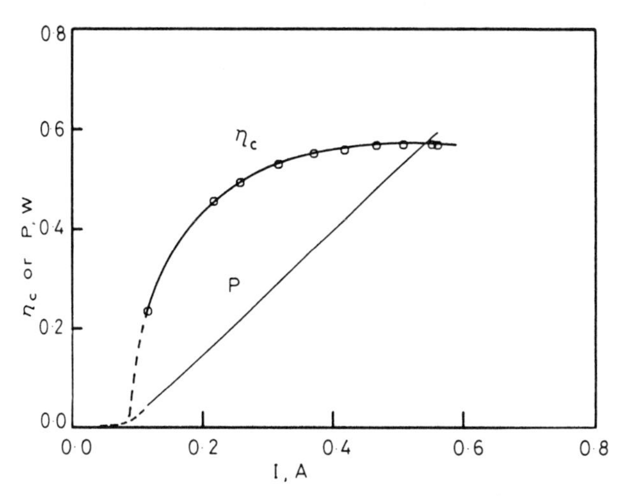

FIG. 2. Measured total optical power and power conversion efficiency as a function of laser drive current.

mW per facet).

The measured efficiency for this laser is indicated by an arrow in Fig. 1, and corresponds to a value of x of 27. Using this value and 82 mA for the threshold current and 1.50 eV for the photon energy, a value of 0.68 Ω is inferred for the series resistance. This is only slightly greater than the value determined from the current-voltage curve. It can also be seen from Fig. 1 that the peak efficiency occurs in a region of diminishing returns where modest increases require substantial reductions in resistance or threshold current. In speculating on how such improvements might be achieved, we note that the threshold current has been minimized with respect to laser length and structure parameters (for the GRINSCH SQW design) so that only stripe width remains to be varied. Although reducing the stripe width will reduce threshold current, it will also cause a reciprocal increase in resistance, making this approach rather problematical. Moreover, the catastrophic power limit will be reduced. We have also considered reducing the series resistance. The diode bulk resistance is about 0.12 Ω, so most of the gains would come from reducing contact, packaging, and fixturing resistances. Assuming a power limit $P = 1.2$ W (both facets) for facet failure, x could conceivably be increased to a value of 134 by this means [see Eq. (4)], corresponding to a peak conversion efficiency of 70%.

We gratefully acknowledge the help of John DeSanctis in the growth of the laser structures, Andy Roza and Mary Mrozack in the fabrication of the lasers, and Tom Guido and Ken Bystrom in device testing. We are also grateful to R. R. Rice whose calculations of diode efficiency stimulated our interest in this topic.

[1]R. L. Thornton, R. D. Burnham, and T. L. Paoli, Appl. Phys. Lett. **48**, 7 (1986).

[2]D. F. Welch, C. F. Schaus, and J. R. Shealy, Appl. Phys. Lett. **46**, 121 (1985).

[3]H. Kressel and J. K. Butler, *Semiconductor Lasers and Heterojunction LEDs* (Academic, New York, 1977), pp. 459–461.

[4]D. S. Hill, D. K. Wagner, R. G. Waters, P. L. Tihanyi, A. J. Roza, H. J. Vollmer, K. J. Bystrom, and T. S. Guido, "High-Power Single-Quantum-Well Lasers Grown by Metalorganic Chemical Vapor Deposition," Southwest Optics '87 Conference, Albuquerque, NM, Feb. 1987, paper WB8.

HIGH-BRIGHTNESS, HIGH-EFFICIENCY, SINGLE-QUANTUM-WELL LASER DIODE ARRAY

D. F. WELCH
M. CARDINAL
W. STREIFER
D. R. SCIFRES
P. S. CROSS

Spectra Diode Laboratories
80 Rose Orchard Way
San Jose, CA 95134, USA

24th August 1987

Indexing terms: Semiconductor lasers, Quantum optics

Single-quantum-well, separate-confinement double-heterostructure laser diode arrays which exhibit a high power conversion efficiency of greater than 54% have been demonstrated. The high efficiency results from a low internal loss of $3\,cm^{-1}$ and high internal conversion efficiency. The maximum output power for a $100\,\mu m$ emitting aperture is 2 W CW and is independent of the cavity length.

Single-quantum-well (SQW), double-heterostructure lasers have been extensively studied because of their low threshold current characteristics.[1–3] Recently, such device structures have also achieved high differential[4] and total power conversion efficiencies.[5,6] In this letter data are presented on SQW separate-confinement, double-heterostructure (SQW-SCH) laser arrays which exhibit a total power conversion efficiency of greater than 54% and threshold currents less than 45 mA for a $100\,\mu m$ aperture. The maximum output power for a $100\,\mu m$ aperture is 2 W CW.

The device structure, which was grown by metalorganic chemical vapour deposition (MOCVD), is similar to that of a SQW-SCH which has been described previously.[7] The wafer is proton-bombarded to define $6\,\mu m$-wide current-conducting regions on $10\,\mu m$ centres. The diodes have a high-reflectivity (~95%) rear facet coating and various front facet reflectivity coatings. The power measurements reported here are CW outputs from the low-reflectivity end of the laser.

The light output as a function of input current for an SQW-SCH laser array is plotted in Fig. 1 for a device with a 32% front facet reflector and a cavity length of $250\,\mu m$. The threshold current is 45 mA with a differential efficiency of 77%. The series resistance is $0{\cdot}67\,\Omega$. Also shown in Fig. 1 is the total power conversion efficiency as a function of current, which peaks at greater than 54% at a power output of 300 mW. The laser is over 50% efficient for power outputs between 200 and 800 mW.

To characterise the internal device properties, threshold and differential efficiency measurements were made as a function of cavity length and front facet reflectivity. The differential efficiency η_d varies with the cavity length L as[8]

$$\eta_d = \frac{\eta_i}{1 + 2\alpha L/\ln(1/R_1 R_2)} \quad (1)$$

where η_i is the internal efficiency, α is the internal loss coefficient (i.e. scattering and free-carrier absorption), and R_1 and R_2 are the front and rear facet reflectivities, respectively. By plotting $1/\eta_d$ as a function of the cavity length, the internal

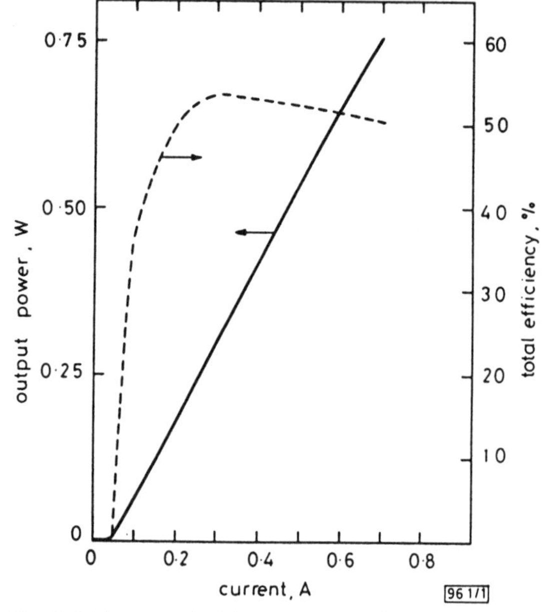

Fig. 1 *Light output (solid curve) and total power conversion efficiency (broken curve) as a function of input current for a 250 μm cavity with a 32% front facet reflectivity for* $\eta_d = 77\%$

efficiency and loss can be determined. Fig. 2*a* shows the data obtained from several diodes of different cavity lengths and front facet reflectivities of 32% and 5%. The internal conversion and optical loss are determined to be 85% and $3\,cm^{-1}$, respectively. The low internal loss results from the low overlap of the optical wave with the active region as specified by the confinement factor Γ. For this structure Γ is calculated to be 4%, which results in minimal free-carrier absorption.

Fig. 2*b* is a plot of the threshold current as a function of the reciprocal of the cavity length. Assuming that the threshold current density J_{th} can be represented by[8]

$$J_{th} = J_t + \frac{d}{\Gamma A}\left[\alpha + \frac{\ln(1/R_1 R_2)}{2L}\right] \quad (2)$$

where J_t is the transparency current, d is the quantum-well thickness, L is the cavity length and α is the internal loss. From the data shown in Fig. 2*b*, the transparency current is $75\,A/cm^2$, while A in eqn. 2 is $0{\cdot}043\,cm\,\mu m/A$. The threshold current density for a $750\,\mu m$ cavity is $130\,A/cm^2$. Essentially

Reprinted with permission from *Electron. Lett.*, vol. 23, no. 23, pp. 1240–1241, Nov. 5, 1987.

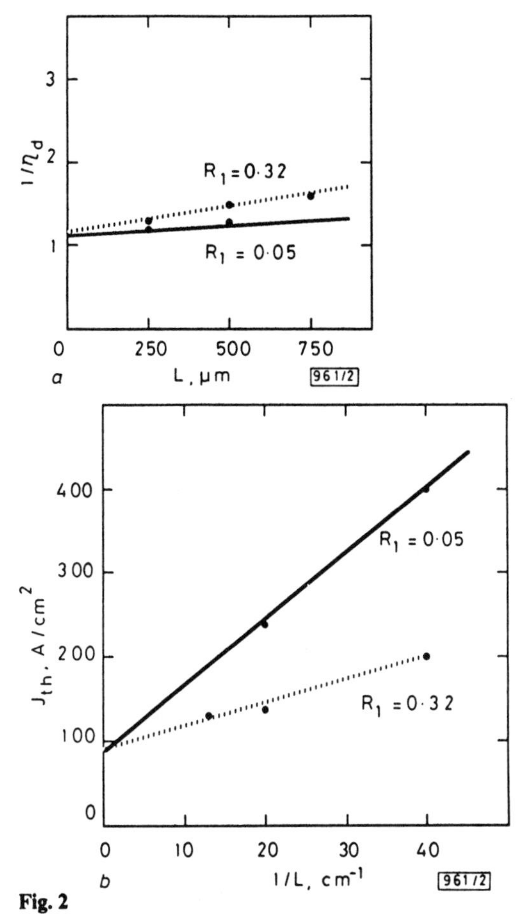

Fig. 2

a Inverse differential efficiency as a function of cavity length for an SQW-SCH laser array
b Threshold current density as a function of inverse cavity length
$A = 0.043$ cm μm/A, $J_t = 75$ A/cm²

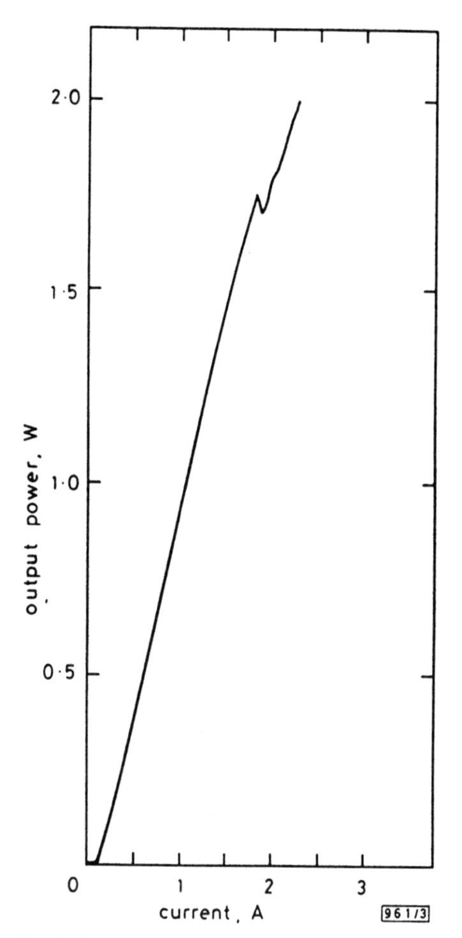

Fig. 3 *Power output as a function of input current for an SQW-SCH with a front facet reflectivity of 5% and a cavity length of 500 μm*

identical values are determined from devices with both 32% and 5% front facet reflectivities.

Fig. 3 shows the light output as a function of drive current for a device with a 5% front mirror reflectivity. The maximum power output for the 100 μm aperture is 2 W CW prior to catastrophic degradation of the output facet. The external differential quantum efficiency is as high as 81%.

In conclusion, SQW-SCH lasers have been demonstrated to emit 2 W CW output power from a 100 μm aperture. The total power conversion efficiency is greater than 54% at 300 mW, and over 50% for a broad output range from 200 to 800 mW. The internal loss of the structure is determined to be 3 cm^{-1} with an internal conversion efficiency of 85%. The transparency current is 75 A/cm^2.

We would like to acknowledge the support of M. Abraham, M. Brown, M. DeVito, P. Tally, E. Taggart, G. Harnagel and B. Quenelle.

References

1 HERSEE, S., BALDY, M., ASSENAT, P., DE CREMOUX, B., and DUCHEMIN, J. P.: 'Low-threshold GRIN-SCH GaAs/GaAlAs laser structure grown by OM VPE', *Electron. Lett.*, 1982, **18**, pp. 618–620

2 TSANG, W. T.: 'Extremely low threshold AlGaAs graded index waveguide separate confinement heterostructure lasers grown by molecular beam epitaxy', *Appl. Phys. Lett.*, 1982, **40**, p. 217

3 BURNHAM, R. D., STREIFER, W., and PAOLI, T. L.: *J. Cryst. Growth*, 1984, **68**, p. 370

4 LARSSON, A., MITTELSTEIN, M., ARAKAWA, Y., and YARIV, A.: 'High-efficiency broad-area single-quantum-well lasers with narrow single-lobed far-field patterns prepared by molecular beam epitaxy', *Electron. Lett.*, 1986, **22**, pp. 79–81

5 HILL, D. S., WAGNER, D. K., WATERS, R. G., TIHANYI, P. L., ROZA, A. J., VOLLMER, B. J., BYSTROM, K. J., and GUIDO, T. S.: 'High power single quantum well lasers grown by metalorganic chemical vapor deposition'. Proc. southwest optics conf., Albuquerque, NM, 1987

6 SHEALY, J. R.: 'Optimizing the performance of AlGaAs graded index separate confining heterostructure quantum well lasers', *Appl. Phys. Lett.*, 1987, **50**, pp. 1634–1636

7 LINDSTROM, C., BURNHAM, R. D., SCIFRES, D. R., PAOLI, T. L., and STREIFER, W.: 'One watt CW visible single-quantum-well lasers', *Electron. Lett.*, 1983, **19**, pp. 80–81

8 THOMPSON, G. H. B.: 'Physics of semiconductor laser devices' (J. Wiley & Sons, 1980), pp. 96–98

Near-ideal low threshold behavior in (111) oriented GaAs/AlGaAs quantum well lasers

T. Hayakawa, T. Suyama, K. Takahashi, M. Kondo, S. Yamamoto, and T. Hijikata
Central Research Laboratories, Sharp Corporation, Tenri, Nara 632, Japan

(Received 5 October 1987; accepted for publication 24 November 1987)

Fundamental characteristics of (111) oriented GaAs/AlGaAs graded-index separate-confinement-heterostructure single quantum well lasers have been compared with conventional (100) oriented lasers. In particular, the threshold current density J_{th} of (111) oriented lasers does not change with the well width L_z in the range of $L_z = 30$–100 Å, which corresponds to an ideal extreme. The lowest J_{th} of 145 A/cm^2 together with a high characteristic temperature T_0 of 186 K in the threshold-temperature dependence has been achieved for an L_z of 40 Å and a cavity length of 490 μm. The dependence of T_0 on L_z showed that T_0 is maximum at $L_z \sim 60$ Å for both (111) and (100) oriented lasers.

Quantum wells (QW's) and superlattices are very important for novel device applications and basic physics studies. These modulated semiconductor structures are based on the one-dimensional modulation of electronic band structure along the growth axis. Thus fundamental properties of these structures are believed to change with their crystal orientation. However, the orientation dependence of quantum effects in modulated semiconductor structures has not been previously investigated, and most structures have been grown on (100) oriented substrates. Recently, we have succeeded in the molecular beam epitaxial growth of high-quality GaAs/AlGaAs QW's on (111)B oriented GaAs substrates by very slightly (0.5°) misorienting the substrate orientation.[1] We found that the photoluminescence efficiency of (111) oriented QW's is enhanced compared with that of (100) oriented QW's by more than one order of magnitude. This enhancement of optical transition rate is due to the large density of states of the heavy-hole band in (111) oriented QW's.[2] It was also demonstrated that the threshold current density J_{th} of (111) oriented GaAs/AlGaAs graded-index separate-confinement-heterostructure (GRIN-SCH) single quantum well (SQW) lasers was lower than that of (100) oriented ones by about 20 A/cm^2 for a well width L_z of 70 Å. In this letter we report the fundamental characteristics in (111) oriented GRIN-SCH SQW lasers. In particular, it is shown that J_{th} does not change with L_z in the range $L_z = 30$–100 Å, which corresponds to the ideal extreme expected from the theory.[3]

GRIN-SCH SQW lasers[4] were grown by molecular beam epitaxy on (111)B GaAs substrates (Sumitomo), which were 0.5° misoriented toward (100). A (100) oriented substrate was also mounted on a Mo block side by side. Laser diodes consist of an n-GaAs buffer layer (1 μm, Si $= 5\times10^{17}$ cm^{-3}), an n-$Al_{0.1}Ga_{0.9}As$ buffer layer (0.2 μm, Si $= 5\times10^{17}$ cm^{-3}), an n-$Al_xGa_{1-x}As$ compositionally graded buffer layer[5] ($x = 0.1$–0.7, 0.2 μm, Si $= 5\times10^{17}$ cm^{-3}), an n-$Al_{0.7}Ga_{0.3}As$ cladding layer (1.4 μm, Si $= 5\times10^{17}$ cm^{-3}), an undoped $Al_yGa_{1-y}As$ GRIN layer (y is parabolically graded from 0.7 to 0.2, 0.15 μm), an undoped GaAs QW, an undoped $Al_yGa_{1-y}As$ GRIN layer ($y = 0.2$–0.7, 0.15 μm), a p-$Al_{0.7}Ga_{0.3}As$ cladding layer (1 μm, Be $= 5\times10^{17}$ cm^{-3}), and a p-GaAs cap layer (0.5 μm, Be $= 2\times10^{18}$ cm^{-3}). L_z was varied in the range 15–300 Å. The substrate temperature was 720 °C and the group V/III flux ratio was ~2–3. Details of the crystal growth were reported previously.[1,6]

Broad-area Fabry–Perot lasers with a cavity length of 490 μm and a width of 120–200 μm were fabricated from an area of $\sim 1\times1$ cm^2 of each wafer. For randomly selected devices from one or two bars, the light output-current curve was measured. The J_{th} was calculated by measuring the actual area of each chip by an optical microscope. Since each chip with a rectangular shape was divided from a cleaved bar by scratching the epitaxial layer with a diamond scriber, the shape of the sidewall is similar to a saw tooth, especially in the case of (111) oriented devices. The pitch and depth of this saw tooth were of the order of 10 μm. This shape of the sidewall is very effective for suppressing the lasing of the circulating mode. We evaluated the area of the device by measuring the width at the dip of the saw tooth, i.e., at the narrowest part so as not to overestimate J_{th}. The distribution of J_{th} for each wafer was measured as was done in Ref. 1, and the lowest J_{th} in each wafer was determined based on this distribution. Some devices showed an extremely low J_{th}, which was slightly ($\gtrsim 10$ A/cm^2) apart from the distribution, possibly because of the nonuniform lasing. These abnormally low J_{th} values were omitted from experimental data. We confirmed that the near-field pattern of normal devices was fairly uniform.

The dependence of J_{th} on L_z for (100) oriented lasers in the present study was compared with previously reported results[7–10] for GaAs/AlGaAs SCH SQW lasers in Fig. 1. The J_{th} in the present study is lowest in the whole range of L_z, which demonstrates the highest quality of material grown under our optimal growth conditions by using a compositionally graded buffer layer.[5,6] In addition, the dependence of J_{th} on L_z is much less than that of previous results.[8,9] The lowest J_{th} of 163 A/cm^2 is achieved at $L_z = 100$ Å for (100) oriented devices.

In the case of $L_z \geqslant 100$ Å, it was found that there is no difference in J_{th} for both (111) and (100) orientations. By contrast, for $L_z < 100$ Å, J_{th} of (111) oriented lasers is considerably lower than that of (100) oriented ones, as shown in Fig. 2. It should be noted that J_{th} of (111) oriented lasers is

Reprinted with permission from *Appl. Phys. Lett.*, vol. 52, no. 5, pp. 339–341, Feb. 1, 1988.

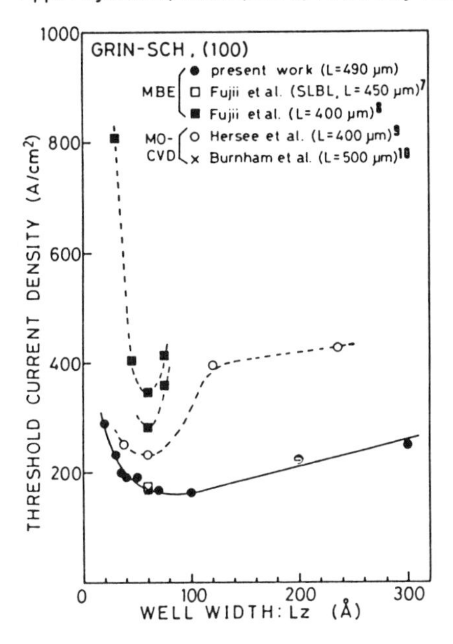

FIG. 1. Well width dependence of threshold current density of (100) oriented graded-index separate-confinement-heterostructure (GRIN-SCH) single quantum well lasers in the present study (closed circles) is compared with previous results for GRIN-SCH (Refs. 7–9) and SCH (Ref. 10) lasers.

almost constant within 160 ± 5 A/cm² for $L_z = 30$–100 Å. The constant J_{th} for the small L_z region is consistent with the theoretical calculation for SCH lasers by Sugimura[3] for the case that all carriers injected into the QW region contribute to the stimulated recombination between ground states of electrons and heavy holes, thus the ideal extreme. The gradual increase of J_{th} with decreasing L_z in (100) oriented lasers also is likely to support the theoretical model by Sugimura, where the nonradiative recombination of electrons from L valleys increases with decreasing L_z.[3] The significant improvement in (111) oriented QW lasers arises from the enhancement of the optical transition rate between ground states of electrons and heavy holes by using the quantization along the [111] axis.[1,2] This enhancement of optical transition rate is due to the larger density of states of the heavy-hole band in (111) oriented QW's.[2] The abrupt increase in J_{th} for $L_z \lesssim 30$ Å is considered to result from the loss of quantum confinement of carriers. By increasing the AlAs mole fraction in the cladding layers from 0.7 to 0.85, J_{th} was further reduced to 145 A/cm² in a (111) oriented device with $L_z = 40$ Å, as plotted in Fig. 2. This is the lowest J_{th} ever reported for semiconductor lasers with a similar cavity length.

The gain-current relationship was derived for both (111) and (100) oriented lasers with $L_z = 40$ Å by the measurement of J_{th} for lasers with different mirror losses. The mirror loss was varied by the change of the cavity length, and the facet reflectivity by adapting the dielectric facet coating. The relationship between mirror loss and J_{th} is plotted in Fig. 3. The gain of (111) oriented devices is 5–10 cm^{-1} higher than that of (100) oriented ones. The gain-current relationship of (100) devices is similar to that obtained by Tsang.[11] However, the present result shows a considerable gain saturation for both orientations, which probably results from the smaller L_z in the present study.

The temperature dependence of J_{th} was measured in the range 15–70 °C. All measured threshold-temperature characteristics followed the relationship of $J_{th} \propto \exp(T/T_0)$, and thus each result can be represented by a single characteristic temperature T_0. In Fig. 4 is shown T_0 as a function of L_z for (111) and (100) oriented devices. T_0 of (111) oriented lasers is slightly higher than that of (100) oriented lasers. It should be noted that T_0 is maximum at $L_z \sim 60$ Å for both orientations, although T_0 tends to decrease with decreasing L_z as a whole. This suggests that the quantum size effect on the threshold-temperature characteristics is most pronounced at $L_z \sim 60$ Å. The highest T_0 measured for a (111) oriented laser with $L_z = 60$ Å is as high as 209 K. It is also

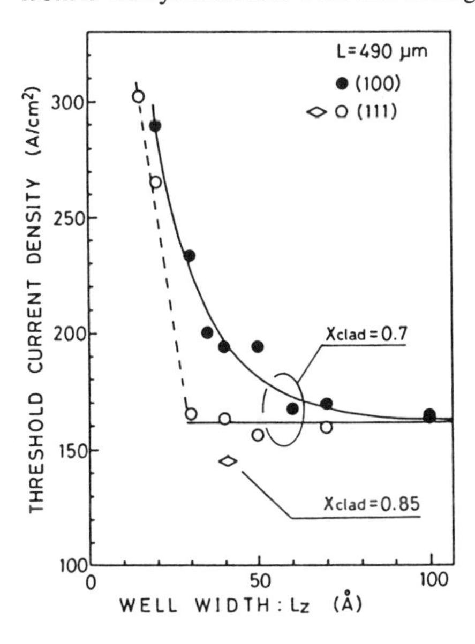

FIG. 2. Well width dependence of threshold current density for (111) oriented graded-index separate-confinement-heterostructure lasers is compared with that for (100) oriented ones; the AlAs mole fraction in the cladding layer is 0.7. The lowest threshold current density of 145 A/cm² achieved for (111) oriented lasers with the AlAs mole fraction in the cladding layer of 0.85 is also plotted.

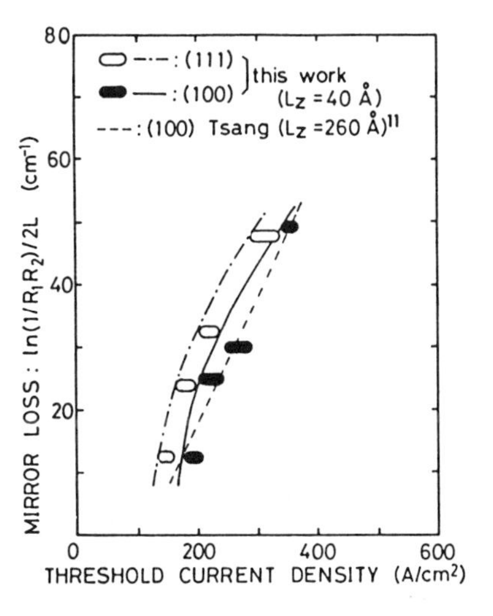

FIG. 3. Relationship between mirror loss and threshold current density for (111) and (100) oriented graded-index separate-confinement-heterostructure single quantum well lasers with a well width of 40 Å. This relationship represents the gain-current relationship. Plotted areas represent the measured distribution of threshold current density.

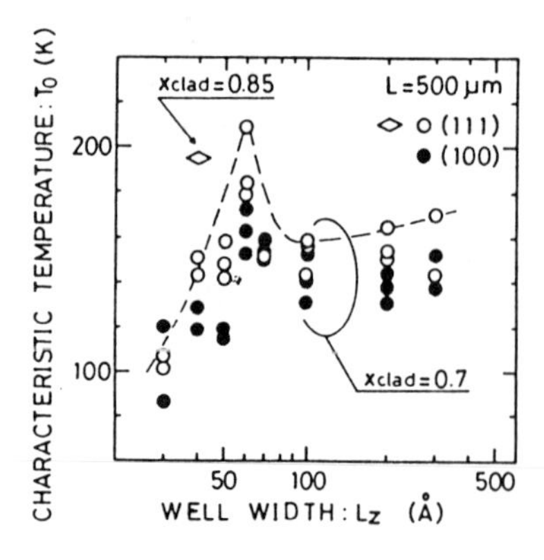

FIG. 4. Well width dependence of the characteristic temperature T_0 for the temperature dependence of threshold current density J_{th} in the form of $J_{th} \propto \exp(T/T_0)$. T_0's of (111) oriented lasers are higher than that of (100) oriented ones in the whole range of well width ($30 \leqslant L_z \leqslant 300$ Å).

interesting to note that the highest T_0 at $L_z \sim 60$ Å in the present study corresponds to the lowest J_{th} at $L_z \sim 60$ Å in the previous reports,[8,9] which are shown in Fig. 1. The highest T_0 at $L_z \sim 60$ Å means that the present devices also show the minimum J_{th} at $L_z \sim 60$ Å when the temperature is very high. Thus we can conclude that J_{th} is minimum at $L_z \sim 60$ Å when the threshold carrier density exceeds a certain value, which in the present study is caused by the increase in the temperature and in the previous studies by the increase in the loss of carriers, probably due to nonradiative recombination.[8,9] The usual mechanism for the loss of high-energy carriers, that is, recombination from L valleys, Auger recombination, and carrier leakage, does not completely explain both the steep change of T_0 with L_z and almost constant J_{th} with L_z for $L_z \leqslant 100$ Å at 300 K in (111) oriented QW lasers. This is because the nonradiative recombination due to these mechanisms increases almost monotonically with decreasing L_z.[3,12] Thus the peculiar change of T_0 with L_z near $L_z \sim 60$ Å is likely to arise from the dependence of the gain-current relationship on L_z. A detailed theoretical analysis, at least including the valence-band mixing effects, is necessary to fully describe the gain-current relationship for $L_z \lesssim 100$ Å.[13] The (111) oriented laser with a high AlAs mole fraction in the cladding layer of 0.85 and $L_z = 40$ Å showed a fairly high T_0 of 186 K, in spite of a very small L_z of 40 Å, as indicated in Fig. 4. There is a possibility that the optimization of L_z will further increase T_0. We also found out that T_0 was more than doubled in gain-guided stripe-geometry lasers because of the current crowding at higher temperatures.[14] For example, (100) oriented stripe-geometry lasers with $L_z = 70$ Å showed extraordinarily high T_0 of 300–400 K. We also noticed in previous reports that T_0 of broad-area devices[9,15–17] is not so high as that of gain-guided stripe-geometry lasers,[18,19] at least for SCH and GRIN-SCH lasers, when the total thickness of the QW is the same. Some part of high T_0 is considered to result from the current crowding effect. Therefore, we cannot expect an extraordinarily high T_0 exceeding 300 K for actual QW lasers together with extremely low J_{th} for which small L_z is required.

In summary, the near-ideal dependence of J_{th} on L_z in (111) oriented QW lasers has been demonstrated. An extremely low J_{th} of 145 A/cm^2 and a high T_0 of 186 K have been achieved in a GRIN-SCH SQW laser with $L_z = 40$ Å. We are convinced that this improvement, compared with conventional (100) oriented devices, is based on the enhancement of the optical transition rate between ground states of electrons and heavy holes in the (111) oriented QW because of the largest density of states along the [111] axis in GaAs. Thus the one-dimensional quantization along the [111] axis will improve performance characteristics in all kinds of optical devices based on the quantum size effect, such as modulators, switches, and bistable devices with the QW region. In addition, improvements will be expected in all (111) oriented QW systems composed of zinc-blende structure materials, such as InGaAs/InAlAs, InGaAs/InP, and GaInP/AlInP.

Note added: After the submission of this letter, we achieved the lowest J_{th} of 124 A/cm^2 in a (111) oriented laser with $L_z = 55$ Å, $L = 490\,\mu$m, and the AlAs mole fraction in the cladding layer of 0.8.

We would like to thank K. Hayashi, I. Fujimoto, and S. Kataoka for continuous encouragement throughout this work.

[1]T. Hayakawa, M. Kondo, T. Suyama, K. Takahashi, S. Yamamoto, and T. Hijikata, Jpn. J. Appl. Phys. **26**, L302 (1987).
[2]T. Hayakawa, K. Takahashi, M. Kondo, T. Suyama, S. Yamamoto, and T. Hijikata (unpublished).
[3]A. Sugimura, IEEE J. Quantum Electron. **QE-20**, 336 (1984).
[4]W. T. Tsang, Appl. Phys. Lett. **40**, 217 (1981).
[5]T. Hayakawa, T. Suyama, M. Kondo, K. Takahashi, S. Yamamoto, and T. Hijikata, Appl. Phys. Lett. **49**, 191 (1986).
[6]T. Hayakawa, M. Kondo, T. Suyama, K. Takahashi, S. Yamamoto, and T. Hijikata, Appl. Phys. Lett. **49**, 788 (1986).
[7]T. Fujii, S. Hiyamizu, S. Yamakoshi, and T. Ishikawa, J. Vac. Sci. Technol. B **3**, 776 (1985).
[8]T. Fujii, S. Yamakoshi, K. Nanbu, O. Wada, and S. Hiyamizu, J. Vac. Sci. Technol. B **2**, 259 (1984).
[9]S. D. Hersee, M. Krakowski, R. Blondeau, M. Baldy, B. de Cremoux, and J. P. Dechemin, J. Cryst. Growth **68**, 383 (1984).
[10]R. D. Burnham, W. Streifer, T. L. Paoli, and N. Holonyak, Jr., J. Cryst. Growth **68**, 370 (1984).
[11]W. T. Tsang, Appl. Phys. Lett. **40**, 217 (1982).
[12]A. R. Reisinger, P. S. Zory, Jr., and R. G. Waters, IEEE J. Quantum Electron. **QE-23**, 993 (1987).
[13]S. C. R. Eppenga and M. F. H. Schuurmans, IEEE J. Quantum Electron. **QE-23**, 960 (1987).
[14]D. Botez, IEEE J. Quantum Electron. **QE-17**, 2290 (1981).
[15]W. T. Tsang, Appl. Phys. Lett. **39**, 786 (1981).
[16]W. T. Tsang, Appl. Phys. Lett. **39**, 134 (1981).
[17]S. D. Hersee, B. de Cremoux, and J. P. Duchemin, Appl. Phys. Lett. **44**, 476 (1984).
[18]P. S. Zory, A. R. Reisinger, R. G. Waters, L. J. Mawst, C. A. Zmudzinski, M. A. Emanuel, M. E. Givens, and J. J. Coleman, Appl. Phys. Lett. **49**, 16 (1986).
[19]G. S. Jackson, D. G. Deppe, K. C. Hsieh, N. Holonyak, Jr., D. C. Hall, R. D. Burnham, R. L. Thornton, and T. L. Paoli, Appl. Phys. Lett. **48**, 1156 (1986).

Author Index

Subject Index

E

F

G

H

I

L

M

N

O

P

Q

R

S

T

U

Editors' Biographies

William Streifer is currently Research Manager for Spectra Diode Laboratories in San Jose, California. A native New Yorker, he is a 1953 graduate of the Bronx High School of Science. He then attended City College, New York, where he graduated magna cum laude with a B.E.E. in 1957, Columbia University (M.S.-E.E., 1959) and Brown University (Ph.D., 1962). During this time, he also served as lecturer at CCNY (1957–1959), and research engineer in the Heat and Mass Flow Analyzer Lab at Columbia (1958–1959). Upon graduation, he joined the E.E. Department at the University of Rochester. During this ten-year period, he taught many courses, supervised six successful Ph.D. students, and he and his students made important contributions to the theory of stable and unstable laser resonant modes, wave and ray properties of optical fibers, tunable dye lasers, mathematical ecology, and algebraic computing. In 1972 he joined the Xerox Palo Alto Research Center as a principal scientist, later becoming Research Fellow and Senior Research Fellow. During this period, he made many important pioneering contributions to the fields of semiconductor laser diodes and integrated optics.

In February 1985, he was appointed Director of the Center of Higher Technology Materials (CHTM) at the University of New Mexico, and in the one-and-a-half-year period that followed, he played a pivotal (and personally rewarding) role in establishing this as a center of excellence: six new laboratories were started in laser-material interactions, nonlinear optics, rotation sensing, III-V crystal growth, semiconductor material processing, and device characterization; the faculty was expanded; and an overall administrative structure for the center was established.

In August of 1986, Dr. Streifer returned to California in his current position as Research Manager at Spectra Diode Laboratories, where he is charged with soliciting and managing government and industrial contracts, directing internal research, and the transfer of technology into production.

His prolific accomplishments are reflected in more than two hundred papers, fifty patents, and innumerable talks, seminars, invited papers, and consulting activities.

Michael Ettenberg received the B.S. degree in Metallurgy from the Polytechnic Institute of New York in 1964, and the M.S. and Ph.D. degrees from New York University in 1967 and 1969, respectively.

Dr. Ettenberg joined David Sarnoff Research Center (formerly RCA Laboratories), Princeton, N.J., in 1969, and has made major contributions in the area of III-V compound semiconductor materials and optoelectronic devices. In the area of material synthesis, he co-developed many of the liquid phase epitaxial processes now used for the production of laser diodes and he was the first to synthesize AlAs. He has also made fundamental studies of the physical and electrical properties of AlGaAs and a host of other III-V compounds and heterostructures now useful in a wide variety of III-V devices.

In the area of devices, Dr. Ettenberg developed the edge-emitting LED for fiber communications, facet mirror passivation coatings, and Al_2O_3/Si dielectric mirror reflectors for laser diodes. He has made significant contributions in device reliability, specifically in the role of device design, synthesis, and processing on reliability. His research has been instrumental in the development of long-lived LEDs and laser diodes.

As part of RCA Corporation, he was involved in the transfer of device technology and fabrication processes to the production division. In that role, beginning as a scientist and later as a manager, he was responsible for transferring the world's first production cw lasers, pulsed lasers for ranging and fusing, the first production lasers for fiber OTDR applications, and the first production InGaAs PIN detectors for fiber-optic communications.

In 1984, Dr. Ettenberg received a David Sarnoff Award for Outstanding Technical Achievement, RCA's highest honor, for leadership in the understanding, development, and manufacture of solid-state optoelectronic devices.

In 1979, Dr. Ettenberg was appointed Head of the Optoelectronic Devices and Systems Research group at the David Sarnoff Research Center. In 1987, he was appointed to Director of the Optoelectronics Research Laboratory.

He has authored or coauthored more than 100 papers and several book chapters and holds 28 U.S. patents. Dr. Ettenberg is a Fellow of both the IEEE and Optical Society of America, and a Member of the American Physical Society and Alpha Sigma Mu Metallurgical Honor Society.